Handbook of Anxiety Disorders

(PGPS-151)

Pergamon Titles of Related Interest

Clarke AGORAPHOBIA: A Clinical & Personal Account

Goldstein/Hersen HANDBOOK OF PSYCHOLOGICAL ASSESSMENT

Hersen/Kazdin/Bellack CLINICAL PSYCHOLOGY HANDBOOK

Meichenbaum STRESS INOCULATION TRAINING

Related Journals*

***Free sample copies available upon request**

CLINICAL PSYCHOLOGY REVIEW

JOURNAL OF ANXIETY DISORDERS

Handbook of Anxiety Disorders

Edited by

Cynthia G. Last

&

Michel Hersen

University of Pittsburgh
School of Medicine

PERGAMON PRESS

New York · Oxford · Beijing · Frankfurt
São Paulo · Sydney · Tokyo · Toronto

U.S.A.	Pergamon Press, Inc., Maxwell House, Fairview Park, Elmsford, New York 10523, U.S.A.
U.K.	Pergamon Press plc, Headington Hill Hall, Oxford OX3 0BW, England
PEOPLE'S REPUBLIC OF CHINA	Pergamon Press, Room 4037, Qianmen Hotel, Beijing, People's Republic of China
FEDERAL REPUBLIC OF GERMANY	Pergamon Press GmbH, Hammerweg 6, D-6242 Kronberg, Federal Republic of Germany
BRAZIL	Pergamon Editora Ltda, Rua Eça de Queiros, 346, CEP 04011, Paraiso, São Paulo, Brazil
AUSTRALIA	Pergamon Press Australia Pty Ltd., P.O. Box 544, Potts Point, N.S.W. 2011, Australia
JAPAN	Pergamon Press, 5th Floor, Matsuoka Central Building, 1-7-1 Nishishinjuku, Shinjuku-ku, Tokyo 160, Japan
CANADA	Pergamon Press Canada Ltd., Suite No 271, 253 College Street, Toronto, Ontario, Canada M5T 1R5

First edition 1988

Library of Congress Cataloging in Publication Data

Handbook of anxiety disorders.
(Pergamon general psychology series; 151)
Includes indexes.
1. Anxiety—Handbooks, manuals, etc. I. Last, Cynthia G. II. Hersen, Michel. III. Series.
[DNLM: 1. Anxiety Disorders. WM 172 H236]
RC531.H27 1988 616.85'223 88–2312

British Library Cataloguing in Publication Data

Handbook of anxiety disorders.—(Pergamon general psychology series; 151).
1. Anxiety — Treatment 2. Phobias — Treatment 2. Obsessive–compulsive neurosis — Treatment
I. Last, Cynthia G. II. Hersen, Michel
616.85'2206 RC531

ISBN 0–08–032766–4

Printed in Great Britain by A. Wheaton & Co. Ltd., Exeter

Contents

Part VI. Special Topics

Part VII. Future Directions

Preface

Although anxiety has been a focal point of study for clinical psychologists, psychiatrists, psychophysiologists, and psychopharmacologists for well over a century, in the last two decades (especially in the 1980s) a wealth of new data has emerged about the topic. As in most areas of psychiatry, the field has become highly specialized, and even the "Renaissance" scholar would have difficulty keeping abreast of the continuous rapid developments.

The purpose of this *Handbook*, therefore, is to put the field into perspective by considering its many manifestations and recent growth. In so doing, we have included 32 chapters divided into seven parts. Part I presents an Overview of the issues, while Part II deals with Clinical Features and Assessment. Part III considers the theories and models that have been postulated to account for the Development and Maintenance of anxiety disorders. The five chapters in Part IV describe the Psychological Treatments, while in Part V the Pharmacological Treatments are reviewed. In Part VI, we look at Special Topics, such as anxiety disorders in childhood and adolescence, anxiety in the elderly, suicide and anxiety, medical illness and anxiety, and the primary prevention of anxiety disorders. Finally, in Part VII, Future Directions are prognosticated.

In a volume of this size, many individuals have given of their time, effort, and expertise. First and foremost, we express appreciation to the respective experts who agreed to write the chapters. Second, we thank our technical assistants for their cooperation and assistance: Jenifer McKelvey, Mary N. Newell, Kim Sterner, and Noelle Thomas. Finally, once more we acknowledge our gratitude to Jerome B. Frank, our editor at Pergamon Press.

Cynthia G. Last
Michel Hersen
Pittsburgh, PA

PART I

Overview

CHAPTER 1

Overview

Cynthia G. Last and Michel Hersen

The role of anxiety in the development and expression of human psychopathology has been acknowledged by mental health practitioners for well over a century. Initially, attention was sparked by the psychoanalytic movement, including Freud and his many students and disciples. In the years that followed, a number of learning theorists and behavioral psychologists focused on the primary role of anxiety in the genesis and maintenance of "neurotic behavior," particularly the phobic disorders.

In the past 20 years, we have witnessed a dramatic increase in the attention paid to anxiety and the anxiety disorders, resulting in the 1980s being labeled as "the decade of anxiety." This growth is reflected by the proliferation of research conducted and published in the area, the number of books appearing on different aspects of anxiety in recent years, and the heightened awareness of anxiety and anxiety-related problems in the community at large, no doubt resulting from the extensive media coverage (i.e., television, newspapers, popular magazines) of this topic.

The *Handbook of Anxiety Disorders* has been designed to present the wealth of information that has accrued in the area of anxiety disorders in one comprehensive volume. The book is interdisciplinary and clinical in nature. Research data and theoretical perspectives are presented to help elucidate the etiology, assessment, diagnosis, and treatment of the anxiety disorders.

The *Handbook* begins with this Overview and then a chapter describing the phenomenology of anxiety. The next section of the book includes chapters focusing on the defining features and assessment of each of the anxiety disorders. Following this, the leading hypothesis concerning the development and maintenance of the anxiety disorders are reviewed. The next two sections of the book include 10 chapters that present the major psychological and pharmacological approaches to treatment. The five chapters that follow address additional specific issues that are of contemporary relevance to the field. Finally, the *Handbook* concludes with a chapter on future directions in the field.

The primary purpose of this Overview is to provide background information that may be useful to understanding the structure and content of the *Handbook.* It is not our intention to introduce or cover every important topic included in the *Handbook.* Rather, we wish to highlight a few specific issues in order to help orient the reader to the contents contained herein.

DIAGNOSTIC ISSUES

Psychiatric diagnosis essentially serves three primary functions: classification, communication, and prediction. In this country, the most widely used diagnostic system is the *Diagnostic and Statistical Manual of Mental Disorders* (DSM) of the American Psychiatric Association (1952, 1968, 1980). Since its inception in 1952, the DSM has undergone substantial revisions, many of which have significantly affected our understanding and classification of the anxiety disorders.

In the most recent version of the manual (DSM-III: American Psychiatric Association, 1980), we witnessed several major changes in regard to the anxiety disorders. First, the anxiety diagnoses no longer were subsumed under the general heading "Neuroses," but instead delegated to a category of their own "Anxiety Disorders"). Second, the number and type of specific anxiety disorders included in this new category changed substantially.

Only three specific anxiety diagnoses had been contained in DSM-II: "anxiety neurosis," "phobic neurosis," and "obsessive–compulsive neurosis." The diagnosis of anxiety neurosis has been used to classify individuals experiencing nonphobic anxiety reactions and/or panic attacks. Subsequently, in DSM-III, this diagnostic category was divided into two separate disorders: panic disorder and generalized anxiety disorder. Chapter 6 outlines the similarities and differences between these two anxiety conditions. Although "phobic neurosis" (phobic disorder) was retained in DSM-III, the diagnostic category was subdivided by type of phobia — agoraphobia, social phobia, and simple phobia — the classification of which depended on the particular objects and/or situations that were feared and/or avoided. Moreover, agoraphobics with a history of panic attacks were distinguished from those who did not have a history of panic attacks. The implications of this diagnostic scheme for the phobic disorders is discussed at length in chapter 4. Finally, it should be noted that the diagnosis of obsessive-compulsive disorder essentially remained unchanged between the two versions of the DSM.

In addition, DSM-III specified a new anxiety condition — "posttraumatic stress disorder" — in the Anxiety Disorders section of the manual. Although this syndrome was "new," in that it had not been included in previous versions of the DSM, the characteristic features of the disorder had been described in the clinical literature for decades. As discussed in chapter 7, the disturbance occurs following a psychologically traumatic event that generally is outside the range of usual human experience (e.g., military combat, rape, natural disasters, etc.).

With the publication of DSM-III, we also saw major changes in the classification of childhood anxiety disorders. Whereas in DSM-II only one anxiety disorder was included in the Childhood and Adolescence section of the manual (overanxious reaction of childhood or adolescence), DSM-III distinguished three childhood anxiety diagnoses: separation anxiety disorder, avoidant disorder, and overanxious disorder. The clinical and associated features of these three disorders are discussed in chapter 27. In addition to these three anxiety conditions that usually first arise in childhood and adolescence, it should be noted that each of the aforementioned anxiety diagnoses can be applied as well to children and adolescents, with the exception of generalized anxiety disorder (which only may be applied to persons 18 years and older).

At the time of writing of this chapter, we are awaiting the publication of yet another version of the DSM: DSM-III-Revised (DSM-III-R). Preliminary drafts of the new manual indicate several further modifications for the anxiety disorders. One of the more important changes will be the ability to diagnose anxiety and affective disorders concurrently. Whereas in DSM-III's hierarchical system affective disorders took "precedence" over anxiety disorders (i.e., a coexisting affective disorder was an exclusion criteria for diagnosing an anxiety disorder), DSM-III-R acknowledges that anxiety and affective disorders (particularly, major depression) may coincide, and that their comorbidity may have important prognastic and treatment implications.

Another important feature of DSM-III-R is the relabeling of "agoraphobia with panic attacks" as "panic disorder with agoraphobia." In this relabeling, the primary role of panic attacks in the development of agoraphobia is acknowledged (see chapter 12), as well as recent pharmacological treatment data indicating that agoraphobic avoidance behavior can be reduced through the blocking of panic attacks (see chapter 24 for a review of the efficacy of tricyclic antidepressants in the treatment of agoraphobia; see chapter 25 for a review on the monoamine oxidase inhibitors).

As indicated earlier, the conceptualization and classification of the anxiety disorders has changed substantially over time. For the most part, these changes have reflected our increased knowledge in the field, through both clinical and research findings. Ultimately, however, the utility of any nosological system must stand the test of empiricism, through rigorous assessments of its reliability and validity. While several of the "newer" anxiety disorders have begun to be examined in this manner (e.g., generalized anxiety disorder, panic disorder, posttraumatic stress disorder), others have not. In this regard, we (CGL, MH) particularly have been concerned about the lack of empirical data on the childhood anxiety disorders, and, as a result, have been conducting a series of studies on their reliability and validity. This topic is covered in detail in chapter 27.

TREATMENT ISSUES

The fourth and fifth sections of this *Handbook* review the major psychological and parmacological approaches to the treatment of anxiety disorders. At this point in time, behavior therapy is considered by many to be the most widely used form of psychological treatment for the anxiety disorders (see chapter 18). Within this orientation, the terms *exposure* and *exposure treatments* have become increasingly popular, and have been used primarily to signify the treatment of individuals by contact with the object(s) and/or situation(s) that elicits anxiety.

Exposure treatments may be conducted in a variety of ways, differing on several dimensions. Some of these dimensions include: imaginal versus live ("in vivo") exposure, graduated versus prolonged exposure, individual versus group exposure, and therapist-assisted versus self-exposure. Each of these dimensions essentially represents a variation in the *manner of approach* to the anxiety-eliciting stimulus, and different combinations of the variables have resulted in a large number of specific exposure-based treatment strategies. For the most part, however, each of these treatment strategies is considered to be effective for the same reason or by the same process: Continued exposure to the anxiety producing stimulus results in a dissipation of the anxiety response.

But why do anxiety reactions subside upon continued exposure? Attempts to answer this question have prompted a number of hypotheses. Five of the more widely acknowledged hypotheses include: (a) *extinction* of conditioned responses, (b) *habituation* of physiological arousal, (c) changes in *emotional imagery* that control physiological and behavioral responses (the bio-information theory of emotional imagery), (d) increases in perceived *self-efficacy* or changes in cognitive "set," and (e) decreases in *catastrophic thoughts* and negative self-verbalizations.

Considerable research activity has been devoted to determining whether one or more of these processes accounts for anxiety reduction during exposure treatments. While this body of literature is far too extensive to be covered in this Overview, suffice it to say that, at this point in time, the answer to this complicated question remains unclear. However, understanding the mechanism of action of this treatment approach remains important because exposure therapy, although proven effective for many of the anxiety disorders, is not nearly as effective as one would hope. Exposure treatments (as are many other forms of treatment) are plagued by failures, dropouts, relapses, and limited clinical improvement.

These deficiencies in exposure therapy have led many to look further into how the treatment is conducted. In this regard, one line of clinical research has focused on the role of interpersonal factors, particularly the marital relationship, in the exposure-based treatment of one of the more prevalent anxiety disorders: agoraphobia. As discussed in chapter 20, such modification of the exposure treatment approach for agoraphobia was spurred by at least two phenomena. First, several clinicians and investigators had reported that the marriages of agoraphobics often deteriorate as the agoraphobic woman becomes increasingly independent, sometimes resulting in husbands pressuring their wives to return to a dependent role. Second, data had been published indicating that agoraphobics with unsatisfactory marriages were less likely than those with satisfactory marriages to improve following exposure treatment and more likely to relapse.

As a result of these findings, clinical researchers began to attend to the marital relationship when conducting exposure therapy with agoraphobic patients. One way in which this was done was by actively including patients' spouses in treatment, by having them participate in exposure sessions, and teaching them more effective means of communicating with their wives during periods of anxiety or panic (see Barlow, O'Brien, & Last, 1984). Another way in which this was done was by including couples communication training sessions as one component of a treatment package for agoraphobia (see Goldstein & Chambless, 1978). Outcome data from such investigations generally have indicated an advantage for inclusion of the spouse in treatment.

Another line of clinical research has focused on the role of cognitions in exposure therapy. Within a cognitive–behavioral framework, catastrophic or negative self-statements are conceptualized as mediators of the maladaptive physiological–emotional and behavioral responses characteristic of the anxiety disorders, and exposure-based treatments are hypothesized to decrease the frequency of such thoughts. However, as outlined in chapter 19, specific cognitive treatment strategies may be utilized to assist in engendering the cognitive change that is believed to be essential to the anxiety reduction process.

A number of studies have been published that have attempted to determine whether teaching cognitive strategies to anxious patients increases the effectiveness of exposure therapy (see Last, 1984, for a review of the cognitive treatment of phobic disorders). Overall, results from these investigations have been mixed. Moreover, clear interpretation of the findings has been hampered by substantial differences in the subjects, measurement techniques, methods, and designs of the studies. Despite the lack of overwhelming empirical support for the cognitive strategies, clinically, we must add, we have found these techniques to be of great value in the treatment of a large number of our anxiety disordered patients, particularly those with generalized anxiety disorder, agoraphobia, or social phobia.

Pharmacological approaches to the treatment of anxiety disorders have undergone marked advances in recent years. Although the benzodiazepines still represent the most widely prescribed and used class of anti-anxiety or anxiolytic agents in this country (see chapter 22), the advantages of known "antidepressant" medications (both the tricyclic antidepressants and monoamine oxidase inhibitors) in the treatment of certain anxiety disorders has become increasingly apparent (see chapters 24 and 15).

One of the greatest potential pitfalls facing the pharmacological treatment approaches is the possibility of relapse following discontinuation of medication. As a result, certain clinicians and investigators have advocated concurrent administration of psychological and pharmacological treatments, in an effort to maximize clinical effectiveness and minimize the likelihood of relapse following drug withdrawal. The advantages of this combination treatment approach are described in detail in chapter 26.

DEVELOPMENTAL ISSUES

Historically, adult models of psychopathology and diagnostic schemes have served as prototypes for classifying psychiatric disturbances in children and adolescents. This may be due, at least in part, to the fact that the study of child psychopathology is of relatively recent origin, lagging a century or more behind that of adult psychopathology (Achenbach, 1980; Ollendick & Hersen, 1983).

Extrapolating diagnostic constructs directly from adults to children implies several relationships between adult and child psychopathology, which may or may not be accurate. First, this framework indirectly suggests that childhood is the root for most adult psychopathology. Second, it similarly implies that there is a direct relationship between symptoms manifested during childhood and those appearing during adulthood (i.e., that early psychiatric disturbances have predictive validity for later psychopathology). Third, and most important, it assumes that differences in level of development (e.g., cognitive, social, biological, psychosexual, educational) are unimportant for understanding child psychopathology, with children essentially representing "little adults."

The diagnostic classification system of the American Psychiatric Association has, over the years, reflected this trend of applying nosological constructs derived from adult disorders to children. Indeed, it was not until the publication of DSM-II in 1968 that childhood disorders (other than adjustment reaction and childhood schizophrenia) were recognized. While in DSM-III the number and type of psychiatric disorders included for children has expanded considerably, it appears that the manual continues to reflect this theoretical bent (i.e., extrapolating from adults to children).

The tradition of applying nosological constructs derived from adult disorders to children is continued in DSM-III in two ways: (a) use of the *same criteria* for adults and children for many major psychiatric disorders (e.g., schizophrenia, major depression, phobic disorders, obsessive–compulsive disorder, somatization disorder, etc.), and (b) inclusion of diagnostic categories in the childhood and adolescence section of the manual that are *functionally equivalent* to other categories that are based on constructs derived from adult psychiatric populations (e.g., separation anxiety disorder–agoraphobia, overanxious disorder–generalized anxiety disorder, conduct disorder–antisocial personality disorder, etc.). While this approach may be valid and useful for understanding and diagnosing certain psychiatric disturbances in children (as ascertained empirically by investigating the reliability and validity of the diagnostic categories in question), its advantages for other disorders are unclear.

For the childhood anxiety disorders, preliminary findings on this approach to diagnosis have been mixed. Early studies (see chapter 27) and investigations employing multivariate taxonomic methods (e.g., Achenbach, 1980) have questioned the reliability and validity of these diagnoses, suggesting that this approach may not be fruitful for this particular population. Further evidence in support of this hypothesis has been provided by Hershberg, Carlson, Cantwell, and Strober (1982) in their study of anxiety and depressive symptoms in anxious and depressed children and adolescents. While results indicated that depressed children, like depressed adults, report many anxiety symptoms, anxious children rarely reported depressive symptoms (and never met criteria for secondary depression) and did not report panic attacks, unlike their adult counterparts.

Alternatively, other data adduced suggest that the DSM-III childhood anxiety diagnoses are reliable and valid, and that anxious children and adolescents are similar to their adult counterparts. A recent investigation by our group has supported the reliability and validity of at least two of the anxiety disorders of childhood: separation anxiety disorder and overanxious disorder (Last, Hersen, Kazdin, Finkelstein, & Strauss, in press). Moreover, research conducted by Gittelman-Klein and Klein (1971, 1973, 1980) suggests that separation-anxious children and agoraphobic adults may share a common psychopathological process, because both have a similar positive response to imipramine. Finally, reports from adult patients with anxiety disorders (Gittelman-Klein, 1975), mothers of child patients with anxiety disorders (Last, Hersen, Kazdin, Francis, & Grubb, 1986; Last, Phillips, & Statfield, in press), and the children of adult patients with anxiety disorders (Weissman, Leckman, Merikangas, Gammon, & Prusoff, 1984), support and relationship between the childhood and adult expression of anxiety disorders.

Currently, we are conducting a large-scale, prospective longitudinal study of children and adolescents with anxiety disorders. Such data should be of considerable value in helping to assess the adequacy of our current nosological system for this population.

CONCLUDING REMARKS

Selected diagnostic, treatment, and developmental issues have been highlighted in this Overview. The issues discussed were meant to be illustrative, to help orient the reader to some of the contents contained in this *Handbook*. It is our hope that this volume will not only educate the reader as to the state of the art in this fascinating area, but spur further clinical research into the many unanswered questions presented in this and subsequent chapters.

REFERENCES

Achenbach, T. M. (1980). DSM-III in light of empirical research on the classification of child psychopathology. *Journal of the American Academy of Child Psychiatry, 19,* 395–412.

American Psychiatric Association. (1952). *Diagnostic and statistical manual of mental disorders (1st. ed.).* Washington, DC: Author.

American Psychiatric Association. (1968). *Diagnostic and statistical manual of mental disorders (2nd ed.).* Washington, DC: Author.

American Psychiatric Association. (1980). *Diagnostic and statistical manual of mental disorders (3rd ed.).* Washington, DC: Author.

Barlow, D. H., O'Brien, G. T., & Last, C. G. (1984). Couples treatment of agoraphobia. *Behavior Therapy, 15,* 41–58.

Gittelman-Klein, R. (1975). Psychiatric characteristics of the relatives of school phobic children. In D. V. S. Sankar (Ed.), *Mental health in children* (pp. 325–334). New York: PJD Publications.

Gittelman-Klein, R., & Klein, D. F. (1971). Controlled imipramine treatment of school phobia. *Archives of General Psychiatry, 25,* 204–207.

Gittelman-Klein, R., & Klein, D. F. (1973). School phobia: Diagnostic considerations in the light of imipramine effects. *Journal of Nervous and Mental Diseases, 156,* 199–215.

Gittelman-Klein, R., & Klein, D. F. (1980). Separation anxiety in school refusal and its treatment with drugs. In L. Hersov & I. Berg (Eds.) *Out of school,* (pp. 321–342). New York: John Wiley & Sons.

Goldstein, A. J., & Chambless, D. L. (1978). A reanalysis of agoraphobia. *Behavior Therapy, 9,* 47–59.

Hershberg, S. G., Carlson, G. A., Cantwell, D. P., & Strober, M. (1982). Anxiety and depressive disorders in psychiatrically disturbed children. *Journal of Clinical Psychiatry, 43,* 358–361.

Last, C. G. (1984). Cognitive treatment of phobia. In M. Hersen, R. M. Eisler, & P. M. Miller (Eds.), *Progress in Behavior Modification: Vol. 16* (pp. 65–82). New York: Academic Press.

Last, C. G., Hersen, M., Kazdin, A. E., Finkelstein, R., & Strauss, C. C. (in press). Comparison of DSM-III separation anxiety and overanxious disorders: Demographic characteristics and patterns of comorbidity. *Journal of the American Academy of Child Psychiatry.*

Last, C. G., Hersen, M., Kazdin, A. E., Francis, G., & Grubb, H. J. (1986). *Psychiatric illness in the mothers of anxious children.* Manuscript submitted for publication.

Last, C. G., Phillips, J., & Statfeld, A. (in press). *Childhood anxiety disorders in mothers and their children. Child Psychiatry and Human Development.*

Ollendick, T. H., & Hersen, M. (1983). A historical overview of child psychopathology. In T. H. Ollendick & M. Hersen (Eds.), *Handbook of child psychopathology* (pp. 3–12). New York: Pergamon Press.

Weissman, M. M., Leckman, J. F., Merikangas, K. R., Gammon, G. D., & Prusoff, B. A. (1984). Depression and anxiety disorders in parents and children. *Archives of General Psychiatry, 41*, 845–852.

CHAPTER 2

The Neuropsychological Basis of Anxiety

Jeffrey A. Gray

The intention of this chapter is to outline an approach to the analysis of anxiety and the anxiety disorders from the perspective afforded by the neurosciences and physiological psychology; that is, the study of how the brain controls behavior. This approach offers a coherent framework within which it is possible to analyze simultaneously the psychology and the neurology of anxiety, in animals as in humans, as well as the personality traits that predispose toward anxiety.

It is conventional to commence the discussion of almost any topic in psychiatry with the problem of classification; and indeed this problem is long-standing and apparently never-ending. A solution would be nearer at hand if we had a clear idea of what it is that we are to classify. The assumption made here is that the aim of psychiatric classification is to group together disorders that reflect the functioning (or malfunctioning) of the same separable subsystem of the brain, and to group apart those that reflect the functioning of different separable subsystems of the brain. This assumption clearly requires that we define the concept of *separable subsystem of the brain,* a matter I will discuss later. But first, by way of an abbreviated justification for the assumption, let me offer this simple syllogism. Psychiatry is the branch of medicine that deals with disordered behavior; behavior is a product of the brain; therefore, psychiatry is a branch of medicine concerned with the orderly and disorderly functioning of the brain. This syllogism (with which, unless one retreats into Cartesian dualism, it is difficult to disagree) defines psychiatry as being much the same as neurology. And indeed it is likely that, with the passage of only tens of years at most, these two branches of medicine will merge.

THE NEUROLOGY OF ANXIETY

What, then, is a separable subsystem of the brain? I shall answer this question by example; but because my example concerns anxiety, it is one that is central to the theme of this chapter.

There have been three quite separate attempts to analyze emotional behavior in animals (of a kind roughly comparable to behavior described in humans as *fearful* or *anxious* and the brain mechanisms that mediate it. One has started from drugs known to reduce anxiety in humans, and has asked about the behavioral and neurochemical effects of these drugs in animals. A second has investigated the effects of infantile stress on later, adult behavior. The third has applied selective breeding (on criteria of open field defecation, derived from the common observation of involuntary defecation in human beings under stress) in the effort to create emotionally "reactive" or "nonreactive" genotypes. There is evidence (considered later) that all three of these approaches — pharmacological, environmental, and genetic — have converged upon the same, unified brain system. It is as though each approach has tugged at this system at a different point, but the same system always comes out as a whole (Gray 1982a; in press). It is in this sense that there appears to be a unified and separable subsystem in the brain whose function is to mediate behavior which, in human beings, is termed *fearful* or *anxious*. If this inference is correct, we may define *anxiety* as the state that is produced by activity in this particular subsystem of the brain, and *anxious behavior* as the behavior that this subsystem controls.

Note that this approach to the problem of psychiatric definition finesses the ancient and honorable quarrel between defenders of the so-called "medical model" in psychiatry and the proponents of the alternative view that psychiatry is concerned rather with extremes of behavior along personality continua (Eysenck, 1960). According to the medical model, the solution to the problem of classification requires that we identify an etiological agent leading to a clearly delineated disorder of function in a system that remains orderly in unaffected individuals. The alternative, "continuum" view rejects the notion that there is such a categorical distinction between the well and the ill; it supposes instead that there is a smooth gradation from one extreme of functioning to another, and that only an arbitrary (or, at best, statistical) decision can be made to segregate some extreme individuals as "ill." But the mode of classification offered here is indifferent to the tension between the medical and the continuum models. Behavior requiring treatment could arise because of brain subsystem functions in a particular manner *either* as the result of trauma, infection, a major gene, and so on, *or* as the result of a cumulation of minor genes and/or environmental experiences. We shall return to one aspect of this issue (namely, the relation between personality and anxiety disorders) at the end of the chapter.

Systems that Mediate Anxiety: The Pharmacological Approach

The most sustained attack on the brain systems that are involved in anxiety has taken the pharmacological approach. This starts from the evidence (Rickels, 1978) that certain drugs can be used clinically to control anxiety and goes on to investigate their mode of action. At present, the most commonly used drugs of this kind belong to the benzodiazepine family. However, the credentials as anti-anxiety agents of two older classes of drug, the barbiturates and ethanol, are almost as good, and in relevant animal experiments the effects of these compounds are virtually indistinguishable from those of the benzodiazepines (Gray, 1977). The chief advantage of the benzodiazepines over these older drugs is the much greater difference between the therapeutic dose and the doses at which sedation, motor incoordination, or lethal effects occur. In the discussion here, therefore, I shall use the terms *anti-anxiety drug* or *anxiolytic* to refer to all three of these drug's classes, as well as other, newer agents (e.g., the triazolopyridazines; Lippa et al., 1980) which again have similar behavioral and clinical effects.

The great advantage of the pharmacological approach to the study of anxiety in animals is that one can be sure that the substance administered to the experimental animal is identical to that which is given to people. In contrast, it is extremely difficult to determine whether some presumed environmental stress causes a state of "anxiety" in animals, or whether a particular form of behavior is a valid index of this state. Nonetheless, the identity of the substances given to animals and human beings does not absolve those who adopt the pharmacological approach from demonstrating that anti-anxiety drugs have effects in animals that are comparable to their therapeutic effects in humans. It is possible that animals do not have a state resembling human anxiety; in that case, whatever the effects of the anti-anxiety drugs on the behavior of animals, they can have little or nothing to do with anxiety. Fortunately, there is excellent evidence that the effects of the anti-anxiety drugs on the behavior of animals resemble those that give these agents their therapeutic value.

A summary of these effects, based exclusively on animal experiments (several hundred of them), is shown in Figure 2.1 (Gray, 1977). This states in diagrammatic form that the anti-anxiety drugs attenuate the behavioral effects of just three classes of stimuli: (a) stimuli associated with pain or punishment, but not pain itself; (b) stimuli associated with nonreward, i.e., the omission of anticipated reward (an event that, in familiar human terms, might be called "frustration" "disappointment" or "failure"), but not nonreward itself; and (c) novel stimuli. Figure 1 further states that these three classes of stimuli all give rise to three behavioral changes: (a) inhibition of all ongoing behavior; (b) increased level of arousal, so that the next action is carried out with unusually great speed, force, or vigor; and (c) increased attention to the environment, and especially novel aspects of the environment. Furthermore, the anti-anxiety drugs (irrespective of the type of eliciting stimulus) attenuate all three of these behavioral changes. The most parsimonious account of this pattern of drug effects (coupled with the lack of effect of these drugs on behavioral responses to other types of stimuli) is that any of the stimuli listed to the left in Figure 2.1 act via a common system (the "behavioral inhibition system") to produce all three of the behavioral outputs listed on the right; and that the anti-anxiety drugs antagonize the activity of the behavioral inhibition system.

Now, a succinct summary of Figure 2.1 is that anxiolytic drugs reduce reactions to threats of pain or failure and reactions to novelty. From here it is a small step to the proposal that anxiety is a state produced by exposure to threats of pain or failure or to novel stimuli; and that in this state one stops, looks, and listens, and prepares for vigorous action (the righthand side of Figure 1). This is such a plausible, common-sense account of anxiety that it is likely to be acceptable to anyone whose conception of emotional life has escaped distortion from the psychodynamic tradi-

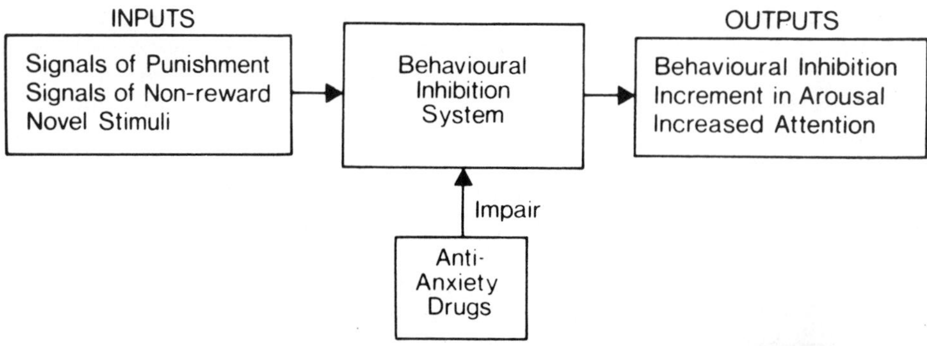

Figure 2.1. The behavioral inhibition system.

tion started by Freud. The only item that may provoke comment is the inclusion of novelty among the list of "axiogenic" stimuli (as we may now term the events listed to the left in Figure 2.1). But the experiments that justify inclusion of this type of stimulus have involved an extreme form of novelty: A rat, for example, that has never before left its home cage is suddenly placed alone in a brightly lit, noisy open arena (the "open field" test). Whatever the equivalent situation might be for a human being, it would be surprising if a person exposed to it did not report anxiety. Thus, Figure 2.1 is derived entirely from experiments with animals, yet gives a plausible account of *human* anxiety. This fact provides strong evidence that animals experience a state of anxiety that closely resembles the human state and which responds in the same manner to anxiolytic drugs (Gray, 1982a).

This conclusion is an important one, from which many consequences flow. First, we now have a definition of anxiety in behavioral terms. It is the state elicited by stimuli associated with punishment, stimuli associated with nonreward, and novelty, and which gives rise to behavioral inhibition, increased arousal, and increased attention. Second, we may at once exclude any explanation of anxiety (e.g., in terms of residues of Oedipal complexes) that draws upon processes unique to our own species. Third, because Figure 2.1 is equally applicable to species (tested in the experiments reviewed by Gray, 1977) ranging from goldfish to chimpanzee, anxiety and the neural systems that mediate it must be phylogenetically relatively old and stable. This conclusion agrees with the results of research on the phylogenetic distribution of the specialized neuronal receptor upon which the benzodiazepines act (discussed later). This receptor is present in higher bony fish and persists in unchanged form throughout the mammals, including humans (Nielsen, Braestrup, & Squires, 1978). Fourth, we have a legitimate scientific basis that allows us to probe the neural basis of anxiety by experiments on the brains of animals. Furthermore, given the third conclusion (above), we should concentrate on such a search on structures that are phylogenetically relatively old, rather than upon structures that have undergone a great deal of recent evolution in the run-up to Homo sapiens.

Mode of Action of Anxiolytics

One way to search the brain for structures that mediate anxiety is to ask about the mode of action of the anxiolytic drugs themselves. The last decade has seen an explosion of knowledge in this field (Bowery, 1984; Trimble, 1983). The focus of this knowledge is the inhibitory transmitter, γ-aminobutyrate (GABA). This acts via two different types of receptor, termed $GABA_A$ and $GABA_B$. Activation of the $GABA_A$ receptor opens a chloride channel, leading to inhibition of firing of the postsynaptic cell or (if the $GABA_A$ receptor is located on a terminal) inhibition of transmitter release. The $GABA_A$ receptor is often closely coupled to two other receptors. One shows high affinity and selectivity for the benzodiazepines (provisionally regarded as agonists at this receptor), and for compounds (so-called "inverse agonists") that have biochemical and behavioral (including anxiogenic) effects that are generally opposite in sign to those of the benzodiazepines (Haefely, 1984). The other ("picrotoxinin") receptor binds the barbiturates and a range of convulsant drugs, such as picrotoxin (Olsen, 1981). The benzodiazepines act via the benzodiazepine receptor, and the barbiturates via the picrotoxinin receptor, so as to increase the opening of the chloride channel gated by GABA at the $GABA_A$ receptor. A model of these interactions proposed by Haefely (1984) is shown in Figure 2.2.

Thus, the common action of the benzodiazepines and barbiturates is to increase inhibition mediated by the $GABA_A$ receptor. In addition, there is evidence that ethanol, too, increases GABAergic inhibition (Nestoros, 1980; Ticku, 1980). These neurochemical data clearly suggest the hypothesis that anxiolytic drug action, whether produced by the benzodiaze-

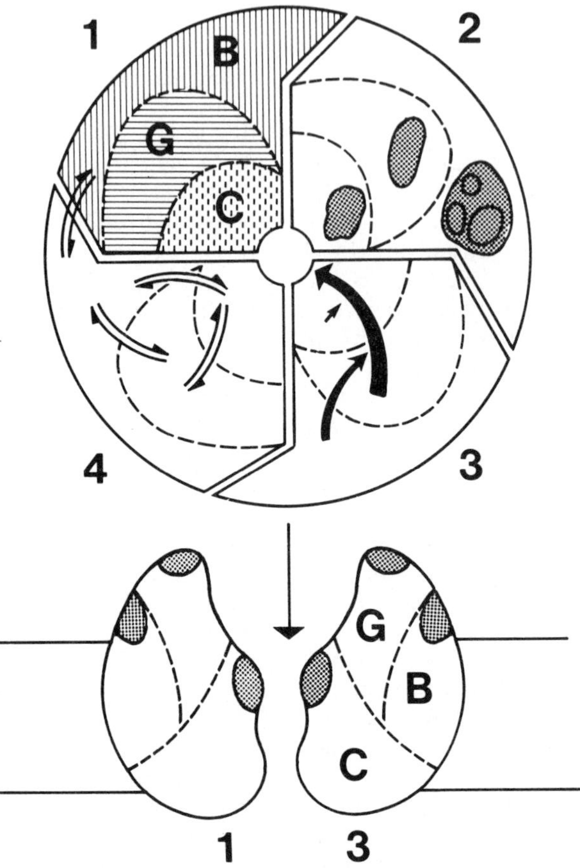

Figure 2.2. Hypothetical anatomy and functions of the receptor-channel complex proposed by Haefely *et al.* (1985). A view from the extracellular space (above) shows the four monomers (1, 2, 3, 4). Four different functions and interactions are depicted. In (1) are shown the three domains: Cl^- channel part (C), GABA binding domain or GABA-R (G), and the regulatory domain with BZ (benzodiazepine) binding site, the BZR (B). In (2) are indicated the ligand binding sites on the channel domain ("picrotoxin binding site," "barbiturate receptor," and "channel ligand site"), on the GABA-R (GABA binding site), and on the BZR (binding site for agonists, antagonists, and inverse agonists, composed of not entirely identical, but adjacent and probably partially overlapping subsites). In (3) is indicated the main function of the complex, namely the GABA-induced gating (opening) of the Cl^- channel (large arrow), with the regulation of this gating process by BZ agonists and inverse agonists (medium arrow), and the regulation of Cl^- channel properties by ligands of the picrotoxinin binding sites. In (4) are shown the four bidirectional coupling functions or domain-domain interactions (between GABA-R and Cl^- channel domain, between BZR and GABA-R, between BZR and channel ligands, and between the BZ binding sites of adjacent subunits). On a cross section through the membrane (see below) are shown the three domains of subunits 1 and 3.

pines, the barbiturates, or alcohol, is due to faciliated GABAergic inhibition. However, there are two problems with this hypothesis.

The first is that, when the hypothesis has been tested in tasks that reflect the specifically anti-anxiety effects of the anxiolytics (as distinct, say, from their sedative or anti-convulsant effects or in purely biochemical experiments), the results have been somewhat variable. There is, in particular, no firm evidence that the barbiturates affect behavior (of the kind illustrated in Figure 2.1) by way of facilitated GABAergic inhibition (Gray et al., 1984; Quintero et al., 1985a, 1985b). There is however, substantial evidence that the benzodiazepines reduce anxiety in this way (e.g., Billingsley & Kubena, 1978; Hodges & Green, 1984; Quintero et al., 1985a, 1985b); and some (but by no means invariable) evidence that $GABA_A$ agonists, such as muscimol, decrease anxiety (e.g., Cananzi, Costa, & Guidotti 1980; Quintero et al., 1985a).

The second problem with the GABA ergin hypothesis of anxiolytic drug action is more theoretical in character. GABAergic neurons, as well as GABA receptors and their associated benzodiazepine and picrotoxinin receptors, are distributed throughout the nervous system, in structures that on other grounds are likely to be concerned with the organization of emotional behavior (e.g., in the limbic system), but also in structures that are quite unlikely to be so concerned (e.g., the neocortex, spinal cord, and cerebellum). Yet, the behavioral effects of the anti-anxiety drugs illustrated in Figure 2.1 are highly specific. To take but one example, anxiolytic drugs (in low, selectively anxiolytic doses) reduce reactions to stimuli that warn of pain, but not reactions to pain itself. If the entire principle of action of these drugs consists in facilitation of GABAergic inhibition, we would expect (given the ubiquitous distribution of GABAergic systems throughout the neuraxis) both kinds of reaction to be reduced. Indeed, this kind of change can be observed, but one needs then to administer larger doses, entering the range at which sedative effects predominate. *These* effects (or the anticonvulsant effects that are also caused by both benzodiazepines and barbiturates) are highly likely to be due to a general facilitation of GABAergic inhibition; but they are not the effects that interest us. Thus (without necessarily departing from the principle that, whatever effects the anxiolytic drugs produce, they do so via enhancement of GABAergic inhibition), we must search for a more specific locus of action within the nervous system in order to account for their capacity to reduce anxiety.

Search for the Behavioral Inhibition System in the Brain

In conducting this search, Figure 2.1 is again a useful guide. This figure suggests that the brain contains a single, unified "behavioral inhibition system," and that the anti-anxiety drugs work by impairing the normal functioning of this system. It follows that a pattern of behavioral change similar to that seen after the administration of anxiolytic drugs should be caused also by other means of interfering with the normal functioning of the behavioral inhibition system. This argument impels one to search the literature for brain lesions that give rise to such a pattern of change. This search leads very rapidly to the septo-hippocampal system. Damage either to the septal area or to the hippocampal formation (with which the septal area is reciprocally connected) causes a series of behavioral changes that overlap to a very considerable degree with those caused by the anxiolytic drugs (Gray, 1982a; Gray & McNaughton, 1983). It is a small step from these data to the hypothesis that the anxiolytic drugs owe their specifically anti-anxiety effects to an impairment in the functioning of the septo-hippocampal system (Gray, 1970a, 1982a, 1982b).

Such an impairment in septo-hippocampal function could be produced by facilitation of inhibition at the many GABAergic synapses within the hippocampal formation and in the septal area. However, a number of specific features of the data from many experiments suggest that much of the action of the anxiolytic drugs upon septo-hippocampal functioning is indirect (Gray, 1982a; Gray & Rawlins, 1986). A particularly important role is played by noradrenergic and serotonergic afferents (originating from the locus coeruleus and the median raphe in the brainstem, respectively) to the septo-hippocampal system. Activity in these fibers is increased by anxiogenic stimulation and stress of other kinds (Lidbrink, Corrodi, Fuxe, & Olson, 1973; Redmond, 1979; Stein, Wise, & Berger, 1973. One consequence of this increased activity (described in greater detail later, is an enhancement in the capacity of the septo-hippocampal system to handle inputs from its major afferent pathway, the perforant path, which transmits information of neocortical origin from the entorhinal area (e.g., Segal, 1980). Anti-anxiety drugs of all kinds reverse the stress-induced increase in noradrenergic and serotonergic activity (Lindbrink et al., 1973; Stein *et al.*, 1973). There are GABAergic synapses both at the relevant cell-bodies in the locus coeruleus and median raphe and at their terminals within the hippocampus (e.g., Fung & Fillenz, 1983). Thus, part of the specifically anti-anxiety action of the anxiolytic drugs is probably mediated by enhancement of GABAergic inhibition at these sites. This would have the effect of blocking the increase in septohippocampal information-handling capacity normally caused by anxiogenic stimulation (Gray, 1982a, 1982b; Redmond, 1979).

Although the ascending noradrenergic and serotonergic pathways appear to be affected similarly by both stress and anxiolytic medication, their roles are probably complementary rather than identical. In particularm the ascending noradrenergic fibers apparently play a more important role in determining the arousal output of the behavioral inhibition system (Figure 2.1) and the serotonergic fibers, the behavioral inhibition output (Gray, 1982a, 1982b; Redmond, 1979; Soubrié, 1986). These functions are mediated in part by way of the noradrenergic and serotonergic projections to the septo-hippocampal system. But projections to other structures, both in the forebrain and in lower brain centers undoubtedly, also play a role. The way in which the noradrenergic and serotonergic projections to the septo-hippocampal system and to other target organs are coordinated during states of anxiety remains unclear. Interactions between the noradrenergic and serotonergic projections themselves may be in part mediated by the reciprocal connections between the locus coeruleus and the raphe nuclei.

The behavioral inhibitions system depicted in Figure 2.1 offers a behaviorist analysis of anxiety (i.e., one couched in terms of stimulus inputs and response outputs). We have now taken the step of identifying some of the brain structures that instantiate the behavioral inhibition system at a neural level, namely, the septal area, the hippocampal formation, the noradrenergic neurons in the locus coeruleus, the serotonergic neurons in the raphe nuclei, and the projections that interconnect these various cell groups. This step into the brain is also a first step from a behaviorist to a cognitive analysis of anxiety (Gray, 1984). The chief function of the brain is to process information so as to make behavior adaptive; and the term *cognitive* is best defined as "relating to the processing of information." Thus, we move on to the cognitive analysis of anxiety when we inquire what information-processing functions are performed by the neural structures that instantiate the behavioral inhibition system.

A Theory of Septo-Hippocampal Function

Theories of septo-hippocampal function have been many and diverse. One notion that is common to views that otherwise differ widely is that the hippocampus acts as a comparator, that is, as a mechanism that compares actual to expected stimuli (Elliott & Whelan, 1978). The application of this notion depends upon the particular hypothesis in which it figures. For example, O'Keefe and Nadel's (1978) theory treats the hippocampus as a device that constructs spatial maps and compares actual and expected locations of objects with respect to such maps; while, according to Vinogradova (1975), the same comparator function serves the detection of novelty versus familiarity. I have recently attempted to distill the common features of these different views (to the extent that they are supported by experimental evidence) and to integrate them into a more general theory of hippocampal function (Gray, 1982a).

The theory maps the functions of the behavioral inhibition system on to the septo-hippocampal system and connected structures; and at the same time it proposes specific ways in which these brain regions act so as to respond appropriately to anxiogenic stimuli (i.e., the inputs listed to the left in Figure 2.1). The theory allots functions to the septal area and hippocampus; to their ascending noradrenergic and serotonergic afferents; to the Papez loop (hippocampus → subicular area → mammillary bodies → anteroventral thalamus → cingulate cortex → subicular area); to the neocortical input to the hippocampus from the entorhinal area; to the prefrontal cortex, which projects to the entorhinal area and cingulate cortex; and to the pathways by which these structures are interconnected. The central task of this overall system is to compare, quite generally, actual with expected stimuli. The system functions in two modes. If actual stimuli are successfully matched with expected stimuli, it functions in the "checking mode," and behavioral control rests with other (unspecified) brain systems. If there is discordance between actual and expected stimuli or if the predicted stimulus is aversive (punishment of nonreward) — conditions jointly termed *mismatch* — it takes direct control over behavior, now functioning in the control mode.

In the control mode, the outputs of the behavioral inhibition system (Figure 2.1) are operated. First, there is an immediate inhibition of any motor program that is in the course of execution. Second, the motor program that was in the course of execution at the time that mismatch was detected is tagged with an indication which, in English, might read "faulty, needs checking." This has two further consequences: (a) On future occasions the relevant program is executed with greater restraint (more slowly, more easily interrupted by hesitations for exploratory behavior, more readiiy abandoned in favor of other programs, etc); and (b) the tagged motor program is given especially careful attention the next time it occurs. That is to say, the system exercises with particular care its basic function of checking predicted against actual events. Third, the system initiates specific exploratory and investigative behavior designed (a) to answer specific questions that arise from the operation of the comparator (e.g., is it turning left or approaching white which, in a typical animal experiment, is followed by footshock); and (b) to try out alternative motor programs that will attain the organism's objectives without mismatch.

It is further supposed that the system is able to identify certain stimuli as being particularly important and requiring especially careful checking. In this connection, the role played by the ascending noradrenergic projection to the septo-hippocampal system is of particular importance. Physiological experiments have shown that impulses coming from the entorhinal cortex to the hippocampus and thence to the subicular area (the major output from the hippocampus) must pass through a "gate" between the dentate gyrus and area CA3 of the hippocampus proper. With stimulus repetition, such impulses either habituate quickly or become consolidated and enhanced (Segal, 1977a, 1977b). It seems, furthermore, that impulses are more likely to pass the dentate/CA3 gate if they are associated with events of biological importance to the animal, such as food or footshock (Segal, 1977a). Segal (1977b) has, in addition, shown that the passage of impulses through the hippocampal formation is facilitated by the simultaneous stimulation of noradrenergic afferents to the hippocampus. The action of these afferents can be characterized as an increase in the signal-to-noise ratio of hippocampal neurons, thereby allowing them to respond more effectively to sensory information (of neocortical origin) entering the system from the entorhinal cortex. In accordance with these data, the theory attributes to the noradrenergic afferents to the septo-hippocampal system the role of labeling such sensory information as "important, needs careful checking," in the manner just outlined. A similar role may be played by the serotonergic afferents to the septo-hippocampal system.

This analysis of the neuropsychology of anxiety lays greatest emphasis upon structures in the limbic system, so updating Papez's (1937) brilliant insight that this part of the brain is ideally placed for the elaboration of emotional experience. Thus, the main comparator function is held to take place in the subicular area, the origin of the major efferents from the hippocampal formation. Predictions as to the next expected state of the world are held to be generated by the Papez circuit; a prediction is initiated by an input to this circuit from the subicular cortex when the previous prediction is successfully matched with the description of the current state of the world reaching the subiculum from the entorhinal area. For a prediction to be made, the predictive circuits require access to stored information describing past regularities in the experience of the animal. These may take the form of stimulus-stimulus regularities, derived from classical conditioning, or response-stimulus regularities, derived from instrumental conditioning. The theory supposed that long-term storage of these regularities is in the temporal lobe. Access to the stored information may go by way of the thalamus (for stimulus-stimulus regularities) or the cingulate cortex (for response-stimulus regularities), both of which lie athwart the Papez circuit; or by way of the subicular projection to the entorhinal area; which lies in the temporal lobe. A further item of information required for the making of predictions is a description of the current motor program: What happens next depends upon what the organism is doing now. It is supposed that this information originates in the prefrontal cortex and reaches the comparator circuits by way of the prefrontal projections to the entorhinal area and the cingulate cortex.

This is an inevitably over-condensed summary of a complex theory. In still further summary, the most important information-processing transactions it postulates are illustrated in Figure 2.3. An indication of how these have been allotted to various brain structures is presented in Figure 2.4.

Brain Systems that Mediate Anxiety: Other Approaches

The major starting point for the theory of anxiety encapsulated in Figures 2.3 and 2.4 has been pharmacological: the action of the anti-anxiety drugs. But, as indicated

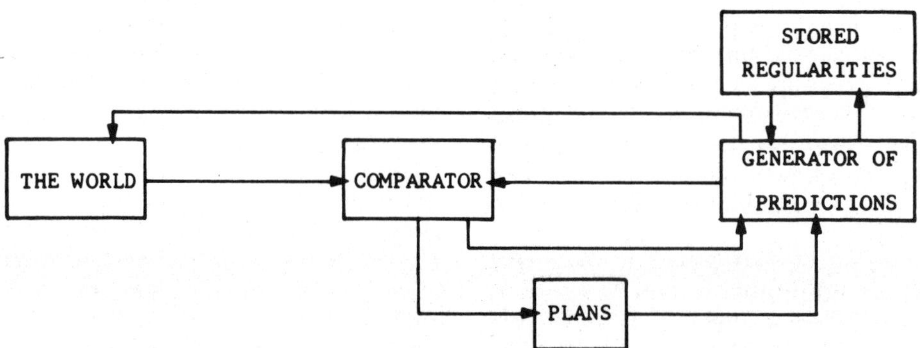

Figure 2.3. The kinds of information processing required for the successful functioning of the hypothetical comparator.

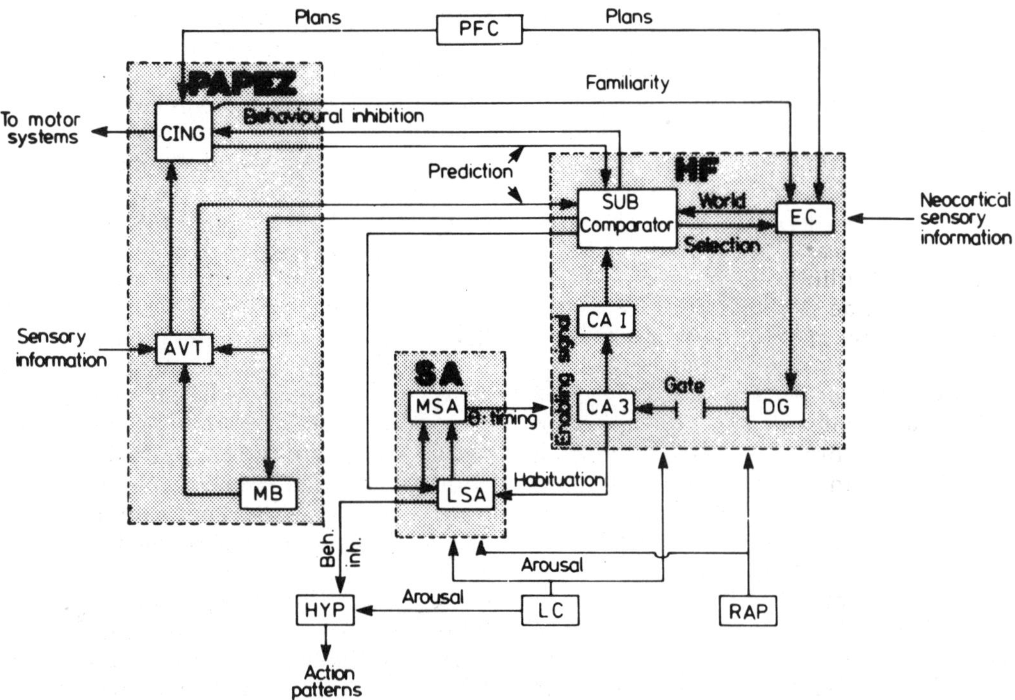

Figure 2.4. A summary of the theory developed in Gray (1982a, b). The three major building blocks are shown in heavy print: HF, the hippocampal formation, made up of the entorhinal cortex, EC, the dentate gyrus, DG, CA_3, CA_1, and the subicular area; the septal area, containing the medial and lateral septal areas, MSA and LSA; and the Papez circuit, which receives projections from and returns them to the subicular area via the mammillary bodies, MB, anteroventral thalamus, AVT, and cingulate cortex, CING. Other structures shown are the hypothalamus, HYP, the locus coeruleus, LC, the raphe nuclei, RAP, and the prefrontal cortex, PFC. Arrows show direction of projection; the projection from SUB to LSA lacks anatomical confirmation. Words in lower case show postulated functions: beh. inh., behavioral inhibition.

earlier, the same neural structures have also turned up in experiments concerned with the effects of infantile experience and selective breeding. I shall not consider these two lines of research in any detail (see Gray, in press), but confine myself to the points at which they have converged with the pharmacological approach to anxiety.

It has been known since the 1960s that the simple technique of picking up a rat pup during the first few days of its life has the permanent effect of lowering its adult level of fearfulness (Denenberg, 1964; Levine, 1962). Among other things, such early handling lowers adult levels of defecation in the open field test, the criterion of fearfulness used in the selective breeding studies that are considered next. In addition, as shown in a number of tests, early handling causes adult behavior to resemble that of an animal treated with an anxiolytic drug. (cf. Gray, 1977; Gray, in press). There are also effects of early handling upon the adrenocortical system: The adrenocortical response to stress is more flexible in the handled animals, showing a finer gradation in relation to the degree of imposed stress and a more rapid return to baseline after termination of the stress. Levine and Mullins (1966) proposed that these endocrine changes, and also the behavioral effects of early handling, might be due to an action of adrenocortical hormones, released in response to infantile stress, upon the dë veloping brain. More specifically, they suggested that the more varied the levels of adrenocortical hormones released during early life (for example, as a consequence of early handling), the greater is the number of distinct levels of activity that the pituitary-adrenocortical system is able to display in adult life. In striking confirmation of this hypothesis, it has recently been discovered that early handling gives rise to a permanent increase in the density of glucocorticoid receptors in the brain. This effect was confined to two regions of the brain: the hippocampus and the prefrontal cortex (Meaney et al., 1985). Glucocorticoid receptors in these regions are believed to play an important part in the negative feedback loop that controls the levels of circulation corticosteroids released in response to stress.

Research on the effects of early handling, then, has implicated the hippocampus and prefrontal cortex, as did research on the effects of anti-anxiety drugs. The parallel with the latter type of research is stronger still when we consider the results of selective breeding experiments. Broadhurst (1960), replicating experiments conducted in the 1930s by C. S. Hall, selectively bred rats for high or low defecation in the open field, creating the Maudsley Reactive and Nonreactive strains in consequence. There have been numerous studies of the behavior of these strains (Broadhurst, 1975), and much evidence has accumulated to show that the reactive strain is in general more fearful than the Nonreactive strain (Gray, 1971). The behavioral differences between the two strains in many (though not all) instances parallel those that discriminate between undrugged animals and animals that have been given an anti-anxiety drug. Furthermore, selective breeding has altered behavioral responsiveness to anti-anxiety drugs in both Maudsley strains (Gray, 1977, 1982a). These behavioral indications that selective breeding has acted upon the same substrate that is responsible for the effects of anxiolytic drugs are supplemented by the results of direct studies of the brain. These have shown strain differences in GABA and serotonin concentrations, benzodiazepine receptor density, noradrenaline release, and the electrophysiology of the septohippocampal system (see Broadhurst, 1975; Gray in press).

The experiments on the electrophysiology of the septo-hippocampal system (Drewett et al., 1977; Gray, 1982a) formed part of a direct comparison between the effects of anxiolytic drugs and those of selective breeding. Neurons in the medial septal area are known to control the rhythmical slow activity, known as the "theta rhythm," that can be recorded from the hippocampus under a variety of behavioral conditions, Stimulation of these cells via chronically indwelling electrodes is able to drive the theta rhythm. If the threshold for such "theta driving" is measured in the free-moving rat as a function of stimulation frequency, there is a minimum threshold at 7.7 Hz. This minimum is due to the activity of the noradrenergic input to the septo-hippocampal system, and may be eliminated by destruction of these fibres. The 7.7-Hz minimum threshold may also be eliminated by administration of any of a range of anxiolytic drugs or by the $GABA_A$ agonist, muscimol. The 7.7-Hz minimum is presend in animals of many strains, including the Maudsley Reactive strain; but it is absent in animals of the Maudsley Nonreactive strain. In this highly specific aspect of the electrophysiology of the septo-hippocampal system, then, the Nonreactive rat resembles an unselected rat that has been given an antianxiety drug. This is strong evidence that selective breeding for low open-field defecation has engaged the same neural systems whose function is altered by acute administration of anxiolytics.

Brain Systems that Mediate Anxiety in Human Beings

These different lines of research give substance to the claim, made at the start of this chapter, that there exists a separable subsystem of the brain, activity corresponds to anxiety. We must next ask whether there is evidence to link this subsystem with clinical evidence of anxiety in human beings.

Such evidence is not easily obtained, for all the usual reasons that impede studies of human brain function. However, there are clear pointers to the same brain systems that have emerged in the animal experiments summarized earlier. The most compelling evidence comes from a recent study using positron emission tomography (PET) to compare patients who suffer from panic attacks with controls (Reiman, Raichler, Butler, Hersovitch & Robins, 1984). Only one brain region differed between the two groups: the one containing the major input to the septo-hippocampal system (the entorhinal area) and its major output (the subicular cortex). This study, then, implicates the septo-hippocampal system. A second series of observations implicates central noradrenergic neurons. It is possible to monitor the activity of these neurons indirectly by measuring plasma concentrations of 3-methoxy-4-hydroxphenylglycol (MHPG), the principal metabolite of brain noradrenaline. Charney, Heininger, and Breier (1984) measured plasma MHPG in response to systemic administration of an γ_2-adrenergic receptor blocker, yohimbine, that increases activity in the locus coeruleus by blocking auto-receptor-mediated negative feedback. The drug gave rise to correlated increases in plasma MHPG levels and self-reported anxiety. Furthermore, both effects were greater in patients who suffer from panic attacks than in controls.

There is also evidence that serotonin discharges the same functions in human beings as in animals. However, this evidence has to be interpreted with caution. Pharmacological blockade of serotonergic transmission in animals alleviates punishment-induced suppression of instrumental behavior (Graeff & Schoenfeld, 1970). This is also a classic effect of the anti-anxiety drugs. Many theorists have therefore supposed that blockade of serotonergic transmission should reduce anxiety in human beings. A closer look at the role played by serotonergic pathways in response suppression, however, shows the flaw in this argument. For the major role of serotonergic mechanisms appears to be that of motor inhibition as such (Gray, 1982a; Soubrié, 1986). Now, consider the effects if environmental anxiogenic stimuli had triggered a state of anxiety which would normally eventuate in the behavioral inhibition output of the behavioral inhibition system (Figure 2.1), but this output were blocked because of impaired serotonergic transmission. Would such a blockade of motor inhibition reduce anxiety? Surely not: The patient would continue to experience anxiogenic stimulation but be unable to cope with it in the normal manner. Under some conditions, such a predicament might even give rise to an increase in anxiety. Just such an increase has been reported by Graeff, Zuardi, Giglio, Lima Filho, and Karniol (1985) when metergoline (a serotonin-receptor blocker) was administered to human subjects during a simulated public speaking task.

More direct evidence for serotonin-mediated response inhibition in human beings comes from a series of studies in which the levels of 5-hydroxyindoleacetic acid (5-HIAA), the principal metabolite of serotonin, have been measured in cerebrospinal fluid (CSF) (see Soubrié, 1986, for review). Data from many animal experiments indicate that serotonergic mechanisms inhibit aggressive behavior. It is consistent with these data that 5-HIAA levels in human CSF correlate negatively with a history of aggressive behavior directed toward either others or oneself (suicide attempts). Low 5-HIAA levels have also been found among criminals, especially those who have been incarcerated for violent and aggressive behavior. Furthermore, in agreement with Graeff et al.'s (1985) results with metergoline (described earlier), patients with low levels of CSF 5-HIAA have been found to be high on measures of anxiety.

One difficulty with these studies is that the 5-HIAA in CSF comes mainly from the spinal cord, not the brain. But, in answer to this objection, Stanley, Virgilio, and Gershon (1982) have investigated post-mortem material from suicides, and report reduced binding of imipramine in the frontal cortex. Because imipramine binding is associated with the neural uptake mechanism for serotonin, this observation suggests a reduced serotonergic input to the frontal cortex in people who commit suicide, in agreement with the lowered CSF 5-HIAA in people who merely attempt it.

Further evidence of continuity between the systems that subserve anxiety in animals and humans comes from patients who, as a last resort, undergo psychosurgery for relief of their symptoms. The operations used for this purpose include cingulectomy and prefrontal leucotomy (Powell, 1979); the latter interrupts the projection from the prefrontal to the cingulate and entorhinal cortices. The majority of patients treated in this way were suffering from chronic and severe obsessive-compulsive symptoms or anxiety state. The success rate has been good. Thus Mitchell-Heggs, Kelly, and Richardson (1976) report a follow-up of 15 cases of anxiety state and 27 obsessional patients who had had severely disabling symptoms for an average of 11 years. Sixteen months after the operation, 89% of the obsessionals and 66% of the patients with anxiety state were improved.

At first glance, these observations fit comfortably with the theory of anxiety outlined earlier, because both cingulectomy and prefrontal leucotomy would be expected to compromise the functioning of the predictive circuits (in the Papez loop, Figure 2.4) that feed into the subicular comparator. A problem is posed, however, by the fact that psychosurgery is used only with patients who have first proved to be resistant to pharmacotheapy; yet the model illustrated in Figures 2.1 and 2.4 has been derived from an analysis of the effects of the drugs. A way out of this difficulty is to suppose that the projections from the prefrontal cortex to the cingulate and enthorhinal cortices provide a route by which the neocortex, and especially neocortical language systems, are able to control the activities of the septo-hippocampal system and its associated predictive and comparator circuits in a way that is more or less independent of the ascending monoaminergic pathways responsible for the effects of the anxiolytic drugs (Gray, 1982a). We need then only suppose that, in patients who are resistant to drug therapy but benefit from psychosurgery, anxious behavior has come largely to depend upon interactions between limbic and neocortical structures rather than upon the ascending monoaminergic route. This assumption is amplified later, when we consider the symptoms observed in one type of patient (the obsessive-compulsive) who has tended to benefit from psychosurgery but not from anxiolytic drugs.

Several of the major components of the system depicted in Figure 2.4 — the hippocampus, the cingulate cortex, central noradrenergic and central serotonergic pathways — appear, then, to play essentially the same roles in human emotional behavior as in that of animals. It seems reasonable to suppose, therefore, that the separable subsystem of the brain which has been picked out in animals by studies of anxiolytic drugs, early handling, and selective breeding (jointly and severally) is the same as the system that mediates anxiety in human beings. If so, it should be possible to apply the knowledge of the anxiety system gained in animals to the understanding of anxiety in human beings. Before we attempt to do this, however, we should take note of another experimental approach to the study of emotional behavior in animals that has led to the description of a quite different brain subsystem.

Brain System for Fight/Flight Behavior

The behavioral inhibition system (Figure 2.1) responds to stimuli associated with unconditioned pain or nonreward, but not to the latter events themselves. There is evidence for a quite separate system that is specialized to respond to unconditioned pain and nonreward. Behaviorally, the responses to such stimuli, as observed in laboratory animals, include striking, biting, the adoption of species-specific defensive postures, flight, upwards rearing and jumping, hissing, and squealing (Adams, 1979). This type of "fight/flight" behavior is quite different from the behavior elicited by conditioned stimuli associated with pain, which consists principally in immobility and silence (Gray, 1975, in press; Myer, 1971) — a phenomenon encapsulated in the "behavioral inhibition" output of the behavioral inhibition system.

Pharmacologically, the difference between the systems that mediate responses to conditioned and unconditioned aversive stimuli is reflected in an important double dissociation between the behavioral effects of anxiolytics and opiates: The former affect reactions to conditioned, but not unconditioned, aversive stimuli; the latter have the reverse pattern of effects. Neurologically, there are again clear differences between the systems concerned. We have already considered the most important brain structures implicated in the organization of responses to conditioned stimuli associated with punishment or nonreward (Figure 2.4). Experiments in which electrical stimulation of the brain has been used to elicit, or brain lesions to suppress, fight/flight behavior have similarly provided a well-documented map of the structures involved in the organization of this behavior (Adams, 1979; Graeff, in press; Panksepp, 1982). The chief components in this map are the amygdala, the ventromedial hypothalamus, and the midbrain central gray. These structures appear to be linked together in the manner shown in Figure 2.5. The central gray component of

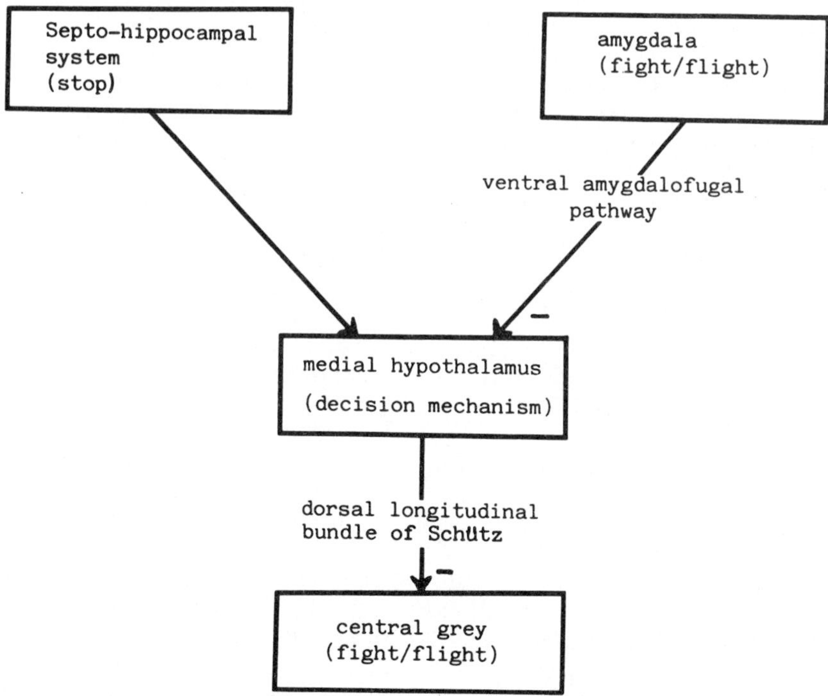

Figure 2.5. The fight/flight system (amygdala, medial hypothalamus and central gray). Also shown is one route by which the behavioral inhibition system is able to influence the fight/flight system (by way of the septo-hippocampal input to the hypothalamus). Arrows indicate direction of flow of information; –, 'inhibits'. From Gray (1987).

this fight/flight system is closely related, and perhaps identical to, neurons that mediate the central experience of pain (Melzack & Wall, 1983).

Most of the experimental evidence concerning fight/flight behavior relates to the effects of pain rather than nonreward. In the case of conditioned aversive stimuli, there is much experimental support for the hypothesis that stimuli associated with nonreward are functionally equivalent to stimuli associated with punishment and act via a common neurological system (Gray, 1975, 1982a), as encapsulated in Figure 2.1. Such evidence as exists suggests that there is a similar functional and neurological equivalence between unconditioned pain and nonreward. Like pain, nonreward elicits aggression against conspecies (e.g., Gallup, 1965). Neurologically, there is only one important experiment, by Henke (1977), to go on. He showed the lesions to the amygdala (known to reduce responses to pain) abolished the double-runway frustration effect (a phenomenon with good credentials as a measure of the unconditioned response to nonrewards; Amsel and Roussel, 1952), but left intact the partial reinforcement extinction effect, which is controlled by conditional stimuli associated with nonreward. Both septal lesions and anxiolytic drugs, in contrast, produce the reverse pattern of effects (Gray, 1982a).

Interactions Between the Behavioral Inhibition and Fight/Flight Systems

The structures illustrated in Figures 2.4 and 2.5, respectively, are clearly different. Furthermore, such interactions as have been demonstrated between the behavioral inhibition and fight/flight systems are primarily inhibitory; in particular, activation of the behavioral inhibition system inhibits reactions to unconditioned aversive stimuli. Thus, Fanselow and Baackes (1982) showed that presentation of a stimulus associated with shock reduces the rat's pain reaction to a subcutaneous injection of formalin. This effect is apparently mediated by endogenous opiates, because it can be blocked by administration of the opiate antagonist, naltrexone.

There are several loci at which the behavioral inhibition system is able to inhibit activity in the fight/flight system. Albert and his co-workers have demonstrated a descending inhibitory pathway from the lateral septal area to the ventromedial hypothalamus (Albert & Chew, 1980). This pathway may be responsible for switching behavior from defensive attack to the display of submissive postures (Adams, 1979; Gray, in press). Another important locus lies in the central gray, where neurons appear to be under three kinds of inhibitory control: GABAergic, serotonergic, and opioid (Graeff, in press). The latter types of inhibitory control may be responsible for the inhibition of pain by conditioned fear stimuli demonstrated by Fanselow and Baackes (1982) (also see Gray, in press).

The existence of both GABAergic and serotonergic inhibitory controls over central gray neurons can account for some otherwise puzzling inconsistencies between the effects of anxiolytic drugs on escape and aggressive reactions elicited by peripheral painful stimuli and by electrical simulation of the central gray, respectively. In the former case, anxiolytics do not normally weaken such reactions; in the latter, they reliably do so (Graeff, in press; Gray, 1977). Now, as we know, anxiolytic drugs facilitate GABAergic inhibition and also reduce stress-induced increases in serotonergic activity (the latter effect probably being secondary to the former). It is likely, therefore, that systemic administration of these drugs will have two opposing effects upon the activity of central gray neurons. Via central gray GABAergic synapses, they will reduce such activity, so tending to oppose fight/flight behavior; at the same time, they will weaken serotonergic inhibition of central gray neurons, so tending to augment fight/flight behavior. This should lead to little net change, or to variable changes depending upon the exact balance of forces in particular cases; and this is a reasonable description of the data (Gray, 1977). Presumably, the serotonergic input to the central gray is at least to some extent by-passed when this region is stimulated electrically, so allowing the tendency of the anxiolytic drugs to oppose fight/flight behavior (by enhanced GABAergic inhibition in the central gray itself) to predominate. This general analysis is supported by the effects of central gray stimulation.

With these interactions in mind, let us consider again the way in which the behavioral inhibition system must operate. The primary function of this system is apparently to suppress behavior that threatens to produce an unwelcome outcome (pain, nonreward, etc.). It follows that the system can only usefully be put to work if some other system is producing behavior that needs to be suppressed. There are essentially two major motivational systems that can do this (Gray, in press): a "reward system" (in which the dopaminergic projections to the corpus striatum and nucleus accumbens appear to play key roles), mediating approach and active avoidance behavior in response to stimuli associated with reward or the omission of anticipated punishment; and the fight/flight system described earlier. To these motivational systems should be added a number of more specialized mechanisms that mediate various forms of unconditioned appetitive behavior (eating, drinking, copulation, etc.). These considerations imply that, at any one time when the behavioral inhibition system is active, the total emotional experience will be an amalgam of the emotional effects of activity in this system and those of activity in the system whose output is under inhibition. It is plausible to suppose that such an amalgam will be maximally negative in affective tone when the system inhibited is the fight/flight system. In the light of his experiments employing electrical stimulation of the central gray (see above), Graeff (1981) suggests, therefore, that the anti-anxiety drugs owe their clinical effectiveness to their capacity to reduce activity simultaneously in both the behavioral inhibition and the fight/flight systems (see also Panksepp, 1982).

SYMPTOMS OF ANXIETY

Detailed descriptions of the syndromes and symptoms of anxiety can be found elsewhere in this *Handbook*. Here I shall consider them only insofar as they may be illuminated by the theoretical framework developed earlier. At the syndromal level it is useful to distinguish between phobias, obsessive–compulsive neurosis, and the anxiety state. But it should be noted that the key symptoms of each of these syndromes are often found together, so that it is unlikely that they correspond to fundamental differences at the level of process. At the level of symptoms, it has become common to distinguish between behavioral, cognitive, and physiological aspects of anxiety (Lang, 1970; Rachman, 1978). This division is useful, so long as it is not taken to correspond in any simple manner to separate systems in the brain. Thus, the behavioral inhibition system, as described here, would be expected to affect the symptomatic picture in all three of these aspects. Behavior is affected by the outputs of this system shown in Figure 2.1. The cognitive aspects of anxiety will reflect the information-processing activities of the septo-hippocampal system and related structures (in a manner considered in more detail later. And the autonomic signs of anxiety (Lader, 1975) depend, at least in part, upon fibers that descend into the spinal cord from the locus coeruleus (Redmond, 1979).

The Phobias

Behaviorally, the chief symptom of the phobias is avoidance of the phobic stimulus. This stimulus is typically something that is not objectively dangerous. In many cases, however, the phobic stimulus evokes fear quite widely in the normal population (e.g., spiders, snakes). Seligman (1971) has proposed that such stimuli are "prepared" (by evolutionary history and Darwinian natural selection) to enter rapidly into association with other, unconditioned stimuli (e.g., a painful shock). If so, they activate the behavioral inhibition system by the definition of this system contained in Figure 1.

Experimental evidence in support of Seligman's hypothesis has been gathered in Öhman's (1979) laboratory. However, the interpretation of this evidence is in doubt (Gray, 1982a), and I prefer the simpler hypothesis that phobic stimuli of this kind are innately capable of activating the behavioral inhibition system. The reason that such "innate fear stimuli" (Gray, 1971) do not appear in the list of inputs to the behavioral inhibition system shown in Figure 2.1 is that the appropriate experiments (investigating the effects of anxiolytic drugs on reactions to such stimuli) have been largely neglected. Whether snakes, spiders, and the like have an innate capacity to act as fear stimuli, or acquire this capacity through very rapid and long-lasting conditioning, is of comparatively little importance to the matter considered here (though it is an important issue with regard to the etiology of the phobias).

An important class of innate fear stimuli is constituted by the emotional expressions emanating from conspecifics during social interaction. Both fearful and aggressive expressions have been shown to elicit fear in experiments using both human and animal subjects (Gray, in press). Innate (or "prepared") reactions to such social stimuli may be of particular importance in the social phobias.

This treatment of the majority of phobic stimuli as being innate contrasts with many earlier treatments of such stimuli as resulting from Pavlovian conditioning (Watson & Rayner, 1920). Eysenck (1979) has summarized the objections to the conditioning theory. The most important are:

1. The stimuli that elicit phobias are not a random sample of stimuli: Some (e.g., snakes, closed spaces) are greatly overrepresented.
2. Phobic stimuli unaccompanied by their unconditioned stimuli ought (if they are conditioned stimuli) to undergo extinction; of course, they do not, or phobias would not constitute a psychiatric problem. To these two objections, Gray (1979) added:
3. The times of onset of phobias are not a random sample of ages; there is a predominance of onsets in early adult life (Marks, 1969).

The first two of these objections are met by treating phobic stimuli as either innate or prepared because prepared conditioning is held to be extremely resistant to extinction). The third is met only by treating them as innate (because there is no reason why prepared conditioning should chance to happen at one time of life rather than another). It is characteristic of innate behavioral propensities that they undergo maturation, appearing at the time they are needed. Thus, the social phobias, for example, appear at the time when the competition for social advantage comes to be played in earnest, that is, in early adult life (Marks, 1969).

This is not to deny, however, all influence to conditioning and learning. On the contrary, these processes play at least three important roles.

First, experience plays a part in the formation of the personality that predisposes to anxiety (discussed later). Studies both of phobic individuals (Torgersen, 1979) and of the personality traits of neuroticism and extraversion (Young, Eaves, & Eysenck, 1980) estimate the contribution of heredity to these conditions at about 50% of the variance. Broadhurst's (1960, 1975) work on the Maudsley rat strains arrived at similar estimates for open-field defecation. But that means, of course, that another 50% of the variance remains to be accounted for, and it is likely that learning plays a determining role in this respect.

Second, there are cases in which phobic stimuli cannot in any manner be described as innate or prepared (Rachman & Seligman, 1976). Some of these clearly require an account in terms of conditioning. Eysenck (1977), for example, describes a case in which a man developed a phobic reaction to a pattern of wallpaper that had been on the walls of a bedroom in which he had been set upon by an irate husband. Cases such as these, however, appear to comprise only a minority of phobias. They offer no problem for the analysis presented here, which treats them as stimuli associated with unconditioned aversive stimuli and therefore capable of acting upon the behavioral inhibition system.

Third, conditioning undoubtedly plays a role in extending phobic reactions. Thus, someone who is afraid of snakes may curtail activities that bring him or her into contact with stimuli only secondarily associated with snakes. These associations may spread along the intricate network of routes offered by stimulus and semantic generalization (Razran, 1971). A particularly important way in which this process can come into play lies in the development of a fear of situations associated with the physiological consequences of fear itself ("anticipatory anxiety" in Klein's terms; discussed later). In this manner, a person who experiences a panic attack in a particular environment may develop a conditioned phobic reaction to that environment; associational spread of this response may then contribute to the development of agoraphobia.

This analysis implicitly treats the panic attacks often seen in agoraphobia and the agoraphobic symptoms themselves as different in kind. This distinction has been forcefully advocated by Klein (1981), who has gathered important pharmacological data in its support. He finds that, whereas anti-anxiety drugs reduce anticipatory anxiety in agoraphobics, these agents do not affect panic attacks, which are in contrast reduced by certain antidepressants. Now, Graeff (in press) points out that the autonomic changes seen in panic attacks resemble those that are produced in animals by electrical stimulation of the central gray (discussed earlier); and also that the drugs that are effective in controlling panic attacks include compounds whose primary mode of action is to inhibit serotonin re-uptake, so facilitating serotonergic transmission. Graeff proposes, therefore, that panic attacks are due to a deficiency in serotonergic inhibition of activity in the central gray, and that antidepressants control the attacks by increasing such inhibition. A physiological analysis of this kind is congruent with an account that treats the panic attacks as unconditioned stimuli (acting via the fight/flight system) for the conditioning of anticipatory anxiety to situational cues (acting via the behavioral inhibition system). An alternative account (not necessarily in conflict with the first) would treat patients who suffer from panic attacks as having high activity in both the fight/flight and the behavioral inhibition systems, with the attacks themselves arising from phasic failures in the inhibition of activity in the fight/flight system normally exercised by the behavioral inhibition system.

Obsessive-Compulsive Syndrome

The phobias constitute a relatively low hurdle for theories of anxiety. A much higher hurdle is posed by the obsessive-compulsive syndrome. In the majority of patients suffering from this disorder there is a ritual behavioral act that makes no obvious sense (the excessive washing of already clean hands is a common example). Prevention of this ritual gives rise to a sharp increase in the subjective experience and physiological signs of anxiety (Roper & Rachman, 1976). At the cognitive level, most such patients also experience obsessions; that is, "intrusive, repetitive thoughts, images, or impulses that are unacceptable and/or unwanted and give rise to subjective resistance" (Rachman, 1978). Not surprisingly, it is the obsessions that are most recalcitrant to explanations derived from the animal laboratory.

The most successful laboratory-based account to date of the compulsive rituals of the obsessional patient treats these as active avoidance responses in distinction to the passive avoidance that characterizes phobic reactions (Gray, 1971; Hodgson & Rachman, 1972). Passive avoidance refers to the kind of behavior in which an animal refrains from making a desired response for fear of punishment, a function attributed to the behavioral inhibition system

(Figure 2.1). Active avoidance, in contrast, is the case in which punishment can be avoided only by making a specified response, all others being followed by punishment (Gray, 1975). The dominant theory of active avoidance behavior for many years attributed its reinforcement and maintenance to the reduction of fear consequent upon escape from stimuli associated with punishment (Mowrer, 1947). Application of this theory to compulsive rituals requires the assumptions that there are fear-eliciting stimuli in the environment (e.g., sources of contamination or dirt) and a consequent increase in anxiety. That performance of the compulsive ritual is followed by a decrease in anxiety and is thus acquired and maintained as an active avoidance response. This account has much to recommend it, and direct tests have provided experimental supported for these assumptions. Thus, it is indeed possible in many cases to identify environmental stimuli that provoke the compulsive ritual; and, as demanded by the theory, exposure to these stimuli without performance of the ritual increases anxiety, while performance of the ritual is followed by a decrease in anxiety (Hodgson & Rachman, 1972; Roper & Rachman, 1976).

Extension of this type of model to obsessional symptoms is more difficult. Rachman (1978) treats obsessions, for example the *thought* of homosexual acts, the *impulse* to jump out of a window, or the *image* of dead people in an open coffin, as aversive internal stimuli which, like phobic objects, give rise to anxiety and attempts at avoidance. Such behavior may be overt. So, one who is troubled by an impulse to jump out of windows may (passively) avoid windows. Or a compulsive behavioral ritual may be used as an active avoidance response (e.g., a patient troubled by sexual thoughts is able to gain relief by going through a hand-washing routine). Alternatively, the avoidance behavior, like the obsession, may remain internal. Thus, Rachman (1978) describes a patient who could gain temporary relief from his obsessional sexual thoughts if he constructed a "good thought" and then repeated the action that had been interrupted by the "bad" one. Similarly a patient troubled by an image of a child in danger may succeed in "putting things right" by forming a counter-image of the child safe and sound. (Rachman, 1976).

Rachman's (1978) attempt to treat obsessions in this way is valiant. But the strain that behavioral concepts suffer when they are pushed like this into the mind is evident. It is also inevitable: Cognitive phenomena are not behavior, they are part of the systems that control behavior; and part of this part (for whatever mysterious reason) happens to reach consciousness and becomes open to introspective account, as in the patients Rachman describes. To suppose that the systems that control behavior follow the same laws as behavior itself is the same kind of categorical mistake as to believe that the neural activity of the visual cortex is watched by a second pair of eyes inside the head.

Even at the level of behavior, the active-avoidance account leaves many crucial aspects of the obsessive-compulsive syndrome unexplained. In one respect the weaknesses of this account are similar to those of the standard conditioning account of the phobias (Eysenck, 1979; discussed earlier): the selectivity of obsessional-compulsive behavior goes unexplained. The rituals seen in this syndrome are not a random sample of the kinds of behavior that might just happen to precede the reduction in anxiety by which they are supposedly reinforced; nor are obsessions a random sample of ideas that could be frightening. On the contrary, there is a great regularity in the kinds of ritual and obsession observed in widely differing places. In New Delhi (Akhtar, Wig, Varma, Pershad, & Verma, 1975) as in England (Rachman, 1978), the commonest obsessional preoccupation is with dirt, disease, or contamination (50%–60% of reported obsessions); followed by orderliness and aggression (35% and 19%, respectively, in England; 23% and 25% in India); and then by religion and sex (10% and 13% in England, 10% and 5% in India). Behavioral rituals similarly consist in the great majority of cases of cleaning, tidying up, and checking that potential threats (dirt, germs, etc.) are absent.

Also unexplained by the active-avoidance model is the intrusive nature of obsessions and the repetitive nature of rituals. If the internal stimulus that constitutes an obsession is aversive, it should be avoided; and the way to avoid such an internal stimulus (because it can only be the patient's own brain that is producing it) is to *stop* producing it. Of course, this does not happen, or there would be no clinical problem. On the contrary, obsessions occur not once, but repeatedly and intrusively. Similarly if compulsive rituals are active avoidance responses, one might expect them to occur once or a few times. But the animal experiments on which the active-avoidance model is based offer no reason to suppose that such responses should be repeated tens or even hundreds of times, as clinically observed.

Checking Functions of the Behavioral Inhibition System

Given these difficulties for the active-avoidance model of obsessive-compulsive symptoms, we should consider an alternative account. Such an account may be developed within the framework provided by the behavioral inhibition system and its neural instantiation, as outlined earlier in the chapter. The chief function of the behavioral inhibition system is to monitor ongoing behavior, checking continuously that outcomes coincide with expectations. In this role, it scans incoming sensory information for threatening or unexpected events and, if they occur, brings all other behavior to a halt, so as to evaluate the nature of the threat. Certain stimuli are tagged "important" and searched for with particular care. Now, there are two ways in which activity in a system of this nature can give rise to anxiety symptoms. First, when the system enters the control mode (having detected mis match), it operates the outputs shown in Figure 2.1, including that of behavioral inhibition. In terms of learning theory, this is the equivalent of passive avoidance; clinically, it is the equivalent of phobic behavior. The second way in which the behavioral inhibition system can give rise to anxiety is by excessive activity in the checking mode: by tagging too many stimuli as "important" searching for them too persistently, as so on. It is plausible to see such an excess of checking activity as corresponding to the obsessive–compulsive syndrome.

Had it not been derived from quite independent sources of data, this description might seem too close to the phenomena to count as an explanation at all. It treats obsessive–compulsive behavior much as does common sense. The patient scans his or her environment to an excessive degree for potential threats: dirt, bacteria, sharp objects, and the like. Much of this scan is carried out overtly, in the form of behavioral checking rituals. The exact form of the ritual will depend, naturally, on the threat the patient is attempting to exclude. If this is a scratch, the person searches for sharp objects; if disorder, for objects out of place. Some rituals may both serve this kind of checking function and act as avoidance responses. Thus, that most common of rituals, hand-washing, is at once an effective means of searching for dirt and a way to remove it. But, if it were only an active-avoidance response, it would not be expected to occur over and over again; its repetitiveness derives from its checking function.

The functions attributed to the behavioral inhibition system also offer a natural account of the cognitive symptoms of the obsessive–compulsive patient. There are two ways these can arise.

First, the scan for potential threats in the external environment can extend to internal repositories of information concerning such threats. These are likely in many cases to be coded verbally; indeed, patients report that obsessions often take a verbal form (Rachman & de Silva, 1978). Information of this kind is presumably stored in the language areas of the temporal lobe (Ojemann & Mateer, 1979). The subicular area has easy access to this region of the neocortex by way of its projection to the entorhinal area, as does the hippocampus itself. This is therefore perhaps the route used when one who is anxious, say, about cutting himself, checks his memory to verify where he disposed of a razor blade. It is easy to see how such an internal scan could involve imagining the relevant scene. So, a person whose greatest fear is of harming her child may imagine scenes in which she has done just that (Rachman & de Silva, 1978).

Second, there are some threats that are themselves purely internal in origin. Rachman and de Silva (1978) describe several cases in which patients are afraid of their own impulses, for example, to jump out of the window to utter swear words. How is the behavioral inhibition system (now, no doubt, under descending neocortical control; see the earlier discussion of psychosurgery and the prefrontal cortex) to check on threats of this nature? This can be done only by an internal scan of the systems that produce the behavior of which the patient is afraid. But at this point the principle of ideo-motor action (James, 1890) is likely to come into play. That is, the thought of a particular action primes the systems that produce it. Thus, checking whether one has a dangerous impulse will increase the probability of experiencing it. The intrusive and repetitive nature of obsessional impulses could in this way arise from the very checking process that attempts to ensure that they are absent; and similar analyses can be applied to obsessional thoughts or images.

The selectivity of rituals and obsessions also finds a reasonably natural account within this framework. Rituals are for the most part fairly obvious examples of checking behavior. In the case of hand-washing, however, other factors may also be at work. As pointed out earlier, this ritual may conveniently serve simultaneously a checking and an active-avoidance function. In the latter capacity, it may be favored by early learning that it is an effective way of removing parental anger (Gray, 1971). There may also be an evolutionary continuity between the human use of soap and water and more ancient forms of grooming behavior. Recall that, as a counterpart to the privileged status of hand-washing among compulsive rituals, so dirt is the commonest of obsessional preoccupations. Thus, natural selection may have favored fear of dirt and its attendant grooming behavior as much as fear of snakes or enclosed spaces; the danger to survival is no less great.

The other common obsessional preoccupations require somewhat different explanations. The need for orderliness may spring from the fact that disorder produces novel arrays of stimuli, which *ex hypothesi* activate the behavioral inhibition system. Obsessions with aggressive and sexual impulses and thoughts arise naturally from the internal origin of these drives, the danger of retribution attendant upon their illicit satisfaction, and the way in which the behavioral inhibition system must use internal scans to check up on them. As to obsessions with religion, the concern that religion has for cleanliness, sex, and aggression probably makes these parasitic on the rest.

The analysis of anxiety presented in this chapter took as its chief starting point the behavioral effects of anti-anxiety drugs in animals. Nonetheless, it is able to tackle some of the most cognitive aspects of this condition. Note, however, that this slippery word, *cognitive*, may be used in at least three senses. First, it may be applied to the information-processing activities carried out by the systems that control behavior. Second, it refers to features of such activities which, for unknown reasons, reach conscious awareness. We have paid some attention to the cognitive phenomena of anxiety in both these senses. The third sense of *cognitive* refers to the verbal reports that figure so heavily, say, in a psychiatric interview. Frequently the word *cognitive*, when it is used in the context of a psychological or psychiatric analysis of anxiety, means only the self-report that the patient is anxious, or even a tick placed at an appropriate point on an adjective checklist. Such self-reports are only of marginal interest to the kind of analysis that has been offered here, because this assumes that language systems (though they clearly interact with the behavioral inhibition system; see earlier discussion) are quite separate from those that mediate the core emotional state of anxiety. Furthermore, the association between *cognitive* phenomena in the first two senses and in the third is quite loose. Some aspects of self-reported anxiety can only be understood on the assumption that patients' observe their own behaviors (rather than their internal information processing), much as do outsiders', and then come to appropriate conclusions concerning their emotional states. This is the most natural explanation, for example, of the fact that, when phobic or obsessional behavior is successfully treated behaviorally, the self-report of improvement often lags behind behavioral and physiological recovery by many weeks (Rachman & Hodgson, 1974).

The Anxious Personality

We do not all run an equal risk of developing symptoms of anxiety. With the exception of simple animal phobias, which are perhaps no more than residual childhood fears (Marks, 1969), such symptoms are predominately observed in individuals who score high on neuroticism and introversion in tests such as those devised by Cattell (1965) and Eysenck and Eysenck (1969). This predisposing effect of permanent personality traits is consistent with the emphasis placed earlier on the capacity of certain kinds of stimuli innately to activate the behavioral inhibition system.

The techniques of factor analysis, which have been used to describe the major dimensions (Eysenck & Eysenck, 1969) and subfactors (Cattell, 1965) of human personality, can establish how many independent dimensions there are in a given personality space, but not where they should be located (Gray, 1981). Thus, if any location of these axes reflects underlying causal influences, this cannot be established by factor-analytic techniques alone, but must be justified by other considerations empirical or theoretical. In terms of the approach adopted in this chapter, the phrase *underlying causal influence* must be interpreted as an influence proceeding from systematic individual differences in the functioning of a separable subsystem of the brain (Gray, 1968). To take an example, factor–analytic methods have established two separate major subfactors of intelligence: verbal and visuo-spatial ability. Subsequently, it transpired that these are likely to reflect individual differences in the activities of the dominant and subdominant cerebral hemispheres, respectively (McFie, 1972). Similarly, in the personality space that describes individual differences in emotional behavior, we should seek to locate our descriptive axes in such a manner that they are most likely to reflect the activities of brain systems that control such behavior.

Because the behavioural inhibition system, as neurally instantiated in the structures illustrated in Figure 2.4, appears to function as a unity (albeit one with differentiated parts), it is reasonable to locate anxious individuals at the pole of a single personality dimension, rather than in a quadrant bounded by two, as does Eysenck's (1981) "neurotic introvert" location. This argument leads to the rotation of Eysenck's axes, shown in Figure 2.6. This preserves two orthogonal axes in the space defined by his dimensions of neuroticism and extraversion-introversion, but now has one of them run from his neurotic introvert to his stable extravert quadrant. Schematically, one can represent this as a 45° rotation of Eysenck's axes. But the fact that cingulectomy and prefrontal lesions reduce neuroticism more than introversion (Powell, 1979), coupled with the observed correlations between the Eysenckian dimensions and scales intended directly to measure the trait of anxiety, suggest a rotation that locates the resulting dimension of *anxiety* closer to Eysenck's dimension of *neuroticism* than to his *extraversion*. The dimension so rotated is close to the trait of anxiety found in the work of Cattell (1965) and Taylor (1953). Arguments and evidence in favor of this rotation are presented elsewhere (Gray, 1970b, 1981, 1983).

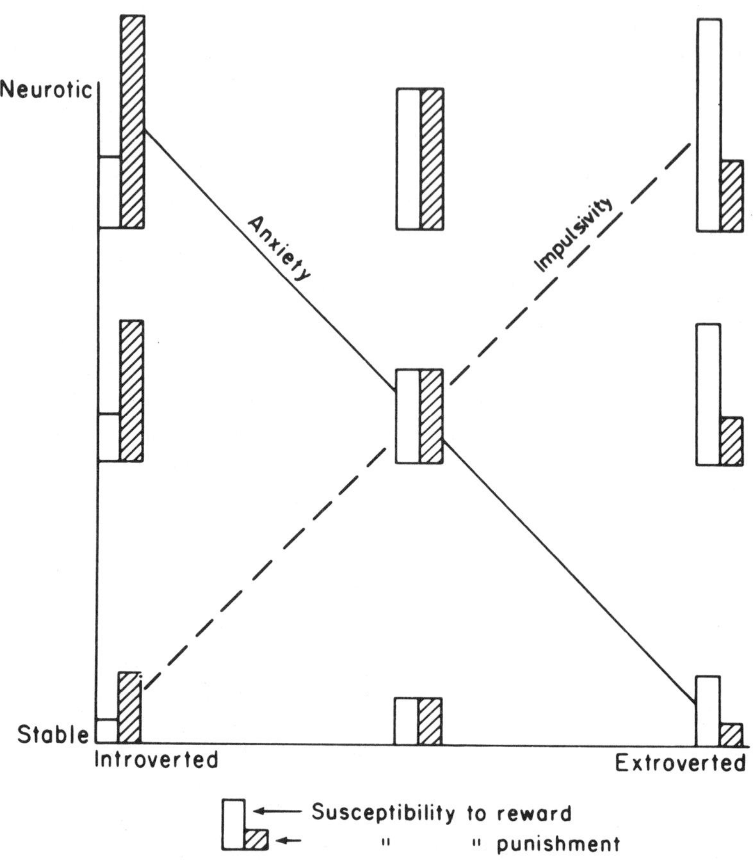

Figure 2.6. Rotation of Eysenck's dimensions of neutroticism and introversion-extraversion proposed by Gray (1970b). The dimension of trait Anxiety represents the steepest rate of growth in susceptibility to signals of punishment (and other adequate inputs to the behavioral inhibition system); the dimension of Impulsivity represents the steepest rate of growth in susceptibility to signals of reward. Introversion–extraversion now becomes a derived dimension, reflecting the balance of susceptibility to signals of punishment and reward, respectively; and neuroticism similarly reflects the sum of these two types of susceptibility to signals reinforcement.

Figure 2.6 can be read as stating that the dimension on anxiety reflects individual differences in susceptibility to the behavioral effects of anxiogenic stimuli, as defined in the model of the behavioral inhibition system illustrated in Figure 2.1, together with the innate fear stimuli which later considerations required us to add to the model. Equivalently, it can be read as stating that the dimension of anxiety reflects individual differences in the reactivity of the neural system outlined in Figure 2.4.

A dimension has two poles. Thus, the schema presented in Figure 2.6 require us to inquire about the behavior, not only of those individuals high on trait anxiety (who are the most likely to develop clinical symptoms of anxiety), but also of those low on this trait. The most plausible answer to this inquiry is that such individuals are predisposed toward primary psychopathy (Hare & Schalling, 1978), presumably because of their lack of fear. This is not the place to enter into the details of the arguments that led to this conclusion (see Gray, 1983). But one consequence that flows from it is germane to the present dicussion. Primary psychopaths differ from individuals high on trait anxiety on not just two, but three of the Eysenckian dimensions: They are low on neuroticism, high on extraversion and high on the Eysenck *P* scale (Eysenck & Eysenck, 1976, 1978). Thus, if we are to describe the location of the anxiety dimension correctly within Eysenckian three-dimensional space (a worthwhile objective, because this remains the most useful available framework for personality description), a more complex diagram than the one shown in Figure 2.6 becomes necessary. Such a diagram is presented in Figure 2.7.

It would take us too far afield to consider the issues raised by Figure 2.7 within personality theory (see Gray, 1981, 1983). My intention in thus touching briefly on the personality of anxious individuals was only to justify further the claim, with which this chapter opens, that the conceptual apparatus developed in the study of brain and behavior allows one to analyze the very diverse problems raised by the concept and phenomena of anxiety within a single coherent framework. In certain respects, this type of analysis is more advanced in the field of anxiety than in any other branch of psychiatry. But other psychiatric problems are likely soon (see, e.g., Willner, 1985) to benefit from a similar approach.

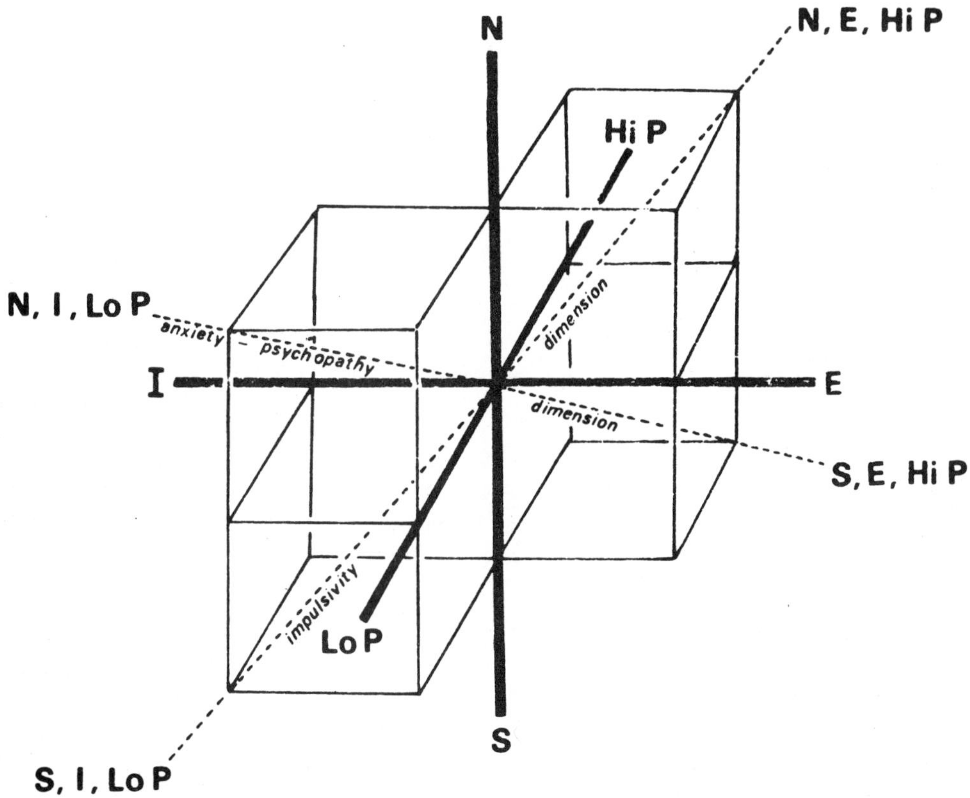

Figure 2.7. Location of an anxiety-psychopathy dimension and an impulsivity dimension (dashed lines) within the three-dimensional space defined by Eysenck's dimensions (thick solid lines) of introversion (1)-extraversion (E), neuroticism (N)-stability (S), and psychoticism (P). For ease of presentation, the anxiety and impulsivity dimensions are drawn as 45° rotations of the Eysenckian dimensions. However, the anxiety dimension probably lies closer to N-S and further from I-E than shown.

CONCLUDING REMARKS

Two brain systems that are likely to be concerned with mediation of the subjective phenomena and objective signs of anxiety are described, largely on the basis of studies of the behavior of experimental animals and of the effects upon such behavior of drugs (including those known to affect anxiety in humans) and interventions in the brain. These systems are: (a) a "behavioral inhibition system," dependent upon neuronal activity in the septohippocampal system and other anatomically related parts of the limbic system; and (b) a fight-flight system, dependent upon activity in the amygdala, hypothalamus) and central gray of the midbrain. Interactions between these two systems are discussed, as there is evidence that they operate in humans in broadly the same manner as in experimental animals.

A theory is offered of the psychological and information-processing functions discharged by the behavioral inhibition and fight/flight systems and of the particular neuronal pathways used for these purposes. The theory is applied to the symptoms and syndromes of anxiety as well as, more briefly, to the personality characteristics that predispose an individual to anxiety. Overall, the approach adopted in this chapter offers an integrated neuropsychological framework within which to analyze anxiety, a framework that is in principle applicable also to other psychiatric disorders.

Acknowledgements — This chapter was largely written while I held the Mary Moody Northen Chair as a visiting Eminent Scholar in the Department of Philosophy and Psychology at the Virginia Military Institute, Lexington, Virginia. I am grateful to all my colleagues at VMI for their unfailing help and kindness during my stay with them. My thanks are also due to Professor W. Haefely and Academic Press for permission to reproduce Figure 2.2.

REFERENCES

Adams, D. B. (1979). Brain mechanisms for offence, defense, and submission. *Behavioral and Brain Sciences, 2*, 201–241.

Akhtar, S., Wig, N., Varma, O., Pershad, D., & Verma, S. (1975). A phenomenological analysis of symptoms in obsessive–compulsive neurosis. *British Journal of Psychiatry, 127*, 342–348.

Albert, D. J., & Chew, G. L. (1983). The septal forebrain and the inhibitory modulation of attack and defense in the rat: A review. *Behavioral and Neural Biology, 30*, 357–388.

Amsel, A., & Roussel, J. (1952). Motivational properties of frustration. I. Effect on a running response of the addition of frustration to the motivational complex. *Journal of Experimental Psychology, 43*, 363–368.

Billingsley, M. L., & Kubena, R. K. (1978). The effects of naloxone and picrotoxin on the sedative and anticonflict effects of benzodiazepines. *Life Sciences, 22*, 897–906.

Bowery, N. G. (Ed.). (1984). *Actions and interactions of GABA and benzodiazepines*. New York: Raven Press.

Broadhurst, P. L. (1960). Applications of biometrical genetics to the inheritance of behaviour. In H. J. Eysenck (Ed.), *Experiments in personality* (Vol. 1). London: Routledge & Kegan Paul.

Broadhurst, P. L. (1975). The Maudsley reactive and nonreactive strains of rats: a survey. *Behaviour Genetics, 5*, 299–319.

Cananzi, A. R., Costa, E., & Guidotti, A. (1980) Potentiation by intraventricular muscimol of the anticonflict effect of benzodiazepines. *Brain Research, 196*, 447–453.

Cattell, R. B. (1965). *The scientific analysis of personality*. Harmondsworth: Pelican.

Charney, D. S., Heininger, G. R., & Breier, A. (1984). Noradrenergic function in panic anxiety. *Archives of General Psychiatry, 41*, 751–763.

Denenberg, V. H. (1984). Critical periods, stimulus input and emotional reactivity: A theory of infantile stimulation. *Psychological Review, 71*, 335–357.

Drewett, R. F., Gray, J. A., James, D. T. D., McNaughton, N., Valero, I., & Dudderidge, H. J. (1977). Sex and strain differences in septal driving of the hippocampal theta rhythm as a function of frequency: Effects of gonadectomy and gonadal hormones. *Neuroscience, 2*, 1033–1041.

Elliott, K., & Whelan, J. (Eds.), (1978). *Functions of the septo-hippocampal system*. Ciba Foundation Symposium 58 (New Series). Amsterdam: Elsevier.

Eysenck, H. J. (1960). Classification and the problem of diagnosis. In H. J. Eysenck (Ed.), *Handbook of abnormal psychology*. London: Pitman.

Eysenck, H. J. (1977). *You and neurosis*. London: Temple Smith.

Eysenck, H. J. (1979). The conditioning model of neurosis. *Behavioral and Brain Sciences, 2*, 155–166.

Eysenck, H. J. (Ed.). (1981). *A model for personality*. New York: Springer.

Eysenck, H. J., & Eysenck, S. B. G. (1969). *The structure and measurement of personality*. London: Routledge & Kegan Paul.

Eysenck, H. J. & Eysenck, S. B. G. (1976). *Psychoticism as a dimension of personality*. London: Hodder & Stoughton.

Eysenck, S. B. G., & Eysenck, H. J. (1978). Impulsiveness and venturesomeness: Their position in a dimensional system of personality description. *Psychological Reports, 43*, 1247–1255.

Fanselow, M. S., & Baackes, M. P. (1982). Conditioned fear-induced opiate analgesia on the formalin test: Evidence for two aversive motivational systems. *Learning & Motivation, 13*, 200–221.

Fung, S-C., & Fillenz, M. (1983). The role of presynaptic GABA and benzodiazepine receptors in the control of noradrenaline release in rat hippocampus. *Neuroscience Letters, 42*, 61–66.

Gallup, G. G. (1965). Aggression in rats as a function of frustrative nonreward in a straight alley. *Psychonomic Science, 3*, 99–100.

Graeff, F. G. (1981). Minor tranquilizers and brain defense systems. *Brazilian Journal of Medical and Biological Research, 14*, 239–265.

Graeff, F. G. (in press). The anti-aversive action of drugs. In T. Thompson., P. B. Dews, & J. Barrett (Eds.), *Advances in behavioral pharmacology* (Vol. 5). Hillsdale, NJ: Erlbaum.

Graeff, F. G., & Scoenfeld, R. I. (1970). Tryptaminergic mechanisms in punished and nonpunished behavior. *Journal of Pharmacology and Experimental Therapeutics, 173*, 277–283.

Graeff, F. G., Zuardi, A. W., Giglio, J. S., Lima Filho, E. C., & Karniol, I. G., (1985). Effect of metergoline on human anxiety. *Psychopharmacology, 86*, 334–338.

Gray, J. A. (1968). The Lister Lecture, 1967: The psysiological basis of personality. *Advancement of Science, 24*, 293–305.

Gray, J. A. (1970a). Sodium amobarbital, the hippocampal that rhythm and the partial reinforcement extinction effect. *Psychological Review, 77*, 465–480.

Gray, J. A. (1970b). The psychophysiological basis of introversion–extraversion. *Behaviour Research and Therapy, 8*, 249–266.

Gray, J. A. (1971). *The psychology of fear and stress*. London: Weidenfeld & Nicolson.

Gray, J. A. (1975). *Elements of a two-process theory of learning*. London: Academic Press.

Gray, J. A. (1977). Drug effects on fear and frustration: Possible limbic site of action of minor tranquilizers. In. L. L. Iversen, S. D. Iversen, & S. H. Snyder, (Eds.), *Handbook of Psychopharmacology* (Vol. 8). New York: Plenum.

Gray, J. A. (1979). Is there any need for conditioning in Eysenck's conditioning model of neurosis? *Behavioral and Brain Sciences, 2*, 169–171.

Gray, J. A. (1981). A critique of Eysenck's theory of personality. In H. J. Eysenck (Ed.), *A model for personality*. Berlin: Springer.

Gray, J. A. (1982a). *The neuropsychology of anxiety: An enquiry into the functions of the septo-hippocampal system*. Oxford: Oxford University Press.

Gray, J. A. (1982b). Précis of "The neuropsychology of anxiety: An enquiry into the functions of the septo-hippocampal system." *Behavioral and Brain Sciences, 5*, 469–484.

Gray, J. A. (1983). Where should we search for biologically based dimensions of personality? *Zeitschrift für Differentielle und Diagnostische Psychologie, 4*, 165–176.

Gray, J. A. (1984). The hippocampus as an interface between cognition and emotion. In H. L. Roitblat, T. G. Bever, & H. S. Terrace (Eds.), *Animal cognition*. Hillsdale, NJ: Erlbaum.

Gray, J. A. (in press). *The psychology of fear and stress*, (2nd ed.). Cambridge: Cambridge University Press.

Gray, J. A., & McNaughton, N. (1983). Comparison between the behavioral effects of septal and hippocampal lesions: A review. *Neuroscience and Biobehavioral Reviews, 7*, 119–188.

Gray, J. A., Quintero, S., Mellanby, J., Buckland, C., Fillenz, M., & Fung, S. C. (1984). Some biochemical, behavioral and electrophysiological tests of the GABA hypothesis of anti-anxiety drug action. In N. G. Bowery (Ed.), *Actions and interactions of GABA and benzodiazepines*. New York: Raven Press.

Gray, J. A., & Rawlins, J. N. P. (1986). Comparator and buffer memory: An attempt to integrate two models of hippocampal function. In R. L. Isaacson & K. H. Pribram (Eds.), *The hippocampus* (Vol. 4). New York: Plenum.

Haefly, W. (1984). Actions and interactions of benzodiazepine agonists and antagonists at GABAergic synapses. In N. G. Bowery (Ed.), *Actions and interactions of GABA and Benzodiazepines*. New York: Raven Press.

Hare, R. D., & Schalling, D. (Eds.). (1978). *Psychopathic behavior: Approaches to research*. Chichester: Wiley.

Henke, P. G. (1977). Dissociation of the frustration effect and the partial reinforcement extinction effect after limbic lesions in rats. *Journal of Comparative and Physiological Psychology, 91*, 1032–1038.

Hodges, H. M., & Green, S. (1984). Evidence for the involvement of brain GABA and serotonin systems in the anti-conflict effects of chlordiazepoxide in rats. *Behavioral and Neurol Biology, 40*, 127–154.

Hodgson, R., & Rachman, S. (1972). The effects of contamination and washing in obsessional patients. *Behavior Research and Therapy, 10*, 111–117.

James, W. (1890). *Principles of psychology*. London: Macmillan.

Klein, D. F. (1981). Anxiety reconceptualized. In D. F. Klein & J. Rabkin (Eds.), *Anxiety: New research and changing concepts*. New York: Raven Press.

Lader, M. H. (1975). *The psychophysiology of mental illness*. London: Routledge & Kegan Paul.

Lang, P. (1970). Stimulus control, response control, and the desensitization of fear. In D. J. Levis (Ed.), *Learning approaches to therapeutic behavior*. Chicago: Aldine Press.

Levine, S. (1962). Psychophysiological effects of infant stimulation. In E. L. Bliss (Ed.), *Roots of behavior*. New York: Hoeber.

Levine, S., & Mullins, R. F. (1966). Hormonal influences on brain organization in infant rats. *Science, 152*, 1585–1592.

Lidbrink, P., Corrodi, H., Fuxe, K., & Olson, L. (1973). The effects of benzodiazepines, meprobamate, and barbiturates on central monoamine neurons. In S. Garattini, E. Mussini, & L. O. Randall (Eds.), *The benzodiazepines*. New York: Raven Press.

Lippa, A. S., Klepner, C. A., Benson, D. I., Critchett, D. J., Sano, M. C., & Beer, B. (1980). The role of GABA in mediating the anticonvulsant properties of benzodiazepines. In H. Lal & S. Fielding (Eds.), *GABA and other inhibitory neurotransmitters* (pp. 861–866). Fayetteville, NY: JANKHO Publishing Co.

McFie, J. (1972). Factors of the brain. *Bulletin of the British Psychological Society, 25*, 11–14.

Marks, I. M. (1969). *Fears and phobias*. London: Heinemann.

Meaney, M. J., Aitken, D. H., Bodnoff, S. R., Iny, L. J., Tatarewicz, J. E., & Sapolsky, R. M. (1985). Early postnatal handling alters glucocorticoid receptor concentrations in selected brain regions. *Behavioral Neuroscience, 99*, 765–770.

Melzack, R., & Wall, P. D. (1983). *The challenge of pain*. New York: Basic Books.

Mitchell-Heggs, N., Kelly, D., & Richardson, A. (1976). Stereotactic limbic leucotomy: A Follow-up at 16 months. *British Journal of Psychiatry, 128*, 226–240.

Mowrer, O. H. (1947). On the dual nature of learning: A re-interpretation of "conditioning" and "problem-solving." *Harvard Educational Review, 17*, 102–148.

Myer, J. S. (1971). Some effects of noncontingent aversive stimulation. In R. F. Brush (Ed.), *Aversive conditioning and learning*. New York: Academic Press.

Nielsen, M., Braestrup, C., & Squires, R. F. (1978). Evidence for a late evolutionary appearance of brain-specific benzodiazepine receptors: An investigation of 18 vertebrate and 5 invertebrate species. *Brain Research, 141*, 342–346.

Nestoros, J. N. (1980). Ethanol selectively potentiates GABA-mediated inhibition of single feline cortical neurons. *Life Sciences, 26*, 519–523.

Öhman, A. (1979). Fear relevance, autonomic conditioning, and phobias: A laboratory model. In P. O. Sjoden, S. Bates, & W. W. Dockens (Eds.), *Trends in behavior therapy*. New York: Academic Press.

Ojemann, G. & Mateer, C. (1979). Human language cortex: Localization of memory, syntax, and sequential motor-phoneme identification systems. *Science, 205*, 1401–1403.

O'Keefe, J., & Nadel, L. (1978). *The hippocampus as a cognitive map*. Oxford: Clarendon Press.

Olsen, R. W. (1981). GABA-benzodiazepine-barbiturate receptor interactions. *Journal of Neurochemistry, 37*, 1–2.

Panksepp, J. (1982). Towards a general psychobiological theory of emotions. *Behavioral and Brain Sciences, 5*, 407–467.

Papez, J. W. (1937). A proposed mechanism of emotion. *Archives of Neurology and Psychiatry, 38*, 725–743.

Powell, G. E. (1979). *Brain and personality*. London: Saxon House.

Quintero, S., Buckland, C., Gray, J. A., McNaughton, N., & Mellanby, J. (1985). The effects of compounds related to γ-aminobutyrate and benzodiazepine receptors on behavioral responses to anxiogenic stimuli in the rat: choice behaviour in the T-maze. *Psychopharmacology, 86*, 328–333.

Quintero, S., Henney, S., Lawson, P., Mellanby, J., & Gray, J. A. (1985b). The effects of compounds related to γ-aminobutyrate and benzodiazepine receptors on behavioral respones to anxiongenic stimuli in the rat: Punished barpressing. *Psychopharmacology, 85*, 244–251.

Rachman, S. (1976). The modification of obsessions: A new formulation. *Behaviour Research and Therapy, 14*, 437–434.

Rachman, S. (1978). An anatomy of obsessions. *Behavior Analysis and Modification, 2*, 253–278.

Rachman, S., & De Silva, P. (1978). Abnormal and normal obsessions. *Behaviour Research and Therapy, 16*, 233–248.

Rachman, S., & Hodgson, R. (1974). Synchrony and desynchrony in fear and avoidance. *Behaviour Research and Therapy, 12*, 311–318.

Rachman, S., & Seligman, M. E. P. (1976). Unprepared phobias: Be prepared. *Behaviour Research and Therapy, 14*, 333–338.

Razran, G. (1971). *Mind in evolution.* Boston: Houghton Mifflin.

Redmond, D. E. (1979). New and old evidence for the involvement of a brain norepinephrine system in anxiety. In W. G. Fann, I. Karacan, A. D. Pokorny, & R. L. Williams (Eds.), *Phenomenology and treatment of anxiety*. New York: Spectrum.

Reiman, E. M., Raichle, M. E., Butler, F. K., Hersovitch, P., & Robins, E. (1984). A focal brain abnormality in panic disorder, a severe form of anxiety. *Nature, 310*, 683–685.

Rickels, K. (1978). Use of anti-anxiety agents in anxious outpatients. *Psychopharmacology, 58*, 1–17.

Röper, G., & Rachman, S. (1976). Obsessional-compulsive checking: Experimental replication and development. *Behaviour Research and Therapy, 14*, 25–32.

Segal, M. (1977a). Changes of interhemispheric hippocampal responses during conditioning in the awake rat. *Experimental Brain Research, 29*, 553–565.

Segal, M. (1977b). The effects of brainstem priming stimulation on interhemispheric hippocampal responses in the awake rat. *Experimental Brain Research, 28*, 529–541.

Segal, M. (1980). The noradrenergic innervation of the hippocampus. In J. A. Hobson & M. A. B. Brazier (Eds.), *The reticular formation revisited.* New York: Raven Press.

Seligman, M. E. P. (1971). Phobias and preparedness. *Behavior Therapy, 2*, 307–320.

Soubrié, P. (1986). Reconciling the role of central serotonin neurons in human and animal behavior. *Behavioral and Brain Sciences, 9*, 319–363.

Stanley, M., Virgilio, J., & Gershon, S. (1982). Tritiated imipramine binding sites are decreased in the frontal cortex of suicides. *Science, 216*, 1337–1339.

Stein, L., Wise, C. D., & Berger, B. D. (1973). Anti-anxiety action of benzodiazepines: Decrease in activity of serotonin neurons in the punishment system. In S. Garattini, E. Mussini, & L. O. Randall (Eds.), *The benzodiazepines.* New York: Raven Press.

Taylor, J. A. (1953). A personality scale of manifest anxiety. *Journal of Abnormal and Social Psychology, 48*, 285–290.

Ticku, M. K. (1986). The effects of acute and chronic ethanol administration and its withdrawal on GABA receptor binding in rat brain. *British Journal of Pharmacology, 70*, 403–410.

Torgersen, S. (1979). The nature and origin of common phobic fears. *British Journal of Psychiatry, 134*, 343–351.

Trimble, M. (Ed.). (1983). *Benzodizepines divided.* Chichester: Wiley.

Vinogradova, O. S. (1975). Functional organization of the limbic system in the process of registration of information: facts and hypotheses. In R. L. Isaacson & K. H. Pribram (Eds.), *The hippocampus* (Vol. 2). New York: Plenum Press.

Watson, J. B., & Rayner, R. (1980). Conditioned emotional reactions. *Journal of Experimental Psychology, 3*, 1–14.

Willner, P. (1985). *Depression: A psychobiological synthesis.* New York: Wiley.

Young, P. A., Eaves, L. J., & Eysenck, H. J. (1980). Intergenational stability and change in the causes of variation in personality. *Personality and Individual Differences, 1*, 35–55.

PART II

Clinical Features and Assessment

CHAPTER 3

Diagnosis and Classification of Anxiety Disorders

Alan Lipschitz

Since antiquity, anxiety has been recognized to be a symptom that is present in a variety of physical and mental diseases. During this long and venerable history, a host of different anxiety syndromes have been described. Behaviorists (Estes & Skinner, 1941), mentalists (Freud, 1894/1962), existentialists (Kierkegaard, 1980), and many others from the various classical and modern schools of psychological thought, contributed their own ideologically derived descriptions of anxiety disorders. Meanwhile, psychiatric practitioners were reporting particular signs, symptoms, and clinical circumstances that occurred together with anxiety and pronounced these constellations to be new syndromes, with little regard for the many similar syndromes already described in other contexts. Posttraumatic stress disorder is a typical example of this phenomenon: After each major war it was discovered afresh, and freshly christened with names like "shell shock," "combat fatigue," or "survivor syndrome." Most of these descriptions of posttraumatic stress disorder conflated it with the "irritable heart" syndrome described by DaCosta in 1871, which was itself subsequently reincarnated under a host of aliases: "neurocirculatory asthenia" (Oppenheimer et al., 1918–1920), "effort syndrome" (Lewis & Engle, 1954), "cardiac neurosis," and "panic disorder" (Ettedgui & Bridges, 1985; Magarian, 1982; Marks & Lader, 1973).

This diagnostic confusion and multiplicity of unreconciled syndromes persists into our own time, paralyzing communication within psychiatry. When experts were surveyed by the World Health Organization during its international review of psychiatric diagnoses (1968–1973), they showed remarkably little agreement in the diagnoses that they assigned to anxious "neurosis" patients (Jablensky, 1985).

A uniform classification system emerged from this World Health Organization survey: the ninth edition of the *International Classification of Diseases* (ICD-9) (World Health Organization, 1978). The ICD-9 is used widely for disease classification, but its clinical usefullness is limited. It is not a diagnostic manual; it is a compilation of diseases for the purpose of statistical reporting of morbidity and mortality. It is limited in the number of categories it can posit, and its descriptions of diagnoses are guides for classification, rather than operational rules for assigning these diagnoses to patients (Kramer, Sartorius, Jablensky, & Gulbinat, 1979). As a result of these constraints, the ICD-9 categories are too ambiguous and overinclusive for it to function as a clinically useful diagnostic manual (Jablensky, 1985).

In the face of this diagnostic anarchy, each clinician applied his or her own diagnostic model to individual patients. Researchers, however, needed operationalized and generalizeable diagnostic criteria in order to apply findings to patients outside their own study populations. A number of such diagnostic systems were developed for research purposes in recent years, and their reliability and validity have been established by comprehensive field trials (Feighner et al., 1972; Wing, Cooper, & Sartorius, 1979). Further gains in reliability have been obtained by explicitly structuring the interview process and diagnostic algorithim (DiNardo, O'Brien, Barlow, Waddel, & Blanchard, 1983; Spitzer & Williams, 1983). From these research-oriented diagnostic systems emerged the third edition of the American Psychiatric Association's *Diagnostic and Statistical Manual of Mental Disorders* (DSM-III) in 1980.

The DSM-III tries to provide for clinical diagnoses the sort of operational criteria that determine research diagnoses by stating explicit inclusion and exclusion criteria for each category, and by supplying in its glossary operational definitions for its terminology. It attempts to derive its classification from the "shared descriptive features" of the syndromes, rather than follow some theory of pathophysiology to establish its diagnostic groups. It hopes to remain "atheoretical in regard to etiology or pathophysiological process, except for those disorders for which this is well established" (American Psychiatric Association, 1980; Spitzer & Williams, 1985). These principles obviate a host of contending ideologically derived classification schemes (e.g., the neuroses). This DSM-III program is restrained, however, by the limitations of our inadequate database, and it is further constrained by the clinical necessity that few patients fall into the "undiagnosed" and "atypical" categories. This approach has earned much criticism (Bayer & Spitzer, 1985; Frances & Cooper, 1981; Michels, 1984; Vaillant, 1984); nonetheless, the DSM-III remains the most popular diagnostic system in the United States today. After its adoption by the American Psychiatric Association in June 1978, the DSM-III was revised in 1987 to accommodate clinical observations, to clarify ambiguous cases, and to incorporate some of its critics' recommendations. This chapter will discuss the anxiety disorders as they are presented in this DSM-III-R revision of the DSM-III (American Psychiatric Association, 1987).

THE ORGANIZATION OF THE DSM-III-R

While fleeing the biases of the past, the DSM-III-R defines its taxonomy by leaning heavily on certain contemporary theories of psychopathology. In recent years, a number of researchers have proposed that there are two primary anxiety syndromes: "exogenous" or "stimulus dependent" anxiety, which is provoked by external stimuli (e.g., phobic anxiety), and "endogenous" or "stimulus independent" anxiety, which is not triggered by any identifiable stimulus in the environment (e.g., panic attacks) (Curtis, 1985; Hallam, 1978; Klein, 1981; Sheehan, Ballenger, & Jacobsen, 1980; Sheehan & Sheehan, 1982a, 1982b). Either syndrome may be elaborated by the development of anticipatory anxiety, and in either one phobias may generalize to formerly neutral stimuli in the environment.

This panic-centered schema has not met with universal approbation. Michels, representing the psychodynamic view in this country, has emphasized that the apparently "unexpected" panic attack might be precipitated by some mental phenomenon that the patient does not disclose on casual questioning (Michels, Frances, & Shear, 1985). Beck and other cognitive therapists have long held this same view (Beck, Laude, & Bohnert, 1974). Outside the United States, anxiety attacks are not given a defining role, as they are regarded as simply more severe presentations of anxiety (Jablensky, 1985; Tyrer, 1984). The evidence currently available is not sufficient to resolve this question of whether panic disorder is distinct from generalized anxiety disorder, a more severe form of generalized anxiety disorder, or a form of depression.

The influence of this endogenous/exogenous dichotimization shows most strongly in the adoption by the DSM-III-R of the anxiety attack as the central figure in its classification, a classification that can be usefully seen as a taxonomy of the contexts in which the anxiety attacks occur. When the attacks are provoked by attempts to escape certain "internal" conscious thoughts or acts, the diagnosis of obsessive compulsive disorder is assigned. When the attacks are severe, "unexpected" and not provoked by any known external or internal (intrapsychic) stimulus, the diagnosis of panic disorder is given. When anxiety is present with no current or past history of panic attacks, one of the "residual" diagnoses is given, that is, agoraphobia without panic attacks or generalized anxiety disorder. Posttraumatic stress disorder has never rested comfortably in this schema. As a state compounded of depressive features, anxiety, and "reexperiencings" of trauma, it is diagnosed regardless of the presence or absence of anxiety attacks, and the DSM-III authors had considered relocating it among the dissociative disorders.

Other symptoms may develop more gradually. They may endure between the attacks and they may persist even after the attacks themselves have remitted with time or with treatment (Davis, Suhayl, Spira, & Vogel, 1981; Grunhaus, Glogen, & Weisstub, 1981). Such an emergent symptom is the avoidance of stimuli associated with these attacks; this avoidance can, in time, generalize to multiple phobias or to agoraphobia (Òst & Hugdahl, 1983). Alternatively, agoraphobia may develop out of the patient's fear of being disabled and helpless if struck by a panic attack when outside the home (Klein, 1981).

A prolonged state of anxiety can develop in anticipation of the anxiety attack. This "anticipatory anxiety" may become autonomous and persist even after the attacks remit. This has been observed when pharmacological treatment abolished patient's panic attacks without eliminating their anticipatory anxiety and avoidance of the associated phobic stimulus (Klein, 1964, 1967).

In all these conditions, the anticipatory component may become manifest as either psychic symptoms or behavioral signs. The phobic patient may tolerate his or her anxiety in the feared situation with only subjective discomfort, or may avoid these situations altogether. This avoidance behavior can be thoroughly integrated into the patient's lifestyle, and years may elapse between the times when he or she confronts the phobic stimulus. The avoidance behavior can persist even if the attacks remit spontaneously or with treatment. It is the avoidance of the phobic stimulus that allows the patient to avoid his or her phobic anxiety. This anxiety-free patient can be given a diagnosis of an anxiety disorder if the avoidant behavior is sufficient in magnitude to cause marked distress, or if it interferes with work or occupational functioning.

This model of pathogenesis links the various DSM-III anxiety disorders. European classifications, however, find little reason to lump together these diverse syndromes (Jablensky, 1985). Anxiety occurs in many of these disorders, but it may be altogether absent, as in the phobic patient who integrates avoidant behavior patterns into his or her lifestyle and so no longer confronts the phobic stimulus. Anxiety is commonplace in other disorders which are not included in this group, for example, in hypochondriasis, which might be regarded as an "illness phobia" (Agras, Sylvester, & Oliveau, 1969). Also, the rationale for including posttraumatic stress disorder among the anxiety disorders has never been compelling, and there have been suggestions that it be placed among the dissociative disorders.

The anxiety disorders frequently cooccur with other syndromes. The DSM-III-R has adopted certain uniform "hierarchy" rules for the assignment of diagnoses in these cases (American Psychiatric Association, 1987 pp. xxiv–xxv):

1. When an Organic Mental Disorder can account for the patient's symptoms a nonorganic diagnosis is excluded.

2. A less pervasive diagnosis is not given when its defining symptoms are symptoms associated with a more pervasive disorder. For example, a diagnosis of simple phobia is not given when a patient with obsessive compulsive disorder avoids dirt or contamination, since such avoidance is commonly associated with obsessive compulsive disorder.

3. A patient assigned an Axis I diagnosis may be given an additional diagnosis of an anxiety disorder if the focus of his concern is not related to the first diagnosis. For example, patients with panic disorder can have concurrent social phobia, if the patient's social fear is not fear of having a public panic attack.

These hierarchy principles do not eliminate all taxonomic ambiguities. Until a less ambiguous system is implemented, the DSM-III-R authors have chosen to err on the side of excess by assigning to the patient all applicable diagnoses that are not specifically excluded by the hierarchy rules. Thus, the more pervasive diagnoses of schizophrenia and mood disorders do not exclude anxiety disorder diagnoses, unless the focus of the patient's anxiety is clearly related to the more pervasive disorder.

CLINICAL FEATURES

Simple Phobia

This is an anxiety disorder marked by two components: intense anxiety when exposed to some specific phobic stimulus, and persistent fear of this stimulus between the episodes of exposure. The genesis of the phobia may have occurred long prior to the patient's presentation for treatment; the initial anxiety attack associated with the phobic stimulus may have been triggered by some transient stressor, or by organic factors, such as marijuana intoxication.

The experience of these anxiety attacks produces a persistent fear of the phobic stimulus, which is either avoided or tolerated only with intense anxiety. This fear of the anxiety attack has been termed "anticipatory anxiety" (Klein, 1964) or "phobophobia" (Van den Hout & Griez, 1982). The anticipatory anxiety may generalize to diverse situations associated with the phobic stimulus, leading the patient to markedly curtail his or her activities. The magnitude of the fearful sensation or avoidant behavior must be sufficient to cause marked distress to the patient or to interfere with social or occupational functioning.

Skillful avoidance of the phobic stimulus can allow patients to function for years, until some circumstance forces them to confront the object of their phobia. Common phobic stimuli are animals, closed spaces (claustrophobia), and heights (acrophobia), but hundreds of phobias have been described, each given the name of its phobic stimulus.

The symptoms of simple phobia may themselves be indistinguishable from panic disorder. However, unlike the "unexpected" anxiety attacks of panic disorder, in simple phobia exposure to the phobic stimulus almost always provokes an attack. In simple phobia, the patient recognizes his or her fear to be excessive or unreasonable. This helps distinguish simple phobia from delusional states, in which the patient's reality testing is impaired and he or she believes his or her fear to be warranted. In a number of other diseases, irrational fears associated with particular stimuli may develop. In obsessive–compulsive disorder, for example, patients typically develop avoidance of situations that trigger the obsession or compulsion. In posttraumatic stress disorder phobias may develop to reminders of the trauma. In childhood, simple phobias commonly are directed at animals, but usually remit spontaneously (Agras, Chapin, & Oliveau, 1972). Phobias persisting into adulthood or developing in adulthood rarely remit without treatment.

Two phobias are given distinct categories in DSM-III-R; fear of humiliation when under public scrutiny (social phobia), and fear of being trapped or helpless while incapacitated (agoraphobia). The suggestion to separate these two phobias comes from Marks (1970), who noted them to be distinguished by their distinct symptomatology, sex ratio, and age of onset. Subsequent studies have confirmed that social phobia starts at a younger age and is more common in males, while agoraphobia is more common in women and often begins later in life (Agras et al., 1969).

Social Phobia

The essential feature of this disorder is a persistent fear of situations in which the individual is exposed to the scrutiny of others, where he or she fears behaving in a way that will be humiliating. The phobic situation is avoided or endured only with intense anxiety. By the time the patient presents for treatment, he or she may have adapted to the phobia by avoidance of the feared stimuli, but at some point in the history he or she must have experienced an intense anxiety response when confronted with the phobic situation. The patient's anxiety or avoidance must be of a sufficient magnitude to either impair functioning or to cause marked distress. The patient recognizes that the fear is unreasonable or excessive. During periods when performance is impaired by other causes, this transient incapacity may further strengthen the anticipatory anxiety component of the phobia.

Such phobias are common in patients with panic disorder, or obsessive–compulsive disorder, and the diagnosis of social phobia is not given if the phobia is due to one of these disorders. Patients with the disorder may have considerable unfocused, generalized anxiety, and often they will have agoraphobia or simple phobia as well. Many patients have avoidant personality in addition to social phobia; while some investigators maintain that a diagnosis of avoidant personality should exclude a concurrent diagnosis of social phobia, there is no body of empirical data to support this exclusion (Greenberg, & Stravynski, 1983). The disorder is most common in males, usually begins in adolescence, persists chronically, and often is complicated by alcoholism (Agras et al., 1969; Aimes, Gelder, & Shaw, 1983; Liebowitz, Gorman, Fyer, & Klein, 1985; Marks, 1970).

History of Panic Disorder

The essential feature of this disorder is anxiety when alone or in a public place, due to the fear of being incapacitated by a sudden symptom. Dizziness, incontinence and cardiac disease are the symptoms most often feared. The magnitude of the fear must be sufficient to either (a) produce intense anxiety when in the phobic situation, or (b) alter the patient's behavior, so that travel is restricted, requiring a companion when the affected person is out of the house; or his or her lifestyle is altered in some other way in order to avoid the phobic stimuli. In order to qualify for this diagnosis, the patient must never have experienced a panic attack; many, however, do experience "limited symptom attacks" of some panic symptoms.

It is difficult to characterize the course and occurrence of this disorder, as few studies have distinguished agoraphobia with panic attacks from agoraphobia without panic attacks, consistent with the views still affirmed in Europe (Jablensky, 1985; Marks, 1985; Tyrer, 1984). The particular feared situation may shift from day to day, and the course of this disorder appears to be variable, with the severity of the anxiety or avoidance waxing and waning. A number of authors have suggested that these fluctuations are due to the availability in the environment of factors that affect the patient's feeling of safety (e.g., the presence of a supportive other person) (Gray, 1971; Hallam, 1978; Rachman, 1984). Women more commonly suffer this disorder, which may start any time after late adolescence, but often begins later in life (Agras et al., 1969; Marks, 1970).

Panic Disorder

Recurrent panic attacks were described as a separate anxiety disorder by DaCosta in 1871. Later in 1894, Freud distinguished the syndrome from neuresthenia and named it anxiety neurosis. In subsequent classifications, the term *anxiety neurosis* was applied to a variety of patients with continuous anxiety, as well as to those whose anxiety was exacerbated in discrete, periodic attacks. Treatment studies since the 1960s showed, however, that spontaneous, discrete anxiety attacks respond to different treatments than precipitated ("phobic") or continuous ("generalized") anxiety states (Klein, 1964, 1967; Klein & Fink, 1962; Klein, Gittelman, Quitkin, & Rifkin, 1980; Klein, Zitrin, Woerner, & Ross, 1983). The DSM-III, therefore, chose to separate this category from the other anxiety disorders, using the criteria of Feighner (Feighner et al., 1972) to describe the panic disorder syndrome.

The essential feature of this disorder is the occurrence of random, unpredictable attacks of panic, but attacks also may occur in certain specific situations. The attacks are marked by pronounced physical signs and psychic symptoms. Common physical signs during the attacks are rapid pulse (tachycardia), shortness of breath (dyspnea), chest pains, sweating, faintness, hot flashes, chills, tremor, and nausea. Common psychic symptoms during an attack include experiences of depersonalization or derealization, and fears of dying, going crazy, or losing control.

Hyperventilation during an attack may be responsible for many of these symptoms. For example, it can produce a respiratory alkalosis which lowers the serum level of ionized calcium sufficiently to affect conduction in the long peripheral nerves, thereby causing the paresthesias of tingling or numbness in the hands or feet (Okel & Hurst, 1961; Weiner, 1985). However, hyperventilation cannot account for all the symptoms of an attack (Magarian, 1982; Marks & Lader, 1973). Hyperventilation cannot reliably reproduce panic attack symptoms in patients who have panic disorder (Gorman, Martinez, Liebowitz, Fyer, & Klein, 1984), and often it is only after the attack begins that the patient will start to hyperventilate (Weiner, 1985).

The patient may associate his or her spontaneous attacks with certain objects or situations, and develop phobias for these stimuli. In panic disorder, unlike simple phobia, the panic attacks sometimes will occur without exposure to a phobic object, and panic will not be produced invariably by exposure to such a phobic stimulus. Some degree of generalized apprehension and nervousness often develops between attacks, with the patient then presenting typical anxiety symptoms, including vigilance, apprehensive expectation, motor tension, and autonomic hyperactivity. Between attacks, the symptom picture may be indistinguishable from generalized anxiety disorder.

The patient's fear of becoming incapacitated by a panic attack while in some public place can lead him or her to avoid leaving home. This is the presumed pathogenesis for agoraphobia, which often develops following panic attacks. In DSM-III-R, the severity of associated agoraphobia graded as "severe", "moderate", "mild" or "without agoraphobia". The course of the disorder may be brief (weeks to months), recurrent, or chronic.

It seems likely that object loss during childhood plays some role in the genesis of panic disorder. Patients with panic disorder frequently give a history of object loss in childhood (Raskin, Peeke, Dickman, & Pinsker, 1982), and object loss often precedes the initial panic episode (Klein, 1981). Panic disorder is more common in adults with a childhood history of separation anxiety disorder, which may be its early presentation (Gittelman-Klein, & Klein, 1985; Klein & Fink, 1962). Noteworthy, too, is the report by many patients that their panic attacks can be prevented or aborted by reassuring contact with another person.

A number of patients with panic disorder have been found to have mitral value prolapse; however, the significance of this finding remains unclear, and there is much reason to doubt that mitral prolapse causes panic attacks (Crowe, 1985). Other biological markers for the disease are under study. In one intriguing study, positron emission tomography (PET) detected an asymmetry in the blood flow to the parahippocamapal gyri in patients between their attacks (Reiman, Raichle, Butler, Herscovitch, & Robins, 1984).

Research studies have used the administration of chemical agents to provoke panic attacks ever since carbon dioxide inhalation first was used for this purpose in 1918 (Drury, 1918–1920). Carbon dioxide, sodium lactate, isoproterenol, yohimbine, and the other provocative agents appear to produce attacks in panic disorder patients at doses that normal subjects can tolerate without panic (Gorman, Dillon, Fyer, Liebowitz, & Klein, 1985). These have remained laboratory procedures, but a recent "cookbook" instruction manual for lactate infusion may popularize this procedure for the diagnostic assessment of patients (Sheehan, Carr, Fishman, Walsh, & Peltier-Saxe, 1985).

Obsessive–Compulsive Disorder

The essential feature here is either obsessions or compulsions. Obsessions are ideas, thoughts, images, or impulses that recur and persist. These are experienced as senseless, intrusive, unwanted, or repugnant phenomena that invade consciousness and produce anxiety despite attempts to suppress or ignore them. Patients often will attempt to "undo" these seemingly alien thoughts by repeating words or conjuring images whose content is opposed to the content of the obsession; other patients try to undo obsessive thoughts by performing rituals to neutralize them. The content of obsessive thoughts most commonly involves violence, contamination, doubt, or the violation of social taboos. Thoughts of attacking someone, contracting diseases, or touching a forbidden person or place are common. Doubts may preoccupy the patient, for example, was the water faucet or gas jet turned off? Commonly, the doubts will concern injuring or offending someone.

Compulsions are repetitive, deliberate, purposeful, goal-directed behaviors that are performed according to certain rules or in a stereotyped fashion. The compulsive behavior is not an end in itself, but is designed to produce or prevent some future event or situation. The behavior is excessive, however, or is not realistically connected with its goal. When the individual attempts to resist the compulsion, he or she feels a mounting sense of tension which is relieved immediately by yielding to the compulsion. Performing the compulsive act does not in itself give pleasure, but it does relieve the anxiety of resistance (Insel 1985; Insel, Zahn, & Murphy, 1985). The relief can be short-lived, however, and the compulsion may soon recur. After repeatedly failing to resist the compulsion the individual may yield to it automatically and without resistance. The most common compulsions involve washing, checking, counting, and touching.

The magnitude of the obsessions or compulsions must be time-consuming, markedly distressing, or must significantly interfere with the patient's normal routine, occupational function, or social activities. Patients frequently will develop phobias for objects or situations linked to their obsessions or compulsions. For example, the patient may fear and avoid situations in which he or she risks contamination. Phobias, obsessions, and compulsions often coexist in the same patient, all centering on avoiding and undoing the anxiety associated with a particular situation. The symptoms typically wax and wane as part of a chronic, life-long course.

Insel (1985; Insel et al., 1985) has noted that a limited repertoire of symptoms occur among the patients with this disorder. He describes compulsive washers who are obsessed with contamination, compulsive checkers who are obsessed with doubts, "pure obsessionals," and patients who have "primary obsessional slowness" without anxiety, obsessions, or compulsions. Studies of biological markers, family history, and treatment response in these patients all suggest that this disorder may be more closely linked to depression than to the anxiety disorders (Insel, 1985; Insel et al., 1985).

Certain excessive activities, such as eating, sexual behavior, gambling, and drinking, commonly are described as "compulsive." These are not true compulsions when the individual derives pleasure from them and resists them only because their consequences are deleterious. Obsessive brooding, rumination, preoccupation with certain situations or events, and indecisive consideration of alternatives, are not true obsessions when the individual regards them as meaningful and appropriate. In psychotic patients, thoughts that appear to be obsessions and compulsions may not in fact be ego-alien, as the patient's ability to test reality is impaired, and he or she may not recognize the behavior as excessive or unreasonable. Alternatively, psychotic patients may fail to identify their obsessive and compulsive thoughts as the products of their own minds, believing them to be alien thoughts that are inserted by some person or other agency.

Generalized Anxiety Disorder

This disorder is characterized by anxious mood or worried preoccupations present on most days for at least 6 months. At least 6 of 18 symptoms must be present during this period. The symptoms fall into three clusters:

1. *Muscle tension* — restlessness, shakiness, trembling, twitching, fidgeting, muscle aches, easy fatigability.
2. *Autonomic hyperactivity* — rapid pulse, dyspnea, sweating, cold clammy hands, dry mouth, dizziness, digestive disturbances, hot or cold flashes, frequent urination, pallor, or a sensation of a lump in the throat.
3. *Vigilance and scanning* — exaggerated startle response, difficulty concentrating, insomnia, irritability, feeling on edge.

The diagnosis can be made if another anxiety disorder is present, as long as the generalized anxiety is not related to the other disorder — thus patients with panic disorder can be given a diagnosis of generalized anxiety disorder if their worry is not about having another panic attack.

Generalized anxiety disorder received little study in recent years, and it is not known if the generalized anxiety disorder symptomatology includes any distinctive features that qualitatively distinguish the disorder from the inter-episode anxiety that accompanies panic disorder, although patients with generalized anxiety disorder seem to have fewer cardiovascular symptoms and fewer symptoms related to hyperventilation (Anderson, Noyes, & Crowe, 1984; Hoehn-Saric, 1982). Many patients with panic disorder will deny any history of symptoms prior to their first attack, but a thorough anamnesis will often contradict their blanket denials. One study of patients with panic disorder found that all had shown symptoms of generalized anxiety disorder for 2 to 10 years prior to their first panic attack (Cloninger, Martin, Clayton, & Guze, 1981). Similarly, the course of the illness remains obscure; some of these patients go on to develop panic disorder (Sheehan & Sheehan, 1983), while others may continue to suffer severe generalized anxiety for years and never have a panic attack (Hoehn-Saric & McLeod, 1985).

No sharp dividing line separates generalized anxiety disorder from the anxieties of everyday life; the listed symptoms differ from normal tension only in magnitude, not in quality. Research studies define this disorder by requiring some arbitrary severity rating on symptom scales, but patients with equal scale ratings often are quite heterogeneous in symptomatology.

Depressed patients often are anxious, and anxious patients depressed; no cross-sectional criteria can reliably distinguish patients with generalized anxiety disorder from those with dysthymic disorder. Longitudinal observation may be necessary in order to assign the correct diagnosis to these patients. In dysthymic patients the dysphoric mood persists while severe anxiety occurs only intermittently, while in patients with generalized anxiety disorder, dysphoric mood is a transient expression of their feelings of defeat and failure in their struggle with anxiety (Clancy, Noyes, & Hoenk, 1978; Roth & Mountjoy, 1982).

Posttraumatic Stress Disorder

The essential feature of this disorder is the development of symptoms after a psychological trauma that is outside the usual human experience. The traumatic stressors experienced would evoke distress in most people and are beyond the range of common experiences, such as bereavement, chronic illness, business losses, or marital conflicts. The trauma generally involves a serious threat to one's life or physical integrity; the destruction of one's home or community; or seeing another person injured, dead, or the victim of physical violence. The trauma may be experienced alone (rape or assault) or in the company of others (military combat). Common stressors are natural disasters (floods, earthquakes) or manmade disasters (car accidents, fires, airplane crashes, bombings, torture, concentration camps). Frequently, some physical damage to the patient takes place.

The symptoms experienced are a mixture of three classes: (a) re-experiencings of the traumatic event, (b) anxiety-like symptoms, and (c) depression-like symptoms. During some phase of the illness, the traumatic event is persistently re-experienced through intrusive distressing recollections, recurrent distressing dreams, or the sudden re-experiencing of the traumatic event. The re-experiencing may take the form of discrete illusions or hallucinations related to the trauma, or it may occur as a dissociated sense of being back in the traumatic scene. It may be experienced when intoxicated or during hypnagogic or hypnapompic periods. In rare instances, there are dissociated states lasting from minutes to days, during which the event is relived (Hendin et al., 1984). Such "reliving" states most often are seen in combat veterans. Conversely, the patient may develop amnesia for certain aspects of the trauma.

Persistent symptoms of increased arousal develop, with anxiety, hypervigilance, an exaggerated startle response, difficulty concentrating, and insomnia. These symptoms may increase when the patient is exposed to circumstances that resemble the original trauma. Patients often avoid such circumstances, as well as any others that arouse recollection of the traumatic events. This avoidance may develop into a full phobia for the situations associated with the trauma.

Depression-like symptoms commonly develop. Patients show a constricted affect with marked loss of interest in previously enjoyed activities. Patients may feel detached or estranged from other people; their ability to feel any emotions may be blunted, with the emotions of tenderness, intimacy, and sexual arousal particularly diminished. Guilty ruminations may preoccupy the thoughts of patients who survived dangerous traumas.

The disorder can begin at any age, from childhood on. Symptoms may begin soon after the trauma, or may be delayed until months or years later. The course of the disorder is variable. The prognosis is good in cases where the symptoms begin within 6 months after the trauma, and have not lasted more than 6 months. The prognosis is more guarded, however, if the symptoms are delayed 6 months or longer, or if they endure for more than 6 months. Pre-existing psychopathology and previous stressful experiences both predispose the patient to the development of this disorder. If another anxiety disorder or any other disorder is present, the patient is given a diagnosis of both posttraumatic stress disorder and the other disorder.

Adjustment Disorder with Anxious Mood

The essential feature of this disorder is a maladaptive reaction occurring within 3 months of an identifiable stressor. It is assumed that the disorder will remit within 6 months of when the stressor ceases, or when some new level of adaptation is reached. The symptoms of this disorder are nervousness, worry, and jitteriness that either exceeds the normal reaction to such a stressor, or causes impairment in the patient's social or occupational functioning.

The stressors may be single or multiple, recurrent (e.g., examinations) or continuous (e.g., chronic illness) and private or affecting a group or community. The specific stressor and its severity should be noted on Axis IV of the DSM-III-R diagnosis. The severity of the patient's reaction may not be predictable from the severity of the stressor. The duration of the disorder may be as brief as a few months if the stressor is transient and ceases, or the duration may be much longer if the stressor continues. Pre-existing disorders and previous stressors may increase an individual's vulnerability to stress and predispose to the development of an adjustment disorder.

This reaction can not be merely one instance of a pattern of overreaction to such stressors, nor can it represent an exacerbation of some disorder present previously. Personality disorders are often exacerbated by stressors, in which case the diagnosis of adjustment reaction is not made unless new, previously unseen symptoms develop. This diagnosis should not be used if the disturbance meets the criteria for some other specific disorder. Further, it is not used if the magnitude of the disturbance is mild. Instead, the patient may be given a diagnosis of one of the "Conditions Not Attributable to a Mental Disorder" from the DSM-III-R "V Codes", for instance, Academic Problem (V.62.30), Occupational Problem (V.62.20), and so on. (American Psychiatric Association, 1987 pp. 359–362).

Separation Anxiety Disorder of Childhood or Adolescence

Some of the adult anxiety disorders are known to be common among children, while for others the childhood incidence is low, unknown, or controversial. The diagnosis of separation anxiety disorder should be given to adults in whom the disorder has persisted from childhood or adolescence.

The essential feature of this disorder is anxiety on separation from familiar surroundings or from people to whom the patient is attached. The anxiety is in excess of that expected at the child's developmental level, and it may be of panic magnitude. When separated from significant objects (people) to whom they are attached, these children often are preoccupied with fears of illnesses or accidents befalling these people or themselves. The patients fear that they themselves or their objects will be harmed or killed by animals, monsters, muggers, car accidents, or airplane travel. Insomnia and fear of the dark are common in these children; nightmares may develop, and the child often fears sleeping alone. The child may display clinging behavior, staying close to their significant object at all times. Some children do not verbalize these specific fantasies, but simply feel homesick, sad, withdrawn, apathetic, anxious, or uncomfortable, and yearn to return home. Children and adolescents often will develop anticipatory fears when separation is impending, and may develop physical symptoms (e.g., abdominal pain, headache, vomiting) which prevent their separation. Often the disorder begins after some life stress or loss, such as the death of a relative or a move to a new environment.

The disorder is equally common in both

sexes and it may develop at any age. It appears more commonly in children from closely knit families, and it presents only rarely in neglected children. The course typically is marked by remissions and exacerbations for many years. In some cases it may not be possible to distinguish this disorder from major depression, in which case both diagnoses should be given. This disorder may be mislabeled "school phobia"; however, when the anxiety response generally is present during most separation situations, and not only during confrontation with school, the correct diagnosis is separation anxiety disorder. Patients with this disorder may be at higher risk for developing agoraphobia or another anxiety disorder in adult life (Gittelman-Klein & Klein, 1985).

Overanxious Disorder of Childhood or Adolescence

This disorder is characterized by generalized fearful behavior and excessive worrying about a variety of situations. While these fears are not focused on any one specific situation or object, they often do center on the child's apprehension about performance in past or anticipated situations. The situations commonly feared include physical examinations, school tests, social situations, and other occasions where the child's performance might be judged. Younger children with this disorder often fear the judgment of some person whom they regard as harsh or critical; adolescents with the disorder often expect that their failures will incite the scorn of their peers.

In addition to these fantasies of failure, unfocused feelings of nervousness may be present, along with the physical signs of anxiety: gastrointestinal distress, nausea, dizziness, headache, dyspnea, and a lump in the throat. These physical signs or other somatic complaints may themselves be a source of anxious concern for the child. The child's anxiety may be expressed as motor restlessness, hair pulling, or nail biting. Perfectionism and obsessional doubting is common in these children, along with a pervasive lack of self-confidence and a strong need to gain the approval of others.

The severity of the disorder may be mild enough to cause the child distress without impairing his or her performance, or the anxiety may be severe enough to interfere with effective performance, thus bringing about the very failure that is feared.

The disorder is seen most frequently in eldest children, only children, children from upper socioeconomic classes, and other children who feel pressured to excel. The disorder is more common in boys than in girls; it can begin gradually or abruptly at any point in childhood or adolescence, and its anxiety or poor self-confidence can persist into adulthood. Its course is usually marked by exacerbations during periods of stress.

Overanxious disorder can coexist with separation anxiety disorder, phobic disorder, obsessive-compulsive disorder, attention deficit disorder, or other DSM-III-R Axis I disorders. It is not diagnosed if the symptoms occur only during the course of a psychotic disorder.

Anxiety Disorder not Otherwise Specified

No explicit criteria are given for this category, which in DSM-III was called atypical anxiety disorder. This diagnosis is to be used for patients who have anxiety or phobic avoidance that does not meet the criteria specified for any of the conditions described.

The Organic Anxiety Syndrome

Anxiety is a common component of the presentation of many medical illnesses, because many patients will become anxious when they observe themselves to be ill. Nonetheless, anxiety appears to be especially common in patients suffering from certain diseases; these have been cataloged in a number of recent reviews (Cameron, 1985; Dietch, 1981; Jefferson & Marshall, 1981; Lader, 1981; Mackenzie &

Popkin, 1983). We might presume that the factor causing the disease also causes the anxiety, or that the disease itself is caused by the anxiety (e.g., peptic ulcer disease), but these assumptions are more faith than fact. Because as little is known about the pathophysiology of anxiety as about the pathophysiology of these diseases, we have little warrant to assert that both flow from a common source. This caveat needs to be kept in mind while we consider the organic diseases presumed to cause anxiety.

These diseases fall in a class that is new in the DSM-III-R: the organic anxiety syndrome. In this syndrome, anxiety may be continuous, as in generalized anxiety disorder, or it may be intermittent, as in panic disorder. A specific organic factor causing the syndrome must be suggested by the patient's history, physical examination, or laboratory tests, and the diagnosis is not assigned if the anxiety is part of a more passive organic disorder, such as delirium or dementia. The most common medical conditions causing anxiety are diseases of the neurologic, endocrine, cardiovascular, or digestive systems, and are summarized in Table 3.1.

Among the neurological diseases, delirium often presents with anxiety, but the disorientation and fluctuating state of consciousness present in delirium make it unlikely to be mistaken for an anxiety disorder. Patients with Parkinson's disease often are anxious (Lishman, 1979). Partial complex seizures, commonly present with anxiety as a component of the pre-seizure aura. At times, this aura will not evolve into the other typical seizure symptoms, and the ictal origin of this anxiety may go unrecognized (Currie, Heathfield, Henson, & Scott, 1971; Roth & Harper, 1962). The development of anxiety symptoms in any epileptic patient should prompt a reevaluation of treatment to determine if the seizures are adequately controlled, or if the anxiety represents an ictal symptom that is "breaking through" the anticonvulsant therapy.

A number of endocrine and metabolic disease are commonly associated with

Table 3.1. Medical Conditions Associated with Anxiety

BODY SYSTEM	MEDICAL CONDITION
Neurological	Partial complex seizures Parkinson's disease Delirium Early dementia
Cardiovascular	Hypertension Angina pectoris Pulmonary embolus Cardiac arrythmias Mitral valve prolapse (?)
Respiratory	Hyperventilation Any condition producing hypoxia
Endocrine/Metabolic	Carcinoid syndrome Cushing's syndrome Hyperthyroidism Hyperparathyroidism Hypoglycemia Pheochromocytoma Acute intermittent porphyria Premenstrual syndrome
Gastrointestinal	Peptic ulcer Spastic colon with diarrhea

anxiety: Cushing's syndrome, hypercalcemia, hyperparathyroidism, both hypo- and hyperthyroidism, carcinoid syndrome, hypoglycemia, and pheochromocytoma (Anger, 1985; Smith, Barish, Correa, Williams, 1972; Williams, Correa, Smith, & Barish, 1970). Anxiety frequently accompanies hypercalcemia, which probably accounts for the higher levels of anxiety seen in patients with hyperparathyroidism (Karpati & Frame, 1964; Petersen, 1968; Weizman et al., 1979). Hypoglycemia can produce anxiety episodically; whether these patients show any other psychological disturbance is controversial (Gorman et al., 1984; Uhde, Roy-Byrne, Vittone, Boulenger, & Post, 1985; Uhde, Vittone, & Post, 1984). Pheochromocytoma is noteworthy because of the episodic nature of the anxiety it produces, with rare generalized anxiety between the episodes (Manger, 1985; Starkman, Zelnik, Nesse, & Cameron, 1985). While no consensus exists on the diagnostic features of the premenstrual syndrome, anxiety is a symptom common to many of the criteria proposed for this disorder (Rubinow & Roy-Byrne, 1984).

Peptic ulcer and other gastrointestinal disturbances have long been felt to be more common in patients with anxiety disorders (Noyes, Clancey, Hoenk, & Slymen, 1978). Elevated levels of anxiety have been demonstrated in patients with the form of irritable colon that is accompanied by diarrhea (Esler & Goulston, 1973; Young, Alpers, Norland, & Woodruff, 1976).

The cardiovascular diseases most often associated with anxiety are those that produce hypoxia and, of course, those that produce pain, preoccupation, and fear in the patient. Patients with hypertension show higher levels of anxiety than do normotensive patients (Sullivan et al., 1981; Wheatley et al., 1975; Whitehead, Blackwell, DeSilva, & Robinson, 1977). For patients with Type A behavior, it is not clear whether they are, in fact, excessively anxious (Blumenthal, Thompson, & Williams, 1979; Dimsdale, Hackett, Block, & Hutter, 1978).

Drug Intoxication and Withdrawal

By far, the most frequent causes of anxiety are drug intoxication and withdrawal from alcohol or other drugs (Dietch, 1981; Drugs, 1984; Lader, 1981).

Caffeine is a ubiquitous drug which frequently causes or exacerbates anxiety (Boulenger, Uhde, Wolff, & Post, 1984; Greden, 1974; Greden, Fontaine, Lubetsky, & Chamberlin, 1978; Gilliland & Andress, 1981; Uhde, Boulenger, Jimerson, & Post, 1984; Uhde, Boulenger, & Post, 1983; Victor, Lubetsky, & Greden, 1981). Patients commonly are unaware of the large doses of caffeine they habitually ingest in sodas, coffee, and headache remedies; this use can produce a state of chronic recurrent caffeine intoxication. When the caffeine addict deliberately or unwittingly stops ingesting the drug, anxiety may be experienced as one symptom of the caffeine withdrawal syndrome, which typically also includes headache and lethargy (Greden, Victor, Fontaine, & Lubetsky, 1980). Aside from its own anxiogenic effects, caffeine can exacerbate the symptomatology already present in patients who have panic attacks or other functional anxiety disorders (Charney, Heninger, & Jatlow, 1985). Theophylline, a methylxanthine compound like caffeine, may have similar effects when it is used in the treatment of asthma (Trembath & Boobis, 1979). Isoproterenol and other β-adrenergic agonists used in the treatment of asthma also have been shown to be anxiogenic (Frohlich, Dunstan, & Page, 1966; Frohlich, Tarazi, & Dunstan, 1969; Pohl et al., 1985). Stimulant compounds available without a prescription are widely used as decongestants in cold and sinusitis preparations (phenylpropanolamine and others), and as appetite suppressants (diethylpropion hydrochloride, phendimetrazine tartrate, and others). These stimulants commonly produce anxiety during the course of their action (Berman & Anderson, 1966). Other stimulating drugs that have dopaminergic effects (amantadine hydrochloride, bromocriptine mesylate, nomifensine maleate) commonly produce anxiety, as may corticosteroids and anticholinergic drugs (Dietch, 1981; Lader, 1981).

Marijuana is commonly anxiogenic. During intoxication it has exacerbated the symptoms of patients with preexisting anxiety disorders, and it can produce recurrent panic attacks in patients who have not previously had any anxiety disorder (Annis & Smart, 1973; Jones, 1978; Meyer, 1978; Pillard, McNair, & Fisher, 1974; Weller & Halikas, 1980; Zuardi, Shirakawa, Finklefarb, & Karniol, 1982). This effect is not limited to novice marijuana users; even patients who have long used marijuana without suffering any adverse effect may abruptly develop panic while intoxicated. The panic may recur after the intoxication subsides, and, as in panic attacks of any etiology, a full phobic anxiety syndrome can ensue. This panic reaction may be more frequent in patients who have previously experienced it while intoxicated, and it appears to be more commonly seen when the marijuana is ingested. Reports on the inadvertant ingestion of marijuana describe anxiety as a transient symptom for many of these patients (Food-borne, 1981). Anxiety reactions also can occur during intoxication with phencyclidine (Siegel, 1978), and other hallucinogens.

Anxiety may be produced by intoxication with nicotine from tobacco or other sources. This anxiety is usually brief in duration, as the nicotine is rapidly cleared from the bloodstream. Polycyclic antidepressants, monoamine oxidase inhibitors, parasympathomimetic drugs, antihypertensive drugs — these and virtually every agent that enters the central nervous system have been implicated as causes of anxiety (Drugs, 1984). Even aspirin can produce anxiety when it is taken in an overdose sufficient to produce acidosis.

Neuroleptic drugs rarely cause anxiety, but they do commonly cause akathesia, a syndrome often mistaken for anxiety because of its hallmark symptom: a subjective sensation of restlessness which leads the patient to fidget and perform repetitive actions, albeit without any subjective sense of nervousness. Akathesia without anxiety can also occur as part of the restless leg syndrome and other neurological movement disorders (Lutz, 1978).

Withdrawal from a variety of drugs can cause anxiety. Alcohol withdrawal is probably the single most common organic cause of anxiety, but withdrawal anxiety also can appear after ceasing virtually any minor tranquilizer. "Rebound" withdrawal from tranquilizers often mimics the very anxiety that necessitated their use, thus perpetuating an iatrogenic state of drug dependence (Allen & Oswald, 1976; Fontaine, Chouinard, & Annable, 1984; Lapierre, Tremblay, Gagnon, Monpremier, Berliss, & Oyewumi, 1982; Morgan & Oswald, 1982; Scharf, Kales, Bixler, Jacoby, & Schweitzer, 1982; Tyrer, Owen, & Dawling, 1983). The time lag to the onset of the tranquilizer withdrawal syndrome varies with the tranquilizer's duration of action. For long-acting agents like flurazepam hydrochloride (Dalmane®) or chlordiazepoxide (Librium®), the withdrawal syndrome can begin after days of abstinence, while for ultra-short acting agents like triazolam or alcohol, anxiety or other withdrawal symptoms can be seen within hours after the last dose (Hoehn-Saric & McLeod, 1985; Kales, Soldatos, Bixler, & Kales, 1983). Anxiety also is common during withdrawal from habitual nicotine use (Nesbitt, 1973; Shiffman, 1979).

Anxiety is a common symptom of narcotic withdrawal. Here, too, the delay in symptom onset varies with the duration of action of the narcotic — heroin withdrawal can occur within hours of the last dose, while methadone withdrawal symptoms may be delayed for days.

DSM-III and DSM-III-R

After their initial publication in 1980, the DSM-III criteria were revised by the American Psychiatric Association Work Group in 1987. It is this revised "DSM-III-R" classification that has been presented in this chapter (American

Psychiatric Association, 1987). Practitioners who are accustomed to the original DSM-III classification may find it useful to examine the changes implemented in the revised version. The revision has effected an overall simplification of the taxonomy by making the criteria more uniform from one disorder to another. Some changes implemented in the revision are pervasive, applying to all diagnoses, while others are specific to particular diagnoses.

Under the revision, uniform hierarchical rules now apply throughout the taxonomy to govern the awarding of multiple concurrent diagnoses (American Psychiatric Association, 1987, pp. xxiv–xxv, 235–253): an organic etiology now excludes diagnosis of all functional anxiety disorders; an anxiety disorder diagnosis is not assigned if the patient's symptoms are symptoms associated with a more pervasive disorder whose diagnostic criteria are met; and a patient with an anxiety diagnosis can be given an additional anxiety diagnosis if the focus of his concern is not related to the first diagnosis.

These revised hierarchy principles allow many concurrent diagnoses to be assigned to patients. Some noteworthy examples are mentioned in the DSM-III-R text: in a patient with panic disorder who meets the generalized anxiety disorder criteria, the concurrent diagnosis of generalized anxiety disorder is allowed if this anxiety is not simply fear of having another panic attack; a patient with panic disorder and social phobia should be given both diagnoses if his social fear is not simply fear of having a panic attack in public; a patient with post-traumatic stress disorder can be given a concurrent diagnosis of simple phobia if his phobic fear is not limited to stimuli related to his post-traumatic stress disorder; a patient with obsessive compulsive disorder can be given a diagnosis of a simple phobia, as long as the patient's phobia is not the fear of contamination which is typically associated with obsessive compulsive disorder. Most importantly, this revision now permits the assignment of anxiety disorder diagnoses to patients who have mood disorders or schizophrenia.

The revised criteria broaden the range of the panic disorder diagnosis and more strictly exclude other overlapping diagnoses. Panic disorder is diagnosed instead of simple phobia or social phobia if the phobic symptoms developed in the past out of panic disorder, or if exposure to the phobic stimulus does not always almost provoke an anxiety attack. The classification now accepts that agoraphobia also emerges from panic disorder in this same way. Following the suggestion of Sheehan (Sheehan & Sheehan, 1982a), the DSM-III-R has subsumed most cases of agoraphobia under the panic disorder rubric, and it requires that the severity of the attacks and the severity of the agoraphobia be separately specified.

In place of the three attacks required by DSM-III, one panic attack is now sufficient to assign the diagnosis, if the attack was followed by a month of persistent fear of having another attack. The defining features of the panic attack have been extended to include nausea, abdominal distress, and derealization, as well as the other diagnostic symptoms.

The revised criteria now recognize that phobic patients may continue to avoid their phobic situations even after their anxiety has disappeared. Patients can now be given the phobia diagnosis if they avoid anxiety by avoiding the phobic stimulus. Ironically, this will allow the diagnosis of an anxiety disorder to be given to patients who have no anxiety, so long as their avoidance behavior continues at a magnitude sufficient to cause them marked distress, or to interfere with their social or occupational functioning.

The criteria for generalized anxiety disorder have become somewhat more restrictive. The duration necessary for the period of anxious mood or worry about misfortune has been extended to 6 months in order to better distinguish this disorder from brief, transient stress reactions. The diagnosis has been restricted further by now requiring the presence of at least 6 of the 18 listed symptoms.

The criteria for posttraumatic stress

disorder have been somewhat broadened in the revision. The classification now specifies that "reexperiencing" the trauma can take many forms: illusions, hallucinations, "flashback," or feelings of reliving the experience. The patient may not be aware of an environmental trigger for these experiences, and they may occur during the altered mental states of awakening or intoxication. The reexperiencing reaction may not even be a conscious one — increased physiological reactivity or intense psychological distress may occur upon exposure to events that have only a symbolic relation to the trauma.

ASSESSMENT

The causes of anxiety are myriad, and there are a host of diagnoses in which anxiety is a prominent symptom. There are many organic, psychotic, and nonpsychotic disorders that present with anxiety in addition to the syndromes collected under the DSM-III-R rubric of "anxiety disorders." If a patient's anxiety is due to an organic etiology, such as a medical disorder, drug intoxication, or drug withdrawal, an anxiety disorder diagnosis is not assigned. An additional anxiety disorder diagnosis can be assigned to patients with functional psychosis, affective illness, or other nonorganic conditions only if the anxiety symptoms are not a feature associated with the condition. Most anxious patients do not have an anxiety disorder, but instead qualify for a diagnosis from one of these other categories.

In order to detect these organic and functional diseases, the evaluation of the anxious patient must include a thorough review of symptoms and medical history. Anxiety can be produced as part of the intoxication or withdrawal syndromes of a host of drugs, so a reliable account must be obtained of the patient's use of drugs including prescription drugs, over-the-counter drugs, intoxicants, and drugs such as caffeine and tobacco from the pharmacopea of everyday life. Only if a careful history has demonstrated the absence of the features associated with these other diagnoses can the patient be assumed to have solely an anxiety disorder.

The particular anxiety disorder diagnosis assigned will depend on the nature of the anxiety symptoms, the type of stimulus that precipitates the anxiety, and the duration of the symptoms themselves. It is critical to determine if the patient suffers a low-grade continuous anxiety; or intermittent, severe, and incapacitating panic atacks; or both continuous anxiety and episodic exacerbations. If the anxiety episodically reaches panic proportions, the stimuli that trigger these episodes must be determined. There may be no provocative stimulus detectable; or the stimulus may be exposure to some "external" object, place, or event; or the stimulus may be some "internal" event or thought. If the patient does not experience panic attacks currently, has he or she ever had them? If a precipitating stimulus is found, will it always provoke the anxiety response? Are some of the anxiety attacks provoked by other stimuli? The symptoms that accompany the anxiety also must be determined. Are there physical symptoms, for example, tachycardia, tachypnea, nausea, paresthesias? Are there dissociative episodes or intrusive memories? Is there marked avoidance behavior? These answers all are crucial in selecting the correct anxiety disorder diagnosis.

Anxiety disorders can begin in childhood, so the examination of the patient must include an evaluation of his or her childhood history. This also may disclose a history of childhood object loss, which appears frequently in patients with panic disorder (Raskin et al., 1982).

The patient's family history can be informative. Anxiety disorders are more common in patients with a family history of anxiety, depression or alcoholism (Weissman, Leckman, Merikangas, Gammon, & Prusoff, 1984). A family history of these disorders does not predict any specific anxiety disorder, but it is for panic disorder that the evidence of familial occurrence appears strongest (Weissman, 1985).

Routine laboratory tests rarely uncover

previously unknown conditions in patients presenting with anxiety (Hall, Popkin, Devaul, Faillace, & Stickney, 1978). The most frequent unexpected finding on these tests is elevated serum levels of liver function enzymes, usually due to occult alcoholism (Hoehn-Saric & McLeod, 1985).

Anxiety and Other Functional Psychiatric Disorders

There is much overlap between the symptoms of the anxiety disorders and the symptoms seen in other functional psychiatric illnesses. Depression and alcoholism frequently develop in patients with anxiety disorders, while anxiety itself is a common symptom in both of these disorders (Brier, Charney, & Heninger, 1985; Small, Stockwell, Canter, & Hodgson, 1984; Stockwell, Small, Hodgson, & Canter, 1984). When an anxiety disorder presents concurrently with another disorder, both diagnoses should be given unless the anxiety symptoms typically are associated features of the other disorder. Under this principle, chronically dysphoric patients with agoraphobia or obsessive–compulsive disorder would not be given an additional diagnosis of dysthymic disorder, because chronic dysphoric mood is a typical associated feature of these anxiety disorders. Another example would be the presence of generalized anxiety during an acute psychotic episode. Here, generalized anxiety disorder would not be diagnosed in addition to the psychotic disorder. A thoroughly executed examination and history may be necessary to disorder. A thoroughly executed examination and history may be necessary to "afraid it might crash." She denies experiencing any anxiety, but for vacations and symptomatology.

Anxiety is a common component of depressive disorders, and the two share many symptoms in common. Separating anxiety from depression can be a difficult and, at times, impossible task. Depression is not common in patients with simple phobias, but it is frequent in patients with panic disorder, agoraphobia (Schapira, Kerr, & Roth, 1970), generalized anxiety disorder, and social phobia (Liebowitz et al., 1985). In many studies, about half of the patients diagnosed as depressed also receive a diagnosis of some anxiety disorder, while nearly half of the patients with anxiety disorders may develop secondary depression (Dealy, Ishiki, Avery, Wilson, & Dunner, 1981; Van Valkenburg, Winokur, Lowry, Behar, & Van Valkenburg, 1983).

The presence of active or residual psychosis distinguishes schizophrenia from the anxiety disorders, but the symptoms of any anxiety disorder can appear in schizophrenia. Not seen in the anxiety disorders, however, are the typical schizophrenic symptoms: delusions; hallucinations; disorganization; abnormal affect; loosening of associations; or deterioration in work, social relations, or self-care. In schizophrenia, and in other psychoses, the anxious patient may relate his or her anxiety to some systematized delusions, for example, believing that obsessive thoughts are being inserted by some other person or machine, that obsessive or compulsive behavior is truly effective in warding off feared consequences, that some external agency is forcing the performance of compulsive acts, or that danger truly lurks outside the door.

Anxiety disorders are common among patients with personality disorder diagnoses, but some personality disorders themselves present symptoms that are confusingly similar to anxiety disorder symptoms. Avoidant personality, thus, may be complicated by the presence of a particular focal phobia, or dependent personality may be confused with agoraphobia.

Other psychiatric disorders may include anxiety as a prominent symptom. Patients with somatization disorder commonly are anxious or depressed; this anxiety often is the symptom that leads them to the psychiatrist's door. Anxiety often is found among patients with hypochondriasis, who believe that they suffer from an undiagnosed and dangerous physical illness. Illness phobia is common among patients with hypochondriasis (Agras et al., 1969). The physiological signs of anxiety themselves can become the focus of hypochondriacal concern (Kenyon, 1976); it can be unclear if the anxiety is caused by the hypochondriasis or if a more complex pathogenetic process is at work. Depersonalization disorder and other dissociative disorders may be accompanied by anxiety symptoms (Roth, 1959).

CASE ILLUSTRATIONS

Case #1

A 56-year-old man is admitted to the hospital for his fifth episode of major depression. He reports that he frequently experiences the symptoms of panic disorder during his depressive episodes, and that he has never had a panic attack at any other time. He believes that his panic attacks are triggered by the fear that he experiences when he is depressed, a fear that he will not recover.

Should this patient receive a diagnosis of panic disorder in addition to the diagnosis of major depression? Under the DSM-III criteria for panic disorder, this diagnosis is not given if the attacks are judged to be due to major depression. In the DSM-III-R, however, the hierarchical principles allow the panic disorder diagnosis, because panic attacks are not a symptom associated with major depression. The patient, therefore, should be assigned the panic disorder diagnosis, as well as the diagnosis of major depression.

Case #2

A month after an appendectomy, an 11-year-old boy refuses to go to school unless accompanied by a parent. He is reluctant to leave home for friends' parties, family outings, and any other cause. When the school bus arrives, he hides or claims to be ill. At home he is clingy and afraid to separate from his parents. Previously he had exhibited no overt psychopathology.

The patient at first appears to present a case of school phobia, but, in fact, his anxiety is not provoked specifically by the school situation, but by separation from his parents. His diagnosis is separation anxiety disorder.

Case #3

A 55-year-old woman reports that she will not fly in an airplane because "I know it's not really going to happen, but I'm afraid it might crash." She denies experiencing any anxiety, but for vacations and for business purposes she travels freely by car, bus, train, or boat — but she has never flown in an airplane.

This patient experiences no anxiety connected with flying only because she has evolved compensatory avoidance behaviors, by which she has adapted to her phobia. Her diagnosis, then, is simple phobia. Although it causes her little active distress, the phobia interferes with her functioning to the extent that she must alter her personal and business life to accommodate her avoidance of the phobic situation.

Case #4

A 33-year-old woman presents complaining of depression, irritability, difficulty in falling asleep, frequent awakenings, difficulty in concentrating, and a loss of interest in social relations. This began a few months after she was raped in an elevator. She cannot recall anything of the event itself, but now does grow anxious when riding in elevators, and she can tolerate them only with difficulty.

This patient's diagnosis is posttraumatic stress disorder. If her symptoms are of sufficient magnitude, she might be given an additional diagnosis of major depression. Her persistent elevator phobia clearly derives from her trauma, even though she cannot recall the event itself. She presents the mixed symptom picture of both depression and anxiety, which is common in this disorder.

Case #5

A 28-year-old man presents complaining that he is unable to leave his home because he fears that he will walk past a funeral parlor, or that a funeral procession will pass him in the street. When either event occurs, he grows anxious and begins to fear that a member of his family will die. This anxiety persists until he can cross himself 100 times while repeating a prayer. He recognizes that his anxiety is unreasonable.

This patient stays at home because he experiences anticipatory anxiety at the prospect of encountering the funereal stimuli, which evoke in him an unpleasant thought and uncomfortable anxiety by performing a stereotyped ritual. Thus, he presents a classic obsessive–compulsive disorder. He has the obsessive thought that a member of his family will die, this thought compells him to perform a ritual to prevent this dreaded event, and to reduce his uncomfortable anxiety. He also has developed a phobia for the stimuli that evoke this thought, and this phobia prevents him from leaving home. He does not have panic disorder with extensive phobic avoidance (agrophobia) because he does not have unexpected panic attacks. His anxiety attacks are, instead, clearly triggered by certain thoughts, which themselves reliably are evoked by the funereal stimuli.

CONCLUSION

Anxiety is a symptom that presents as a part of a number of different organic and functional illnesses. Medical illnesses, drug intoxication or withdrawal, and a number of functional disorders must be ruled out before a patient is given a diagnosis of an anxiety disorder. Diagnosis of the patient with anxiety thus requires that he or she receive a full psychiatric evaluation in addition to a detailed history of the anxiety symptoms. The history obtained from the patient must extend back into childhood, to determine if object losses occurred and if the anxiety symptoms began then.

A large number of different anxiety syndromes have been described in the past; some of these derived from clinical observation, some from attempts to organize the diagnostic taxonomy, and some from theoretical positions. Today, the most widely used diagnostic system in the United States is the DSM-III, now revised as the DSM-III-R. This classification has introduced three innovations into clinical practice:

1. Reliable operationalized criteria are used for the assignment of diagnoses.
2. Multiple concurrent diagnoses are assigned wherever not specifically excluded. For example, an anxious patient with any functional psychiatric illness can be given an additional diagnosis of an anxiety disorder, as long as the anxiety symptoms are not typically a part of the illness.
3. An integrated model of pathogenesis is used which distinguishes among the anxiety disorders according to the locus of the stimulus (random, external, internal) that provokes the anxiety. When the attacks are "unexpected" panic disorder is diagnosed; when the attacks are provoked by exposure to some external stimulus, a simple phobia is diagnosed; when the attacks are provoked by some thought, obsessive–compulsive disorder is diagnosed. Posttraumatic stress disorder is diagnosed when both symptoms of anxiety and depression are present, along with either experiences of reliving the trauma or anxious reactions to trauma-linked stimuli. The diagnoses of generalized anxiety disorder and limited symptom attacks with phobic avoidance (agoraphobia without panic attacks) are restricted to patients who have never had a panic attack.

Whatever the stimulus that evokes the anxiety attack, it may become associated with certain external stimuli that the patient then fears. This "anticipatory anxiety" can lead the patient to reorganize his or her life so as to avoid the provocative stimulus. Some patients succeed so well at avoiding this phobic stimulus that they no longer experience anxiety attacks, and the persistence of the avoidant behavior pattern may be the only sign that the patient has an anxiety disorder. Alternatively, the anxiety may generalize to other stimuli, which the patient then avoids. Agoraphobia can arise from these multiple phobias, or it can develop from the patient's fear of being incapacitated by an anxiety attack while away from home.

These moves toward rationalizing the nosology are profound in their effects. Whatever doubts may be inspired by the DSM-III program, it does provide a reliable, testable, and "falsifiable" taxonomy. The standard of reliability it sets will guide any study seeking to establish valid diagnostic groups in the coming years.

REFERENCES

Agras, W. S., Chapin, H. N., & Oliveau, D. C. (1972). The natural history of phobia: Course and prognosis. *Archives of General Psychiatry, 26,* 315–317.

Agras, W. S., Sylvester, D., & Oliveau, D. (1969). The epidemiology of common fears and phobias. *Comprehensive Psychiatry, 10,* 151–156.

Aimes, P. L., Gelder, M. G., & Shaw, P. M. (1983). Social Phobia: A comparative clinical study. *British Journal of Psychiatry, 142,* 174–179.

Allen, S., & Oswald, I. (1976). Anxiety and sleep after forsazepam. *British Journal of Clinical Pharmacology, 3,* 165–168.

Anderson, D. J., Noyes, R., Crowe, R. R. (1984). A comparison of panic disorder and generalized anxiety disorder. *American Journal of Psychiatry, 141,* 572–576.

American Psychiatric Association. (1980). *Diagnostic and statistical manual of mental disorders* (3rd Ed.). Washington, DC: Author.

American Psychiatric Association. (1987). *Diagnostic and statistical manual of mental disorders* (3rd Ed. Revised). Washington, DC: Author.

Annis, H. M., & Smart, R. G. (1973). Adverse reactions and recurrences from marijuana use. *British Journal of Addiction, 68,* 315–319.

Bayer, R., & Spitzer, R. L. (1985). Neurosis, psychodynamics, and DSM-III; a history of the controversy. *Archives of General Psychiatry, 42,* 187–196.

Beck, A. T., Laude, R., & Bohnert, M. (1974). Ideational components of anxiety neurosis. *Archives of General Psychiatry, 31,* 319–325.

Berman, M. I., & Anderson, I. R. (1966) Comparison of weight losses with three reducing regimens: Diet therapy, phenmetrazine, and an amphetamine combination (Obetrol). *Journal of the American Geriatrics Society, 14,* 623–630.

Blumenthal, J. A., Thompson, L. W., & Williams, R. B. (1979). Anxiety-proneness and coronary heart disease. *Journal of Psychosomatic Research, 23,* 17.

Boulenger, J. P., Uhde, T. W., Wolff, E. A., & Post, R. M. (1984). Increased sensitivity to caffeine in patients with panic disorders: Preliminary evidence. *Archives of General Psychiatry, 41,* 1067–1072.

Cameron, O. G. (1985). The differential diagnosis of anxiety: psychiatric and medical disorders. *Psychiatric Clinics of North America, 8,* 3–24.

Charney, D. S., Heninger, G. R., & Jatlow, P. I. (1985). Increased anxiogenic effects of caffeine in panic disorders. *Archives of General Psychiatry, 42,* 233–243.

Clancy, J., Noyes, R., & Hoenk, P. R., (1978). Secondary depression in anxiety neurosis. *Journal of Nervous and Mental Disease, 166,* 846.

Cloninger, C. R., Martin, R. L., Clayton, P., & Guze, S. B. (1981). A blind follow-up and family study of anxiety neurosis: Preliminary analysis of the St. Louis 500. In D. F. Klein & J. G. Rabkin (Eds.), *Anxiety: New research and changing concepts* (pp. 137–154). New York: Raven Press.

Crowe, R. R. (1985). Mitral valve prolapse and panic disorder. *Psychiatric Clinics of North America, 8,* 63–72.

Currie, S., Heathfield, K. W. G., Henson, R. A., & Scott, D. F. (1971). Clinical course and prognosis of temporal lobe epilepsy: A survey of 666 patients. *Brain, 94,* 173–190.

Curtis, G. C. (1985). Anxiety and anxiety disorders: Toward a conceptual reorientation. *Psychiatric Clinics of North America, 8,* 159–168.

DaCosta, J. M. (1871). On irritable heart: A clinical study of a functional cardiac disorder and its consequences. *American Journal of Medical Science, 61,* 17–52.

Davis, J., Suhayl, N., Spira, N., & Vogel, C. (1981). Anxiety: Differential diagnosis and treatment from a biological perspective. *Journal of Clinical Psychiatry, 42,* 4–14.

Dealey, R. R., Ishiki, D. M., Avery, D. H., Wilson, L. G., & Dunner, D. L. (1981). Secondary depression in anxiety disorders. *Comprehensive Psychiatry, 22,* 612–618.

Dietch, J. T. (1981). Diagnosis of organic anxiety disorders. *Psychosomatics, 22,* 661–669.

Dimsdale, J. E., Hackett, T., Block, P. C., & Hutter, A. M., Jr. (1978). Emotional correlates of Type A behavior pattern. *Psychosomatic Medicine, 40,* 580–583.

DiNardo, P. A., O'Brien, G. T., Barlow, D. H., Waddell, M. T., & Blanchard, E. B. (1983). Reliability of DSM-III anxiety disorder categories using a new structured interview. *Archives of General Psychiatry, 40,* 1070–1075.

Drugs that cause psychiatric symptoms (1984). *The Medical Letter on Drugs and Therapeutics, 26,* 75–79.

Drury, A. N. (1918–1920). The percentage of carbon dioxide in the alveolar air and the tolerance to accumulating carbon dioxide in cases of so-called "irritable heart" of soldiers. *Heart, 7,* 165–173.

Esler, M. D., & Goulston, K. J. (1973). Levels of anxiety in colonic disorders. *New England Journal of Medicine, 288,* 16–20.

Estes, W. K., & Skinner, B. F. (1941). Some quantitative properties of anxiety. *Journal of Experimental Psychology, 29,* 390–400.

Ettedgui, E., & Bridges, M. (1985). Posttraumatic stress disorder. *Psychiatric Clinics of North America, 8,* 89–104.

Feighner, J. P., Robins, E., Guze, S. B., Woodruff, R. A., Winokur, G., & Munoz, R. (1972). Diagnostic criteria for use in psychiatric research. *Archives of General Psychiatry, 38,* 57–63.

Fontaine, R., Chouinard, G., & Annable, L. (1984). Rebound anxiety in anxious patients after abrupt withdrawal of benzodiazepine treatment. *American Journal of Psychiatry, 141,* 848–852.

Food-borne illness due to inadvertent consumption of marijuana — California (1981). *Morbidity and Mortality Weekly Report, 30,* 527–528, 533.

Frances, A., & Cooper, A. M. (1981). The DSM-III controversy: A psychoanalytic perspective. *American Journal of Psychiatry, 138,* 1198–1202.

Freud, S. (1962). On the grounds for detaching a particular syndrome from neurasthenia under the description "anxiety neurosis." In J. Strachey (Ed. and Trans.), *The standard edition of the complete psychological works of Sigmund Freud,* (Vol. 3, pp. 90–115). London: Hogarth Press, (Original work published 1894).

Frohlich, E. D., Dunstan, H. P., & Page, I. H. (1966). Hyperdynamic beta-adrenergic circulatory state. *Archives of Internal Medicine, 17,* 614–617.

Frohlich, E. D., Tarazi, R., Dunstan, H. P., & Page, I. H. (1969). Hyperdynamic beta-adrenergic circulatory state. Increased beta-receptor responsiveness. *Archives of Internal Medicine, 123,* 1–7.

Gilliland, K., & Andress, D. (1981). Ad lib caffeine consumption: Symptoms of caffeinism and academic performance. *American Journal of Psychiatry, 138,* 512–514.

Gittelman-Klein, R., & Klein, D. F. (1985). Childhood separation anxiety and adult agoraphobia. In A. H. Tuma & J. D. Maser (Eds.), *Anxiety and the anxiety disorders* (pp. 389–402). Hillsdale, NJ: Lawrence Erlbaum Associates.

Gorman, J. M., Dillon, D., Fyer, A. J., Liebowitz, M. R., & Klein, D. F. (1985). The lactate infusion model. *Psychopharmacology Bulletin, 21,* 428–433.

Gorman, J. M., Martinez, J. M., Liebowitz, M. R., Fyer, A., Klein, D. F. (1984). Hypoglycemia and panic attacks. *American Journal of Psychiatry, 141,* 101–102.

Gray, J. A. (1971). *The psychology of fear and stress.* New York: McGraw-Hill.

Greden, J. F. (1974). Anxiety or caffeinism: A diagnostic dilemma. *American Journal of Psychiatry, 131,* 1089–1092.

Greden, J. F., Victor, B. S., Fontaine, P., & Lubetsky, M. (1980). Caffeine-withdrawal headache: A clinical profile. *Psychosomatics, 21,* 411–413, 417–418.

Greden, J. F., Fontaine, P., Lubetsky, M., & Chamberlin, D. (1978). Anxiety and depression associated with caffeinism among psychiatric inpatients. *American Journal of Psychiatry, 135,* 963–966.

Greenberg, D., & Stravynski, A. (1983). Social phobia. *British Journal of Psychiatry, 143,* 526.

Grunhaus, L., Glogen, S., & Weisstub, E. (1981). Panic attacks: A review of treatments and pathogenesis. *Journal of Nervous and Mental Disease, 169,* 608–613.

Hall, R. C. W., Popkin, M. K., Devaul, R. A., Faillace, L. A., & Stickney, S. K. (1978). Physical illness presenting as psychiatric disease. *Archives of General Psychiatry, 35,* 1315–1320.

Hallam, R. R. (1978). Agoraphobia: A critical review of the concept. *British Journal of Psychiatry, 133,* 314–319.

Hendin, H., Haas, A. P., Singer, P., Houghton, W., Schwartz, M., & Wallen, V. (1984). The reliving experience in Vietnam veterans with posttraumatic stress disorder. *Comprehensive Psychiatry, 25,* 165–173.

Hoehn-Saric, R. (1982). Comparison of generalized anxiety disorder with panic disorder patients. *Psychopharmacology Bulletin, 18,* 104–108.

Hoehn-Saric, R., & McLeod, D. R. (1985). Generalized anxiety disorder. *Psychiatric Clinics of North America, 8,* 73–88.

Insel, T. R. (1985). Obsessive–compulsive disorder. *Psychiatric Clinics of North America, 8,* 105–118

Insel, T. R., Zahn, T., & Murphy, D. L. (1985). Obsessive–compulsive disorder: An anxiety disorder? In A. H. Tuma & J. D. Maser (Eds.), *Anxiety and the anxiety disorders* (pp. 577–589). Hillsdale, NJ: Lawrence Erlbaum Associates.

Jablensky, A. (1985). Approaches to the definition and classification of anxiety and related disorders in European psychiatry. In A. H. Tuma & J. D. Maser (Eds.), *Anxiety and the anxiety disorders* (pp. 735–758). Hillsdale, NJ: Lawrence Erlbaum Associates.

Jefferson, J. W., & Marshall, J. R. (1981). *Neuropsychiatric features of medical disorders.* New York: Plenum Medical Books.

Jones, R. T. (1978). Marijuana: Human effects. In L. L. Iversen, S. D. Iversen, & S. H. Snyder (Eds.), *Handbook of psychopharmacology. Volume 12: Drugs of abuse* (pp. 129–146). New York: Plenum Press.

Kales, A., Soldatos, C. R., Bixler, E. O., & Kales, J. D. (1983). Early morning insomnia with rapidly eliminated benzodiazepines. *Science, 220,* 95–97.

Karpati, G., & Frame, B. (1964). Neuropsychiatric disorders in primary hyperparathyroidism. *Archives of Neurology, 10,* 388.

Kenyon, F. E. (1976). Hypochondriacal states. *British Journal of Psychiatry, 129,* 1–14.

Kierkegaard, S., (1980). *The concept of anxiety.* R. Thomte & A. B. Anderson (Eds.) pp. 41–45. Princeton University Press.

Klein, D. F. (1964). Delineation of two drug responsive anxiety symptoms. *Psychopharmacologia, 5,* 397–408.

Klein, D. F. (1967). Importance of psychiatric diagnosis in prediction of clinical drug effects. *Archives of General Psychiatry, 16,* 118–126.

Klein, D. F. (1981). Anxiety reconceptualized. In D. F. Klein & J. Rabkin (Eds.), *Anxiety: New research and changing concepts* (pp. 235–265). New York: Raven Press.

Klein, D. F., & Fink, M. (1962). Psychiatric reaction patterns to imipramine. *American Journal of Psychiatry, 119,* 432–438.

Klein, D. F., Gittelman, R., Quitkin, F. M., & Rifkin, A. (1980). *Diagnosis and drug treatment of psychiatric disorders: Adults and children (2nd Ed.)* (pp. 500–507; 543–548) Baltimore: Williams and Wilkins.

Klein, D. F., Zitrin, C. M., Woerner, M. G., & Ross, D. C. (1983). Treatment of phobias: II. Behavior therapy and supportive psychotherapy: Are there any specific ingredients? *Archives of General Psychiatry, 40,* 139–145.

Kramer, M., Sartorius, N., Jablensky, A., & Gulbinat, W. (1979). The ICD-9 classification of mental disorders. *Acta Psychiatrica Scandinavica, 59,* 241–262.

Lader, M. H. (1981). Assessment methods and the differential diagnosis of anxiety. *Journal of Clinical Psychopharmacology, 1,* 342.

Lapierre, Y. D., Tremblay, A., Gagnon, A., Monpremier, P., Berliss, H., & Oyewumi, L. K. (1982). A therapeutic and discontinuation study of clobazam and diazepam in anxiety neurosis. *Journal of Clinical Psychiatry, 43,* 372–374.

Lewis, N. D. C., & Engle, B. (1954). *War time psychiatry.* New York: Oxford University Press.

Liebowitz, M. R., Gorman, J. M., Fyer, A. J., & Klein, D. F. (1985). Social phobia: Review of a neglected anxiety disorder. *Archives of General Psychiatry, 42,* 729–36.

Lishman, W. A. (1979). *Organic psychiatry.* London: Blackwell.

Lutz, E. G. (1978). Restless legs, anxiety, and caffeinism. *Journal of Clinical Psychiatry, 39,* 693–698.

Mackenzie, T. B., & Popkin, M. K. (1983). Organic anxiety syndrome. *American Journal of Psychiatry, 140,* 342–344.

Magarian, G. J. (1982). Hyperventilation syndromes: Infrequently recognized common expressions of anxiety and stress. *Medicine, 61,* 219–236.

Manger, W. M. (1985). Psychiatric manifestations in patients with pheochromocytomas. *Archives of Internal Medicine, 145,* 229–230.

Marks, I. M. (1970). The classification of phobic disorders. *British Journal of Psychiatry, 116,* 377–386.

Marks, I. M., & Lader, M. (1973). Anxiety states (anxiety neurosis): A review. *Journal of Nervous and Mental Disease, 156,* 3–18.

Meyer, R. E. (1978). Behavioral pharmacology of marihuana. In M. A. Lipton, M. A. DeMascio, & K. F. Killam (Eds.), *Psychopharmacology: A generation of progress* (pp. 1639–1652). New York: Raven Press.

Michels, R. (1984). First rebuttal. *American Journal of Psychiatry, 141,* 548–551.

Michels, R., Frances, A. J., & Shear, M. K. (1985). Psychodynamic models of anxiety. In A. Tuma & J. Maser (Eds.), *Anxiety and the Anxiety Disorders* (pp. 595–618). Lawrence Erlbaum Associates.

Morgan, K., & Oswald, I. (1982). Anxiety

caused by a short-life hypnotic. *British Medical Journal, 284,* 942.

Nesbitt, P. D. (1973). Smoking, physiological arousal, and emotional response. *Journal of Personality and Social Psychology, 25,* 137–145.

Noyes, R., Clancey, J., Hoenk, P. R., & Slymen, D. J. (1978). Anxiety neurosis and physical illness. *Comprehensive Psychiatry, 19,* 407–413.

Okel, B. B., & Hurst, J. W. (1961). Prolonged hyperventilation in man: Associated electrolyte changes and subjective symptoms. *Archives of Internal Medicine, 108,* 157–163.

Oppenheimer, B. S., Levine, S. A., Morison, R. A., Rothschild, M. A., St. Lawrence, W., & Wilson, F. N. (1918–1920). Report on neurocirculatory asthenia and its management. *Military Surgeon, 42,* 409–426, 711–719.

Öst, L. G., & Hugdahl, K. (1983). Acquisition of agoraphobia, mode of onset, and anxiety response patterns. *Behaviour Research and Therapy, 21,* 623–631.

Petersen, P. (1968). Psychiatric disorders in primary hyperparathyroidism. *Journal of Clinical Endocrinology and Metabolism, 28,* 1491.

Pillard, R. C., McNair, D. M., & Fisher, S. (1974). Does marijuana enhance experimentally induced anxiety?, *Psychopharmacologia, 40,* 205–210.

Pohl, R., Rainey, J., Ortiz, A., Balon, R., Singh, H., & Berchou, R. (1985). Isoproterenol-induced anxiety states. *Psychopharmacology Bulletin, 21,* 424–427.

Rachman, S. (1984). Agoraphobia: A safety signal perspective. *Behaviour Research and Therapy, 22,* 59–70.

Raskin, M., Peeke, H. V. S., Dickman, W., & Pinsker, H. (1982). Panic and generalized anxiety disorders: Developmental antecedents and precipitants. *Archives of General Psychiatry, 39,* 687–689.

Reiman, E. M., Raichle, M. E., Butler, F. K., Herscovitch, P. & Robins, E. (1984). A focal brain abnormality in panic disorder: A severe form of anxiety. *Nature, 310,* 683–685.

Roth, M. (1959). The phobic anxiety-depersonalization syndrome. *Proceedings of the Royal Society of Medicine, 52,* 587–595.

Roth, M., & Harper, M. (1962). Temporal lobe epilepsy and the phobic anxiety, depersonalization syndrome. Part II. Practical and theoretical considerations. *Comprehensive Psychiatry, 3,* 215–226.

Roth, M., & Mountjoy, C. Q. (1982). The distinction between anxiety states and depressive disorders. In E. S. Paykel (Ed.), *Handbook of affective disorders* (pp. 70–92). New York: Guilford Press.

Rubinow, D. R., & Roy-Byrne, P. (1984). Premenstrual syndrome: Overview from a methodologic perspective. *American Journal of Psychiatry, 141,* 163–172.

Schapira, K., Kerr, T. A., & Roth, M. (1970). Phobias and affective illness. *British Journal of Psychiatry, 117,* 25–32.

Scharf, M. B., Kales, A., Bixler, E. O., Jacoby, J. A., & Schweitzer, P. K. (1982). Lorazepam-efficacy, side effects, and rebound phenomena. *Clinical Pharmacology and Therapeutics, 31,* 175–179.

Sheehan, D. V., Ballenger, J., & Jacobson, G. (1980). Treatment of endogenous anxiety with phobic, hysterical, and hypochondriacal symptoms. *Archives of General Psychiatry, 37,* 51–59.

Sheehan, D. V., Carr, D. B., Fishman, S. M., Walsh, M. M., & Peltier-Saxe, D. (1985). Lactate infusion in anxiety research: Its evolution and practice. *Journal of Clinical Psychiatry, 46,* 158–165.

Sheehan, D. V., & Sheehan, K. H. (1982a). Diagnostic classification of anxiety and phobic disorders. *Psychopharmacology Bulletin, 18,* 35.

Sheehan, D. V., & Sheehan, K. H. (1982b). The classification of anxiety and hysterical states. Part II. Toward a more heuristic classification. *Journal of Clinical Psychopharmacology, 2,* 386.

Sheehan, D. V., & Sheehan, K. H. (1983). The classification of phobic disorders. *International Journal of Psychiatry in Medicine, 12,* 243–266.

Shiffman, S. M. (1979). The tobacco withdrawal syndrome. In N. A. Krasnegor (Ed.), *Cigarette smoking as a dependence process* (National Institute of Drug Abuse Research Monograph 23) (pp. 158–184). Washington, DC: U.S. Government Printing Office.

Siegel, R. K. (1978). Phencyclide and ketamine intoxication: A study of four populations of recreational users. In R. C. Petersen, & R. C. Stillman (Eds.), *Phencyclidine abuse: An appraisal* (National Institute of Drug Abuse Research Monograph 21) (pp. 119–147). Washington, DC: U.S. Government Printing Office.

Small, P., Stockwell, T., Canter, S., & Hodgson, R. (1984). Alcohol dependency and phobic anxiety states: I. A prevalence study. *British Journal of Psychiatry, 144,* 53–57.

Smith, C. K., Barish, J., Correa, J., & Williams, R. H. (1972). Psychiatric disturbance in endocrinologic disease. *Psychosomatic Medicine, 34,* 69–86.

Spitzer, R. L., & Williams, J. B. W. (1983). Structured clinical interview for DSM-III (SCID). New York: Biometrics Research Department, New York State Psychiatric Institute.

Spitzer, R. L., & Williams, J. B. W. (1985). Proposed revisions in the DSM-III classification of anxiety disorders based on research and clinical experience. In A. H. Tuma & J. D. Maser (Eds.), *Anxiety and the anxiety disorders.* Hillsdale, NJ: Lawrence Erlbaum Associates.

Starkman, M. N., Zelnik, T. C., Nesse, R. M., Cameron, O. G. (1985). Anxiety in patients with pheochromocytomas. *Archives of Internal Medicine, 145,* 248–252.

Stockwell, T., Small, P., Hodgson, R., & Canter, S. (1984). Alcohol dependence and phobic anxiety states: II. A retrospective study. *British Journal of Psychiatry, 144,* 58–63.

Sullivan, P., Schoentgen, S., DeQuattro, V., Procci, W., Levine, D., Vandermeulen, J., & Bornheimer, J. (1981). Anxiety, anger, and neurogenic tone at rest and in stress in patients with primary hypertension. *Hypertension, 3,* 119–123.

Trembath, P. W., & Boobis, S. W. (1979). Plasma theophylline levels after sustained-release aminophylline. *Clinical Pharmacology and Therapeutics, 26,* 654–659.

Tyrer, P. (1984). Classification of anxiety. *British Journal of Psychiatry, 144,* 78–83.

Tyrer, P., Owen, R., & Dawling, S. (1983). Gradual withdrawal of diazepam after long-term therapy. *Lancet I,* 1402–1406.

Uhde, T. W., Boulenger, J. P., & Post, R. M. (1983). Psychopathological effects of caffeine in psychiatric patients and normal controls. *American College of Psychopharmacology Abstracts, p. 35.*

Uhde, T. W., Boulenger, J. P., Jimerson, D. C., & Post, R. M. (1984). Caffeine — relationship to human anxiety, plasma MHPG, and cortisol. *Psychopharmacology Bulletin, 20,* 426–430.

Uhde, T. W., Roy-Byrne, P. P., Vittone, B. J., Boulenger, J. P., & Post, R. M. (1985). Phenomenology and neurobiology of panic disorder. In A. H. Tuma & J. D. Maser (Eds.), *Anxiety and the anxiety disorders* (pp. 557–576). Hillsdale, NJ: Lawrence Erlbaum Associates.

Uhde, T. W., Vittone, B. J., & Post, R. M. (1984). Glucose tolerance testing in panic disorder. *American Journal of Psychiatry, 141,* 1461–1463.

Vaillant, G. E. (1984). The disadvantages of DSM-III outweigh its advantages. *American Journal of Psychiatry, 141,* 542–545.

Van den Hout, M., & Griez, E. (1982). Cardiovascular and subjective responses to inhalation of carbon dioxide: A controlled test with anxious patients. *Psychotherapy and Psychosomatics, 37,* 75–82.

Van Valkenburg, C., Winokur, G., Lowry, M., Behar, D., & Van Valkenburg, D. (1983). Depression occurring in chronically anxious persons. *Comprehensive Psychiatry, 24,* 285–289.

Victor, B. S., Lubetsky, M., & Greden, J. F. (1981). Somatic manifestations of caffeinism. *Journal of Clinical Psychiatry, 42,* 185–188.

Weizman, A., Eldar, M., Schoenfield, Y., Hirschorn, M., Wijsenbeek, H., & Pinkhas, J. (1979). Hypercalcemia-induced psychopathology in malignant diseases. *British Journal of Psychiatry, 135,* 363–366.

Weiner, H. (1985). The psychobiology and pathophysiology of anxiety and fears. In A. H. Tuma & J. D. Maser (Eds.), *Anxiety and the anxiety disorders* (pp. 333–354). Hillsdale, NJ: Lawrence Erlbaum Associates.

Weissman, M. M. (1985). The epidemiology of anxiety disorders: Rates, risks, and familial patterns. In A. H. Tuma & J. D. Maser (Eds.), *Anxiety and the anxiety disorders* (pp. 275–296). Hillsdale, NJ: Lawrence Erlbaum Associates.

Weissman, M. M., Leckman, J. F., Merikangas, K. R., Gammon, G. D., & Prusoff, B. A. (1984). Depression and anxiety disorders in parents and children: Results from the Yale family study. *Archives of General Psychiatry, 41,* 845–852.

Weller, R. A., & Halikas, J. A. (1980). Objective criteria for the diagnosis of marijuana abuse. *Journal of Nervous and Mental Disease, 168,* 98–103.

Wheatley, D., Balter, M., Levine, J., Lipman, R., Bauer, M. L., & Bonato, R. (1975). Psychiatric aspects of hypertension. *British Journal of Psychiatry, 127,* 327–336.

Whitehead, W. E., Blackwell, B., DeSilva, H., & Robinson, A. (1977). Anxiety and anger in hypertension. *Journal of Psychosomatic Research, 21,* 383–389.

Williams, R. H., Correa, J., Smith, K., & Barish, J. (1970). Metabolism and mentation. *Journal of Clinical Endocrinology and Metabolism, 31,* 461–479.

Wing, J. K., Cooper, J. E., & Sartorius, N. (1979). *The measurement and classification of psychiatric symptoms.* London: Cambridge University Press.

Work Group to Revise DSM-III. (1985). *DSM-*

III-R in development. Washington, DC: American Psychiatric Association.

World Health Organization. (1978). *International classification of diseases — clinical modification (9th ed.).* Ann Arbor, MI: Edwards Brothers.

Young, S. J., Alpers, D. H., Norland, C. C., & Woodruff, R. A. (1976). Psychiatric illness and the irritable bowel syndrome. *Gastroenterology, 70,* 162–166.

Zuardi, A. W., Shirakawa, I., Finklefarb, E., & Karniol, I. G. (1982). Action of cannabidiol on the anxiety and other effects produced by delta-9-THC in normal subjects. *Psychopharmacology, 765,* 245–250.

CHAPTER 4

Phobic Disorders

Paul M. G. Emmelkamp

The purpose of this chapter is to describe the clinical features and assessment of phobic disorders. After discussing the prevalence of phobias among children and adults, the clinical features of the various disorders are described. The clinical value of various assessment procedures are discussed, including self-report, psychophysiological assessment, and behavioral measures. Finally, the diagnosis and assessment of phobic disorders are illustrated with a few case illustrations.

Prevalence of fears and phobias

Fears are quite common among children (Morris & Kratochwill, 1983). Miller, Barret and Hampe (1974) estimated children from 2 to 6 years of age to have about three to four fears, on the average, but the number of excessive fear reactions is small. In a study by Ollendick (1983), girls between 8 and 14 years reported an average of 13 excessive fears, while boys of this age reported an average of 9 excessive fears. Several factor analytic studies have been conducted on the structure of fears in children. Generally, these studies found three (Miller, Barrett, Hampe, & Noble, 1972) to five (Ollendick, 1983) interpretable factors. The following factors were obtained in the Ollendick study: (a) fear of failure and criticism, (b) fear of the unknown, (c) fear of injury and small animals, (d) fear of danger and death, and (e) medical fears.

These studies, as well as others, have shown that girls report more fears than boys. Most fears of younger children are passing episodes in a normal developmental process, and disappear within a few months. In a prevalence study in the Netherlands (Verhulst, 1985) parents of over 2,000 children from 4 to 18 years of age were interviewed with respect to the fears and phobias of their children. Results revealed that the number of fears reported significantly decreased with age.

While the fears of younger children appear to diminish with age, the fears of those around 6 years and up to adolescence remain relatively constant, consisting primarily of social anxiety and fears related to natural events and injury (Ollendick, Matson, & Helsel, 1985).

While fears are quite common among

children, the prevalence of clinical phobias among children is rare (Graziano & Graziano, 1979; Miller et al., 1974; Rutter, Tizard, & Whitmore, 1970). Rutter et al. (1970), for example, in a survey involving more than 2,000 10- to 11-year-old children, found that no more than 0.7% of children had clinically significant and disabling phobias. School phobia is the main phobic condition referred for treatment, although its occurrence in the general population has been estimated ranging from 1% (Miller et al., 1974) to 2% (Verhulst, 1985). Presumably, school phobia has such serious repercussions that parents must seek professional help. In adolescence, social fears are the most common. Fears of blushing and fears of being looked at peaked in girls approximately 2 years earlier than in boys (Abe & Masui, 1981).

Fears and phobias exist in a fairly high proportion of the adult general population, but only a minor proportion of those who are affected ever consult health services. Agras, Sylvester, and Olivieau (1969) investigated the prevalence of fears and phobias in the general population. The total prevalence of phobias was estimated at 77/1,000 people. Only 9 out of 1,000 had seen a psychiatrist for treatment of a phobia. Thus, although severe fears are common among the general population, only a small percentage of "phobics" receive treatment.

In a subsequent study (Agras, Chapin, & Oliveau, 1972), the course of the phobias of a subgroup of the phobics studies by Agras et al. (1969). was investigated. None of the group had received treatment during the 5-year period. Most of the fears of children and adolescents had disappeared. At follow-up, 100% were improved or symptom free. Of the adult group, only 6% lost their phobic symptoms entirely. Moreover, 37% of the adult group showed a worsening of their main phobia. Those patients with a generalized main phobia (e.g., agoraphobia) had worse prognosis than the patients with specific phobias. This study confirmed the findings that children's fears often improve spontaneously.

In the Epidemiologic Catchment Area program on the lifetime prevalence of specific psychiatric disorders, it was found that phobia and depression were the predominant disorders among women (Robins et al., 1984). Interviews were held with over 9,000 persons from large general population samples in three metropolitan areas: New Haven, Baltimore, and St. Louis. The lifetime prevalence of a disorder is stated as the proportion of persons in a representative sample of the population who have ever experienced that disorder up to the date of assessment. The lifetime prevalence of phobic disorders was 7.8% for New Haven, 23.3% for Baltimore, and 9.4% for St. Louis. Rates of agoraphobia and simple phobia were significantly higher for women than men in all sites. The intersite difference in the prevalence of phobic disorders between Baltimore, on the one hand, and New Haven and St. Louis, on the other, are presumably attributable to minor variations in the questions used for assessing phobic disorder.

Meyers et al. (1984) focused on the prevalence rates for the 6-month period immediately preceding the interview in the Epidemiologic Catchment Area program. The 6-month prevalence rates for social phobia, simple phobia, and agoraphobia are presented in Table 4.1. The most common diagnoses were phobias, alcohol abuse, dysthymia, and major depression. Phobic disorder was the most common diagnosis for women across all ages, while phobia was the second most common disorder for men older than 25 years.

While these studies indicate that phobic disorders are quite common in the United States, results cannot be generalized to other cultures. Reports from the Sudan (Rahim & Idris, 1976), Nigeria (Leighton & Lambo, 1963; Odejide, 1976), and Botswana (Ben-Tovim, 1985) indicate that phobic disorders have been difficult to identify in Africa. In India, Verghese and Beig (1974) and Nandi, Ajmany, Banerjee, Ghosh, and Sarkar (1975) found only one case of phobia in two epidemiological studies in rural communities. In a west-

Table 4.1: Six-Month Prevalence of Phobias

TYPE OF PHOBIA	NEW HAVEN (Percentage)	BALTIMORE (Percentage)	ST. LOUIS (Percentage)
Social	–	2.2	1.2
Simple	4.7	11.8	4.5
Agoraphobia	2.8	5.8	2.7

Note. Adapted from "Six Month Prevalence of Psychiatric Disorders in Three Communities" by J. K. Meyers et al., 1984, *Archives of General Psychiatry, p. 963.* Copyright 1984 by American Medical Association. Copyright Holder. Adapted by permission.

ernized city area, however, the prevalence rate of phobic disorder was 2.7% (Nandi et al., 1980). The remarkable difference in prevalence rates of phobic disorder in these studies probably is due to rural/ urban differences and associated cultural factors. While in studies in Western Europe and the United States, female agoraphobics usually outnumber male agoraphobics by a ratio of 4 to 1, Raguram and Bhide (1985) found a striking male preponderance among phobics in a South Indian State, which may be attributable to cultural factors. As Raguram and Bhide (1985) note, an Indian woman is mostly housebound, and inability to venture out by herself without the presence of a male may not be construed as abnormal behavior, but is culturally normal behavior in the traditional Indian society. The gross difference in prevalence rates of phobias in different countries may be accounted for by sociocultural factors. Presumably, the way in which anxiety is expressed varies from culture to culture. For example, it is a common experience in African psychiatry that distress tends to be expressed more in bodily than in psychic symptoms (Morakinyo, 1985). As one of the workers in a developing country remarked with respect to culture-bound syndromes:

> They are usually thought of as exotic problems from far away places, but it is not clear why abuse of injectable opiates, anorexia nervosa, and agoraphobia — all of which are currently unknown in Botswana — should not also be viewed as culture-bound disorders of Western origin. (Ben-Tovim, 1985, p.344).

CLINICAL FEATURES

Though phobias are common in other psychiatric disorders, the frequency of phobic disorders in clinical practice is about 3% (Marks, 1969). Agoraphobics constitute about 50% to 80% of all phobics seen in clinical practice (Burns & Thorpe, 1977; Chambless, 1982). The bulk of the remaining clinical phobias consist of illness phobias and social anxieties. Very few individuals with specific or "simple" phobias come for treatment; animal phobics are rarely seen.

Agoraphobia

The term *agoraphobia* refers to a syndrome in which the most characteristic feature is an attack of anxiety or panic in a variety of public places, such as streets, crowds, stores, or buses. This causes "fear of fear" and leads to an avoidance of these situations. Agoraphobics become anxious when walking, shopping, going by bus, or visiting cinemas and churches. Most-agoraphobics feel less anxiety when accompanied by a trusted person (partner), but they usually remain anxious, although to a lesser degree. The few agoraphobics who succeed in visiting churches, cinemas, and parties choose a chair near the exit.

Foa, Steketee and Young (1984) proposed that the fears of agoraphobics can be grouped into three main categories: (a) fears of external situations, such as being alone, being in a crowd, being in enclosed spaces, travelling on public-transportation, etc; (b) fears of internal physical sensations (e.g., heart palpitations, dizziness, weakness in the limbs); and (c) fears of catastrophes, such as heart attack, fainting, or loss of control.

Although fear of open spaces is common among agoraphobics, it does not have the central function as was once thought. Marks and Bebbington (1976) suggested that "space phobia" is characterized by a fear of absent visuospatial support (open spaces) and by a fear of falling, unlike the fears of public places found in agoraphobia. Marks (1981) proposed that this pseudoagoraphobic syndrome may be the result of disturbed integration of vestibularocular reflexes. More recently Jacob, Bjüro Möller, Turner, and Wall (1985) investigated the audiovestibular system in patients with panic disorder or agoraphobia with panic attacks, whose panic symptoms included the experience of dizziness. They found that with this *selected* group of patients a high proportion had abnormal vestibular and audiological functions. Further controlled studies carried out in a blind fashion are needed to establish whether such neurological abnormalities are indeed characteristic for a subgroup of agoraphobics.

Associated problems

Agoraphobia appears to be associated with "spontaneous" panic attacks (Marks, 1969) and depression (Bowen & Kohout, 1979; Gardos, 1981; Jasin & Turner, 1980). The depression may be secondary to anxiety (Chambless, 1985b). Further, somatic symptoms (Arrindell, 1980; Gardos, 1981), illness phobias (Bianchi, 1971; Buglass, Clarke, Henderson, Kreitman, & Presley, 1977) and hypochondriasis (Jasin & Turner, 1980) often are associated with agoraphobia. These somatic complaints and preoccupations may be related to hyperventilation, which can result in heart palpitations, chest pains, sweating, and light-headedness, and which might play a causal role in the onset of agoraphobia (Emmelkamp, 1982). The somatic complaints of agoraphobics may be the cause rather than the consequence of fear. It has been proposed that persons with a bad breathing habit are inclined to hyperventilate when confronted with stressful events or when emotionally aroused. The concept of vicious-circle effect may be helpful to understand the course of the hyperventilation and the development of the agoraphobia after the first hyperventilation attack. A hyperventilation attack with the concomitant bodily sensations usually is accompanied with severe anxiety that by itself may provoke hyperventilation in the future. This fear of panic may lead to avoidance of a number of situations, which ultimately may result in agoraphobia.

Evidence for a relationship between agoraphobia and hyperventilation can be found in a study by Arrindell (1980). A higher order factor analysis on the data of a large sample of phobics on the Fear Survey Schedule (FSS-III: Wolpe & Lang, 1964) and the Symptom Check List (SCL-90: Derogatis, 1977) revealed a "factorial" definition of agoraphobia. A number of symptoms that are typically associated with hyperventilation appeared to be substantially related to the Agoraphobia-FSS factor. Further evidence for the hyperventilation theory of agoraphobia was provided by Ley (1985a,b). Agoraphobics who suffered panic attacks indicated clearly that the symptoms of hyperventilatory hypocapnea preceded the onset of fear. Finally, Garssen, Van Veenendaal, and Bloemink (1983) found that most agoraphobics could be diagnosed as hyperventilators.

Others have suggested that mitral valve prolapse syndrome (MVPS) may be related to agoraphobia (Kantor, Zitrin, & Zeldis, 1980). MVPS is a cardiological disease with symptoms similar to those of anxiety. The palpitations and the dyspnea associated with MVP can lead to panic attacks, thus further aggravating the symptoms and so creating a vicious circle as in the case of hyperventilation.

Marital complications

It has been suggested that the intimate relationship of agoraphobic patients with their marital partner may be of critical importance in the development and maintenance of the patient's agoraphobic symptoms. A number of different authors (e.g., Andrews, 1966; Chambless & Goldstein, 1981; Fry, 1962; Goodstein & Swift, 1977; Hafner, 1982; Hand & Lamontagne, 1976; Lazarus, 1966; Webster, 1953) have suggested that agoraphobia more suitably may be described in terms of both an interpersonal, particularly marital, conflict and an intrapsychic conflict. For instance, it has been observed clinically that marital satisfaction increases in proportion to improvement of agoraphobic symptoms, or that improvement in the phobia is associated with more marital satisfaction in the patients but with *dissatisfaction* in the spouse (Hafner, 1982; O'Brien, Barlow, & Last, 1982).

Given the emphasis that has been put on the possible role of marital difficulties in the etiology and maintenance of agoraphobia, it is surprising that hardly any methodologically sound study has been conducted to investigate whether the marriages of agoraphobics differ from those of controls. Most of the available studies emphasizing the importance of marriage quality in the etiology of agoraphobia (e.g., Fry, 1962; Hafner, 1982; Holmes, 1982; Torpy & Measy, 1974; Webster, 1953) are based on confusing methodologies which limit the drawing of definite conclusions. Despite these shortcomings, these studies have, at times, provided an abundance of comments concerning the quality of marriage in agoraphobics and their partners.

Buglass et al. (1977) compared agoraphobic housewives and their spouses with normal control couples in terms of domestic activities (i.e., the execution of specified family tasks), decision-making in a number of areas, and manifest interaction ratings (assertion-compliance and affection-dislike). The most striking feature of the comparison between the two groups of couples was their similarity with respect to the above criterion measures. Arrindell and Emmelkamp (1986a) investigated the quality of the marital relationship of agoraphobic patients and their partners by comparing their marriages with those of three groups: (a) nonphobic psychiatric patients and their partners, (b) maritally distressed couples, and (c) nondistressed (happily married) couples. The findings of this study indicate that agoraphobics and their spouses tend to be comparable to happily married subjects in terms of marital adjustment, intimacy, and needs, while nonphobic psychiatric patients and their partners are comparable to maritally distressed subjects. Similarly, Fisher and Wilson (1985) also found no difference in reported marital satisfaction between agoraphobics and controls. It could be argued that agoraphobics are more inclined to repress conflicts than other groups, but a controlled study found little or no evidence that this was the case (Arrindell & Emmelkamp, 1985a). Furthermore, marital dissatisfaction is not related to agoraphobia severity (Bland & Hallam, 1981; Chambless, 1985b; Milton & Hafner, 1979).

Finally, it has been investigated whether partners of agoraphobics are themselves psychiatrically disturbed. In a recent study (Arrindell & Emmelkamp, 1985b) that investigated this particular issue, it was clearly shown that the partners of female agoraphobics were not more defensive or psychologically more disturbed than controls.

The finding that clinical reports, with respect to the marital functioning of agoraphobics, are not in line with results from empirical studies may be ascribed to a self-perpetuating myth "with clinicians seeing in their own patients only what has been reported by other clinicians. The more powerful the myth, the wider the clinical consensus, which in turn strengthens the myth" (Hafner, 1982, p. 83).

Psychological characteristics

It has often been suggested that agoraphobics have a dependent personality, but recent reviews suggest that there only is meager support for the existence of a consistent "agoraphobic personality" (Chambless, 1982; Emmelkamp. 1982; Foa et al., 1984). Arrindell and Emmelkamp (1986) compared female agoraphobics with control groups of non-phobic psychiatric and nonpatient normal subjects on a large number of measures. Agoraphobics were not found to be more dependent than the other groups. This finding, in conjunction with other studies showing agoraphobics not to have experienced their parents as more overprotective than controls (Arrindell, Emmelkamp, Monsma, & Brilman, 1983; Parker, 1979; Thyrer, Nesse, Cameron, & Curtis, 1985), does not support the popular notion that agoraphobics have premorbid dependent personalities. In the Arrindell and Emmelkamp (1987) study, however, agoraphobics were found to be more introverted and more socially anxious than controls. Similarly, Chambless (1982) reported a significant correlation between severity of agoraphobic symptoms and fear of criticism.

Emmelkamp (1982) has suggested that locus of control and faulty attributional processes may be important variables in the development of agoraphobia. Emmelkamp and Cohen–Kettenis (1975) found that phobic anxiety was related to external locus of control in agoraphobics. Persons with an external control orientation experiencing anxiety in a stressful period are likely to mislabel the anxiety and attribute it to external sources (e.g. crowded areas) or to a disease (e.g., heart attack or stroke). Others may even interpret it as a sign of losing control or going crazy. Thus, they may perceive the experienced anxiety as being outside their control. At present, it is unclear whether social anxiety and external locus of control is of etiological significance, or merely the result of the agoraphobia. At the time agoraphobics are assessed, they may evidence many "traits" mistakenly assumed to have existed premorbidly (Tearman, Telch, & Keefe, 1984).

Social Phobia

According to DSM-III, (American Psychiatric Association, 1980) the essential feature of social phobia is a persistent irrational fear of, and compelling desire to avoid, situations in which the individual may be exposed to scrutiny by others. Examples are fears of speaking or performing in public, eating in public, or writing in the presence of others.

Social phobia is distinguished from the shyness and social anxiety many individuals experience by the intensity of the fears and the avoidance of social situations involved. DSM-III asserts that social phobics generally have only one fear, implying that patients with multiple social fears or more generalized social anxiety are either rare or should be included in some other diagnostic category (e.g., avoidant personality disorder) (Liebowitz, Gorman, Fyer, & Klein, 1985). As argued by Liebowitz et al., there is no empirical justification to exclude patients from the social phobia category whose social anxiety symptoms are due to avoidant personality disorders.

Recent cognitive–behavioral research has isolated a number of differences between socially anxious and nonanxious persons. Socially anxious persons are characterized by anxious self-preoccupation (Smith, Ingram, & Brehm, 1983). It has been shown that socially anxious persons endorse a high frequency of negative self-statements (Glass, Merluzzi, Biever, & Larssen, 1982) and negatively evaluate the quality of their social performance (Edelman, 1985). Further, socially anxious persons also have been found to be preoccupied with the evaluation of others (Goldfried, Padauer, & Robins, 1984; McEwan & Devins, 1983). Smith, Ingram, and Brehm (1983) demonstrated that anxious self-preoccupation occurred only in a socially evaluative situation.

The skills-deficits hypothesis holds that anxiety experienced in social situations is the result of inadequate handling of these situations. Results of studies investigating whether socially anxious persons are less skillful and less socially competent than nonanxious individuals are inconclusive (Beidel, Turner, & Dancu, 1985; Dow, Biglan, & Glaser, 1985). Studies on *clinically* socially anxious subjects suggest that social skills deficits are of less importance in the etiology of social anxiety than once thought (Edelman, 1985; Newton, Kindness, & McFayden, 1983). This suggests that individuals experience social anxiety not because they are unable to behave in a socially competent manner per se, but because they *believe* that they are socially inadequate. In a similar vein, Hartman (1983) has argued that social inadequacy of socially anxious people may be the result of a difference in the attentional focus of high and low socially anxious persons during interpersonal encounters. The socially anxious person is impaired by the effort to divide attention between internal cues (self-depicatory thinking and perception of autonomic arousal) and external cues in the social situation, while nonanxious persons concentrate on the interpersonal interaction only.

Simple phobia

According to DSM-III, the essential feature of simple phobia is a persistent irrational fear of, and compelling desire to avoid, an object or situation other than being alone or in public places away from home (agoraphobia), or of humiliation or embarrassment in certain social situations (social phobia). The most common clinical simple phobias are claustrophobia (fear of closed spaces) and acrophobia (fear of heights). Illness phobias are not a special category in DSM-III and sometimes are diagnosed as somatoform disorders rather than as an anxiety disorder. Blood and injury phobias that are outside the context of an unrealistic belief of having a disease should be diagnosed as simple phobia.

Age of onset

A number of studies have investigated the onset age of the various phobic disorders. Previous studies (Marks & Gelder, 1966; Mendel & Klein, 1969) found a bimodal distribution of the onset of agoraphobia in late adolescence and in the 30s, but this has not been confirmed in later studies. Sheehan, Sheehan, and Michiello (1981) found a unimodal distribution in the age of onset of agoraphobics with "spontaneous" panics. Mean age of onset was 24 years. They conclude that the bimodal distribution found in the earlier studies resulted from artifacts inherent in the small sample sizes. Simple phobia was found to start on the average 4.4 years earlier than agoraphobia in the Sheehan et al. (1981) study.

Thyrer, Parrish, Curtis, Nesse, and Cameron (1985) also studied the onset of various phobic conditions. The age of onset of agoraphobia presented a normal unimodal distribution. As far as simple phobia is concerned, 70% acquired their phobia before they reached the age of 20. Also, most cases (66%) of social phobia appeared to develop in childhood or teenage years. Öst (1986) studied the onset age in 370 phobic patients. Animal phobics had the earliest onset age (7 years), followed by blood phobics (9 years), dental phobics (12 years), social phobics (16 years), claustrophobics (20 years), and agoraphobics (28 years). Although the exact figures vary from study to study, the overal impression is that simple phobias nearly always start in childhood or adolescence. The onset of social phobia usually is in adolescence, while agoraphobia usually starts in adulthood. The difference in onset age between the various phobic conditions may point to a different etiology for the various phobic conditions.

ASSESSMENT

Di Nardo, O'Brien, Barlow, Waddell, and Blanchard (1982) developed the *Anxiety Disorders Interview Schedule* (ADIS) to make differential diagnoses among the DSM-III anxiety disorder categories. Barlow (1985) studied reliability and comorbidity of the anxiety disorder categories using the ADIS. The interrater agreement was quite high for agoraphobia (κ = ·85) and social phobia (κ = ·91), but less satisfactory for simple phobia (κ = ·56). In approximately one half of the agoraphobic and social phobic cases, additional diagnoses were assigned. It further was noted that a substantial percentage of most anxiety disorder categories would meet criteria for panic disorder. In fact, there were no differences among patients' reports of panic attacks among the diagnostic categories (Barlow, 1985). These results demonstrate that there is considerable overlap between the various anxiety disorder categories. Rather than consider them as distinct diagnostic categories, anxiety disorders are better viewed as lying on a number of different continua. The actual clinical diagnosis depends on the predominant features in a particular patient.

Three-Systems-Approach

Following Lang's (1971) repudiation of the "lump theory" of fear, it has become commonplace to consider anxiety as a constellation of three different response channels: (a) verbal-cognitive, (b) behavior-motoric, and (c) psychophysiological. There is an ongoing debate among behavioral researchers in the field of anxiety disorders about the necessity to represent all three channels of anxiety/fear in the assessment of these disorders. This multimethod approach is based on the notion that these three channels are partly independent (discordance), and may change independently from each other in the course of therapy (desynchrony).

There are, indeed, a number of studies that demonstrate that the intercorrelations among self-report scales, behavioral measures, and pschophysiological indices typically are low (Emmelkamp, 1982; Williams, 1985). Self-reports of fear generally correlate moderately with avoidance behavior, but only modestly with autonomic indices (Rachman, 1978). Results of studies on concordance of the three systems of anxiety are difficult to interpret, because often only mildly fearful individuals were used. When clinically severe reactions are concerned, a greater concordance between the response systems was found (Craske & Craig, 1984; Sallis, Lichstein, & McGlynn, 1980).

The notion of the "triple response mode" has been criticized on methodological grounds (Cone 1979; Emmelkamp, 1982; Hugdahl, 1981). Cone (1979) called attention of basic flaws in the methodology of studies that investigated relationships among systems: "Research has varied both method of assessment and content area when computing correlations" (p. 87). For example, self-report can consist of such different statements as "I feel heart palpitations" or "I would like to run away." The former self-statement is more likely to be related to heart rate, whereas the latter probably is associated with behavioral indices. However, self-report of anxiety — irrespective of content — has usually been considered to refer to the "cognitive channel," thus neglecting the specific content of the self-statements. This lack of consistency concerning the definition of the cognitive component is problematic because it makes comparison between various studies intending to measure the relationship between components difficult. In a similar vein, Hugdahl (1981) has noted that the "cognitive component" may mean at least three different things. The first conceptualization of the cognitive component is that the subject has perceived his or her autonomic arousal and cognitively relabeled it as anxiety. Further, the cognitive component may mean worrying and brooding about the forthcoming fear-provoking event, and, finally, the cognitive component may refer to the thinking style of the phobic patient when confronted with the phobic stimulus. In line with this, Chambless, Caputo, Gallagher, and Bright (1985) have recommended measuring at least two cognitive components with agoraphobics: (a) cognitions concerning imagined disasterous consequences of having panic attacks, and (b) fear of interoceptive cues of arousal body sensations).

There is some evidence that the correlation between self-report and avoidance measures of fear may increase when self-report measures provide a more accurate description of the fear-provoking stimuli. For example, Lick, Sushinsky, and Malow (1977) demonstrated that the low relationship between the self-assessment of fear and actual behavior in a behavioral avoidance test situation could be increased by giving the subjects more information about the task they were required to perform in the laboratory test. Subsequent studies by Bandura and his colleagues demonstrated a high correlation between self-report ("efficacy expectations") and performance on a behavioral avoidance test (Bandura & Adams, 1977; Williams, 1985). Self-efficacy is measured by having phobics indicate which of a series of specific behavioral tasks they believe they can perform. Thus, subjects rate their confidence in their ability to "go with an elevator to the 20th floor," not whether they are able to stay in "enclosed spaces."

To summarize, lack of concordance between the different response systems is at least partly a function of methodological inadequacies associated with the measurement of the different "channels." As noted by Cone (1979); "the conclusions of response system independence (e.g., Lang, 1971) are premature and that a sorting out of behavior method confounds would lead to different interpretations" (p. 80).

A final aspect of the issue of discordance among the three systems of fear concerns the reliability and validity of the measurement of each component by itself. Although the concurrent validity of self-report measures that purport to evaluate the same construct is satisfactory, the validity of psychophysiological indices of anxiety and standardized behavior tests is questionable. Generally, there is a low intercorrelation among different psychophysiological measures that purport to measure the same state of arousal (e.g. Hersen, Bellack, & Turner, 1978; Marks & Huson, 1973), which may be due to individual differences in physiological reaction patterns (Lacey, 1962). In addition, type of phobia may be related to a specific response pattern. For example, blood-injury phobics deviate from the generally observed pattern of heart-rate increase when confronted with their phobic stimuli (Connolly, Hallam, & Marks, 1976). Blood phobics show heart-rate deceleration rather than acceleration, which can result in fainting. Individual differences in psychopysiological responding also may be due to personality characteristics. For example, repressors, who have a defensive coping style, were found to show a different psychophysiological reaction pattern than low- and high-anxious subjects (Weinberger, Schwartz, & Davidson, 1979).

A related issue is the unreliability of the psychophysiological assessment typically used with phobics. Results from a study by Arena, Blanchard, Andrasik, Cotch, and Myers (1983) cast serious doubts upon the reliability of psychophysiological measures. Heart rate was found not quite reliable and skin conductance appeared completely unreliable over time. To quote Arena et al.:

> If subjects can one day respond with a heart rate of 65 beats per minute to a stressful stimulus and the next day respond with a heart rate of 125 beats per minute, what clinical utility is a psychophysiological measure? (1983, p. 458)

Holden and Barlow (1984) assessed the reliability and validity of heart rate as a measure of anxiety in agoraphobia during an in vivo standardized behavioral avoidance test. The test-retest reliability for heart rate was low. In addition, not only phobics but also *nonphobic* controls were found to improve over the course of time on heart rate! Results by Arena et al. (1983) and Holden and Barlow (1984) suggest a cautious use of physiological assessment with phobic patients.

At present, there is little reason to recommend psychophysiological assessment as routine practice with phobics. Although a few recent studies suggest that such psychophysiological indices may have prognostic utility (Michelson, 1984; Vermilyea, Boice, & Barlow, 1984) results at present are far from conclusive, and the lack of reliability and validity of the measures used suggest caution in the interpretation of the results from the physiological measurements obtained in these studies. Apart from the methodological issues just discussed, there also are theoretical issues that limit the applicability of psychophysiological measurement. For instance, heart rate, a measure that is now widely used in treatment research studies, may reflect other processes than fear. Several studies in the area of social anxiety indicate that *nonsocially* anxious subjects react with increased heart rate when they have to deliver a speech. For example, Lang, Levin, Miller, and Kozak (1983) found that snake phobics generated an equally marked heart rate change during speech exposure as speech-anxious subjects. As Lang et al. note, the cardiovascular demand required by a speech task is so pronounced that it may mask any evidence of an affective component in this system. Similarly, it is unknown whether heart rate recording of agoraphobics, when confronted with their phobic situations, reflects purely fear or of alternatively, reflects fear and other processes (e.g., attention, cognitive activity, physical exercise).

It may be worthwhile to investigate the utility of other physiological measures than those currently used. Agoraphobia often is associated with hyperventilation and ventilation, which therefore may be a more relevant measure than heart rate, but research into reliability and validity with phobics is nonexistent. Tyrer and Lader (1976) have suggested that physiological measurement directly concerned with cerebral functions (resting electroencephalogram and averaged evoked potentials) may be better correlates of anxiety than heart rate, but this recommendation does not seem to have been noticed by researchers in the area of phobic disorders.

Psychophysiological indices only can be recommended as measures when they can be reliably measured over time and are found to discriminate between phobics and normal subjects when confronted with the phobic situation. Even then, it is questionable whether these measures would significantly add information to information that is much more easily obtained by behavioral measures and self-report of anxiety, including self-report of awareness of physiological arousal. Using psychophysiological assessment is very time-consuming and costly and may lead to a number of technical and mechanical failures during the assessment. For example, Mavissakalian and Michelson (1982) could use only the complete set of data of 6 out of 32 agoraphobics, because of equipment failure or missed appointments. In sum, psychophysiological recording is very time-consuming and costly, with questionable reliability and validity.

Behavioral Measures

Agoraphobia

Behavioral approach tests are a widely used measure to assess phobic behavior in analogue studies. In the early 1970s, both Emmelkamp and his colleagues in the Netherlands and Mathews and his colleagues in Oxford felt the need to develop behavioral measures to assess agoraphobic fears in treatment outcome studies. Emmelkamp (1974, 1982) had agoraphobic patients walk along a preselected route leading to progressively more crowded places; they were instructed to return when they became anxious. Both time and distance walked away from a "safe" place can be measured.

Another behavioral test with agoraphobics has been used by Mathews, Gelder, and Johnston (1981). This test consists of a hierarchy of progressively more difficult items. This hierarchy attempted to sample the whole range of phobic situations from very easy to exceedingly difficult. An attempt was made to ensure that before treatment began, the patient could carry out three or four of the items on the hierarchy, thereby allowing room for significant deterioration as well as for improvement. A serious problem with the Mathews et al. test is that, due to the idiosyncratic nature of this test, different subjects' scores cannot be meaningfully compared with one another. In recent years other researchers have used slight variations of these in vivo tests (Williams, 1985). Subjective anxiety, psychophysiological arousal, and cognition also have been assessed during or immediately after the in vivo tests.

Few data are available with respect to psychometric characteristics of the in vivo tests. Correlations between Emmelkamp's behavioral measure and phobic anxiety and avoidance ratings have been found to be fairly high. Furthermore, this behavioral measure was found to be relatively stable over time with untreated patients. Finally, this measure could detect significant differences in effectiveness between treatments (Emmelkamp, 1982). Results on the behavioral test of Mathews et al. correlated highly with phobic severity rating by assessors, but less so with patients' ratings.

Both in vivo tests were developed to evaluate the effects of treatment of agoraphobia and are of little clinical utility. There is no advantage in using the in vivo tests as a diagnostic instrument, except perhaps in a supplementary capacity. A clear disadvantage of Emmelkamp's measure is that only a part of the cluster of agoraphobic fears is measured behaviorally, although presumably the most important part. Although the assessment approach of the Oxford group attempts to encompass the breadth of generality of agoraphobic fears and their idiosyncratic patterning by constructing for each subject a single hierarchy, there are a number of other disadvantages (e.g., Williams, 1985) that prevent its clinical use, the most important being that such a test is very difficult and expensive to organize. Because both behavioral tests have been found to correlate highly with other measures of agoraphobic fears, there is no need to include these tests in routine clinical practice.

Given the difficulty in organizing in vivo tests and the costs involved, it might be worthwhile to develop less expensive methods to assess in vivo behavior of agoraphobics. Probably the most economical approach is to reply on patients' self-reports about their actual behavior in potentially phobic situations. Mathews et al. (1981) had their patients complete diaries of their daily comings and goings and found that time spent away from home was a satisfactory measure. Research needs to be undertaken into the reliability and validity of such behavioral diaries.

For research purposes, in vivo tests still may be required. A potentially fruitful area of future research involves the measurements of thoughts during behavioral tests discussed later.

Social Phobia

Behavioral tests of social anxiety are not easy to standardize because of the idiosyncratic character of the patients' phobias. Social phobics might differ widely concerning the social situations they fear. Nevertheless, a number of research studies into the nature and treatment of social anxiety have included behavioral tests. In most studies, assessment was accomplished either through role-playing interactions in standardized real-life interaction tests or role-playing test with taped stimulus material (Emmelkamp, 1982).

Although role playing now appears to be increasingly popular as a behavioral measure for social anxiety in research studies, the clinical utility is questionable. First, no single assessment procedure has been thoroughly validated on clinically socially-anxious patients. Second, it generally is assumed that behavior in these analogue situations is quite similar to real-life behavior in the patients' natural environment. However, behavior in these tests may be only minimally related to social anxiety (Trower, Yardley, Bryant, & Shaw, 1978). there is increasing evidence that role-played behavior does not accurately represent behavior in more naturalistic settings (e.g., Bellack, Hersen, & Lamparski, 1979; McNamara & Blumer, 1982). Finally, a related problem of role-playing is that the behavior of the patient is assessed in only one or a few standard situations. However, a situation that is relevant for one patient may be trivial for another and vice versa.

Behavior of patients in these standardized tests can be rated on molar (global judgment of social anxiety) or molecular level. With the latter approach, a number of specific behavioral components are measured using frequency counts and duration. While global ratings of social anxiety are much easier to obtain than the more specific behavioral components, the latter are clinically more useful to help sort which behavior needs to be targeted for change and which specific treatment (e.g., social skills training) should be chosen. As a compromise, Monti et al. (1984) developed a midi-level behavioral measure of social anxiety in a standardized behavioral role-play test, the Simulated Social Interaction Test (Monti, Curran, Corriveau, De Lancey, & Hagerman, 1980). Nine categories of "midi-level" behavior (including facial expression, posture, gestures, and voice quality) were rated on a Likert-type scale for anxiety. All nine categories were found to be significantly related to global ratings of social anxiety in a patient sample (Monti et al., 1984). Although this measure provides much more clinically relevant information than a global rating of social anxiety, the behavioral test and the rating of patient's behavior still is very time-consuming and not easy to use in routine clinical practice.

Indirect measures of phobic behavior are much more economical. Bryant and Trower (1974) developed the Social Situation Questionnaire, which provides an index of patients' social participation in 30 everyday situations. Other researchers have made use of standardized social diaries (Marzillier, Lambert, & Kellett, 1976). Such self-reports about behavior in potentially phobic situations might prove to be quite useful as behavioral measures. Research needs to be undertaken into the reliability and validity of these questionnaires.

Fear Questionnaires

There are several fear questionnaires that may be used for the assessment of phobic patients. In clinical practice, *general* fear questionnaires are particularly useful, because this type of questionnaire provides information on a wide range of specific phobic situations. The Fear Survey Schedule (FSS-III; Wolpe & Lang, 1964) has been used clinically and experimentally in various forms for over 20 years, and has enjoyed considerable prestige among behavior therapists and researchers as a measure of phobic anxiety. This questionnaire lists 76 fears that are common in phobic patients. Factor analyses revealed five interpretable factors: (a) social anxiety; (b) agoraphobia; (c) fears related to bodily injury, death, and illness; (d) fears of sexual and aggressive scenes; and (e) fears of harmless animals. These factors were, to a high degree, generalizable across phobic and nonphobic populations (Arrindell, Emmelkamp, & Van de Ende, 1984). Scale reliability for the subscales (Cronbach's coefficient α) all were very high.

Another general inventory is the Fear Questionnaire (FQ: Marks & Mathews, 1979). This form includes the 15 most common phobias and five associated anxiety-depression symptoms found in clinical practice. The phobia score is composed of (a) agoraphobia, (b) social fears, and (c) blood and injury fears. Arrindell et al. (1984) factor analyzed FQ scores of various phobic and nonphobic samples and found that *all* items, a priori hypothesized to load on their respective factors, were found to do so in a meaningful fashion; most of the items evidenced very high ($\geqslant$ ·70) loadings on their theoretically related factor, and only moderate, and in most cases low ($\leqslant$ ·20), loading on their unrelated counterparts. As could be expected on the basis of the smaller number of items that are captured by its subscales, the α figures obtained for the FQ were smaller than those for the FSS-III. The FQ was found to possess acceptable temporal stability over a 1-year period. However, the Anxiety-Depression subscale evidenced very low stability, which might be due to the episodic nature of panic attacks and depressed mood. It should be noted, however, that findings from this study and a study by Michelson and Mavissakalian (1983) indicate that small to moderate decreases occur over both relatively short (5–10 weeks) and relatively long (13 months) periods of time (if there have been no interventions). In making judgments about change in individual cases, the standard errors of measurement of the phobic subscales should be taken into account, which can be calculated by means of the reliability figures given by Arrindell el at. (1984). To exclude measurement error as the primary source of the difference between a first and a second test score, the observed change (the first score minus the second score) should at least exceed the standard error of measurement.

In addition to the general fear questionnaires, a number of questionnaires dealing with *specific* fears have been constructed (e.g., questionnaires dealing specifically with fear of snakes, spiders, and mutilation; and test-anxiety), but most of these are of little clinical use. Useful questionnaires, that provide information on social anxiety, are the Social Avoidance and Distress (SAD) and the Fear of Negative Evaluation Scale (FNE), both developed by Watson and Friend (1969).

Cognitive Measures

Given the recent interest in cognitive therapy procedures for anxiety disorders, there has been surprisingly little attention paid to the development of cognitive assessment methods for phobic patients. Questionnaires, such as the Irrational Beliefs Test (Jones, 1968) and the Rational Behavior Inventory (Shorkey & Whiteman, 1977), were developed to assess more general irrational beliefs and are not particularly suited to assess cognitions associated with specific phobic situations. Last (1984) provides an overview of cognitive measures that have been used to assess the thoughts of phobic patients. Generally, phobics are confronted with their phobic stimulus, either in vivo or imaginally, and are requested to record their thoughts on precoded sheets (thought-listing) or are requested to report whatever they are thinking about into a tape recorder (in vivo cognitive assessment). Few investigations have evaluated the reliability of cognitive assessment with phobic patients, and the findings of these studies cast doubt on the reliability of these measures (Last, 1984). However, as noted by Last (1984), it is questionable whether stability in cognitions should be expected, because thoughts of phobic patients may fluctuate over time.

To assess the fear of fear in agoraphobics, Chambless et al. (1985) developed the Agoraphobic Cognitions Questionnaire and the Bodily Sensations Questionnaire. The former is composed of 14 thoughts concerning disastrous consequences of panic that are commonly reported by agoraphobics. The Bodily Sensations Questionnaire is made up of 17 items concerning internal responses associated with anxiety in agoraphobics. Reliability and validity of these questionnaires are satisfactory.

CASE ILLUSTRATIONS

The differential diagnosis of phobic disorders usually provides little problems for experienced clinicians (Barlow, 1985), although in a few cases the distinction between various anxiety disorder categories can be difficult. For example, agoraphobia may be confused with social phobia, because social phobics feel anxious in public crowded places and buses, agoraphobics may avoid certain social situations. The differential diagnosis is illustrated in the following case.

David is a 24-year-old single man who is referred for agoraphobic complaints by his general practitioner. Detailed interviewing, however, reveals that his avoidance of public situations (e.g., shops, crowded areas, buses) is the result of social anxiety rather than of agoraphobia. The characteristic fear of fear is absent; he is not worrying about bodily sensations or possible disastrous consequences of panic, typical for agoraphobics. His maladaptive thoughts in phobic situations all are centered on the impression he will make on others. In such situations he usually blushes, and he believes that other people notice his blushing. This belief leads to more anxiety.

Agoraphobic-like avoidance behavior also may be the result of other problems, for example, obsessive–compulsive disorder. Mary is a 33-year-old woman who on initial interview presents herself as an agoraphobic. She is afraid of leaving her house, shopping, riding on buses, and so on. Detailed inquiry into the pattern of avoidance and associated thoughts reveals that the avoidance behavior, in this case, is mediated by an obsessive concern with contamination. She fears being contaminated by germs, and by avoiding public places she prevents possible contamination. Also, in this case there was no fear of fear or of associated bodily sensations.

In clinical practice, assessment is something different from establishing what diagnostic labels are to be given. Although patients may have the same diagnosis, this often says little about the treatment the patient ought to have. From a cognitive-behavioral perspective, a functional behavioral analysis is very important for treatment planning.

Case of Julia

Julia is a 42-year-old female with agoraphobic complaints. For several years now she has been afraid to do all kinds of things alone, such as walking, travelling by public transport, shopping, going to the cinema, or sitting in a chair at the hairdresser. When accompanied by her partner, she usually feels less anxious than when alone. Her first anxiety attack occurred several years ago when driving on a highway with her children in the car. She suddenly felt extremely anxious without knowing why, felt dizzy, and experienced palpitations. The next weeks and months anxiety was felt in a number of related situations from which escape was difficult. As is usually the case, anxiety increased when she was far from home, unaccompanied and in crowded places.

In addition to an initial clinical interview, Julia completed the Fear Questionnaire (Marks & Mathews, 1979). Results on this questionnaire revealed a score of 28 (range of subscale scores is 0–40) on the agoraphobia subscale. The scores for social phobia (10) and blood and injury phobia (9) were relatively low. To get a more accurate idea of the relative degree of anxiety and avoidance in agoraphobic situations, Julia scored five different agoraphobic situations on 0 through 8 rating scales (Emmelkamp, 1979). Walking down a busy street, walking away from hospital, travelling by bus, and shopping in a supermarket all were rated as 8. Sitting in a restaurant appeared to be less of a problem (rating of 2 and 4 for anxiety and avoidance, respectively). Thus, there appeared to be concordance between anxiety and avoidance in typically agoraphobic situations. To assess the actual behavioral competence and her in vivo cognitions, Julia was requested to walk a route from the hospital leading to a progressively more crowded place with the instruction to return when feeling anxious. She managed to stay away for 13 minutes, and had to return because she felt anxious. Immediately after the behavioral test, Julia completed modified versions of the Agoraphobic Cognitions Questionnaire and the Body Sensation Questionnaire (Chambless et al., 1985), in order to explore which thoughts run through her head during the in vivo tests. The cognitive questionnaire revealed that Julia's thoughts centered around suffocating, losing control, and being paralyzed through anxiety. The bodily sensation questionnaire revealed that a number of complaints typically associated with hyperventilation (e.g., shortness of breath, dizziness, dry throat) had caused considerable anxiety during the in vivo test.

Finally, Julia was requested to keep a precoded behavioral diary of her activities (Mathews et al., 1981). An extract of this diary is shown in Table 4.2. This behavioral diary showed that Julia did almost nothing outside home unaccompanied. The few instances that she visited a friend nearby unaccompanied by her husband resulted in considerable anxiety.

Taking into account the information gathered in interviews, behavioral assessment, fear questionnaires, and cognitive measures, Julia met DSM-III (American Psychiatric Association, 1980) diagnostic criteria for agoraphobia. On the basis of this information, it was hypothesized that a hyperventilation attack when driving her car several years ago led to escape and avoidance behavior, which eventually spread to typical agoraphobic situations, due to the fear of panicking again. When exposed to potentially anxious situations, Julia's anticipatory anxiety easily could result in hyperventilation for which symptoms further increased the anxiety, thus creating a vicious circle.

Table 4.2. Behavioral Diary

Date	Time			Anxiety	Destination and/or Purpose of Trip				Transport			
(April)	Out	Back	Medication	(0–10)	(with approximate distance from home)	Accompanied	Met	Alone	Walk	Car	Bus	Other
25	10:00	11:00	—	8	Visiting friend (50 meters)			X	X			
25	18:00	19:00	—	0	Walk (1 kilometer)	X			X			
26	13:30	15:30	—	3	Shopping	X				X		
26	18:00	19:00	—	0	Walk	X			X			
26	20:00	00:30	—	0	Visiting friends (6 km)	X				X		
27	09:30	11:00	—	6	Shopping (12 km)	X				X		

CONCLUDING REMARKS

The DSM-III categories of phobic disorder generally can be easily discriminated, but it should be noted that there is considerable overlap, especially between agoraphobia and social phobia. Results of research by Barlow (1985) suggest that multiple presenting problems perhaps are the rule rather than the exception. Although there are various studies that suggest that the various phobic disorders may have a different etiology (Arrindell et al., 1983; Emmelkamp, 1982; Hugdahl & Öst, 1985), different patterns of autonomic symptoms experienced in phobic situations (Amies, Gelder, & Shaw, 1983; Hugdahl & Öst, 1985; Marks, Thyrer, Himle, & Curtis, 1985) and distinct negative cognitions experienced when confronted with the phobic situation (Chambless, 1985), further studies are needed to establish whether the current diagnostic conditions indeed are different categories rather than various manifestations on the same theme of anxiety.

It recently has been suggested (Spitzer & Williams, 1985) that agoraphobia and panic disorder should be changed to a single category of panic disorder with three subdivisions: (a) uncomplicated panic disorder, (b) panic disorder with limited phobic avoidance, and (c) panic disorder with extensive phobic avoidance (i.e., agoraphobia). As argued by Cerney, Himadi, and Barlow (1984), there is a clear conceptual shift implied in the proposed reclassification of agoraphobia, because this revision would split agoraphobia across nonphobic anxiety states (panic disorder with agoraphobia) and phobic disorders (agoraphobia without panic attacks). It is highly questionable whether the central role of panic attacks in diagnosing the various forms of agoraphobia is tenable, in light of the recent findings that panic also is frequently found among most of the other anxiety disorders (Barlow, 1985). Further studies into the assessment and clinical features of the various phobic conditions are needed before the current DSM-III criteria for these disorders are changed.

REFERENCES

Abe, K., & Masui, T. (1981). Age-sex trends of phobic and anxiety symptoms in adolescense. *British Journal of Psychiatry, 138,* 297–302.

Agras, W. S., Chapin, H. N., & Oliveau, D. C. (1972). The natural history of phobia: Course and prognosis. *Archives of General Psychiatry, 26,* 315–317.

Agras, S., Sylvester, D., & Oliveau, D. (1969). The epidemiology of common fears and phobias. *Comprehensive Psychiatry, 10,* 151–156.

American Psychiatric Association. (1980) Diagnostic and statistical manual of mental disorders (3rd ed.) Washington, DC: Author.

Amies, P. L., Gelder, M. G., & Shaw, P. M. (1983). Social phobia: A comparative clinical study. *British Journal of Psychiatry, 142,* 174–179.

Andrews, J. D. W. (1966). Psychotherapy of phobias. *Psychological Bulletin, 66,* 455–480.

Arena, J. G., Blanchard, E. B., Andrasik, F., Cotch, P. A., & Myers, P. E. (1983). Reliability of psychophysiological assessment. *Behaviour Research and Therapy, 21,* 447–460.

Arrindell, W. A. (1980). Dimensional structure and psychopathology correlates of the fear survey schedule (FSS-III) in a phobic population: A factorial definition of agoraphobia. *Behaviour Research and Therapy, 18,* 229–242.

Arrindell, W. A., & Emmelkamp, P. M. G. (1985a). A test of the repression hypothesis in agoraphobics. *Psychological Medicine, 15,* 125–129.

Arrindell, W. A., & Emmelkamp, P. M. G. (1985b) Psychological profile of the spouse of the female agoraphobic patient: Personality and symptoms. *British Journal of Psychiatry, 146,* 405–414.

Arrindell, W. A., & Emmelkamp, P. M. G. (1987). Psychological states and traits in female agoraphobics: A controlled study. *Journal of Behavioural Assessment & Psychopathology* (in press).

Arrindell, W. A., & Emmelkamp, P. M. G. (1986). Marital adjustment, intimacy and needs in female agoraphobics and their partners: A controlled study. *British Journal of Psychiatry. 149,* 592–602.

Arrindell, W. A., Emmelkamp, P. M. G., & Van der Ende, J. (1984). Phobic dimensions: I. Reliability and generalizability across samples, gender and nations. *Advances in Behaviour Research and Therapy, 6,* 207–253.

Arrindell, W. A., Emmelkamp, P. M. G., Monsma, A., & Brilman, E. (1983). The role of perceived parental rearing practices in the aetiology of phobic disorders: A con-trolled study. *British Journal of Psychiatry, 143*, 183–187.

Bandura, A., & Adams, N. E. (1977). Analysis of self-efficacy theory of behavioral change. *Cognitive Therapy and Research, 1*, 287–310.

Barlow, D. H. (1985). The dimensions of anxiety disorders. In A. H. Tuma & J. D. Maser (Eds.), *Anxiety and the anxiety disorders.* Hillsdale, NJ: Lawrence Erlbaum Associates.

Beidel, D. L., Turner, S. M., & Dancu, C. V. (1985). Physiological, cognitive and behavioral aspects of social anxiety. *Behaviour Research and Therapy, 23*, 109–117.

Bellack, A. S., Hersen, M., & Lamparski, D. (1979). Role play test for assessing social skills: Are they valid? Are they useful? *Journal of Consulting and Clinical Psychology, 47*, 335–342.

Ben-Tovim, D. I. (1985). DSM-III in Botswana: A field trial in a developing country. *American Journal of Psychiatry, 142*, 342–345.

Bianchi, G. N. (1971). Origins of disease phobia. *Australian and New Zealand Journal of Psychiatry*, 241–257.

Bland, K., & Hallam, R. S. (1981). Relationship between response to graded exposure and marital satisfaction in agoraphobics. *Behaviour Research and Therapy, 19*, 335–338.

Bowen, R. C., & Kohout, I. (1979). The relationship between agoraphobia and primary affective disorders. *Canadian Journal of Psychiatry, 24*, 317–322.

Bryant, B., & Trower, P. E. (1974). Social difficulty in a student sample. *British Journal of Educational Psychology, 44*, 13–21.

Buglass, D., Clarke, J., Henderson, A. S., Kreitman, N., & Presly, A. (1977). A study of agoraphobic housewives. *Psychological Medicine, 7*, 73–86.

Burns, L. E., & Thorpe, G. L. (1977). The epidemiology of fears and phobias (With particular reference to the National Survey of Agoraphobics). *Journal of International Medical Research, 5*, 1–7.

Cerny, J. A., Himadi, W. G., & Barlow, D. H. (1984). Issues in diagnosing anxiety disorders. *Journal of Behavioral Assessment, 6*, 301–329.

Chambless, D. L. (1982). Characteristics of agoraphobia. In D. L. Chambless & A. J. Goldstein (Eds.), *Agoraphobia.* (pp. 1–18). New York: Wiley.

Chambless, D. L. (1985a November). *Fear of fear and the anxiety disorders.* Paper presented at the meeting of the Association for Advancement of Behavior Therapy, Houston, TX.

Chambless, D. L. (1985b). The relationship of severity of agoraphobia to associated psychopathology. *Behaviour Research and Therapy, 23*, 305–310.

Chambless, D. L., & Goldstein, A. (1980). The treatment of agoraphobia. In A. Goldstein & E. B. Foa (Eds.), *Handbook of behavioral interventions.* New York: Wiley (pp. 322–415).

Chambless, D. L., Caputo, G. C., Gallagher, R., & Bright, P. (1985). Assessment of fear of fear in agoraphobics: The Body Sensations Questionnaire and the Agoraphobic Cognitions Questionnaire. Unpublished manuscript.

Cone, J. D. (1979). Confounded comparisons in triple response mode assessment research. *Behavioral Assessment, 1*, 85–95.

Connolly, J., Hallam, R. S., & Marks, I. (1976). Selective association of fainting with bloodinjury phobias. *Behavior Therapy, 7*, 8–13.

Craske, M. G., & Craig, K. D. (1984). Musical performance anxiety: The three systems model and self-efficacy theory. *Behaviour Research and Therapy, 22*, 267–280.

Derogatis, L. R. (1977). *SCL-90: Administration scoring and procedures manual — I for the (Revised) version.* John Hopkins University School of Medicine, Clinical Psychometrics Research Unit, Baltimore.

Di Nardo, P. A., O'Brien, G. T., Barlow, D. H., Waddell, M. T., & Blanchard, E. B. (1983). Reliability of DSM-III anxiety disorder categories using a new structured interview. *Archives of General Psychiatry, 40*, 1070–1075.

Dow, M. G., Biglan, A., & Glaser, S. R. (1985). Multimethod assessment of socially anxious and socially unanxious women. *Behavioral Assessment, 7*, 273–282.

Edelman, R. J. (1985). Dealing with embarassing events: Socially anxious and nonsocially anxious groups compared. *British Journal of Clinical Psychology, 24*, 281–288.

Emmelkamp, P. M. G. (1974). Self-observation versus flooding in the treatment of agoraphobia. *Behaviour Research and Therapy, 12*, 229–237.

Emmelkamp, P. M. G. (1979). The behavioral study of clinical phobias. In M. Hersen, R. M. Eisler, & P. M. Miller (Eds.), *Progress in Behaviour Modification* (Vol. 8). New York: Academic Press (pp. 55–125).

Emmelkamp, P. M. G. (1982). *Phobic and*

obsessive-compulsive disorders: Theory, research & practice. New York: Plenum.

Emmelkamp, P. M. G. & Cohen-Kettenis, P. Relationship of locus of control to phobic anxiety and depression. *Psychological Reports,* 1975, *36,* 2, 390.

Fisher, L. M., & Wilson, G. T. (1985). A study of the psychology of agoraphobia. *Behaviour Research and Therapy, 23,* 97–107.

Foa, E. B., Steketee, G., & Young, M. C. (1984). Agoraphobia: Phenomenological aspects, associated characteristics, and theoretical considerations. *Clinical Psychology Review, 4,* 431–451.

Fry, W. F. (1962). The marital context of an anxiety syndrome. *Family Process, 1,* 245–252.

Gardos, G. (1981). Is agoraphobia a psychosomatic form of depression? In D. F. Klein & J. Rabkin (Eds.), *Anxiety: New research and changing concepts.* New York: Raven Press.

Garssen, B., Van Veenedaal, W., & Bloemink, R. (1983). Agoraphobia and the hyperventilation syndrome. *Behaviour Research and Therapy, 21,* 643–649.

Glass, C. R., Merluzzi, T. V., Biever, J. L., & Larsen, K. H. (1982). Cognitive assessment of social anxiety: Development and validation of a self-statement questionnaire. *Cognitive Therapy and Research, 6,* 37–55.

Goodstein, R. K., & Swift, K. (1977). Psychotherapy with phobic patients: The marriage relationship as the source of symptoms and focus of treatment. *American Journal of Psychotherapy, 31,* 284–293.

Graziano, A. M., & De Giovanni, I. S. (1979). The clinical significance of childhood phobias: A note on the proportion of child-clinical referrals for the trreatment of children's fears. *Behaviour Research and Therapy, 17,* 161–162.

Hafner, R. J. (1982). The marital context of the agoraphobic syndrome. In D. L. Chambless & A. J. Goldstein (Eds.), *Agoraphobia: Multiple perspectives on theory and treatment.* (pp. 77–118). New York: Wiley.

Hand, I., & Lamontagne, Y. (1976). The exacerbation of interpersonal problems after rapid phobia-removal. *Psychotherapy: Theory, Research and Practice, 13,* 405–411.

Hartman, L. M. (1983). A metacognitive model of social anxiety: Implications for treatment. *Clinical Psychology Review, 3,* 435–456.

Hersen, M., Bellack, A. S., & Turner, S. (1978). Assessment of assertiveness in female psychiatric patients: Motor and autonomic measures. *Journal of Behavior Therapy and Experimental Psychiatry, 9,* 11–16.

Holden, A. E. & Barlow, D. H. (1984) Heart rate and heart rate variability recorded in vivo in agoraphobics and non-phobics. Unpublished manuscript.

Hugdahl, K. (1981). The three-systems- model of fear and emotion — A critical examination. *Behaviour Research and Therapy, 19,* 75–86.

Hughdahl, K., & Öst, L. G. (1985). Subjectively rated physiological and cognitive symptoms in six different clinical phobias. *Personality and Individual Differences, 6,* 175–188.

Jacob, R. J., Bjüro Möller, M., Turner, S. M., & Wall, C. (1985). Otoneurological examination in panic disorder and agoraphobia with panic attacks: A pilot study. *American Journal of Psychiatry, 142,* 715–720.

Jasin, S. E., & Turner, R. (1980 November). *Multivariate analysis of agoraphobics', anxiety neurotics', and depressive neurotics' responses to the MMPI and Beck Depression Inventory.* Paper presented at the American Association of Behavior Therapy Convention, New York.

Jones, R. (1968). *A factored measure of Ellis' irrational beliefs systems with personality and maladjustment correlated.* Unpublished doctoral dissertation, Texas Technological University, Lubbock, TX.

Kantor, J. S., Zitrin, C. M., & Zeldis, S. M. (1980). Mitral valve prolapse syndrome in agoraphobic patients. *American Journal of Psychiatry, 137,* 467–469.

Lacey, J. I. (1962). Psychophysiological approaches to the evaluation of psychotherapeutic process and outcome. In F. Rubenstein & M. B. Parloff (Eds.), *Research in psychotherapy* (Vol. II). Washington, DC: American Psychological Association.

Lang, P. J. (1971). The application of psychophysiological methods to the study of psychotherapy and behavior modification. In A. E. Bergin & S. L. Garfield (Eds.), *Handbook of psychotherapy and behavior change.* (pp. 75–125). New York: Wiley.

Lang, P. J., Levin, D. N., Miller, G. A., & Kozak, M. J. (1983). Fear behavior, fear imagery, and the psychophysiology of emotion: The problem of affective response integration. *Journal of Abnormal Psychology, 92,* 276–306.

Last, C. G. (1984). Cognitive treatment of phobia. In: M. Hersen, R. M. Eisler, & P. M. Miller (Eds.), *Progress in behavior modification* (Vol. 16, pp. 65–82). New York: Academic Press.

Lazarus, A. A. (1966). Broad-spectrum behavior therapy and the treatment of agoraphobia. *Behaviour Research and Therapy, 4,* 95–97.

Leighton, A. H., & Lambo, T. A. (1963). *Psychiatric disorders among the Yoruba.* New York: Cornell University Press.

Ley, R. (1985a). Agoraphobia, the panic attack and the hyperventilation syndrome. *Behaviour Research and Therapy, 23,* 79–81.

Ley, R. (1985b). Blood, breath and fears: A hyperventilation theory of panic attacks and agoraphobia, *Clinical Psychology Review, 5,* 271–285.

Lick, J. R., Sushinsky, L. W., & Malow, R. (1977). Specificity of fear survey schedule items and the prediction of avoidance behavior. *Behavior Modification, 1,* 283–307.

Liebowitz, M. R., Gorman, J. M., Fyer, A. J., & Klein, D. F. (1985). Social phobia: Review of a neglected anxiety disorder. *Archives of General Psychiatry, 42* 729–736.

Marks, I. M. (1969). *Fears and phobias.* New York: Academic Press.

Marks, I. M. (1981). Space "phobia": A pseudo-agoraphobic syndrome. *Journal of Neurology, Neurosurgery and Psychiatry, 44,* 387–391.

Marks, I. M., & Bebbington, P. (1976). Space-phobia: Syndrome of agoraphobic variant. *British Medical Journal, 2,* 345–347.

Marks, I. M., & Gelder, M. G. (1966). Different ages of onset in varieties of phobias. *American Journal of Psychiatry, 123,* 218–221.

Marks, I. M., & Huson, M. (1973). Physiological aspects of neutral and phobic imagery: Further observations. *British Journal of Psychiatry, 122,* 567–572.

Marks, I. M., & Mathews, A. M. (1979). Brief standard self-rating for phobic patients. *Behaviour Research and Therapy, 17,* 263–267.

Mathews, A. M., Gelder, M. G., & Johnston, D. W. (1981). *Agoraphobia: Nature and treatment.* London: Tavistock.

Marzillier, J. S., Lambert, C., & Kellett, J. (1976). A controlled evaluation of systematic desensitization and social skills training for social inadequate psychiatric patients. *Behaviour Research and Therapy, 14,* 225–228.

Mavissakalian, M., & Michelson, L. (1982). Patterns of psychophysiological change in the treatment of agoraphobia. *Behaviour Research and Therapy, 20,* 347–356.

McEwan, K. L., & Devius, G. M. (1983). Is increased arousal in social anxiety noticed by others? *Journal of Abnormal Psychology, 92,* 417–421.

McNamara, J. R., & Blumer, C. A. (1982). Role playing to assess social competence. Ecological validity considerations. *Behavior Modification, 6,* 519–549.

Mendel, J. G. C., & Klein, D. F. (1969). Anxiety attacks with subsequent agoraphobia. *Comprehensive Psychiatry, 10,* 190–195.

Meyers, J. K., Weissman, M. M., Tischler, G. L., Holzer, C. E., Leaf, P. J., Orvaschel, H., Anthony, J. C., Boyd, J. H., Burke, J. D., Kramer, M., & Stoltzman, R. (1984). Six-month prevalence of psychiatric disorders in three communities. *Archives of General Psychiatry, 41,* 959–970.

Michelson, L. (1984). The role of individual differences, response profiles, and treatment consonance in anxiety disorders. *Journal of Behavioral Assessment, 6,* 349–367.

Michelson, L., & Mavissakalian, M. (1983). Temporal stability of self-report measures in agoraphobia research. *Behaviour Research and Therapy, 21,* 695–698.

Miller, L. C., Barrett, C. L., & Hampe, E. (1974). Phobia of childhood in a prescientific era. In A. Davids (Ed.), *Child personality and psycho-pathology: Current topics* (Vol. 1). New York: Wiley.

Miller, L. C., Barrett, C. L., Hampe, E., & Noble, H. (1972). Factor structure of childhood fears. *Journal of Consulting and Clinical Psychology, 39,* 264–268.

Milton, F., & Hafner, J. (1979). The outcome of behavior therapy for agoraphobia in relation to marital adjustment. *Archives of General Psychiatry, 36,* 807–811.

Monti, P. M., Boice, R., Fingeret, A. L., Zwick, W. R., Kolko, D., Munroe, S., & Grunberger, A. (1984). Midi-level measurement of social anxiety in psychiatric and non-psychiatric samples. *Behaviour Research and Therapy, 22,* 651–660.

Monti, P. M., Curran, J. P., Corriveau, D., DeLancey, A. L., & Hagerman, S. M. (1980). Effects of social skills training groups and sensitivity training groups with psychiatric patients. *Journal of Consulting and Clinical Psychology, 48,* 241–248.

Morakinyo, O. (1985). Phobic states presenting as somatic complaints syndromes in Nigeria. *Acta Psychiatria Scandinavia, 71,* 356–365.

Morris, R. J., & Kratochwill, T. R. (1983). *Treating children's fears and phobias: A behavioral approach.* New York: Pergamon Press.

Nandi, D. N., Ajmany, S., Banerjee, G. C., Ghosh, A., & Sarkar, A. (1975). Psychiatric disorders in a rural community in West Bengal — an epidemiological study. *Indian Journal of Psychiatry, 17,* 87–89.

Nandi, D. N., Das, N. N., Chaudry, A., Banerjee, G., Dalta, P., Ghosh, A., & Boral, G. C. (1980). Mental morbidity in urban life — an

epidemiological study. *Indian Journal of Psychiatry, 22,* 324–330.
Newton, A., Kindness, K. & McFadyen, M. (1983). Patients and social skills groups: do they lack social skills? *Behavioural Psychotherapy, 11,* 116–126.
O'Brien, G. T., Barlow, D. H., & Last, C. G. (1982). Changing marriage patterns of agora-phobics as a result of treatment. In R. L. Du Pont (Ed.), *Phobia. A comprehensive sum-mary of modern treatment.* New York: Brunner/Mazel.
Odejide, A. O. (1976). A psychiatric service in a Nigerian general hospital. *African Journal of Psychiatry, 3,* 97–102.
Ollendick, T. H. (1983). Reliability and validity of the Revised Fear Survey Schedule for Children (FSSC-R). *Behaviour Research & Therapy, 21,* 685–692.
Ollendick, T. H., Matson, J. L., & Helsel, W. J. (1985). Fears in children and adolescents; Normative data. *Behaviour Research and Therapy, 23,* 465–467.
Ost, L. G. (1986). Age at onset in different phobia. Manuscript submitted for publication.
Parker, G. (1979). Reported parental characteristics of agoraphobics and social phobics. *British Journal of Psychiatry, 135,* 555–560.
Rachman, S. (1978). *Fear and courage.* San Francisco: Freeman.
Raguram, R., & Bhide, A. Y. (1985). Patterns of phobic neurosis: A retrospective study. *British Journal of Psychiatry, 147,* 557–560.
Rahim, S., & Idris, A. (1976). Epidemiology of neuroses in the Sudan. *African Journal of Psychiatry, 1,* 21–31.
Robins, R. N., Helzer, J. E., Weissman, M. M., Orvaschel, H., Gruenberg, E., Burke, J. D., & Regier, D. A. (1984). Lifetime prevalence of specific psychiatric disorders in three sites. *Archives of General Psychiatry, 41,* 949–958.
Rutter, M., Tizard, J., & Whitmore, S. (1970). *Education, health and behavior.* London: Longmans.
Sallis, J., Lichstein, K., & McGlynn, F. (1980). Anxiety response patterns: A comparison of clinical and analogue populations. *Journal of Behaviour Therapy and Experimental Psychiatry, 11,* 179–183.
Sheehan, D. V., Sheehan, K. E., & Michiello, W. E. (1981). Age of onset of phobic disorders: A reevaluation. *Comprehensive Psychiatry, 22,* 544–553.
Shorkey, C., & Whiteman, V. (1977). Development of the Rational Behavior Inventory: Initial validity and reliability. *Educational and Psychological Measurement, 37,* 527–533.
Smith, T. W., Ingram, R. E., & Brehm, S.S. (1983). Social anxiety, anxious self-preoccupation, and recall of self-relevant information. *Journal of Personality and Social Psychology, 44,* 1276–1283.
Spitzer, R. L., & Williams, J. B. W. (1985). *DSM-III-R working draft.* New York: American Psychiatric Association.
Tearman, B. H., Telch, M. J., & Keefe, I. (1984). Etiology and onset of agoraphobia: A critical review. *Comprehensive Psychiatry, 25,* 51–62.
Thyrer, B. A., Himle, J., & Curtis, G. C. (1985). Blood-injury-illness phobia: A review. *Journal of Clinical Psychology, 41,* 451–459.
Thyrer, B. A., Nesse, R. M., Cameron, O. G., & Curtis, G. C. (1985). Agoraphobia: A test of the separation anxiety hypothesis. *Behaviour Research and Therapy, 23,* 75–78.
Thyrer, B. A., Parrish, R. T., Curtis, G. C., Nesse, R. M., & Cameron, O. G. (1985). Age of onset of DSM-III anxiety disorders. *Journal of Nervous and Mental Disease,* 113–122.
Torpey, D., & Measy, L. (1973). Marital interaction in agoraphobia. *Journal of Clinical Psychology, 30,* 351–354.
Trower, P., Yardley, K., Bryant, B. M., & Shaw, P. (1978). The treatment of social failure: A comparison of anxiety-reduction and skills-acquisition procedures on two social problems. *Behavior Modification, 2,* 41–60.
Tyrer, P. J. & Lader, M. H. (1976). Central and peripheral correlates of anxiety: A comparative study. *Journal of Nervous and Mental Disease, 62,* 99–104.
Verghese, A., & Beig, A. (1974). Neurosis in Vellore Town — an epidemiological study. *Indian Journal of Psychiatry, 16,* 1–8.
Verhulst, F. C. (1985). Normaal en niet-normale angsten in de kinderontwikkeling. In H. Ras, T. van Rijthoven, & R. Beunderman (Eds.), *Angsten en Fobieën.* Utrecht: (pp. 102–130). Nederlandse Vereniging voor Psychotherapie.
Vermilyea, J. A., Boice, R., & Barlow, D. H. (1984). Rachman and Hodgson a decade later: How do desynchronous response systems relate to the treatment of agoraphobia? *Behaviour Research and Therapy, 22,* 615–621.
Watson, D., & Friend, R. (1969). Measurement of social-evaluative anxiety. *Journal of Consulting & Clinical Psychology, 33,* 448–457.
Webster, A. S. (1953). The development of phobias in married women. *Psychological Monographs, 67,* whole (No. 367).
Weinberger, D. A., Schwartz, G. E., & Davidson R. J. (1979). Low-anxious, high-anxious, and repressive coping styles: Psychometric

patterns and behavioral and physiological responses to stress. *Journal of Abnormal Psychology*, *88*, 369–380.

Williams, S. L. (1985). On the nature and measurement of agoraphobia. In M. Hersen, R. M. Eisler & P. M. Miller (Eds.), *Progress in behavior modification* (Vol. 19 pp. 109–144). New York: Academic Press.

Wolpe, J., & Lang, P. (1964). Fear Survey Schedule for use in behavior therapy. *Behaviour Research and Therapy*, *2*, 27–30.

CHAPTER 5

Obsessive–Compulsive Disorder

Michael J. Kozak, Edna B. Foa and Paul R. McCarthy

The definition and description of obsessive–compulsive disorder has changed little since it was first offered by Equirol in 1838. Obsessive–compulsive syndrome is typically described as a

> recurrent or persistent idea, thought, image feeling or movement which is accompanied by a sense of subjective compulsion and a desire to resist it, the event being recognized by the individual as foreign to his personality, and into the abnormality of which he has insight. (Pollitt, 1956, p. 842)

Variously labeled obsessional state, obsessional neurosis or illness, and obsessional compulsive disorder, it has been most commonly described in recent writings by the DSM-III (American Psychiatric Association, 1980) term *obsessive–compulsive disorder* (e.g., Emmelkamp, 1982; Foa, Steketee, & Ozarow, 1985; Insel, 1982; Marks, 1981; Salzman & Thaler, 1981).

Obsessive–compulsive disorders have usually been classified according to the nature of the ritualistic behavior, namely washing and/or cleaning, checking, and less frequent forms such as repeating and ordering. Case examples of the most common manifestations, washing and checking rituals, and their associated obsessional thoughts are given here.

Case 1

Sara is a 33-year-old married woman with two children. She felt contaminated (a nonspecific feeling of being dirty, accompanied by extreme anxiety and discomfort) when in contact with her mother. Her symptoms started 10 years prior to treatment when she was pregnant with her second child and her mother had touched her once in order to feel the movements of the fetus. Sara felt highly anxious immediately after that touch and was relieved after a normal shower. She came for treatment when she felt contaminated by everything that could have been even remotely in contact with her mother: persons living in the area where her mother lived, persons who were in contact with her mother, mail from the area where her mother lived, and so forth. She avoided contaminated places and controlled her husband's and children's movements to avoid being contaminated through them. In spite of all attempts to avoid contamination, Sara needed to clean herself actively. The daily washing activity gradually increased to include about 50 hand washings, three 30-minute showers, and several hours of cleaning various objects in her environment.

Case 2

Mike, a 32-year-old patient, performed checking rituals that were preceded by a fear of harming other people. When driving, he had to stop the car often and return to check whether he had run over people, particularly babies. Before flushing the toilet, he had to check to be sure that a live insect had not fallen into the toilet, because he did not want to be responsible for killing a living thing. At home he repeatedly checked to see that the doors, stoves, lights, and windows were shut or turned off so that no harm, such as fire or burglary, would come to his family due to his negligence. He particularly worried about his 15-month-old daughter, repeatedly checking the gate to the basement to be sure that it was locked. He did not carry his daughter while walking on concrete floors in order to avoid killing her by accidentally dropping her. Mike performed these and many other checking rituals for an average of 4 hours a day. Checking behavior started several months after his marriage, 6 years prior to treatment. It increased 2 years later, when his wife was pregnant with their first child, and continued to worsen over the years.

Traditional attempts to categorize obsessive–compulsive symptoms were descriptive in nature, usually focusing on the specific ritualistic behaviors or on the content of the ruminative material. This is quite clear in the division of obsessive-compulsive patients into "washers," "checkers," or "orderers," and the like. Although many patients manifest more than one type of ritualistic behavior, in most cases one specific type prevails. Washing/cleaning and checking rituals are the most common compulsions encountered (Stern & Cobb, 1978). "Repeaters" are a subgroup of checkers who repeat an action, usually a specified "magical" number of times in order to prevent a particular disaster from occurring. These individuals differ from other checkers, in that their rituals are not related to feared consequences in a direct, rational way. A third group consists of patients who manifest ordering rituals in which certain objects must be precisely arranged in order to achieve a satisfying state of symmetry or balance. Disturbance of this order provokes extreme discomfort. A rarer category of "obsessional slowness" has been suggested by Rachman and Hodgson (1980). These patients do not appear to have distinct obsessions followed by ritualistic behavior designed to reduce anxiety. Rather, they carry out their everyday activities, particularly toileting, with meticulous care and many hours of effort. Other authors have attempted to provide a classification based on the form of obsessions (e.g., Akhtar, Wig, Varma, Pershad, & Verma, 1975; Capstick & Seldrup, 1973; Dowson, 1977).

A shortcoming of all the traditional classifications is that they fail to bear on treatment strategies. To be most useful, nosology must be related to etiology and/or treatment. Foa, Steketee, and Ozarow (1985) proposed a classification that rests on the cues that evoke anxiety and the type of activity (cognitive or overt) that reduces it. This classification enables us to relate subtype to treatment.

All obsessive-compulsives complain of the presence of intrusive thoughts, images, or impulses. These thoughts may be triggered by an external event, such as touching a contaminated object or locking a door, or they may arise without apparent external cues. A further categorization can be made with respect to the presence or absence of ideas of disastrous consequences. For instance, the thought "Did I lock the door properly?" may be associated with the idea of a rapist invading one's home; the spontaneous image of Jesus' penis may give rise to a thought of going to hell. On the other hand, the intrusive thought "Is my hand contaminated?" may elicit discomfort in the absence of any idea of disturbing consequences. Thus, obsessions can be divided into several different kinds: (a) presence of intrusive ideas, external cues, and fears of disasters; (b) presence of intrusive ideas and external cues without thoughts of disasters; and (c) presence of intrusive ideas and thoughts of disasters with external cues.

An additional kind of obsession, with neither external cues nor fear of disasters, is theoretically possible, but we have not observed patients with such obsessions, nor have we come across reports of them in the literature. Rachman's (1976) division of compulsions into "restorative" and "preventative" can provide an explanation for the absence of this pattern. It seems unlikely that a repetitive thought without either the urge to restore a state of relative calm or to prevent a future disaster would be associated with the degree of anxiety that characterizes an obsession. Thus, fears of disasters and/or associated external cues seem to be prerequisites for an obsession.

How can rituals be classified? Because our present conceptualization posits that all rituals are anxiety reducing, the type of ritual (e.g., washing, checking) becomes irrelevant because it does not lead to differential treatment. A more useful approach is to categorize compulsions on the basis of their mode (i.e., cognitive or behavioral). Although these two classes do not differ in their functional relationship to anxiety, they do carry different treatment implications (Foa, Steketee, & Ozarow, 1985).

Clarifying obsessions and compulsions on the dimensions just mentioned yields eight types of obsessive-compulsives. These are shown in Figure 5.1. As we have discussed, only six types have been observed. It is notable that these types are not mutually exclusive: A patient may have obsessions of several different types. Similarly, a given obsession may give rise to both covert and overt rituals. As seen in Figure 5.1, the second, fourth, and sixth types are all distinguished by the absence of overt rituals. Patients manifesting this pattern have been labeled as obsessional. They may vary, however, with respect to whether or not their obsessions include external cues and/or anticipated disasters. Type 1, overt compulsions associated with external cues and with ideas of future disasters, is found in nearly all patients with checking rituals and in many of those with washing and cleaning rituals. The third type, obsessions triggered by external cues without feared consequences, is characteristic of many patients with ordering rituals and also of some with washing rituals. The fifth type represents obsessions triggered by ideas, especially those of future disasters; it is most often observed in patients who exhibit repeating rituals.

THEORETICAL CONSIDERATIONS

The validity of any nosology depends on its usefulness in relation to treatment procedures and etiology. An advantage of a theoretically based classification is the guidance it provides for forming hypotheses about etiology and treatment. A relationship between treatment procedures and the above typology has already been proposed by Foa, Steketee, and Ozarow (1985). In this chapter, we will conceptualize the different symptoms of obsessive–compulsive disorder as manifestations of cognitive structures. Those structures are thought to be the targets of treatment; therefore, they require systematic assessment. The nature of these structures and methods of their assessment will be addressed here. We will begin with a general discussion of the cognitive struc-

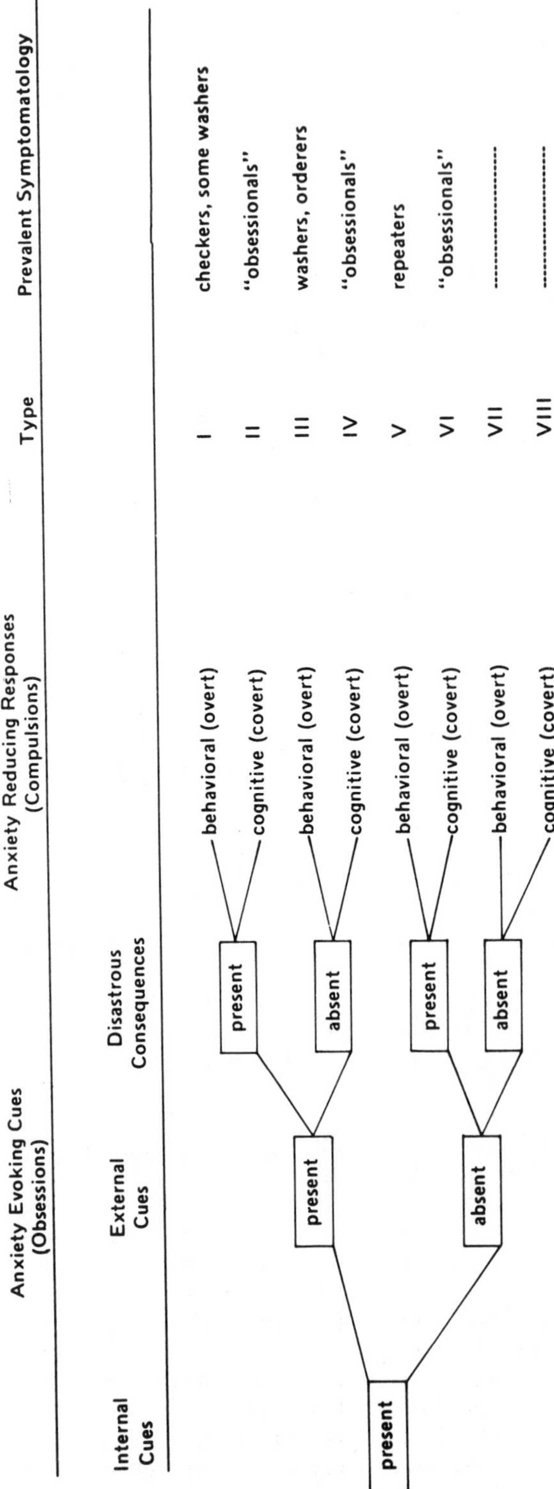

Figure 5.1. Classification of obsessions and compulsions according to anxiety-evoking cues, anticipated consequences, and mode of anxiety reduction.

ture of fear and proceed to a more specific discussion of fear structures of obsessive–compulsive disorder.

Fear Structures of Anxiety Disorders

A starting point for considering the structure of obsessive–compulsive fears can be found in Lang's (1977, 1979) bioinformational conceptualization of fear. Accordingly, fear is represented as a network in memory that includes three kinds of information: (a) information about the feared stimulus situation; (b) information about verbal, physiological, and overt behavioral responses; and (c) interpretive information about the meaning of the stimulus and response elements of the structure. This information structure is conceived of as a program for escape or avoidance behavior.

If the fear structure is indeed a program to escape danger, it must involve information that stimuli and/or responses are dangerous, as well as information about physiological activity preparatory for escape. Thus, a fear structure is distinguished from other information structures not only by response elements, but also by certain meaning information it contains (Foa & Kozak, 1986). For example, the programs for running ahead of a baton-carrying competitor in a race and for running ahead of a club-carrying assailant on a racetrack are likely to involve similar stimulus and response information. That which distinguishes the fear structure is the *meaning* of stimuli and responses. Only the fear structure involves a representation of danger coupled with motor behavior preparatory to escape.

Disordered fear structures are characterized by persistence, coherence, and irrationality (Foa & Kozak, 1986). This view entails that either the phobic structure itself differs from a non-neurotic fear structure and/or that anxiety-disordered individuals are impaired in the mechanisms by which fear is usually modified. With regard to their fear structures, Foa and Kozak (1986) suggested that *both* normal and pathological fears involve stimulus and response elements as well as representations of their meaning. Disordered anxiety, however, is characterized by unusually high negative valances associated with the fear structure. That is, for some disordered individuals, the "badness" of an event is simply much greater than for other individuals. Only sometimes, however, is valence related to an erroneous evaluation about the consequences of the event. In addition, high negative valence in a fear structure can derive from erroneously high estimates of the probability of occurrence of an event. Thus, one individual may fear making a social faux pas because the embarrassment feels terrible; another may be convinced that a single faux pas will bring job dismissal; a third may believe he or she will almost surely make a faux pas at any social occasion.

Anxiety disorders are also characterized by large fear responses. The excessive responses may reflect a more elaborate fear structure, that is more stimulus and response elements are present in the network. Another possible explanation for the excessive responses is that the associations in the disordered fear structure are more strongly formed. In either case, a pathological fear structure would be more readily evoked than a normal one. Of course, it is also possible that magnitude information is coded into the response structure, and that some individuals are predisposed to larger responses (Lader & Wing, 1966).

Obsessive–Compulsive Fear Structures

Of all those with anxiety disorders, obsessive–compulsives appear to show the most hetereogeneous symptom manifestations. We suppose that such heterogeneity reflects a variety of fear structures in these patients, The most common fear involves harm to self or to others which stems from contact with contaminants, and attempts to ensure safety via passive avoidance and washing rituals.

This fear structure is exemplified in the patient who is concerned with contracting venereal disease from public bathrooms, and washes even on suspicion of the most indirect contact. As with simple phobics, analysis of the structure into stimulus, response, and meaning elements is straightforward. However, the plethora of stimulus and response associations distinguishes this structure from that of simple phobics. Because of the preponderance of stimulus associations, effective passive avoidance becomes impossible, and active rituals are necessary for safety. Often, inquiry fails to reveal an external source of harm associated with contamination (e.g., disease). In this case, washing is performed to reduce discomfort associated with the contaminant rather than to prevent harm. The absence of reported harm is puzzling given a definition of anxiety as subserving overt escape from threat. It suggests that individuals may not be aware of all the elements of their fear structure. This challenges us to develop assessment methods to examine fear structures independently of verbal report.

Less common than washing and checking rituals are others such as repeating, counting, hoarding, praying, and ordering. With the exception of ordering, these rituals are often reported as protecting the individual from some harm. For example, a person may hoard thousands of newspapers to prevent loss of access to information that may be needed at some later time. In contrast, orderers, as a rule, report no anticipated harm associated with asymmetric placement of objects; for them the rituals simply reduce discomfort.

Some obsessive–compulsives are without rituals but suffer from intrusive, repetitive, unwanted, discomfort-evoking thoughts, images, or impulses; we refer to them as obsessionals. Most of them are concerned with specific harmful events. Examples are individuals who worry that they may impulsively harm a child and therefore avoid being alone with children, or those who worry that they may stab themselves or others and consequently avoid knives.

These examples illustrate the heterogeneity of obsessive–compulsive disorder with respect to both feared harm and types of protective rituals. What conceptual commonality allows us to view these diverse symptoms as one disorder? We propose that what distinguishes obsessive–compulsive patients is the complexity of the associations with harm in their fear structures. Obsessive–compulsives exhibit a capacity to associate a wide variety of apparently unrelated stimuli with ideas of threat or danger. This capacity is interpretable as a form of cognitive impairment.

Clinical observations as well as experimental investigations indicate that obsessive–compulsives show cognitive impairments in the following four major areas: (a) epistemological reasoning, (b) estimates of the probability of harm, (c) negative valence associated with the feared harm, and (d) rules for generalization and discrimination.

Epistemological Reasoning

Most people operate on the assumption that in the absence of valid evidence for danger, a given situation is safe. Foa and Kozak (1985) have suggested that obsessive–compulsives, when considering fear material, assume that in the absence of evidence for safety, the situation is dangerous. Because evidence for the complete safety of a situation is rarely available, the obsessive–compulsive is tormented with indecisiveness and doubt regarding what is dangerous and what is safe. Evidence for indecisiveness in obsessive–compulsives has, in fact, been reported by several authors. Milner, Beech, and Walker (1971) observed that, compared with depressed patients, obsessive–compulsives requested more repetitions of trials when asked to disinguish auditory tones presented in white noise. Similar results were obtained by Volans (1976) in comparing normals, phobics, and obsessional checkers on a decision-making task; even when neuroticism was partialled out, the obsessional group still required more evidence before making a decision. In the same vein,

Sartory and Master (1984), comparing obsessionals and matched normal controls on a motor set contingent negative variation (CNV) paradigm, found that the former demonstrated greater uncertainty and doubt.

In addition to their doubts about the safety of a circumstance, obsessive–compulsives, particularly those with checking rituals, are afflicted with uncertainty as to whether their ritualistic efforts have succeeded in preventing a feared harm. Indeed, students who scored high on the checking subscale of the Maudsley Obsessive-Compulsive Inventory showed deficits in memory for prior actions (Sher, Frost, & Otto, 1983; Sher, Mann, & Frost, 1984).

Evaluation of Threat: Probability and Valence

In a questionnaire study, anxious and depressed patients exhibited higher estimates of subjective cost and probability of threatening events compared to normals. Moreover, they were more likely to interpret ambiguous situations as threatening (Butler & Mathews, 1983). With respect to obsessive–compulsives' attitudes toward mistakes, Walker (1967) proposed that they would be reluctant to take risks, preferring the low cost/high probability alternative. She further hypothesized that obsessive–compulsives overestimated the degree of unpleasantness as well as the probability of making a mistake. The results indicated no abnormalities regarding estimated probabilities of making mistakes. Some obsessionals offered exaggerated estimates of the unpleasantness of making a mistake, whereas others did not. Walker concluded that this impairment is not general, but rather specific to certain areas of the patient's life.

Expanding Walker's hypothesis to include all types of unfavorable events, Carr (1974) suggested that "in *all* situations the compulsive neurotic has an abnormally high subjective estimate of the probability of occurrence of the unfavorable outcome" (p. 289). He proposed that threat appraisal "is some multiplicative function of the subjective cost of an event and its subjective probability" (p. 315). Unlike Walker, Carr did not hypothesize a difference between obsessive–compulsives and normals in the *strength* of the negative valence associated with threatening situations. The higher degree of perceived threat in obsessive–compulsives, he suggested, was attributable entirely to their exaggerated subjective probability of danger. Walker's (1967) results, however, seem to contradict this assertion with respect to mistake making, a major concern of obsessive–compulsives.

McFall and Wollersheim (1979) share Walker and Carr's view that obsessive–compulsives show an abnormally high appraisal of threat. Like Walker but unlike Carr, they advanced a theoretical formulation of obsessive–compulsive, which focused on impairment in the assigned valence of unpleasant events. Specifically, they proposed that this valence is influenced by a set of unreasonable beliefs held by obsessive–compulsives that (a) they should be perfectly competent to be worthwhile, (b) making mistakes or failing to meet such standards of perfection should result in condemnation and punishment, (c) certain thoughts or feelings are unacceptable and may lead to catastrophe.

Organization of Information: Rules for Generalization and Discrimination.

Reed (1968) proposed that obsessionals suffer from functional impairment in the organization and integration of experience. Accordingly, he predicted that in a classification task, these patients would be overly specific and therefore too strict in their rules for including an event in a given class. This prediction was supported in a verbal-conceptual task. When asked to select only the essential features in order to define an object, obsessionals tended to allocate fewer members to any class and therefore required more categories. Moreover, they appeared to show more indecision and more anxiety during the task (Reed, 1969).

Reed's conceptualization and the methods he used to test it assumed that obsessive–compulsives have general impairments in how they organize information. But the presence of general deficits does not account for the specificity of obsessive–compulsives' fears. Persons and Foa (1984) investigated whether obsessive–compulsives differed from other patients in the way in which they categorize information and whether such deficits are global (pertaining to all information) or specific to fear-related information. The results indicated a general deficit; obsessive–compulsives used more piles when sorting both neutral and feared items, (i.e., they over-discriminated). In addition, they required more time to sort feared than neutral items, whereas for controls, no such differences were found. Persons and Foa suggested that the latter finding may indicate an exaggeration of the general deficit when fear-related information is processed.

In evaluating the effects of behavioral treatment, Foa and Steketee (1979) proposed that treatment by exposure and response prevention ameliorates obsessive–compulsive symptoms but often leaves cognitive style unchanged. Difficulties in categorizing events and making decisions about danger and safety appeared to continue. They concluded that,

> Exposure treatment brings about a reversal in the limited system of classification employed by patients but does not promote increased discrimination. Now, instead of categorizing bathroom faucets, trash cans, and floors as "dirty", they are taught to label them "clean" and forced to act accordingly by not avoiding. The original deficit, however, is not corrected. (p. 42).

In summary, clinical observations and empirical data suggest that obsessive–compulsives have specific impairments in information processing. Accordingly, several investigators have suggested that techniques aimed directly at correcting cognitive impairments would yield a successful outcome (Carr, 1974; Foa & Kozak, 1985; Foa & Steketee, 1979; McFall & Wollersheim, 1979; Reed, 1983). This proposition can be evaluated in light of what is known about the efficacy of behavioral (exposure and response prevention) and cognitive treatments for obsessive–compulsives (cf. Foa & Kozak, 1986).

The foregoing discussion suggests that two aspects of the pathology of obsessive–compulsives require assessment. First is delineation of pathological elements in the fear structure, which usually is accomplished by assessment of symptoms such as rituals, avoidance and obsessions. As will be discussed later, assessing symptoms is not the only way to delineate a fear structure, and sometimes may be unsatisfactory. Regarding the second aspect, impairments in information processing, standardized assessment procedures are unavailable. However, the several studies mentioned earlier have provided methods that can serve as a foundation for developing such procedures.

ASSESSMENT OF OBSESSIVE–COMPULSIVE SYMPTOMS

Clinical Interview and Rating Scales

A major technique for assessing symptoms is the clinical interview. Guidelines for this inquiry with obsessive–compulsive symptoms are given as follows.

Obsessions (anxiety/discomfort evoking material)

1. *External Cues*: objects or situations that are sources of high anxiety or discomfort, such as urine, pesticides, locking a door, driving over bumps, and so on.
2. *Nonexternal Cues*: thoughts, images or impulses that provoke anxiety, shame or disgust, such as images of Jesus' penis, certain numbers, impulses to stab one's child, thoughts of being contaminated, thoughts of negligence about the gas burners left on, bodily sensations that disturb the patient, such as tachycardia, pains, and swallowing.

3. *Anticipated Harm*: harm anticipated from external sources, for example disease from touching a contaminated object, burglary if a door is not properly locked. Harm consequent to non-external cues may be from:
   (a) Thoughts, images or impulses, e.g., "God will punish me. I may actually stab my child."
   (b) Bodily sensations, e.g., "I'll lose control."
   (c) The long-term experience of high anxiety, e.g., "This anxiety will never go away and I'll always be highly upset."

Avoidance and Escape

1. *Passive Avoidance*: situations or objects that are avoided, for example public bathrooms, stepping on brown spots on the sidewalk, carrying one's child over a concrete floor, driving; subtle avoidance practices, for example, touching doorknobs on the least used surface, driving at times of least traffic.
2. *Rituals*: ritualistic behavior including washing, cleaning, checking, repeating an action, ordering objects, requesting reassurance, and cognitive rituals, such as praying, neutralizing thoughts, "good" numbers; subtle rituals such as the use of "Handiwipes" or lotion to decontaminate hands.

Relationship Between Avoidance and Fear Cues

The functional relationship between the fear cues and the avoidance associated with it is assessed by interview. In our clinic, this interview yields three focal areas which are rated on 8-point scales in the areas of fear, avoidance, and rituals. In research protocols, these areas are then rated by the patient, therapist, and/or an independent assessor. Examples of these ratings appear in the Appendix.

In describing the three main fears, we attempt to specify both the feared situation and the anticipated harm. Although describing the fear solely in terms of anticipated harm is tempting (e.g., getting sick), it is important to specify stimulus situations associated with that concern. This is essential for designing exposure tasks for assessment and treatment. In rating the severity of the fears, we take into account both the amount of discomfort and the strength of conviction about harm. In selecting avoidance items, we attempt to identify naturally occurring situations that are avoided in everyday living, rather than merely a feared object, for example, "grass where dogs defecate" versus "dog feces." An obstacle to reliable rating of rituals is that either the frequency or duration can indicate severity. Our scale attempts to compensate for this via overlapping guidelines according to frequency and duration.

The information gleaned from the interview suggests a fear structure. One individual may show little avoidance and much ritualizing whereas another may mostly avoid and ritualize only when contact occurs. The oft-found discordance among these measures might be understood in terms of their function; both avoidance and rituals are threat reducing, so only one or the other may be "needed."

Reliability and Validity of Rating Scales.

Behavioral researchers in the area of phobias and obsessive–compulsive disorder have often used ratings such as those described in the previous section. Several outcome studies with obsessive–compulsives (Boersma, Den Hengst, Dekker, & Emmelkamp, 1976; Foa *et al.*, 1983, Foa & Goldstein, 1978; Foa, Grayson, & Steketee, 1982; Marks, Hodgson, & Rachman, 1975) have reported findings based on such scales, mainly used by an independent assessor. Reliability of rating scales has been estimated mainly by measures of interrater agreement.

Marks, Hallam, Connolly, and Philpott (1977) examined interrater reliability for measures of target problem ratings. Correlation coefficients for ratings of 34 patients and their therapists were .96 for time spent in rituals per day and .79 for discomfort during rituals. With 72 obsessive–compulsives, Foa et al. (1983) found interrater reliabilities between two independent assessors on the various clinical scales ranging from .92 to .97. In a later study with 38 patients, somewhat lower coefficients among assessor, self, and therapist ratings (.64 to .83) were found (Foa, Steketee, Kozak, & Dugger, 1985).

Similar rating scales have been used to assess the efficacy of behavioral treatment with phobics. Interrater reliabilities varied across studies in Watson and Marks' (1971) study; interrater reliability across patient, assessor, and therapist ranged from .82 to .89 (N = 48). Lower values were reported by Chambless, Foa, Groves, and Goldstein (1982) for agoraphobics: Interrater correlations between therapist and patient ranged from .35 to .88 (N = 21) with a mean of .62.

In summary, whereas some studies have evidenced the interrater reliability of symptom ratings, information about their psychometric properties is generally lacking. Nevertheless, support for their validity lies in their demonstrated sensitivity to treatment effects. For example, in the Chambless, Foa, Groves and Goldstein (1980) study, the effects of flooding and placebo procedures were distinguished. Likewise, symptom ratings were sensitive to differences among these variants of exposure treatment in another study with obsessive–compulsives (Foa et al., 1984). Thus, the available evidence supports the use of such scales in assessing obsessive–compulsive disorder.

Standardized Instruments

Several standardized instruments have been developed to assess obsessive–compulsive symptoms. The most commonly used are discussed here.

Leyton Obsessional Inventory (LOI)

This 69-item true-false inventory was developed by Cooper (1970) as a card sort task. Forty questions are concerned with obsessional symptoms and 23 are concerned with obsessive traits, thus yielding both a symptom and a trait score. Thirty-five of the cards provide a resistance score (severity) and an interference score (disability). Because the four LOI subscales (trait, symptoms, resistance, interference) are considered interdependent, all the cards must be sorted four times. This makes test-administration rather cumbersome.

Numerous studies have investigated the reliability and validity of these scales. Cooper (1970) found the LOI to differentiate obsessional patients from normals. Further evidence for the test's discriminant validity was reported by Murray, Cooper, and Smith (1979) who found 73 obsessive–compulsives to have a mean score of 43.8 (*SD* 10.6) and 100 normals a mean score of 10.3 (*SD* 6.2). The administration procedure was simplified with the development of a self-report version (Kazarian, Evan's, & Lefave, 1977) which correlated quite well (.72 to .77) with the original LOI (Snowden, 1980).

Although the LOI is a reliable instrument and was found to discriminate obsessional patients from normals and from "house-proud housewives," it suffers from several shortcomings. First, the four subscales that comprise this questionnaire are interdependent. Second, its content focuses heavily on compulsive personality traits rather than on symptoms of obsessive–compulsive disorder. Third, many items seem to relate specifically to British culture.

Lynfield Obsessional–Compulsive Questionnaire (LOCQ).

In an effort to devise a more convenient measure of obsessive–compulsive symptoms, Allen and Tune (1975) and Allen (1977) constructed a 20-item self-report instrument called the Lynfield Obsessional/Compulsive Questionnaire, which was derived from the LOI. This version expanded the dichotomous format of its predecessor to a 5-point rating scale and yielded two subscale scores, resistance and interference. The LOCQ was found reliable and sensitive to change after treatment. However, it has been tested on only 19 obsessive–compulsives. Unfortunately, like the LOI, it too focuses heavily on items that measure compulsive personality traits; only 10 of the 20 items refer to the symptoms of obsessive–compulsive disorder.

Correlations between LOI and LOCQ scores for a group of 15 obsessional patients were significant for interference scores (r = .77) and resistance scores (r = .43) (Allen, 1977). Sixteen obsessionals yielded a mean score of 44.5 (*SD* 13.13) for the interference scale and 42.69 (*SD* 12.95) for resistance. Two groups of nonpsychiatric patients had mean interference scores of 15.31 (N = 13, *SD* 10.92) and 17.06 (N = 17, *SD* 8.08) and mean resistance scores of 13.31 (N = 13, *SD* 8.14) and 18.29 (N = 17, *SD* 8.29).

Compulsive Activity Checklist (CAC).

Parallel with attempts to simplify the LOI, two instruments focusing on obsessive–compulsive symptoms, rather than on compulsive traits, have been developed: the Compulsive Activity Checklist (CAC) and the Maudsley Obsessive–Compulsive Inventory (MOCI). The CAC was developed by Hallam and reported by Philpott (1975). The name of the instrument has changed several times. Its original title, "Obsessive–Compulsive Interview Checklist" (Marks et al., 1977; Philpott, 1975) was altered to "Compulsive Checklist" (Marks, Stern, Mawson, Cobb, & MacDonald, 1980) and finally to "Compulsive Activity Checklist" (Mawson, Marks, & Ramm, 1982). Originally it contained 62 items describing specific activities, each of which was rated by an assessor on a 4-point scale of severity. Each point on the scale was anchored with quantitative written descriptors. Data reported by Marks et al. (1977) and by Insel, Murphy, Cohen, Alterman, Kilts, and Linnoila (1983), using the 62-item version, indicated that the CAC was sensitive to changes in symptoms following behavioral and drug treatments. Similar changes following treatment were reported by Marks et al. (1980) using a 37-item CAC and by Foa, Steketee, Grayson, Turner, and Latimer (1984) with one additional item.

Compulsive Activity Checklist data for a normal population are unavailable. Pre- and post-treatment (M = 43.84, *SD* 13.30; M = 16.45, *SD* 14.67) means for 32 obsessive–compulsives have been reported by Foa et al. (1984) and by Freund, Steketee, and Foa (1985) (M = 39.71, *SD* 17.55; M = 14.37, *SD* 17.55, N = 68). Estimates of interrater reliability have ranged from .90 between self and assessor ratings (Marks et al., 1980) to .62 between two assessors (Freund et al., 1985). Estimates of test-retest reliability were .63 for one rater and .84 for another rater (Freund et al., 1985).

A factor analysis (N = 99) (Freund et al., 1985) revealed two major factors: one for washing rituals representing 60% of the variance, and the other for checking compulsions accounting for 40% of the variance. A further analysis of 63 washers and checkers revealed that these items could correctly discriminate washers from checkers 85% of the time. With respect to sensitivity to treatment effects, total CAC scores changed in a positive direction in all treatment studies, thus demonstrating the sensitivity of this instrument.

After an extensive review of the psychometric properties of the CAC, Freund (1986) concluded that: (a) the CAC has been the only published, standardized symptom severity measure of interference with day-to-day functioning of OCD patients; (b) sensitivity of the CAC to treatment effectiveness by behavior therapy and by drugs has been demonstrated; (c) high interrater correlations, satisfactory construct validity, reliability of factor items for internal consistency, and (to some extent) test-retest reliability have been reported for varying uses of the instrument; and (d) discriminant analysis of the factor items yielded two subscales which correctly classified two subtypes of obsessive–compulsives: washers and checkers.

Maudsley Obsessional–Compulsive Inventory (MOCI)

The MOCI is a 30-item self-report questionnaire with a true-false response format (Hodgson & Rachman, 1977), which assesses cognitive and behavioral aspects of obsessive–compulsive disorder. It yields four subscales: washing, checking, slowness, and doubting, as well as a total score. A scoring key may be found in Rachman and Hodgson (1980).

Data from 100 obsessive–compulsive patients were reported by Rachman and Hodgson (1980). Alpha coefficients for the four subscales; checking, washing, slowness, and doubting, were .7, .8, .7 and .7, respectively. Pearson correlations examining test-retest reliability for 39 washers and checkers were .69 for the total score, .81 for the washer scale, and .67 for the checker scale (Freund, Steketee, & Foa, in press). With a population of 50 normal controls, Rachman and Hodgson (1980) found a test-retest reliability of .80 (Kendall τ).

Concurrent validity of the MOCI has been calculated using the LOI. A moderate correlation (.60) emerged between the total scores of each measure (Rachman & Hodgson, 1980). A lower correlation with the CAC (.33) has been reported (Freund et al., in press). Data from several studies indicate the sensitivity of the MOCI to treatment effects (Emmelkamp & Delange, 1983; Foa, Steketee, & Grayson, 1985; Foa et al., 1984). In addition, the MOCI has been found to differentiate normals, neurotics (including phobics), and obsessive–compulsives (Rachman & Hodgson, 1980; Volans, 1976). For an extended review, see Freund (1986).

Yale-Brown Obsessive–Compulsive Scale (Y-BOCS).

The Y-BOCS is a relatively new 10-item instrument constructed to exclude symptoms of depression or other anxiety disorders. Items are clinician-rated on a 0–4 scale of severity with five items focused on obsessions and five items on compulsions, yielding a maximum score of 40. Preliminary estimates of interrater reliability among six clinicians ranged from .7 to 1.0 (Spearman correlations). A pilot study of convergent validity with 26 patients revealed a correlation of .72 between pretreatment Y-BOCS scores and MOCI ratings. With the same sample, the Y-BOCS was found unrelated (Pearson r = .12) to Hamilton Depression Scale scores (24-item, excluding obsession item). Preliminary evidence for the sensitivity of the Y-BOCS to treatment effects was found in a pilot study of 11 patients treated with medication (Goodman, Price, Rasmussen, Mazure, Charney, & Heninger, 1986).

Although evidence on the psychometric properties of the Y-BOCS is now quite preliminary, ongoing evaluation of the instrument by the Yale-Brown group is underway.

One question that might be addressed in such work is the contribution of Y-BOCS items coding "resistance" to obsessions and compulsions. Although more resistance is scored as less pathological, it could be argued that *not* "fighting" obsessional ideas represents improvement. The Y-BOCS is included here as a standardized instrument because preliminary efforts have been made to control its psychometric characteristics. It should be noted, however, that the instrument actually consists of ten 0-4 point rating scales, whose individual psychometric properties have not been ascertained.

PSYCHOPHYSIOLOGICAL ASSESSMENT

Rating scales and standardized questionnaires have been developed mainly to assess overt behavior as well as ideation that was accessable to patients' conscious awareness. Physiological assessment has been used for two purposes. Cortical measures (i.e., electroencephalogram (EEG) and event-related-potentials (ERP) have been recorded primarily to explore hypotheses about psychopathology and have not been used to evaluate treatment effects. On the other hand, autonomic measures (e.g., cardiac and electrodermal activity) have been recorded mainly as indices of anxiety under different conditions, often in the context of behavioral treatment.

Brain Electrical Activity

EEG Studies.

Early studies examined the role of neurological factors in obsessive–compulsive disorder and suggested a connection between early traumatic or infectious processes and the development of the disorder (e.g., Grimshaw, 1964; Ingram & McAdam, 1960; Pacella, Polatin, & Nagler, 1944; Schilder, 1938). Neurological examinations and clinical EEG recordings typically revealed that some obsessive–compulsives exhibited mild abnormalities. The number of patients with this neurologically abnormal subgroup varied widely from study to study (10% in Ingram & McAdam, 1960; 65% in Pacella, Polatin, & Nagler, 1944).

Within the past 10 years, only a few studies have examined the EEG recordings of obsessive–compulsives. In one such study, Flor-Henry, Yendall, Koles, and Howarth (1979) examined the neuropsychological profiles and EEGs of 11 (8 women, 3 men) obsessive–compulsives. Neuropsychological testing indicated a bilateral frontal dysfunction with a greater left hemisphere involvement for 10 of the 11 patients. Electrocortical activity was recorded for the patients and for 23 normal controls during mental rest, and verbal, and spatial tasks. The EEGs of obsessive–compulsives differed significantly from those of normals, showing reduced left temporal lobe variability in the beta 1 (13–20 Hz) band with eyes closed for obsessive–compulsives as compared to controls. Second, patients showed a relative increase in right parietal variability. Taken together, these findings were suggested to indicate a frontal dysfunction in obsessive–compulsives, impairing the inhibitory processes of that region. This may account for the obsessive–compulsive's inability to inhibit thoughts and images.

An attempt to replicate the findings of left frontal lobe dysfunctions in obsessive–compulsives was apparently unsuccessful (Insel, Donnelly, Lalakee, Alterman, & Murphy, 1983). A clinically based method of EEG analysis (visual inspection for hyperventilation, and photic stimulation) yielded no indication of these anomalies.

Although these findings appear disparate, the results of Flor-Henry et al. (1979) and Insel et al. (1983) may be compatible. Visual analysis of the EEG is useful in detecting gross manifestations of organic dysfunction. However, the more subtle discriminations afforded by spectral analytic techniques are typically used to examine correlates of cognitive processes. As indicated, Insel et al. (1983) used experimental conditions which would be expected to activate the subject physically. Although this method is useful in evoking EEG anomalies of gross organic bases, it would probably be insensitive to more subtle EEG phenomena. Therefore, if obsessive–compulsive disorder is manifested in cognitive impairments, Flor-Henry et al.'s paradigm might be expected to reveal related EEG phenomena, whereas the method used by Insel et al. would not.

Most recently, McCarthy (1985) studied obsessive–compulsives, anxious controls, and normal controls via the spectral analysis of EEG recorded while various attentional tasks were performed. At rest, obsessive–compulsives showed EEG patterns different from normals, but similar to anxious controls. During cognitive task performance, however, excessive bilateral frontal slow-wave activity distinguished obsessives from both control groups. These results were interpreted as pointing to some frontal lobe dysfunction during information processing, and as compatible with the findings of Flor-Henry and colleagues.

Event Related Potentials (ERP).

One of the first studies to investigate ERPs with obsessive–compulsives found no difference from normals in the major component (P130) of simple flash-induced potentials (Ceiseilski, Beech, & Gordon, 1981). However, when a patterned flash was presented, obsessive–compulsives showed a lower amplitude P130 than did normals (Ceiseilski et al., 1981). They also showed decreased latency and amplitude for the N220 component during cognitive activity (same vs. different figure matching). With a more complex, three-shape matching task, obsessive–compulsives showed decreased latency for the P350 and N220 components, compared to normals, although the amplitudes were equivalent (Beech, Ceiseilski, & Gordon, 1983). Taken together, these results suggest that obsessive–compulsives show shorter latency and lower amplitude ERPs than normals as information processing task complexity is increased.

In a recent study, Shagass, Roemer, Straumanis, and Josiassen (1984) examined evoked potentials using stimulation in several different sensory modalities: visual, auditory, and tactile (shock-stimulated). Only ERP components with latencies under 100 ms distinguished obsessive–compulsives from non-obsessive–compulsive neurotics and normals. For auditory stimuli, a smaller P60 component was seen for obsessive–compulsives; for visual stimuli, decreased amplitude and latency of the N75 was evident.

Although the Shagass et al. results appear to contradict those of Beech et al., these differences may reflect paradigm variations. Whereas Shagass et al,'s subjects received sensory stimuli with little information processing demand beyond attention, Beech et al.'s subjects performed figure matching tasks. Notably, differences in later ERP components found by Beech et al. became more pronounced as task complexity was increased. In sum, the results from both paradigms point to ERP differences between obsessive–compulsives and normals: The former show lower amplitudes in several components. A better understanding of these differences will require programmatic investigation of the paradigms used.

Autonomic Activity

Several studies have assessed the cardiac and electrodermal activity of obsessive–compulsives. The assumption that anxiety characterizes this disorder underlies such research. Accordingly, psychophysiological measures are used to assess anxiety. Some studies have investigated the resemblance of obsessive–compulsive pathology to that of phobics. Other studies have focused on the processes and outcome of treatments aimed at anxiety reduction for obsessive–compulsives.

Several studies have tested the hypotheses that like phobics, obsessive–compulsives would (a) show increased autonomic responding when confronted with their feared situations, and (b) show decreased responding after performing their rituals, that is, after threat is reduced. These hypotheses were supported for both washers and checkers (Hodgson & Rachman, 1972; Roper, Rachman, & Hodgson, 1973; Roper & Rachman, 1976). The studies of Rachman and his colleagues investigated the heart rates of obsessive–compulsives under different experimental conditions (neutral exposure, contaminant exposure, after washing). Boulougouris (1977) compared responses during neutral fantasy, obsessive fantasy, neutral talk, flooding talk, and flooding in vivo, measuring both heart rate and skin conductance. Results indicated that cardiac and skin conductance were elevated for fear situations relative to non–fear situations. Interestingly, the responses to fantasized material were comparable in size to those for in vivo exposure. In contrast, simple phobics appear to show larger responses to in vivo material (e.g., Watson, Gaind, & Marks, 1972). Perhaps because of their obsessive worrying, obsessive–compulsives are more practiced than simple phobics at accessing their fear structures fully in the absence of their feared situation.

In another study comparing cardiac responses to imagined neutral and feared situations, Grayson, Nutter, and Mavissakalian (1980) examined heart-rate waveform. Results indicated that neutral scripts evoked orienting responses (OR) and fear scenes were characterized by attenuated ORs or by defensive responses (DR). These findings converge with those of other studies with simple phobics, indicating that fear-relevant material will prompt DRs, whereas neutral materials will evoke ORs (Grayson, 1979; Hare, 1972; Hare & Blevings, 1975).

The above-mentioned studies of autonomic physiology indicate that obsessive–

compulsives do show larger reactions to feared material than to neutral material, just as would be expected for phobics. Several studies have assessed responses associated with exposure therapy to investigate treatment efficacy and mechanisms underlying fear reduction. Hypothesizing a deficit in habituation, these studies have mainly focused on the habituation of autonomic responding during exposure to some form of fear-evoking material.

When repeatedly threatened with physical or psychological harm, not only have obsessive–compulsives — been found to show greater heart rate and skin conductance responses than those of normals, but they have also been found to show slower habituation of their electrodermal responses across trials (Boulougouris, 1977).

To assess outcome of therapy, Boulougouris (1977) recorded autonomic physiology before and after therapy, using the test stimuli described earlier. Cardiac and electrodermal responding differed for fear and neutral material before but not after therapy. The smaller responses to feared material after treatment evidenced successful therapy. Studies examining the effects of various behavioral and psychopharmacological treatments have reported a relationship between habituation and treatment efficacy.

In a study conducted in our laboratory with 14 obsessive–compulsives treated by imaginal and in vivo exposure, cardiac and electrodermal responses were recorded during sessions (Kozak, Foa, & Steketee, 1986). Outcome was assessed via the rating scales previously described. Peak response during a session was compared to the response at the end of that session to yield a measure of within-session habituation. Peak-response early in therapy was compared to peak-response at the end of treatment, providing a measure of between-session habituation. An overall habituation within session, but not between session, was evident. Peak heart-rate during exposure and between-session habituation were found positively correlated to reduction of obsessive–compulsive symptoms. Although at first sight, the failure to find overall between-session habituation seems inconsistent with Boulougourie's findings, the correlative findings implicate both fear reaction and its habituation across sessions as predictors of outcome. Thus, both studies point to a positive relationship between habituation and treatment outcome.

The hypothesis that anxiety disordered patients show a deficit in capacity for autonomic habituation has been studied with various diagnostic groups (cf. Lader & Wing, 1966). Two recent studies have focused on obsessive–compulsives, measuring cardiac and electrodermal activity. Zahn, Insel, and Murphy (1984) compared the effects of clomipramine and clorgyline on obsessive–compulsive symptoms and on autonomic responding to a variety of simply physical stimuli. Whereas both drugs reduced tonic skin conductance level, only clomipramine reduced obsessive–compulsive symptoms as well as both electrodermal reactivity and cardiac variability in response to stimulation. Zahn et al. concluded that reductions in autonomic reactivity, but *not* in tonic arousal, may be associated with clinical improvement in obsessive–compulsives. In our laboratory, we used Lader and Wing's (1966) paradigm to examine autonomic habituation and symptom reduction in obsessive–compulsives (Kozak, Rossi, McCarthy, Steketee, & Foa, 1986). Of 26 obsessive–compulsives, half received imipramine and half placebo; all received symptom evaluations and tone habituation assessments before and after drug administration. The imipramine group showed decreased electrodermal activity, increased tonic heart rate, and a tendency to decreased heart rate variability in response to tones, but neither group showed significant improvement in obsessive–compulsive symptoms. Our physiological findings were similar to those of Zahn et al. for clomipramine, but our results failed to reveal a relationship between drug-induced decreases in autonomic reactivity and clinical improvement.

In summary, for obsessive–compulsives, ruminative or obsessive material can be discriminated from neutral material using autonomic nervous system measures (heart rate and electrodermal activity). Palpable reactions are measureable in these systems during such exposure, particularly for heart rate. Some data have hinted at the possibility that the habituation deficit (i.e., retarded habituation rate) may be one mechanism in obsessive–compulsive disorder, but further research is needed to clarify this issue. Finally, some studies measuring heart rate and electrodermal activity have indicated a decrease in arousal and reactivity to feared situations for patients who showed clinical improvement, but the hypothesis of drug-induced decreases in general autonomic reactivity as a mechanism for clinical improvement remains questionable.

CONCLUDING REMARKS

The measurements described in this chapter were of two types. One type is based on reports by the patient about symptoms, either in interview or questionnaire format. The second type does not rely directly on patients' reports, for example physiological monitoring or behavioral observation. Although these measures appear to conform to the three-systems method (Lang, 1968) of fear assessment, a caveat is in order. A conceptual danger lies in making strong inferences about cognitive processes solely from data based on patients' reports. Although certain aspects of a fear structure may be identifiable through introspection, ample evidence (cf. Van Den Berg & Eelen, 1985) suggests that a fear structure can contain elements (and relationships among elements) in the absence of conscious knowledge about them. Because of our imperfect knowledge about their fear structures, non-introspective information about them is probably also required for understanding any particular pathology. One way of investigating unconscious aspects of a fear structure is through certain paradigms used by cognitive experimental psychologists.

One such approach that has been employed in our laboratory consists of a dichotic listening paradigm. In this procedure, subjects are presented simultaneously with two prose passages, one to each ear. They are requested to shadow (repeat aloud) the passage presented to the dominant ear ("attended" passage). They are also asked to detect target words inserted in each passage. Typically, subjects readily detect targets in the attended passage, but have great difficulty recognizing targets in the unattended passage, unless the words are unusually salient, for example one's name.

Previous results indicated that phobics were especially sensitive to fear-relevant words in a dichotic listening test (Burgess, Jones, Robertson, Radcliffe, & Emerson, 1981). A similar dichotic listening test was used in our laboratory to assess the fear structures of obsessive–compulsives before and after treatment (Foa & McNally, 1986). Before treatment, patients showed greater sensitivity to fear-relevant words, as indicated by behavioral (button press) and physiological (skin conductance) measures. After treatment, such differential sensitivity disappeared, suggesting successful modification of the fear structures of these patients. This experiment exemplifies a way to assess semantic elements of fear and treatment effects on such elements without introspection. Assessment of fear via paradigms of this sort can complement assessment via introspective reports, because it supplies information about aspects of the structure that are simply not available from an interview.

The foregoing examination of assessment of obsessive–compulsives reveals that at present there are several useful methods to assess gross symptoms and they can be used to evaluate treatment effects. In addition, psychophysiological assessment has proven useful with subtle aspects of obsessive–compulsive functioning. Procedures for non-introspective assessment of semantic aspects of fear are generally undeveloped, but the application of certain "cognitive" paradigms holds promise for advances in this area. Standardized psychometric instruments to assess impaired thinking are also in preliminary stages of evolution and require further development.

Acknowledgement — The preparation of this paper was supported in part by NIMH Grant No. 31634 awarded to Edna B. Foa.

REFERENCES

Akhtar, S., Wig, N. A., Varma, V. K., Pershad, D., & Verma, S. K. (1975). A phenomenological analysis of symptoms in obsessive-compulsive neurosis. *British Journal of Psychiatry, 127*, 342–348.

Allen, J. J. (1977). The measurement of obsessionality: First validation studies of the Lynfield Obsessional/Compulsive Questionnaire. *Journal of International Medical Research, 5*, 12–15.

Allen, J. J., & Tune, G. S. (1975). The Lynfield Obsessional/Compulsive Questionnaire. *Scottish Medical Journal, 20*, 21–24.

American Psychiatric Association. (1980). Diagnostic and statistical manual of mental disorders. (3rd ed.). Washington, DC: Author.

Beech, H. R., Ceiselski, K. T., & Gordon, P. K. (1983). Further observations of evoked potentials in obsessional patients. *British Journal of Psychiatry, 142*, 605–609.

Boersma, K., Den Hengst, S., Dekker, J., & Emmelkamp, P. M. G. (1976). Exposure and response prevention: A comparison with obsessive–compulsive patients. *Behaviour Research and Therapy, 14*, 19–24.

Boulougouris, J. C. (1977). Variables affecting the behavior modification of obsessive–compulsive patients treated by flooding. In J. C. Boulougouris & A. D. Rabavilas (Eds.), *The treatment of phobic and obsessive–compulsive disorders.* New York: Pergamon Press. pp. 73–84.

Burgess, I. S., Jones, L. M., Robertson, S. H., Radcliffe, W. N., & Emerson, E. (1981). The degree of control exerted by phobic and non-phobic verbal stimuli over the recognition behavior of phobic and non-phobic subjects. *Behaviour Research and Therapy, 19*, 233–243.

Butler, G., & Mathews, A. (1983). Cognitive processes in anxiety. *Advances in Behavior Research and Therapy, 5*, 51–62.

Capstick, N., & Seldrup, J. (1973). Phenomenological aspects of obsessional patients treated with clomipramine. *British Journal of Psychiatry, 122*, 719–720.

Carr, A. T. (1974). Compulsive neurosis: A review of the literature. *Psychological Bulletin, 81*, 311–318.

Ceiseilski, K. T., Beech, H. R., & Gordon, P. K. (1981). Some electrophysiological observations in obsessional states. *British Journal of Psychiatry, 138*, 479–484.

Chambless, D. L., Foa, E. B., Groves, G. A., & Goldstein, A. J. (1982). Exposure and communications training in the treatment of agoraphobia. *Behaviour Research and Therapy, 20*, 219–231.

Chambless, D. L., Foa, E. B., Groves, G. A., & Goldstein, A. (1980). Flooding with Brevital[R] in the treatment of agoraphobia: Counter effective? *Behaviour Research and Therapy, 17*, 243–251.

Cooper, J. E. (1970). The Leyton Obsessional Inventory. *Psychological Medicine, 1*, 48–64.

Dowson, H. H. (1977). The phenomenology of severe obsessive–compulsive neurosis. *British Journal of Psychiatry, 131*, 75–78.

Emmelkamp, P. M. G. (1982). *Phobic and obsessive–compulsive disorders: Theory, research and practice.* New York: Plenum Press.

Emmelkamp, P. M. G., & Delange, I. (1983). Spouse involvement in the treatment of obsessive–compulsive patients. *Behaviour Research and Therapy, 21*, 341–346.

Esquirol, J. E. D. (1838). *Des maladies mentales* (Vol. II). Paris: Bailliere.

Flor-Henry, P., Yendall, L. T., Koles, Z. J., & Howarth, B. G. (1979). Neuropsychological and power spectral EEG investigations of the obsessive–compulsive syndrome. *Biological Psychiatry, 14*, 119–130.

Foa, E. B., & Goldstein, A. (1978). Continuous exposure and complete response prevention of obsessive–compulsive neurosis. *Behavior Therapy, 9*, 821–829.

Foa, E. B., Grayson, J. B., & Steketee, G. (1982). Depression, habituation and treatment outcome in obsessive–compulsives. In J. C. Boulougouris (Ed.), *Practical applications of learning theories in psychiatry.* New York: Wiley. pp. 129–142.

Foa, E. B., Grayson, J. B., Steketee, G. S., Doppelt, H. G., Turner, R. M., & Latimer, P. R. (1983). Success and failure in the behavioral treatment of obsessive–compulsives. *Journal of Consulting and Clinical Psychology, 51*, 287–297.

Foa, E. B., & Kozak, M. J. (1985). Treatment of anxiety disorders: Implications for psychopathology. In A. H. Tuma & J. D. Maser (Eds.), *Anxiety and the anxiety disorders.* Hillsdale, NJ: Lawrence Erlbaum Associates, pp. 421–452.

Foa, E. B., & Kozak, M. J. (1986). Emotional

processing of fear: Exposure to corrective information. *Psychological Bulletin, 99*, 20–35.

Foa, E. B., & McNally, R. J. (1986). Sensitivity to feared stimuli in obsessive–compulsives: A dichotic listening analysis. *Cognitive Therapy and Research, 10*(4), 477–485.

Foa, E. B., & Steketee, G. (1979). Obsessive-compulsives: Conceptual issues and treatment interventions. In M. Hersen, R. M. Eisler, & P. M. Miller (Eds.), *Progress in behavior modification* (Vol. VIII). New York: Academic Press. pp. 1–53.

Foa, E. B., Steketee, G. S., & Grayson, J. B. (1985). Imaginal and in vivo exposure: A comparison with obsessive–compulsive checkers. *Behavior Therapy, 16*, 292–302.

Foa, E. B., Steketee, G. S., Grayson, J. B., Turner, R. M., & Latimer, P. R. (1984). Deliberate exposure and blocking of obsessive–compulsive rituals: Immediate and long-term effects. *Behavior Therapy, 15*, 450–472.

Foa, E. B., Steketee, G. S., Kozak, M. J., & Dugger, D. (1985, September). *Effects of imipramine on depression and on obsessive–compulsive symptoms.* Paper presented at the European Association for Behavior Therapy, Munich, F. R. Germany.

Foa, E. B., Steketee, G. S., Grayson, J. B., Turner, R. M., & Latimer, P. R. (1984). Deliberate exposure and blocking of obsessive–compulsive rituals: Immediate and long-term effects. *Behavior Therapy, 15*, 450–472.

Foa, E. B., Steketee, G. S., & Ozarow, B. J. (1985). Behavior therapy with obsessive–compulsives: From theory to treatment. In M. Mavissakalian (Ed.), *Obsessive-compulsive disorders: Psychological and pharmacological treatments.* New York: Plenum Press. pp. 49–129.

Freund, B. (1986). *Comparison of measures of obsessive–compulsive symptomatology: Rating scales of symptomatology and standardized assessor- and self-rated.* Unpublished doctoral dissertation, Southern Illinois University, Carbondale, IL.

Freund, B., Steketee, G., & Foa, E. B. (1985). Comparison of obsessive–compulsive symptomatology measures: Standardized versus Global Rating Scales, assessor versus self-rated. Unpublished manuscript.

Freund, B., Steketee, G. S., & Foa, E. B. (in press). Compulsive activity checklist. In M. Hersen & A. S. Bellack (Eds.), *Dictionary of behavioral assessment techniques.* New York: Pergamon Press.

Goodman, W. K., Price, L. H., Rasmussen, S. A., Mazure, M., Charney, D. S., & Heninger, G. R. (1986). The Yale-Brown Obsessive–Compulsive Scale (Y-BOCS): Proposal to Study Reliability and Validity. Unpublished Manuscript.

Grayson, J. B. (1979). *Orienting and defensive responses in phobic imagery and the incremental stimulus intensity effect.* Paper presented at the 13th annual meeting of the Association for the Advancement of Behavior Therapy, San Francisco. December.

Grayson, J. B., Nutter, D., & Mavissakalian, M. (1980). Psychophysiological assessment of imagery in obsessive–compulsives: A pilot study. *Behaviour Research and Therapy, 18*, 580–593.

Grimshaw, L. (1964). Obsessional disorder and neurological illness. *Journal of Neurological and Neurosurgical Psychiatry, 27*, 229–231.

Hare, R. D. (1972). Cardiovascular components of orienting and defensive responses. *Psychophysiology, 9*, 606–614.

Hare, R. D., & Blevings, G. (1975). Conditioned orienting and defensive responses. *Psychophysiology, 12*, 289–297.

Hodgson, R. J., & Rachman, S. (1972). The effects of contamination and washing in obsessional patients. *Behaviour Research and Therapy*, 10, 111–117.

Hodgson, R. J., & Rachman, S. (1977). Obsessional–compulsive complaints. *Behaviour Research and Therapy, 15*, 389–395.

Ingram, I. M., & McAdam, W. A. (1960). The electroencephalogram, obsessional illness and obsessional personality. *Journal of Mental Science, 106*, 686–691.

Insel, T. R. (1982). Obsessive–compulsive disorder — five clinical questions and a suggested approach. *Comprehensive Psychiatry, 23*, 241–251.

Insel, T. R., Donnelly, E. F., Lalakee, M. L., Alterman, I. S., & Murphy, D. L. (1983). Neurological and neuropsychological studies of patients with obsessive–compulsive disorder. *Biological Psychiatry, 18*, 741–751.

Insel, T. R., Murphy, D. L., Cohen, R. M., Alterman, I., Kilts, C., & Linnoila, M. (1983). Obsessive–compulsive disorder: A double blind trial of clomipramine and clorgyline. *Archives of General Psychiatry, 40*, 605–612.

Kazarian, S. S., Evans, D. R., & Lefave, K. (1977). Modification and factorial analysis of the Leyton obsessional inventory. *Journal of Clinical Psychology, 33*, 422–425.

Kozak, M. J., Foa, E. B., & Steketee, G. S. (1986). *Process and outcome of exposure treatment with obsessive–compulsives: Psychophysiological in-*

dicators of emotional processing. Unpublished manuscript.

Kozak, M. J., Rossi, M., McCarthy, P. R., Steketee, G. S., & Foa, E. B. (1986). *Effects of imipramine on the autonomic responding of obsessive–compulsives.* Manuscript in preparation.

Lader, M. H., & Wing, L. (1966). Physiological measures, sedative drugs, and morbid anxiety. London: Oxford University Press.

Lang, P. J. (1968). Fear reduction and fear behavior: Problems in treating a construct. In J. M. Schlien (Ed.), *Research in psychotherapy: Vol. 3.* Washington, DC: American Psychological Association. pp. 90–103.

Lang, P. J. (1977). Imagery in therapy: An information processing analysis of fear. *Behavior Therapy, 8,* 862–886.

Lang, P. J. (1979). A bio-informational theory of emotional imagery. *Psychophysiology, 16,* 495–512.

Marks, I. M. (1981). Review of behavioral psychotherapy, I.: Obsessive–compulsive disorders. *American Journal of Psychiatry, 138,* 584–592.

Marks, I. M., Hallam, R. S., Connolly, J., & Philpott, R. (1977). *Nursing in behavioral psychotherapy.* London: Royal College of Nursing of the United Kingdom.

Marks, I. M., Hodgson, R., & Rachman, S. (1975). Treatment of chronic obsessive–compulsive neurosis by in vivo exposure. *British Journal of Psychiatry, 127,* 349–364.

Marks, I. M., Stern, R. S., Mawson, D., Cobb, J., & MacDonald, R. (1980). Clomipramine and exposure for obsessive–compulsive rituals: I. *British Journal of Psychiatry, 136,* 1–25.

Mawson, D., Marks, I. M., & Ramm, L. (1982). Clomipramine and exposure for chronic obsessive–compulsive rituals: III. Two year follow-up and further findings. *British Journal of Psychiatry, 140,* 11–18.

McCarthy, P. R. (1985). *Cognitive influences on autonomic and central nervous system activity in obsessive–compulsive disorder.* Unpublished doctoral dissertation, Pennsylvania State University, University Park, PA.

McFall, M. E., & Wollersheim, J. P. (1979). Obsessive–compulsive neurosis: A cognitive behavioral formulation and approach to treatment. *Cognitive Therapy and Research, 3,* 333–348.

Milner, A. D., Beech, H. R., & Walker, V. J. (1971). Decision processes and obsessional behavior. *British Journal of Social and Clinical Psychology, 10,* 88–89.

Murray, E. J., Cooper, J. E., & Smith, R. (1979). The Leyton Obsessional Inventory: An analysis of the responses of 73 obsessional patients. *Psychological Medicine, 9,* 305–311.

Pacella, B. L., Polatin, P., & Nagler, S. H. (1944). Clinical and EEG studies in obsessive–compulsive states. *American Journal of Psychiatry, 100,* 830–838.

Persons, J. B., & Foa, E. B. (1984). Processing of fearful and neutral information by obsessive–compulsives. *Behaviour Research and Therapy, 22*(3), 259–265.

Philpott, R. (1975). Recent advances in the behavioral measurement of obsessional illness: Difficulties common to these and other instruments. *Scottish Medical Journal, 20,* 33–40.

Pollitt, J. (1956). Discussion: Obsessive–compulsive states (abridged). *Proceedings of the Royal Society of Medicine, 49,* 842–845.

Rachman, S. (1976). Obsessional–compulsive checking. *Behaviour Research and Therapy, 14,* 269–277.

Rachman, S., & Hodgson, R. (1980). *Obsessions and compulsions.* Englewood Cliffs, NJ: Prentice Hall.

Reed, G. F. (1968). Some formal qualities of obsessional thinking. *Psychiatria Clinica, 1,* 382–392.

Reed, G. F. (1969). "Under-inclosion" — A characteristic of obsessional personality disorder: II. *British Journal of Psychiatry, 115,* 787–790.

Reed, G. F. (1983). Obsessional–compulsive disorder: A cognitive/structural approach. *Canadian Psychology, 24,* 169–180.

Roper, G., & Rachman, S. (1976). Obsessional–compulsive checking: Experimental replication and development. *Behaviour Research and Therapy, 14,* 25–32.

Roper, G., Rachman, S., & Hodgson, R. (1973). An experiment on obsessional checking. *Behaviour Research and Therapy, 11,* 271–277.

Salzman, L., & Thaler, F. H. (1981). Obsessive–compulsive disorders: A review of the literature. *American Journal of Psychiatry, 138,* 286–296.

Sartory, G., & Master, D. (1984). Contingent negative variation in obsessional–compulsive patients. *Biological Psychology, 18,* 253–267.

Schilder, P. (1938). The organic background of obsessions and compulsions. *American Journal of Psychiatry, 94,* 1397–1430.

Shagass, C., Roemer, R. A., Straumanis, J. J., & Josiassen, R. C. (1984). Evoked potentials in obsessive–compulsive disorder. *Advances in Biological Psychiatry, 15,* 69–75.

Sher, K. K., Frost, R. O., & Otto, R. (1983). Cognitive deficits in compulsive checkers:

An exploratory study. *Behaviour Research and Therapy, 21,* 357–364.

Sher, K. J., Mann, B., & Frost, R. O. (1984). Cognitive dysfunction in compulsive checkers: Further explorations. *Behaviour Research and Therapy, 22,* 493–502.

Snowdon, J. (1980). A comparison of written and post hoc forms of the Leyton obsessional inventory. *Psychological Medicine, 10,* 165–170.

Stern, R. S., & Cobb, J. P. (1978). Obsessive thoughts: The problem of therapy. *British Journal of Psychiatry, 133,* 200–205.

Van Den Berg, O., & Eelen, P. (1985). *Unconscious processing and emotions.* Unpublished manuscript, University of Leuven, Department of Psychology, Belgium.

Volans, P. J. (1976). Styles of decision-making and probability appraisal in selected obsessional and phobic patients. *British Journal of Social and Clinical Psychology, 15,* 305–317.

Walker, V. J. (1967). *An investigation of ritualistic behavior in obsessional patients.* Unpublished doctoral dissertation, Institute of Psychiatry, University of London.

Watson, J. P., Gaind, R., & Marks, I. M. (1972). Physiological habituation to continuous phobic stimulation. *Behaviour Research and Therapy, 10,* 269–278.

Watson, J. P., & Marks, I. M. (1971). Relevant and irrelevant fear in flooding — A crossover study of phobic patients. *Behavior Therapy, 2,* 275–293.

Zahn, T. P., Insel, T. R., & Murphy, D. L. (1984). Psychophysiological changes during pharmacological treatment of patients with obsessive–compulsive disorder. *British Journal of Psychiatry, 145,* 39–44.

APPENDIX

Rating Scales for Obsessive–Compulsive Symptoms

Briefly state the nature of your three worst *fears* on the appropriate line below. For each fear write the number from the scale which best indicates how much it upsets you.

0	1	2	3	4	5	6	7	8
does not		slightly sometimes		definitely often		markedly very often		very severely continuously

	Description	Rating
1. The worst fear:	hitting a pedestrian while driving	
2. The second worst fear:	strangling a child who is alone	
3. The third worst fear:	contracting VD from a toilet seat	

Please rate the degree to which you tend to *avoid* situations which are associated with the three fears you described above.

0	1	2	3	4	5	6	7	8
I never avoid this situation		I hesitate to enter this rarely avoid it		I sometimes avoid this situation		I usually avoid this situation		I always avoid this situation

Rating

Avoidance of most feared situation:	driving
Avoidance of second worst feared situation:	being alone with a child
Avoidance of third worst feared situation:	public bathrooms

For each of the three main *ritualistic activities* you engage in select the number on the scale which best indicates your situation. For each activity write the chosen number in the space provided.

COMPARED TO MOST PEOPLE THIS ACTIVITY IN MY CASE IS:

0	1	2	3	4	5	6	7	8
no different		twice as lengthy or different		three times as lengthy or frequent		four times as lengthy or frequent		five times as lengthy or frequent

	Description	Rating
Activity A:	retracing the route	
Activity B:	seeking information (checking) about the safety of children they've been near	
Activity C:	washing and showering	

CHAPTER 6

Panic and Generalized Anxiety Disorders

Rudolf Hoehn-Saric and Daniel R. McLeod

Anxiety is a universal experience. It serves as a warning system and signals a situation of danger that usually is associated with uncertainty. Anxiety becomes abnormal when it is excessively strong, when it lasts beyond the exposure to potential danger, when it is triggered by situations that are known to be harmless, or when it occurs without any apparent cause. Abnormal anxiety may be of a transitory nature or may become chronic. In the latter form, it manifests itself either as a panic disorder, that is, in frequently unexpected paroxysms of anxiety, or as a generalized anxiety disorder, in which anxiety is present on a more or less continuous basis.

PANIC DISORDER

The *Diagnostic and Statistical Manual of Mental Disorders, Third Edition,* (DSM-III) (American Psychiatric Association, 1980) defines panic disorder as a condition in which anxiety manifests itself in paroxysms of apprehension, fear, or terror, often associated with feelings of impending doom, and is accompanied by a variety of physical symptoms, to be described later. To be diagnosed as having panic disorder, a person should have at least three panic attacks within a 3-week period. The attacks should not occur as the result of marked physical exertion or in life threatening situations. Moreover, they should occur, at least at times, spontaneously, that is, without being precipitated by exposure to a circumscribed phobic stimulus. Panic attacks lead to the avoidance of situations in which they have been experienced previously because re-exposure to those situations frequently elicits new attacks. Avoidance leads to restriction of activities which, in extreme form, results in a person being practically housebound. When avoidance behavior is present, the patient is said to have agoraphobia with panic attacks.

Representative Cases

Case 1

Mr. A was a 27-year-old businessman who was referred to the Anxiety Disorders Clinic by his internist. Four months earlier, while driving home on an expressway, he suddenly experienced palpitations, tightness and pain in the chest, shortness of breath, feelings of dizziness, shakiness, upset stomach, and a feeling of intense fear. The patient thought that he was having a heart attack and pulled off to the side of the road. A passing police officer called an ambulance, and the patient was taken to the nearest hospital. A thorough medical examination was negative. He was told that he had suffered an anxiety attack and was discharged after a few hours. He initially felt reassured, but 3 days later while driving again on the expressway he experienced a similar attack. A second medical examination by his internist was negative. Subsequently, Mr. A experienced similar attacks not only while driving on the expressway, but also in other situations, particularly in situations in which he felt confined, such as crowds, church, restaurants, and elevators. Gradually he began to fear situations in which he had previously experienced panic attacks. While he forced himself to go to work, he began to restrict his social life and avoided leaving town. He became increasingly more tense, even between panic attacks, and experienced difficulties sleeping, increased muscular tension, palpitations, butterflies in the stomach, and urinary frequency, in anticipation of further attacks.

Family history of the patient was positive for panic attacks on the maternal side and alcoholism on the paternal side. His childhood and adolescence were normal, except that he was always somewhat tense. For instance, when having to speak in public in school he experienced palpitations and sweaty palms. A month prior to the first panic attack, his mother died, after which he became mildly depressed and suffered from moderate insomnia and increased tension.

In the Anxiety Disorders Clinic, the patient was placed on imipramine and alprazolam. He reported improvement within several days. He reported having only a few panic attacks, and those were comparatively mild. Over 3 weeks, imipramine was gradually increased, while alprazolam was decreased from a regular dose to a dose to be taken only when unusually tense. At that time, he was free of panic attacks but still felt moderately tense and continued to avoid leaving town and attending various social functions. During the next 2 months, supportive psychotherapy and encouragement to engage in situations that he had been avoiding helped him to overcome his fears. He was followed on medication for a year, after which both medications were tapered off. He subsequently continued to do well.

This patient represents a "classic" case of panic disorder, with a positive family history, some signs of increased autonomic reactivity to stress since his teens, and increased feelings of stress and distress several weeks prior to the first panic attack, which occurred spontaneously without any clear precipitating event. Subsequent panic attacks gradually became associated with certain stimuli, which by themselves became triggers for further attacks. The development of anticipatory anxiety increased general tension and fear of new attacks induced avoidance behavior. The patient responded well to medication and reassurance, and gradually overcame the anticipatory anxiety and phobias.

Case 2

Mr. M was a 42-year-old high level business executive in a multinational company who had experienced his first panic attack 16 years earlier. At that time he was under no unusual stress. While waiting for the delivery of a new car at the dealership, he suddenly experienced a tightness in the chest, palpitations, and feelings of dread and anxiety. He believed that he had had a heart attack, but his family physician declared him physically healthy and gave him no explanation for the attack. He continued to have attacks approximately once every 2 weeks and had numerous medical examinations, all of which were negative. Gradually he also developed "minor attacks," that is, attacks similar in quality to a full-blown attack but of lesser intensity and shorter duration. Over the years, he continued to have panic attacks, although sometimes he was free of them for 2 to 3 months. He noticed no difference in the frequency of attacks while under pressure at work or during relaxing vacations. However, he was more likely to have an attack on days that followed an evening of drinking or on days when he woke up feeling more tense or physically run down. Therefore, he gave up alcoholic beverages. Mr. M never developed avoidance behavior and continued with his daily life routine. His family history was negative except for alcoholism on the paternal side. His developmental history was normal. He had a very successful career as a business executive, and had served in several multinational companies. He did not think of himself as a workaholic. He usually left work at 5:00, rarely took work home, and spent the weekends sailing or playing golf. His family life was satisfactory. His panic attacks were completely controlled within 2 weeks of being placed on imipramine and, except for an explanation about panic attacks, no formal psychotherapy was necessary.

This patient represents a case of pure panic disorder without any complicating features: The only symptoms are sudden spontaneous panic attacks. Such cases occur mostly in men and these men rarely seek treatment from psychiatrists (Uhde et al., 1985).

Case 3

Ms. J was a 22-year-old married woman who had her first panic attack at the age of 17. Because of panic attacks, she had quit high school, but was able to work as a nurse's aid. She was married at the age of 18 to a truckdriver who drank heavily and abused drugs. Her panic attacks continued to increase in severity and frequency to the point where she experienced several panic attacks each day. Eventually, she was unable to go to work and left home only in the company of others. Family history was positive for panic disorder on the maternal side; impulsive, criminal acting-out behavior on the paternal side; and alcoholism on both sides. She had a very low frustration tolerance, was easily excited, and tried to overcome pressures within her family and marriage through obsessive cleaning and housekeeping. This patient was prescribed a variety of medications, including benzodiazepines, beta-blockers, tricyclic antidepressants, and MAO inhibitors. In addition, because her husband refused to participate in marital therapy, she received individual psychotherapy. Medication improved her condition moderately, but she soon showed a tendency toward abusing benzodiazepines. Showing little progress for over a year, she was hospitalized. Within the hospital setting, it was possible to withdraw her from medication (phenelzine sulfate and alprazolam) in a few days. She continued to experience one or two panic attacks a day, but these were mild and transitory. Close observation revealed that whenever she became stressed, she hyperventilated. Her comparatively mild panic attacks led to hyperventilation, which magnified the severity and the duration of the attacks. Assertiveness training and breathing exercises, combined with her husband's eventual willingness to participate in family therapy, led to a quick improvement. After discharge, the patient showed a partial relapse, but her ability to cope with life situations had improved, her panic attacks were milder, and she remained functional on a minimal amount of medication.

This patient has a strong family history of anxiety disorders, including panic attacks, personality problems, low frustration tolerance, and an inability to cope with family problems. Her tendency to hyperventilate complicates the picture by magnifying the severity of her panic attacks. Medication alone was of little help, but intensive psychological interventions within a hospital setting led to improvement.

Case 4

For Ms. J, agoraphobia was not associated with secondary gain, but this was the prominent feature in the case of Ms. P, a 25-year-old wife of a graduate student who, soon after her first panic attack, developed extensive agoraphobia which forced her husband to take her everywhere she wanted to go. In this case, marital problems dominated the picture. Her husband, a rather dry and perfectionistic engineer, constantly argued with his rather emotional and somewhat disorganized wife. Her agoraphobia served to control her husband, and only intensive therapy with both partners led to a modest improvement in the marriage and a reduction in avoidance behavior.

Prevalence and Onset

Estimates of the prevalence of anxiety disorders depend on the criteria used in the survey and on the qualities of the interviewers. Therefore, the results vary considerably. Epidemiological studies report a 6-month prevalence rate of 0.6/100 to 1.0/100 for panic attacks and a rate of 2.7 to 5.8 for agoraphobia, a condition usually associated with panic attacks (Weisman, 1985). Panic disorder tends to have a two to one female preponderance. It usually begins in young adults between the ages of 18 and 35, with an average age of 26 years (Thyer, Parrish, Curtis, Nesse, & Cameron, 1985). However, occasional onset in the early teens or as late as the fifth decade have been observed.

Predisposing Factors

Biological predisposing factors

Familial occurrence, suggesting genetic transmission of panic disorder, is well established, with a morbidity risk of 25% to 32% for anxiety disorders in relatives of panic disorder patients. Relatives of patients with agoraphobia also have been found to be at higher risk for alcohol disorders (Reich, 1986). Mitral valve prolapse occurs more frequently in patients with panic disorder than in either patients with generalized anxiety disorder or nonanxious persons (Dager, Comess, & Dunner, 1986; Liberthson, Sheenan, King, & Weyman, 1986). However, the majority of patients with mitral valve prolapse never to develop panic disorder. Hormonal diseases, such as thyroid disturbances (Lindemann, Zitrin, & Klein, 1984), or pheochromocytoma (Starkman, Zelnick, Nesse, & Cameron, 1985), can be associated with panic disorder, but the occurrence of these disorders in panic disorder patients is comparatively rare. Such conditions may, at times, trigger a panic disorder in a predisposed individual, but they are not of primary etiological significance. Not all anxiety evoking biological changes trigger panic attacks. Hypoglycemia, for example, may induce anxiety, but it has not been found to trigger attacks in patients with panic disorder (Uhde et al., 1985). Thus, various physiological disturbances may increase anxiety and probably induce panic attacks in predisposed individuals, but they have no primary etiological significance.

Psychological Predisposing Factors

Gittelman and Klein (1984) found a high incidence of separation anxiety during childhood in agoraphobic patients and theorized that agoraphobia resembles separation anxiety in children. Others were not able to duplicate their findings, however (Thyer, Nesse, Cameron & Curtis, 1985). Raskin, Peeke, Dickman, & Pinsker (1982), for example, reported a higher incidence of environmental disturbances rather than separation anxiety. Thus, the effect of disturbances during childhood on subsequent panic disorder remains unknown. A recent survey by Deltito (1986) found that patients who developed agoraphobia had a high incidence of school phobias, while patients who had panic attacks without agoraphobia had no such disturbances during childhood. This finding suggests that the etiology of panic attacks is not linked to separation anxiety disorder, but that the presence of the latter disorder may indicate a heightened vulnerability for avoidance behavior that develops secondary to the panic attacks.

Panic disorder usually is associated with generalized anxiety (Barlow, 1985; Uhde et al., 1985), but reports differ as to whether and to what degree generalized anxiety precedes panic attacks. Uhde et al. (1985) reported that the majority of their patients developed pathological degrees of generalized anxiety after, rather than before, the onset of the first panic attack, while Hibbert (1984) found that in half of the patients the first panic attacks were preceded by a period of somatic symptoms such as palpitations, sweating, difficulties breathing, tightness in the chest, or muscular tension, which could be interpreted as signs of increased anxiety. In a longitudinal follow-up, Cloninger, Martin, Clayton, and Guze (1981) found that symptoms of generalized anxiety preceded panic disorder in all patients. In our experience, most of the patients who develop panic attacks have been more anxious than the average population prior to the first attack. However, anxiety levels that developed after the onset of the panic disorder often were so high that the presence of preceding anxiety could be detected only after careful questioning. The question of whether prolonged periods of anxiety predispose persons to develop panic disorder remains unanswered.

Precipitating Factors

For some patients, the first panic attack appears to occur without a precipitating factor. However, the majority of patients experience significant stressors in the months preceding the first panic attack (Uhde et al., 1985). The types of stressors range from interpersonal problems, difficulties at work, adjustment to new environment, or personal losses, to increased physiological vulnerability after physical illnesses. For a period of time prior to the first attack, patients may have felt mildly to moderately distressed, but continued to function until the first panic attack occurred. The attack usually occurs, however, under trivial everyday circumstances, and takes the patient by complete surprise.

Symptoms

Panic attacks usually start with paroxysms of intense fear and apprehension which strike suddenly without warning and for no apparent reason (Sheehan, 1982). Symptoms are predominantly cardiorespiratory combined with shakiness, but frequently including feelings of lightheadedness and depersonalization. Along with intense terror and fear, patients may complain of rapid heart rate, palpitations, discomfort in the chest, rapid or difficult breathing, sweating, hot and cold spells, urgency to urinate or defecate, trembling, nausea, dizziness, and feelings of fainting. The symptoms may last from a few minutes to half an hour, after which they gradually fade away. Patients may continue to feel tense, shaky, or exhausted for hours. Besides full-blown major attacks, patients also may experience "minor attacks," which are similar in nature to the major attack but are less intense and shorter in duration. During early panic attacks, patients believe that they are having a heart attack or stroke, or that they are losing their sanity. Even patients who are well informed about the nature of the attacks continue to fear them, in part because of the dreadfulness of the experience, but also because of the social humiliation that is brought on by the obvious manifestation of anxiety in an everyday situation, the need of the patient to escape the dreaded place, and the lack of understanding of his or her behavior by others.

Objective measures of physiological changes during panic attacks are rare. Lader and Mathews (1970) observed spontaneous panic attacks in three of their patients and recorded increased heart rate and skin conductance during the attacks. Taylor et al. (1986), using an ambulatory heart rate monitoring device, detected increased heart rate disproportionate to activity levels during 58% of reported panic attacks. Intense panic attacks were more likely than less severe attacks to be accompanied by changes on the recording. The elevated heart rates were due to sinus tachycardia and did not occur during anticipatory anxiety episodes. Freedman, Ianni, Ettedgui, and Putthezhath (1985), also using an ambulatory device, found increases in heart rate and changes in finger temperature during spontaneous panic attacks. There is some disagreement as to whether the tonic levels of autonomic activity displayed by patients who suffer from panic attacks do (Kelly, Mitchell-Heggs, & Sherman, 1971; Liebowitz et al., 1984; 1985) or do not (Freedman et al., 1985; LaPierre, Knott, & Gray, 1984) differ from those of persons who do not have panic attacks.

Sleep studies show little difference between normals and patients with panic attacks. The sleep architecture in panic disorder patients is not grossly disturbed, but panic disorder patients are more restless and have shorter sleep duration, which suggests hyperarousal (Uhde et al., 1985). Some patients wake up from sleep with panic attacks. The attacks start usually, although not always, during Stage 2 sleep. Typically, the eyes suddenly start to move, the heart rate speeds up, sleep becomes restless, and the patient then awakens 1 or 2 minutes after the disturbance has begun, reporting the experience of a panic attack (Hauri, Ravaris, & Friedman, 1986).

Hyperventilation regularly accompanies panic attacks. Panic disorder patients show lower carbon dioxide tension and bicarbonate levels in the blood even before panic attacks. This suggests that they may be chronic hyperventilators (Margraf, Ehlers, & Roth, 1986). Some panic attacks may be the consequence of hyperventilation, which by itself induces somatic changes similar to those observed in panic attacks. In other attacks, panic precedes hyperventilation (Bass & Gardner, 1985). The relationship between hyperventilation and panic disorder needs further clarification.

Increased levels of anxiety may predispose patients to panic attacks. Many patients notice that when they wake up in the morning feeling tense, they are more likely than usual to have a panic attack. The fact that patients who have had spontaneous panic attacks in certain environments, such as while driving on a highway, are more likely to develop panic attacks when reexposed to the same circumstances (particularly if they have developed anticipatory anxiety), suggests that heightened anxiety levels may lower the threshold for panic attacks. Moreover, patients who are more anxious are more likely to develop a panic attack when exposed to a sodium lactate challenge (Margraf et al., 1986).

Patients with fully developed panic disorder experience, in addition to panic attacks, two types of anxiety: (a) anticipatory anxiety, namely, the fear of developing a panic attack when going out and engaging in activities that have led to attacks previously, and (b) a generalized feeling of anxiety phenomenologically comparable to generalized anxiety. Anticipatory anxiety develops in most patients within 6 months after their first panic attack (Uhde et al., 1985), and may range from mild discomfort to severe anxiety prior to certain activities. For example, high levels of anxiety may be present for several days preceding a social event. This anxiety may be decreased in the company of a familiar person, and the patient may become very dependent on such a person. The reduction in anxiety may occur even in the presence of persons who may not fail only to help the patient in the case of an emergency, but may actually be a hinderance. One of our patients was able to drive when she took along her 8-month-old daughter, but not when she was alone. Anticipatory anxiety may persist after panic attacks have been brought under control and, in more severe cases, psychological interventions, particularly behavior therapy, may be necessary to overcome it. Generalized anxiety occurs in over 80% of patients with panic disorder (Barlow, 1985; Uhde et al., 1985). It can precede the panic disorder or develop during the disorder. In most cases, preexisting generalized anxiety becomes exaggerated. Severe cases may experience a more or less continuous hyperarousal. Patients without generalized anxiety are mostly men who have infrequent attacks (Uhde et al., 1985). Like anticipatory anxiety, generalized anxiety may have a life of its own and persists even when the panic attacks have been brought under control (Waddell, Barlow, & O'Brien, 1984.)

While physiological measures are rarely taken during spontaneous panic attacks, such measures have been taken during attacks produced in the laboratory by agents such as sodium lactate (Pitts & McClure, 1967). During lactate-induced panic attacks, increases have been found in forearm blood flow (Kelly et al., 1971), heart rate (LaPierre et al., 1984; Liebowitz et al., 1985) diastolic blood pressure (Liebowitz et al., 1985), electromyographic and electrooculographic activity (Knott, Chaudhry, & LaPierre, 1981; LaPierre et al., 1984), and in cortisol and norepinephrine levels (Liebowitz et al., 1985). Decreases have been found in bicarbonate levels (Liebowitz et al., 1985). Change in electroencephalographic activity and auditory evoked potentials also have been reported (Knott et al., 1981; LaPierre et al., 1984). Caution should be taken in the interpretation of lactate-induced physiological changes because they may not correspond to those of spontaneous panic attacks (Margraf et al., 1986).

Longitudinal Course and Complicating Factors

A person may have only a few panic attacks during his or her lifetime or may experience them regularly. Attacks may vary in frequency within the same person and between persons. They may occur from once every few months to several times a day. However, no cyclicity comparable to that observed in affective disorders has been observed (Uhde et al., 1985). In general, panic disorder takes a chronic course. Patients who have become free of panic attacks have a tendency to relapse, particularly when under psychological pressure. At times a panic disorder may change into a generalized anxiety disorder, but more frequently a person with generalized anxiety develops panic attacks.

The majority of patients who experience panic attacks on a regular basis begin to avoid situations in which they have experienced panic attacks or encounters that socially embarrass them. Avoidance behavior might be comparatively mild, such as cancellation of unimportant social events, or it may reach such a level of severity that a person becomes totally homebound. Patients generally fear situations from which they cannot escape, for instance, being stuck in traffic, on a bridge, in the midst of a church service, or in a restaurant or airplane. They fear that if they have a panic attack under such circumstances they will not be able to escape. These patients also fear situations that remove them from potential sources of help, such as being out of town, in an unknown environment, or without a telephone. Often patients still are able to function within the most important areas of life and they continue to work. However, they increasingly avoid interactions that are not essential for their survival. In severe cases, avoidance may reach such proportions that the patient becomes unable to go to the dentist, or obtain new glasses or clothing for years. He or she becomes pathologically dependent on others for transportation and other services, thus placing great burdens on family and friends. Some persons feel reassured in the presence of trusted persons, or even when carrying an inanimate object for a talisman, while others remain fearful under any circumstances. Occasionally a new, emotionally satisfactory friendship or love relationship may temporarily improve or apparently "cure" the condition. Avoidance behavior generally starts a few weeks to a few months after the onset of the first panic attack and has a tendency to generalize and increase in severity over time.

Patients often are too embarrassed to divulge their affliction to others. Margaret West (1981), an English writer, describes vividly the web of deceptions necessary to avoid the humiliating admission that an everyday social obligation, such as going to an art exhibit or a dinner invitation, terrifies an adult with a successful career.

Depression is a frequent complication of panic disorder. It may be a transitory response to the recurrence of a panic attack or to the failure to attend a social event. Because of the chronic course of the disorder, many patients become demoralized, but they do not exhibit the pervasively depressed mood and loss of interest seen in patients with major depressive illness. Patients with panic attacks are likely, however, to develop episodes of major depression at some point in their life. The incidence of depression in panic disorder and agoraphobia patients has been reported to be as high as 91% (Bowen & Kohout, 1979), but when stricter diagnostic criteria are applied, prolonged depression is found in only 24% (Uhde et al., 1985) to 41% (Munjack & Moss, 1981) of the examined population. At times, panic attacks occur only during depressive episodes. In this case, panic attacks present a symptom of depression rather than an independent coexisting disorder.

Panic disorder also increases the risk of a premature death from suicide in those patients who become depressed and from cardiovascular death (Coryell, Noyes, & House, 1986). Whether this increased mortality can be attributed to the panic disorder or to a concomitant mitral valve prolapse is unknown. Alcohol and anxiolytic medications relieve anticipatory and generalized anxiety and lessen, at least temporarily, the symptoms of panic. Therefore, patients with the disorder are at increased risk for substance abuse and dependency.

Assessment

Due to the absence of reliable laboratory tests, the diagnosis of panic disorder remains clinical. Provocation methods, such as the application of yohimbine (Charney, Heninger, & Breier, 1984) or sodium lactate (Liebowitz et al., 1986) induce panic only in 50% to 70% of patients with panic disorder. The dexamethasone suppression test generally is in the normal range (Roy/Byrne, Bierer, & Uhde, 1985). Physical illnesses, particularly thyroid disorders, pheochromocytoma, or cardiac arrythmia, may mimic panic disorder and have to be ruled out. More frequently, such disorders trigger a latent predisposition for panic attacks which persist even when the underlying physical illness has been brought under control. Dizziness is frequently associated with panic attacks, and one study suggests that otologic disturbances are frequent in patients with this disorder (Jacob, Moller, Turner, & Wall, 1985).

The reliability of the clinical diagnosis of panic disorder without concomitant agoraphobia is fairly low (Barlow, 1985). This may be due to the rigid criteria of DSM-III, which requires three panic attacks within 3 weeks to qualify for the diagnosis. Some panic attacks are "minor" and their inclusion depends on the judgment of the evaluators. Moreover, DSM-III leaves a diagnostic gray area for conditions having definite but less frequent panic attacks, although family studies suggest that they are related to panic disorder (Crowe, Noyes, Pauls, & Slymen, 1983). Diagnostic difficulties also arise in the case of patients with generalized anxiety disorder, who exhibit rapid increases in anxiety under stress that can be mistaken for panic attacks. In these patients, the increase in anxiety is related to events perceived as stressful and occurs gradually before reaching a plateau. This form of anxiety does not have the paroxysmal appearance of panic attacks. In patients who tend to hyperventilate, it may be difficult to distinguish between anxiety attacks that were induced through hyperventilation and panic attacks in which hyperventilation follows.

In general, it is easy to differentiate between circumscribed phobias and phobic conditions secondary to panic disorder. Circumscribed phobias invariably elicit anxiety whenever a person approaches the feared situation. On the other hand, agoraphobic patients experience panic attacks frequently, but not always, in situations associated with previous attacks. Moreover, circumscribed phobias generally remain static, while phobias of untreated panic disorder patients tend to generalize.

GENERALIZED ANXIETY DISORDER

Generalized anxiety disorder was described for the first time in DSM-III. This disorder occurs more frequently than panic disorder, but is less well investigated. It is defined as anxiety that has persisted for at least 1 month, and symptoms from three of the following four categories must be present: (a) motor tension, (b) autonomic hyperactivity, (c) apprehensive expectation, and (d) vigilance and scanning. Symptoms occurring in phobic, obsessive-compulsive, and panic disorders should be absent. Patients should be at least 18 years of age and the symptoms should not be part of another mental disorder, such as depression or schizophrenia.

Representative Cases

Case 1

Ms. W. was a 25-year-old white, single computer assistant with 1 year of college education, who had been feeling tense since her teens. In school she felt self-conscious because she was taller and thinner than others, and she had the tendency to have sweaty palms and to perspire when tense. Between the ages of 15 and 16, she developed spastic colon and her family physician gave her chlordiazepoxide, which she took periodically. She remained somewhat shy and tended to worry excessively. Two years ago, she developed palpitations, breathing difficulty, sweaty palms, increased muscular tension, tension headaches, that were bipolar and lasted for hours, butterflies in the stomach, nausea, abdominal cramps in the right lower quadrant, and frequent loose bowel movements. She had difficulty falling asleep and, at times, woke up after 2 or 3 hours with dreams of failure. Her condition was present almost continuously in a mild form, but became worse whenever she was under interpersonal stress or had financial worries. The exacerbation of her symptoms during the last year was attributed to adjustment problems with her boyfriend. In addition, she had a mild fear of closed spaces and a tendency to worry excessively, but had no clear obsessive–compulsive symptoms.

Her medical history was positive for spastic colon. She also had increased premenstrual tension lasting for 1 or 2 days. She did not smoke or drink alcohol and rarely drank caffeinated beverages.

Family history was positive for chronic anxiety in her mother. Early childhood and school adjustment were satisfactory until high school, when she became self-conscious about her height (which eventually reached 6 feet). In general, she was a shy child. After she finished high school, she started to work for the government as a computer assistant. She performed adequately at work, but found it boring. Therefore, she attended evening classes with the intention of eventually becoming a drug counselor. She dated infrequently, but had serious involvements with two men.

Ms. W. provides a fairly typical case of chronic generalized anxiety disorder. She grew up in a household with an anxious and tense mother. As a child she was shy, but had no overt symptoms until she felt under increased social pressure in school. Subsequently, she continued to have a variety of psychological and physical symptoms that were generally mild but became severe whenever she came under an even minimal degree of stress. The patient was given psychotherapy and was placed on alprazolam. She subsequently became more relaxed, had fewer physical symptoms, and eventually learned to cope more effectively with stressful situations. She continued to be somewhat symptomatic, however, and needed medication from time to time.

Case 2

Mr. B was a 44-year-old white, married, college-educated sales manager who had been tense throughout most of his life, but had become definitely more tense during the last 15 years, particularly over the last 8 months. He complained that he felt constantly tense, had frequent increased muscular tension, particularly in the back and neck, which led to headaches, and he tended to wake up in the middle of the night worrying about work and business. In addition, he experienced butterflies in the stomach, but had no palpitations, increased perspiration, or symptoms of hyperventilation. On occasion, he had intrusive obsessive thoughts, but they were rarely bothersome. His habits were rather perfectionistic. His general health was good. He did not smoke, drank alcohol socially, and had one cup of coffee per day. He noticed during his vacations that his symptoms, particularly the headaches, while still present, decreased.

The patient's father was described as having been a constant worrier who developed peptic ulcers. He was loud and argumentive, and the patient never felt close to him. The patient's mother was more easygoing. The patient's early childhood was uneventful. His academic performance was good, but his social adjustment was only fair because he tended to be a loner who had only a few close friends. After college, he fulfilled his military obligation and subsequently began to work for a large corporation where he steadily advanced. He married a woman he had known since high school and now has one daughter who attends college. The patient's relationship with his wife is fairly good, except for some tension brought on by his excessive preoccupation with work and work performance.

Personality-wise, the patient appeared to be a highly driven perfectionist who placed high demands on himself and his co-workers. When frustrated at work, he tended to lose self-control and have temper tantrums.

The patient was given alprazolam, first regularly, and later on an irregular basis. He did very well on psychotherapy involving a cognitive/behavior therapy orientation. His ability to tolerate frustration gradually improved, and the medication reduced his headaches and permitted him to sleep better.

This patient represents a chronically anxious person who has predominantly muscular symptoms leading to tension headaches, hypervigilance, and a tendency to worry excessively. Having a Type A personality, he converted his anxieties into high work performance, driving himself and placing high demands on both himself and his co-workers, at times displaying temper tantrums. Therapy permitted him to see his life in more balanced terms and continue to perform satisfactorily with less anxiety.

Case 3

Ms. F was a 40-year-old single, white, saleswoman who had been rather tense all of her life. As a child, she was shy and anxious and tended to avoid unpleasant situations. After high school she began to work for a department store as a saleswoman. She remained in this job until she was laid off shortly before coming to the clinic. The patient's father died when she was 12 years old, leaving the family in financial difficulties. Her mother was described as an anxious, overprotective person. The patient never married and continued to live with her mother. She had a few friends from high school with whom she spent vacations. When the old friends eventually married or left town, the patient did not replace them with new friends. Her life became increasingly more centered around work and home. After losing her job, she became almost housebound, being afraid of going for job interviews or travelling downtown. This fear, however, was not as severe as the agoraphobia seen in panic disorder. When sufficiently motivated, she was quite capable of taking a bus and reaching her destination with moderate but tolerable levels of anxiety, which consisted of feelings of anxiety, tension, tightness in the throat, increased perspiration and, occasionally, rapid heartbeat.

Like Mr. B, this patient also suffered from chronic anxiety. However, having an avoidant personality, she generally escaped higher levels of tension through social withdrawal. For all of her life she had remained on the same job. When this security was taken away, she was unable to replace it with new social contacts or work opportunities. Therapy consisted of dealing with her psychological problems.

Little progress was made until she ran out of her unemployment insurance. Only when financial necessities outweighed her tendency to avoid unpleasantness did she seriously look for another job. Eventually, she found a sales job which, after a period of heightened anxiety, permitted her to continue the life she had led before losing her previous position.

Case 4

Ms. O was a 23-year-old laboratory technician who complained of increased feelings of anxiety which at times overwhelmed her. Symptoms consisted of tension, palpitations, shortness of breath, breaking into a sweat, and trembling. When upset, she tended to become quite agitated, which concerned people at work to the point that they eventually brought her to the clinic. The patient stated that she was a tense person and that small things triggered anxiety. She felt under increased pressure at work due to problems with her supervisor, but obtained comfort from a boyfriend with whom she had a good relationship. She appeared to be a vivacious, outgoing person who easily related to the interviewer. Her pulse rate, however, was increased and her hands, upon handshake, were moist.

The patient's family history was positive for alcoholism on the paternal side. Her father was described as a fairly quiet person, whereas her mother was rather outgoing and "emotional." Childhood was fairly uneventful, except for a school phobia and separation anxiety during one year. The patient was comfortable in the company of friends and started to date when she was 15-years-old. Her school performance varied and tended to depend on the interest she had in a particular subject. After two years of college, she began to work as a laboratory technician and her performance was adequate except for her tendency to become excessively emotional when under pressure. Therapy consisted of psychotherapy and alprazolam was prescribed on a p.r.n. basis. The patient showed a moderate degree of improvement in therapy.

In contrast to the previously described cases, this patient was an outgoing, somewhat histrionic person who, nevertheless, showed symptoms of chronic anxiety. Unlike the previously described patient, she reacted to heightened anxiety not through withdrawal, but through interaction with other people, either in a help-seeking or in an acting-out manner.

Prevalence and Onset

Prevalence of generalized anxiety disorder is difficult to establish because the diagnostic criteria are poorly defined. Surveys have reported a 1-year prevalence rate of 2.3/100 to 6.4/100, making it the most frequent anxiety disorder, occurring two to five times more frequently than panic disorder (Weissman, 1985). The majority of patients with generalized anxiety disorder are not treated in psychiatric clinics, but are seen by family physicians. The onset of generalized anxiety disorder is earlier than in panic disorder, with a median of 21 years and onset of symptoms between the ages of 16 and 26. Many patients report that they have been anxious "all their life," which led Akiskal (1985) to propose that patients with generalized anxiety disorder actually suffer from an anxious personality.

Predisposition

In contrast to panic disorder, no clear evidence of a genetic predisposition to generalized anxiety disorder has been established (Torgersen, 1983). However, the possibility that certain subtypes of generalized anxiety have genetic predisposition cannot be excluded.

Thomas and Chess (1977 and 1984), who followed children from the age of 3 months to their late teens, noted that various personality traits, including a tendency toward anxiety, were present already in young infants. A recent study indicates a higher incidence of adjustment disorders with anxiety in families of patients with generalized anxiety disorders (Noyes, personal communication). These findings suggest the existence of a genetic predisposition toward heightened anxiety, which may manifest itself either as a prolonged disorder or, intermittently, as a heightened vulnerability to stress. No organic precipitating factors have been related etiologically to generalized anxiety but, as is true of panic disorder, certain physical illnesses may precipitate anxiety that may continue even if the physical illness has been treated successfully. A variety of environmental stressors occurring during childhood, particularly high levels of anxiety in the mother (Windheuser, 1977), or the death of a parent (Torgersen, 1986), and stressors occurring in later life, predominantly disturbances in interpersonal relationships, have been found to be related to the emergence and the maintenance of anxiety (Ilfeld, 1979). The question of whether chronic anxiety disorders can be precipitated by trauma in adults with healthy personalities remains unanswered. Extreme conditions, such as concentration camps (Levav & Abramson, 1984) frequently leave permanent scars, but the etiological importance of less stressful events on long-term anxiety remains controversial (Lader, 1983). Precipitating factors are frequently present in the development of shorter lasting anxiety and in the exacerbation of chronic anxiety disorders.

Symptoms

Psychological symptoms of generalized anxiety can be divided into affective/cognitive symptoms, consisting of various degrees of fear, and the tendency to worry constantly. This apprehension may be internalized, manifesting itself as insecurity about one's own abilities and performance, or externalized into expectation of disasters that may stike one's self or important persons in one's life. The concomitant hyperarousal manifests itself in *somatic symptoms.* These consist of muscular tension, which results in feelings of achiness, fatigue, tension headaches, and, in severe cases, tremor; autonomic symptoms attributable to sympathetic hyperarousal, such as palpitations, increased perspiration, symptoms secondary to hyperventilation, along with its secondary symptoms of tightness in the chest, air hunger, paresthesia, and feelings of dizziness; and predominantly parasympathetically induced symptoms, such as butterflies in the stomach, nausea, and, in severe cases, vomiting, loose bowels, and urinary frequency. Appetite, as well as sex drive, can be increased or decreased. Somepeople find overeating or an orgasm tension releasing; other people lose interest in food or sex when under great pressure. Initial insomnia (difficulty falling asleep) is frequent, but many patients also complain of waking up during the night, particularly around 4 o'clock in the morning. Dreams with threatening content or dreams of disaster are frequently present. The somatic symptoms experienced in generalized anxiety disorder vary greatly between patients and probably depend on constitutional predisposition. In some persons, anxiety affects mainly the cardiovascular system, causing rapid heartbeat and palpitations, irregular heartbeat, and increases in blood pressure. Other persons experience predominantly gastrointestinal symptoms, consisting of gastric and intestinal spasms, nausea, and irregular bowel movements. Still other persons complain predominantly of muscular symptoms (Weiner, 1985). However, the cardiopulmonary symptoms generally are less severe than those of panic disorder (Anderson, Noyes, & Crowe, 1984; Hoehn-Saric, 1982a).

Objective studies of physiological patterns in anxiety are limited by measuring techniques. Thus, most frequently reported are changes in heart rate, blood pressure, blood flow in extremities, electrodermal activity, pupil diameter, respiration, and muscle activity; less frequently, gastrointestinal activity is measured. In normal subjects, stress generally heightens these activities. In chronically anxious patients, baseline activities frequently differ from those of nonanxious subjects, but response patterns resulting from stress are often difficult to predict in anxious patients. Moreover, patients with similar self-ratings vary considerably in their physiological responses. Indeed, the relationships between self-ratings and physiological response patterns are tenuous at best. It should be pointed out, however, that while low correlations between self-reports and physiological activity generally are found, patients are able to accurately perceive the direction of change in some physiological activities under stress (McLeod, Hoehn-Saric, & Stefan, 1986). It also appears that the responses of some body systems, for example, those of the cardiovascular system, change not only as the result of prolonged anxiety and exposure to specific situations, but depend on constitutional factors as well. Hormonal changes are equally complex. When exposed to stress, normal subjects tend to show a variety of hormonal responses, including the elevation of catecholamines, cortisol, growth hormones, and prolactin, along with the suppression of testosterone (Ursin, Baade, & Levine, 1978). The hormonal responses of chronically anxious patients are less predictable (Curtis, Nesse, Buxton, & Lippman, 1979; Mathew, Ho, Kralik, & Claghorn, 1979). It is premature at the present time to make general statements concerning psychophysiological response patterns in generalized anxiety disorder.

The effects of anxiety on sleep architecture, on the waking electroencephalogram, on various autonomic and electromyographic measures, and on hormonal levels have been studied. Sleep is frequently disrupted in anxiety disorders. Reynolds and colleagues (Reynolds, Shaw, Newton, Coble, & Kupfer, 1983) compared the sleep patterns of anxious patients with those of depressed patients and found impairment of sleep continuity and reduction of delta sleep in both groups. Patients with generalized anxiety disorder differed from depressed patients in exhibiting greater reduction in Stage 1 sleep and REM percentage, whereas patients with primary depression exhibited shorter REM latencies. Because the number of examined patients was small, the findings are not necessarily representative of the entire spectrum of generalized anxiety patients. Akiskal (personal communication) noticed that patients with generalized anxiety disorder adapt less well to the sleep laboratory during the first night of recording than patients with other diagnoses, suggesting that a novel situation, even when not objectively threatening, may cause hyperarousal in these patients.

The EEGs of patients with anxiety are characterized by a low output in the alpha-band, a poor alpha-organization, and a reduced amplitude of the contingent negative variation. According to Koella (1981) these signs "indicate a disbalance in the activity and reactivity of the neuronal systems that control the level of general and discrete vigilance" (p. 187).

The behavioral manifestation of generalized anxiety disorder depends on the intensity of the anxiety, type of stressors, available, coping mechanisms, and personality factors. Patients with mild or moderate anxiety are able to hide it from other people. When they become highly anxious, their faces appear flushed or pale, they may exhibit some tremor, their hands may be sweaty and cold, and, in interactions with other people, they may show various levels of disorganization. A person with an outgoing Type A personality may try to cope with anxiety through aggressive activities, while a passive and avoidant person may retreat into a shell. Persons with obsessive personality traits worry continuously, while persons with hysterical traits demonstrate their anxieties in a dramatic manner, but are able to put them out of their minds when they are not facing the stressors directly.

Longitudinal Course and Complicating Factors

Generalized anxiety tends to have a prolonged course (Anderson et al., 1984; Barlow, Blanchard, Vermilyea, Vermilyea, & Di Wardo, 1986). The course tends to fluctuate and severity frequently depends on the degree and number of perceived external stressors.

Anxious patients acquire phobic reactions faster than nonanxious persons and are less likely to desensitize (Ohman, Fredrikson, & Hugdahl, 1978). Therefore, patients with increased anxiety are prone to form avoidance behavior which can take on phobic characteristics. The phobic reactions, however, usually are less intense than those in circumscribed phobias or in patients with severe agoraphobia. An anxious patient, for instance, who had an unpleasant experience on a bus may start to avoid taking buses, but will travel by bus if absolutely necessary. Constant worrying is a characteristic of generalized anxiety disorder and, at times, these ruminations may approach obsessive-compulsive proportions. Moreover, some patients with mild and clinically irrelevant obsessive-compulsive symptoms may find that these symptoms are exaggerated and disturbing at times of increased anxiety. Because patients with chronic anxiety frequently become demoralized, they also are prone to transitory depressions. Finally, chronic anxiety predisposes certain people to substance abuse.

Assessment

To diagnose generalized anxiety disorder, one must first exclude various physical illnesses, such as endocrine, cardiovascular, and pulmonary diseases, which may cause increased anxiety. In addition, patients who engage in substance abuse may present themselves as having generalized anxiety disorder. The dividing line between generalized anxiety disorder and other psychiatric disorders, especially other anxiety disorders and depression, is a fluid one (Hoehn-Saric & McLeod, 1985a). For example, the definition of where normal anxiety ends and pathological anxiety begins frequently is left to the judgment of the clinician. The dividing line between phobic disorders and obsessive–compulsive disorders is equally fluid because many normal persons have clinically insignificant phobic or obsessive symptoms. If such symptoms become amplified during times of heightened anxiety, a patient may be classified in one or the other category. The distinction between a case of generalized anxiety disorder and one of depressive disorder may also cause problems. Some elements of depression frequently are present in anxiety disorders, while a large number of depressed people also experience anxiety.

The differential diagnosis between generalized anxiety disorder and dysthymic disorder depends more on the level of depression than on the severity of anxiety (Hoehn-Saric, 1983; Lipman, 1982). Moreover, in anxiety disorders, symptoms of anxiety are persistent while depression is short-lived and occurs as a reaction to some discrete event. In depressive disorders, symptoms of depression are pervasive, while anxiety occurs more intermittently. Finally, anxiety disorders usually begin at an early age; if a person has the first bout of anxiety in his or her 40s or 50s, an agitated depression rather than a primary anxiety disorder should be suspected.

BIOLOGY OF ANXIETY DISORDERS

The psychobiology of anxiety is complex. Several neurotransmitter systems play an important role in the regulation of anxiety (Hoehn-Saric, 1982b, 1985). The benzodiazepine-GABA system lowers hyperarousal and decreases somatic symptoms. The noradrenergic system appears to serve as an amplification system which may increase the level of anxiety and be responsible for fluctuations in anxiety, including panic attacks (Hoehn-Saric, Merchant, Keyser, & Smith, 1981; Redmond & Huang, 1979). Both the noradrenergic and the serotonergic systems may be involved in alteration of psychic symptoms of anxiety, especially excessive worrying and rumination (Hoehn-Saric, McLeod, & Zimmerli, 1986). Recently a number of medications that affect selectively the serotonergic receptors have been found to be anxiolytic (Hoehn-Saric, 1985). Anxiety disorder patients appear to be in a state of hyperarousal and are oversensitive to medications that increase noradrenergic activity or antagonize adenosine (Charney et al., 1984). The primary cause of hyperarousal, however, is not known. Endogenous ligands affecting the benzodiazepine receptor have been postulated, but not confirmed (Hoehn-Saric, 1982b).

The underlying causes of panic disorder remain obscure. Abnormality in chemoreceptors, which may affect the locus coeruleus–noradrenergic system, have been postulated (Carr & Sheehan, 1984). This theory attempts to explain why such diverse challenges as hyperventilation, inhalation of CO_2, or sodium lactate infusion can induce panic attacks. Other theories focus on a possible malfunction of the locus coeruleus, which may act as an "alarm system" when overstimulated. Animal studies (Redmond & Huang, 1979), as well as the finding that reduction of noradrenergic activity blocks panic attacks, support this hypothesis (Hoehn-Saric et al., 1981). Recently, Reiman et al. (1986) demonstrated circulatory and metabolic abnormalities in the parahippocampal gyrus of patients with panic attacks. The threshold for panic attacks may be lowered by heightened anxiety, or by procedures that increase arousal but generally do not cause panic attacks in the normal population. Such procedures include yohimbine administration (Charney et al., 1984), CO_2 inhalation (van den Hout & Griez, 1984), caffeine ingestion (Charney, Henirger, & Jatlow, 1985), and infusion of isoproterenol (Rainey et al., 1984). On the other hand, a decrease in anxiety due to psychological interventions (Guttmacher & Nelles, 1984) increases the threshold for panic attacks, as does desensitization due to repeated administration of certain panic-inducing substances, such as CO_2 (Griez & van den Hout, 1983) or sodium lactate infusion (Bonn, Harrison, & Rees, 1973). These findings may explain why panic attacks respond both to pharmacological and to psychological interventions.

CONCLUDING REMARKS

Generalized anxiety disorder phenomenologically is closer to normal anxiety than other anxiety disorders, and may occur alone or as a part of other anxiety disorders, such as panic disorder, phobic disorder, or obsessive-compulsive disorder. It also occures frequently in depressive disorders and often a sharp division between the two disorders cannot be made (Hoehn-Saric & McLeod, 1985a). Within the context of other disorders, generalized anxiety can exist independently, it may precede the appearance of other symptoms, or it may remain present even when symptoms of other disorders have disappeared. For instance, patients with panic disorder may no longer suffer from panic attacks, but may retain high levels of generalized anxiety. The manifestations of generalized anxiety disorder are influenced by a physiological predisposition that results in a diversity of somatic symptoms. They also are determined by personality traits. For example, we may observe aggressive activities in a Type A personality, withdrawal in an avoidant personality, dramatic responses in the histrionic, or quiet and persistent rumination in the obsessive person. The manifestations of generalized anxiety disorder and panic disorder also are influenced by a patient's locus of control (Hoehn-Saric & McLeod, 1985b). Generalized anxiety disorder tends to occur early in life and have a protracted course, with alternating periods of improvement and relapse.

In contrast to generalized anxiety, panic disorder occurs in persons with a definite family history and predisposition. It appears that heightened arousal induced through anxiety or by pharmacological means lowers the threshold for panic attacks. The first attack frequently occurs during periods of heightened stress, and subsequent attacks are elicited in tension-producing situations or after ingestion of stimulants. Panic disorder varies considerably in severity and frequency of the attacks and can lead to phobic avoidance of situations in which attacks have occurred in the past. The type and degree of avoidance depends on the severity of the disorder, but is modified by personality characteristics.

The prognosis and treatment of both anxiety disorders depend on the severity of the condition, on personality factors, and on the presence of external stressors. Psychological interventions are necessary for the patient to learn to cope with everyday problems. In addition, a panic disorder patient needs to accept the attacks and to overcome avoidance behavior. Antidepressants are useful in modifying psychic symptoms, specifically the tendency to worry excessively and the dysphoria that frequently accompanies both disorders. In addition, antidepressants, as well as alprazolam, help to prevent the recurrence of panic attacks. Acute symptoms of both conditions respond to benzodiazepines, and these drugs remain the treatment of choice in reducing hyerarousal and physical symptoms on an acute basis.

REFERENCES

Akiskal, H. S. (1985). Anxiety: Definition, relationship to depression, and proposal for an integrative model. In A. H. Tuma & J. Maser (Eds.), *Anxiety and the anxiety disorders* (pp. 787–797). Hillsdale, NJ: Lawrence Erlbaum.

American Psychiatric Association (1980). *Diagnostic and statistical manual of mental disorders* (3rd ed.). Washington, DC: Author.

Anderson, D. J., Noyes, R. Jr., & Crowe, R. R. (1984). A comparison of panic disorder and generalized anxiety disorder. *American Journal of Psychiatry, 141,* 572–575.

Barlow, D. H. (1985). The dimensions of anxiety disorders. In A. H. Tuma & J. Maser (Eds.), *Anxiety and the anxiety disorders* (pp. 479–500). Hillsdale, NJ: Lawrence Erlbaum.

Barlow, D. H., Blanchard, E. B., Vermilyea, J. A., Vermilyea, B. B., & DiNardo, P. A. (1986). Generalized anxiety and generalized anxiety disorder: Description and reconceptualization. *American Journal of Psychiatry, 143,* 40–44.

Bass, C., & Gardner, W. (1985). Emotional influences on breathing and breathlessness. *Journal of Psychosomatic Research, 29,* 599–609.

Bonn, J., Harrison, J., & Rees, W. (1973). Lactate infusion in the treatment of "free-floating anxiety." *Canadian Psychiatric Association Journal, 18,* 41–45.

Bowen, R. C., & Kohout, J. (1979). The relationship between agoraphobia and primary affective disorders. *Canadian Psychiatric Association Journal, 24,* 317–322.

Carr, D. & Sheehan, D. (1984). Panic anxiety: A new biological model. *Journal of Clinical Psychiatry, 45,* 323–330.

Charney, D. S., Heninger, G. R., & Breier, A. (1984). Noradrenergic function in panic anxiety. *Archives of General Psychiatry, 41,* 751–763.

Charney, D. S., Heninger, G. R., & Jatlow, P. I. (1985). Increased anxiogenic effects of caffeine in panic disorders. *Archives of General Psychiatry, 42,* 233–243.

Cloninger, C. R., Martin, R. L., Clayton, P., & Guze, S. B. (1981). A blind follow-up and family study of anxiety neurosis: Preliminary analysis of the St. Louis 500. In D. F. Klein & J. G. Rabkin (Eds.), *Anxiety: New research and changing concepts* (pp. 137–154). New York: Raven Press.

Coryell, W., Noyes, R. Jr., & House, J. D. (1986). Mortality among outpatients with anxiety disorders. *American Journal of Psychiatry, 143,* 508–510.

Crowe, R. R., Noyes, R. Jr., Pauls, D. L., & Slymen, D. (1983). A family study of panic disorder. *Archives of General Psychiatry, 40,* 1065–1069.

Curtis, G. C., Nesse, R., Buxton, M., & Lippman, D. (1979). Plasma growth hormone: effect of anxiety during flooding in vivo. *American Journal of Psychiatry, 136,* 410–414.

Dager, S. R., Comess, K. A., & Dunner, D. L. (1986). Differentiation of anxious patients by two-dimensional echocardiographic evaluation of the mitral valve. *American Journal of Psychiatry, 143,* 533–536.

Deltito, J. A. (1986, April). *The relationship of childhood separation anxiety to panic disorder in a multinational sample.* Paper presented at the Panic Disorder Biological Research Workshop, Washington, DC.

Freedman, R. R., Ianni, P., Ettedgui, E., & Puthezhath, N. (1985). Ambulatory monitoring of panic disorder. *Archives of General Psychiatry, 42,* 244–248.

Gittelman, R., & Klein, D. F. (1984). Relationship between separation anxiety and panic and agoraphobic disorders. *Psychopathology, 17,* (Suppl. 1), 56–65.

Griez, E., & van den Hout, M. A. (1983). Treatment of phobophobia by exposure to CO_2-induced anxiety symptoms. *The Journal of Nervous and Mental Diseases, 171,* 506–508.

Guttmacher, L. B., & Nelles, C. (1984). In vivo desensitization alteration of lactate-induced panic: A case study. *Behavior Therapy, 15,* 369–372.

Hauri, P. J., Ravaris, C. L., & Friedman, M. J. (1986, April). *Sleep laboratory evaluation and double-blind medication trials in patients with panic disorder*. Paper presented at the Panic Disorder Biological Research Workshop, Washington, DC.

Hibbert, G. A. (1984). Ideational components of anxiety: Their origin and content. *British Journal of Psychiatry, 144*, 618–624.

Hoehn-Saric, R. (1982a). Comparison of generalized disorder with panic disorder patients. *Psychopharmacology Bulletin, 18*, 104–108.

Hoehn-Saric, R. (1982b). Neurotransmitters in anxiety. *Archives of General Psychiatry, 39*, 735–742.

Hoehn-Saric, R. (1983). Affective profiles of chronically anxious patients. *Hillside Journal of Clinical Psychiatry, 5*, 43–56.

Hoehn-Saric, R. (1985). Neurotransmitters in anxiety: A reappraisal. In G. D. Burrows, T. R. Norman, & L. Dennerstein (Eds.), *Clinical and pharmacological studies in psychiatric disorders* (pp. 105–110). London: John Libbey.

Hoehn-Saric, R., & McLeod, D. R. (1985a). Generalized anxiety disorder. In G. C. Curtis, B. A. Thyer, & J. M. Rainey (Eds.), *Psychiatric clinics of North America 8* (No. 1), (pp. 73–88). Philadelphia: W. B. Saunders Co.

Hoehn-Saric, R., & McLeod, D. R. (1985b). Locus of control in chronic anxiety disorders. *Acta Psychiatrica Scandinavica, 72*, 529–535.

Hoehn-Saric, R., & McLeod, D. R., & Zimmerli, W. D., (1986). Differential effects of alprazolam and imipramine in generalized anxiety: I. Somatic versus psychic symptoms. Manuscript submitted for publication.

Hoehn-Saric, R., Merchant, A., Keyser, M., & Smith, V. K. (1981). Effects of clonidine on anxiety disorders. *Archives of General Psychiatry, 38*, 1278–1282.

Ilfeld, F. W. J. (1979). Persons at high risk for symptoms of anxiety. In B. Brown (Ed.), *Clinical anxiety/tension in primary medicine*. Princeton, NJ: Excerpta Medica.

Jacob, R. G., Moller, M. B., Turner, S. M., & Wall, C. III. (1985). Otoneurological examination of panic disorder and agoraphobia with panic attacks: A pilot study. *American Journal of Psychiatry, 142*, 715–719.

Kelly, D., Mitchell-Heggs, N., & Sherman, D. (1971). Anxiety and the effects of sodium lactate assessed clinically and physiologically. *British Journal of Psychiatry, 119*, 129–141.

Knott, V., Chaudhry, R., & LaPierre, Y. D. (1981). Panic induced by sodium lactate-Electrophysiological correlates. Progress in Neuro-Psychopharmacology, 5, 511–514.

Koella, W. P. (1981). Electroencephalographic signs of anxiety. *Progress in Neuro-Psychopharmacology, 5*, 187–192.

Lader, M. (1983). Behavior and anxiety: Physiological mechanisms. *Journal of Clinical Psychiatry, 44*, 5–10.

Lader, M. & Mathews, A. (1970). Physiological changes during spontaneous panic attacks. *Journal of Psychosomatic Research, 14*, 377–382.

LaPierre, Y. D., Knott, V. J., & Gray, R. (1984). Psychophysiological correlates of sodium lactate. *Psychopharmacology Bulletin, 20*, 50–57.

Levav, I., & Abramson, J. H. (1984). Emotional distress among concentration camp survivors: A community study in Jerusalem. *Psychological Medicine, 14*, 215–218.

Liberthson, R., Sheehan, D. V., King, M. E., & Weyman, A. E. (1986). The prevalence of mitral valve prolapse in patients with panic disorder. *American Journal of Psychiatry, 143*, 511–515.

Liebowitz, M. R., Fyer, A. J., Gorman, J. M., Dillon, D., Appleby, I. L., Levy, G., Anderson, S., Levitt, M., Palij, M., Davies, S. O., & Klein, D. F. (1984). Lactate provocation of panic attacks: I. Clinical and behavioral findings. *Archives of General Psychiatry, 41*, 764–770.

Liebowitz, M. R., Gorman, J. M., Fyer, A., Dillon, D., Levitt, M., & Klein, D. F. (1986). Possible mechanisms for lactate's induction of panic. *American Journal of Psychiatry, 143*, 495–502.

Liebowitz, M. R., Gorman, J. M., Fyer, A. J., Levitt, M., Dillon, D., Levy, G. Appleby, I. L., Anderson, S., Palij, M., Davies, S. O., & Klein, D. F. (1985). Lactate provocation of panic attacks: II. Biochemical and physiological findings. *Archives of General Psychiatry, 42*, 709–719.

Lindemann, C. G., Zitrin, C. M., & Klein, D. F. (1984). Thyroid dysfunction in phobic patients. *Psychosomatics, 25*, 603–606.

Lipman, R. S. (1982). Differentiating anxiety and depression in anxiety disorders: Use of rating scales. *Psychopharmacology Bulletin, 18*, 69–72.

Margraf, J., Ehlers, A., & Roth, W. T. (1986). Sodium lactate infusions and panic attacks: A review and critique. *Psychosomatic Medicine, 48*, 23–51.

Mathew, R. M., Ho, B. T., Kralik, P., & Claghorn, J. L. (1979). Anxiety and serum prolactin. *American Journal of Psychiatry, 136*, 716–717.

McLeod, D. R., Hoehn-Saric, R., & Stefan, R. L. (1986). Somatic symptoms of anxiety: Comparison of self-report and physiological measures. *Biological Psychiatry, 21,* 301–310.

Munjack, M., & Moss, H. B. (1981). Affective disorder and alcoholism in families of agoraphobics. *Archives of General Psychiatry, 38,* 869–871.

Ohman, A., Fredrikson, M., & Hugdahl, K. (1978). Towards an experimental model for simple phobic reactions. *Behavioural Analysis and Modification, 2,* 97–114.

Pitts, F., & McClure, J. (1967). Lactate metabolism in anxiety neurosis. *New England Journal of Medicine, 277,* 1329–1336.

Rainey, J. M., Pohl, R. B., Williams, M., Knitter, E., Freedman, R. R., & Ettedgui, E. (1984). A comparison of lactate and isoproterenol anxiety states. *Psychopathology, 17,* (Suppl. 1), 74–82.

Raskin, M., Peeke, H. V. S., Dickman, W., & Pinsker, H. (1982). Panic and generalized anxiety disorders. *Archives of General Psychiatry, 39,* 687–689.

Redmond, D. E. Jr., & Huang, Y. H. (1979). Current concepts II. New evidence for a locus coeruleus — norepinephrine connection with anxiety. *Life Science, 25,* 2149–2162.

Reich, J. (1986). The epidemiology of anxiety. *The Journal of Nervous and Mental Diseases, 174,* 129–136.

Reiman, E. M., Raichle, M. E., Robins, E., Butler, F. K., Herscovitch, P., Fox, P., & Perlmutter, J. (1986). The application of positron emission tomography to the study of panic disorder. *American Journal of Psychiatry, 143,* 463–477.

Reynolds, C. F. III, Shaw, D. H., Newton, T. F., Coble, P. A., & Kupfer, D. J. (1983). EEG sleep in outpatients with generalized anxiety: A preliminary comparison with depressed outpatients. *Psychiatry Research, 8,* 81–89.

Roy-Byrne, P. P., Bierer, L. M., & Uhde, T. W. (1985). The dexamethasone suppression test in panic disorder: Comparison with normal controls. *Biological Psychiatry, 20,* 1234–1237.

Sheehan, D. V. (1982). Panic attacks and phobias. *The New England Journal of Medicine, 307,* 156–158.

Starkman, M. N., Zelnik, T. C., Nesse, R. M., & Cameron, O. G. (1985). Anxiety in patients with pheochromocytomas. *Archives of Internal Medicine, 145,* 248–252.

Taylor, C. B., Sheikh, J., Agras, S., Roth, W. T., Margraf, J., Ehlers, A., Maddock, R. J., & Gossard, D. (1986). Ambulatory heart rate changes in patients with panic attacks. *American Journal of Psychiatry, 143,* 478–482.

Thyer, B. A., Nesse, R. M., Cameron, O. G., & Curtis, G. C. (1985). Agoraphobia: A test of the separation anxiety hypothesis. *Behavior Research and Therapy, 23,* 75–78.

Thyer, B. A., Parrish, R. T., Curtis, G. C., Nesse, R. M., & Cameron, O. G. (1985). Ages of onset of DSM-III anxiety disorders. *Comprehensive Psychiatry, 26,* 113–122.

Thomas, A., & Chess, S. (1977). *Temperament and development.* New York: Brunner-Mazel.

Thomas, A., & Chess, S. (1984). Genesis and evolution of behavioral disorders: From infancy to early school life. *American Journal of Psychiatry, 141,* 1–9.

Torgersen, S. (1983). Genetic factors in anxiety disorders. *Archives of General Psychiatry, 40,* 1085–1089.

Torgersen, S. (1986). Childhood and family characteristics in panic and generalized anxiety disorders. *American Journal of Psychiatry, 143,* 630–632.

Uhde, T. W., Boulenger, J. P., Roy-Byrne, P. R., Geraci, M. F., Vittone, B. J., & Post, R. M. (1985). Longitudinal course of panic disorder: Clinical and biological considerations. *Progress in Neuro-Psychopharmacology and Biological Psychiatry, 9,* 39–51.

Ursin, H., Baade, E., & Levine, S. (1978). *Psychobiology of stress.* New York: Academic Press.

van den Hout, M. A., & Griez, E. (1984). Panic symptoms after inhalation of carbon dioxide. *British Journal of Psychiatry, 144,* 503–507.

Waddell, M. T., Barlow, D. H., & O'Brien, G. T. (1984). A preliminary investigation of cognitive and relaxation treatment of panic disorder: Effects on intense anxiety vs "background" anxiety. *Behavior Research and Therapy, 22,* 393–402.

Weiner, H. (1985). The psychobiology and pathophysiology of anxiety and fear. In A. H. Tuma & J. Maser (Eds.), *Anxiety and the anxiety disorders* (pp. 333–354). Hillsdale, NJ: Lawrence Erlbaum.

Weissman, M. M. (1985). The epidemiology of anxiety disorders: rates, risks and familial patterns. In A. H. Tuma & J. Maser (Eds.), *Anxiety and the anxiety disorders* (pp. 275–296). Hillsdale, NJ: Lawrence Erlbaum.

West, M. (1981). Agoraphobia. *The Lancet, 2,* 1039–1040.

Windheuser, H. J. (1977). Anxious mothers as models for coping with anxiety. *Behavioural Analysis and Modification, 2,* 39–58.

CHAPTER 7

Posttraumatic Stress Disorder*

Herbert Hendin and Ann Pollinger Haas

Much of what we know about what is now called posttraumatic stress disorder has been learned through war. From seeing the effects of exposure to violent death in combat soldiers, prisoners of war, concentration camp survivors, and survivors of the atomic explosions of Hiroshima and Nagasaki, clinicians came to recognize the distinct symptoms of this disorder.

When some of the symptoms such as nightmares, insomnia, an excessive startle reaction to loud noise, and outbursts of anger were first recognized among hospitalized veterans of World War I, the condition was assumed to be relatively rare. If we pitied "shell-shocked" combat survivors, we also judged them to be an unfortunate minority who paid a high price for their participation in the war. Only since World War II have we begun to realize that exposure to the possibility of sudden death and witnessing the violent deaths of others — whether in the context of war or through civilian accidents, crime, or disasters — have lasting traumatic consequences for a high percentage of individuals.

CONCEPTUAL DEVELOPMENT

Even before World War I, long-term reactions had been observed in victims of civilian traumas, ranging from railway accidents to being struck by lightning. This was considered a consequence of physical injury to the nervous system, carrying the names of various agents thought to have provoked it; for example, "lightning neurosis" or "railway spine" (Timble, 1981). The common use of the

*This chapter is based on an intensive study of Vietnam veterans, published by the authors in *Wounds of War: The Psychological Aftermath of Combat in Vietnam* (N.Y.: Basic Books, 1984), and on research with civilian victims which is currently being funded by the Harry Frank Guggenheim Foundation.

term *shell shock* to describe combat reactions among soldiers in World War I was a natural extension of this prevailing view. Although personality changes involving alternations between apathy and overexcitability were also observed in trauma victims, these responses were seen as secondary to physical injury.

Early in his career, Sigmund Freud recognized the similarity of the way in which symptoms developed in what was then called traumatic neurosis and hysteria. In both disorders, he found that strong emotion associated with a traumatic situation had been repressed, with subsequent development of symptoms that were psychologically linked to the original trauma (Breuer & Freud, 1955). During the early part of World War I, Freud's colleagues believed they had confirmed his views in their observations of the traumatic reactions of soldiers to combat. The predominance of neuropsychiatric opinion, however, continued to favor the view that the disorder was primarily physical.

By the end of World War I, when it was evident that the symptoms of traumatic war neurosis were seen in combat soldiers who had experienced no physical trauma, there began a growing acceptance of Freud's view of the psychological basis of the disorder (Freud, Ferenczi, Abraham, Simmel, & Jones, 1921). Freud himself had begun to approach the problem in a somewhat different direction, stimulated by a contradiction that traumatic neurosis seemed to pose to his theories. How were repetitive nightmares of combat to be reconciled with his belief that wish fulfillment was the motivating force behind dreams? Peacetime nightmares could be linked to punishment for forbidden sexual wishes, but repetitive combat nightmares could not be so easily explained.

Consideration of this question led Freud to a new view of trauma. In *Beyond the Pleasure Principle* (1948), he considered trauma to involve a breaking through of the individual's defense against stimuli (*reitzschutz*). He saw traumatic neurosis as a result of fright (*schreck*) — a condition occurring when one encountered a danger without being adequately prepared. The repetitive dream was an attempt to be prepared after the fact, to dissipate by repetition the anxiety generated by the experience. For a comparable example of mastery by repetition, Freud used observations he had made of an infant who dealt with the anxiety of being separated from his mother by repeating a game in which he threw his toys away and then took considerable pleasure in finding them again.

Using Freud's *reitzschutz* theory as a starting point, Kardiner incorporated reactions to trauma into an adaptational frame of reference, providing the basis for much of contemporary thinking on post-traumatic stress (Kardiner & Spiegel, 1947). Kardiner saw trauma as an alteration in the individual's usual environment in which the adaptive maneuvers suitable to previous situations no longer sufficed. With the balance between the organism and its adaptive equipment broken, a new adaptation was not possible, and the individual accommodated his or her shrunken inner resources with the development of symptoms.

In his work with World War I veterans with chronic traumatic neuroses, Kardiner saw certain constant features of the disorder: fixation on the trauma, repetitive nightmares, irritability, exaggerated reactions to unexpected noise (startle reactions), proclivity to explosive aggressive behavior, and a contraction of the general level of functioning, including intellectual ability. He also saw loss of interest in activity as a result of the breakup of organized channels of action which were replaced by periodic outbursts of disorganized aggression. The internal conception of the self became altered, confidence was lost, the world was seen as a hostile place, and the patient lived in perpetual dread of being overwhelmed. To Kardiner, combat nightmares were the result of this altered conception of oneself and the outer world.

After World War II observations of concentration camp survivors (Eitinger, 1969; Krystal, 1968; Niederland, 1968), studies of the Japanese survivors of atomic explosions (Lifton, 1968), studies of the survivors of natural disasters (Lifton & Olson, 1976) and other traumatic experiences in civilian life (Horowitz, 1976), and additional work with combat veterans (Archibald & Tuddenham, 1965; Futterman & Pumpian-Mindlin, 1951) added new perspectives to our understanding of posttraumatic stress. The American involvement in Vietnam gave even further impetus to the conceptualization of the disorder (Horowitz & Solomon, 1975; Hendin & Haas, 1984b).

Among combat veterans, concentration camp survivors, and victims of civilian trauma, many individuals were observed who seemed to adjust well immediately after their traumatic experience, but later developed symptoms, in some cases many years afterward. The concept of "delayed stress," so dramatically apparent in Vietnam combat veterans, was actually a reaffirmation of what had been observed in earlier studies. Moreover, among all stressed populations, it became evident that in large numbers of cases the incapacitating consequences of trauma not only persisted, but often worsened when reenforced by stresses in the individual's subsequent life.

Work with both soldiers and civilians exposed to life-threatening trauma emphasized the relationship of two contrasting aspects of the stress response: the tendency to re-experience the anxiety of the trauma in nightmares or daytime thoughts, images, and emotions; and a mechanism of numbing or emotional withdrawal. The repetition continued to be seen as a reflection of an effort toward completion or mastery of the trauma, while the numbing came to be considered an attempt to ward off or diminish the intense anxiety of intolerable ideas and emotions.

DIAGNOSTIC ISSUES

These contrasting aspects of the stress response were used as the basis for defining the initial set of diagnostic criteria for a posttraumatic stress disorder (PTSD), which appeared in the third edition of the *Diagnostic and Statistical Manual of Mental Disorders* (American Psychiatric Association, 1980). According to the DSM-III definition, the diagnosis of PTSD depends on the presence of a recognizable traumatic stressor, specified as a psychologically traumatic event "that is generally outside the range of usual human experience". (DSM III, p. 236.) Most who work with posttraumatic stress emphasize the roots of the disorder in the encounter with the possibility of sudden violent death. Indeed, memories and images associated with death are so central that Lifton (1968) has described such trauma as causing a "death imprint."

In the presence of the traumatic stressor, persistent re-experiencing of the event — in the form of recurrent nightmares, intrusive recollections, or reliving experiences (flashbacks) — were deemed essential to the diagnosis as was emotional numbing. The DSM-III diagnostic criteria included six other symptoms, at least two of which had to be present to make the diagnosis: exaggerated startle response, insomnia, exacerbation of symptoms by events that recall the trauma, avoidance of such events, guilt over what might have been done to survive or guilt over surviving when others had died, and difficulty with memory and concentration. Anxiety, depression, and irritability with explosive outbursts of anger were listed as frequently associated symptoms, but not as necessary criteria for the diagnosis of the disorder.

By making it possible for researchers to study and communicate shared diagnostic criteria, the DSM-III description widened the scope of clinical work on PTSD while serving as a powerful research stimulus. A bibliography recently compiled for the Veterans Administration (Arnold, 1984) lists over 600 citations dealing with posttraumatic stress and related problems stemming from combat experiences. Likewise, a National Institute of Mental Health bibliography focusing on the psychological aftermath of environmental and community disasters in civilian life (Ahearn & Cohen, 1984) currently includes almost 300 citations, a large proportion dealing specifically with PTSD. Although less attention has been given to traumatic experiences involving only one or a few people in any particular occurrence, considerable evidence has emerged that PTSD frequently develops among victims of rape (Martin, Warfield, & Braer, 1983; Nadelson, Notman, Jackson, & Gornick, 1982), survivors of vehicular accidents (Burnstein, 1983), and police officers involved in life-threatening situations (Stratton, Parker, & Snibbe, 1984).

The extensive empirical work of PTSD has refined the conceptualization of the disorder and prompted considerable discussion of symptom reclassification. This has led to a revision of the DSM-III diagnostic criteria, recently published as DSM-III-R (American Psychiatric Association, 1987).

In the revised definition, posttraumatic stress symptoms are reorganized under three key headings:

A. Persistent re-experiencing of the traumatic event in at least one of the following ways: (1) recurrent and intrusive recollections of the event, (2) recurrent distressing dreams of the event, (3) reliving experiences, or (4) intense psychological distress at exposure to events resembling the trauma.
B. Persistent avoidance of stimuli associated with the trauma of numbing of general responsiveness (not present before the trauma), as indicated by at least three of the following: (1) efforts to avoid thoughts or feelings associated with the trauma, (2) efforts to avoid activities or situations that arouse recollections, (3) psychogenic amnesia, (4) markedly diminished interest in significant activities, (5) feelings of detachment or estrangement from others, (6) restricted range of affect, or (7) sense of a foreshortened future.
C. Persistent symptoms of increased arousal (not present before the trauma), as indicated by at least two of the following: (1) difficulty falling or staying asleep, (2) irritability or outbursts of anger, (3) difficulty concentrating, (4) hypervigilance, (5) exaggerated startle response, or (6) physiologic reactivity upon exposure to events resembling the trauma.

For the diagnosis of PTSD to be made, DSM-III-R requires that all three categories of symptoms must be met during the same period of at least 1 month. A delayed onset is specified if the symptoms first occurred at least 6 months after the trauma. Finally, in the revised criteria, guilt is no longer among the symptoms used in making the actual diagnosis of PTSD, although it is regarded as an associated feature in cases where a life-threatening trauma is shared with others.

DSM-III represented an essentially successful attempt to embrace within one diagnostic framework the consequences of very different traumatic experiences, and this is likely to be found true as well for DSM-III-R. These consequences have enough in common to make the criteria usable for diagnostic purposes, but that should not blur important differences among survivors of different kinds of trauma (Krupnick & Horowitz, 1981).

It is true, for example, that traumatic stress reactions without survivor guilt are frequently seen among both soldiers and civilians exposed to life-threatening danger — especially if no one's life was actually lost. In the case of other individuals, however — perhaps most notably, survivors of the concentration camps and the Japanese atomic explosions — guilt appears to be at the core of the disorder. The fact that the likelihood of survival for Jewish inmates of concentration camps was remote, and that those who died were often close family members, undoubtedly contributed to the high incidence of survivor guilt in this population. A similar high casualty rate among family members was probably responsible for the high frequency of survivor guilt among the survivors of the atomic explosions.

Among survivors of other traumatic experiences, feelings of guilt as a central feature of the stress disorder are often related to what might have been done to save others from dying, or to one's behavior during the trauma. To a degree unparalleled in our earlier wars, combat in Vietnam involved the killing of women, children, and the elderly: Some of those killed were armed fighters, some were killed inadvertently, and some were killed in retaliation for deaths caused by their countrymen. Regardless of the circumstances, and even in situations where the veteran had to kill to save his life, guilt over such killing is profoundly disturbing to most veterans and plays, in comparison with other wars and traumas, a far more significant role in the stress disorders of Vietnam veterans.

In a related vein, survivors of traumatic experiences vary considerably in their expression of anger and aggression. The absence of physical aggression in concentration camp survivors has been documented, particularly among those who reacted to their persecution with overwhelming fear and a profound sense of helplessness (Trautman, 1964). But physical aggression, often explosive in character, is a common feature of the stress disorder in veterans of war. While physical aggression was not compatible with survival in concentration camp inmates, the soldier learned during combat to use his aggression toward the enemy to reduce his anxiety, epitomized in the basic act of firing his gun. That the veteran who develops posttraumatic stress continues to use his aggression to diminish fear in peacetime is not surprising.

THE MEANING OF TRAUMA

Knowledge of either the specific stress symptoms produced or the nature of the trauma that produced them is not sufficient to understand or treat posttraumatic stress disorders. Our own work with Vietnam combat veterans (Hendin & Haas, 1984a, 1984b; Hendin, Haas, Singer, Gold, & Trigos, 1983; Hendin, Pollinger, Singer, & Ulman, 1981), as well as with civilians suffering from PTSD, has made clear that the response to trauma is not only a function of the event the individual encountered, but also of the specific ways he or she experienced that event, what it meant at the time, and what it continues to represent in the posttraumatic period.

Two veterans we have seen, for example, had nearly identical experiences of witnessing, from the ground, captured Vietcong being pushed to their deaths from helicopters during aerial interrogation. One man identified strongly with the helplessness of the victims, a response that was related to his dominant perception of combat as entailing being the victim of events over which he had no control. His perception was the outgrowth of attitudes stemming from early family experiences in which he had been unable to influence the favored treatment his parents gave to his older and younger brothers. The second man felt strongly that had he been in the plane, he could have prevented the prisoner's death. His perception, too, was consistent with his reactions throughout combat. He was a much-decorated squad leader, proud that none of the men in his command was killed. His posttraumatic stress disorder was triggered after his return home when he learned that one of the men in his squad was killed following a foolish order by the new squad leader. He felt that had he still been there, this man would have lived. The attitudes and behavior he displayed in combat were the outgrowth of a preservice adaptation in which he and his siblings effectively supported each other because of the emotional unavailability of their parents.

Although the first veteran would likely have had difficulties in adult life whether or not he went to Vietnam, the second man, who functioned well in combat and who both before and during the war demonstrated a capacity for caring, supportive relationships, would probably not have developed serious problems as an adult had it not been for combat. Yet, his pre-existing personality was an integral part of the meaning he gave to his combat experience, and directly affected the form and expression of his posttraumatic stress disorder.

Understanding the role of the subjective experience or *meaning* of trauma permits us to resolve some of the confusion surrounding the impact of pre-existing personality factors on the development of posttraumatic stress disorder. Those who consider such factors to be critical have tended to see the stress syndrome as a more usual form of neurosis. Those who have seen them as having minimal importance in the development of posttraumatic stress disorders have tended to view the traumatic event as sufficiently and inherently stressful to result in long-term reactions among most who are exposed to it.

Such a dichotomy, in our experience, is conceptually misleading. The fact that a posttraumatic stress disorder may develop in anyone subjected to a sufficient amount of stress does not mean that precombat personality factors do not play a critical role. We have found that who the individual was prior to the traumatic experience is, in most cases, significant and sometimes decisive in shaping the way in which the posttraumatic stress disorder develops. This does not imply that a personality disorder was present or would have developed without the traumatic stress or even that such individuals are more vulnerable to stress in any general sense. Rather, it is indicative of the importance of close examination of pretraumatic as well as traumatic factors in attempting to understand the meaning of the experience to the individual and his or her subsequent adaptation to it. The following case of a civilian trauma victim is illustrative:

CASE STUDY

Mrs. W is a married woman in her late 20s who lives with her husband and 2-year-old son. She was referred by her attorney for evaluation of the traumatic psychological effects produced by a head-on automobile collision in the spring of 1981, and was seen for a total of 5 hours. Her manner in the interviews was cooperative and friendly, but when taken back to the specific events of the accident and its aftermath, she became upset and tearful. At times she had difficulty grasping questions related to the accident, although she appeared generally intelligent and had no difficulty understanding and responding quickly to questions on any other subject.

Mrs, W was the third child of a couple who divorced soon after her birth. She saw her father a few times, but only during the first years of her life. When as a teenager she tried to contact him, she learned he had died. Her mother was a chronic alcoholic and lived for a number of years with a man, whom Mrs. W regarded as her stepfather and toward whom she felt somewhat closer than to her mother. He also drank excessively, frequently abusing her mother physically when he was intoxicated; her mother in turn was often physically abusive to her children after drinking. During her adolescence she lived for various periods of time with other relatives. With their help and her own self-determination she managed to finish high school.

At the age of 19, she moved to another state to make a new life for herself. In her new environment, she became deeply involved with a conservative religious group in which she found both spiritual peace and a longed-for sense of family. In early 1981 she decided to go abroad with several members of her church. She was back in her hometown making preparations for her trip when she was involved in the automobile accident.

The Trauma

On the night of the accident, Mrs. W was driving with her older brother, with whom she had had a close relationship during her childhood. They were on a two-lane road when she saw the high-beam lights of a car approaching her from around a sharp curve. She recalled telling her brother that she was going to flash her lights to signal the driver to turn down his high beams. Before she could do so, the other car was around the curve, driving in her lane and coming straight at her. She remembers a feeling of terror, and then the cars collided.

On impact she briefly lost consciousness and woke up lying on the door of her car, which had turned over onto its left side. She was bleeding profusely from her mouth and was having trouble catching her breath. Her brother was lying on top of her; he was moaning and so was she.

Following the lengthy period it took rescue workers to extract them from the car, she and her brother were taken to a nearby hospital. There she learned that she had lost her front teeth, her remaining teeth were knocked out of alignment, and her jaw was damaged. Her brother had dislocated his hip and had glass splinters in his eyes. While waiting to be extricated from the car, she remembered feeling certain that the driver of the other car had been killed, but she subsequently learned that he and his passengers had been able to walk away from the accident.

Posttraumatic Life

After the accident, she felt her whole life had been altered. Because of her injuries, she had to stay with relatives for several months and it became impossible for her to go abroad as planned. In a larger sense, she felt that the accident had shattered her security, both in her religion and in relation to what she wanted in life. During this period she felt vulnerable, irritable, and withdrawn. When she returned home, she resumed her previous job as a secretary in a large corporation. Shortly thereafter, she met a man who she described as the only person she could talk to about the accident. They became close friends, eventually married, and had a child in 1984.

Shortly after the birth of her child, Mrs. W had reconstructive jaw surgery. This involved breaking her jaw, removing bone from her hip to replace missing bone in the jaw, removing several of her remaining teeth to make possible the insertion of a bridge to replace teeth lost in the accident, and wiring her jaws so that she was not able to talk for 6 weeks. The pain during the healing was excruciating and in this period, she recalled occasionally thinking of suicide as an escape.

Her new teeth are larger than her original teeth, and the shape of her jaw has changed. Comments on these changes by those who knew her before are painful to her. In addition, the surgery to repair the damage to her mouth was only partially successful, and additional procedures have been recommended. Her physical discomfort and her sense of being changed and damaged physically have undermined her self-confidence and contributed to her psychological distress.

Symptoms of Posttraumatic Stress Disorder

Reexperiencing

At the time she was seen, more than 4 years after the accident, she reported having a recurrent nightmare in which she is in the dark, a light comes right at her, she hears the screeching brakes of a car, and feels a sense of terror just before awakening. She began having this dream almost immediately after the accident, and had it two or three times a week for 2 years before it began to diminish in frequency, although not in intensity.

A great deal of her time and energy subsequent to the accident has been spent going over what happened, and she has experienced almost constant intrusive thoughts about it. She has been preoccupied with both the specific details of the accident and the consequences it has had for her.

More than 2 years after the accident she had a reliving experience while a passenger in a car driven by her husband. She heard the brakes of a car screech and saw its lights out of the corner of her eye. She became terrified, had the feeling that she was lying on the door of the car as she had been after the accident, and began sobbing uncontrollably. She has also evidenced marked physiological reactivity, experiencing a sense of tightness and pain in the back of her neck whenever she drives.

Avoidance and numbing

In the years since the accident, Mrs. W has experienced marked discomfort when exposed to reminders of it. She described a tense, frightened feeling in the pit of her stomach whenever she sees a movie, a television program, or reads about a car accident. Subsequent to the accident, she felt a sense of terror whenever she was in a car. Although this feeling has subsided, fearfulness concerning driving has persisted, and she avoids nighttime driving. The apprehensiveness and sense of vulnerability she feels in a car extends to being alone at night, and she has attempted whenever possible to avoid this, even in her own house. During the initial months after the accident, she also showed a marked withdrawal from people in general, and especially from her relatives. Of particular significance is the fact that she has never been able to discuss the accident or her feelings about it with her brother.

Her emotional withdrawal is also evident in her relationship to her religion. Although she does not feel the accident has shaken her basic religious belief, she described herself as feeling less close to God since it happened.

Increased arousal

Mrs. W has shown marked symptoms of increased arousal which were not previously present. In the several-month period after the accident, she had difficulty falling asleep; if she fell asleep and woke up in terror from her dreams, she would be unable to go back to sleep. She also experienced considerable difficulty concentrating during this period.

Describing herself as a mild and "mellow" person prior to the accident, she said the irritability and anger she showed toward family members during the months she stayed with them was a shock to her and them. She has remained more irritable than she was prior to the accident, but feels she has learned how to control it.

She remains hypervigilant when out alone, especially after dark, experiencing a fear of harm being done to her by strangers. She has persistently had a severe startle reaction to the sound of car brakes screeching. She has a similar reaction if a car's headlights catch her eyes.

Course of Illness

In an attempt to cope with the intense tension and anxiety she felt during the first year after the accident, Mrs. W resumed the smoking habit she had stopped at the time she joined her church several years prior. She also resumed drinking alcohol during this period, and at the peak of her symptoms was consuming over a gallon of wine per week. She stopped smoking and drinking when she learned she was pregnant and, since the birth of her child, has resumed only on a social basis.

Over the 4 years since the accident, Mrs. W's severe posttraumatic stress disorder has moved from an acute to a chronic form, and her symptoms have waxed and waned in severity. Following her reconstructive surgery, her nightmares and other symptoms increased in intensity. They did so again some months later after the reliving experience she had while driving with her husband. Her fears and tension when driving, her fear of being alone or going out alone at night, and her general view of the world as a more frightening place than she had seen it before have persisted.

Meaning of Trauma

The meaning of the particular trauma for Mrs. W is centered in a loss of confidence and trust — in herself, other people, and in God and her religion. Her sense of vulnerability is heightened by the feeling that the accident happened despite the fact that she had done nothing to contribute to it.

Her association of trauma and loss of trust in those to whom she was close extends to events prior to the accident. One event, which occurred when she was 14, stands out in particular.

She and a close friend who was sleeping over had been boisterous while her mother was entertaining a male friend. Mrs. W locked herself in the bathroom to avoid punishment. Her mother persuaded her to open the door by saying she would not hit her and wanted only to talk to her. Her mother then beat her savagely, banging her head repeatedly against the door lock. Mrs. W was afraid she would be killed, but connects the event as much to her feeling that she would never trust her mother again.

This feeling paralleled one she had had a few years before in relation to her older brother. As a young child she had felt close to and supported by him, but when he became a teenager he did not want her around. She recalled the shock she felt one time when he punched her in the stomach to drive her away.

Mrs. W recalled experiencing similar feelings as a young adult, in the context of a relationship with a man with whom she had lived during the first 2 years following her move from her hometown. Their relationship had ended after he became involved with other women. Whether this way of viewing her earlier life was influenced by the accident, whether the accident was viewed in the context of earlier traumas, or, as seems likely, both are operative, was not possible to determine with certainty. It was clear, however, that the accident has heightened her sense that the world is an unsafe place in which she is perpetually vulnerable to physical or psychological trauma.

Mrs. W is a woman who overcame the handicaps of an extremely difficult early family situation to make a relatively successful life for herself. Although the security and confidence she had begun to develop were severely damaged by the accident, she shows the same determination to overcome her present difficulties.

During the course of the evaluation interviews, she experienced relief in discussing the accident and its meaning to her in the context of her life. In a telephone follow-up a few months later, she reported less apprehension when driving, a diminuation in the frequency of her recurrent nightmare of the accident, and a significant change in its content. Whereas in the past, she had always awakened with terror just before the collision, she now dreamed that the car lights were coming toward her but that she was able to swerve to the other side of the road, thereby evading the collision.

STRESS-ORIENTED PSYCHOTHERAPY

The preceding case is illustrative of the large majority of patients with posttraumatic stress disorder, for whom exploration of the traumatic event and its meaning is beneficial in alleviating stress symptomatology. The essential goal of psychotherapeutic treatment of the trauma-derived stress disorder is to open up and explore in detail the content of the specific traumatic experience with the individual, his or her feelings about the experience both at the time of its occurrence and currently, and the particular meanings the experience had and continues to have in light of both the person's pretraumatic and posttraumatic life. We have found that only through direct, sustained, and repeated exploration of events, feelings, and meanings can patients achieve sufficient resolution to make the trauma no longer dominant in their subsequent behavior and emotions. In using the term *stress-oriented psychotherapy*, we wish to emphasize the essential focus of treatment on the stress disorder and its roots — perceptual as well as objective — in the specific traumatic experience.

From the time the psychological symptoms caused by trauma were first recognized, treatment of the disorder was seen as a unique psychotherapeutic problem. Initially, the symptoms were seen by Breuer and Freud (1955) as amenable to the "talking cure" (catharsis), in which the patient was helped to recover repressed traumatic memories and to express the emotions associated with them (abreaction). When Freud realized that catharsis and abreaction were not usually sufficient to effect a cure, emphasis shifted to childhood conflicts, which were relived and worked out in the relationship with the therapist (Freud, 1955; Futterman & Pumpian-Mindlin, 1951; Lidz, 1946; Saul, 1945). Later, a consensus emerged that the development of posttraumatic stress is not dependent on childhood precursors, and the roles of both abreaction and catharsis came to be reconsidered in the treatment of reactions to trauma.

The role given to catharsis by most modern observers is somewhat different from that attributed to it by Freud. For Abram Kardiner, the critical therapeutic factor was not merely the expression of traumatic memories and the emotions associated with these, but also involved systematic reconstruction of the traumatic event and filling in of the amnesia that accompanied trauma (Kardiner, 1959; Kardiner & Spiegel, 1947). Kardiner documented the successful use of short-term psychotherapy in the treatment of World War I veterans seen 6 or 7 years after their combat experiences. In each of the cases, single traumatic combat experiences were responsible for a variety of symptoms and inhibitions. The patients could not recall many of the details of the experiences, but with the aid of their dreams, Kardiner was able to reconstruct with them what had happened. These events were gone over many times until the patient could tolerate the recollection of these details with no untoward effects. Then the more difficult task began of showing the patient the relation of his current inhibitions to the traumatic event.

In working with World War II soldiers with acute war neurosis, Grinker and his associates (Grinker & Spiegel, 1947) produced emotional recall of traumatic combat events through the use of "narcoanalysis," a procedure in which patients were interviewed under the influence of barbiturates (Horsley, 1936). Although in some cases positive results were achieved in a short period of time, these clinicians eventually concluded that additional therapeutic sessions without medication were necessary to allow a full working through of the traumatic material. Although narcoanalysis and hypnosis are sometimes still used to diagnose posttraumatic stress or to stimulate recall of traumatic events (Belson & Dempster, 1980; Brende & Benedict, 1980; Cavener & Nash, 1977; Spiegel, 1981), our experience is consistent with the conclusion reached by others that the recovery of memories and the emotions associated with them regularly occurs in the context of effective psychotherapy, and generally does not need to be elicited through drugs or hypnosis (Blank, 1982; Egendorf, 1978).

Many patients with posttraumatic stress, moreover, do recall the details of the traumatic events that precipitated their stress disorder, and may utilize a variety of defenses other than repression and amnesia. A thorough description of the defensive maneuvers utilized by posttraumatic stress patients is contained in the writings of Horowitz (1974, 1976). He points out that some patients will recall a traumatic event in words, but will not picture the experience. Others will recall traumatic events, but will not relate them to anything else in their lives; the events remain isolated and unintegrated. Still others will recall traumatic events in detail, but will express no feeling in connection with the recall. Horowitz emphasized the role of therapy in helping patients to achieve an integration of the cognitive and emotional elements in their response to trauma.

Many civilian cases are seen relatively soon after the trauma, an opportune time for exclusive focus on reactions to it, especially because acute symptoms are usually responsible for bringing the patient to seek help. In other cases, including many war veterans, we are dealing with individuals who have had the disorder in an untreated chronic form for many years. We have found that some such patients have managed, albeit at a great price, to separate their stress disorders from the rest of their lives. They may work and function adequately in their families apart from episodes of stress symptomatology. With others, every aspect of their life is affected by their efforts to cope with their stress symptoms. With these patients the responses to the traumatic experience have often become merged with their reactions to subsequent stressful events, such as the loss of employment, separation from family, or problems with the law. These stressful civilian events must also become the focus of the therapeutic intervention. Here, principles we have learned from therapy with posttraumatic stress victims must be integrated with principles more generally applicable to short-term psychotherapy if treatment is to be effective.

Another key distinction concerns the nature of the trauma to which the individual seeking treatment has been exposed. In many cases the patient is reacting to a single traumatic event: an accident, a disaster, or an instance of sudden loss of a loved one. The therapeutic task in such instances, if not simpler, is more focused. In other cases, most notably in combat veterans, several specific traumatic experiences usually converge in the disorder. Often a variety of traumatic combat events experienced by the veteran will be organized around certain themes unique to his particular perception. Understanding the common meanings of such experiences is central to the treatment of the patients for whom the disorder is not confined to one overwhelming traumatic event (Williams, 1983).

In order for the therapist to discern what the trauma has meant to the individual patient, a thorough knowledge of specific traumatic events must first be obtained. As Horowitz has noted, because individuals have a variety of ways to defend themselves against trauma, the therapist may have to make a number of different interventions during the process of attempting to explore traumatic experiences. In some cases, patients may try to avoid any discussion of the trauma, focusing instead on current difficulties. Especially when the individual is undergoing a crisis, current circumstances will need therapeutic attention. When a posttraumatic stress disorder is present, however, the source of current difficulties in the unresolved traumatic experience must be suspected, and this will necessitate opening up the issue of the trauma at the earliest opportunity.

Even in cases where patients are willing or even eager to talk about the trauma, specific details of the experience can be obscured or events can be related with no sense of the individual's involvement, reaction, or emotion. Here, too, while respecting the patient's need to set his or her own manageable pace, the therapist must continually pursue the essential task of reconstructing the experience until the entire setting, events, behaviors, and accompanying feelings are communicated and understood. Even though it is important to recognize that additional details of traumatic events which add to the therapist's understanding frequently emerge much later in the therapeutic process, the initial process of exploration is not complete until the therapist has a sense of comprehending the essence of the particular event or action.

In attempting to identify what specific traumatic events meant and continue to mean to patients, we have found that trauma-related dreams and nightmares provide invaluable clues. They are also of critical help in treating the disorder (Wilmer, 1982). In the context of individual stress-oriented psychotherapy, patients should be encouraged to relate their dreams and nightmares and to associate details of the trauma connected to them. Repressed details and feelings connected with specific traumatic events often emerge only after the event has been repeatedly discussed over an extended period. But specific parts of dreams can often point to aspects of the patient's experience that have not emerged through conscious reconstruction. The particular detail may seem minor, but if it has not been related before there is usually significant emotion bound up in it. Moreover, the events in the individual's current life that precipitate traumatic nightmares help to clarify the ongoing ways in which trauma distorts current perceptions.

As patients recover from posttraumatic stress disorder, their dreams often reflect their progress. This was seen in the accident victim earlier described who persistently reenacted the head-on collision in her nightmares. After she had begun to make progress toward resolving her stress disorder, she dreamed that she was able to avoid the oncoming car by swerving into the other lane.

Another essential aid in identifying and

understanding traumatic events is the individual's flashbacks, revisualizations, or reliving experiences. Although some who have worked with Holocaust survivors have reported that treatment possibilities are limited among those who relive their traumatic experiences in a state of altered consciousness (Krystal, 1975, 1981), we have not found this to be true for Vietnam combat veterans, where the symptom has been most often described (Hendin *et al.*, 1984). Systematically exploring the content of reliving experiences provides a valuable therapeutic tool for understanding the meaning of the individual's traumatic experiences and for eliciting the accompanying emotions. A cessation of this form of re-experiencing is also an important sign of therapeutic progress.

One veteran, a former helicopter pilot, frequently relived Vietnam combat experiences. Reliving an incident in which he had been shot, he would fall backward. While driving he would relive a time in which his helicopter went out of control and he would actually drive off the road. As the fear related to these combat events diminished in his therapy, he moved from reacting to the events, to perceiving them as unreal, to recognizing that they were happening only in his head. In time, the anxiety and palpitations accompanying his recollections ceased and though they remained unpleasant memories, they were no longer disruptive.

Although knowledge of the individual's specific traumatic experiences underlies our understanding of the posttraumatic stress reaction, in our experience an understanding of pretraumatic factors is often an important part of stress-oriented psychotherapy. In this respect, our approach differs from that of Kardiner and Horowitz, who both saw the posttraumatic stress reaction as essentially rooted in and determined by the particular traumatic experience. Neither explores the role of pre-existing personality factors in determining the particular way in which the trauma was perceived and experienced or the way in which the stress disorder is manifested. We have found, however, that understanding the patient's pretraumatic personality and functioning facilitates an assessment of his or her adaptive resources prior to the trauma which influenced how it was experienced.

Having a general knowledge of the patient's pretraumatic functioning also helps the therapist to understand how a posttraumatic stress disorder is expressed in the context of the individual's personality and character. Virtually all patients with posttraumatic stress, for example, show a markedly diminished capacity for pleasure (anhedonia), supporting Henry Krystal's (1981) observation that this condition is a characteristic and reliable indication of posttraumatic states. We have found that with progress in therapy, however, as fear, anger, and guilt cease to dominate the patient's life, a remarkable improvement in the capacity for pleasure takes place, at least among those individuals who had demonstrated an ability to enjoy themselves and their relationships with others prior to the trauma. Knowledge of pretraumatic functioning is obviously necessary in determining what degree of improvement to expect in a particular patient.

Finally, with regard to the significance of pretraumatic experience, it may be noted that Kardiner assumed that attempts by patients to link traumatic events with earlier life experiences represented retrospective attempts to defend themselves against the stress disorder. Our experience with Vietnam veterans and with rape and accident victims seen in civilian life is that they seldom try to make such linkages. If anything, they tend to see their lives as beginning — and often ending — with their traumatic experience. The ability to see trauma in the context of other life experiences is usually a sign of a lessening of the stress disorder.

Particular attention in the treatment of combat veterans must be given to the relationship between the therapist and the veteran. Although all combat veterans may be expected to feel some initial reluctance or mistrust when attempting to communicate their experiences to a therapist, with veterans of the Vietnam War this tendency often appears to be especially pronounced because of the lack of support and understanding they received from those at home during and following their time in Vietnam. Obviously there needs to be a minimum core of trust for therapy to begin, but many veterans, we have found, make the primary determinant of whether such trust is possible the manner in which the therapist deals with their combat experiences.

Supervising the treatment of Vietnam veterans, we have frequently found tha therapy flounders at the point when the veteran has shared at least some of the specifics of his combat tour. The therapist may respond to stories of cruelty or brutality in combat with revulsion, or fear that such behavior indicates a potential for violence and possibly personal danger. Some veterans will try to intimidate the therapist in this way, but usually cease these tactics if they see the therapist is not frightened or angered.

More frequently, the therapist's discomfort is communicated in the need to convey understanding and acceptance before he or she is really in a position to do so. This reaction often reflects an unconscious desire to curtail unpleasant communications related to combat. In other cases, the therapist may not feel personally threatened by the veteran's potential aggression, but may be afraid that elaboration of combat descriptions will interfere with his or her ability to like and respect the veteran. When this happens, it is the therapist's discomfort rather than what is specifically said that the veteran responds to, leaving him feeling even more unacceptable and isolated.

Veterans who felt their aggression was out of control in combat often see any relationship, including their therapeutic one, as having the potential to release their destructiveness. Before exploration and relief of some of the distress produced by traumatic experiences, however, most veterans are not able to explore in any significant way the complexity of emotions that will develop toward a therapist. Usually, only after the therapist has helped the veteran to begin to deal with the continuing impact of combat on his postwar relationships with family, friends, and co-workers will the veteran permit his feelings to be explored directly in relation to the therapist. The dreams of veterans with posttraumatic stress provide an early clue that combat trauma rather than feelings toward the therapist should be dealt with first. In the repetitive combat nightmares of most veterans, the therapist does not usually appear, even in disguised form. In our experience, it is only after considerable therapeutic progress has been made that combat-derived nightmares become less stereotyped and the therapist may appear in them.

Another salient factor in stress-oriented psychotherapy with Vietnam veterans is the difficulty most have in managing the powerful feelings that are set off by discussion of their wartime experiences. In our work, we have found the intensity of emotions associated with recalling and reconstructing traumatic combat events dictates that the veteran be seen no more than twice a week, and in many cases, only once a week. Frequently, veterans will "forget" or consciously choose to miss appointments when the sessions become particularly painful. We have found it important to respect these attempts to regulate the therapeutic pace. In this respect, our experience is consistent with the observations of Zetzel (1970), who treated British soldiers in World War II, and Krystal (1975), who treated survivors of the Holocaust, that therapy must be tuned to the "affect tolerance" of the traumatized individual. As we have indicated, however, the affect tolerance of the therapist is of comparable significance in determining the outcome in treatment.

If, during the treatment, symptoms such as anxiety, depression, rage, or insomnia become too incapacitating, a limited amount of medication may provide necessary but temporary relief. Although a considerable amount has been written about chemotherapeutic treatment of posttraumatic stress (Hogben & Cornfield, 1981; Kolb, 1984; Marshall, 1975; Thompson, 1977; Walker, 1982), the specific objectives and effects of such treatment remain largely unknown due to the lack of systematic, large-scale study. There is ample support, however, for our conclusion that behavioral rather than pharmacologic interventions are preferred whenever possible (Domash & Sparr, 1982; Friedman, 1981). Specifically, because the patient's dreams and nightmares provide the fundamental insight into what continues to trouble him about the traumatic experience, medications that aim at their suppression should be avoided whenever possible.

In recent years, techniques other than individual psychotherapy have been used in the attempt to help patients work through the disturbing effects of trauma. Perhaps the most widely adopted of these has been the use of group therapy, or "rap groups." In the case of combat veterans, in particular, clinicians have reported beneficial outcomes among veterans resulting from the mutual trust, understanding, and support supplied by the group (Egendorf, 1975; Frick & Bogart, 1982; Walker & Nash, 1981).

While acknowledging the value of the therapy group, our experience supports the conclusion of others that without the simultaneous process of individual psychotherapy (not necessarily with the same therapist), this technique in most cases is inadequate for patients to work through their posttraumatic stress disorders (Brende, 1981).

Although the group can help patients feel less isolated through the sharing of common experiences and emotions, we have found that most do not explore the most intensely personal meanings of trauma in a group setting. Individual therapy, if properly focused, does permit such an exploration. The meanings of the trauma will vary, as we have tried to indicate, not merely because of the nature of the trauma — rape, accident, combat, etc. — but because individuals bring different ways of perceiving and reacting to the same trauma. The fact that posttraumatic stress patients have in common exposure to an overwhelming encounter with death and a common set of symptoms should not obscure these differences. Helping the individual understand the personal meaning of the trauma for him or herself is a necessary step in resolving the disorder.

REFERENCES

Ahearn, F. L., & Cohen, R. E. (1984). *Disasters and mental health: An annotated bibliography*. Rockville, MD: National Institute of Mental Health.

American Psychiatric Association. (1980). *Diagnostic and statistical manual of mental disorders*. (3rd ed.). Washington, DC: Author.

American Psychiatric Association. (in press). DSM-III-Revised. Washington, DC: Author.

Archibald, H., & Tuddenham, R. (1965). Persistent stress reaction following combat: A twenty-year follow-up. *Archives of General Psychiatry, 12*, 475–481.

Arnold, A. L. (1984). *Selected bibliography: Posttraumatic stress disorder with special attention to Vietnam veterans*. Phoenix, AZ: Veterans Administration Medical Center.

Belson, P. M., & Dempster, C. R. (1980). Treatment of war neurosis from Vietnam. *Comprehensive Psychiatry, 21*, 167–175.

Blank, A. (1982). Apocalypse terminable and interminable: Operation outreach for Vietnam veterans. *Hospital and Community Psychiatry, 33*, 913–918.

Brende, J. O. (1981). Combined individual and group therapy for Vietnam veterans. *Inernational Journal of Group Psychotherapy, 31*, 367–378.

Brende, J. O. & Benedict, B. (1980). The Vietnam combat delayed stress response syndrome: Hypnotherapy of "dissociative symptoms." *American Journal of Clinical Hypnosis, 23*, 34–40.

Breuer, J. & Freud, S. (1955). *Studies in hysteria* (2nd ed.). London: Hogarth Press.

Burnstein, A. (1983). Post-traumatic revisualizations. *Psychosomatics, 24*, 166–167.

Cavener, J. O., & Nash, J. L. (1977). Narcoanalysis: The forgotten diagnostic aid. *Military Medicine, 142*, 553–555.

Domash, M., & Sparr, L. (1982). Posttraumatic stress disorder masquerading as paranoid schizophrenia: Case report. *Military Medicine, 147*, 772–774.

Egendorf, A. (1975). Vietnam veteran rap groups and themes of post-war life. *Journal of Social Issues, 31*, 111–124.

Egendorf, A. (1978). Psychotherapy with Vietnam veterans. In C. R. Figley (Ed.), *Stress disorders among Vietnam veterans: Theory, research and treatment.* New York: Brunner/ Mazel.

Eitinger, L. (1969). Psychosomatic problems in concentration camp survivors. *Journal of Psychosomatic Research, 13,* 183–189.

Freud, S. Ferenczi, S., Abraham, K., Simmel, E., & Jones, E. (1921). *Psychoanalysis and the war neurosis.* London: International Psychoanalytic Press.

Freud, S. (1948). *Beyond the pleasure principle.* London: Hogarth Press.

Freud, S. (1955). *Psychoanalysis and the war neurosis.* London: Hogarth Press.

Frick, R., & Bogart, L. (1982). Transference and countertransference as group therapy in Vietnam veterans. *Bulletin of the Menninger Clinic, 46,* 429–444.

Friedman, M. (1981). Post-Vietnam syndrome: Recognition and management. *Psychosomatics. 22, 921–943.*

Futterman, S., & Pumpian-Mindlin, E. (1951). Traumatic war neurosis five years later. *American Journal of Psychiatry, 108,* 401–408.

Grinker, R. P., & Spiegel, J. P. (1947). *Men under stress.* Philadelphia: Blakistan Co.

Hendin, H., & Haas, A. P. (1984a). Combat adaptations of Vietnam veterans without posttraumatic stress disorders. *American Journal of Psychiatry, 141,* 956–960.

Hendin, H., & Haas, A. P. (1984b). *Wounds of war: The psychological aftermath of combat in Vietnam.* New York: Basic Books.

Hendin, H., Haas, A. P., Singer, P., Gold, F., & Trigos, G. (1983). The influence of precombat personality on posttraumatic stress disorder. *Comprehensive Psychiatry, 24,* 530–534.

Hendin, H., Haas, A. P., Singer, P., Houghton, W., Schwartz, M., & Wallen, V. (1984). The reliving experience in Vietnam veterans with posttraumatic stress disorder. *Comprehensive Psychiatry, 25,* 165–173.

Hendin, H., Pollinger, A., Singer, P., & Ulman, R. (1981). Meanings of combat and the development of posttraumatic stress disorder. *American Journal of Psychiatry, 138,* 1490–1493.

Hogben, G., & Cornfield, R. B. (1981). Treatment of traumatic war neurosis with phenelzine. *Archives of General Psychiatry, 38,* 440–455.

Horowitz, M. J. (1974). Stress response syndromes. *Archives of General Psychiatry, 31,* 768–781.

Horowitz, M. J. (1976). Stress response syndromes. New York: Jason Aronson.

Horowitz, M. J., & Solomon, G. (1975). Delayed stress response syndromes in Vietnam veterans. *Journal of Social Issues, 4,* 67–80.

Horsley, J. (1936). Narcoanalysis. *Journal of Mental Science, 82,* 416–422.

Kardiner, A. (1959). Traumatic neuroses of war. In S. Arieti (Ed.), *American handbook of psychiatry (Vol. I).* New York: Basic Books.

Kardiner, A., & Spiegel, H. (1947). *War stress and neurotic illness.* New York: Hoeber.

Kolb, L. C. (1984). The posttraumatic stress disorders of combat: A sub-group with a conditioned emotional response. *Military Medicine, 149,* 237–243.

Krupnick, J., & Horowitz, M. J. (1981). Stress response syndromes — recurrent themes. *Archives of General Psychiatry, 38,* 425–435.

Krystal, H. (1968). *Massive psychic trauma.* New York: International Universities Press.

Krystal, H. (1975). Affect tolerance. *Annual of Psychoanalysis, 3,* 179–219.

Krystal, H. (1981). The aging survivor of the Holocaust: Integration and self-healing in posttraumatic states. *Journal of Geriatric Psychiatry, 14,* 165–189.

Lidz, T. (1946). Nightmares and the combat neurosis. *Psychiatry, 9,* 37–49.

Lifton, R. J. (1968). *Death in life: Survivors of Hiroshima.* New York: Random House.

Lifton, R. J., & Olsen, E. (1976). The human meanings of total disaster: The Buffalo Creek experience. *Psychiatry, 39,* 1–18.

Marshall, J. R. (1975). The treatment of night terrors associated with the posttraumatic syndrome. *American Journal of Psychiatry, 132,* 293–295.

Martin, C., Warfield, M., & Braer, R. (1983). Physicians' management of the psychological aspects of rape. *Journal of the American Medical Association, 249,* 501–503.

Nadelson, C., Notman, M., Zackson, H., & Gornick, J. (1982). A follow-up study of rape victims. *American Journal of Psychiatry, 139,* 1266–1270.

Niederland, W. (1968). Clinical observations on the "survivor syndrome." *International Journal of Psychoanalysis, 49,* 313–315.

Saul, L. (1945). Psychological factors in combat fatigue with special reference to hostility and the nightmares. *Psychosomatic Medicine, 4,* 257–272.

Spiegel, D. (1981). Vietnam grief work using hypnosis. *American Journal of Clinical Hypnosis, 24,* 33–40.

Stratton, J. G., Parker, D. A., & Snibbe, J. R. (1984). Posttraumatic stress: Study of police officers involved in shootings. *Psychological Reports, 55,* 127–131.

Thompson, G. (1977). Posttraumatic psychoneurosis: Evaluation of drug therapy. *Diseases of the Nervous System, 38,* 617–619.

Trautman, E. C. (1964). Fear and panic in Nazi concentration camps: A biosocial evaluation of the chronic anxiety syndrome. *International Journal of Social Psychiatry, 10,* 134–141.

Trimble, M. (1981). *Post-traumatic neurosis: From railway spine to the whiplash.* New York: John Wiley & Sons.

Walker, J. I. (1982). Chemotherapy of traumatic war neurosis. *Military Medicine, 147,* 1029–1033.

Walker, J. I., & Nash, J. L. (1981). Group therapy in the treatment of Vietnam combat veterans. *International Journal of Psychotherapy, 31,* 379–389.

Williams, C. (1983). The mental foxhole: The Vietnam veteran's search for meaning. *American Journal of Orthpsychiatry, 53,* 4–17.

Wilmer, H. (1982). Vietnam and madness: Dreams of schizophrenic veterans. *Journal of the American Academy of Psychoanalysis, 10,* 47–65.

Zetzel, E. (1970). *The capacity for emotional growth.* New York: International Universities Press.

CHAPTER 8

Distinguishing Between Anxiety and Depressive Disorders

Max Hamilton

There is a long tradition in psychiatry, now waning in importance, of believing that all mental disorders are of the same essence and that the notion of separate mental "diseases" has no real meaning. In its modern form, this idea dates from the 19th century theory of the "unitary psychosis." In the United States, this tradition was continued and developed by Adolf Meyer, who regarded all mental disturbance as a reaction to the environment, with the form based on the circumstances, constitution, and personality of the individual. When psychoanalysis began to dominate clinical psychiatry, this theory fit well with psychoanalytic ideas, which minimized the difference between diagnostic categories and instead emphasized the importance of mental mechanisms. The difference between different "disorders" was then regarded as essentially one of individual balance between the mental mechanisms. Most clinical psychologists adhere to variations of this theme, even when unconscious mechanisms are replaced by conditioning and learning theories.

Although sociologists recognize, to some extent, the differences between different disorders, because they are concerned solely with the social factors relating to incidence and prevalence, they too have an essentially unitary approach.

In particular, concerning anxiety and depressive states, the fundamental unity of these two syndromes is implied in both Seligman's theory of "learned helplessness" (Abramson, Seligman, & Teasdale, 1978) and Bowlby's concept of "separation anxiety" (Bowlby, 1969).

There is, of course, considerable justification for this way of looking at the affective disorders, comprising the three groups of manias, depressions (melancholias), and anxiety states. Affective disorders involve a change in mood, are more common in women than in men, and have overlapping symptoms. These characteristics apply when we consider anxiety states and "neurotic" depression, but apply also to mania and depression, much more than one would gather from traditional clinical descriptions. It is not only that patients may swing from one mood disorder to another (most easily recognized in manic-depressive disorder), but that in any one phase there is overlap of symptoms.

Nevertheless, on the basis of accumulating evidence, opinion is swinging over to emphasizing the differences and distinctions between the affective disorders. This chapter concentrates on depressive and anxiety disorders.

The problems of classification of the anxiety disorders are dealt with in other chapters, so there will be no need to deal with them here other than very briefly. The acute posttraumatic disorders, whether acute, chronic, or delayed, will not be considered. However, anxiety states, with or without phobias (including agoraphobia) and with or without panic states, will be discussed in this chapter, but only those cases in which general symptoms of anxiety are present in addition to the phobias and panic attacks. The definition here of anxiety state corresponds very closely to that of anxiety disorder in the *Diagnostic and Statistical Manual of Mental Disorders,* third edition (DSM-III) (American Psychiatric Association, 1980), but does not include obsessional neurosis.

Depressive disorders are now classified as either bipolar or unipolar, but the relationship of the latter to those depressive conditions variously described as "reactive" or "neurotic" is still under debate. This is partly a legacy of the distinction, once regarded as central in psychiatry, between the psychoses and the neuroses. Clearly, the recurrent depressions, both bipolar and unipolar, could be classified as psychotic disorders, but the reactive depressions fit very badly into this category, as is shown by the alternative name of "neurotic depression."

It has been increasingly recognized that the dichotomy between psychosis and neurosis, however useful it may have been once, has become increasingly a handicap rather than an aid to classification in psychiatry. An example of this is the abandonment in DSM-III of the term *neurotic.* Before going further, it would be useful to review briefly this old distinction, to make clear why it has been abandoned. It could be said that it was made on five criteria.

1. *Etiology* — Psychoses were said not to be psychogenic, in contrast to the neuroses. This distinction has become very thin, now that the role of environmental experiences in the precipitation of acute phases of mania and schizophrenia have become increasingly recognized. On the other hand, the role of infantile experiences in the causation of neuroses has received much adverse criticism.
2. *Response to treatment* — It was said that neuroses responded to psychotherapy and psychoses did not. The value of social therapy and rehabilitation is quite clear even for chronic schizophrenics, and many respond to behavioral therapy. The continual proliferation of psychotherapies for the neuroses suggests that these treatments are not as effective as has been suggested in the past.
3. *Insight* — Psychotics were said to have no insight into their condition, but in the early stages of the disorder, schizophrenics are often only too well aware of what is happening to them, and there are few patients who show less insight than the classical hysterics.
4. *The personality is wholly involved in psychosis, but not in neurosis.* — It is difficult to make out what this means, but in manic-depressive disorder and some types of schizophrenia, the patient may show complete restoration between acute phases, indicating that however severe may have been the patient's disorganization and maladjustment, the personality survived intact.

5. *Social adaptation* — This is largely a question of the severity of the disorder, not of type.

Once it is accepted that the distinction between psychotic and neurotic can be ignored, the depressions can be left as depressions, with differences in the clinical manifestations (anxious vs. retarded) and in precipitating stresses (endogenous vs. reactive) recognized to be varying in quantity rather than quality. However, another distinction remains important, that between a normal reaction to environmental stresses and an abnormal or pathological condition. This applies equally to both depressive and anxiety states. A terrifying experience (fright) may produce appropriate reactions which may take considerable time to fade away. Even though the person's condition is recognized as not being pathological (diseased state), it is accepted that, in addition to sympathy and understanding, it is appropriate that such help as can be provided by modern medicine should be available. In some cases, it is nevertheless recognized that the response to the precipitating stress has produced a state that continues independently of its origin (i.e., the stress has introduced a pathological condition).

The same applies to those persons who have undergone a severe loss. Even when taking into account the significance of the loss to the individual and the reactivity of the personality (the variations here are greater than most psychiatrists recognize), it may become evident that the original stress has precipitated a pathological process which then continues independently of its origin. There are some features that help to distinguish between normal and abnormal reactions, but however carefully examined, there remains a residuum of cases where the nature of the condition remains in doubt. This does not invalidate the general usefulness of the distinction. The same considerations apply to those patients suffering from a severely debilitating or mortal illness.

The problems relating to the differences between the various forms of depressive states are not irrelevant to the distinction between depressions and anxiety states. If all the forms of depressive disturbances are included, then the distinction between them and the anxiety states is easy, but if the reactive (anxious, neurotic) depressions only are considered, then the distinction becomes difficult.

The best way of approaching the subject is to separate the two aspects: The first is to consider the theoretical problem of whether the two groups of disorders are truly separate, though overlapping in their manifestations; and the second is to make a practical decision (e.g., as a basis for treatment).

GENETIC AND FAMILY STUDIES

Both family and twin studies have given clear evidence that there is a hereditary component to depressive disorders. Thus, the incidence of such disorders in parents of children of patients is about 10 %; in monozygotic twins the concordance rate is 68 %; and in same-sexed dizygotic twins it is only 23 %. Much of the work on the genetics of the depressions has been on manic-depressive disorder, obviously because it is the most clinically identifiable. The evidence indicates that there are different genes producing the same clinical effect. Many reports have shown that there is a sex-linked dominant gene (e.g., Dunner & Fieve, 1975; Winokur 1970), though Loranger (1975) and Fieve, Mendlewicz, Rainer et al. (1975) have warned that this applies only to some families. Where there is no evidence of the presence of the disorder in the family, it has been suggested (Mendlewicz, Fieve, & Rainer, 1973) that the inheritance is polygenic.

Unipolar depressions appear to have a distinct mode of inheritance. The pattern of risks in children and parents is incompatible with an X-linked dominant gene, despite the marked preponderance of depressions among the female relatives of female probands. Cadoret, Winokur, and Clayton (1970) have suggested that there are at least two genetic varieties of depressive disorder: one in which the sex is limited to women, and the other in which the two sexes have equal morbidity rates. Although most series of depressives include twice as many women as men, it is not yet certain that this represents the true prevalence in the general population.

Other evidence for the genetic heterogeneity of the depressions is derived from the response to treatment. This response is much the same among first-degree relatives given a particular antidepressant drug, but not for different antidepressants. This suggests that there is more than one biochemical abnormality underlying the depressions and that these are genetically specific (Pare & Mack, 1971).

In contrast to unipolar and bipolar depressive illnesses, neurotic depressions (which must in practice overlap the latter to some extent) show little evidence of genetic factors. Torgersen (1980) found that the proband concordance rate was 21% for monozygotic twins and 28% for same-sexed dizygotic twins. This conforms to the general opinion that those with neurotic depressions are a very mixed group. In my opinion, it also accords well with the supposition that the group of people with neurotic depressions often includes those who are not ill (i.e., not in a pathological state, but "overreacting" to the stresses of life). In other words, they are constitutionally different from most persons.

Much of the genetic work on the anxiety states was made before the current subdivisions came into use and therefore need be considered only briefly. Suffice it to say that there is good evidence for genetic factors, though further work that distinguishes between the varieties of anxiety states will have to be done in due course. The prevalence of anxiety states in the population is estimated to be 3.4 % among women and 1.5 % among men (Cloninger, Martin, Clayton, & Guze, 1981). Corresponding to this, there is a higher prevalence among the female relatives of anxiety patients (19 %) than among the male relatives (8 %), that is, a ratio of about two to one. The pooled risk for second-degree relatives (6 %) is slightly less than half that for first-degree relatives (16 %). Roth, Gurney, Garside, and Kerr (1972) found that 20% of the parents and 17% of the siblings of anxiety state patients suffered from neurotic disorder. The corresponding figures for depressives were 5% and 9%. Personality disorder was found in the parents of anxiety state patients in 68% of all cases and in the siblings 32% of the time. The corresponding figures for the depression were 28% and 14%.

Torgersen (1980) found that the proband concordance rate for anxiety states was 39% for monozygotic twins and 12% for dizygotic sames-sexed pairs. These figures are close to those reported by Slater and Shields (1969), which were 41% and 4%, respectively. Even more to the point, all investigators agree that the genetic factors for depressions are distinct from those for anxiety states.

PREMORBID PERSONALITY

Persons with anxiety disorders, on the whole, tend to have poorly adjusted personalities. They have what is commonly described as an anxious disposition. In other words, they have a low threshold for the appearance of anxiety, including minor nondisabling phobias. Their most important traits are immaturity, lack of confidence, dependence on relatives, hypersensitivity, a shy and anxious disposition, and hysterical features. All these go a long way back in the life of the individual and are evident in a poor record during school life. On the Maudsley Personality Inventory, those with anxiety disorder show higher Neuroticism and more Introversion than depressives (Kerr, Roth, Schapira, & Gurney, 1972). Among women, 39 % show premorbid frigidity; whereas among the depressives, this is found in only 8 % (Roth et al., 1972).

Neurotic depressives tend to have the same personality characteristics as those suffering from anxiety states (Zerssen, 1980). In contrast, endogenous depressives tend to have rigid personality structures, and to be orderly and traditionally minded, with a tendency to close personal relationships with family members. They are solid characters, oriented toward achievement, reliable in social relations, and conforming to social roles (Tellenbach, 1980). None of these characteristics are necessarily beyond the normal range; this type of personality is very common. Bech, Shapiro, Sihm, Nielsen, Sorensen, and Rafaelsen (1980) tested 13 unipolar and 23 bilpolar depressives on the Marke-Nyman Temperament (Bech, Allerup, & Rosenberg, 1978), the Zerssen Personality and the Cesarec-Marke Personality Scales, and the Eysenck Personality Inventory, and found that the score patterns of their subjects lay within the normal range. The bipolar cases scored significantly lower on Neuroticism than did neurotics. It must be said that there is little evidence for a "depression-prone" personality.

PRECIPITATING EVENTS

We are all afraid when we are in a potentially harmful situation and we become depressed when we experience a major loss or feel that our circumstances are hopeless. These are normal reactions, but the important question is whether this is true of the precipitation of pathological states. Finlay-Jones and Brown (1981) have no doubt. They found that the frequency of such appropriate precipitating stresses in the year previous to the onset of illness in 164 young women attending, a general practitioner was significantly greater than in a control series. They even found that cases of mixed anxiety and depression had experienced both a severe loss and a severe danger before the onset of their illness.

This would be conclusive evidence if it could be certain that the young women investigated by Finlay-Jones and Brown were suffering from true pathological disorders, and there is still controversy on this. Another investigation adds to this doubt. Popkin, Callies, and MacKenzie (1985) examined the data pertaining to 50 medical inpatients suffering from various illnesses such as malignant neoplasm, insulin-dependent diabetes, and epilepsy, and who had been diagnosed by a psychiatric consultant as suffering also from a major depressive syndrome. Earlier investigators had concluded that over two thirds of such disorders were reactive responses to physical illness. The patients were treated with anti-depressant drugs and only 40 % responded, a result that is very inferior to that usually experienced. Incidentally, 16 of the patients had to terminate their antidepressant treatment because of unacceptable side effects (half of which were delirium). As this inquiry was retrospective and uncontrolled, its relevance is by no means great, but it would have been very important had the results of treatment been a good response in 70 % to 80 %. In contrast to this report, Clayton and Lewis (1981) found that depressive disorders arising secondarily to other nonaffective psychiatric illness responded to drugs in the same manner as primary depressive disorders.

However, there is no doubt that both anxiety states and depressive illness are quite frequently precipitated by external events. Roth et al. (1972) found that physical and psychological stresses were more severe and more numerous in anxiety cases. Is there any fundamental difference between primary depressive disorder with or without a precipitating stressful life event? Garvey, Schaffer, and Tuason (1984) found no difference, after 4 and 6 weeks, in the response to treatment.

COURSE

During the course of the illness, the anxiety states are, in general, much more responsive to the situation of the patient than the depressive illnesses. Thus the placebo response is much greater in the former than in the latter. Recovery from an acute phase is often incomplete and is followed by a subsequent recrudescence. Noyes, Clancy, Holuk, and Slymen (1980) followed up 112 anxiety neurotics for 6 years and compared them with 110 surgical subjects. Recovery or mild impairment was found in 68 % of the patients, with the majority showing persisting symptoms and some social impairment. Patients who originally had an illness of less than 5 years duration showed a more favorable outcome than those who had been ill for 6 years or more. Thus, the course of the illness is irregularly recurrent with periods of remission, which are not always complete. This might account for the usual descriptions of the personalities of these patients.

In contrast, the course of the depressions shows a regular cycle of acute phases with (usually) clear intervening periods. The frequency distribution of the length of acute phases and of cycles is log-normal, and there is a tendency for the cycles to become shorter in the course of time (Angst, Grof, Hippius, Poldinger, Varga, Weis, & Wyss, 1969). On the whole, although about 40 % of depressives do recover spontaneously (i.e., they have no further attacks), the prognosis of these patients is not good in the long run (Angst, 1980) in the sense that, however well they may be between acute phases, recurrence is to be expected.

According to Keller, Kierman, Lavori, Coryell, Endicott, and Taylor (1984), in the shorter run, after 2 years, only about 20 % of depressives will still not have recovered and 65 % will have made a complete recovery. These authors give the ultimate complete recovery rate as approaching 80 %.

Although anxiety states are usually not as disabling during the acute phase as are the depressions, in between acute periods those suffering from anxiety disorders are more likely to experience symptoms and to have recurrences. It is of particular interest that these patients almost invariably remain in the same diagnostic category (Schapira, Roth, Kerr, & Gurney, 1972).

RESPONSE TO TREATMENT

The treatment for anxiety states has always been essentially some form of psychotherapy. This was true also for the depressions, until the discovery of the first of the modern antidepressant, Imipramine pamoate, except that more severe cases were treated with convulsive therapy. As antidepressant drugs came increasingly into use, the range of severity of depressions treated with convulsive therapy was considerably reduced. At the same time, introduction of the benzodiazepine drugs also diminished the emphasis on psychotherapy for anxiety states. In recent years there has been a recrudescence of interest in the psychotherapy for the depressions, so that in one sense, the differences in the approach to treatment for these disorders has become much less.

As stated earlier, one way of examining the relationship betweeen the two types of disorder is to examine their response to treatment. When the nature of the treatment is clearly understood, together with its mode of action, this can be very illuminating, but otherwise it can be very misleading. In the first place, most treatments are not completely effective, as there are always some patients who do not respond. Only rarely do we know why this should be so. In the long-term treatment of endogenous depressions with nortriptyline hydrochloride, Kragh-Sørenson, Hansen, Larsen, Naestoft, and Hvidberg (1974) found that in the few cases where relapse occurred, the plasma levels of the drug were too low. Paykel (1972) found that there was no significant difference between psychotic and neurotic depressives in the results of treatment with amitriptyline. However, when he classified his patients into the four groups he had described (using a clustering method), he found that the psychotics had the best outcome, the anxious depressives the worst, and the other two groups came in between. Subsequently, Paykel, Klerman, and Prusoff (1974) found that the outcome of treatment with amitriptyline was better among endogenous than reactive depressions. In these cases, the different outcomes between different groups adds plausibility to the distinction made between them.

It would be very unwise to be more certain about this conclusion. For example, aspirin is used for the long-term treatment of both rheumatoid arthritis and coronary thrombosis. We understand why this does not imply that they are the same or even related disorders, because the treatment effects depend on two different action of the drug. In the treatment of bacterial infections, the same antibiotic will be used for different infections, and different antibiotics will affect the same infection. Were the nature of the diseases and the mode of action of the treatments unknown, it would be impossible to draw conclusions about the classification of either.

Accepting these reservations, it is still worthwhile considering what light is shed on the distinction between the depressions and anxiety states by their response to different treatments. Even within the depressive disorders, it was quickly realized that the disorder that responded best to convulsive therapy was the endogenous or psychotic syndrome. For example, Carney, Roth, and Garside (1965) found that the similarity between the features that distinguished depressions from anxiety states were very similar to those that indicated the response to convulsive therapy. In their diagnostic index and Electroconvulsive therapy (ECT) predictive index (Carney, Roth, & Garside, 1965) it was loss of weight, early wakening, and a previous episode that favored the diagnosis of depressive disorder and good response to the treatment. On the opposite side were anxiety, worsening of symptoms late in the day, together with hysterical and hypochondriacal features in the illness.

Mendels (1965) similarly found that those features characteristic of anxiety states and neurotic depressions were inimical to a good outcome with convulsive therapy. These included, among others, inadequate personality and neurotic traits in childhood and adult life.

The response to antidepressant drugs was similar. Clinical experience soon showed that the tricyclic antidepressants were more effective for the retarded depressions than for the anxious type, and this was fully confirmed in a double-blind controlled trial by Hollister et al. (1967), whose report went as far as to recommend the phenothiazines for the latter syndrome. Raskin, Schulterbrandt, Reatig, Crook, and Odle (1974) found in their double-blind controlled trial that whereas phenelzine sulfate was effective for most depressions, for the anxiety-depressives, diazepam was a better treatment, as shown by the subsidence of symptoms when it was taken and their worsening when it was discontinued. Rickels, Hesbacher, and Downing (1970) evaluated drug treatments for neurotic depressives and found that tricyclics were better for high depression and low anxiety, but chlordiazepoxide was better for the reverse pattern. In a controlled trial of amitriptyline hydrochloride, phenelzine, and placebo, Rowan, Paykel, and Parker (1982) found that both drugs were effective antidepressants, but differed in detail in their effects. Examination of the changes in individual symptoms showed that phenelzine produced greater improvement on ratings of anxiety, and amitriptypine on anergia and loss of interest.

With the exception of convulsive therapy, drug treatment of the depressions seems to show a gradation in the response to treatment corresponding to the changeover from typical retarded depressions to anxious depressions.

Comparisons between the outcome of treatment in depressions and anxiety states yield much to same results. Once again, convulsive therapy is obviously better for the depressions (Gurney, Roth, Kerr, & Schapira, 1970). Drug therapy does not show such clear results. In a controlled trial comparing diazepam with phenelsine or with placebo on groups with anxiety, depressive and phobic neuroses, Mountjoy, Roth, Garside, and Leitch (1977) found that phenelzine did better than placebo in the depressive neuroses but, if anything, it fared worse than placebo in the anxiety groups. This is an unusual finding, as most controlled trials of phenelzine have shown it to be an effective treatment in anxiety states, though often in an unpredictable fashion. For example, Tyrer, Candy, and Kelly (1973) found it to be an effective treatment for chronic agoraphobic and social phobic patients when compared with placebo, though the difference between the results of the two treatments had diminished at follow-up a year later (Tyrer & Steinberg, 1975).

The first report on the effect of Imipramine on agoraphobia and panic attacks was by Klein (1964). This has since been confirmed many times, for example, by Zitrin, Klein, and Woerner (1980), who showed in a controlled trial that the drug was more effective than placebo for primary phobias and spontaneous panic attacks. It is of interest that in this trial the more depressed patients fared worse than those who were less depressed.

Other antidepressant drugs have also been found effective in the treatment of agoraphobia and panic attacks and particular interest has been directed toward the monoamine oxidase inhibitors (e.g., phenelzine). The effectiveness of phenelzine was confirmed by Nies, Howard, & Robinson, (1982) (who emphasized the importance of adequate dosage) especially on the phobic, somatic, and psychic components of anxiety. In a controlled trial comparing the effect of imipramine, phenelzine, and placebo, combined with supportive group therapy, on chronic anxiety states (mean length of illness 13 years), Sheehan, Ballenger, and Jacobsen (1980) found that although all patients showed improvement, those receiving the active drugs did significantly better. Phenelzine was better than imipramine for phobic avoidance, and work and social disability.

Concerning the relationship between depressive and anxiety disorders, it would appear that the response to treatment is equivocal. On the one hand, convulsive therapy and the tricyclics show obviously better results with the retarded type of depressions than with the anxious depressions and anxious states, though they are not ineffective in the last two. On the other hand, the monoaminase oxidase inhibitors, although sometimes effective for retarded depressions, produce a response that is much the same in the anxious depressions and anxiety states, and that appears to ignore the difference between them.

Psychotherapy is too big a subject to be dealt with adequately in this chapter, but it cannot be ignored. Psychotherapy has always been regarded as the basic and essential treatment for the anxiety states, aside from symptomatic treatment with sedatives (anxiolytics). However, since the last century, new approaches and techniques have been continually proposed, which suggests that none of them was all that satisfactory. The last two decades have witnessed the increasing development and use of behavioral techniques, and controlled trials have demonstrated their value. For the depressions, clinicians have tended to use psychotherapy only when other treatments were unavailable or had failed.

A new technique, cognitive psychotherapy, has been introduced in the last decade and has aroused not only considerable interest, but even attempts at evaluation with controlled trials. Two examples will suffice: Blackburn and Bishop (1983) tested cognitive and drug therapy and their combination and found that in hospital outpatients the combination was significantly superior to cognitive therapy and about equal in general practice. Drugs alone came out most poorly. It is particularly meaningful clinically that the improvement was not only on cognitive variables, but also on measures of mood and overall severity. "Treatment as usual," with or without cognitive therapy, was evaluated by Teasdale, Fennell, Hibbert, and Amies (1984), who found that the combined treatment was significantly better. At 3 months follow-up, there was no difference between the two groups.

Even when the ultimate outcome of different treatments is the same, this does not imply that these treatments are of equal value. Any treatment that shortens the duration of suffering and of deprivation of normal life for the patients is of value. Perhaps in the milder cases the cost in time, effort, and money, and so on may have to be weighed in relation to the benefit from a shorter duration of illness; but this is very much an individual matter.

COMPARISON OF FEATURES

The clear difference in the dominant mood of the two disorders is obviously the basis on which they were first distinguished. But moon is not an abstract entity, it is a form of (internal and external) behavior of human beings, and the difference between the two moods is easy to demonstrate on most physiological variables. For example, differences between the two were found by Shagass (1955) in the photically activated electroencephalogram; by Kelly and Walter (1969) in forearm blood flow and heart rate, both under resting conditions and experimentally induced anxiety; and also by Noble and Lader (1972) together with differences in the electromyogram, skin conductance and its fluctations, and rate of salivation.

Depression and anxiety can be subdivided into many symptoms, many of which are quite different, but some of which are similar. It is an obvious step, once the data have been gathered systematically, to apply factor analysis and discriminant function analysis to them to see what light these mathematical techniques cast on the distinction under consideration. Of course, such mathematical analyses must be confirmed in the end by independent information, (e.g., genetic studies, course and prognosis, and response to treatment).

Roth et al. (1972) factor analyzed their data by the method of principal components. The first component clearly distinguished between anxiety and depressive states. The distribution of scores on this component was unimodal, but the patients diagnosed as depressive or anxious occupied different ends of the distribution, with considerable overlap. However, discriminant function analysis of the same data (Gurney, Roth, Garside, Kerr, & Schapira, 1972) produced a bimodal distribution of the discriminant function scores. The conclusion was that the two diagnostic categories formed two distinct groups with overlapping manifestations. Subsequent follow-up studies (Schapira et al., 1972) confirmed the distinction. The items that contributed most to the discriminant function (in descending order of importance) were panic attacks, neuroticism, suicidal tendencies, retardation, and agoraphobia.

Most of the patients in these studies had been admitted into the hospital. Prusoff and Klerman (1974) studied outpatients and did not obtain such clear-cut results. Using self-assessment questionnaire items, they found that a discriminant function led to a 35 % incorrect assignment of the patients' diagnoses.

At the time the mathematical analyses are made, they are validated against clincial diagnosis. Despite constant efforts to refine diagnostic criteria and procedures, these are still by no means satisfactory. In a follow-up study by Nelson, Charney, and Vingiano (1978), among the 40 patients who had been diagnosed as reactive depression and who had responded to treatment with psychosocial therapy without antidepressant drugs, 18 *clearly* met the research diagnostic criteria for primary affective disorder and 11 *probably* did so. Feinberg, Carroll, Steiner, and Commorato (1979) confirmed that the research diagnostic criteria mixed together endogenous and neurotic depressions, and were convinced that no mere checklist of clinical features could be expected to select a completely homogeneous group of patients.

CLINICAL PRACTICE

It must not be forgotten that whereas an organic condition can present as a psychiatric disorder (e.g., thyrotoxicosis may look like an anxiety state and dementia may resemble a depressive illness), the reverse is also true. This will be particularly important when patients are reluctant to mention their psychological symptoms, for fear of being labeled "neurotic," or sometimes when they think that doctors are concerned only with somatic symptoms. Either way, the patients do not mention their psychological symptoms or minimize them or explain them away. For this reason, even when the diagnosis seems obvious, it is wise to consider the possibility of organic disease. A simple clinical examination should rule out the possibility of the commonest organic conditions. After that, it is not worth carrying out investigations for uncommon diseases. Because they are uncommon, most of the time nothing will be found and a fruitless search for the uncommon is obviously wasteful when one considers that anxiety and depressive states are common. The same applies to uncommon psychiatric conditions. Careful routine history taking will soon reveal the hallucinations of the paraphrenic who presents as a depressive, or the compulsive rituals of the obsessional who mentions only the symptoms of anxiety.

In the majority of cases, there is no difficulty in recognizing the anxiety or depressive disorders. In the case of the depressions, the chief difficulty is when the various symptoms associated with anxiety are prominent and "mask" the underlying disorder. In ordinary clinical practice, symptoms of anxiety are extremely common in depressive illness, as has been pointed out above. Thus, anxiety is present in 96 % and somatic symptoms of anxiety in 86 %, difficulty in falling asleep in 86 % of men and 79 % of women, and agitation in 61 % of men and 72 % of women (Hamilton, 1980). Even attacks of panic occur in a minority of patients (Klein, 1964).

The diagnosis of depressive disorder is therefore made on positive grounds. Apart from the depressed mood which, however mild it may be, is always more persistent than in the anxiety states and is usually worse in the mornings, the most important symptom to look for is a loss of interest in life, work, hobbies, and normal activities. After that the clinician places great weight on the somatic symptoms of loss of appetite, energy, libido, and weight. Feelings of self-reproach, guilt, and thoughts of suicide will often be present, but usually will be elicited only on questioning. Delayed insomnia is relatively specific for depressive illness, but is very much related to the severity of illness. A particularly useful sign when it is detected is psychomotor retardation. Finally, if there is still doubt about the diagnosis, it is well to take into account the background of the current illness: a first attack in the 30s, a history of previous attacks of depression, and/or family history of depression or suicide. The patients may have well-adjusted personalities when they are well.

In anxiety states, although the patient may suffer from depressed mood, depression tends to be episodic and fluctuating, responsive to external circumstances, similar to but not as markedly as anxious mood. Patients often say that they can more or less easily "shake themselves out of it." Agoraphobic patients may not mention their disability, even when they are almost completely housebound, and they have even been known to deny its existence even when questioned. In case of doubt, the patients' statements should be checked with the relatives. Somatic symptoms are frequent and may dominate the clinical picture. They are of the type associated with over-activity of the adrenergic autonomic nervous system. Sexual function is disturbed. In men, it takes the form usually of premature ejaculation or inability to maintain an erection; in women, it appears as dyspareunia or anorgasmia. Inquiry into the background will sometimes reveal a history of symptoms in childhood and a family history of neurosis, personality disorder, or alcoholism. The onset of anxiety states tends to be more abrupt than the depressions and the first breakdown occurs earlier, in the 20s or teens.

CONCLUDING REMARKS

The importance of distinguishing between anxiety and depressive illnesses lies in the approach to treatment which, in the current state of the art, differs considerably between them. For the depressions, the basic treatment is antidepressant drug therapy supplemented, if appropriate, by psychotherapy. For the more severe cases, convulsive therapy should be considered, especially if there is any possibility of suicide. Long-term treatment would also possibly involve administration of lithium. For the anxiety states, psychotherapy is the basic treatment, supplemented by anxiolytic drugs for short-term use. For the phobic anxieties, behavior therapy may be the most appropriate form of treatment.

REFERENCES

Abramson, L. Y., Seligman, M. E. P., & Teasdale, J. (1978). Learned helplessness in humans: critique and reformulation. *Journal of Abnormal Psychology, 87,* 49–74.

American Psychiatric Association (1980). *Diagnostic and Statistical Manual of Mental Disorders* (3rd. Ed.) Washington D.C.: American Psychiatric Association.

Angst, J., Grof, P., Hippius, H., Poldinger, W., Varga, E., Weis, P., & Wyss, F. (1969). Verlaufsgesetzlichkeiten depressiver Syndrom in H Hippius and H Selbach (Ed.) *'Das depressiver Syndrom'* Munich: Urban & Schwarzenberg,

Angst, J. (1980). Verlauf unipolar depressiver, bipolar manisch-depressiver und schizoaffectiver Erkrankungen und Psychosen. Ergebnisse einer prospectiveren Studie. *Fortschrift Neurologia und Psychiatria, 48,* 3–30.

Bech, P., Allerup, P., & Rosenberg, R. (1978). The Marke-Nyman Temperament Scale. *Acta psychiatrica Scandinavica 57,* 49–58.

Bech, P., Shapiro, R. W., Sihm, F., Nielsen, B. F., Sørensen, B., and Rafaelsen, O. J. (1980). Personality in unipolar and bipolar manic-melancholic patients. *Acta Psychiatrica Scandinavia, 62,* 245–247.

Blackburn, I. M., & Bishop, S. (1983). p, S. (1983) Changes in cognition with pharmacotherapy and cognitive therapy. *British Journal of Psychiatry, 143,* 609–717.

Bowlby, J. (1969). Attachment and Loss. Hogarth Press, London.

Cadoret, R. J., Winokur, G., & Clayton, P. J. (1970). Family history studies: VI. Manic-depressive disease versus depressive disease. *British Journal of Psychiatry, 116,* 625–635.

Carney, M. W. P., Roth, M., & Garside, R. F. (1965). The diagnosis of depressive syndromes and the prediction of ECT response. *British Journal of Psychiatry, 111,* 659–674.

Cesarec, L., & Marke, S. (1968). Mätning av psypkogena behavmed frageformulärsteknik. Stockholm, Skand. Testförlaget.

Clayton, P. J., & Lewis, C. E. (1981). The significance of secondary depression. *Journal of Affective Disorders, 3,* 25–35.

Cloninger, C. R., Martin, R. L., Clayton, P., & Guze, S. B. (1981). A blind follow-up and family study of anxiety neurosis: Preliminary analysis of the St. Louis 500 in D. F. Klein and J. G. Rabkin (Ed.) *'Anxiety: New Research and Changing Concepts',* pp. 137–148.

Dunner, D. L., & Fieve, R. R. (1975). Psychiatric illness in fathers of men with bipolar primary affective disorder. *Archives of General Psychiatry, 32,* 1134–1137.

Eysenck, H. J., & Eysenck, S. B. G. (1964). Manual of the Eysenck Personality Inventory. London, University of London Press.

Feinberg, M., Carroll, B. J., Steiner, M., & Commorato, A. J. (1979). Misdiagnosis of endogenous depression with research diagnostic criteria. *Lancet, 1,* 267, Feb. 3rd.

Fieve, R. R., Mendlewicz, J., Rainier, J. D., et al. (1975). A dominant-linked factor in manic-depressive illness: studies with color blindness. *Proceedings of the American Psychopathological Association, 63,* 241–255.

Finlay-Jones, R., & Brown, G. W. (1981). Types of stressful life events and the onset of anxiety and depressive disorders. *Psychological Medicine, 11,* 803–815.

Garvey, M. J., Schaffer, C. B., & Tuason, V. B. (1984). Comparison of pharmacological treatment response between situational and non-situational depressions. *British Journal of Psychiatry, 145,* 363–365.

Gurney, C., Roth, M., Kerr, T. A., & Schapira, K. (1970). The bearing of treatment on the classification of the affective disorders. *British Journal of Psychiatry, 117,* 251–255.

Gurney, C., Roth, M., Garside, R. F., Kerr, T. A., & Schapira, K. (1972). Studies in the classification of affective disorders. The relation between anxiety states and depressive illnesses II. *British Journal of Psychiatry, 121,* 162–166.

Hamilton, M. (1980). Psychopathology of depressions: quantitative aspects in K. Achte, V. Aalberg and J. Lonnqvist (Ed.) "Psychopathology of Depression". *Psychiatria Fennica Supplementum,* pp. 201–205.

Hollister, L. E., Shelton J., Overall, J. E., Pennington, V., Kimbell, I., & Johnson, M. (1967). Selective choice for drugs for depression. *Archives of General Psychiatry, 17,* 486-493.

Keller, M. B., Klerman, G. L., Lavori, P. W., Coryell, W., Endicott, J., & Taylor, J. (1984). Long-term outcome of episodes of depression. *Journal of the American Medical Association, 252,* 788–792.

Kelly, D., & Walter, C. J. S. (1969). A clinical and physiological relationship between anxiety and depression. *British Journal of Psychiatry, 115,* 401–406.

Kerr, T. A., Roth, M., Schapira, K., & Gurney, C. (1972). The assessment and prediction of outcome in affective disorders. *British Journal Psychiatry, 121,* 167–174.

Klein, D. F. (1964). Delineation of two drug-responsive anxiety syndromes. *Psychopharmacologia, 5,* 397–408.

Kragh-Sørenson, P., Hansen, C. E., Larsen, N. E., Naestoft, J., & Hvidberg, E. F. (1974). Long-term treatment of endogenous depression with nortriptyline with control of plasma levels. *Psychological Medicine, 4,* 174–180.

Loranger, A. W. (1975). X-linkage and manic-depressive illness. *British Journal Psychiatry, 127,* 482–488.

Mendels, J. (1965). Electroconvulsive therapy and depression I. The prognostic significance of clinical factors. *British Journal of Psychiatry, 111,* 675–681.

Mendlewicz, J., Fieve, R. R., Rainier, J. D. et al. (1973). Affective disorder on paternal and maternal sides. Observations in bipolar (manic-depressive) patients with and without a family history. *British Journal Psychiatry, 122,* 31–34.

Meyer, A. (1951). The Collected Papers Vol. II. Psychiatry, Ed. By Eunice Winters. Baltimore, Johns Hopkins Press.

Mountjoy, C. Q., Roth, M., Garside, R. F., & Leitch, I. M. (1977). A clinical trial of phenelzine in anxiety, depressive and phobic neuroses. *British Journal of Psychiatry, 131,* 486–492.

Nelson, J. C., Charney, D. S., & Vingiano, A. W. (1978). False positive diagnosis with primary affective disorder criteria. *Lancet, 2,* 1252–1253, Dec. 9th.

Niles, A., Howard, D., & Robinson, D. S. (1982). Anti-anxiety effects of MAO inhibitors. In *"The Biology of Anxiety"* ed. by R. J. Matthew, pp. 123–133. New York, Brunner/Mazel.

Noble, P., & Lader, H. (1972). A physiological comparision of 'endogenous' and 'reactive' depression. *British Journal of Psychiatry, 120,* 541–542.

Noyes, R., Clancy, J., Holuk, P. R., & Slymen, D. J. (1980). The prognosis of anxiety neurosis. *Archives of General Psychiatry, 37,* 173–178.

Pare, C. M., & Mack, J. W. (1971). Differentiation of two genetically specific types of depression by the response to antidepressant drugs. *Journal Medical Genetics, 8,* 306–309.

Paykel, E. S. (1972). Depressive typologies and response to amitriptyline. *British Journal of Psychiatry, 120,* 147–156.

Paykel, E. S., Klerman, G. L., & Prusoff, B. A. (1974). Prognosis of depression and the endogenous-neurotic distinction. *Psychological Medicine, 4,* 57–64.

Popkin, M. K., Callies, A. L., & Mackenzie, B. (1985). The outcome of antidepressant use in the medically ill. *Archives of General Psychiatry, 42,* 1160–1163.

Prusoff, G., & Klerman, G. L. (1974). Differentiating depressed from neurotic outpatients. Use of discriminant function analysis for separation of neurotic affective states. *Archives of General Psychiatry, 30,* 301–309.

Raskin, A., Schulterbrandt, J. G., Reatig, N., Crook, T. H., & Odle, D. (1974). Depression subtypes and response to phenelzine, diazepam, and a placebo. *Archives of General Psychiatry, 30,* 66-75.

Ravaris, C. L., Nies, A., Robinson, D. S., Ives, J. O., & Bartlett, D. (1976). A multiple dose controlled study of phenelzine in depressive-anxiety states. *Archives of General Psychiatry, 33,* 347–350.

Rickels, K., Hesbacher, P., & Downing, R. W. (1970). Differential drug effects in neurotic depression. *Diseases of the Nervous System, 31,* 468–?

Roth, M., Gurney, C., Garside, R. F., & Kerr, T. A. (1972). Studies in the classification of affective disorders. The relationship between anxiety states and depressive illness I. *British Journal of Psychiatry, 121,* 147–161.

Rowan, P. R., Paykel, E. S., & Parker, R. R. (1982). Phenelzine and Amitriptyline: Effects on symptoms of neurotic depression. *British Journal of Psychiatry,140,* 475–483.

Schapira, K., Roth, M., Kerr, T. A., & Gurney, C. (1972). The prognosis of affective disorders: the differentiation of anxiety states from depressive illnesses. *British Journal of Psychiatry, 121,* 175–181.

Shagass, C. (1955). Differentiation between anxiety and depression by the photically activated EEG. *American Journal of Psychiatry, 112,* 41–46.

Sheehan, D. V., Ballenger, J., & Jacobsen, G. (1980). Treatment of endogenous anxiety with phobic, hysterical and hypochondriacal components. *Archives of General Psychiatry, 37,* 51–59.

Slater, E., & Shields, J. (1969). Genetical aspects of anxiety. In *"Studies of Anxiety"*, Ed. by Lader M. H., pp. 62–71. British Journal of Psychiatry Special Publications No. 3, Ashford, Kent, England.

Teasdale, J. D., Fennell M. J. V., Hibbert, G. I., & Amies, P. L. (1984). Cognitive therapy for major depressive therapy in primary care. *British Journal of Psychiatry, 144,* 400–406.

Tellenbach (1976). Melancholie. Berlin, Springer.

Tellenbach (1980). Zur Phänomenologie des Gesundseins and deren Konsequenzen für den Arzt. Z. Klin. *Psychol. Psychother., 28,* 57–67.

Torgersen, S. (1980). Hereditary and environmental differentiation of general neurotic, obsessive, and impulsive hysterical personality traits. *Acta Genetica Medica Genrellol, 29,* 193–207.

Torgersen, S., (1983). Genetic factors in anxiety disorders. *Archives of General Psychiatry, 40,* 1085–1089.

Tyrer, P., & Steinberg, D. (1975). Symptomatic treatment of agoraphobia and social phobias: A follow-up study. *British Journal of Psychiatry, 127,* 163–168.

Tyrer, P., Candy, J., & Kelly, D. (1973). A study of the clincial effects of phenelzine and placebo in the treatment of phobic anxiety. *Psychopharmacologia, 432,* 237–254.

Winokur, G. (1970). Genetic findings and methodological considerations in manic-depressive disease. *British Journal of Psychiatry, 117,* 267–274.

Zerssen, D. v. (1980). Personlichkeitsforschung bei Depressionen, in *"Neue Perspektiven in der Depressionsforschung"*, ed. by Heimann, H. and Gideke, H. pp. 155–178. Bern, Huber.

Zerssen, D. v. (1977). Premorbid personality and affective disorders. In *"Handbook of Studies on Depression"*, Ed. by Burrows, G. D. pp. 79–103. Amsterdam, Excerpta Medica.

Zitrin, C. M., Klein, D. F., & Woerner, M. G. (1980). Treatment of agoraphobia with group exposure in vivo and imipramine, *Archives of General Psychiatry, 37,* 63–71.

PART III

Development and Maintenance

CHAPTER 9

Genetics

Svenn Torgersen

The nature-nurture problem will always emerge when the development of a psychiatric disorder is discussed. To what extent is the manifestation of the disorder determined by hereditary factors and to what extent by environmental factors? The question is not easily answered, as a direct examination of genes is impossible. The indirect way to study genetic factors is to apply family studies, twin studies, or adoption studies.

In family studies, the biological relatives of a proband with a certain disorder are examined, either through the proband's report or through a personal interview. If there is a higher frequency of the disorder among the relatives of a the proband compared to the the relatives of the controls, the disorder may seem to have a familial transmission. However, the reason may be environmental as well as genetic, as family members not only share genes, but also live in the same environment, are exposed to similar environmental stimuli, and are imitating and identifying with each other. What we can do with family studies is to make a negative proof, that is, if a higher frequency of the disorder is not observed among the relatives, then genetic factors cannot be involved.

Twin studies are an improvement compared to family studies. Both monozygotic (MZ) and dizygotic (DZ) twins are usually growing up in the same family and hence exposed to similar environmental factors. However, MZ twins are genetically identical, while DZ twins are no more similar genetically than other siblings. Hence, if the same disorder (concordance) is found more often in MZ than in DZ pairs, genetic factors seem to be involved in the development of the disorder.

Critics of the twin method, however, have argued that twin studies are not more successful in separating environmental and genetic factors than family studies. Monozygotic twins are not only more similar genetically than DZ twin partners, they are also exposed to a more similar environment. As MZ twins are frequently confused, approached as a unit, they are treated more similarly and have the same friends. Hence, the higher concordance in MZ twin pairs compared to DZ pairs may be due to environmental similarity as well as genetic identity.

One way to avoid this mingling of environmental and genetic factors is to study adoptees, and observe the concordance of the disorder between the adopted-away offspring and their biological relatives. In a few instances the two methods have been combined, as twins reared apart have been studied. However, it is rare to find a proband with a certain disorder who is both twin and adopted-away to another family than that of the co-twin.

Even if the most refined methods are used in the study of genetic factors in the development of the disorder, problems of interpretation and validity of results remain. First, the probands are usually treated patients and it is not known whether the etiology of the disorder is the same in all individuals as in individuals seeking treatment for their disorder. Second, there is the question of whether twins or adoptees are representative of the total population. Third, and most important; it is a mistake to think that a universal estimation of the genetic contribution to the development of the disorder can be found once and for all. The relative importance of genetic and environmental factors is dependent upon the variation in genetic and environmental factors in the population. If a population with small environmental variation and large genetic variation is studied, the results have to be that genetic factors are important in the development of the disorder. Conversely, if the genetic variation in the population is small, and the environmental variation large, the results will be that environment is important in the development. This always holds when *both* genetic and environmental factors are involved, and this is usually the case with psychiatric disorders.

Hence, there is reason to believe that what we find about genetic factors in the development of anxiety disorders is limited to the culture we are studying and the historical time of the study.

RESEARCH REVIEW

The anxiety disorders are classified as anxiety neuroses and phobic neuroses in international classifications of psychiatric disorders. The same was the case in the United States until the introduction of the American Psychiatric Association's *Diagnostic and Statistical Manual of Mental Disorders,* third edition (DSM-III) in 1980. The DSM-III divided anxiety neuroses into two groups: panic disorder and generalized anxiety disorder, and the phobic disorders into four: agoraphobia with and without panic attacks, social phobia, and simple phobias. In addition, obsessive–compulsive disorder and post-traumatic stress disorder were included among the anxiety disorders. The family and twin studies will first be discussed according to the more global international classification, and then to the more specific DSM-III classification.

Anxiety neuroses

The early family studies of anxiety neuroses applied a rather crude classification system where the anxiety neuroses were designated as irritable heart (Oppenheimer & Rotschild, 1918), DaCosta's syndrome (Wood, 1941), effort syndrome (Wheeler, White, Reed, & Cohen, 1948), as well as anxiety neurosis (McInnes, 1937) and anxiety states (Brown, 1942). However, all the studies clearly showed a (two times or more) higher frequency of anxiety neuroses in the relatives of the patients compared to the relatives of normal controls.

Two twin studies have investigated the concordance rates for anxiety states (Shields & Slater, 1966) and anxiety neurosis according to the International Classification of Diseases, ninth edition (ICD-9) (Torgersen, 1985). Shields and Slater (1966) found a concordance rate of 41% among 17 MZ pairs and a concordance rate of 4% among 28 DZ pairs. The concordance rate in Torgersen's (1985) study of 28 MZ twins was 36%, and 13% among the 48 DZ pairs. The low concordance rate among the DZ twin pairs in the study of Shields and

Slater seems strange and may have something to do with the diagnostic methods.

As mentioned earlier, the higher concordance rate in MZ pairs might be ascribed to the MZ twins being together more in childhood, being treated as a unit, having the same friends, and generally being exposed to more similar environmental factors than DZ twins. However, Shields (1962), in his study of twins reared apart, presented three MZ twin pairs who demonstrated a similar development of marked anxiety tendencies despite having been separated shortly after childhood and reared in different families. Taken together, the family and twin studies indicate that genetic factors are involved in the development of anxiety neuroses, globally perceived.

Panic disorder

The term *neurocirculatory asthenia* is an early forerunner of the diagnosis of panic disorder. Cohen, White, and Johnson (1948), Cohen, Badal, Kilpatrick, Reed, and White (1951), and Wheeler et al. (1948) observed a frequency between 13% and 58% of neurocirculatory asthenia among the first-degree relatives of patients with neurocirculatory asthenia. The corresponding frequency among relatives of controls was between zero and 2%.

Around the time of the introduction of the DSM-III, a number of family studies of panic disorder appeared. They all demonstrated a remarkably high frequency of panic disorder among the first-degree relatives of panic disorder probands (ranging from 16% to 31%) compared to 1% to 4% among the first-degree relatives of controls, as shown in Table 9.1 (Crowe, Pauls, Slyman, & Noyes, 1980; Crowe Goffney, & Kerber, 1982; Crowe, Noyes, Pauls, & Slyman, 1983; Harris, Noyes, Crowe, & Chaudry, 1983).

As it appears, the early family studies of neurocirculatory asthenia and the studies of DSM-III panic disorder displayed similar results: There is a strong familial accumulation of panic disorder. Whether this is due to genetic transmission or to common family environment may be elucidated by a twin study. Torgersen (1983) observed panic attacks in 4 of 13 MZ co-twins of index twins with panic disorder or agoraphobia with panic attacks, compared to none in 16 DZ co-twins. The concordance rates were not influenced by whether the twins had been together a lot as children or later, or whether they strongly identified with each other or had been treated as a unite by their parents. Consequently, genetic factors seem to influence the transmission of panic disorder within families.

Generalized anxiety disorder

As mentioned earlier, the DSM-III classification system splits the older category of anxiety neurosis into panic disorder and generalized anxiety disorder. While many studies have investigated the familial transmission of panic disorder, only two have looked at the families of

Table 9.1. Morbidity Risk for Panic Disorder among First-Degree Relatives of Probands with Panic Disorder and Controls

STUDY	FIRST-DEGREE RELATIVES OF PROBANDS (Percentage)	CONTROLS (Percentage)
Crowe et al. (1980)	31	4
Crowe et al. (1982)	16	1
Crowe et al. (1983)	17	2
Harris et al. (1983)	21	4

probands with generalized anxiety disorder. Cloninger, Martin, Clayton, and Guze (1981) observed an anxiety disorder frequency of 3.1% among first-degree relatives of probands with anxiety states other than panic disorder (presumably mainly generalized anxiety disorder). Nearly the same frequency of anxiety disorder (3.5%) was observed among the first-degree relatives of controls. Davidson, Schwartz, Storck, Krishnan, and Hammett (1985) found a morbidity risk of 3.8% of generalized anxiety disorder among the parents of probands with generalized anxiety disorder and a morbidity risk of 3.2% among the siblings. This was very similar to what they observed among the first-degree relatives of probands with depression and posttraumatic stress disorder. Both the lack of difference in the morbidity risk for generalized anxiety disorder between relatives of probands with generalized anxiety disorder, relatives of probands with posttraumatic stress disorder and with depression, and the low risk, indicate that the specific familial transmission of generalized anxiety disorder is negligible. On the other hand, many other psychiatric disorders were observed among the first-degree relatives of probands with generalized anxiety disorder. In the study of Davidson et al. (1985) only 1 of 13, or 7%, of the patients with generalized anxiety disorder lacked a first-degree relative with a psychiatric disorder, compared to 21% among the depressive probands and 34% among the probands with posttraumatic stress disorder. Consequently, an unspecific familial transmission seems to exist.

A twin study (Torgersen, 1983) confirms that neither a genetic nor a specific familial transmission is involved in the development of generalized anxiety disorder. None of the 12 MZ co-twins of index twins with generalized anxiety disorder had generalized anxiety disorder, and 2 (17%) had other anxiety disorders. One of the 20 DZ co-twins (5%) had generalized anxiety disorder, and 3 (15%) had other anxiety disorders.

The twin study displayed another interesting result: as much as 25% of the MZ co-twins, and the same percentage of the DZ co-twins, had another psychiatric disorder than anxiety disorder. This result is in accordance with the observation of Davidson et al. (1985), and indicates the unspecific familial transmission of generalized anxiety disorder.

These observations might challenge the diagnostic validity of generalized anxiety disorder, as Breier, Charney, and Heninger (1985) suggest. However, it may be that generalized anxiety disorder is a consequence of environmental factors, which may lead to a number of psychiatric disorders. An examination of the childhood experiences of the twins with anxiety disorders disclosed that 31% of twins with generalized anxiety disorder had lost their mother, father, or both by death in childhood, compared to 10% of the twins with panic disorder or agoraphobia with panic attacks (Torgersen, 1986). These results fit nicely with the results of the concordance rate analysis, and show that generalized anxiety disorder, in contrast to panic disorders, is nongenetic, and consequently completely a product of environmental factors. Among these, childhood loss due to death seems to be prominent.

Phobic disorders

Phobic disorders especially represent classification problems. Phobic traits are very common in the population. On the other hand, phobias so severe that they deserve treatment are rather rare, only a small percentage of the total population. Consequently, to define a case may be difficult. Futhermore, to differentiate between what constitutes phobic anxiety and phobic obsessions is difficult. This means that different studies of phobias may include different groups of disorders. In the following, studies of phobic traits in the common population as well as clinical cases will be included.

Solyom, Bech, Solyom, and Hugel (1974) investigated the first-degree relatives of persons with undifferentiated phobias and observed a frequency of 19% among the relatives, compared to 4% among the first-degree relatives of controls. Buglass, Clarke, Henderson, Kreitman, and Presley (1977) studied agoraphobia and found a frequency of 7% phobics among the first-degree relatives, compared to 2% among the relatives of controls. Harris et al. (1983) classified the first-degree relatives of agoraphobics by means of DSM-III and observed 9% agoraphobics among the relatives, compared to 4% among the first-degree relatives of controls. When all phobias were included, they observed a frequency of 15% among the first-degree relatives of agoraphobics, compared to 5% among the relatives of controls. The frequency of other anxiety disorders were 12% among the relatives of agoraphobics, compared to 10% among the relatives of controls. The frequency of anxiety disorders other than the phobias was, thus, not higher among the relatives of agoraphobics than among the relatives of controls.

Looking at the twin studies, Young, Fenton, and Lader (1971) observed a heritability of .64 for a phobic anxiety subscale of the Middlesex Health Questionnaire in a common twin population. Torgersen (1979) observed a heritability between .23 and .53 for different groups of phobic traits assessed by means of a questionnaire in a common twin population. Rose and Dilto (1983) found a heritability from .24 to .78 for different kinds of phobic traits by means of a questionnaire given to twins of college age. Thus, phobic traits in the common population do seem to be influenced by genetic factors.

Studies of clinical twin cases of phobias are rare. Carey and Gottesman (1981) observed phobic symptoms or features in seven of eight MZ co-twins of index twins with a phobic disorder, compared to the same symptoms and features in 4 of 13 DZ co-twins. Torgersen (1983) did not find any phobias among the 12 MZ co-twins or 18 DZ co-twins of probands with phobias. However, 42% of the MZ co-twins compared to 11% of the DZ co-twins had other anxiety disorders.

Taken together, phobias in the common population and in the studies of clinical cases indicate that the development of phobias is influenced by genetic factors. However, it is a question of how specific the genetic transmission may be. It might be expected that some phobias, for instance, animal phobias or other simple phobias and social phobias, are less influenced by genetic factors than agoraphobias. However, especially the study of Torgersen (1979), but also the study of Rose and Dilto (1983), show that this is not the case.

Obsessive–compulsive disorder

The classification of obsessive–compulsive disorder is also complicated because obsessive–compulsive symptoms are abundant in many psychiatric disorders, and also in the common population, without representing any adjustment problems. The delineation between obsessive–compulsive symptoms and the obsessive personality traits area is also difficult to draw. With these reservations in mind, I will present some (mostly older) family and twin studies.

Luxenburger (1930) observed a frequency of 15% compulsions and obsessive personality among the first-degree relatives of patients with obsession. Lewis (1935) found 14% severe obsessions and 12% mild obsessions among the relatives. Brown (1942) also included controls and observed 7% obsessions among the relatives of obsessive patients, compared to none among the relatives of controls. The frequency of anxiety states among the relatives of obsessive patients was 28% compared to 10% among the relatives of controls. Rüdin (1953) observed only 4% obsessions among the relatives of obsessive patients. Kringlen (1965) also included phobias among the index patients. He observed 10% obsessions among the relatives of the obsessive/phobic patients, compared to none among the relatives of controls, and 31% with obsessive personality compared to 8% among the relatives of controls. Rosenberg (1967) found that 0.3% of the first-degree relatives of patients with obsessions had been treated for obsessions, and 3% for anxiety. He had no controls. Finally, Rasmussen and Tsuang (1986) observed in a recent study that 5%

of the parents of probands with DSM-III obsessive–compulsive disorder met the criteria for the same disorder, while 11% had obsessive–compulsive traits. The family studies show that obsessive–compulsive disorder is familially transmitted and related to anxiety and obsessive personality.

The twin samples are small, as obsessions are a rare disorder. Rüdin (1953) summarized cases from the literature and observed that six of nine MZ pairs were concordant, compared to none of only one DZ pair. Inouye (1972) observed in his summary of cases that 19 of 25 MZ twin pairs were concordant, compared to none of seven DZ pairs. Ihda (1961) found that 8 of 10 MZ pairs were concordant. He had no DZ pairs. Inouye (1965) observed 8 of 10 concordant MZ pairs compared to one of four DZ pairs. Carey (1978) observed that 17 of 20 (85%) MZ co-twins had obsessive or phobic symptoms, compared to 12 of 24 (50%) DZ co-twins. Carey and Gottesman (1981) reported that 13 of 15 MZ co-twins had obsessive symptoms or features, compared to 7 of 15 (47%) DZ co-twins. It is important to note that these three studies essentially included the same Maudsley twin population. Torgersen (1983) observed that none of three MZ and nine DZ co-twins had an obsessive compulsive disorder, though one MZ co-twin had an agoraphobia without panic attacks, and one DZ co-twin a generalized anxiety disorder.

The low frequency of DZ cases compared to MZ cases among the older twin samples suggests that the studies were not too representative. Even so, the twin studies seem to indicate that obsessive–compulsive disorder is genetically influenced. Futhermore, the family and twin studies suggest that obsessions are not genetically separate from phobias.

Posttraumatic stress disorder

As the term indicates, environmental factors have to be of importance in the development of posttraumatic stress disorder. Even so, genetic factors may be of importance too. Only one family study is published (Davidson et al., 1985), and there are no twin studies dealing with this disorder. The family study shows a high morbidity risk of alcoholism among the first-degree relatives, compared to relatives of patients with depression and generalized anxiety disorder. The risk of other psychiatric disorders is not higher than among the relatives of the comparison groups, especially when it comes to the relatives of patients with generalized anxiety disorder, and this disorder does not seem to be influenced by genetic factors. So, today, we do not know if posttraumatic stress disorder is influenced by genetic factors, but it does not seem likely.

Conclusions from family and twin studies

The family and twin studies indicate that generalized anxiety disorder is not influenced by genetic factors. Panic disorder, phobic disorder, and obsessive–compulsive disorder, however, seem to be influenced by genetic factors. As for posttraumatic stress disorder, we do not know, but it is probably not. It may be stated that twin studies give no evidence, as partners of MZ pairs are more exposed to the same environmental factors than partners of DZ pairs. However, Torgersen (1983) controlled for this factor without any influence on the concordance rates.

The specificity of genetic transmission

When genetic factors are involved in the development of anxiety disorders, except in the case of generalized anxiety disorder and posttraumatic stress disorder, the question arises whether the same genetic factors are involved in all anxiety disorders that are genetically transmitted.

A way to answer this question is to examine the family and twin studies and see whether the relatives or co-twins have different anxiety disorder than the probands. The study of Harris et al. (1983)

gives an especially good opportunity for such an analysis. As mentioned earlier, the relatives of probands with agoraphobia and panic disorder were investigated and an important difference was found between the two groups of relatives. The total morbidity risk for anxiety disorders was almost the same in both groups of relatives. However, concordance for the specific disorder was different. The morbidity risk for panic disorder was 20.5% among the relatives of probands with panic disorder. On the other hand, the morbidity risk for agoraphobia among the relatives of probands with agoraphobia was only 8.5%. The rest of the anxiety disorders consisted of panic disorder, generalized anxiety disorder, atypical anxiety, social phobia, simple phobia, and obsessive–compulsive disorder.

The research group later extended the number of probands and reached essentially the same results (Noyes et al., 1986). The frequency of panic disorder was 14.9% among the relatives of probands with panic disorder, compared to 7.0% among the relatives of probands with agoraphobia, and 3.5% among the relatives of controls (see Table 9.2). The frequency of agoraphobia was 9.4% among the relatives of probands with agoraphobia, compared to only 1.7% among the relatives of probands with panic disorder, and 3.5% among the relatives of controls. The frequency of the combined group of social phobia, simple phobia, and obsessive–compulsive disorder was 7.0% among the relatives of the probands with agoraphobia, compared to 3.4% among the relatives of probands with panic disorder, and 2.7% among the controls.

Astonishingly, the authors conclude that agoraphobia and panic disorder are familially related, despite the fact that only 1.7% of the relatives of probands with panic disorder had agoraphobia. They meant that agoraphobia is a more severe variant of panic disorder. My own interpretation is that panic disorder and agoraphobia with panic attacks are related on the one hand, and agoraphobia without panic attacks, the other phobias, and obsessive–compulsive disorder are related, on the other.

The twin study (Torgersen, 1983) confirms this hypothesis, even if the number of twin pairs in the different categories is low. The study showed that a MZ co-twin of a proband with panic disorder had agoraphobia with panic attacks, and, correspondingly, that a MZ co-twin of a proband with agoraphobia with panic attacks had panic disorder. Futhermore, two more MZ co-twins of one index twin with panic disorder and one with agoraphobia with panic attacks, had panic attacks, without fulfilling the criteria of panic disorder because of fewer than three

Table 9.2. Frequency of Various Anxiety Disorders among the First-Degree Relatives of Probands with Panic Disorder and Agoraphobia

	FIRST-DEGREE RELATIVES OF PROBANDS WITH:		
	PANIC DISORDER (Percentage)	AGORAPHOBIA (Percentage)	CONTROLS (Percentage)
Panic disorder	14.9	7.0	3.5
Agoraphobia	1.7	9.4	3.5
Other anxiety disorders[a]	3.4	7.0	2.7

Note. Data from Noyes et al., 1986
[a]Social phobia, simple phobia, and obsessive–compulsive disorder

attacks within 3 weeks. Panic disorder and agoraphobia with panic attacks thus seem to be related. Correspondingly, the twin study showed concordance between agoraphobia without panic attacks and obsessive–compulsive disorder. Even if it is too early to draw a definite conclusion from these two studies, the observations indicate that panic disorder and agoraphobia with panic attacks are genetically related, and so are other phobias and obsessive–compulsive disorder.

It has also been proposed that there is a genetic relationship between panic disorder and major depression, as both disorders respond positively to antidepressive medication. Leckman, Weissman, Merikangas, Pauls, and Prusoff (1983) observed a higher frequency of both depression and anxiety disorders among the adult relatives of probands with major depression plus panic attacks. Weissman et al. (1984) also observed an increased risk of major depression and anxiety disorder among the children of probands with major depressive and panic disorder. Finally, Breier, Charney, and Heninger (1984) found that episodes of depression were common prior to the first panic attack.

However, these studies do not prove any familial or genetic relationship between anxiety and depression, but only that the relatives of probands with both the two disorders frequently have the same two disorders, and that different affective states can occur in the course of a disorder. When the frequency of depression is specifically studied among the relatives of probands with agoraphobia and panic disorder, divergent results are observed. Munjack and Moss (1981) found a higher frequency of depression among first-degree relatives of probands with panic disorder compared to relatives of controls. Bowen and Kohut (1979) also observed a high rate of major depression among the relatives of probands with agoraphobia with panic attacks. However, Cloninger et al. (1981) did not observe an increased risk of depression among the relatives of probands with panic disorder. The same was true for Crowe et al. (1980, 1983). In the preliminary (Harris et al., 1983) and final (Noyes et al., 1986) report from the Iowa study of panic disorder and agoraphobia, the results were also negative. In my own twin study (Torgersen, 1983), I did not find any MZ co-twin of probands with panic disorder or agoraphobia with panic attacks who had an affective disorder. On the other hand, among the non — co-twin relatives of index twins with panic disorder and agoraphobia with panic attacks, the frequency of affective disorder was 16.0%, compared to 3.9% among the relatives of index twins with generalized anxiety disorder (Torgersen, 1986). My own interpretation of the results of the family and twin studies is that anxiety disorders with panic and depression may show some common familial, environmental variance, but no common genetic variance.

The various studies also seem to indicate a familial association between panic disorders and agoraphobia, on the one hand, and alcohol disorders on the other (Crowe et al., 1980; Crowe et al., 1983; Noyes et al., 1986; Torgersen, 1986). The results may not lead to any speculation about a common genetic diathesis, only indicate the simple relationship that alcohol abuse is a common complication to more severe anxiety disorders because of the sedative effects of alcohol.

The mode of genetic transmission

If it is established that all anxiety disorders except generalized anxiety disorder and posttraumatic stress disorder are genetically transmitted, the question arises whether the transmission is polygenetic or by an autosomal dominant gene. Crowe et al. (1981) have tried to answer this question. They investigated up to four generations of ancestrals of probands with panic disorder. Two analyses were performed. First, the number of unilateral ancestral cases was compared to the number of bilateral cases. In unilateral cases, two cases come from one side of the kindred; bilateral cases are those in which one case comes from the maternal side and one from the paternal. If a single dominant gene is involved, more unilateral pairs are expected. The results showed that almost all ancestral cases were unilateral, indicating a single cominant gene. In addition, a more advanced pedigree analysis was performed, taking into account variable age at onset and ascertainment bias. A maximum-likelihood estimate analysis showed a very good fit to a Mendelian single-gene model.

Even if the existence of a single locus for panic disorder is not established, the observations may indicate that panic disorder is inherited as an autosomal dominant trait. However, Carey (1982) has criticized the study on two grounds. First, the higher frequency of panic disorder among women compared to men speaks against a single-gene transmission. Second, with an autosomal dominant genetic transmission the observed concordance is less than half of the expected. His explanation is that the Iowa sample is a highly selected severe sample, and a polygenetic model would also predict results similar to what Crowe et al. observed. So, just as for schizophrenia, the question as to the mode of genetic transmission is not yet settled.

What is inherited?

Even if the family and twin studies indicate that genetic factors are involved in the development of panic disorder and the phobias, nothing is known about what exactly is inherited. Some studies indicate that patients with panic disorder and phobias experienced much anxiety in childhood (Tearnan, Telch, & Keefe, 1984; Torgersen, 1986). However, the observations are conflicting. Even so, the question remains why these individuals are more prone to anxiety. Since Pitts and McClure's (1967) famous study of lactate-induced panic attacks, a number of biochemical theories of anxiety proneness have been proposed. The most popular hypothesis today is that of an inherited weakness in the locus coeruleus. The locus coeruleus contains most of the central nervous system's noradrenergic neurons. A low threshold of discharge from the locus coeruleus may abruptly increase the total central noradrenergic activity and give rise to the acute panic attacks. However, the theory is still being debated (Gorman, Dillon, Fyer, Liebowitz, & Klein, 1985). Futhermore, a change in the function of the locus coeruleus may be a consequence and not the cause of the development of disorders with panic attacks. In fact, neither biochemical research, studies of the effects of various medication, nor genetic investigation have invalidated the old psychoanalytical theories of an exaggerated drive strength or the behavior theories assumptions about proneness to conditioned learning. Genetic research tells only that some people have a higher inherited proneness to anxiety, not why this is so.

CONCLUDING REMARKS

The family and twin studies indicate that all anxiety disorders except generalized anxiety disorder and posttraumatic stress disorder are influenced by genetic factors in their development. It is possible that panic disorder and agoraphobia with panic attacks are influenced by one set of genetic factors, and the other phobias and obsessive–compulsive disorder by another. Anxiety disorders with panic attacks may be a consequence of an autosomal dominant gene, although more studies are necessary before this hypothesis is confirmed.

No common genetic diathesis seems to exist between any anxiety disorders and affective disorders. Alcohol abuse seems to be related to anxiety disorders with panic attacks, not because of a common genetic basis, but because the individuals use alcohol as self-medication.

However, even if genetic factors are involved, environment plays an important part in the development, as most MZ pairs are discordant. Kendler, Heath, Martin, and Eaves (1986) calculated the environmental variance for different anxiety symptoms of more than 50%.

Nothing is known about what biochemical mechanisms are inherited and what makes some individuals more prone to anxiety disorders, and even less about the interaction between heredity and environment. However, the study of Kendler et al. (1986) indicates that unique environmental factors specific to the individual are far more important than familial environment. The problem with these statistical models is that they find a high unique and a low familial variance for almost all disorders. So, the possibility exists that the models are wrong, perhaps because the development of twins cannot be calculated mechanically. An intentional polarization within the twin pair will violate the assumptions of the models and may give an exaggerated unique variance and a diminuated familial variance.

Genetic research cannot be of any help in choosing between different theories about the development of anxiety disorders, and is irrelevant to the question of what kind of therapy is the best choice. There is no evidence that a disorder partly caused by genetic factors is more successfully treated by biochemical therapy than a disorder solely caused by environmental factors. Similarly, psychological therapy does not need to be more effective for a disorder caused by environmental factors than for a disorder strongly influenced by genetics.

Progress in the prevention and treatment of anxiety disorders awaits studies of the interaction between genetic and environmental factors in the development of the disorder. However, a breakthrough of this kind of research assumes the detection of genetic markers. Today nothing is known about such markers, as is the case for most other psychiatric disorders.

REFERENCES

American Psychiatric Association. (1980). *Diagnostic and statistical manual of mental disorders* (3rd ed.). Washington, DC: Author.

Bowen, R. C., & Kohut, J. (1979). The relationship between agoraphobia and primary affective disorders. *Canadian Journal of Psychiatry, 24,* 317–322.

Breier, A., Charney, D. S., & Heninger, G. R. (1984). Major depression in patients with agoraphobia and panic disorder. *Archives of General Psychiatry, 41,* 1129–1135.

Breier, A., Charney, D. S., & Heninger, G. R. (1985). The diagnostic validity of anxiety disorders and their relationship to depressive illness. *American Journal of Psychiatry, 142,* 787–797.

Brown, F. N. (1942). Heredity in the psychoneuroses. *Journal of the Royal Society of Medicine, 35,* 785–790.

Buglass, D., Clarke, J., Henderson, A. S., Kreitman, N., & Presley, A. S. (1977). A study of agoraphobic housewives. *Psychological Medicine, 7,* 73–86.

Carey, G. (1978). A clinical genetic twin study of obsessive and phobic states. *Dissertation Abstracts International, 39,* 2975B (Order No. 7823880).

Carey, G. (1982). Genetic influences on anxiety neuroses and agoraphobia. In P. J. Mathew (Ed.), *The biology of anxiety.* New York: Brunner/Mazel.

Carey, G., & Gottesman, I. I. (1981). Twin and family studies of anxiety, phobic and obsessive disorders. In D. F. Klein & J. Rabkin (Eds.), *Anxiety: New research and changing concepts.* (pp 117–136). New York: Raven Press.

Cloninger, C. R., Martin, R. L., Clayton, P., & Guze, S. B. (1981). A blind follow-up and family study of anxiety neurosis: Preliminary analysis of the St. Louis 500. In D. F. Klein & J. Rabkin (Eds.), *Anxiety: New research and changing concepts.* (pp 137–154). New York: Raven Press.

Cohen, M. E., Badal, D. W., Kilpatrick, A., Reed, E. W., & White, P. D. (1951). The high familial prevalence of neurocirculatory asthenia (anxiety neurosis, effort syndrome). *American Journal of Human Genetics, 3,* 126–158.

Cohen, M. E., White, P. D., & Johnson, R. E. (1948). Neurocirculatory asthenia, anxiety neurosis or the effort syndrome. *Archives of Internal Medicine, 81,* 260–281.

Crowe, R. R., Goffney, G., & Kerber, R. (1982). Panic attacks in families of patients with mitral valve prolapse. *Journal of Affective Disorder, 4,* 121–125.

Crowe, R. R., Noyes, R., Pauls, D., & Slyman, D. (1983). A family study of panic disorder. *Archives of General Psychiatry, 40,* 1065–1069.

Crowe, R. R., Pauls, D. L., Kerber, R. E., & Noyes, R. (1981). Panic disorder and mitral valve prolapse. In D. F. Klein & J. Rabkin (Eds.), *Anxiety: New research and changing concepts.* (pp 103–114). New York: Raven Press.

Crowe, R. R., Pauls, D. L., Slyman, D. J., & Noyes, R. (1980). A familial study of anxiety neurosis: morbidity risk in families of patients with and without mitral valve prolapses. *Archives of General Psychiatry, 37,* 77–79.

Davidson, J., Schwartz, M., Storck, M., Krishnan, R. R., & Hammett, E. (1985). A diagnostic and family study of posttraumatic stress disorder. *American Journal of Psychiatry, 142,* 90–93.

Gorman, J. M., Dillon, D., Fyer, A. J., Liebowitz, M. R., & Klein, D. F. (1985). The lachtate infusion model. *Psychopharmacology Bulletin, 21,* 428–433.

Harris, E. L., Noyes, R., Crowe, R. R., & Chaudry, D. R. (1983). Family study of agoraphobia; report of a pilot study. *Archives of General Psychiatry, 40,* 1061–1064.

Ihda, S. (1961). A study of neurosis by twin method. *Psychiatrica Neurologica Japanese, 63,* 861–892.

Inouye, E. (1965). Similar and dissimilar manifestations of obsessive–compulsion neurosis in monozygotic twins. *American Journal of Psychiatry, 121,* 1171–1175.

Inouye, E. (1972). Genetic aspects of neurosis: a review. *International Journal of Mental Health, 1,* 176–189.

Kendler, K. S., Heath, A., Martin, N. G., & Eaves, L. J. (1986). Symptoms of anxiety and depression in a volunteer twin population: The etiologic role of genetic and environmental factors. *Archives of General Psychiatry, 43,* 213–221.

Kringlen, E. (1965). Obsessional neurotics: A long-term follow up. *British Journal of Psychiatry, 111,* 709–722.

Leckman, J. F., Weissman, M. M., Merikangas, K. R., Pauls, D. L., & Prusoff, D. A. (1983). Panic disorder and major depression: Increased risk of depression, alcoholism, panic and phobic disorders in families of depressive probands with panic disorder. *Archives of General Psychiatry, 40,* 1055–1060.

Lewis, A. (1935). Problems of obsessional illness. *Proceeding from the Royal Society of Medicine, 29,* 325–336.

Luxenburger, H. (1930). Heredität und familientypus der zwangsneurotiker (anankastis cher psychopaten). *Archiv für Psychiatrie und Nervenkrankheiten, 90,* 590–594.

McInnes, R. G. (1937). Observations of heredity in neurosis. *Journal of the Royal Society of Medicine, 30,* 895–904.

Munjack, D. J., & Moss, H. B. (1981). Affective disorder and alcoholism in families of agoraphobics. *Archives of General Psychiatry, 38,* 869–871.

Noyes, R., Crowe, R. R., Harris, E. L., Hamra, B. J., McChesney, C. M., & Chaudry, D. R. (1986). Relationship between panic disorder and agoraphobia. A family study. *Archives of General Psychiatry, 43,* 227–232.

Oppenheimer, B. S., & Rotschild, M. A. (1918). The psychoneurotic factor in the "irritable heart" of soldiers. *British Medical Journal, 2,* 29–31.

Pitts, F. N., & McClure, J. N. (1967). Lactate metabolism in anxiety neurosis. *New England Journal of Medicine, 277,* 1329–1336.

Rasmussen, S. A., & Tsuang, M. T. (1986). Clinical characteristics and family history in DSM-III obsessive–compulsive disorder. *American Journal of Psychiatry, 143,* 317–322.

Rose, R. J., & Dilto, W. B. (1983). A developmental-genetic analysis of common fears from early adolescence to early adulthood. *Child Development, 54,* 361–368.

Rosenberg, C. M. (1967). Familial aspects of obsessional neurosis. *British Journal of Psychiatry, 113,* 404–413.

Rüdin, E. (1953). Ein Beitrag zur frage der zwangskrankheit, inbesondere ihrer hereditären beziehungen. *Archiv für Psychiatrie und Nervenkrankheiten, 191,* 14–54.

Shields, J. (1962). *Monozygotic twins brought up apart and brought up together.* London: Oxford University Press.

Shields, J., & Slater, E. (1966). La similarité du diagnostic chez les jumeaux et la problème de la specificité biologique dans les nevroses et les troubles de la personalité. *Evolutione Psychiatrie, 31,* 441–451.

Solyom, L., Bech, P., Solyom, C., & Hugel, R. (1974). Some etiological factors in phobic neurosis. *Canadian Psychiatric Association Journal, 19,* 69–78.

Tearnan, B. H., Telch, M. J., & Keefe, P. (1984). Etiology and onset of agoraphobia: A critical review. *Comprehensive Psychiatry, 25,* 51–62.

Torgersen, S. (1979). The nature and origin of common phobic fears. *British Journal of Psychiatry, 134,* 343–351.

Torgersen, S. (1983). Genetic factors in anxiety disorders. *Archives of General Psychiatry, 40,* 1085–1089.

Torgersen, S. (1985). Hereditary differentiation of anxiety and affective neuroses. *British Journal of Psychiatry, 146,* 530–534.

Torgersen, S. (1986). Childhood and family characteristics in panic and generalized anxiety disorder. *American Journal of Psychiatry, 43,* 630–632.

Weissman, M. M., Gershon, E. S., Kidd, K. K., Prusoff, B. A., Leckman, J. F., Dibble, D. L., & Guroff, J. J. (1984). Psychiatric disorders in the relatives of probands with affective disorders. *Archives of General Psychiatry, 41,* 13–21.

Wheeler, E. D., White, P. D., Reed, E. W., & Cohen, M. E. (1948). Familial incidence of neurocirculatory asthenia ("anxiety neurosis," "effort syndrome"). *Journal of Clinical Investment, 27,* 562.

Wood, P. (1941). Aetiology of Da Costa's syndrome. *British Medical Journal, 1,* 845–851.

Young, J. P. R., Fenton, C. W., & Lader, M. J. (1971). The inheritance of neurotic traits: A twin study of the Middlesex Hospital Questionnaire. *British Journal of Psychiatry, 119,* 393–398.

CHAPTER 10

Animal Models

William T. McKinney

Animal models are basically experimental preparations developed in one species for the purpose of studying phenomena occurring in another species. There is no such thing as a single, comprehensive animal model for anxiety or for any psychiatric syndrome. In the case of animal models of any human disorder, one seeks to develop syndromes in animals that resemble as closely as possible the human condition. However, one is still working with "models," and therefore they will not resemble all aspects of the human clinical syndrome. There will inevitably be differences and, in some instances, the study of these differences may be more important than the similarities.

Comparisons are typically made between the proposed animal model and the human disorder in terms of etiology, symptoms, underlying mechanisms, and treatment responsiveness. There can only be successive approximations or simulation of specific, but limited, aspects of a given syndrome. Nevertheless, there is much to be learned from a comparative approach in psychiatry.

Before reviewing the various proposed animal models of anxiety, this chapter will first discuss the general approaches to understanding and developing animal models of any psychiatric disorder. There are at least four different categories of animal models (McKinney, 1984). These include those designed to: (a) simulate specific signs or symptoms of the human disorder; (b) evaluate specific etiological theories; (c) study underlying mechanisms; and (d) primarily evaluate preclinical drug's.

These different categories will be discussed in more detail in the first part of this chapter. Obviously, some proposed animal models bridge these four different areas, but the animal modeling field is now at a stage of development when no single paradigm will suffice for all four categories of studies. For example, there is no single animal model of anxiety that accomplishes all four purposes.

One of the particularly confusing things in the literature on animal models of "anxiety" is an extreme degree of confusion about pain, fear, stress (acute or chronic), and learning. As the different approaches to modeling anxiety in animals are reviewed, it will become apparent that some paradigms basically involve the study of fear, but implications are proposed about human "anxiety." The relationship between situation specific fear and generalized anxiety is a matter of some controversy, and there needs to be more clarity in the animal literature about this relationship. In particular, extreme caution needs to be exercised in reasoning to human anxiety from animal paradigms that involve situation-specific fear induction, even though such behaviors in animals might be altered by anti-anxiety agents. Such agents might be working in animal paradigms by mechanisms that have absolutely nothing to do with their effectiveness as anti-anxiety agents in humans.

Likewise, there is a lack of clarity in most discussions of animal paradigms that basically involve learning or conditioning of various kinds. Such approaches may have very high cross species empirical validity in terms of predicting drug responsiveness, but have very little to do with human anxiety on other grounds.

The preceding illustrative comments are not meant to be critical of these particular approaches to developing studying "anxiety" in animal paradigms. They have their contributions to make as long as the limitations are recognized. Any single approach to "modeling" anxiety in animals has advantages and limitations, and a theme of this chapter is to urge readers and workers alike to recognize this and cease needless advocacy of one model as being "better" than another. Which animal model is "better" depends on what one wants to study. This applies to anxiety and to any other psychiatric syndrome.

KINDS OF ANIMAL MODELS

Models Designed to Simulate Specific Signs or Symptoms

In this approach to animal modeling one tries to produce, in animals, certain specific aspects of the human disorder. The reason for developing these kinds of models is to focus on the study of a particular symptom or a cluster of symptoms. The primary intent is not to evaluate either a specific etiological theory or treatment responsiveness. The validity of the model is judged by how closely it approximates the human condition from a phenomenological standpoint. From one standpoint, the inducing condition is irrelevant in that one is interested in the study of a set of behaviors, per se, regardless of how they were produced. The significance of this type of work is likely to cut across syndromes rather than be linked with any one disorder. For example, stereotypic behaviors in animals can be produced by many methods ranging from pharmacological techniques to alteration of rearing conditions. In animal paradigms, one can study many aspects of stereotype without having to anchor the work to only one clinical syndrome. It is a fundamental psychopathological behavior that is important in its own right. Likewise, the study of fear-induced behaviors or of learning behaviors has implications that transcend animal models of anxiety.

Models Designed to Test a Specific Etiological Theory

In this type of modeling research, one begins with a specific etiological theory of a given form of psychopathology or, alternatively, with a general theory about the importance of certain variables in a number of forms of psychopathology.

This approach obviously involves the development of paradigms that reasonably simulate theories developed from clinical research. It should be emphasized that this use of animal models does not make any a priori assumptions about the validity of the theory. Rather, the attempt is to operationalize the theory and to develop experimental paradigms to evaluate the effects of such inducing conditions. Animal models such as these are sometimes called "theory driven" models and can be distinguished from the previous kinds of models involving behavioral similarities that are considerably more atheoretical. Though these kinds of animal models are theory driven in the sense that a theory drives the development of the paradigm, the form of behavior is then subject to an analysis which may confirm, modify, or bring into question the original theory.

Models Designed to Study Underlying Mechanisms

This is a complex topic which at present includes at least two different views. To some, the term *mechanisms* is synonymous with neurobiological mechanisms, and the value of animal models is directly related to how easily direct studies of underlying molecular mechanisms can be done. There are many examples of such approaches, mostly in invertebrates and rodents. Typically, in such studies the description of social behavior is quite limited, though the neurobiological aspects will be very precise. To the developmentalist or the behaviorist the term *mechanism* might have very different meanings. Typically, in such studies the behavioral descriptions, whether they be of social behavior or operant behavior, will be quite precise, but neurobiological indices will be limited to those that can be done while still studying social behavior.

It is hoped that these approaches will come to be viewed as complementary rather than antagonistic, which is too often the case at present. Some more socially oriented paradigms are negatively criticized because they do not permit "direct" studies of neurobiological mechanisms at the cellular or subcellular level. These kinds of criticisms are increasingly being directed at animal studies using nonhuman primates as subjects. There is particular relevance of this criticism to the issue of animal models of anxiety, where it may be desirable to utilize primates so that one can assess social behavior and do developmentally oriented work. Not all valid and important neurobiological work, even in these times, needs to be at the molecular level. The continued study of neurobiology using techniques that are compatible with the ongoing study of social behavior has considerable merit even though such studies may not be "direct" studies of neurobiological mechanisms at the cellular level. The limitations in this regard may be more than counterbalanced by the unique advantages in the areas of controlling developmental parameters and assessing social behaviors.

Models Designed to Permit Preclinical Drug Evaluation

If one is mainly interested in developing an experimental system in which potential clinical pharmacological agents can be evaluated, the method by which the syndrome is induced, and even issues of behavioral similarity, become secondary. One evaluates these paradigms by how well the drug effects in the preclinical model predict clinical effectiveness. This is called empirical validity. A high degree of predictive or empirical validity, however, does not necessarily have mechanistic or etiological implications. Drugs can have quite similar effects in two different species, but for different reasons.

This use of models represents one of the oldest and most widely known ones and one widely used in the pharmaceutical industry. Many well-known animal models of anxiety are of this kind.

In an ideal, empirically based model there should be no false positives and no false negatives. That is, in all instances a drug that works in the animal model should also work clinically in humans, and vice versa. This goal has never been achieved nor is it likely that it will, although there are a number of experimental paradigms for anxiety that have high empirical validity.

ANIMAL MODELING RESEARCH IN RELATIONSHIP TO OTHER APPROACHES TO PSYCHIATRIC RESEARCH

The evaluation of an animal model should closely relate to the purposes for which the model is being developed in the first place. To cite an extreme example, an animal model created to screen for anti-anxiety drugs may have high empirical validity in that context, but be completely inappropriate for studying various etiological theories of anxiety. On the other hand, a model developed to evaluate a given etiological variable in anxiety might be completely inappropriate or impractical for drug screening. It is not a matter of one kind of modeling approach being better or worse. To the contrary, it is a question of why the model is being developed in the first place and how it is to be used.

ANIMAL MODELS OF ANXIETY

Operant Conditioning Paradigms

In general, these approaches utilize operant techniques to elicit a behavior with a high frequency of occurrence. After the response is well established, the behavior is then suppressed by punishing it when it occurs. Potential anti-anxiety drugs are then screened by their ability to restore responding to their presuppression levels (Cook & Sepinwall, 1975; Davidson & Cook, 1969; Hill & Tedeschi, 1971; Cook & Davidson, 1973; McMillan, 1975). The analogy to fear is the conditioned association between the behavior and the punishment.

One example of such tests is the Geller Conflict Test (Geller, Kulak, & Seifter, 1962; Geller & Siefter, 1960; Howard & Pollard, 1977), which is widely used in screening for potential anti-anxiety drugs. In the original Geller paradigm, rats were trained on multiple variable interval VI 2-minute/CRF schedule for milk reinforcement. This involves a two-component operant behavior schedule. In the variable interval (VI) portion, signaled by one stimulus, bar pressing is reinforced at variable intervals with the mean interval being 2 minutes. In the continuous reinforcement (CRF) portion, signaled by a different stimulus, every bar-pressing is reinforced. When footshock is given concurrently with positive reinforcement, response rates are suppressed. Drug-induced increases in rate of punished responding are interpreted as an index of anti-anxiety activity, whereas decreases in unpunished responding are interpreted as indicating depressant activity. In other words, the type of behavior that originally had a high frequency of occurrence but was subsequently suppressed by certain manipulations is highly sensitive to the benzodiazepines and to meprobamate but not chlorpromazine.

In general, this test, along with many subsequent modifications, identifies clinically active anxiolytic agents, predicts their clinical potency, and is generally insensitive to stimulant, antipsychotic antidepressant, or analgesic drugs. It seems to work in different species and to be relatively independent of the schedules of positive reinforcement or punishment. Thus, this operant conflict approach seems to have high empirical validity in terms of predicting clinical drug responsiveness. In addition, this paradigm has more recently been used to study several neurobiological hypotheses concerning the mechanism of action of anti-anxiety drugs.

There would be very little disagreement that these approaches have high empirical validity. The question is how well response-contingent punishment paradigms in animals model human anxiety from other standpoints. Howard and others (Cook & Sepinwall, 1975; Fishman, Schuster, & Uhlenhuth, 1977; Howard & Pollard, 1977) have written some about this relationship, but surprisingly, there is not a large literature. The suppression of responding in the punishment paradigms has been considered as a passive avoidance response, and it has been suggested that a component of human anxiety arises from passive avoidance of social situations. This is a complex area in human anxiety which is more appropriately discussed in other chapters of this book. These possible connections with human anxiety are, of course, highly speculative, but do indicate that attempts have been made to relate these kinds of experimental paradigms on a theoretical level to human clinical theories.

There have been modifications of the original Geller Conflict Test (Cook & Davidson, 1973) that consist of a multiple schedule of reinforcement in which the alternative components are a variable interval 30-second (VI30) schedule reinforced by food in the presence of a white houselight, and a fixed ratio 10 response (FR10) schedule reinforced simultaneously with food and footshock in the presence of a red houselight. The development of suppression aftershock was introduced during the FR components. The suppressed FR rates were operationally designated as "conflict behavior." Psychotropic drugs are evaluated in this paradigm by their ability to alternate the conflict by increasing responding during the punishment periods. Benzodiazepines, carbonic acid esters, and some barbituates increase responding during the punishment periods, whereas amphetamine actually produces a greater amount of suppression during the FR segments. Neuroleptics, antidepressants, antihistamines, and morphine are all inactive.

A Model Based on Alteration of Locus Coerulus Function

Another animal model of anxiety has been proposed based on studies of the locus coerulus in the cat, macaque monkey, and squirrel monkey. The locus coerulus is a brain structure with a very high density of norepinephrine-containing neurons plus numerous projections to other brain regions. The strategy behind this paradigm is to perturb these systems in various ways and to study the effects. Techniques that have been employed include electrical stimulation, ablation, and pharmacological probes.

To summarize, the locus coerulus has been studied in many species, with variable effects (Huang, Redmond, Snyder, & Maas, 1975; Redmond, 1977, 1979, 1983; Redmond, Huang, Snyder, Maas, & Baulu, 1977). Increasing locus coerulus function, whether by electrical stimulation or with appropriate drugs, leads to an increase in threat-associated behaviors, whereas decreasing locus coerulus function decreases threat-associated behaviors. Some have argued that these behavioral effects are consistent with an essential role for the locus coerulus in mediating anxiety and fear, and can be related to some extent to human reports of the effects of similar drugs. The contention is that the behavioral measures associated with locus coerulus function in primates are the same ones that change with environmental stimuli associated with fear in humans and that they are lessened by diazepam. However, as the authors point out, this paradigm does not permit a distinction between fear as a response to an externally threatening situation and anxiety which is characteristically more free floating and less related to a specific environmental precipitant. The relationship between fear and anxiety is complex, and one must be careful in discussion of the significance of this set of studies not to use them interchangeably. This approach has been most useful in improving our understanding of the ralationship between central noradrenergic functioning and a specified set of behaviors.

A Model Based on Studies of Aplysia

It has been proposed that not only anxiety as a general state, but several specific subcategories of anxiety can be modeled in the sea snail, *Aplysia Californica*. Because of its relatively simple nervous system, it is argued that the molecular basis of anxiety can be studied in this type of animal preparation. Currently, there is great interest in this kind of approach because it does offer the advantage of the possibility of more direct approaches to studying the cellular mechanisms of behavior. "Behavior" in this type of preparation has a very different meaning from that in some of the previous models. It is not social behavior and is closest to a variant of conditioning paradigms that have been utilized for some time.

Kandel (Kandel, 1983; Walters, Carew, & Kandel, 1979, 1981) argues that in *A. Californica*, classically conditioned fear models anticipatory anxiety and what is termed *long-term sensitization* models chronic anxiety. The basic paradigm used is as follows. The aversive or unconditioned stimulus (US) is strong shock to the head of *A. Californica*. This is followed by the trauma of a weak test probe to the tail, which elicits an unconditioned response — a reflex or instinctive response — which, in the case of the sea snail, is escape locomotion and other defensive reflexes. A conditioned stimulus (CS) does not elicit the reflex response before repeated pairing with the unconditioned stimulus. In the case of the sea snail, the conditioned stimulus used is extract of shrimp. By pairing with the US (head shock), the CS (extract of shrimp) can come to elicit the reflex or unconditioned response. This is fairly straightforward classical or Pavlovian conditioning, which has been used for some time in the study of experimental neuroses. However, some newer and important neurophysiological techniques have been applied in studies utilizing these paradigms and a controversial reconceptualization of their relationship to clinical anxiety has been proposed that, if correct, would extend the implication of this line of work beyond the mechanisms of learning (Brunelli, Castellucci, & Kandel, 1976; Hawkins, Castellucci, & Kandel, 1981).

Models Based Primarily on Social Manipulations

It is in this area that one encounters terms such as *fear, anxiety, agitation, stress,* and *neurosis* being used interchangeably with a resultant extreme degree of confusion. For example, the initial stage of reaction to maternal or peer separation in nonhuman primates has historically been labeled the "agitation or protest" stage. More recently, this stage has been conceptualized by some in an anxiety context (Suomi, Kraemer, Baysinger, & Delizio, 1981). The first phase is characterized, as previously discussed, by the infant's being behaviorally very active. They show large increases in activity levels and in vocalization. It has also been found that the infants have marked activation of pituitary adrenal system during this "protest" stage and an increase in the enzymes involved in catecholamine synthesis (Breese *et al.*, 1973). These findings, and many others, support the view of separation as a very powerful event from both behavioral and neurobiological standpoints, and are consistent with a large body of literature regarding the behavioral and biological effects of a variety of stressors. It is not yet known to what extent this initial stage of reaction responds to anxiolytic pharmacological agents and how specific this response may be. This would be an important line of research to pursue.

The initial protest stage following maternal separation of primates has even been likened to a panic attack, and the fact that monkeys on imipramine pamoate do not exhibit either the protest or depair stage has been used as support for this argument (Suomi, Seaman, Lewis, Delizio, & McKinney, 1978). However, in the original imipramine study the medication was begun during the despair or depressive phase and continued throughout subsequent separations. It affected the behavior in both stages and it is impossible, from that study, to sort out which was primary and which was secondary. What is needed is a series of pharmacological trials with anti-anxiety drugs, antidepressants, and neuroleptics.

Other experimental situations in primates that have been reported to model anxiety include introduction of strangers, rearing in conditions of social deprivation followed by exposure to a more socially stimulating environment, and early experience with a rejecting real or surrogate mother. There is one report to suggest that early autonomic responsivity, as measured by heart rate change in reaction to certain stimuli, correlates with later responses to certain stressors (Suomi *et al.*, 1981). This needs to be replicated.

Phobias and Other Neuroses

This area has been well reviewed in an article by Isaac Marks (1977). Marks, in that article, reminds us of the distinction between *fear*, which comes from an old English term for sudden calamity or danger, and *anxious*, which is from the Greek root meaning "press tight" or "strangle." According to Marks and others, fear is an emotion produced by present or impending danger. The cause is apparent. Anxiety, on the other hand, is the emotion when the cause is vague or less understandable. Fear can lead to either freezing or becoming mute. Much stress literature in animals reports the same thing (e.g., rats freezing in an open field) as being stress.

There is one study (Sackett, 1966) with the potential for study of phobias that bears replication and extension. In this study, monkeys in isolation were shown slides on the inside of the cage. They also had levers they could press to make them appear. None of the pictures disturbed them except those of other monkeys threatening. This was especially true when the monkeys were about 2.5 to 4 months of age. It is suggested that there may be innate mechanisms of recognition in monkeys that lead to social interaction. The speculation is that during this time of 2.5 to 4 months, monkeys may be particularly prone to acquire new fears of neutral stimuli that are paired with innately fear releasing stimuli, such as threat. It is surprising that very few proposed models of anxiety incorporate developmental considerations in view of the extensive clinical literature about the developmental origins of anxiety.

Marks discusses conditioning models and theories in relation to anxiety and phobia models and points to a number of their shortcomings in relation to human phobias. Many animal experiments assume that fear, which is induced by conditioning techniques, is a model for human phobic (or anxiety) reactions. A similar assumption is often made for paradigms that involve the use of trauma to induce avoidance reactions. While it is true that such induction techniques to produce fear of relatively specific stimuli and enable one to study the variables that are important for the learning of fear in humans, a clearly definable event (i.e., a definable US) can rarely be found at the start of human phobias (or anxiety).

Marks thinks that research on animals has little to tell us about human anxiety that exists internally and symbolically, often without observable motor or autonomic concomitants. The operational definition of anxiety is difficult. He feels that either Pavlovian or Skinnerian conditioning paradigms are useless as far as modeling human phobias (anxieties). Human phobias and anxiety just do not fit into conditioning language or paradigms. He feels that conditioning language makes assumptions about etiology and treatment that are not borne out in practice, and that the terminology is difficult to apply to clinical events.

One other additional approach to the study of phobias has been done. This involves the development of two lines of pointer dogs (Dykman, Murphree, & Ackerman, 1966; Dykman, Murphree, Oddist, Rees, & William, 1979; Murphree & Newton, 1971; Peters, Murphree, & Dykman, 1967). One line was bred for fearfulness and lack of friendliness toward people. Another was bred for the opposite characteristics. The basic hypothesis of this work was that inheritance would determine in large part many behavioral characteristics of the dog, including susceptibility to breakdown under acute and chronic stress. Throughout 10 generations, about 80% of each litter were similar in temperament to the parents. Through this process of selection and inbreeding, it was possible to establish the two lines of dogs and to study their behavior on a number of parameters.

The "phobic" line of dogs was extremely timid, avoided humans, and showed decreased exploratory activity. They showed an excessive startle response, a slower heart rate, and an increased incidence of atrioventricular heart block. Interestingly, even those with the most severe disturbance could learn operant conditioning bar pressing, but it was necessary to facilitate this process with benzodiazepines — the most efficacious drugs. Amphetamine and cocaine both disrupted the behavioral responses of genetically nervous dogs to a far greater extent than the stable line (Murphree, Angel, & Deluca, 1974).

These pointer dogs genetically predisposed to nervous behavior could be partially rehabilitated. By means of a program of gradual desensitization, involving graduated exposure, reciprocally competitive responses, and social facilitation, it was possible to train them as hunting dogs. However, such rehabilitated behavior did not extend to laboratory tests where they were probably being challenged on stress (McBryde & Murphree, 1974; Murphree, Angel, & Deluca, 1974).

Social Interaction

In this test developed by File and Hyde (1977, 1978), two male rats are placed in a neutral arena, and the time they spend interacting (i.e., sniffing, grooming, kicking, boxing, and wrestling) is scored. The rats can either be in high or low light, or familiar or unfamiliar with the area. The use of increased light or an unfamiliar area lead to less social interaction, and this can be overcome by anxiolytics (File, 1985). This test is specific for anxiolytics and appears able to distinguish sedative from anxiolytic effects. The use of stimulants increases social interaction; however they increase it under all conditions, unlike anxiolytics (Guy & Gardner, 1985).

The neurobiology of the aforementioned model has also been studied. Small 5,7-dihdroxytryptamine lesions, specifically in the dorsal raphe, had an anxiolytic effect, as did lesions into the lateral spetum. These effects are quite specific, and general lesions or 5HT uptake inhibitors have no effect in this test. This model appears to have excellent pharmacological specificity, and uses naturally occurring behavior, and it may be particularly promising for further neurobiological studies.

CONCLUDING REMARKS

In the area of anxiety, as well as any other psychiatric disorders, it is important to keep in mind that animal models are basically experimental preparations developed to study specific aspects of a particular psychopathological syndrome. Some paradigms will be appropriate for the study of phenomenological aspects, in that there is a high cross-species behavioral similarity. Other paradigms will be designed and utilized primarily for the prediction of drug effectiveness. These paradigms might have high empirical validity, but from a phenomenological or etiological standpoint have little usefulness. Certain paradigms might basically involve the study of the mechanisms of learning and be of great value in this context.

The field of animal modeling of anxiety is still very much in a formative stage; there is still a good deal of conceptual confusion. This may, in part, reflect the fact that our concepts of human anxiety and its relationship to fear, learning, stress, and conflict are being reconsidered. The core defining characteristics of human anxiety are experimental and psychophysiological and, therefore, it is difficult to evaluate animal models from the standpoint of behavioral similarities.

Most animal modeling work in the anxiety area involves the study of how animals react to external threats, conflicts, trauma, and unpredictability, and so on. There is a large body of work that involves response-contingent paradigms and punishment-induced suppression of responding. These paradigms have high empirical validity. Another approach involves alteration of locus coerulus function, while yet another involves studies of conditioning phenomena in invertebrates. There are also several proposed models based on social manipulations that emphasize developmental parameters.

Such an extensive range of approaches is a good sign for the animal modeling of anxiety area because each potentially has special advantages and limitations. In the future, this research area will continue to develop and, both from conceptual and practical standpoints, have an effective interface with clinical research on the anxiety disorders.

REFERENCES

Breese, G. R., Smith, R. D., Mueller, R. A., Howard, J. L., Prange, A. J., Lipton, M. S., Young, L. D., McKinney, W. T., & Lewis, J. K. (1973). Induction of adrenal catecholamine synthesizing enzymes following mother-infant separation. *Nature New Biology, 246,* 94–96.

Brunelli, M., Castellucci, V., & Kandel, E. R. (1976). Synaptic facilitation and behavioral sensitization in aplysia: Possible role of serotonin and cyclic AMP. *Science, 194,* 1178–1181.

Cook, L., & Davidson, A. B. (1973). Effects of behaviorally active drugs in a conflict-punishment procedure in rats. In S. Garattini, E. Mussini, & L. O. Randall (Eds.), *The benzodiazepines.* (pp. 327–346). New York: Raven Press.

Cook, L., Sepinwall, J. (1975). Reinforcement schedules and extrapolations to humans from animals in behavioral pharmacology. *Federation Proceedings, 34,* 1889–1897.

Davidson, A. B., & Cook, L. (1969). Effects of combined treatment with trifluoperazine HCL and amobarbital on punished behavior in rats. *Psychopharmacology, 15,* 159–168.

Dykman, R. A., Murphee, O. D., & Ackerman, P. T. (1966). Litter patterns in the offspring of nervous and stable dogs: II. Automatic and motor conditioning. *Journal of Nervous and Mental Disease, 141,* 419–431.

Dykman, R. A., Murphee, O. D., Oddist, D., Reese, W. G., & William, G. (1979). Familial anthrophobia in pointer dogs. *Archives of General Psychiatry, 36,* 988–993.

File, S. E. (1985). Animal models for predicting clinical efficiency of anxiolytic drugs: Social behavior. *Neuropsychobiology, 13,* 55–63.

File, S. E., & Hyde, J. R. G. (1977). The effects of *p*–chlorophenylalanine and ethanolamine-o-sulphate in an animal test of anxiety. *Journal of Pharmacology and Pharmacy, 29,* 735–738.

File, S. E., & Hyde, J. R. G. (1978). Can social interaction be used to measure anxiety? *British Journal of Pharmacology, 62,* 19–24.

Fishman, M., Schuster, C. R., & Uhlenhuth, E. H. (1977). Extension of animal models to clinical evaluation of antianxiety agents. In I. Hanin & E. Usdin (Eds.), *Animal models in psychiatry and neurology.* (pp. 339–349). New York: Pergamon Press.

Geller, I., Kulak, J. T., & Seifter, J. (1962). The effects of chlordiazepoxide and chlorpromazine on a punishment discrimination. *Psychopharmacologica, 3,* 374–385.

Geller, I., & Seifter, J. (1960). The effects of meprobamate, barbiturates, diamphetamines and promazine on experimentally, induced conflict in the rat. *Psychopharmacologica, 1,* 482–492.

Guy, A. P., & Gardner, C. R. (1985). The behavioral effects of RU 24969, a suggested 5-HT1 receptor agonist in rodents and the effect on the behavior of treatment with antidepressants. *Neuropsychobiology, 13,* 194–200.

Hawkins, R. D., Castellucci, V. F., & Kandel, E. R. (1981). Interneurons involved in mediation and modeulation of gill-withdrawal reflex in aplysia II. Identified neurons produce heterosynaptic facilitation contributing to behavioral sensitization. *Journal of Neurophysiology, 45,* 315–339.

Hill, R. T., & Tedeschi, D. H. (1971). Animal testing and screening procedures in evaluating psychotropic drugs. In R. Rech & K. Moore (Eds.), *An introduction to psychopharmacology.* (pp. 237–288). New York: Raven Press.

Howard, J. L., & Pollard, G. T. (1977). The Geller conflict test: A model of anxiety and a screening procedure for anxiolytics. In I. Hanin & E. Usdin (Eds.), *Animal models in psychiatry and neurology.* (pp. 269–278). New York: Pergamon Press.

Huang, Y., Redmond, D. E., Snyder, D. R., & Maas, J. R. (1975). In vivo location and destruction of the locus coerulus in the stumptail macaque (*Macaca arcoides*). *Brain Research, 100,* 157–162.

Kandel, E. R., (1983). From metapsychology to molecular biology: Explorations into the nature of anxiety. *American Journal of Psychiatry, 140,* 1277–1993.

Marks, I. (1977). Phobias and obsessions: Clinical phenomena in search of a laboratory model. In J. Maser & M. Seligman (Eds.), *Psychopathology: Experimental models.* (pp. 174–213). San Francisco: W. H. Freeman and Co.

McBryde, W. C., & Murphree, O. D. (1974). The rehabilitation of genetically nervous dogs. *Pavlovian Journal of Biological Sciences, 9,* 76–84.

McKinney, W. T. (1984). Animal models of depression: An overview. *Psychiatric Developments, 2,* 77–96.

McMillan, D. E. (1975). Determinants of drug effects on punished responding. *Federation Proceedings, 34,* 1870–1879.

Murphree, O. D., Angel, C., & Deluca, D. C. (1974). Limits of therapeutic change: specificity of behavioral modification in genetically nervous dogs. *Biological Psychiatry, 9,* 99–101.

Murphre, O. D., & Newton, J. (1971). Cross-breeding and special handling of genetically nervous dogs. *Pavlovian Journal of Biological Sciences, 6,* 129–136.

Peters, J. E., Murphree, O. D., & Dykman, R. A. (1967). Genetically determined abnormal behavior in dogs: Some implications for psychiatry. *Pavlovian Journal of Biological Sciences, 2,* 206–215.

Redmond, E. A. (1977). Alterations in the function of the nucleus locus coerulus: A possible model for studies of anxiety. In I. Hanin & E. Usdin (Eds.), *Animal models in psychiatry and neurology.* (pp. 293–306). New York: Pergamon Press.

Redmond, D. E. (1979). The effects of destruction of the locus coerulus on nonhuman primate behaviors. *Psychopharmacology Bulletin, 15*(2), 26–27.

Redmond, D. E. (1983). Social effects of alterations on brain noradrenergic function on untreated group members. In Steklis, Horst, D., & Kling, Arthur S. (Eds.), *Hormones, drugs, and social behavior in primates.* (pp. 271–280). New York: Spectrum.

Redmond, D. E., Huang, Y. H., Snyder, D. R., Maas, J. W., & Baulu, J. (1977). Hyperdipisia after locus coerulus lesions in the stump-tailed monkey. *Life Sciences, 20,* 1619–1628.

Sackett, G. P. (1966). Monkeys reared in isolation with pictures as visual input: Evidence for an innate learning mechanism. *Science, 154,* 1468–1472.

Suomi, S. J., Kraemer, G. W., Baysinger, C. M., & Delizio, R. D. (1981). Inherited and experiential factors associated with individual differences in anxious behavior displayed by rhesus monkeys. In D. F. Klein & J. Rabkin (Eds.), *Anxiety: New research and changing concepts.* (pp. 179–200). New York: Raven Press.

Suomi, S. J., Seaman, S. F., Lewis, J. K., Delizio, R. D., & McKinney, W. T. (1978). Effects of imipramine treatment of separation-induced social disorders in rhesus monkeys. *Archives of General Psychiatry, 35,* 321–325.

Walters, E. T., Carew, T. J., & Kandel, E. R. (1979). Classical conditioning in *Aplysia californica. Proceedings of the Natural Academy of Science, 76,* 6675–6679.

Walters, E., Carew, T., & Kandel, E. (1981). Associated learning in aplysia: Evidence for conditioned fear in an invertebrate. *Science, 211,* 504–506.

CHAPTER 11

Pharmacologic Models

Marianne Z. Wamboldt and Thomas R. Insel

One might well wonder why pharmacologists involved in the treatment of disease would study compounds that induce rather than reduce symptoms. Actually, pharmacologic models of several medical illnesses, from peptic ulcer to Parkinson's disease, have contributed greatly to defining the pathophysiology and improving the treatment of these disorders. In psychiatry, pharmacologic models of depression (e.g., reserpine) and schizophrenia (e.g., hallucinogens) have been imperfect but still useful tools for research into the pathophysiology of these syndromes.

That drugs also might provide useful models of anxiety should not be particularly surprising, as anxiety is a common side effect of a number of medications, including antihistamines, pentazocine hydrochloride, theophylline, and indomethacin (Abramowicz, 1981). The extent to which drugs may precipitate anxiety was noted by an anonymous physician volunteer, who, following self-administration of pentylenetetrazol described, this experience:

> within a matter of seconds, I experienced catastrophic anxiety and said to myself now I know what these patients are going through, I can't possibly take that. It was a sense of utter distress and impending catastrophe. There is no doubt that this was one of the most anxiety-producing events of my life. (Cited in Lal & Emmett-Oglesby, 1983, p. 1427)

THEORETICAL CONSIDERATIONS

What is a Pharmacologic Model?

A pharmacologic model, like an animal model or a cognitive model, is simply a research tool used to investigate some aspect of a clinical problem. Investigators usually think in terms of homologous models, that is, models that not only mimic the subjective, physiologic, and biochemical features of the clinical disorder, but also are mediated by the same etiologic factors. However, in the study of psychopathology, where etiologic factors are unknown, models are never truly homologous. At best, one seeks to be able to induce several features of the clinical syndrome under controlled conditions and to infer something about etiology. In pharmacologic studies, two overall approaches to modeling anxiety can be discerned: Agents can be used to induce a state as similar to spontaneous anxiety as possible, that is, a "complete model"; or agents can be used to select a vulnerable population, that is, a "provocative challenge model."

In the first approach, a compound is given to a healthy subject and measures of subjective, physiologic, and biochemical changes are recorded. If these changes simulate what occurs during naturalistic states of anxiety, the compound is said to be "anxiogenic" and one assumes that by defining its pharmacology some inferences about the neurochemical systems mediating anxiety would be forthcoming. One might hypothesize, for instance, that abnormal amounts of an endogenous compound, similar to the agent administered exogenously, cause pathological anxiety. In addition, studies in animals given this same compound might define which neural pathways are involved in the genesis of anxiety, providing a guide for regional imaging studies in man. Unfortunately, there are several problems with this approach. First, the pharmacologic challenge may not discriminate between adaptive and pathologic anxiety. Second, bahaviorally active drugs have a panoply of central nervous system effects, thus precluding a simple correlation of "one symptom to one system." Third, there are marked species variabilities in both the behavioral and neurochemical responses to many drugs, so that the effects of a drug such as yohimbine hydrochloride in the rat may not really be analogous to the effects of the same drug in man (indeed, Unnerstall, Kopajtic, and Kuhan, 1984, have shown that the regional distribution of brain receptors for this particular drug differ between rodents and primates). Nevertheless, by studying anxiogenic compounds in man, the relationship of subjective states to physiologic and biochemical changes can be explored. And by studying the neural systems activated by several anxiogenic compounds in animals, certain patterns should emerge — patterns that ultimately could define those brain regions mediating the symptoms of anxiety disorders.

The second pharmacologic approach to modeling anxiety has a more modest goal. If a compound were found to induce anxiety in patients with one particular anxiety disorder but had no such effect in normals or, more importantly, in patients with other disorders, then the compound might provide a diagnostic test. Such tests, often called "provocative tests," are used widely in medicine, including, for example, the glucose tolerance test for diabetes mellitus or the Tensilon test for myasthenia gravis. Provocative tests are useful for detecting vulnerable subjects in a population at risk for the disorder and, within a clinically homogeneous group, they can distinguish subgroups who are differentially responsive to treatment. As we review later, administration of sodium (Na) lactate appears to induce panic attacks in patients with panic disorder, but not in patients with social phobias. Although the syndromes resemble each other in several ways, they respond to different treatments and follow a different clinical course. The intravenous administration of Na lactate has helped to identify panic disorder as a discrete diagnostic entity, even though this infusion test remains a research tool rather than a practical clinical test. This approach assumes very little about the specific mechanism of drug action. Sodium lactate administration might affect panic disorder patients more because they are predisposed to panic with an intravenous fluid load or because they are, at baseline, closer to the panic state than are the social phobics. Even though the mechanism might be nonspecific, the drug can still have predictive power for making a diagnosis. What counts is not the mechanism, but the specificity and sensitivity of the test.

There are two other uses of anxiogenic compounds that we will mention only briefly. The first is their use as therapeutic agents to desensitize patients with anxiety. The second is their use as a challenge to test the success of clinical therapies. For example, pharmacologically induced anxiety states provide a rapid test of anxiolytic agents.

So, pharmacologic agents can be used to model anxiety in order to study the pathophysiology of this affect or they can be used to provoke anxiety for diagnostic purposes. Here we will focus primarily on studies investigating anxiogenic drugs with effects mediated through either adrenergic, benzodiazepine, or adenosine receptors. Then we will review studies with Na lactate and CO_2, specifically as provocative agents in panic disorder. Finally, we will try to define how these various pharmacologic models differ and how they interact. But first, let us take a look at what the drugs are attempting to model.

Problems with Modeling Anxiety

All current models suffer from some common handicaps. First and foremost, the use of the term *model* implies that one knows what one is trying to artificially induce or replicate. Yet what exactly is anxiety? *Anxiety* is used to describe both an affect and a syndrome. As an affect, it has been defined as an internal apprehension or a future-oriented sense of danger. However, few persons who complain about feeling anxious would describe their subjective distress in these terms. When Buss (1962) surveyed patients about what they meant by *anxiety*, he found two main categories of complaints. The first category included symptoms of autonomic over-reactivity: such physiological changes as sweating, flushing, shallow breathing, heart palpitations, intestinal discomfort, and aches and pains. The second category included more symptoms of "conditioned" anxiety, such as restlessness, worry, and tension. Buss subdivided these into symptoms of striate muscle tension, namely, aches, pains, twitching, shaking; and "feelings of anxiety," namely, inability to concentrate, worry, compulsive mannerisms, insecurity, sleep and relaxation problems, feelings of fear. panic, or dread.

What kind of affect is being precipitated by anxiogenic substances? Early investigators (Marañon, 1924) noted that adrenaline would cause a state of physiologic arousal, perhaps akin to Buss's first category, without causing any emotional overtones or cognitive changes that would be included in Buss's second category. Marañon labeled this state as one of an "as if" or "cold" emotion. Rodin (1958) described responses to pentylenetetrazol as being more in Buss's second category, or symptoms of "feelings of anxiety." Curiously, many modern researchers fail to define the phenomenology of the "anxiety" associated with drug administration. In part, this is due to the paucity of psychometric tools that can discriminate subtypes of anxious affect, and in part it is because modern researchers have focused more on anxiety as a syndrome.

One might consider three basic syndromes of anxiety, based on the complex of fear-related behavioral acts and the environmental stimulus involved:

1. Anticipatory or signaled anxiety (e.g., phobic).
2. Chronic anxiety (generalized and usually unsignaled).
3. Panic (acute, largely unsignaled, profound, perhaps akin to startle).

Although each of these states may have served some adaptive role in phylogeny, the pathological or clinical state is associated with symptoms that are disabling and thus no longer adaptive. In DSM-III (American Psychiatric Association, 1980) terms, these states are known as phobic disorders, generalized anxiety disorder, and panic disorder, respectively. Most of the recent researchers using pharmacologic challenges have cited "panic attack" as their dependent variable. However, they often report a range of physiologic symptoms and subjective distress that may well qualify as chronic anxiety or signaled anxiety.

In order to make clear distinctions between the various anxiety disorders, more descriptive research needs to be done to elucidate the critical affective states, physical symptoms, physiologic signs, and biochemical measures that distinguish each syndrome from the others. Just as we know that all fear states do not share the same patterns of autonomic activation (e.g., most panic states have elevated heart rate, whereas the anxiety connected with blood and mutilation phobias is associated with decreased heart rate (Curtis & Thyer, 1983)), we may well discover that each syndrome has pathognomonic patterns of affective, visceral, and somatic activation.

Spontaneous Anxiety States

In Table 11.1, we review representative results of the physiologic and biochemical results from laboratory studies of "naturalistic" anxiety. Several approaches have been attempted. Ekman, Levenson, and Friesen (1983) evaluated anxiety as an affect. They artificially induced various emotive states by having professional actors mimic facial expressions that Ekman found to be essential for each affect, then monitored heart rate and skin temperature. This technique distinguishes six major affects including fear. Others have looked at separate syndromes of anxiety, monitoring various physiologic and biochemical changes associated with each type of anxiety as it spontaneously occurs. Uhde et al. (1982) experimentally provoked anxiety in healthy volunteers who agreed to participate in a study assessing their pain sensitivity to mildly painful electric shocks. Curtis and colleagues (Curtis, Buxton, Lippman, Nesse & Wright, 1976; Curtis, Nesse, Buxton, & Lippman, 1979; Nesse, Curtis, & Brown, 1982; Nesse, Curtis, Brown, & Rubin, 1980) monitored phobia patients during flooding sessions with their feared object. Zohar et al. (in press) exposed obsessive-compulsive patients to their object of avoidance while monitoring cerebral blood flow. Ko et al. (1983) took some physiologic and biochemical measurements 30 minutes following a spontaneously occurring panic attack. Woods, et al. (Woods, Charney, McPherson, Gradman, Heninger, 1987) and Freedman, Janni, Ettedgui, & Puthezhath (1985) have placed Holter type monitors on panic disorder (PD) or panic disorder with agoraphobia (PDA) outpatients to study outside of the laboratory the physiologic concomitants of a naturally occurring panic attack. The patients also were asked to keep detailed journals. Interestingly, Freedman et al. (1985) noted that subjects reported highly charged interpersonal interactions as precipitants of their attacks.

All of these techniques are promising. The methods differ across studies, but several consistent findings have emerged. Although it is widely believed that plasma cortisol and the norepinephrine metaboite 3-methoxy-4-hydroxyphenylethyleneglycol (MHPG) reflect levels of stress, neither of these indices was found to increase consistently in these studies, even though subjective ratings reflect very high levels of "anxiety." By contrast, heart rate and blood pressure generally correlate well with subjective reports, although they do not distinguish among the syndromes. Other measures, such as peripheral or cerebral blood flow, skin temperature, skin conductance, or EEG may be more useful. Freedman et al.'s (1985) data offer a suggestion that the time course of autonomic changes may provide a crucial clue. They found that increased skin temperature preceeded the event mark, while decreased skin temperature coincided with the event mark. Taking Ekman et al.'s (1983) work into account, where increased heart rate and increased skin temperature were associated with anger, while increased heart rate and decreased skin temperature were associated with fear, the physiologic data may be corroborating the patients' reports of angry interactions preceeding their attacks. Perhaps the anger-anxiety sequence is of significance in panic attacks and could easily be tested by more studies of this nature.

Clearly, if pharmacologic models are to be more useful, we need more naturalistic studies of the phenomenology and physiology of spontaneous forms of anxiety. To describe different forms of anxiety induced by different compounds, the researchers must first know the concomitants of those affects they attempt to model. To go beyond affects and to model distinct syndromes of anxiety requires a clear map of the boundaries between the different disorders. Although we now have clinical criteria for the various disorders based primarily on symptoms (APA, 1980), we do not know if there are distinct physiologic and biochemical changes, let alone separate neural pathways associated with each.

REVIEW OF THE RESEARCH: SPECIFIC MODELS

An overview of the types of substances known to provoke anxiety in healthy volunteers is given in Table 11.2. As can be seen, each of these substances has specific brain receptors with a discrete regional distribution. Although we discuss individual drugs as models, each drug is representative of a class of compounds, some of which are present endogenously as neurotransmitters.

Adrenergic Agents

The catecholamines epinephrine and norepinephrine have been implicated in anxiety since Cannon's classic experiments carried out between 1910 and 1935 (Cannon, 1929). Using a paradigm where healthy cats were held on their backs in the presence of barking dogs, Cannon was able to show that the tachycardia, pupillary dilatation, piloerection, and decreased visceral activity that accompanied the cat's hissing, clawing, and attempts to escape were associated with the release of epinephrine from the adrenals and could be replicated by the intravenous administration of epinephrine. These findings led to a series of investigations of anxiety states associated with intramuscular injections of epinephrine in man. The history of this field has been recently reviewed elsewhere (Guttmacher, Murphy, & Insel, 1983). There are several shortcomings in all of these studies: Epinephrine is quickly metabolized and may not reach the central nervous system; "adrenaline" used in older studies was a poorly defined mixture of epinephrine and norepinephrine; and the subjects, in these studies, were usually only partly characterized. Still, there are two points of note: first, epinephrine appeared generally to produce "cold emotion," that is, subjects complained of the somatic symptoms without the full affective components of anxiety. This may reflect the very limited bioavailability for brain adrenergic receptors when epinephrine is given peripherally. The second point derives from an important study by Schachter and Singer (1962). These workers noted that parenteral epinephrine in normals engendered a wide variety of affects, ranging from anxiety to amusement depending on the social cues of the environment. This is a key point that needs to be kept in mind throughout this review: The behavioral effect of a drug reflects not only its pharmacology but the context, cognitive set, and expectancy of the subject.

The field of adrenergic neuropharmacology has been advanced greatly by more selective agents that bind with high affinity to the receptor and penetrate the blood-brain barrier. We now recognize at least four different classes of adrenergic receptors, all of which are present in brain. The alpha-1 receptor, which is activated by norepinephrine, is present postsynaptically on cells in the cortex, the hippocampus, and other regions of the "limbic" forebrain (Young & Kuhar, 1980). The alpha-2 receptor has a presynaptic inhibitory role at noradrenergic cell bodies in the brainstem, particularly the locus coeruleus, the nucleus of the solitary tract, and the lateral tegmental nuclei. These sites, each comprising a few thousand cells, represent the source for nearly all the noradrenergic pathways in the brain. Note that activating these presynaptic alpha-2 receptors with an agonist (such as clonidine hydrochloride) will *decrease* the activity of noradrenergic neurons going to the forebrain, whereas an alpha-1 receptor agonist (such as methoxamine hydrochloride) will *increase* the activity of the postsynaptic neurons, that is, whatever cells the noradrenergic neuron innervates. Additionally, the alpha-2 receptor exists as a postsynaptic receptor in the forebrain (see Figure 11.1), where its function is less clear.

The beta adrenergic receptors also are of

Table 11.1. Pathophysiology of Spontaneous Panic Attacks or Anxiety

CITATION	PHYSIOLOGIC AND SUBJECTIVE CHANGES	PLASMA BIOCHEMICAL CHANGES	COMMENTS
Lader & Mathews, 1970	Abrupt decrease in skin resistance; abrupt increase in heart rate (HR) (range 40–50 beats per minute); increase in forearm blood flow.	—	3 Cases with probable attacks while subject undergoing continuous physiologic monitoring for other purposes.
Curtis et al., 1976, 1979 Nesse et al., 1980, 1982	Produced "great anxiety" with weeping, tremor, piloerection, perspiration, attempts to get away, chattering teeth; increase in HR.	Increased growth hormone; no change in cortisol, prolactin, TSH.	7–9 Phobics exposed with in vivo flooding. Blood sampled every 20 min during five sessions of 3 hr each. Exposure in 2nd hr of 3rd and 4th sessions.
Uhde et al., 1982	Increased anxiety on Spielberger State-Trait Anxiety Inventory.	Increased MHPG correlated with increased anxiety.	Studied relationship between State anxiety and MHPG in 12 normals exposed to a laboratory controlled, anxiety-inducing situation.
Ekman et al., 1983	High HR, low skin temp — fear and sadness; high HR, high skin temp — anger; low HR — happy, disgust, surprise.	—	Used 12 actors and 4 scientists to elicit 6 emotions in 2 carefully designed and controlled tasks. Fear distinguished by pattern of ↑ HR, ↓ skin temperature changes.
Ko et al., 1983	Increased anxiety measured by ratings, increased BP.	Increased MHPG with panic, attenuated by pretreatment with clonidine, but not imipramine.	6 Agoraphobics studied 30 min after visiting typical fear- inducing situation. Levels compared to non-panic days for same patients, no control subjects for comparison. Increased anxiety correlated with increased MHPG and increased BP.

Freedman et al., 1985	↑ HR [16–38 bpm], ↑ skin temp [0.3–2.3°C] (prior to event mark); decrease skin temp at event mark; increase skin temp as HR normalized. Patients and controls did not differ in baseline HR, average temp or patterns of variation.	—	Studied 12 panic disorder patients and 11 controls. Used ambulatory monitoring *via* recorder worn on 2 consecutive days. 8 panic attacks occurred in 5 patients. 6/8 attacks were preceeded by a social event (usually angry exchange.)
Woods et al., 1987	Increased BP; increased HR; increased anxiety on VAS (Visual Analogue Scale)	No change MHPG; no change cortisol when compared to controls.	Studied 15 panic disorder and/or agoraphobic patients with exposure to phobic stimuli. Used ambulatory monitors. Increased MHPG noted in patients but also in nonanxious controls (n = 13) studied simultaneously.
Zohar et al., 1985	rCBF increases during imaginal flooding; decreases during in vivo exposure. Changes greatest in left temporal region. Increased BP, HR; no change in pCO_2 or respiratory rate.	—	Used xenon ^{133} inhalation technique to measure regional cerebral blood flow (rCBF) in 7 obsessive–compulsive disorder patients during relaxation, imaginal flooding, and exposure in vivo.

Table 11.2. Receptor Systems for Anxiogenic Drugs

RECEPTOR SYSTEM	RECEPTOR SUBTYPE	AGONIST	ANTAGONIST	ENDOGENOUS LIGAND
Adrenergic				
	Alpha-2	Clonidine	*Yohimbine*	Norepinephrine
	Beta	*Isoproterenol*	Propranolol	Norepinephrine
Benzodiazepine-GABA-Cl-Channel				
	BZD	Diazepam	β-CCE, FG-7142	DBI
	CL-Channel	Ethanol (?)	*Pentylenetetrazol*	
Adenosine				
	A_1	PIA (phenyl-isopropyl-adenosine)	*Caffeine* Theophylline	Adenosine, Inosine

Note. Putative anxiogenic compound italicized.

two types (Minneman, Pittman, & Molinoff, 1981). The beta-1 receptor (for which isoproterenol hydrochloride is an agonist and propranolol hydrochloride an antagonist) is present throughout the forebrain. The role of the beta-2 receptor in the brain is not entirely clear; although most evidence suggests that this receptor is predominantly localized to the cerebellum, this receptor may have a role in cerebrovascular control.

Alpha adrenergic agents. In terms of their potency for eliciting anxiety-like symptoms, there is a clear hierarchy among alpha-adrenergic agents. Yohimbine hydrochloride, an alpha-2 antagonist, appears more potent than epinephrine, whereas norepinephrine (perhaps for reasons of bioavailability) and alpha-1 agonists have very little effect when administered peripherally. Yohimbine, through its blockade of the inhibitory presynaptic receptors in the brainstem, leads to a widespread "disinhibition" of noradrenergic activity, manifested by increases in heart rate, blood pressure, MHPG, and behavioral activation.

Pharmacologic studies done by Gershon and Lang (1962) over 20 years ago indicated that yohimbine produced central stimulatory actions in conscious animals that might be considered a model of anxiety. Redmond, in a series of elegant studies, activated the locus coeruleus either electrophysiologically or pharmacologically with local administration of yohimbine and demonstrated "alarm-like" behavior in nonhuman primates (Redmond, 1979; Redmond & Huang, 1979). Early studies of yohimbine in both psychiatric patients and normals produced autonomic and subjective feeling states that closely resembled anxiety (see Table 11.3). These early studies used intravenous yohimbine in doses of 0.5 mg/kg over 5 to 6 minutes. Garfield, Gershon, Sletten, Sundland, and Ballow (1967) found that 13 symptoms of anxiety were reproduced consistently with yohimbine, while only six were elicited more inconsistently by epinephrine on repeated administrations.

Although yohimbine was found to produce anxiety more effectively than epinephrine or norepinephrine, remarkably little was done to exploit the model until the early 1980s. Since then, several groups have used oral yohimbine in doses of 20 to 60 mg to induce anxiety in panic disorder patients and normals. The results have

a.

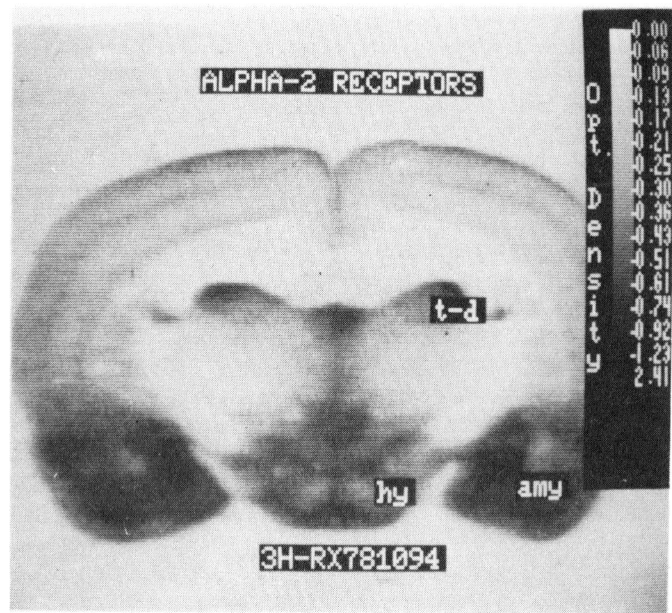

b.

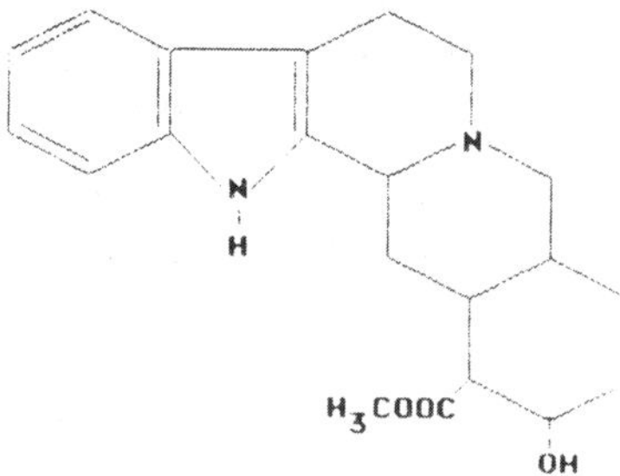

Figure 11.1. A. Brightfield autoradiogram of alpha-2 receptor distribution in rat forebrain labeled with selective ligand ^{3}H-Rx 781094. Method involves incubating slide-mounted thin coronal sections of brain with radioactively labeled drug in vitro. Sections are then exposed to tritium sensitive film to generate image of receptor distribution. Dark areas (hy = hypothalamus, t-d = dorsal nucleus of thalamus, amy = amygdala) represent highest concentration of receptors. Other areas of dense binding, not visible in this section, include locus coeruleus and nucleus of the solitary tract in the brainstem. (Autoradiogram courtesy of James Unnerstall, Ph.D., National Institute of Neurologic Communicative Disorders and Stroke.) B. Chemical structure of yohimbine, a selective alpha-2 receptor antogonist similar to Rx 781094.

been somewhat contradictory. Henauer, Gillespie, and Hollister (1983) found an increase in blood pressure and heart rate but few other autonomic symptoms and widely variable increases in anxiety in nine normals and one patient with "epiosodic anxiety" given yohimbine. The results from this group, therefore, caused the authors to question the validity of oral yohimbine as an agent to model panic or

Table 11.3. Yohimbine

STUDY	SUBJECTS	DESIGN	RESULTS	COMMENTS
Holmberg & Gershon, 1961	50 psychiatric patients (pts.), 9 controls.	—	Anxiety: "restless, irritable, tremulous, impatient and unrestful affect as well as reluctance to complete study." ↑ HR, flushing, perspiration, salivation, lacrimation, and pupillary dilatation.	Blocked by amobarbital and chlordiazepoxide; potentiated by imipramine (over 3 wks).
Ingram, 1962	25 psychiatric pts.	Single-blind, placebo-controlled study using 0.5 mg/kg IV over 5 min.	Anxiety: "restlessness, irritability, tense facial expression, obvious anxiety, and marked reluctance to repeat the drug test." ↑ HR, ↑ BP, ↑ respirations, ↓ skin resistance, ↑ skin temperature. Flushing, respiration, lacrimation, salivation, dilated pupils, and tremors.	Also compared epinephrine and norepinephrine. Blocked by amobarbital and reserpine. Potentiated by chlorpromazine
Garfield et al., 1967	12 psychiatric pts.	Double-blind, placebo-controlled study where each subject received each situation twice. Dose 0.5 mg/kg IV over 6 min.	"Anxious and upset" ↑ HR, ↑ BP, flushing, perspiration abdominal distress, nausea, and vomiting.	On second replication, no significant difference between saline and drug.
Charney et al., 1983	10 Normals.	Single-blind, placebo-controlled study using dose of 30 mg po.	Increase in anxiety measured on Visual Analogue Scale (VAS), ↑ BP, perspiration, urinary frequency, hot/cold flashes, piloerection. ↑ MHPG.	Anxiety blocked by clonidine or diazepam. Clonidine, not diazepam, also blocked rise in MHPG and autonomic symptoms.

Henauer et al., 1983	9 Normals, 1 "episodic anxiety" pt.	Single-blind, placebo-controlled study using 30 mg and 60 mg po.	No panic attacks. Anxiety greater than placebo in only 50% of subjects as measured by State-Trait Anxiety Inventory, SCL-90, POMS, and Clyde Mood Scale	Anxiety scales not as sensitive as VAS.
Charney et al., 1984a	39 Panic disorder pts, 20 normals.	Single-blind, placebo-controlled study using 20 mg po.	Increased anxiety in patients, not controls, using VAS. Patients claim anxiety was similar to panic attacks. ↑ MHPG.	More autonomic symptoms in patients than controls at baseline and after challenge.
Uhde, Boulenger, Jimerson, & Post, 1984	11 Panic disorder pts, 5 normals.	Placebo-controlled study using 20 mg po. Blind not specified.	"Profound anxiety" in 9/11 patients, "several" had panic attacks. No anxiety in normals.	—
Charney & Heninger, 1985a	10 PDA, 4 PD pts.	Single-blind, placebo-controlled study using 20 mg po.	11/14 "panicked" and reported ↑ anxiety on VAS. ↑ BP, perspiration, palpitation, tremor, piloerection, hot/cold flashes, lacrimation, anorexia. ↑ MHPG.	Blocked by alprazolam.
Charney & Heninger, 1985b	11 PDA pts.	Single-blind, placebo-controlled study using 20 mg po.	Same results as above.	Imipramine did NOT block or attenuate response.

anxiety. Charney and associates in several studies (Charney & Heninger, 1985a,b; Charney, Heninger, & Redmond, 1983) have demonstrated that yohimbine produces numerous autonomic symptoms, as well as increased subjective endorsements of "nervousness" and "anxiety," on a very sensitive visual analogue scale in both normals and patients. These increases were greater in patients than controls, and increased subjective anxiety was correlated with increased plasma MHPG. Although it is not clear whether the symptoms experienced would have qualified for a panic attack, the correlation of physiologic and subjective changes, taken together with reports of the anxiolytic effects of the alpha-2 agonist clonidine, suggest that this neurochemical system has a role in anxiety, if not panic disorder, per se.

Given that the earlier intravenous studies of yohimbine produced robust effects in both normals and patients, whereas the lower oral doses seem to provoke anxiety consistently only in PD or PDA patients, one wonders if patients are more sensitive to alpha-2 receptor blockade. Differences between patients and controls in MHPG or endocrine measures following yohimbine (or clonidine) administration would support a difference in the sensitivity of the alpha-2 receptor, possibly indicating compensation from chronic stimulation. Although such differences have been demonstrated in patients with affective illness, the evidence for alterations in alpha-2 receptor number or sensitivity in the anxiety disorders is not entirely consistent (Cameron, Smith, Hollingsworth, Pesse, & Curtis, 1984). Thus, it is not yet clear whether yohimbine will be useful as an agent that provokes an anxiety syndrome, capable of discriminating patient populations, as well as a general probe for eliciting the affect of anxiety.

It seems likely that yohimbine's behavioral effects are mediated via the alpha-2 receptor, possibly the presynaptic inhibitory receptor in the brainstem. Not only does pharmacologic stimulation of the locus coeruleus produce "alarm-like" behavior in nonhuman primates (Charney & Redmond, 1983; Redmond, 1979), but in clincial studies the autonomic and subjective effects of yohimbine have been totally blocked by clonidine, an alpha-2 agonist (Charney, et al., 1983). If yohimbine produces anxiety by disinhibiting noradrenergic cells in the brainstem, then yohimbine's anxiogenic effect should be blocked by propranolol, which blocks postsynaptic beta-receptors at noradrenergic terminals. Propranolol has been found to block the fearful behavior produced by electrical stimulation of the locus coeruleus (Redmond, 1979), but has not yet been used in humans to attempt to block yohimbine's effects. Imipramine pretreatment (which should decrease beta-adrenergic receptors) has been tried with conflictual results either potentiating yohimbine (Holmberg & Gershon, 1961) or giving no effect (Charney, Heninger, 1985b).

On the other hand, sodium amobarbital, chlordiazepoxide hydrochloride, and diazepam block the subjective anxiety but not the autonomic changes or the rise in MHPG in normals (Charney, et al., 1983; Holmberg & Gershon, 1961; Ingram, 1962). Because plasma MHPG does not increase consistently in studies of naturalistic anxiety, yohimbine may be increasing anxiety independent of the increase in noradrenergic turnover (although the effects appear correlated). Or, in other words, the increase in plasma MHPG may not be essential for the neural mediation of anxiety, induced either environmentally or pharmacologically. If this is the case, then yohimbine's anxiogenic effects may be related to its actions at the postsynaptic alpha-2 receptors in the forebrain (see Figure 11.1) and propranolol should have little effect in blocking yohimbine's actions.

Beta adrenergic agents.

If yohimbine were thought to produce anxiety via its effects on the noradrenergic system, it will be useful to see the actions of the beta-adrenergic agents themselves. The primary substance used to probe the beta-adrenergic system is *isoproterenol hydrochloride*. In contrast to yohimbine, isoproterenol thus far has been most useful as a tool to discriminate patient populations from nonpatient controls. It is not clear whether higher doses also would induce anxiety in nonpatient groups, or if patient groups have a more sensitive beta-adrenergic system.

Isoproterenol was first used as a probe by Frohlich, Tarazi, and Dustan (1969) who described its effects on patients with hyperdynamic beta-adrenergic circulatory state, a syndorme of labile hypertension, chest pain, and anxiety. Nine of these 14 patients had "spontaneous hysterical outbursts" during the infusion, as well as higher heart rates than controls that were infused. Since then, several open studies and one major double-blind study have been reported (see Table 11.4). Studies have used intravenous doses of isoproterenol ranging from 0.4 to 3.0 μg/min over 5 to 6 minutes or total doses of 7 to 20 μg of isoproterenol. In studies using lower doses, few panic attacks have been noted, although subjects have expereinced symptoms of "fatigue, chest pain, palpitations, anxiety, and breathlessness" (Boudoulas, King, & Wooley, 1984), as well as tachycardia and decreased cortisol and growth hormone (Nesse, Cameron, Curtis, McCann, & Huber-Smith, 1984). The major double-blind placebo controlled study tested 39 panic disorder patients and 18 controls with isoproterenol 20 μg IV, lactate, and placebo (Rainey, Frohman et al., 1984; Rainey, Pohl, et al., 1984; Rainey, Ettedgui et al., 1984). Using criteria of intense fear and at least 3 of 10 RDC criteria for panic attack, 29 of 39 patients and 1 of 18 controls "panicked" on isoproterenol. Of these, 20 of 34 attacks were rated as being similar to spontaneous attacks, although most of the isoproterenol attacks were judged to be "mild" by the patients (by contrast, lactate attacks were rated as "moderate").

The symptoms following isoproterenol administration appear to be mediated by the beta adrenergic receptor, as they are reversed by the beta adrenergic receptor antagonist, propranolol (Easton & Sherman, 1976; Frohlich et al., 1969), and prevented by long-term treatment with imipramine (Rainey, Ettedgui, et al., 1984) which decreases brain beta adrenergic receptors. No other blockers have been tested. It is not clear how much of a parenterally administered dose of isoproterenol actually reaches brain receptors, and it should be noted that isoproterenol infusions may be dangerous for their peripheral effects. In patients with coronary artery disease, isoproterenol administration has been associated with ischemic EEG changes: Continuous monitoring is prudent. See Figure 11.2 for the structure of isoproterenol and distribution of brain beta adrenergic receptors.

Benzodiazepine or GABA System

The benzodiazepines, such as diazepam and chlordiazepoxide, have long been known to be anxiolytic, but the mechanism for this effect remained unclear until recently. Early theories that the effects of these drugs were mediated by GABA, glycine, or serotonin receptors gave way in 1977, when two independent research groups described high-affinity stereospecific receptors for benzodiazepines in the mammalian central nervous system (Mohler & Okada, 1977; Squires & Braestrup. 1977). This brain benzodiazepine receptor was later shown to be functionally and structurally coupled to both a receptor for gamma-aminobutyric acid (GABA) and a chloride ionophore, existing as part of a "supramolecular receptor complex" (Skolnick & Paul, 1982). Considerable evidence supports the notion that the central pharmacologic actions of the benzodiazepines (i.e., anxiolytic, anticonvulsant, sedative, and muscle relaxant actions) are mediated through this receptor complex (Costa & Guidotti, 1979; Tallman, Paul, Skolnick, & Gallager, 1980). The model currently in vogue is that the benzodiazepines potentiate GABA's effects on the chloride ion channel, increasing the duration of channel openings, and thus inhibiting neuronal activity. Unlike the catecholamines, which are limited to less than 1% of forebrain neurons, GABA can be demonstrated in as many as 30% of neurons distributed widely throughout the brain. It appears,

Table 11.4. Isoproterenol

STUDY	SUBJECTS	DESIGN	RESULTS	COMMENTS
Frohlich et al., 1969	14 Patients (pts.) with "hyperdynamic β-adrenergic circulatory state." 13 hypertensives, 25 controls.	Open design using continuous infusions of 1, 2, and 3 μg/min, increasing dose to next level when HR stabilized.	9/14 Pts. had anxiety and/or "spontaneous outbursts, almost uncontrollable." None of the controls had anxiety. ↑ HR noted, patients > controls.	IV propranolol reversed symptoms.
Easton & Sherman, 1976	5 Patients with "anxiety attacks."	Open design using continuous infusions of 0.4–2.6 μg/min.	5/5 Had "anxiety attacks," identical to spontaneous occurring attack.	Blocked by IV propranolol.
Nesse et al., 1984	14 Panic disorder pts., 6 controls	Single-blind placebo-controlled study using a control of patients who knew they would not receive drug. Isoproterenol IV bolus injections 0.06–4.0 μg, 10 min apart.	No panic attacks reported; anxiety decreased during trial. Adr, Nor, GH, and cortisol greater in patients than controls, actually decreased through trial. Lactate, cAMP – no change.	Patients did not respond more to placebo than controls. Anxiety was measured by State-Trait Anxiety Inventory.
Boudoulas et al., 1984	16 mitral valve prolapse pts., 6 controls.	Open design, no placebo. Infused 0.5, 1.0, and 2.0 μg/min for 6 min.	14/16 Pts. noted "anxiety, fatigue, chest pain, palpitations, and breathlessness," and ↑ HR. 2/16 pts. had "panic attacks." No controls had symptoms.	Noted a dose response relationship.

Rainey, Frohman, et al., 1984 Rainey, Pohl, et al., 1984	39 Panic disorder pts., 18 controls.	Well designed double-blind, placebo-controlled study using 20 μg isoproterenol in 6 ml/kg DSW over 20 min.	29/39 Pts. and 1/18 controls had a panic attack using the criteria of "intense fear and at least 3 RDC symptoms of panic attack." Patients rated attacks as "mild" and 20/34 noted the attacks were similar to spontaneous attacks.	Blocked by imipramine therapy in 7 cases. Compared lactate challenge in same patient group.
Rainey, Ettedgui, et al., 1984 Rainey et al., 1985	22 Panic disorder pts., 17 controls.	Same study as above.	Patients were distinguished from controls by lower finger temperature and higher skin conductance. ↑ HR, ↓ respirations, and ↓ muscle tension during infusion.	No physiologic data separated those who panicked from those who did not.

a.

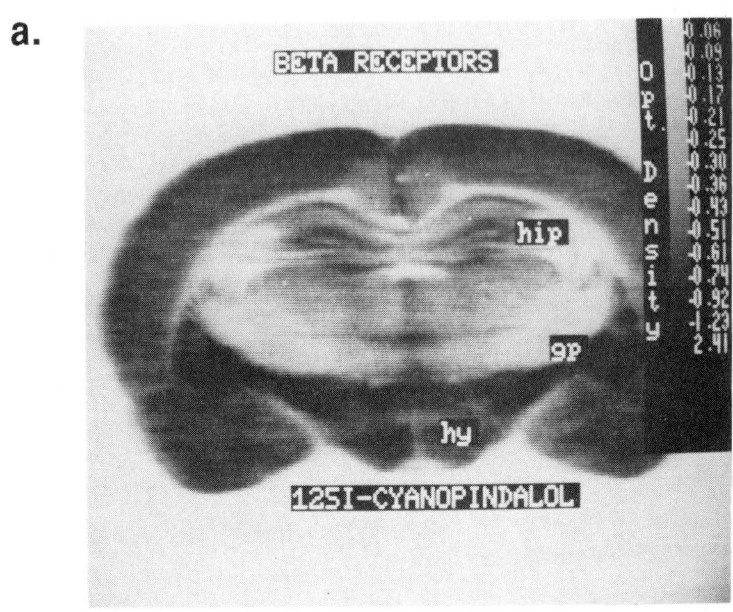

b.

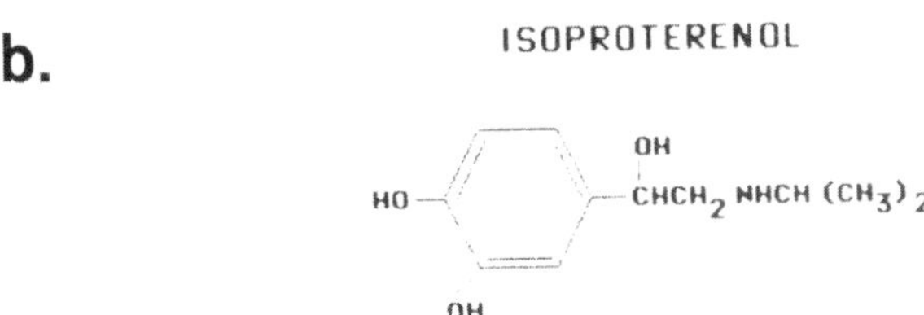

Figure 11.2. A. Brightfield autoradiogram of beta receptor distribution in rat forebrain labeled with ^{125}I-cyanopindalol. Method as in figure 11.1. Dark areas (hy = hypothalamus, gp = globus pallidus, hip = hippocampus) represent highest concentrations of receptors. Receptors are also present in high concentrations in cortex, caudate putamen, and cerebellum. (Autoradiogram courtesy of James Unnerstall, Ph.D., NINCDS.) B. Chemical structure of isoproterenol, a beta receptor agonist.

however, that only a limited number of GABA receptors are functionally linked to the ion channel and the benzodiazepine receptor.

Another recent advance in the study of benzodiazepine receptors was the development of several potent benzodiazepine receptor ligands, such as beta-carboline-3-carboxylic acid ethyl ester (β-CCE) (see Figure 11.3). The affinity of β-CCE for the benzodiazepine receptor in vitro is roughly equivalent to the most potent benzodiazepines and is approximately eightfold greater than diazepam (Mohler & Richards, 1981). Unlike diazepam, which is anticonvulsant, β-CCE and other beta-carboline esters lower the threshold for pentylenetetrazol-induced seizures and actually block the anticonvulsant effects of benzodiazepines in rodents (Oakley & Jones, 1980). These observations led to the classification of these beta-carboline esters as "inverse agonists," and raised the possibility that lower doses of β-CCE, or a closely related analogue — FG-7142 (beta-carboline monomethylamide), also might induce anxiety (see Table 11.5).

a.

b.

B-CCE

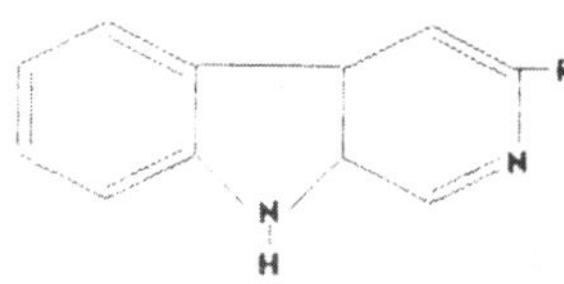

Figure 11.3. A. Brightfield autoradiogram of benzodiazepine receptor distribution in rat forebrain labeled with ^{3}H-flunitrazepam. Method as in Figure 11.1, with approximately same brain region selected. Note high receptor concentrations in amygdala (amy), hippocampus (hip), and cortex (cor) similar although not identical to Figure 11.2. Receptors are also present in high concentrations in the olfactory bulb, septal nuclei, and cerebellum. B. Chemical structure of beta-carboline, with the anxiogenic drugs such as β-CCE substituting an ester moiety at the R. Note similarity with yohimbine structure in Figure 11.1.

Beta-carbolines

In pilot studies in which adult male rhesus monkeys were injected intravenously with 2.5 mg/kg of β-CCE, the behavioral changes were dramatic and rapid, usually manifested within minutes after injection (Ninan, Insel, Cohen, Skolmick, & Paul, 1982). These changes included struggling in the restraining chair, marked head and body turning, increased vocalizing, refusing food or drink, and defecating and urinating immediately after infusion. Accompanying these behaviors were marked elevations in heart rate, blood pressure, plasma cortisol, and plasma catecholamines.

In subsequent studies, it was shown that lower doses of β-CCE (25–500 μg/kg) were associated with dose-related changes in behavioral activation (Insel et al., 1984). The most striking and long-lasting alterations in behaviors were

Table 11.5. Agents Working Via the BZD-GABA-Cl Complex

STUDY	SUBJECTS	DRUG	DESIGN	RESULTS	COMMENTS
Rodin, 1958	40 Normals	5% Pentylenetetrazol IV; 50 mg/min (max dose= 650 mg).	Open	At least 25/40 had extreme "anxiety" and numerous physiologic symptoms. Many had spike/wave discharges on EEG or frank seizures.	Mean dose yielding symptoms was 5.5 mg/kg. Used as a challenge test for epilepsy. Full data on anxiety symptoms not given.
Dorow et al., 1983	12 Normals	FG-7142 200 mg po.	Single-blind, no placebo-controlled.	2/12 Experienced "extreme uneasiness," sense of "impending doom," and ↑ HR, ↑ BP, ↑ muscle tension, ↑ cortisol.	Only the two with anxiety showed measurable blood levels of FG-7142. Blocked in 1 subject with IV Lormetazpam.
Insel et al., 1984	6 Chair-adapted rhesus monkeys.	β-CCE 25-2500 μg/kg IV; FG-7142 3 mg/kg IV.	Blind, vehicle control given.	6/6 Showed "extreme agitation" characterized by head and body turning, distress vocalization, defecation, urination, fearful response to caretaker, ↑ HR, ↑ BP. ↑ cortisol, no change MHPG.	Dose related effects seen. All effects blocked by RO-15-1788 or diazepam less effectively by clonidine. Behavioral effects not blocked by propranolol.

observed during interactive sessions using relatively low doses of β-CCE. Although animals varied in the intensity and character of their responses, these individual responses resembled those observed following a naturalistic threat and generally apperaed as species typical defense reactions. Similar responses were observed following injection of FG-7142 (3 mg/kg IV) in the same monkeys.

The behavioral and physiologic changes following β-CCE administration were entirely blocked by pretreatment with RO 15-1788, a benzodiazepine antagonist without intrinstic actions, and by anxiolytic doses of diazepam (Insel et al., 1984). By contrast, treatment with propranolol blocked the tachycardia, but not the behavioral or endocrine changes. Clonidine pretreatment blunted the behavioral activation and blocked the drug induced increases in blood pressure and pulse, suggesting some interaction between the benzodiazepine and alpha-2 adrenergic systems (Crawley et al., 1985; Insel et al., 1984).

To date, there has been only one study of administration of a benzodiazepine receptor inverse agonist in humans. Dorow, Horowski, Paschelke, Amin, and Braestrup (1983) gave FG-7142 to 12 normal volunteers. Only two subjects were found to have measurable blood levels of the compound and both experienced intense motor unrest and "almost intolerable tension," which one subject described as a feeling of impending doom. In one case these symptoms were so severe that the subject was given lormetazepam, which reversed the unpleasant behavioral effects in minutes. In addition to these changes, plasma cortisol, systolic blood pressure, and heart rate all increased significantly following administration of FG-7142.

As with yohimbine, there is little doubt that the benzodiazapine receptor inverse agonists produce intense behavioral and autonomic activation. What is not clear is whether this activation phenomenologically is specific to anxiety, panic, or fear. For instance, in the primate studies, administration of β-CCE was associated with increases in aggressive displays, reminiscent of Cannon's descriptions of restrained cats subjected to barking dogs. A recent study looked more closely at the behavioral effects of β-CCE in rhesus monkeys with different rearing histories. In animals raised in a peer group with control over their environment, responses to a natural stress (separation) were brief, and β-CCE administration was associated with aggression and threat vocalizations. In a second cohort of monkeys that were yoked so that they received identical items, but only when chosen by the "control" group, responses to separation were more catastrophic, and β-CCE administration was followed by withdrawal and distress or "coo" vocalizations (Insel, Scanlan, Champoux, & Suomi, unpublished data). The drug, then, induces a neurochemical state that has different manifestations depending on rearing history and response style.

In human terms, this suggests that the behavioral response to β-CCE might be different in patients vulnerable to anxiety compared to those without a history of an anxiety disorder. It also is possible that early experiences might produce a lasting change in the number or the sensitivity of benzodiazepine receptors, leaving certain individuals more vulnerable to endogenous anxiogenic substances. One such substance that binds to the benzodiazepine receptor is an 18 amino acid peptide, derived from the precursor diazepam binding inhibitor (DBI), which has recently been isolated and purified (Ferrero, Guidotti, Conti-Tronconi, & Costa, 1984; Guidotti et al., 1983). In the near future, we should know whether anxious patients have more of this peptide in the cerebrospinal fluid than nonanxious controls. Since administration of FG-7142 elicited such marked distress even in nonanxious subjects, it is doubtful whether the current beta-carbolines will be ethically useful as clinical pharmacologic probes. Other strategies, including in vivo receptor imaging, may be more useful in evaluating whether anxious patients indeed have a more sensitive benzodiazepine-GABA system than nonanxious controls (Persson et al., 1985).

Pentylenetetrazol

Still within the benzodiazepine-GABA system, but working downstream from the benzodizepine receptor, is a different class of anxiogencis. One such anxiogenic, pentylenetetrazol (Metrazol®), is a "cage convulsant" that appears to bind to a site on the chloride channel (Squires, Sqederup, Crawley, Skolnick, & Paul, 1984). In the 1940s and 1950s, it was widely used as a means to induce either electroencephalographic seizure discharges or overt clinical seizures in patients suspected of having a convulsive disorder (Moore, Kellaway, and Kagawa, 1954). As such, it was given intravenously in doses from 50 mg to 1,000 mg to over 1,000 "normal" volunteers and to an unknown number of neurologic patients. It often produced definite EEG paroxysms of frank grand mal seizures (Buchthal & Lennox, 1953). In this early literature, much attention was paid to EEG changes occurring with pentylenetetrazol administration, but relatively little information appeared about the symptoms that subjects noted, Rodin (1958) noted that there was marked variability in the amount of subjective discomfort induced by the pentylenetetrazol challenge procedure, with some subjects having little discomfort and others complaining of such symptoms as dizziness, profound tension, anxiety, muscular twitchings, panic sensations, changes in body image, or hallucinatory experiences.

Accordingly, in 1958, Rodin undertook a systematic study of 40 normal controls during which he collected verbatim transcripts of the subjects' reports of their experiences. For example, one report included "muscle tension, some anxiety, worry about what was going to happen, swimming sensation in head, pulsating sensation in head and body, dry mouth, pain in the arm and shoulder." Another subject felt the experience was frightening, "I got more scared than I've ever been in my life, so scared, really scared. This kept building up. Then I thought this was ridiculous and then it was all right" (Rodin, 1958, p. 438). It was difficult to evaluate whether the symptoms would qualify for a panic attack or not, but clearly many subjects experienced both subjective feelings of anxiety and autonomic and physiologic sensations consistent with anxiety. Because of the risk of seizures, human administration of pentylenetetrazol has not continued and there are no recent human studies, although in the animal literature pentylenetetrazol still is seen as one of the best pharmacologic models for anxiety (Lal & Emmett-Oglesby, 1983). Indeed, the potency for blocking pentylenetetrazol-induced seizures probably is the most sensitive measure of a benzodiazepine's anxiolytic potential.

What about these agents makes them anxiogenic substances? One obvious implication from the literature on β-CCE and pentylenetetrazol is that there appears to be a continuum between anxiogenic and convulsant effects. The converse statement also is true: several excellent anxiolytics, such as the benzodiazepines and the barbiturates, also are anticonvulsant. This relationship raises the possibility that anxiety could be conceptualized as subconvulsive cortical activation from a variety of causes. The relationship of seizures to anxiety may be a fruitful area for further study, and the new techniques for monitoring cortical electrophysiologic and blood flow changes should be productive in anxiety states.

Adenosine System

The adenosine system has been implicated as one of the neurochemical systems involved with anxiety because of data that link the stimulant properties of caffeine with its effects on the adenosine system. Although it previously has been assumed that caffeine produces its effects either by inhibition of phosphodiesterase, an enzyme that mediates the catabolism of cyclic adenosine monophosphate, or by direct actions at the benzodiazepine receptor, recent evidence indicates that caffeine is a potent antagonist at brain adenosine receptors (see Figure 11.4). Adenosine has inhibitory effects on neurotransmission mediated through the blockade of release of excitatory neurotransmitters (Synder, 1985). Thus, caffeine's stimulant effects are probably mediated via the antagonism of the depressant actions of adenosine.

Caffeine, a methylxanthine (see Figure 11.4), is widely consumed for its psychostimulant properties. The average North American adult consumes 200 to 250 mg of caffeine daily. Such doses are known to increase alertness, stimulate attention, and reduce deterioration of performance due to boredom or fatigue (Gilbert, 1981). Consumption of caffeine in high doses (greater than 600 mg/day) reportedly has induced a syndrome of "caffeinism" with symptoms of anxiety, nervousness, sleep disturbances, and psychophysiologic complaints that may be indistinguishable from anxiety neurosis (Greden, 1974).

Several studies have suggested an association between caffeine consumption and anxiety and/or depression in both college students (Gilliland & Andress, 1981; Primavera, Simon, & Camiza, 1975) and

a.

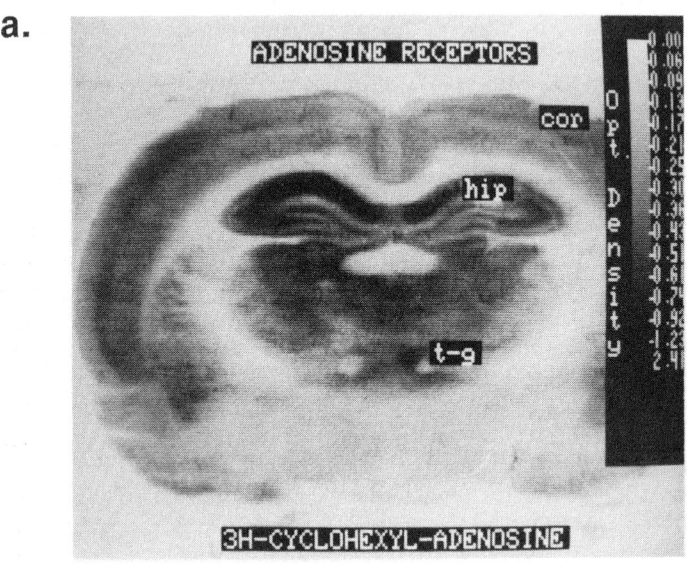

b.

CAFFEINE

Figure 11.4. A. Brightfield autoradiogram of adenosine receptor distribution in rat forebrain labeled with selective ligand ^{3}H-cyclo-hexyl-adenosine. Method as in Figure 11.1, with approximately same brain region selected. Receptor concentrations are highest in hippocampus (hip), cortex (cor), and thalamus (especially nucleus glomerulosus-t-g). In addition, adenosine receptors are present in high concentrations in the cerebellum, lateral septum, and medial geniculate. B. Chemical structure of caffeine, an adenosine receptor antagonist.

psychiatric inpatients De Freitas & Schwartz, 1979; Greden, Fontaine, Lubetsky, & Chamberlin, 1978; Winstead, 1976). However, the meaning of this relationship is unclear, as caffeine consumption was self-selected, and caffeine consumption is correlated with a host of other variables characterizing the "style of life," any of which may be related to increased anxiety (Dews, 1984).

There has been a recent interest in caffeine both as an anxiogenic substance and as a challenge test for anxiety disorders. Boulenger, Uhde, Wolff, and Post (1984) have argued that because panic disorder patients reported increased anxiety following a single cup of coffee and reported giving up coffee because of unpleasant effects more than either depressives or matched normal controls, perhaps panic disorder patients have an increased sensitivity to caffeine. This group and others have undertaken controlled studies of caffeine challenges in both normals and panic disorder patients. Caffeine differs from the other substances we have reviewed because it is so widely available, and therefore a confounding variable in using it as a challenge drug is the subject's prior usage and level of tolerance.

Because caffeine has so recently been reintroduced into this field, there are very few studies administering caffeine in protocols similar to those using the other substances we have reviewed. On the other hand, the older caffeine literature is replete with studies looking for behavioral effects of caffeine. We will refer the reader to Dews' (1984) comprehensive review of this extensive older literature, and briefly survey only the more relevant recent studies (see Table 11.6).

These studies were not all set up to evaluate caffeine as a challenge substance for panic attacks or even anxiety. Nonetheless, several generalizations emerge: First, caffeine in general induces anxiety with a dose-related effect regardless of usage pattern; second, caffeine does not induce a rise in MHPG; and third, there are groups of patients (and "normal" children) that respond differently to caffeine both behaviorally and physiologically than others. More information defining the factors that contribute to the variance in the behavioral response to caffeine may be useful in understanding the pathophysiology of anxiety because adenosine and related purines are remarkably abundant in brain (though difficult to measure). The recent finding that rodents inbred to be emotionally reactive have different numbers of adenosine receptors is of importance in this regard (Marangos, Insel, Montgomery, 1987).

Other substances clearly differentiate some anxiety patients from nonanxious patients, yet there is no clear etiologic rationale for why they do so. We will now review two of these — sodium lactate and carbon dioxide.

Sodium Lactate

Lactate was first investigated due to the belief that anxiety patients were exercise-intolerant and developed unusually high blood levels of lactic acid. The original Pitts and McClure (1967) model was well designed and, in most cases, has been followed with only minor revisions. The results across all studies using a 20-minute intravenous infusion (10 ml/kg) of 0.5 M Na lactate (a mixture of D and L stereoisomers) are quite consistent (see Table 11.7 for recent studies; others reviewed by Guttmacher et al., 1983). Across 16 separate studies, approximately 70% of 286 panic disorder patients and 10% of 113 healthy controls experienced anxiety states meeting the operational criteria for panic attacks (Appleby, Klein, Sachar & Levi, 1981; Arbab, Bonn & Hicks, 1971; Bonn, Harrison & Rees, 1971; Carr et al., 1986; Fink, Taylor & Volavka, 1970; Fyer, Liebowitz, Gaman, Davies & Klein, 1985; Gorman et al., 1983; Haslam, 1974; Kelly, Mitchell-Heggs & Sherman, 1971; Knott, Chaudhry & Lapierre, 1981; Lapierre, Knott, Phil & Gray, 1984; Liebowitz et al., 1984; Liebowitz, Fyer et al., 1985; Liebowitz, Gorman et al., 1985; Pitts & McClure, 1967; Rainey, Frohman, Freedman, Pohl, Ettedgui & Williams, 1984a; Rainey, Ettedgui, Pohl & Bridges, 1985; Rifkin, Klein, Dillon & Levitt, 1981). Symptoms, which

Table 11.6. Caffeine

CITATION	SUBJECTS	DESIGN	RESULTS
Uhde et al., 1984	5 Panic disorder pts., 8 controls.	Double-blind, placebo-controlled study using po doses of caffeine 240 mg, 480 mg, and 720 mg.	Dose related increased anxiety in all subjects; 2/8 controls had panic attacks with high dose; cortisol; no change in MHPG.
Charney et al., 1984b	11 Normals.	Single-blind, placebo-controlled study giving po doses of 10 mg/kg.	Increased anxiety using visual analogue scale (VAS), ↑ BP, ↑ HR, no change in MHPG.
Spindel et al., 1984	7–10 Normals per test all 18–30-yr-old students who drank 1–3 cups coffee qd.	Placebo-controlled single-blind study giving 250 mg or 500 mg po.	Beta-endorphin like immunoreactivity increased with high dose. No change in TSH, GH, prolactin, cortisol, T_3 with either dose.
Veleber & Templer, 1984	157 Normals separated as to high, moderate, or low caffeine use.	Placebo-controlled double-blind study using 300 mg or 600 mg.	Increased anxiety with dose effect regardless of prior usage.
Rapport, Berg, Ismond, Zahn, & Neims, 1984	38 Children, ages 6–13 years. 19 high caffeine use; 19 low caffeine use.	Placebo-controlled, double-blind crossover outpatient study using 5 mg/kg po BID for 2 weeks.	High consumers had increased anxiety on placebo, no change on caffeine. Low consumers had increased restlessness, fidgeting, moodiness, and inattention with caffeine. No difference in BP, HR.
Charney, Heninger, & Jatlow, 1985	21 Panic disorder pts., 17 controls	Single-blind, placebo-controlled study using 10 mg/kg po caffeine.	15/21 Patients reported panic attack. Nausea, palpitations, restlessness, anorexia, and tremors; patients > controls. Slight ↑ BP, ↓ HR-controls; ↑ BP, ↑ HR-patients. No change in MHPG. ↑ cortisol.

are reported as quite close to "moderate" spontaneous attacks, peak after approximately 15 minutes and cease several minutes after the drug is discontinued. If the infusion is stopped immediately, there are few residual effects.

Numerous researchers have tried to differentiate panickers from non-panickers on the basis of baseline or pre-infusion anxiety levels, physiological signs and biochemical measurements (see Table 11.7). These studies have consistently shown that those persons who panic have a higher pre-infusion level of anxiety and fearfulness, heart rate, and blood pressure than those patients who do not panic or than control groups. No other changes are consistently found. The heightened sympathetic arousal seems to be an acute process, for at least in one study (Liebowitz, Gorman, et al., 1985) the patient-control difference in heart rate the day before the lactate infusion was less marked. If there were some threshold at which anyone would panic, are the patients merely closer to the threshold at

Table 11.7. Summary of Sodium Lactate Infusion Studies

STUDY	SUBJECTS	DESIGN	RESULTS	COMMENTS
Pits & McClure, 1967	14 Anxiety neurosis (probable panic disorder), 10 normals.	Double-blind placebo-controlled.	13/14 Pts., 1/10 controls developed anxiety symptoms. With addition of calcium to lactate, only 1/14 pts. panicked.	Symptoms ablated upon cessation, but residua lasted over 24 hr.
Knott et al., 1981	6 Panic disorder pts.	Single-blind, placebo-controlled study.	6/6 Pts. had "panic episodes." No criteria for panic were given. ↑ HR, ↑ EOG, ↑ EMG; ↓ alpha, ↑ delta on EEG.	—
Gorman et al., 1983	6 Panic disorder pts.	Single-blind noncontrolled study, repeated with pretreatment of propranolol .2 mg-kg IV over 30 min.	6/6 Pts. had panic "typical of ordinary attacks." With propranolol, 2/6 had "milder attacks."	—
Lapierre et al., 1984	23 Panic disorder pts. 16 generalized anxiety disorder pts.	Double blind.	6/23 Panic disorder pts., 2/16 GAD pts. panicked (not a significant difference). No baseline differences between panickers and non-panickers were seen.	With panic attack, ↑ blink frequence, ↑ EMG tension, ↑ HR, and ↑ in delta EE.
Rainey et al., 1984b, 1985	39 Panic disorder pts., 17 normals.	Double-blind placebo-controlled study comparing lactate and isoproterenol induced panic attacks.	34/39 Pts., 6/17 controls panicked using DSM-III criteria for panic attack. 4 patients reinfused after TCA therapy: all experienced attenuated symptomatology.	Used 1.0 M DL Na lactate at 6 ml/kg over 20 min. (different methodology than other studies). Panickers had increased anxiety at baseline and developed greater tachycardia than controls.

Liebowitz et al., 1984, 1985b	43 Panic disorder pts., 20 normals.	Single-blind, placebo-controlled.	31/43 Pts., 0/20 controls panicked using DSM-III criteria for panic attack and "crescendo of extreme apprehension or fear." With infusion, lactate, pyruvate, prolactin, pH and HC_3 increased; Ca^+, phophate, cortisol, and pCO_2 decreased. No change in EPI or NOR.	Also treated 27 patients with TCA. Of these, 4 of 27 panicked with reinfusion. Panickers had increased baseline anxiety and somatic complaints, lower pCO_2 and HCO_3 compared to controls.
Liebowitz et al., 1985a	29 Panic disorder pts., 15 social phobia pts.	Physician infusing was blind to diagnosis; staff was not blind to infusate.	14/29 Panic disorder pts., 1/15 social phobics had panic attack using above criteria.	—
Fyer et al., 1985	15 Panic disorder pts.	Nonclear; reinfused following treatment with TCA	9/15 Pts. panicked using criteria of DSM-III panic symptoms and "crescendo of fear."	Lower response to infusion if in remission.
Carr et al., 1986	30 Panic disorder pts., 10 normals.	Double-blind, placebo-controlled study.	"90% Of patients raised panic intensity" but criteria for measuring anxiety not specified in this paper. With infusion, prolactin, GH, and NOR increased; EPI and MHPG decreased and cortisol and LH remained stable.	Lactate was given to 25 patients and 10 controls. Placebo was given to 5 patients. 4 patients were dropped from study because did not respond to lactate. Patients had increased EPI and panic ratings at baseline. Symptoms attenuated upon reinfusion following alprazolam therapy.
		TCA.		

baseline? This hypothesis could be tested by increasing the lactate dose in nonpatient groups, or by increasing the controls' baseline anxiety and arousal, either with adrenergic agents or situationally, and then challenging them with lactate. There are clear dose-dependent effects seen with pentylenetetrazol, yohimbine, and caffeine such that normals will appear anxious, although at higher doses than is required for panic disorder patients.

Because the panickers are more aroused, could the lactate effect simply be explained by the expectations of the patients? There are some reasonable data to suggest this is not true, that is, the effects of lactate are less attributable to social cues than the adrenergic agents. In Pitts and McClure's (1967) original study, they gave lactate, lactate with calcium, and glucose in saline in a double-blind, random order design. Despite similar environment, previous experience, and current expectations, patients did not panic on placebo. A representative verbatim quote from an anxiety neurosis patient with glucose in saline infusion is, " 'Nervous when came in here after those other two times but this one causes nothing — in fact, I think I feel somewhat better, a little stronger' " (Pitts & McClure, 1967, p.1331). It is clear that increased baseline arousal alone is not sufficient to precipitate a panic attack — the trigger also is specific.

As of yet, there is no agreement about lactate's mechanism of action. Pitts and McClure (1967) originally suggested that lactate-induced hypocalcemia was the cause of anxiety, because addition of calcium to the lactate infusion attenuated panic. However, their report that EDTA, a powerful calcium chelator, did not produce panic in panic disorder patients refutes this hypothesis. Grosz and Farmer (1972) advanced the theory that alkalosis, caused by the metabolic conversion of lactate to bicarbonate, precipitated the panic attack. Although they showed that sodium bicarbonate produced similar anxiety symptoms as lactate in normals, they never attempted this with patients, therefore it is unclear if bicarbonate alone can cause panic attacks in vulnerable patient groups. This theory currently is being investigated by Klein and colleagues (Klein, Gorman, Liebowitz, & Fyer, 1985). One of the most consistent findings during a lactate-induced panic attack is a precipitous drop in blood CO_2 concentration, indicating hyperventilation (Gorman et al., 1985). Yet simply hyperventilating patients to the point of respiratory alkalosis does not precipitate panic attacks, whereas breathing carbon dioxide does. This has led Gorman et al. (1985) to speculate that lactate's effects are mediated via CO_2 (see CO_2 section for discussion of its mechanisms). One final approach documented a possible anatomic difference in lactate responders. Reiman, Raichle, Butler, Herscouitch and Robins (1984) described a discrete characteristic asymmetry of cerebral blood flow in PD patients responding to lactate, but not in controls. Certainly, this novel approach deserves increased attention in the future.

The lactate model is relatively simple to execute (for a good summary of procedures, see Sheehan, Carr, Fishman, Walsch, & Peltier-Saxe, 1985), replicable, and quantifiable. It may be unsafe in subjects with compromised cardiovascular function because of the large vascular fluid load over a short period of time.

Carbon Dioxide

Carbon dioxide (CO_2) has long been associated with anxiety, although often in contradictory ways. Drury first observed in 1919 that inhalation of CO_2 produced intolerable hyperpnea in World War I soldiers complaining of irritable heart or the effort syndrome (predecessor terms for anxiety neurosis and panic disorder). In 1950, Cohen and White studied patients with "neurocirculatory asthenia" (another predecessor term for anxiety neurosis). They had these patients use a rebreathing technique to increase concentrations of CO_2 to 4% over 12 minutes. Approximately 80% of 43 patients and none of 27 controls had "anxiety attacks" with this procedure. It would seem that CO_2

provoked anxiety in susceptible groups. Yet clinical lore encouraged patients in the midst of anxiety attacks to rebreath CO_2 (such as breathing into a bag) in order to decrease their anxiety and attenuate the attack. Indeed, in the 1950s carbon dioxide was used as an anxiolytic intervention, which was claimed by Wolpe (1958) to be specific for pervasive anxiety. He reported a powerful inhibition of anxiety which lasted for some hours to several days after one or more inhalations. In the first controlled trial, immediate reduction of subjective anxiety after CO_2 intake was observed (Slater & Leavy, 1966). This finding was replicated (Ley & Walker, 1973), but the results are difficult to interpret because both groups told the subjects to expect a decrease in anxiety and neither group specifically tested PD patients. It may be that CO_2 affects PD patients and "neurotic patients" or nonpatients in opposite ways. Alternatively, CO_2 may be similar to the catecholamines in that the effect it produces is highly dependent upon the expectations of the subject. Yet a third possibility is that CO_2 has different effects depending upon where in the temporal sequence of an anxiety state it is administered. In any case, it would seem prudent to settle these historically discrepant observations before definitively touting CO_2 as an anxiogenic agent.

Nonetheless, CO_2 is fast becoming a popular agent in the pharmacologic modeling of anxiety, and Table 11.8 summarizes the most recent CO_2 challenge work. Griez and Van Den Hout (Griez, 1984; Van Den Hout & Griez, 1984) compared CO_2 to lactate-induced panic attacks and found that CO_2 replicated eight of nine DSM-III panic symptoms in at least 50% of subjects, whereas lactate produced three of nine symptoms in 50% of subjects. Testing CO_2 with lactate-responsive panic patients, Gorman et al. (1984) found that most of these patients also panicked with CO_2 and described these attacks as similar to their spontaneous attacks. Woods, Charney, Lake, Goodman, Redmond, and Heninger (1986) compared spontaneous panic to that induced by CO_2, caffeine, and yohimbine. Most recently, Gorman et al. (1985) have studied 31 PD or PDA patients and compared them with healthy controls as well as with patients with other anxiety disorders. Recent work seems to indicate panic disorder patients will panic at lower concentrations of CO_2 than controls; however, it also appears that higher doses of CO_2 will induce anxiety in non–panic disorder patient groups (Gorman et al., 1985; Woods et al., 1986).

The mechanism for CO_2-induced panic is not known. Because breathing CO_2 drives respiration, it has been hypothesized that CO_2 panic is secondary to the feeling that one's breathing is out of control, an experience that may be intolerable for patients, but not controls. Donald Klein has suggested that panic patients may have a pathologically lowered threshold in a "suffocation alarm mechanism" that is triggered by CO_2 (personal communication, November 4, 1983). In this regard, Woods et al. (1986) have shown that panic disorder patients do *not* have an increased respiratory response to CO_2 administration; they differ from normals only in their subjective response. Carbon dioxide is also a potent stimulator of locus coeruleus discharge, which has been hypothesized as central to the panic attack (Elam, Yoa, Thoren, & Svensson, 1981). Acute intravenous administration of the alpa-2 adrenergic receptor agonist clonidine, which decreases firing of the locus coeruleus, does not prevent lactate-induced panic (Rainey et al., 1985). Whether clonidine will block CO_2-induced anxiety remains to be seen.

A major advantage of using carbon dioxide is the ease and safety of administration. The technique, which is well described by Griez and Van den Hout (1982), is self-administered, quantifiable, and replicable. When used therapeutically several administrations can be given in a half-hour session. The induced symptoms and physiological changes are very short-lived and no serious side effects have been observed. It is hoped that with larger and more carefully controlled studies, carbon dioxide's role in the syndrome of panic-type anxiety can be better assessed.

Table 11.8. Carbon Dioxide

STUDY	SUBJECTS	DESIGN	RESULTS	COMMENTS
Salter & Leavy, 1966	12 Psychiatric inpatients with "high anxiety."	Double-blind, placebo-controlled study using single inhalation of 35% CO_2/65% O_2 mixture.	↓ anxiety with CO_2; no change in anxiety with air or hyperventilation.	Anxiety rated by 1–10 analogue scale, subj. and obj. Subjects told to expect anxiety.
Ley & Walker, 1973	10 "Neurotics," 10 controls.	Single-blind, placebo-controlled study using single inhalation of 35% CO_2/65% O_2 mixture.	↓ anxiety ↓ HR, no change BP with both CO_2 and with air; no difference between groups.	Anxiety rated by subjective scale. Subjects told to expect anxiety.
Griez & Van den Hout, 1983b	1 General anxiety disorder patient with panic attacks.	Single case report, 35% CO_2/65% O_2.	Inhalations treated "phobophobia" as form of densensitization therapy.	—
Van de Hout & Griez, 1983	20 Normals.	Single-blind, placebo-controlled study using inhalation of 35% CO_2/65% O_2 mixture.	Provoked symptoms of panic — dyspnea, palpitations, chest pains, choking, dizziness, paresthesies, cold, faintness, shakiness,	Not clear if subjects actually had cognitive components of anxiety.
Gorman et al., 1984	12 Panic disorder pts., 4 normals.	Single-blind, placebo-controlled study using breathing of 5% CO_2 for 20 min.	7/12 Pts., 0/4 controls developed panic attacks similar to naturally occurring attacks.	Also, used Na lactate in same subjects.

Woods et al., 1985; in press	14 PDA pts., 23 controls.	Open study, no placebo, using technique of rebreathing a 5% CO_2 mixture for up to 5 min.	7/10 Pts., 4/22 controls developed panic attacks. Used criteria of DSM-III P.A. plus extreme fear. 8/10 pts. described attack as similar to spontaneous.	Pts. more sensitive to anxiogenic effects but not to ventilatory stimulation induced by CO_2. Panic blocked by chronic alprazolam therapy.
Gorman et al., 1985	31 PD or PDA pts., 13 normals, 12 "other anxiety disorders" (8 soc. phobia, 3 GAD, 1 OCD).	Single-blind, placebo-control study using rebreathing 5% or 7% CO_2 by hood for up to 20 min.	12/13 Pts., 1/13 normals, 0/12 "other" anxiety pts. had panic attacks with 5% CO_2. 6/9 pts., 3/3 social phobes, 0/6 normals had panic with 7% CO_2. With CO_2 NE and respiratory rate higher in panickers than controls. EPI, cortisol, lactate, and BP, panickers = controls.	Also used hyperventilation and lactate infusion in some pts. Baseline ↑ HR, ↑ BP, ↑ anxiety, ↓ pCO_2, ↓ Ca, ↑ dBP in PD or PDA compared to norm.

CONCLUDING REMARKS

Pharmacologic models of anxiety have yet to provide a coherent picture of the pathophysiology of anxiety. The most ambitious hope, that an anxiogenic agent would lead us to a single endogenous substance that mediates the pathophysiology of anxiety, has not yet been realized. However, as more experience is gained with each agent, several generalizations emerge as to how certain classes of compounds might fit into the total picture.

Anxiogenic Drugs: Putting it all Together

The adrenergic agents consistently cause the autonomic signs and physical symptoms associated with anxiety, similar to Buss' (1962) first category of complaints. Yohimbine seems to be the most potent, producing such symptoms as palpitations, tremor, perspiration, piloerection, hot and cold flashes, increased urinary frequency, rhinnorhea, and increased diastolic and systolic blood pressure in both normals and panic disorder patients (Charney et al., 1983). Subjects receiving adrenergic agents may experience fear, anxiety, introspection, or euphoria (Schachter & Singer, 1962), depending on their expectations and the environmental setting. It may be, then, that the adrenergic agents are responsible for a general state of arousal, vigilance, and activation, reflecting their actions on phylogenetically primitive brainstem nuclei, such as the locus coeruleus.

By contrast, administration of anxiogenic agents working through the benzodiazepine/GABA/Cl-channel complex, such as the beta-carboline esters and pentylenetetrazol, appear to be associated with the subjective "feelings" of anxiety that Buss (1962) described. The beta-carbolines have not been tested extensively, yet two human subjects with measurable blood levels experienced a sense of "impending doom." The older pentylenetetrazol literature is replete with numerous graphic descriptions of fear states, as seen in Rodin's work (1958). It is interesting that diazepam, a benzodiazepine, blocks the subjective anxiety experienced with a yohimbine challenge, yet does not block the increase in MHPG or the autonomic changes.

One way of conceptualizing the difference between the benzodiazepine-GABA-Cl channel system and the adrenergic system, is that the former is a phylogenetically recent development, concentrated in the neocortex and limbic structures (see Figure 11.3), with a role in higher cognitive processes such as apprehension and coping with conflict. In line with this approach, animal models of anxiety that are sensitive to benzodiazepines generally involve a "conflict" test, whereas nonconflict tests such as acoustic startle appear most sensitive for adrenergic agents (Patel & Malick, 1983).

It would be misleading, however, to assume that yohimbine and β-CCE work on entirely independent neural systems. Lesioning noradrenergic pathways in the forebrain leads to as much as a 30% reduction in benzodiazepine receptors, suggesting that many of these receptors are actually located on noradrenergic terminals (Sabato, Novas, Lowenstein, Ziehere, & De Robertis, 1981). Conversely, benzodiazepines decrease the firing rate of the locus coeruleus (Grant, Huang, & Redmond, 1980). So it seems most likely that both systems are involved in the neural mediation of anxiety.

A second point, emanating from the overlap in the autoradiograms shown in Figures 11.1 through 11.3, is that certain brain areas appear to mediate the effects of all of the "anxiogenic" drugs. The central and basolateral nuclei of the amygdala, the lateral septal nuclei (not shown), and various hypothalamic nuclei appear as "hot spots" for adrenergic, benzodiazepine, and adenosine receptors. These limbic sites define a network, with efferents to sympathetic nuclei in the brainstem, that very likely mediate the neural experience of anxiety. As imaging techniques improve, it should become possible to examine these same regions in human brain for blood flow, metabolic activity, or receptor binding in normal and pathologic anxiety states

It should, however, be kept in mind that drugs may be selective for brain receptors, but nonselective in their ultimate effects. The brain is not organized pharmacologically. Individual neurons may share receptor sites for hundreds of different chemicals and each neuron may synapse with thousands of chemically unrelated neurons. Descriptions of the adrenergic or adenosine "system" may be overstating the case — these are not systems in the sense of having a homogeneous function or sharing well-defined internal relationships.

Anxiogenic Drugs as a Challenge Model: What have We Learned?

A more modest goal of pharmacologic challenges has been to provide a provocative test that would discriminate subtypes of anxiety. Sodium lactate has certainly been successful in this regard. In numerous studies, panic disorder patients consistently panic and healthy volunteers do not panic with a standardized Na lactate infusion. Additionally, the actions of lactate can be blocked by the usual clinical therapies for panic disorder. This body of work has helped to define panic disorder as a distinct clinical entity, perhaps the most important contribution thus far of pharmacologic models of anxiety.

The challenge models also have been useful heuristically in trying to establish the etiology of panic attacks. Although current theories looking for neurochemical lesions still are inconclusive, a different school of thought views the etiology as being based in the larger system — the person. Is it possible that both patients and normals experience the same physiologic changes, but the patients have a different subjective response to them? Proponents of the "phobophobia" model of panic disorder would argue that patients have become sensitized to and fearful of the internal sensations experienced during autonomic arousal, and react to autonomic arousal much as a phobic patient would react to their feared stimulus. In support of this theory is the fact that repeated exposures to autonomic arousal, either by in vivo desensitization or with lactate or CO_2 induced panic, is a viable therapy. Additionally, the naturalistic study of Freedman et al. (1985) suggested that panic attacks were preceeded by charged interpersonal situations where autonomic arousal most likely occurred. Charney et al, (1983) demonstrate that diazepam blocked the subjective distress but not the autonomic arousal of a yohimbine challenge in normals. Would this effect be replicated in panic disorder patients? Using the anxiogenic agents in this way can help test out etiologic therories at a higher systems level, as well as at a basic neurochemical level.

Future Directions

The pharmacologic study of anxiety promises to move in several fruitful directions in the near future. The development of imaging techniques to assess in vivo receptor binding of benzodiazepines has already given a first glimpse of brain receptor distribution in anxious and nonanxious subjects (Persson et al., 1985). This method applied to patients and to normal volunteers during episodes of anxiety should help to define if the benzodiazepine receptor has a role in anxiogenesis, as well as anxiolysis.

Although the recent studies of yohimbine, caffeine, CO_2, and other challenge agents have stressed the distinctive features of each agent, in the future researchers will need to devote more attention to what these various compounds have in common. The common threads that link these agents as "anxiogenics" may be the most useful for ultimately developing a neurochemical model of anxiety. In animal studies, the effects of these agents on behaviorally active brain peptides, such as corticotropin releasing factor or the opiates, needs to be explored.

Finally, there is a continuing need to enlarge the assumptions underlying this entire area of research. Do these pharmacologic agents act consistently across different environmental situations? What are the concomitant effects of expectational set, previous experience, and social cues? Do subjects respond to drugs differently if they are in conflict situations, reassuring situations, or perceptibly dangerous situations? These all are larger questions that can be tested using these same agents.

In conclusion, pharmacologic models of anxiety provide useful heuristic tools with which to generate and test hypotheses regarding the etiology of pathologic forms of anxiety as well as the neurochemical mediating systems involved in anxiogenesis and anxiolysis. Whether or not the models exactly mimic a spontaneous state of anxiety, these probes may ultimately allow us to tease apart the mystery underlying much of human suffering.

> One thing is certain, that the problem of anxiety is a nodal point, linking up all kinds of most important questions; a riddle, of which the solution must cast a flood of light upon our whole mental life. (Freud, 1917/1960, p. 401)

REFERENCES

Abramowicz, M. (1981). Drugs that cause psychiatric symptoms. *Medical Letter, 23,* 9–12.

American Psychiatric Association. (1980). *Diagnostic and statistical manual of mental disorders* (3rd ed.). Washington, DC: Author.

Appleby, I. L., Klein, D. F., Sachar, E. J., & Levi, H. M. (1981). Biochemical indices of lactate-induced panic: A preliminary report. In D. F. Klein & J. Rabkin (Eds.), *Anxiety: New research and changing concepts* (pp. 411–423). New York: Raven Press.

Arbab, A. G., Bonn, J. A., & Hicks, D. C. (1971). Effect of propranolol on lactate induced phenomena in normal subjects. *British Journal of Pharmacology, 41,* 430.

Bonn, J. A., Harrison, J., & Rees, W. L. (1971). Lactate induced anxiety: Therapeutic application. *British Journal of Psychiatry, 119,* 468–471.

Boudoulas, H., King, B. D., & Wooley, C. F. (1984). Mitral valve prolapse: A marker for anxiety or an overlapping phenomenon? *Psychopathology, 17* (Suppl. 1), 98–106.

Boulenger, J. P., Uhde, T. W., Wolff, E. A. III, & Post, R. M. (1984). Increased sensitivity to caffeine in patients with panic disorders. *Archives of General Psychiatry, 41,* 1067–1071.

Buchthal, F., & Lennox, M. (1953). The EEG effect of metrazol and photic stimulation in 682 normal subjects. *Electroencephalography and Clinical Neurophysiology, 5,* 545–558.

Buss, A. H. (1962). Critique and notes: Two anxiety factors in psychiatric patients. *Journal of Social Psychology, 65,* 426–427.

Cameron, O. G., Smith, C. B., Hollingsworth, P. J., Nesse, R. M., & Curtis, G. C. (1984). Platelet α_2-adrenergic receptor binding and plasma catecholamines. *Archives of General Psychiatry, 41,* 1144–1148.

Cannon, W. (1929). *Bodily changes in pain, hunger, fear and rage.* New York: Appleton Century Croft.

Carr, D. B., Sheehan, D. V., Surman, O. S., Spiro, T. E., Greenblatt, D. J., Heninger, G. R., Jones, K. J., Levine, P. H., & Watkins, W. D. (1986). Neuroendocrine correlates of lactate-induced anxiety and their response to chronic alprazolam therapy. *American Journal of Psychiatry, 143:* 483–494.

Charney, D. S., Galloway, M. P., & Heninger, G. R. (1984b). The effects of caffeine on plasma MHPG, subjective anxiety, autonomic symptoms and blood pressure in healthy humans. *Life Sciences, 35,* 135–144.

Charney, D. S., & Heninger, G. R. (1985a). Noradrenergic function and the mechanism of action of antianxiety treatment. I. The effect of long-term alprazolam treatment. *Archives of General Psychiatry, 42,* 458–467.

Charney, D. S., & Heninger, G. R. (1985b). Noradrenergic function and the mechanism of action of antianxiety treatment. II. The effect of long-term imipramine treatment. *Archives of General Psychiatry, 42,* 473–481.

Charney, D. S., Heninger, G. R., & Breier, A. (1984a). Noradrenergic function in panic anxiety. *Archives of General Psychiatry, 41,* 751–763.

Charney, D. S., Heninger, G. R., & Jatlow, P. I. (1985). Increased anxiogenic effects of caffeine in panic disorders. *Archives of General Psychiatry, 42,* 232–243.

Charney, D. S., Heninger, G. R., & Redmond, D. E. (1983). Yohimbine induced anxiety and increased noradrenergic function in humans: Effects of diazepam and clonidine. *Life Sciences, 33,* 19–29.

Charney, D. S., & Redmond, D. E., Jr. (1983). Neurobiological mechanisms in human anxiety. Evidence supporting central noradrenergic hyperactivity. *Neuropharmacology, 22*, 1531–1536.

Cohen, M., & White, P. (1950). Life situations, emotions, and neurocirculatory asthenia (anxiety neurosis, neurasthenia, effort syndrome). *Proceedings Association for Research in Nervous and Mental Disease, 29*, 832–869.

Costa, E., & Guidotti, A. (1979). Molecular mechanisms in the receptor action of benzodiazepines. *Annual Review of Pharmacology and Toxicology, 19*, 531–545.

Crawley, J. N., Ninan, P. T., Pickar, D., Chrousos, G. P., Linnoila, M., Skolnick, P., & Paul, S. M. (1985). Neuropharmacological antagonism of the β-carboline-induced "anxiety" response in rhesus monkeys. *The Journal of Neuroscience, 5*, 477–485.

Curtis, G., Buxton, M., Lippman, D., Nesse, R., & Wright, J. (1976). Flooding "in vivo" during the circadian phase of minimal cortisol secretion: Anxiety and therapeutic success without adrenal cortical activation. *Biological Psychiatry, 11*, 101–107.

Curtis, G. C., Nesse, R., Buxton, M., & Lippman, D. (1979). Plasma growth hormone: Effect of anxiety during flooding in vivo. *American Journal of Psychiatry, 136*, 410–414.

Curtis, G. C., & Thyer, B. (1983). Fainting on exposure to phobic stimuli. *American Journal of Psychiatry, 140*, 771–774.

De Freitas, B., & Schwartz, G. (1979). Effects of caffeine in chronic psychiatric patients. *American Journal of Psychiatry, 136*, 1337–1338.

Dews, P. B. (1984). Behavioral effects of caffeine, In P. B. Dews (Ed.), *Caffeine: Perspectives from recent research* (pp. 86–103). Berlin, New York: Springer-Verlag.

Dorow, R., Horowski, R., Paschelke, G., Amin, M., & Braestrup, C. (1983). Severe anxiety induced by FG 7142, a β-carboline ligand for benzodiazepine receptors. *Lancet, II*, 98–99.

Drury, A. N. (1918–1920). The percentage of cabon dioxide in the alveolar air and the tolerance to accumulating carbon dioxide in cases of so-called "irritable heart" of soldiers. *Heart*, (London), *7*, 165–173.

Easton, D., & Sherman, D. G. (1976). Somatic anxiety attacks and propranolol. *Archives of Neurology (Chicago), 33*, 689–691.

Ekman, P., Levenson, R. W., & Friesen, W. Y. (1983). Autonomic nervous system activity distinguishes among emotions. *Science, 221*, 1208–1210.

Elam, M., Yoa, J., Thoren, P., & Svensson, T. H. (1981). Hypercapnia and hypoxia: Chemoreceptor-mediated control of locus ceruleus neurons and splanchnic, sympathetic nerves. *Brain Research, 222*, 373–381.

Ferrero, P., Guidotti, A., Conti-Tronconi, B., & Costa, E. (1984). A brain octadecaneuropeptide generated by tryptic digestion of DBI functions as a proconflict ligand of benzodiazepine recognition sites. *Neuropharmacology, 23*, 1359–1362.

Fink, M., Taylor, M. A., & Volavka, J. (1970). Anxiety precipitated by lactate. *New England Journal of Medicine, 281*, 1129.

Freedman, R. R., Ianni, P., Ettedgui, E., & Puthezhath, N. (1985). Ambulatory monitoring of panic disorder. *Archives of General Psychiatry, 42*, 244–248.

Frohlich, E. O., Tarazi, R. C., & Dustan, H. P. (1969). Hyperdynamic beta-adrenergic circulatory state. *Archives of Internal Medicine, 123*, 1–7.

Fyer, A. J., Liebowtz, M. R., Gorman, J. M., Davies, S. O., & Klein, D. F. (1985). Lactate vulnerability of remitted panic patients. *Psychiatry Research, 14*, 143–148.

Garfield, S. L., Gershon, S., Sletten, I., Sundland, D. M., & Ballou, S. (1967). Chemically induced anxiety. *International Journal of Neuropsychiatry, 6*, 426–433.

Gershon, S., & Lang, W. J. (1962). A psychopharmacological study of some indole alkaloids. *Archives of International Pharmacodynamics, 135*, 31–56.

Gilbert, R. M. (1981). Caffeine: Overview and anthology. In S. A. Miller (Ed.), *Nutrition and behavior* (pp. 145–166). Philadelphia: Franklin Institute Press.

Gilliland, K., & Andress, D. (1981). Ad lib caffeine consumption, symptoms of caffeinism and academic performance. *American Journal of Psychiatry, 138*, 512–514.

Gorman, J. M., Askanazi, J., Liebowitz, M. R., Fyer, A. J., Stein, J., Kinney, J. M., & Klein, D. F. (1984). Response to hyperventilation in a group of patients with panic disorder. *American Journal of Psychiatry, 141*, 857–861.

Gorman, J. M., Fyer, A. F., Gliklich, J., King, D., & Klein, D. F. (1981). Effect of sodium lactate on patients with panic disorder and mitral valve prolapse. *American Journal of Psychiatry, 138*, 247–249.

Gorman, J., Fyer, M. R., Goetz, R., Askanazi, J., Martinez, J., Liebowitz, M. R., Fyer, A. J., Kinney, J., & Klein, D. F. (1985). *Ventilatory physiology of patients with panic disorder.* Unpublished manuscript.

Gorman, J. M., Levy, G. F., Liebowitz, M. R., McGrath, P., Appleby, I. L., Dillon, D. J., Davies, S. O., & Klein, D. F. (1983). Effect of acute α-adrenergic blockade on lactate-induced panic. *Archives of General Psychiatry, 40,* 1079–1084.

Grant, S. J., Huang, Y. H., & Redmond, D. E., Jr. (1980). Benzodiazepines attenuate single unit activity in the locus coeruleus. *Life Sciences, 27,* 2231–2236.

Greden, J. F. (1974). Anxiety or caffeinism: A diagnostic dilemna. *American Journal of Psychiatry, 131,* 1089–1092.

Greden, J. F. Fontaine, P., Lubetsky, M., & Chamberlin, K. (1978). Anxiety and depression associated with caffeinism among psychiatric inpatients. *American Journal of Psychiatry, 135,* 963–966.

Griez, E. (1984). Experimental models of anxiety — problems and perspectives. *Acta Psychiatrica Belgica, 84,* 511–532.

Griez, E., & Van Den Hout, M. A. (1982). Effects of carbon dioxide–oxygen inhalations on subjective anxiety and some neurovegetative parameters. *Journal of Behavioral Therapy and Experimental Psychiatry, 13,* 27–32.

Griez, E., & Van Den Hout, M. A. (1983a). Carbon dioxide and anxiety: Cardiovascular effects of a single inhalation. *Journal of Behavioral Therapy and Experimental Psychiatry, 14,* 297–304.

Griez, E., & Van Den Hout, M. A. (1983b). Treatment of phobophobia by exposure to CO_2 induced anxiety symptoms. *Journal of Nervous and Mental Disease, 171,* 506–508.

Grosz, H. J., & Farmer, B. B. (1972). Pitts and McClure's lactate-anxiety study revisited. *British Journal of Psychiatry, 120,* 415–418.

Guidotti, A., Forchetti, C. M., Corda, M. G., Konkel, D., Bennett, C. D., & Costa, E. (1983). Isolation, characterization, and purification to homogeneity of an endogenous polypeptide with agonistic action on benzodiazepine receptors. *Proceedings of the National Academy of Sciences of the United States of America, 80,* 3531–3535.

Guttmacher, L. B., Murphy, D. L., & Insel, T. R. (1983). Pharmacologic models of anxiety. *Comprehensive Psychiatry, 24,* 312–326.

Haslam, M. T. (1974). The relationship between the effect of lactate infusion on anxiety states, and their amelioration by carbon dioxide inhalation. *British Journal of Psychiatry, 125,* 88–90.

Henauer, S. A., Gillespie, H. K., & Hollister, L. E. (1983). Yohimbine and the model anxiety state. *Journal of Clinical Psychiatry, 45,* 512–515.

Holmberg, G., & Gershon S. (1961). Autonomic and psychic effects of yohimbine hydrochloride. *Psychopharmacologia, 2,* 93–106.

Ingram, C. G. (1962). Some pharmacologic actions of yohimbine and chlorpromazine in man. *Clinical Pharmacology and Therapeutics, 3,* 345–352.

Insel, T. R., Ninan, P. T., Aloi, J., Jimerson, D., Skolnick, P., & Paul, S. (1984). A benzodiazepine receptor-mediated model of anxiety. Studies in non-human primates and clinical implications. *Archives of General Psychiatry, 41,* 741–750.

Kelly, D., Mitchell-Heggs, N., & Sherman, D. (1971). Anxiety and the effects of sodium lactate assessed clinically and physiologically. *British Journal of Psychiatry, 119,* 129-141.

Klein, D. F., Gorman, J. M., Liebowtz, M. R., & Fyer, A. J. (1985, December). Mechanism of action of lactate induced panic anxiety. Abstact presented at American College of Neuropsychopharmacology XXIV, Maine, Dec. 1985.

Knott, V, Chaudhry R., & Lapierre, Y. D. (1981). Panic induced by sodium lactate: Electrophysiological correlates. *Progress in Neuro-Psychopharmacology and Biological Psychiatry, 5,* 511–514.

Ko, G. N., Elsworth, J. D., Roth, R. H., Rifkin, B. G., Leigh, H., & Redmond, D. E. (1983). Panic-induced elevation of plasma MHPG levels in phobic-anxious patients. *Archives of General Psychiatry, 40,* 425–430.

Lader, M., & Mathews, A. (1970). Physiological changes during spontaneous panic attacks. *Journal of Psychosomatic Research, 14,* 377–382.

Lal, H., & Emmett-Oglesby, M. W. (1983). Behavioral analogues of anxiety. *Neuropharmacology, 22,* 1423–1441.

Lapierre, Y. D., Knott, V. J., Phil, D., & Gray, R. (1984). Psychophysiological correlates of sodium lactate. *Psychopharmacology Bulletin, 20,* 50–57.

Ley, R., & Walker, H. (1973). Effects of carbon dioxide-oxygen inhalation on subjective anxiety, heart rate and blood pressure. *Journal of Behavior Therapy and Experimental Psychiatry, 4,* 223–228.

Liebowitz, M. R., Fyer, A. J., Gorman, J. M., Dillon, D., Appleby, I. L., Levy, G., Anderson, S., Levitt, M., Palij, M., Davies, S. O., & Klein, D. F. (1984). Lactate provocation of panic attacks, I. Clinical and behavioral findings. *Archives of General Psychiatry, 41,* 764–770.

Liebowitz, M. R., Fyer, A. J., Gorman, J. M., Dillon, D., Davies, S. Stein, J. M., Cohen, B. S., & Klein, D. F. (1985a). Specificity of lactate infusions in social phobia versus panic disorders. *American Journal of Psychiatry, 142,* 947–950.

Liebowitz, M. R., Gorman, J. M., Fyer, A. J., Levitt, M., Dillon, D., Levy, G., Appleby, I. L., Anderson, S., Palij, M., Davies, S. O., & Klein, D. F. (1985b). Lactate Provocation of panic attacks: II. Biochemical and physiological findings. *Archives of General Psychiatry, 42,* 709–719.

Marañon, G. (1924). Contribution a l' étude de l' action émotive de l' adrenaline. *Revue Francaise Endocrinology, 2,* 301–325.

Minneman, K. P., Pittman, R. N., & Molinoff, P. B. (1981). β adrenergic receptor subtypes: Properties, distrubution, and regulation. *Annual Review of Neuroscience, 4,* 419–461.

Mohler, H., & Okada, T. (1977). Benzodiazepine receptor; Demonstration in the central nervous system. *Science, 198,* 849–851.

Mohler, H., & Richards, J. G. (1981). Agonist and antagonist in benzodiazepine receptors interaction "in vitro." *Nature, 294,* 763–765.

Marangos, P. J., & Insel, T. R., Montgomery, P. (1987). Brain adenosine receptors in maudsley reactive and non-reactive rats. Brain Research.

Moore, F. T., Kellaway, P., & Kagawa, N. (1954). Metrazol activation as a diagnostic adjunct in electroencephalography. *Neurology, 4,* 325–338.

Nesse, R. M., Cameron, O. G., Curtis, G. C., McCann, D. S., & Huber-Smith, M. J. (1984). Adrenergic function in patients with panic anxiety. *Archives of General Psychiarty, 41,* 771–776.

Nesse, R. M., Curris, G. C., & Brown, G. M. (1982). Phobic anxiety does not affect plasma levels of thyroid stimulatory hormone in man. *Psychoneuroendocrinology, 7,* 69–74.

Nesse, R. M., Curtis, G. C., Brown, G. M. & Rubin, R. T. (1980). Anxiety induced by flooding therapy for phobias does not elicit prolactin secretory response. *Psychosomatic Medicine, 42,* 25–31.

Ninan, P., Insel, T. R., Cohen, R. M., Skolnick, P., & Paul, S. M. (1982). A benzodiazepine receptor mediated model of anxiety. *Science, 218,* 1332–1334.

Oakley, N., & Jones, B. (1980). The proconvulsant and diazepam-reversing effects of ethyl-β-carboline-3-carboxylate. *European Jouranl of Pharmacology, 68,* 381–382.

Patel, J. B., & Malick, J. B. (1983). Neuropharmacological profile of an anxiolytic, In J. B. Malick, S. J. Enna, & H. Yamamura (Eds.), *Anxiolytics: Neurochemical, behavioral, and clinical perspectives* (pp. 173–188). New York: Raven Press.

Persson, A., Ehrin, E., Eriksson, L., Farde, L., Hedström, C. G., Litton, J. E., Mindus, P., & Sedvall, G. (1985). Imaging of [^{11}C]-labelled RO 15-1788 binding to benzodiazepine receptors in the human brain by positron emission tomography. *Journal of Psychiatric Research, 19,* 609–622.

Pitts, F. N., & McClure, J. N. (1967). Lactate metabolism in anxiety neurosis. *New England Journal of Medicine, 277,* 1329–1336.

Primavera, L. H., Simon, W., & Camiza, J. (1975). An investigation of personality and caffeine use. *British Journal of Addiction, 70,* 213–225.

Rainey, J. M., Ettedgui, E., Pohl, R. B., & Bridges, M. (1985). Effect of acute β-adrenergic blockade on lactate-induced panic. *Archives of General Psychiarty, 42,* 104–105.

Rainey, J. M., Frohman, C. E., Freedman, R. R., Pohl, R. B., Ettedgui, E., & Williams, M. (1984a). Specificity of lactate infusion as a model of anxiety. *Psychopharmacology Bulletin, 20,* 45–49.

Rainey, J. M., Pohl, R. B., Williams, M., Knotter, E., Freedman, R. R., & Ettedgui, E. (1984b). A comparison of lactate and isoproterenol anxiety states. *Psychopathology, 17* (Suppl. 1), 74–82.

Rainey, M., Jr., Ettedgui, E., Pohl, B., Balon, R., Weinberg, P., Yelonek, S., & Berchou, R. (1984c). The β-receptor: Isoproterenol anxiety states. *Psychopathology, 17,* (Suppl. 3), 40–51

Rapoport, J. L., Berg, C. J., Ismond, D. R., Zahn, T. P., & Neims, A. (1984). Behavioral effects of caffeine in children. *Archives of General Psychiatry, 41,* 1073–1079.

Redmond, D. E., Jr, (1979). New and old evidence for the involvement of a brain norepinephrine system in anxiety. In W. E. Fann (Ed.), *The phenomenology and treatment of anxiety* (pp. 153–203). New York: Spectrum Press.

Redmond, D. E., Jr., & Huang, Y. H. (1979). New evidence for locus coeruleus–norepinephrine connection with anxiety. *Life Sciences, 25,* 2149–2162.

Reiman, E. M., Raichle, M. E., Butler, F. K., Herscovitch, P., & Robins, E. (1984). A focal brain abnormality in panic disorder, a severe form of anxiety, *Nature, 310,* 683–685.

Rifkin, A., Klein, D. F., Dillon D., & Levitt, M. (1981). Blockade by imipramine or desipramine of panic induced by sodium lactate. *American Journal of Psychiatry, 138,* 676–677.

Rodin, E. (1958). Metrazol tolerance in a "normal" volunteer population. An investigation of the potential significance of abnormal findings. *Electroencephalography and Clinical Neurophysiology, 10,* 433–446.

Sabato, U. C., Novas, M. L., Lowenstein, P., Ziehere, L. M., & De Robertis, E. (1981). Action of 6-hydroxydopamine on benzodiazepine receptors in rat cerebral cortex. *European Journal of Pharmacology, 73,* 381–382.

Schachter, S., & Singer, J. E. (1962). Cognitive, social, and physiological determinants of emotional state. *Psychological Review, 69,* 379–399.

Sheehan, D. V., Carr, D. B., Fishman, S, M., Walsh, M. M., & Peltier-Saxe, D. (1985). Lactate infusion in anxiety research: Its evolution and practice. *Journal of Clinical Psychiatry, 46,* 158–165.

Skolnick, P., & Paul, S. M. (1982). Molecular pharmacology of the benzodiazepines. *International Review of Neurobiology, 23,* 103–140.

Slater, S. L., & Leavy, A. (1966). The effects of inhaling a 35% CO_2–65% O_2 mixture upon anxiety level in neurotic patients. *Behaviour Research Therapy, 4,* 309–316.

Snyder, S. H. (1985). Adenosine as a neuromodulator. *Annual Review of Neuroscience, 8,* 103–124.

Spindel, E. R., Wartmen, R. J., McCall, A., Carr, D. B., Conlay, L., Griffith, L, & Arnold, M. A. (1984). Neuroendocrine effects of caffeine in normal subjects. *Clinical Pharmacology and Therapeutics, 36,* 402–407.

Squires, R. F., & Braestrup, C. (1977). Benzodiazepine receptors in rat brain. *Nature, 266,* 732–734.

Squires, R. F., Saederup, E., Crawley, J. N., Skolnick, P., & Paul, S. M. (1984). Convulsant potencies of tetrazoles are highly correlated with actions on GABA/ benzodiazapine/picrotoxin receptor complexes in brain. *Life Sciences, 35,* 1439–1444.

Tallman, J. F., Paul, S. M., Skolnick, P., & Gallager, D. W. (1980) Receptors for the age of anxiety: Pharmacology of the benzodiazepines. *Science, 207,* 274–281.

Uhde, T. W., Boulenger, J. P., Jimerson, D. C., & Post, R. M. (1984). Caffeine: relationship to human anxiety, plasma MHPG, and Cortisol. In J. Rapoport (Ed.), *Caffeine and behavior: Relation to psychopathology and underlying mechanisms. Psychopharmacology Bulletin, 20,* 426–430.

Uhde, T., Siever, L., Post, R. Jimerson, D., Boulenger, J. P., & Buchsbaum, M. (1982). The relationship of plasma-free MHPG to anxiety and psychophysical pain in normal volunteers. *Psychopharmacology Bulletin, 18,* 129–132.

Unnerstall, J. R., Kopajtic, T. A., & Kuhar, M. J. (1984). Distribution of α_2 agonist binding sites in the rat and human central nervous system: Analysis of some functional, anatomic correlates of the pharmacologic effects of clonidine and related adrenergic agents. *Brain Research Reviews, 7,* 69–101.

Van Den Hout, M. A., & Griez, E. (1984). Panic symptoms after inhalation of carbon dioxide. *British Journal of Psychiatry, 144,* 503–507.

Veleber, D. M., & Templer, D. I. (1984). Effects of caffeine on anxiety and depression. *Journal of Abnormal Psychology, 93,* 120–122.

Winstead, D. K. (1976). Coffee consumption among psychiatric inpatients. *American Journal of Psychiatry, 133,* 1447–1450.

Wolpe, J. (1958). *Psychotherapy by reciprocal inhibition.* Stanford, CA: Stanford University Press.

Woods, S. W., Charney, D. S., McPherson, C. A., Gradman, A. H., & Heninger, G. R. (1987). Situational panic attacks: Behavioral, physiologic, and biochemical characterization. *Archives of General Psychiatry,* 44: 365–375.

Woods, S. W., Charney, D. S., Lake, J., Goodman, W. K., Redmond, D. E., Jr., & Heninger, G. R. (1986). Carbon dioxide sensitivity in panic anxiety. Ventilatory and anxiogenic response to CO_2 in healthy subjects and panic anxiety patients before and after alprazolam treatment. *Archives of General Psychiatry,* 43; 900–909.

Young, W. S., & Kuhar, M. J. (1979). Noradrenergic α_1 and α_2 receptors: Autoradiographic visualization. *European Journal of Pharmacology, 59,* 317-319.

Young, W. S., & Kuhar, M. J. (1980). Noradrenergic α and α_2 receptors: Light microscopic autoradiographic localization. Presented at the meeting of the National Academy of Sciences of the United States of America, Philadelphia, PA.

Zohar, J., Insel, T. R., Foa, E. B., Steketee, G., Berman, K. F., Weinberger, D. R., Kozak, M., & Cohen, R. M. (in press). Physiological and psychological changes during *in vivo* exposure and imaginal flooding of obsessive compulsive disorder patients. *Proceedings of the IV World Congress of Biological Psychiatry.* Philadelphia.

CHAPTER 12

Psychophysiology

James F. Papillo, Patrick M. Murphy and Jack M. Gorman

Most contemporary behavioral scientists would agree that the concept of anxiety can best be defined as a multidimensional phenomenon comprised of physiological, psychological, and behavioral response components. As a result of this view, a wide variety of self-report, central and autonomic nervous system, and behavioral measures have been developed and utilized for assessing anxiety in human subjects (Bellack & Lomardo, 1985; Bernstein & Nietzel, 1974; Borkovec, Weerts, & Bernstein, 1977; Paul & Bernstein, 1973). However, the repeated finding of small magnitude and statistically nonsignificant correlations among anxiety measures (Lang 1968, 1971, 1977) has prompted many investigators to question the validity of the multidimensional view of anxiety. The terms *discordance, desynchrony* (Rachman & Hodgeson, 1974), *asynchrony* (Lick & Katkin, 1976) and *dissociation* (Schwartz, 1978) have been widely used in the recent literature to denote the low magnitude and sometimes paradoxical nature of the correlations observed among the various measures of anxiety.

Several theories for explaining the lack of covariation among anxiety measures have recently been proposed. A number of investigators attribute the phenomenon of discordance to the partial independence or "imperfect coupling" of the three response systems (Lang, Rice, & Sternbach, 1972; Rachman & Hodgson, 1974). According to this view, each response system may react more or less independently of the others both in the expression of anxiety and in response to therapeutic treatment (Hugdahl, 1981). A contrasting interpretation of discordance comes from Schwartz's "biopsychosocial" model of emotion. In emphasizing the importance of the interaction among response systems for both the experience and expression of emotion, Schwartz (1978) argues that the lack of concordance among anxiety measures may result primarily from a failure to assess patterns of responding within and between systems.

Various sources of measurement error and related methodological deficiencies have also been implicated as major factors contributing to the low concordance among anxiety measures. For example, the persistent use of categorical scales for assessing cognitive or affective reactions provide a relatively crude (i.e., ordinal) level of measurement, at best, and thus can provide only qualitative information regarding the psychological dimension of anxiety. The lack of consensus among investigators as to the definition and identification of relevant physiological, psychological, and behavioral parameters of anxiety has also been cited as an important factor contributing to discordance. Issues related to the limited reliability and validity of measures used to assess specific responses within response systems also probably contribute to low concordance.

While the data are clear in indicating that anxiety is a multidimensional phenomenon, it is becoming equally clear that anxiety reactions involve different forms of responding not only in different systems, but in different individuals and different situations as well. It is therefore imperative that individual difference factors and situational factors be evaluated. With the recent advent of sophisticated mathematical and statistical techniques, it is now becoming possible to tease out patterns of responses among the dimensions of anxiety from statistically noisy data.

While it seems reasonable to speculate that poor measurement is not the only explanation for the low degree of correspondence among measures of anxiety, what makes the measurement issue particularly important is that as a consequence of poor measurement, it is difficult to determine whether discordance results from weaknesses in our theoretical formulations or deficiencies in our measures of anxiety. In order for the researcher or clinician to achieve the goal of specifying relationships among the different dimensions of anxiety, the ability to accurately and reliably measure each of them must first be demonstrated.

Significant advances in our ability to assess the psychological and behavioral dimensions of anxiety have recently been achieved and are discussed elsewhere in this volume. The goal of the present chapter is to provide an overview of past and recent developments in the field of psychophysiology as they relate to the measurement and analysis of the physiological dimension of anxiety. Specifically, a number of important and theoretical and practical issues as they relate to the collection, analysis, and interpretation of the most widely employed psychophysiological measures of anxiety, that is, cardiovascular, respiratory, and electrodermal activity will be discussed. Throughout the chapter, we will attempt to underscore the importance of adopting a biological perspective in analyzing and interpreting physiological measures of anxiety. A selective review of the experimental literature pertaining to the psychophysiological assessment of normal as well as pathological anxiety states will also be presented. It is suggested that the issues considered may serve to enhance both the reliability and validity of psychophysiological assessments of the clinical anxiety disorders.

CARDIOVASCULAR FUNCTION

Heart Activity

Measurement of the electrical activity associated with contraction of cardiac muscle (i.e., the electrocardiogram or ECG) have served as the basis for the most widely recorded physiological variable in both laboratory and clinical assessment of the emotions. Specifically, the frequency, or rate, at which the heart beats over time has been extensively employed as a dependent measure in the study of emotions such as anger (Ax, 1953), depression (Dawson, Schell, & Catania, 1977), anxiety (Borkovec et al., 1976; Van Egeren, Feather, & Hein, 1971; Mathews & Lader, 1971), and fear (Ax, 1953; Lang, Melmead, & Hart, 1970).

Because the human body is a good volume conductor, the relatively large bioelectric signal associated with myocardial contraction can be reliably and continuously recorded by the placement of electrodes at the body's surface. Other cardiovascular measures that are time-locked to the heartbeat, such a finger pulse volume or arterial blood pressure oscillations, have also been used for obtaining measures of heartbeat frequency. However, in some pathological vascular conditions, the rates obtained in this manner may be in error.

Two methods of reporting the frequency of heartbeats over time are heart rate and heart period. Heart rate (HR) is expressed in terms of the number of heartbeats per unit of time, typically 1 minute, and can be obtained by simply counting the number of beats (R-waves) during the time period of interest. More often, however, an electronic device known as a cardiotachometer is used for obtaining a continuous beat-by-beat measure of heart rate. This is accomplished by the circuitry of the cardiotachometer which, in response to detection of R-waves on the ECG signal, electronically calculates the reciprocal of the time interval between successive heart cycles. The voltage output of this device is calibrated in terms of beats per minute (bpm) and displayed on a polygraph and/or sampled by computer.

The second method of reporting heartbeat data, heart period (HP), is based directly on the time interval (milliseconds) between successive heartbeats. Several devices for recording and evaluating HP have been developed (Brener, 1980; Shimizu, 1977).

Much debate has ensued concerning the appropriate unit of measure for expressing heartbeat frequency. While both HR and HP measures share a common base (that is, time) conversion of the data from one unit of measure to another may cause statistical problems due to the nonlinear relationship between them (Jennings, Stringfellow, & Graham, 1974; Khachaturian, Kerr, Kruger, & Schachter, 1972).

As a result, it is possible to reach different conclusions depending on which unit of measure is employed (Montgomery, 1977). It has also been shown that whether HR or HP is computed on the basis of real time (e.g., the number of beats in 30 seconds) or "biological time" (e.g., the amount of time elapsed during 30 beats) can effect the analysis and interpretation of heart rate data. Graham (1979) has indicated that the appropriate measure of heart rate can vary depending on whether the analysis is based on individual or group data, if adults or infants are used as subjects, and if raw scores or change scores serve as the primary data. Hence, the exact method of measuring heart rate should be carefully chosen on a study-by-study basis depending on the subjects to be studied and the specific research question being examined.

Another consideration of extreme importance to investigators, particularly in the study of clinical anxiety disorders, concerns the choice of an appropriate baseline for studying physiological activity. Merely being in a laboratory environment or wearing an ambulatory monitor in a natural setting can have a profound effect on functions mediated by the autonomic nervous system. Analysis of physiological measures obtained without first obtaining an adequate baseline may result in incorrect interpretation of the data and the inability to make meaningful comparisons of data collected within and between research facilities.

Wilder (1957) was the first to formalize the Law of Initial Values (LIV) which states that both the magnitude and, in extreme cases, the direction of elicited physiological responses is partly determined by the prestimulus, or baseline level of activity. Specifically, the LIV states that with respect to response magnitude, there is an inverse relationship between prestimulus levels and the degree of change brought about by the stimulus. Simply stated, if the tonic prestimulus level of activity is low, then larger phasic responses will be observed. Conversely, with higher prestimulus levels, smaller responses will be observed. At extremely high or low prestimulus levels of activity, paradoxical responses may be observed. Several measures of cardiovascular activity including heart rate (Hord, Johnson, & Lubin, 1964), vasomotor activity (Lovallo & Zeiner, 1975), and blood pressure (Lacey & Lacey, 1962) have been shown to be lawfully related to prestimulus levels as predicted by the LIV. These observations further emphasize the importance of utilizing adequate baseline measurement procedures.

A variety of statistical techniques for correcting the variation in baseline levels observed among subjects and for neutralizing the effects of the LIV have been developed (Benjamin, 1967; Cronbach & Furby, 1970; Jennings & Wood, 1976; Lacey & Lacey, 1962).

Recently, Hastrup (1986) surveyed the literature and found a lack of consensus among investigators as to the length of baseline time reported. In addition, a significant negative correlation between the length of baseline recording period used and the mean heart rate levels obtained was found. On the basis of this survey, it was suggested that a 15-minute pre-assessment baseline period should be employed. It was further suggested that baseline period duration be individualized whenever feasible. Obrist (1981) has recently provided evidence indicating that baseline measures obtained during a period of relaxation on a day when no laboratory task is scheduled may provide a more appropriate assessment of baseline heart rate level, especially in psysiologically reactive individuals. Additional guidelines for obtaining adequate baseline measures of physiological activity may be found in Meyers and Craighead (1978).

Several excellent overviews of the technical and methodological considerations related to the measurement and evaluation of cardiac function are available (Geddes & Baker, 1968; Siddle, Turpin, Spinks, & Stevenson, 1980). Specific considerations related to the assessment of heart rate variability (Heslegrave, Ogilivie, & Furedy, 1979; Varni, Clarke, & Giddon, 1971), the handling of individual differences in the range of heart rate response (Lykken, 1972), and the use of sophisticated statistical techniques such as trend analysis (Wilson, 1974), time series analysis, and spectral analysis (Sayers, 1973) and a variety of multivariate procedures for evaluating cardiac measures have received much attention in the recent literature. Recently, recommended standards and guidelines for the collection, quantification, and analysis of heart rate data have been published (Jennings et al., 1981).

The study of cardiovascular function in general, and of heart rate in particular, has dominated psychophysiological investigations in the anxiety disorders (Borkovec, et al., 1977; Martin & Stroufe, 1970; Mathews, 1971; Van Egeren et al., 1971; Freedman, Ianni, Ettedgui, Pohl, & Rainey 1984). Many studies have utilized heart rate measures for obtaining an objective index of anxiety states. In most studies, variations in heart rate are interpreted as reflecting the state of autonomic nervous system tone, leading to the assumption that a fast heart rate in an anxious individual equates with heightened adrenergic action. Some points related to these assumptions need to be considered.

According to activation theory, global unidirectional changes in physiological activity accompany varying states of emotional arousal (Duffy, 1962; Lindsley, 1951; Malmo, 1959). Lacey (1967) observed, however, that while some behavioral manipulations, such as mental arithmetic, produce the classic pattern of physiological arousal (e.g., increases in both HR and electrodermal activity), other manipulations, such as those involving perceptual processing, produce "directionally fractionated" response patterns (simultaneous decrease in heart rate and increase in electrodermal activity). The phenomenon of directional fractionation cannot be adequately explained by arousal theory.

Lacey (1950) was also one of the first investigators to systematically explore and verify the large individual differences in the patterning of physiological reactivity elicited by stressful conditions. Two basic principles have emerged from this work: *stimulus-response specificity* and *individual-response stereotypy*. The concept of stimulus-response specificity refers to the observation that an individual's pattern of physiological response will vary as a function of the stimulus conditions but will tend to remain stable with repeated replications of the same stimulus configuration. The formulation of this concept provided the impetus for much of the early work attempting to differentiate among the emotions based on psychophysiological measures (Ax, 1953; Engel, 1960, 1972). The concept of individual-response stereotypy, on the other hand, refers to the observation that individuals tend to respond in a stereotypical, or idiosyncratic fashion to a wide variety of stimulus situations both in terms of the patterning of physiological activity ("response stereotypy") and in terms of a single response system that responds maximally ("response specificity"). Engel (1960) and Engel and Bickford (1961) demonstrated the coexistence of both stimulus-response specificity and individual-response stereotypy intraindividually. Taken together, these findings indicate that observed physiological responses are determined by factors related to both the stimulus conditions and the individual. These findings also underscore the importance of obtaining measures from several autonomic nervous system functions for evaluating psychophysiological relationships.

In evaluating observed variation of heart rate in response to anxiety provoking stimuli, it is important to be cognizant of the multiple factors that continuously influence cardiac activity. In particular, the investigator must bear in mind that the behavior of the heart, in addition to being controled by intrinsic autoregulatory mechanisms, is also influenced by complex interactions with peripheral hemodynamic and central nervous system factors. It is through these interactions that the heart serves its primary function: to assist in maintaining metabolic homeostasis within the organism through adequate perfusion of the tissues with blood.

Obrist and his co-workers (Obrist, 1981; Obrist, Webb & Sutterer, 1969; Obrist, Webb, Sutterer, & Howard, 1970; Obrist, Howard, Lawler, Galosy, Meyers, & Gaebelein, 1974) have provided strong empirical evidence indicating that under normal conditions, heart rate and somatomotor activity are tightly coupled. Simply stated, an increase in somatomotor activity, such as during exercise, is associated with an increase in heart rate. The increase in heart rate serves functionally to supply the additional oxygen and nutrients (i.e., blood flow) required by the working muscles of the active organism. Inhibition of somatomotor activity, such as occurs when going from exercise to rest, reduced metabolic requirements and is therefore accompanied by a reduction in heart rate. The covariation of heart rate and somatomotor activity can be seen even during periods of quiet rest when minimal variations in metabolic requirements occur. Several lines of evidence indicate that the integration of somatomotor and cardiac activities takes place within the central nervous system (Obrist, 1981).

Obrist and his colleagues have, in addition, sought to delineate the neurogenic mechanisms underlying cardiac-somatic coupling. In a series of elegantly designed experiments involving both animals and human subjects, they demonstrated that the momentary heart rate changes reliably observed during many laboratory procedures, such as aversive classical conditioning (phasic HR increases) and signaled reaction time tasks (phasic HR decreases), are mediated by the parasympathetic branch of the autonomic nervous system. By administering pharmacologic agents that block either vagal influences (atropine) or beta-adrenergic influences (propranolol hydrochloride) on the heart during such tasks, they were able to empirically verify the role of the vagal innervations to the heart in "linking" cardiac and somatic activity (Obrist, Lawler, Howard, Smithson, Martin, & Manning, 1974; Obrist et al., 1969; Obrist et al., 1970).

A particularly relevant aspect of this research for the study of anxiety disorders concerns the finding that under certain stressful conditions, having both motivational and emotional significance for subjects, an uncoupling of cardiac and somatic activity can be observed. For example, in an unsignaled reaction time task, where subjects are threatened with shock for slow response time, increases in heart rate that are in excess of metabolic requirements have been consistently demonstrated. Futhermore, such metabolically excessive heart rate increases have been shown to be mediated by an increased beta-adrenergic tone. It seems reasonable to speculate that some portion of heart rate increase determined to be metabolically excessive may represent an "anxiety component." This is certainly an interesting research path to pursue.

In view of the complex processes involved in the regulation of heart activity, it is suggested that inquiries into the relationship between cardiac function and clinical anxiety states should be designed with the following points in mind.

First, there is virtually no beta adrenergic stimulation to the heart at rest. Theoretically, the administration of beta adrenergic blocking drugs to a subject in a completely nonanxious state, at absolute rest, should have no effect on either the rate or force of cardiac contraction. Vagal stimulation to the heart, on the other hand, remains constant, even at rest. Most scientists agree that respiratory sinus arrythmia — the normal fluctuation in heart rate that occurs in synchrony with inspiration (HR acceleration) and expiration (HR deceleration) — depends almost entirely on intact vagal tone to the heart.

While there are probably no alpha-adrenergic receptors located within the heart, the alpha-adrenergic system can have considerable influence over cardiac function. First, beta receptors in the myocardium appear to be far more sensitive to norepinephrine than are other beta-adrenergic receptors. Most peripheral norepinephrine is generated from the synapses of alpha-adrenergic nerves on peripheral vessels. Second, the influence of alpha-adrenergic stimulation on the caliber of peripheral vessels affects cardiac function enormously through alteration in arterial pressure (i.e., afterload) and venous return to the right heart (i.e., preload).

Finally, cardiac function can be altered through complicated interactions between peripheral and central nervous system influences. Animal studies have elegantly demonstrated, for example, that stimulation of certain areas of the brain immediately produces ventricular premature contractions. Patients with diabetic peripheral neuropathy lose vagal tone to the heart and consequently demonstrate drastically reduced respiratory sinus arrythmia. Stimulation of the pontine nonadrenergic center of the brain, the locus ceruleus, increases heart rate in monkeys, but administration of noradrenalin peripherally increases blood pressure, and, thus, produces a reflexive decrease in heart rate.

Against this backdrop of theoretical considerations, the repeated finding that anxious individuals have higher resting heart rates than normals cannot be taken to mean that they are adrenergically stimulated.

White and Gilden (1937) were among the first to observe that anxious patients have higher heart rates than normal subjects. Similarly, Kelly and Walter (1968) found the resting heart rates of 41 patients with chronic anxiety state to be 97 bpm compared to 74 bpm for a group of 60 normal subjects. Several other investigators have reported tachycardia associated with anxiety (Lader & Wing, 1966).

Liebowitz et al. (1985) have recently demonstrated that patients diagnosed as having panic disorder display higher resting levels of heart rate prior to sodium lactate infusion when compared to normal controls. Furthermore, patients who go on to have a panic attack during the infusion have higher resting heart rate levels than those panic disorder patients who do not experience a panic attack during the infusion. Liebowitz et al. (1985) interpreted this finding as indicating that patients with panic disorder are in a chronic, hyperadrenergic state and that those patients who respond to sodium lactate infusion with panic attack must be adrenergically "primed" to panic.

Using 24-hour ambulatory monitoring of heart rate, Rother, Ticklenberg, and Doyle (1976) reported positive correlations throughout the day between levels of stress and increased heart rate. In addition, patients with neurocirculatory asthenia, a condition that overlaps various categories of anxiety disorder, were found to experience significantly more tachycardia and cardiac arrhythmias during routine activities and during sleep than did normals.

Freedman, Ianni, and Ettedgui (1985) and Taylor et al. (1986) have recently conducted ambulatory monitoring studies of panic disorder patients and agoraphobics. Both studies demonstrated that panic attacks occurring under conditions of naturalistic stress are associated with significant and "paroxysmal" increases in heart rate.

In the study reported by Freedman et al. (1985), panic disorder patients were compared to controls on measures of heart rate, finger temperature, and self-rated anxiety throughout the 24-hour period. During this period, eight spontaneous panic attacks were reported by patients. The results indicated no difference between patients and controls or between patients who experienced a panic attack and those who did not with respect to tonic physiological activity or self-rating of anxiety through the 24-hour period. However, substantial increases in heart rate and vasomotor activity were observed during panic attacks. The finding that mean heart rate levels for patients and controls did not differ significantly in the natural setting is in direct contradiction to the findings of elevated resting heart rates in laboratory studies of panic disorder patients in comparison to normal controls (Freedman, Ianni, & Ettedgui, 1985; Kelly, Mitchel-Heggs, & Sherman, 1971; Liebowitz et al., 1985). This suggests that higher resting heart rate levels observed in laboratory studies may result from greater levels of anticipatory anxiety in patients as compared to controls.

In the field study reported by Taylor et al. (1986), the heart rate and activity levels of 12 female patients meeting DSM-III criteria for panic disorder and 12 control subjects were monitored continuously for periods of up to 6 days. Thirty-three panic attacks occurred in patients during this time. During a substantial proportion of these panic attacks (58%), heart rates in excess of concurrent activity levels were observed. Interestingly, heart rate elevations in excess of activity levels were found to occur more often in patients than controls during non-panic periods as well. This finding suggests that the physiological mechanism(s) underlying cardiac-somatic coupling may be disregulated in patients with panic disorder.

As mentioned previously, the rather sudden and dramatic increase in heart rate observed during "in vivo" panic attacks has been documented by several investigators using lactate infusion induction of panic in the laboratory (Ehlers, Margraf, & Roth, 1986; Lapierre, Knott, & Gray, 1984; Liebowitz, et al., 1985). However, precise quantification of the heart rate response associated with lactate induced panic is complicated by two factors. First, infusion of sodium lactate produces a steady rise in heart rate during the course of the infusion in all subjects, both patients and normals alike. A second complication results from the fact that panic disorder patients have significantly higher resting heart rate levels as compared to normal controls.

This is particularly true for patients who go on to panic during the infusion. Thus, in evaluating the heart rate response associated with panic, it is important to correct both for differences in resting heart rate levels among subjects and for the ubiquitous rise in heart rate resulting from the infusion.

In our laboratory, the application of statistical procedures designed to correct for both factors has shown that lactate-induced panic is indeed associated with a precipitous rise in heart rate. It is important to note, however, that large magnitude elevations in heart rate were observed in association with the point of panic only when panic attacks occurred within the first 15 minutes of the 20-minute infusion period. Attacks reported during the last 5 minutes of infusion were associated with substantially smaller increases in heart rate. This latter observation may be the result of a ceiling effect. That is, in accordance with the Law of Initial Values, because lactate infusion raises heart rate over time, increases in heart rate associated with panic during the last 5 minutes of infusion may be severely dampened.

In addition to differences in heart rate level, evidence also indicates that patients with anxiety disorders differ from normals in the rate of habituation of heart rate responses to stressful or anxiety provoking stimuli (McGuinness, 1973). However, it remains unclear as to whether the slower habituation rates observed in anxious patients represent some specific biological abberation or, instead, reflect various cognitive factors (i.e., thoughts and feelings) associated with attending to novel stimuli.

The results of recent studies indicate that anxious subjects may be more aware of variations in heart activity than non-anxious subjects (Tyrer, 1986) Tyrer, Lee, and Alexander (1980), for example, have reported significant, positive correlations between subjective ratings of heart rate and actual heart rate during exposure to anxiety provoking films in groups of patients with anxiety neurosis and hypochondriasis. Patients with phobic anxiety (agoraphobia and social phobia), on the other hand, showed no ability to accurately perceive variations in their heart rate. Schandry (1980) found that subjects classified as good perceivers of spontaneous fluctuations in heart activity scored significantly higher on Spielberger's State-Trait anxiety inventory and on a test of emotional lability than did subjects classified as poor perceivers. In view of the putative role of the perception of autonomic nervous system activity for both the generation and experience of emotion, further research into the ability of patients with anxiety disorder to perceive autonomically mediated functions seems warranted. Recent advances in the development of methods and procedures for assessing visceral perception in human subjects (Pennebaker 1982) may be usefully employed in studies involving clinically anxious patients.

Few studies have been reported that explore the possible connection between anxious patients' frequent complaints of "palpitation" or "skipped beats" and actual dysrhythmias. The experiments of Lown and colleagues (Lown & DeSilva, 1978) have shown that psychological stress is capable of inducing ventricular arrhythmias in experimental animals and that the manifestation of these disturbances requires an intact vagal innervation. Shear and her colleagues (L. Shear, 1985, personal communication) have observed increases in both atrial and ventricular arrhythmias in patients with panic disorder. In our previous investigations of lactate-induced panic, we have failed to observe significant increases in either ventricular or atrial ectopic beats or in the incidence of serious arrhythmias in patients.

On the basis of the evidence accumulated, it seems fair to conclude that heart rate is faster in anxious patients and that panic attacks are accompanied by sudden and often dramatic elevations in heart rate. Anxious patients may also be differentiated on the basis of a slower rate of habituation to stressful stimuli, greater awareness of variations in cardiac activity, and greater beat-to-beat variability in heart rate. Stress can provoke arrythmias in experimental animals, but the relevance of this to humans with anxiety disorders is yet to be determined.

It may surprise many to recognize that although it has been known for 50 years that the hearts of anxious patients beat faster, the precise physiological and/or neurological mechanism underlying this phenomenon remains entirely obscure. One possibility is that anxious patients have increased adrenergic stimulation to the heart, perhaps mediated by increased catecholamine secretion. The results of two experiments dispute this idea. Gorman et al. (1983) has shown that intravenous propanolol, in sufficient dose to block beta adrenergic innervation to the heart, was not effective in supressing the surge of heart rate produced by lactate-induced panic. This indicates that the observed tachycardia is not secondary to beta adrenergic stimulation. Nesse, Cameron, Curtis, McCann, and Huber-Smith (1984), using bolus injections of isoproterenol, showed that beta adrenergic tone is actually subnormal in patients with panic disorder.

Could deficient vagal tone to the heart be responsible for the tachycardia observed during panic attacks? Little evidence exists on this point. In a pilot study conducted in our laboratory, we did not observe a decrease in heart rate variability during lactate-induced panic. This would tend to mitigate against reduced vagal tone as a contributing factor leading to the elevated heart rates observed in clinically anxious patients. These findings clearly indicate the need for further research directed toward delineating the neurogenic mechanism underlying cardiac activity in patients with anxiety disorders.

Detailed assessment of the complex mechanical and neurogenic influences on heart function using noninvasive recording techniques has received much recent attention from cardiovascular psychophysiologists (Schneiderman & Pickerins, 1986). Several measures of cardiac activity allow for the assessment of the relative contribution of sympathetic (i.e., beta-adrenergic) and parasympathetic influences on heart function. A few of these measures will be briefly described here.

Unlike the sinoatrial node and the atria areas of the heart receiving both parasympathetic and sympathetic innervations, the ventricles are innervated predominately by the sympathetic branch of the autonomic nervous system (Guyton, 1985). Therefore, a relatively pure index of beta-adrenergic influences on the heart may be obtained by measuring the strength of ventricular contraction (i.e., contractile force) during each heart cycle.

Several measures are available for assessing contractile force on a continuous (i.e., beat-to-beat) basis. One such measure can be obtained by determining the first derivative (i.e., slope) of the pulse pressure waveform recorded at the carotid artery (Obrist, Howard, Lawler, Sutterer, Smithson & Martin, 1972; Lawler & Obrist, 1974). However, because a highly sensitive transducer is required for detecting the pressure pulse at the carotid artery, this measure of contractility is especially susceptible to movement artifact (e.g., head turning and swallowing) and thus its reliability may be limited, particularly in studies of the emotions, such as anxiety.

An alternative, less obtrusive measure of contractile force is based on the amplitude of the T-wave of the ECG signal (Heslegrave & Furedy, 1979a). The ECG T-wave represents the electrical activity associated with repolarization of the left ventricle during each heart cycle and, depending on electrode placements, is usually recorded as a positive-going waveform. An increased beta-adrenergic outflow to the heart results in an increased synchrony in the firing of heart muscle which, in turn, results in either a diminution or, in some cases, an inversion of T-wave amplitude. While this measure of contractile force has the advantage of being directly obtainable from the ECG signal, thereby obviating the need for additional recording transducers, the small magnitude of the T-wave (20–30 mv) usually requires special amplification and processing techniques to reliably detect variations in the amplitude of this wave form.

While each of the above measures of contractility may be employed in a wide variety of laboratory situations, issues related to their reliability and validity for indexing beta-adrenergic influences on the heart have been raised (Furedy & Heslegrave, 1983; Heslegrave & Furedy, 1979b; Obrist, 1981; Obrist & Light, 1979). For example, it has been shown that under certain conditions parasympathetic activation and various cardiodynamic as well as hemodynamic factors (e.g., preload, afterload, and heart rate) can influence each of these measures independently of intraventricular contractility. Also, neither measure can be calibrated and therefore cannot be used for obtaining absolute indices of ventricular function.

The relative timing of the mechanical events associated with the systolic phase of the cardiac cycle has been shown to provide reliable information concerning the contractile state of the heart (Newlin & Levenson, 1979; Schneiderman, McCabe, & Hausman, 1984). The systolic time intervals (STIs) can be measured from simultaneous recordings of the ECG Q-wave, a peripheral pressure pulse wave, and the heart sound ("lub-dub") recorded from a highly sensitive transducer placed on the chest (i.e., phonocardiography). The three STIs of importance for assessing ventricular function include the preejection period

(PEP), left ventricular ejection time (LVET), and electrochemical systole (EMS). PEP has been shown to be highly correlated with invasive measurements of contractility. Determined noninvasively, PEP represents the duration of time from onset of the systolic phase of the heart cycle, as indicated by the Q-wave of the ECG signal, to the opening of the aortic valve (first heart-sound — "lub"). Thus, PEP is a measure of the duration of ventricular events prior to ejection of blood. Due to difficulties in obtaining reliable first heart-sound recordings, PEP is usually derived from the two other STIs: LVET and EMS. Electrochemical systole represents the total duration of the electrical and mechanical events associated with the systolic phase of the cardiac cycle. It is measured as the time from the Q-wave of the ECG signal (i.e., onset of ventricular contraction) to the occurrence of the second heart sound ("dub") produced by the closing of aortic valve (i.e., end of ventricular contraction). Left ventricular ejection time represents the period of time blood is being ejected from the left ventricle on each heart cycle and is determined as the time period commencing with detection of the first heart-sound (i.e., opening of the aortic valve) and ending with the detection of the second heart sound (i.e., closing of the aortic valve). However, because of the difficulty in reliably detecting the first heart-sound, LVET is normally determined from a peripherally recorded pulse wave obtained at either the carotid artery, finger, or pinna of the ear. Because the timing of both the opening and closing of the aortic valve is faithfully encoded on the pulse waveform (foot of the upswing and the dicrotic notch, respectively), LVET may be reliably determined as the difference between these two aspects of the recorded pulse waveform. The preejection period may then be expressed as the difference between LVET and EMS (i.e., PEP = EMS − LVET).

For indexing beta-adrenergic influences on the heart, PEP is generally preferred over other measures of contractility for the following reasons. First, there is substantial evidence showing that PEP is less influenced by intracardiac and/or vascular events and thus provides a purer measure of beta-adrenergic influences on the heart. Second, beacuse the STIs are time-based measures, each can be calibrated. Therefore, unlike other measures of contractile force, measures based on STIs allow meaningful comparisons to be made both between and within subjects concerning variations in heart function.

Two important measures of heart function, cardiac output (CO) and stroke volume (SV), have been shown to be responsive to anxiety provoking stimuli (Bogdonoff, Combs, Bryant, & Warren, 1959; Stead, Warren, Merrill, & Brannon, 1945; Stevenson, Duncon, Wolf, Ripley, & Wolf, 1949). Cardiac output is the quantity of blood pumped by the heart each minute, while SV measures the quantity of blood pumped during each heart cycle. Cardiac output can be expressed mathematically as the product of heart rate and SV. Thus, equivalent changes in CO may be accompanied by different combinations of heart rate and SV which vary both in direction and magnitude.

Noninvasive measures of CO, SV, and each of the STIs just described may be obtained using the technique of impedance cardiography (Buell, 1984). This technique involves measuring the electrical impedance to low energy, high frequency alternating current applied to electrode bands positioned around the patient's neck and abdomen. Two additional electrode bands each positioned around the thorax — one above and one below the heart — are used for measuring the phasic alterations in electrical impedance of the thorax region produced by heart function. Based on temporal and morphologic characteristics of the differentiated waveform of the impedance signal, a variety of cardiodynamic indices may be determined for each heart cycle. The results of studies assessing the validity of CO and SV measures obtained using impedance cardiography have generally been positive (Kubicek et al., 1970; Miller & Horvath, 1978). Additional information concerning a number of important methodological considerations and analytical issues related to impedance cardiography may be obtained from Buell (1984), Miller and Horvath (1978), and Kubicek et al. (1970). Although further efforts toward establishing the validity of the technique are required, impedance cardiography appears to have great potential as a useful clinical and laboratory tool for conducting extensive assessments of cardiac function in psychophysiological studies of the anxiety disorders.

In a recently conducted study (Sherwood, Allen, Obrist, & Langer, 1986), the technique of impedance cardiography was employed for assessing the cardiac responses of healthy normal male subjects to a stressful reaction time task and cold pressor test. As part of the experimental protocol, each subject underwent a graded exercise task so that the linear relationship between cardiac output (CO) and oxygen consumption (O_2) could be determined. The CO-O_2 relationship to exercise, describing metabolically appropriate adjustments in CO across the range of 0_2 provoked during exercise, was then used to evaluate CO changes observed during the stress and cold pressor tasks. During the reaction time task, increases in CO, the Heather index, and systolic blood pressure, as well as decreases in PEP were similar to those observed during mild exercise. The CO during the reaction time task was, however, in excess of metabolic demand as measured by O_2. Cardiac output and other measured reactions to cold pressor, on the other hand, were found to be consistent with changes in metabolic demand. Interestingly, although the stress and cold pressor tasks produced different CO responses, the magnitude of the heart rate increase during each task was comparable. Analysis of the SV data revealed that the difference in CO between tasks resulted from a reduced SV during the cold pressor task as compared to the reaction time task. Consistent with previous reports (e.g., Obrist, 1981), the metabolically excessive CO response to the reaction time task was found to be mediated by the sympathetic nervous system. Blockade of the beta-adrenergic system with propranolol was more effective in reducing the CO response to the reaction time task than to cold pressor.

As indicated earlier, the parasympathetic (i.e., vagal) innervation to the heart plays an important role in modulating heart rate. Respiratory sinus arrhythmia (RSA) — the normal variation in heart rate occurring in synchrony with the inspiratory (HR acceleration) and expiratory (HR deceleration) phases of respiration — depends almost entirely on an intact vagal innervation to the heart. Elimination of vagal activity to the heart, either through surgical ablation or pharmacological manipulation, has been shown to abolish RSA almost completely. Elimination of sympathetic activity to the heart has no effect on RSA. Therefore, a noninvasive measure of vagal influences on the heart may be obtained by quantifying RSA.

Because under normal resting conditions RSA accounts for a significant portion of the variation in heart rate, an index of the vagal tone to the heart may be obtained simply by measuring variability (e.g., range of variance) of heart rate. However, under more usual conditions where unrestricted subjects are being monitored, various sources in addition to RSA (e.g., movement and fluctuations in both body temperature and blood pressure) may contribute to heart rate variability. Under these conditions, the accuracy of measures of RSA based on heart rate variability may be seriously in error. An alternative measure proposed by Katona and Jih (1975) has been shown to provide more reliable estimates of RSA (Fouad, Taruzi, Ferrerio, Fighaly, & Alicandri, 1984). This measure assesses the difference between the minimum heart period during the inspiratory phase and the maximum heart period during the expiratory phase of each respiratory cycle.

Porges and his colleagues (Porges, 1986; Porges, McCabe, & Yongue, 1982) advocate the use of spectral analysis, a statistical procedure, for precisely quantifying RSA. Much as a prism breaks down sunlight into its constituent frequencies (i.e., colors), spectral analysis may be used to break down the total variance in heart rate into its constituent components. The output of spectral analysis, a spectral density function, provides a measure of the variance attributed to each frequency comprising the heart rate data. By determining the power density of heart rate corresponding to the prevailing respiratory frequency, a measure of RSA (i.e., vagal tone) may be obtained. While the spectral density function typically shows the greatest power at the frequency associated with respiration, nonzero power is usually observed at other frequencies as well. Recent studies have demonstrated that certain low-frequency peaks in the heart rate power spectrum represent the influence of physiological factors other than respiration on heart rate variability (Akselrod et al., 1981).

Although the mathematics involved are quite complex (Bohrer & Porges, 1982), spectral analysis techniques uniquely allow the investigator to reliably distinguish among the various sources of variability contributing to observed patterns of heart rate. As such, it is vastly superior to other measures of heart rate variability for providing an accurate index of vagal influences on the heart.

A major shortcoming of previous work on the psychophysiology of anxiety concerns the failure to obtain detailed assessments of heart function in studies of patients with anxiety disorder. Cardiovascular symptoms are frequently reported by anxious patients, and that patients with some forms of anxiety disorder experience a higher incidence of cardiac abnormalities, such as mitral valve prolapse (Gorman, Fyer, Gliklich, King, & Klein, 1981). Such patients also have higher mortality rates resulting from increased cardiovascular disease (Coryell, Noyes, & Clancy, 1982). Therefore, detailed assessments of heart function in clinically anxious patients may shed significant light on the relationship between cardiovascular function and anxiety disorder.

A more obvious deficiency of previous work on the psychophysiology of anxiety concerns the failure to differentiate among the various forms of anxiety disorder. Patients with agoraphobia and panic disorder have been the most extensively studied subgroups with respect to cardiovascular variables. Few data have been specifically reported for patients with generalized anxiety disorder or obsessive-compulsive disorder since the DSM-III became available.

Vasomotor Activity

An important component of the pattern of physiological activity typically associated with the "fight-flight" response is the shunting of peripheral blood flow away from the skin, splanchnic bed, and the kidney and toward skeletal muscles. Most authorities are now in agreement that this redistribution of blood flow occurs via two primary mechanisms: (a) alpha-adrenergic mediated constriction of blood vessels in the skin, gastointestinal tract, kidney, and liver; and (b) beta-adrenergic as well as mechanical dilation of the blood vessels supplying skeletal muscles.

Two measurement strategies are employed by psychophysiologists to assess both phasic and tonic alterations in the distribution of peripheral blood flow. One strategy involves measuring the blood flow through skin capillary beds in the finger (i.e., finger blood flow). The other strategy involves measuring the quantity of blood flow through skeletal muscles (i.e., forearm blood flow).

Finger blood flow can be easily recorded using a photoplethysmograph. This device is affixed to the fingertip and consists of a light source on one side (i.e., positioned on the top of the finger) and a photocell on the other side (i.e., positioned on the bottom of the finger). In one variation of the technique, changes in the intensity of the light passing through the tissues of the finger, resulting from moment-to-moment variations in the quantity of blood flowing to the finger, are detected by the photocell. Two components of this measure may be derived from the same device using different gain and filter settings. Pulsatile changes in blood flow, referred to as pulse amplitude or pulse volume, reflect variations in the quantity of blood flowing to the finger following each heart cycle. The characteristics of this component are primarily determined by the pulsatile features of blood flow following each heartbeat and are therefore sensitive to alteration in cardiodynamic as well as hemodynamic events. Pulse volume can be faithfully recorded through AC coupling (high gain) of the output of the photocell. The second component, referred to as blood volume, provides a measure of the relatively slow changes in the overall engorgement of the vasculature within the finger. Blood volume recordings provide a relatively pure measure of the state of the vasculature in that they are relatively free from transient cardiodynamic factors. Blood volume is recorded through DC coupling (low gain) of the photocell's output signal.

Evidence indicates that the two components of blood flow to the finger (i.e., pulse and volume) may be differentially responsive to a variety of psychological and environmental situations (Cook, 1974; Ginsberg & Furedy, 1974; Lavender, Lidberg, & Schalling, 1974). Cook (1974) has noted that, in addition to reflecting variations in blood flow, the finger pulse volume response is also affected by factors such as the position of the limb, and variations in venous pressure and environmental temperatures. Thus, in obtaining measures of finger pulse volume amplitude for indexing the state of alpha-adrenergic tone on the cardiovascular system, it is important to control for these potential influences on the response. It is also important to note that finger blood flow measures obtained using photoplethysmographic devices cannot be calibrated and can therefore only provide an index of relative, as opposed to absolute, changes in blood flow. Finally, if the photoplethysmograph must be removed and then reattached, it is important to note this event, as even small changes in the location of the transducer can have profound effects on the characteristics of the recorded finger pulse volume waveform.

Measures of forearm blood flow (FBF) are usually obtained by venous occlusion plethysmography (Kelly, 1980; Williams, 1984). In this technique, one standard-sized blood pressure cuff is positioned around the upper arm and one smaller cuff is positioned around the wrist. Most modern applications of the technique employ a mercury strain gauge, the output of which provides the measure of blood flow (Whitney, 1953). The strain gauge is positioned around the forearm midway between the two applied blood pressure cuffs. To determine FBF, the wrist cuff is initially inflated to suprasystolic level (e.g., 200 mm Hg) in order to occlude the hand circulation. Following inflation of the wrist cuff, the upper arm cuff is rapidly inflated to a level that effectively occludes venous outflow without inhibiting arterial inflow (e.g., 50 mm Hg). Once the upper arm cuff is inflated, the arm begins to engourge. The increase in the circumference of the forearm is measured by the strain gauge which provides a venous occlusion slope that is typically displayed on a polygraph. The rate of increase in forearm circumference (i.e., rate of rise in the venous occlusion slope) is directly proportional to the rate of increase in blood flow. By properly calibrating the strain gauge prior to its placement, an absolute measure of FBF may be determined.

Combined measures of FBF and mean arterial blood pressure can be used to determine forearm vascular resistance, or the total resistance to blood flow in the forearm. Knowledge of forearm vascular resistance allows one to determine to what extent observed changes in FBF are a result of active (i.e., neurogenic) or passive (i.e., mechanical) changes in forearm vasomotor activity.

Cook (1974) provides a full discussion of the physiological mechanisms underlying the control and regulation of peripheral blood flow as well as the many factors that must be considered in the measurement and analysis of pulse volume, blood volume, and limb blood flow. Several other papers provide extensive overviews of the history and variety of noninvasive techniques employed for measuring variations in peripheral blood flow (Brown, 1967; Jennings, Tahmoush, & Redmond, 1980).

Whereas the heart is innervated by both the sympathetic and parasympathetic branches of the autonomic nervous system, the peripheral vasculature is innervated solely by the sympathetic branch. Therefore, measures of finger pulse volume and finger blood volume may provide a relatively pure measure of the sympathetic (alpha-adrenergic) tone during emotional or stressful events. However, it is important to be aware that in addition to its direct neural innervation, the peripheral vasculature is also highly sensitive to circulating catecholamines. Differentiating between these two influences on the vasculature cannot, therefore, be made on the basis of measures of peripheral vascular events.

Several studies have examined the effects of psychological stress on peripheral blood flow through the finger (Abramson & Ferris, 1940; Blair, Glover, Greenfield, & Roddie, 1959; Gelder & Mathews, 1968). More recent studies have focused on the reactivity of finger blood flow measures to experimentally induced states of stress and anxiety (Bloom, Houston, & Burish, 1976; Bloom & Trautt, 1977; Knight & Borden, 1979; Smith, Houston, & Stucky, 1984).

In a series of experiments, Bloom and his associates (Bloom et al., 1976; Bloom & Trautt, 1977) observed small but statistically significant correlations between levels of self-reported anxiety (Affect Adjective Check List) and reductions in finger pulse volume amplitude during periods when normal subjects expected to receive series of electric shocks. Finger pulse volume amplitude was more strongly correlated with self-rated anxiety than was heart rate (Bloom et al., 1976). These investigators also observed differences in the temporal patterning of finger pulse volume and heart rate responsivity to their anxiety manipulation, which could account for the small intercorrelations often observed among measures (Bloom & Trautt, 1977). Finger pulse volume reactivity occurred sooner and recovered earlier following removal of the threat than did heart rate.

Smith, Houston, and Zurawski (1984) obtained measures of finger pulse volume amplitude, heart rate, and self-ratings of anxiety in normal subjects during an experiment designed to compare the physiological and subjective manifestations of anxiety produced by high and low levels of social-evaluative threat (i.e., videotaped interview). During anticipation of the interview, the observed correlation between subjective levels of anxiety and reductions in finger pulse volume amplitude was significant.

In the previously mentioned study reported by Freedman et al. (1985), spontaneous panic attacks were associated with marked decreases in finger temperature, which is indicative of a decreased blood flow to the finger. In our laboratory, we have recently observed marked reductions in finger pulse volume amplitude in panic disorder patients during sodium lactate–precipitated panic attacks.

Dramatic reductions in finger pulse volume amplitude are consistently observed in response to the cold pressor test (Lovallo, & Zeiner, 1975). This maneuver, which involves submerging an extremity into icewater, provokes a generalized peripheral vasoconstriction mediated by alpha-adrenergic receptor stimulation. In one experiment, a cold pressor test failed to provoke panic attacks in patients with panic disorder. Furthermore, no difference was observed in the magnitude of the finger pulse volume amplitude response to cold pressor between patients with panic disorder and normals.

Several studies have examined the reactivity of forearm blood flow to situational and chronic states of anxiety (Blair et al., 1959; Gelder & Mathews, 1968; Kelly, 1966; Kelly, Brown, & Shaffer, 1970; Kelly & Martin, 1969; Kelly & Walter, 1968; Konzett, Brener, & Lochs, 1973; Mathews & Lader, 1971; Kelly, 1968). These studies have generally found that the typical response to stressful or anxiety provoking conditions is an increase in forearm blood flow.

Kelly, et al. (1970) observed significantly higher resting levels of forearm blood flow in anxious patients compared to controls. In addition, significant correlations were obtained between resting levels of forearm blood flow and several measures of anxiety.

Gelder and Mathews (1968) observed increased forearm blood flow when anxious patients were instructed to imagine scenes incorporating their phobias. Harper et al. (1955) obtained similar results in patients with phobic anxiety. However, it has also been demonstrated that patients with phobic anxiety do not differ significantly from normal controls with respect to either resting or stress-induced forearm blood flow levels (Kelly, 1980).

High correlations often reported between forearm blood flow and heart rate (Kelly, 1980; Mathews & Lader, 1971) raise serious questions concerning the usefulness of the forearm blood flow measures to provide independent information related to the cardiovascular component of anxiety. However, the volume of the finger pulse has been shown to provide a sensitive index of vascular action which is independent of heart rate.

Arterial Blood Pressure

As previously indicated, the main function of the cardiovascular system is to help maintain adequate blood flow through the various body tissues in the face of constantly changing metabolic requirements. Even slight alterations in the need of most body tissues for energy will trigger a highly complex pattern of cardiovascular adjustments involving neural, humoral, and mechanical factors serving to modify the quantity and/or distribution of blood flow through the circulation. The complex nature of these adjustments serves to enhance the flexibility and precision by which the ever changing metabolic demands of the body are satisfied. The cost of this complexity, however, comes in the form of an increased chance that some component may have potential pathophysiological consequences for the entire cardiovascular system.

The normal adjustments to blood flow resulting from an increase in metabolic activity, such as during exercise, involve modifications to three major cardiovascular variables: (a) an increase in cardiac output, (b) the redistribution of blood flow from less active to more active tissue sites, and (c) an increase in arterial blood pressure. At a more molecular level of analysis, the various cardiodynamic and hemodynamic factors considered earlier (e.g., stroke volume, heart rate, vasomotor tone, etc.) also figure significantly in the control of blood flow.

The single factor having the greatest on the control and regulation of blood flow through the circulation is blood pressure (BP). Blood pressure refers to the force that the blood exerts on the walls of blood vessels, and is determined by the relationship between the cardiac output and the total peripheral resistance ($BP = CO \times TPR$). An alteration in either one of these factors, without a compensatory change in the other, will effect the BP.

The primary function of BP is to drive the output of the heart through the circulatory system. On each beat of the heart, contraction of the left ventricle forces blood (i.e., the stroke volume) into the aorta, causing it to distend creating pressure within it. The absolute pressure level within the circulatory system drops steadily as the distance from the heart increases. As a result of this pressure gradient, the blood ejected from the heart is forced through the circulatory system — first through the aorta and major arteries, followed in series by the arterioles, capillaries, venules, veins, and eventually, returning to the heart. In addition to serving as the medium for the transport of blood through the circulatory system, the vasculature functions to smooth the pulsatile pressure wave as it travels progressively through the circulation. This effectively transforms the intermittent, pulsatile output of the heart to a more steady and continuous flow which facilitates the exchange of nutrients and waste products between tissues and blood at capillary sites.

It is incorrect to view measures of BP as indexing a specific physiological process or event. Rather, BP measures should be interpreted as reflecting the net result of the multiple and complex interactions among cardiodynamic and hemodynamic events operating to help maintain metabolic homeostasis. Equivalent changes in BP (either systolic or diastolic) may be produced by very different patterns of cardiodynamic and hemodynamic adjustments. For this reason, arterial BP can provide only a general index of cardiovascular function, providing little insight into the mechanics underlying cardiovascular activity.

An important characteristic of BP concerns the fact that it is both an important *controlled* and *controlling* variable with respect to cardiac function. Through the operation of physiological negative-feedback control mechanisms, the level of BP is normally maintained within a narrow range. The "baroreceptor reflex" is one such mechanism by which BP is regulated. Pressure receptors (i.e., baroreceptors) concentrated in the arch of the aorta and carotid sinus are stimulated by the stretching of the vessel walls caused by BP fluctuations and relay this information, via afferent pathways, directly to neural control centers located in the medulla. In response to abrupt alterations in BP, the medullary control centers initiate appropriate compensatory adjustments to heart and vasomotor functioning, via efferent pathways, to return BP toward its original, homeostatic level. As a result of this neurogenic feedback mechanism, an inverse relationship between the direction of change in BP and the direction of change both in HR and vasomotor tone is typically observed. However, several higher brain centers including the thalamus, hypothalamus, and forebrain — important areas for both the experience and expression of emotion — may override the operation of the baroreceptor reflex thus leading to large, unbuffered cardiovascular changes.

Studies have shown that individuals may differ in the efficiency of the baroreceptor reflex to regulate BP in the manner just described. Several measurement strategies have been devised for assessing the integrity of the baroreceptor reflex noninvasively in human subjects (Eckberg, Cavanaugh , & Aboud, 1975; Smyth, Sleight, & Pickering, 1969).

Several additional physiological feedback mechanisms for regulating BP involving highly specialized mechanoreceptors chemoreceptors, and humoral factors have received extensive experimental study and each may play an important role in modulating cardiovascular function during emotional states (Cohen & Macdonald, 1974).

Although BP may be determined at any point along the circulatory system, measures are usually obtained from on of the major arteries (e.g., brachial or radial) of the body. The pusatile nature of BP within the arteries reflects the various phases of ventricular contraction during each cardiac cycle. Systolic blood pressure (SBP) is the peak pressure and the diastolic blood pressure (DBP) is the lowest pressure exerted in an artery following each heart cycle. Another frequently reported BP measure, pulse pressure, is simply the arithmetic difference between the systolic and diastolic pressure values. Mean arterial pressure (MAP) represents the average pressure during the cardiac cycle and may be approximated using the formula: 1/3 (DBP + (SBP−DBP)). Mean arterial pressure is a particularly important BP measure as it reflects the average effective pressure that drives the blood through the circulatory system. At any instant, the MAP must be sufficient to cause the CO to flow through the total peripheral resistance.

There is substantial evidence indicating that systolic and diastolic arterial pressures may be differentially affected by specific patterns of cardiodynamic and hemodynamic adjustments. Within normal limits, SBP is influenced primarily by variations in heart rate and stroke volume, while DBP is influenced mainly by changes in heart rate and the degree of peripheral resistance (Guyton, 1985).

Several excellent reviews of the methods and procedures utilized by psychophysiologists for measuring arterial blood pressure have been recently published (Larsen, Schneiderman, & Pasin, 1986; Steptoe, 1980). The interested reader should consult the classical work by Geddes (1970) for an extensive and detailed presentation of standard laboratory techniques for recording blood pressure in both human and animal subjects. A recent paper has reviewed a number of commercially available ambulatory BP recording devices that may be used for monitoring BP in the field (Chesney, 1984).

The only method currently available that provides accurate and continuous (i.e., beat-to-beat) measures of BP involves inserting a cannula directly into one of the major blood vessels, such as the brachial or radial arteries. By connecting a calibrated pressure transducer to the cannula, one may obtain precise measurements of SBP, DBP, and MAP during each heart cycle. Ethical and practical considerations, however, often preclude the use of the intra-arterial method of recording BP in psychophysiological studies involving human subjects. As a result, much effort has been focused on developing non-invasive procedures for obtaining reliable and accurate BP measures.

The most commonly employed non-invasive techniques for measuring BP involve the use of a blood pressure cuff for providing counterpressure to arterial blood flow.

The auscultatory method of determining BP has become the universally accepted standard for obtaining both clinical and laboratory assessments. In this technique, a blood pressure cuff is placed snuggly around the upper arm and initially inflated to above the occluding level. The bell of a stethescope (a simple acoustic amplification device) is then positioned over the brachial artery, just distal to the lower edge of the cuff, and used on the actual determination of systolic and diastolic BP. Determinations of systolic and diastolic BP are made by listening, through the stethoscope, for the characteristic Korotkoff sounds (K-sounds) that are produced when the pulse wave passes through the occluded artery underneath the cuff. With the cuff pressure initially set to above the occluding level, no K-sounds will be detected because transmission of pressure waves along the artery are interrupted at the point of occlusion. At this level, the cuff pressure exceeds the arterial BP level. As the cuff pressure is slowly reduced from the occluding level, the difference between cuff pressure and arterial pressure is reduced, eventually reaching the point at which arterial pressure just exceeds the applied cuff pressure level. At this level of applied cuff pressure, the pulse wave will penetrate the point of occlusion, force open the artery, and pass to the other side. The bell of the stethoscope is positioned to detect the turbulence produced by the passing of the pulse wave through the (now) partially occluded artery (i.e., a K-sound will be heard). Upon detection of the first K-sound, the level of cuff pressure can be read from a manometer (a pressure indicator calibrated in millimeters of mercury (mm Hg units) which is attached to the cuff. The pressure level indicated on the manometer when the initial K-sound is detected represents the arterial systolic BP level. As cuff pressure continues to be slowly reduced (2–3 mm Hg per heartbeat rate of reduction is recommended), arterial pressure now exceeds cuff pressure following each heart cycle and a series of K-sound will be detected. However, as less and less counterpressure is applied to the artery, a gradual increase followed by a gradual diminution in the amplitude (i.e., loudness) of the K-sounds is detected as the pulse wave gradually begins to flow unimpeded through the arterial segment underneath the cuff. Depending on the particular criteria employed (American Heart Association, 1975), the pressure reading on the manometer at the point where the K-sounds either become muffled or completely disappear marks the arterial diastolic pressure level.

Although the auscultatory technique has become the standard method for measuring BP in both clinical and laboratory setting, it is not entirely satisfactory for use in many psychophysiological studies. Specifically, because the auscultatory technique can provide measures of BP approximately once every minute (at least 30 seconds between measures is recommended to allow the return of normal blood flow to the arm), studies requiring more frequent assessments of BP must employ a different technique. An additional problem with this technique concerns the fact that it consistently underestimates the true SBP and DBP levels. In establishing the SBP and DBP pressure points, the cuff pressure must be less than the true arterial pressure for either a K-sound to be detected (SBP) or for the disappearance of K-sounds (DBP). An additional problem limiting the accuracy of the ascultatory method relates to the inherent lability of BP. Tursky (1972) has indicated that normal beat-to-beat variability in BP can be quite large, reaching 30 mm Hg in some individuals over a short period of time. This fact, coupled with the fact that BP measurements are usually based on the pressure level associated with a single heart cycle, may add significantly to errors in determining BP using the ascultatory technique.

Tursky and his colleagues (Tursky, Shapiro, & Schwartz, 1972; Tursky, 1974) have developed a method of recording BP designed to circumvent many of these problems. The constant-cuff technique involves inflating a standard BP cuff to either the systolic or diastolic level and holding the pressure constant at this level for a series of 30 or 40 heart cycles. Rather than using a stethoscope, a crystal microphone is placed over the brachial artery distal to the lower edge of the cuff for electronically detecting the occurrence of a K-sound following each heart cycle. The median systolic or diastolic BP level is defined as the applied cuff pressure level producing a K-sound on approximately 50% of heart cycles. An attractive feature of the constant-cuff technique is that the median BP level can be reliably tracked from trial to trial based on the percentage of K-sounds detected during each cuff inflation. It has been demonstrated that when between 25% and 75% of the heart cycles during a cuff inflation trial produce a K-sound, the cuff pressure level equals the true arterial pressure level with an accuracy of ± 2 mm Hg. The detection of fewer than 25% or more than 75% K-sounds will result in an adjustment (± 2 mm Hg) to the applied cuff pressure level on the next cuff inflation. In this way, the arterial pressure can be tracked automatically from one trial to the next during a protracted period of time.

Shapiro, Greenstadt, Land, and Rubinstein (1981) have recently modified this technique to allow for the tracking of arterial BP on each beat of the heart. Following each heart cycle, the applied cuff pressure is either increased or decreased by 2 mm Hg depending on whether or not a K-sound was detected. Within-subject comparisons of BP measures obtained using the beat-to-beat tracking technique with measures obtained intra-arterially have shown good agreement. However, due to its inherent hysteresis, large, rapid variations in BP such as typically occur during anxiety or panic may be difficult to track using this technique. Further work examining the relationship between actual changes in BP and various characteristics of K-sounds (e.g., amplitude and/or frequency composition) may lead to a greater precision in the ability of the cuff pressure to track arterial BP fluctuations on a beat-to-beat basis.

Posey, Geddes, Williams, and Moore (1969) have demonstrated that the gradual reduction in applied cuff pressure from the occluding level is accompanied by a series of cuff pressure oscillations that are first detected at approximately the SBP, increase in amplitude until peaking at approximately the MAP level, and then are gradually reduced in amplitude as cuff pressure approaches the DBP level. Earlier studies (Geddes, 1970) had shown that these cuff pressure oscillations result from the transmission of turbulence in the artery, produced when arterial blood flow is partially occluded, directly into the medium (i.e., air) of the occluding cuff. By attaching a pressure transducer to the BP cuff, the slight oscillations in cuff pressure following each heart cycle can either be amplified and displayed on a polygraph or sampled and processed by computer. Recent studies have shown that by holding the cuff pressure constant for a period of time at a level within the range that produces cuff pressure oscillations (i.e., between SBP and DBP), a beat-to-beat measure of relative BP fluctuations can be obtained (Geddes & Newberg, 1977; Papillo, Tursky, & Friedman, 1981; Tursky, Papillo, & Friedman, 1982).

In addition to the experimental and methodological problems just cited, several other important issues related to BP measurement in general, and the use of an occluding cuff in particular, should be mentioned. Individual different factors, such as the subject's age, gender, weight, race, physical health (e.g., cardiovascular disease), posture, medication usage, caffeine and nicotine consumption, and so on may each have a profound effect on BP and therefore must be controlled by the investigator either experimentally or statistically. The effects of periodic and sustained cuff inflations, both physiological and psychological, may also influence BP measurements. Additional methodological factors including the width of the occluding cuff, placement of the K-sound detecting instrument, time of day measures are obtained, and differences in the skills of the individuals assessing BP can each have a significant impact on the reliability and accuracy of measurements obtained. As for other cardiovascular measures, obtaining adequate baseline assessments is essential for correctly evaluating and interpreting BP data.

An alternative method for obtaining a continuous, beat-to-beat measure of arterial BP — one that does not involve the use of an occluding BP cuff — has received much recent attention from cardiovascular psychophysiologists. Pulse Transit Time (PTT) is a measure of the time it takes (in milliseconds) for a peripheral pulse to travel between two points along an artery (P-PTT) or, alternatively, the time between the R-wave of the ECG signal and the arrival of a peripheral pulse at a single site (R-PTT). The underlying assumption is that each of these time intervals varies inversely with changes in arterial BP. However, studies examining the relationship between BP and PTT have produced ambiguous results. At the prsent time, it remains uncertain as to which aspect of BP (i.e., SBP, DBP, or MAP) is most closely associated with variations in PTT (Lane, Greenstadt, Shapiro, & Rubinstein, 1983).

The results of recent studies indicate that the two measures of PTT (R-PTT and P-PTT) may, depending upon conditions, reflect different cardiovascular events (Obrist, 1981). For example, because the time interval represented by R-PTT includes most of PEP, variations in R-PTT may reflect changes in beta-adrenergic influences on the heart. P-PTT, on the other hand, does not include the PEP and should therefore provide a purer index of vascular events in comparison to R-PTT.

Together, these findings suggest that extreme caution is necessary when interpreting the results of studies reporting BP data based on measures of PTT. Further research into the patterning of factors contributing to changes in PTT should enhance the reliability and accuracy of this measure for monitoring BP on a continuous, beat-to-beat basis. A recent study has demonstrated that by assessing patterns of R-PTT, HR, and MAP activity it is possible to differentiate among alpha-adrenergic, beta-adrenergic, and parasympathetic influences on the cardiovascular system (Weiss, Del Bo, Reichek, & Engelman, 1980).

Several basic studies involving normal subjects have attempted to examine the relationship between BP and the emotions. In a classic experiment in psychophysiology, Ax (1953) observed that the emotions of anger and fear could be differentiated on the basis of patterns of cardiovascular responses. Specifically, anger was found to be associated with relative increases in peripheral resistance and diastolic BP, while fear was associated with relative increases in cardiac output and systolic BP. Weerts and Roberts (1976) observed a similar pattern of results in normal subjects instructed simply to imagine anger and fear provoking situations.

Schwartz, Weinberger, and Singer (1981) observed distinct patterns of SBP, DBP, and HR activity in normal subjects instructed to imagine experiencing and expressing the emotions of happiness, sadness, anger, and fear. It is interesting, although not surprising, that when subjects were instructed to imagine each emotion while, at the same time, engaging in exercise (walking up and down a single step), DPB no longer varied as a function of the different emotional states. The authors speculated that the large reduction in peripheral resistance produced by exercise caused a uniform reduction in DBP level which served to overshadow the differences in DBP observed when subjects simply imagined the emotions. This finding underscores the importance of considering the behavioral state of subjects in evaluating cardiovascular activity. An additional finding from this study was that although SBP failed to differentiate anger from fear during exercise, a slower recovery of the SBP response to anger was observed in comparison to fear.

Few studies of the anxiety disorders have examined the nature of BP responses in clinically anxious patients. Kelly and Martin (1969) found significantly higher resting levels of systolic and diastolic BP in patients with "anxiety states" (129/85) as compared to "neurotic" patients (119/78) and normal controls (117/77). Consistent with the Law of Initial Values, the BP response during performance of a stressful mental arithmetic task was smaller, percentage-wise, in anxiety patients as compared to neurotics and normal controls.

The results of a recent study conducted in our laboratory (Liebowitz et al., 1984b) showed that patients diagnosed as having panic disorder and who went on to panic during the infusion of sodium lactate had significantly higher resting baseline levels of diastolic BP as compared to non-panicking patients and normal controls. During the period of lactate infusion, significant increases in systolic BP were observed in patients and normals alike.

In a study reported by Ehlers et al. (1986), systolic BP was the only recorded physiological variable that showed a statistically different response to sodium lactate infusion between panic disorder patients and normal controls. At the end of the infusion, both the systolic and diastolic BPs were significantly elevated in patients as compared to controls.

Charney, Heninger, and Jatlow (1985) recently studied the anxiogenic effects of caffeine in patients meeting DSM-III criteria for agoraphobia with panic attacks or panic disorder and normal controls. Following caffeine consumption, significantly greater increases in systolic and diastolic BP were observed in patients as compared to controls.

RESPIRATORY FUNCTION

Psychophysiologists routinely measure respiratory function primarily as a means of assessing artifacts observed in other physiological response measures (Shean & Stange, 1971). Rarely heave measures of respiratory function served as primary measures in psychophysiological research.

Relatively few studies concerning the psychophysiology of emotion have focused specific attention on the use of respiratory measures for indexing or differentiating among the various emotional states (Dudley, 1969; Feleky, 1916; Finesinger, 1944; Stevenson et al., 1949).

However, more recent studies have demonstrated the responsivity of the respiratory system to psychological stress (Garssen, 1980; Mavissakalian & Michelson, 1982), the modulating effects of paced respiration on both physiological and psychological components of stress response (Harris, Katkin, Lick, & Habberfield, 1976; McCaul, Solomon, & Holmes, 1979), and similarities in symptoms produced by stress-induced respiratory changes with those most often reported by anxious individuals (Clark & Hemsley, 1982). These demonstrations have generated strong interest in the psychophysiological assessment of ventilatory function in anxiety disorders.

The basic function of the respiratory system involves supplying the tissues of the body with oxygen, removing carbon dioxide from tissues, and maintaining a constant balance in blood acidity. Intervening in the process of gas exchange between the lungs and body tissues is the cardiovascular system, which is responsible for the distribution of oxygen to the various tissues of the body. Thus, it should not be surprising to find a high degree of interaction, both centrally and peripherally, between the cardiovascular and respiratory systems. Recently, Grossman (1983) has published comprehensive reviews regarding the nature and extent of these interactions as well as their implications for cardiovascular competence and dysfunction.

The process of respiration is complexly regulated, involving interactions among neurological, chemical, and mechanical factors. Neurologically, both the central and autonomic nervous systems play a role in modulating respiratory function. With respect to autonomic nervous system influences, the parasympathetic branch plays a particularly important role. Chemical control of respiration involves chemoreceptors located at the arch of the aorta and the carotid sinus which are stimulated by the relative concentrations of oxygen (O_2) and carbon dioxide (pCO_2) in the blood. In addition to peripheral chemoreceptors, central chemoreceptors located in the medullary brainstem can be directly stimulated by increasing blood levels of CO_2. Mechanical control of respiration is enabled via stretch receptors located throughout the lungs that are stimulated by the degree of distention during the inspiratory phase of the respiration cycle.

Neural centers located in the pons and medulla process respiratory information arriving, via afferent pathways, from peripherally located chemoreceptors and from the stretch receptors of the lungs. The processing of this information results in reflexive adjustments which attempt to maintain homeostatic conditions. The medulla and pons also receive inputs from the hypothalamus and reticular formations. Additional information concerning the neurophysiology of respiratory control can be found in Comroe (1974).

The primary respiratory measures of interest to most psychophysiologists are the rate and depth of breathing. Both measures are typically obtained by placing a stretchable device around the thoracic and abdominal regions. These devices monitor changes in the diameter of these regions when the subject inhales and exhales. Depending on the type of device used, changes in diameter can be quantified in terms of changes in resistance (strain gauge), changes in air pressure (pneumograph), or changes in electrical impedance (impedance pneumograph). Another frequently employed technique involves the placement of a thermistor near the nasal passages. The thermistor senses the relative temperature difference between inhaled (cool) and exhaled (warm) air during each respiratory cycle.

The major drawback associated with each of these measurement techniques concerns the fact that, while absolute measures of respiratory frequency (i.e., rate) may be obtained, absolute measures of respiratory depth (i.e., tidal volume) cannot be derived. Several studies have documented the relative independence of rate and tidal volume response to both psychologically and stress induced ventilatory changes. In light of the fact that respiratory depth may be the more important parameter in studies of anxiety disorders, it is important that the measurement techniques provide accurate assessment of both rate and depth breathing.

To obtain absolute measures of tidal volume, spirometry techniques may be employed. However, spirometry requires the placement of a mask over the subject's face and may provoke adverse reactions in some individuals. An alternative technique involves the less intrusive methodology operating on the principle of inductive plethysmography. A commercially available respiratory monitoring system provides for measures of absolute rate and tidal volume associated with the separate volume components of thoracic and abdominal breathing. By prior calibration of this system, which involves having the subject breathe into a known volume air bag, absolute volume measures for each component may be obtained (Cohn, 1982). In our laboratory, online collection and processing of these measures by computer provides a continuous breath-by-breath analysis of tidal volume, respiratory rate, and minute volume separately, for both the thoracic and diaphragmatic components of respiratory action (Papillo, Pijacki, & Tursky, 1984).

A number of studies have investigated the relationship between patterns of respiration and specific emotional states. In addition, several studies have focused on the reactivity of the respiratory system to stress in both normal and clinical populations. Recent interest has centered on the role of a specific pattern of respiration, hyperventilation, in the pathogenesis of clinical anxiety disorders.

Several early studies showed characteristic alteration in respiratory patterns to be associated with various emotional states. For example, Feleky (1916) observed specific patterns of respiratory activity to six emotions (i.e., pleasure, pain, fear, anger, disgust, wonder) that subjects were required to imagine. Stevenson and Ripley (1952) described specific patterns of respiration occurring in a wide variety of emotional states elicited during an interview. Ancoli, Kamiya, and Ekman (1980) have recently demonstrated a differential pattern of respiratory activity in normal subjects during the viewing of a film designed to induce either a positive affect (i.e., happiness) or a negative affect (i.e., disgust). It was found that the experience of positive affect was associated with predominately abdominal breathing, while negative affect produced a pattern dominated by thoracic breathing.

Taking a different approach to investigating the relationship between respiratory parameters and emotional response, several investigators have examined the effects of paced respiration on autonomic nervous system reactivity to a variety of threatening situations (Clark, 1978; Foss, 1975; Harris et al., 1976; McCaul, Solomon, & Homes, 1979). In a study reported by McCaul et al. (1979), subjects who were instructed to pace their breathing at a rate of eight breaths per minute (i.e., half the normal resting rate) were less respondent in skin resistance change and finger pulse volume levels than were those who were paced at a normal rate (i.e., 16 breaths per minute). Heart rate was also measured, but was not significantly affected by the breathing manipulation. Clark (1978) found that subjects who paced their breathing rates at eight breaths per minute experienced less anxiety while watching a stressful film as compared to subjects taking 16 or 24 breaths per minute. The group who paced their breathing at 24 breaths per minute reported the highest level of anxiety during the procedure. In addition, significant correlations between self-reports of anxiety and respiration rate were obtained in this study, while no relationship was observed between self-reports of anxiety and changes in either cardiac or electrodermal measures. Additional evidence indicating positive correlations between respiratory rate and subjective levels of anxiety has been reported (Lande, 1981; Mathews & Gelder, 1969; McCollum, Burch, & Roesler, 1969; Oken et al., 1962).

A particular respiratory pattern, hyperventilation, has been regarded as both a cause and an effect of anxiety. By hyperventilating, the organism exhales or "blows off" more carbon dioxide than is simultaneously produced by cellular aerobic metabolism. This results is a lowered arterial concentration of CO_2 (hypocapnia) which, in turn, raises the arterial pH level above normal limits (respiratory alkalosis). This series of events has been shown to produce an almost immediate cerebral vasoconstriction and concomitant slowing in the frequency of electrical brain wave activity (i.e., EEG). As a consequence, the subject becomes dizzy, lightheaded, nauseated, confused, tremulous, and breathless.

A distinction between chronic and acute states of hyperventilation must be made. Acute hyperventilation is reflected by increased minute volume, decreased end-tidal CO_2, decreased CO_2 production, decreased arterial CO_2 concentration (pCO_2), increased pH, and decreased serum inorganic phosphate. As hyperventilation is sustained, however, several compensatory mechanisms intervene. The relative cerebral anoxia caused by vasoconstriction produces a reciprocal vasodilation. The kidney reabsorbs extra titratable acid and excretes excess bicarbonate to restore pH to a nearly normal level.

Chronic hyperventilators do not appear to be breathing fast despite profound hypocapnia. This is because once the hyperventilatory state is established, only a few deep breaths each hour are required to maintain the conditions just described.

The results of several studies provide clear evidence linking psychogenic stress and acute episodes of hyperventilation (Clark, 1978; Mathews & Gelder, 1969). For example, Suess, Alexander, Smith, Sweeny, and Marion (1980) observed significant reductions in end-tidal CO_2 levels accompanied by significant increases in both respiration rate and scores on the state portion of the State-Trait Anxiety Inventory, during a task involving threat of electric shock in normal subjects. Garssen (1980), also using normal subjects, observed a statistically significant hyperventilatory pattern (i.e., decrease in pCO_2) in response to the threat of an examination. No change in respiration rate was observed in response to this stressor.

Other studies showing a relationship between psychological stress and hyperventilation report substantial individual differences in respiratory response to stress. Recent studies designed to examine the nature of these individual differences have focused on behavioral and psychological factors (Clark & Hemsley, 1982; McCollum et al., 1969; Oken et al., 1962).

Recent interest in the connection between hyperventilation and clinical anxiety disorder has focused on the response of anxious patients to inhalation of carbon dioxide.

A number of studies have shown that anxious patients breathe more rapidly and exhibit lower end-tidal CO_2 than normal subjects. However, many of these studies have either failed to control for stress of the laboratory or have made no attempt to differentiate acute from chronic states of hyperventilation in their subjects.

Mills (1973) observed that some anxious subjects continue to hyperventilate following a hyperventilation test. Normal subjects, on the other hand, hypoventilate following the test to bring the pCO_2 levels down to normal. This finding provides further evidence suggesting a possibly disregulated respiratory system in anxious patients.

L. C. Lum (1976) has theorized that patients with panic disorder are chronic hyperventilators who have acquired the bad habit of thoracic breathing. By retraining patients to breathe diaphragmatically, the normal way for adults, he has demonstrated success in blocking future attacks.

In one study (Clark et al., 1985), psychiatric patients who suffered from recurrent panic attacks received training in slow breathing and were encouraged to practice the technique at home as a coping skill when anxious. During a 2-week period, there were significant reductions in the number of panic attacks and their severity. In addition, the symptoms continued to decrease during an 11-week period following training and were maintained at 6-month and 2-year follow-up reports. Additional treatment techniques were implemented following the 2-week slow breathing training period, and therefore the long-tern effectiveness of the breathing technique per se cannot be isolated.

In a series of recent experiments, we have explored the possible role of ventilatory disturbances in patients with panic disorder and found that patients had indices compatible with a state of chronic hyperventilation. During lactate-induced panic, there was a significant decrease in pCO_2, which indicates acute hyperventilation superimposed on chronic hyperventilation.

Signs of ventilatory disturbance dissipated in patients once the panic attacks were pharmacologically blunted. There is evidence that training patients not to hyperventilate may attenuate the panic response to sodium lactate infusion in a manner analogous to anti-panic medications. Finally, panic disorder patients who undergo a second lactate infusion following successful pharmacological treatment of their anxiety disorder typically complain less of hyperventilation related symptoms as compared to their first infusion.

The evidence reviewed so far suggests that hyperventilation may play a significant role in both the etiology and pathogenesis of panic disorder, but does not explain why patients hyperventilate in the first place.

In an effort to more precisely evaluate the role of hyperventilation in panic disorder, we have recently initiated a series of studies designed to investigate the ventilatory responses of anxious patients in a tightly controlled environment. We were primarily interested in ascertaining whether the cluster of symptoms reported by anxious patients during acute panic attacks is caused by hyperventilatory induced alkalosis. As a control for the alkalotic state, subjects were administered increased amounts of carbon dioxide in room air inhaled to breath. Five percent carbon dioxide in room air has been shown to triple minute ventilation in most subjects without producing either hypocapnia or alkalosis.

We were surprised to discover that 5% CO_2 was a more potent panicogenic agent for panic disorder patients than room air hyperventilation. Patients who typically panic to 5% CO_2 usually do not panic to room air hyperventilation; the reverse is also true. The results also indicated that normal controls as well as patients with other anxiety disorders (e.g., social phobia and obsessive-compulsive) do not panic to either 5% CO_2 or room air hyperventilation. Some patients with social phobia did have anxiety attacks when the dose of CO_2 was raised to 7%. Efforts to replicate these findings are currently under way.

The response to CO_2 inhalation observed in panic disorder patients may be the result of a disregulated central nervous system feedback mechanism involved in respiratory control. Increased amounts of carbon dioxide in arterial blood results in stimulation of peripheral and medullary chemoreceptors that initiate increased ventilation. It is conceivable that in patients with anxiety disorder, these chemoreceptors are hypersensitive, so that CO_2 inhalation results in an exaggerated hyperventilatory response.

Based on these results, and the finding that CO_2 inhalation induces panic, we have speculated that chronic hyperventilation may be an adaptive response to maintain CO_2 concentration at low levels in order to avoid triggering the hypersensitive CO_2 regulators. Anti-panic medications may act to "desensitize" these receptors. Breathing retraining may prevent the hyperventilatory reaction that follows stimulation of these receptors. In a related study, we found that minute ventilation correlated with subjective anxiety level better than heart rate or plasma epinephrine level in a group of social phobics undergoing epinephrine infusion.

ELECTRODERMAL ACTIVITY

Measures of electrodermal activity (EDA) have been used to index variations in physiological arousal and emotional reactivity in a large number of studies, both clinical and analogue. The principal effector involved in EDA measurement is the sweat gland, which serves an important role in thermoregulatory processes of the organism and is responsive to a wide range of psychological manipulation.

There are two basic types of sweat glands, appocrine and eccrine, distributed with varying densities throughout the surface of the body. Appocrine sweat glands are locally distributed in areas such as the armpit and around the genitals. These glands are not directly controlled by the nervous system and are not involved in thermoregulation. The result is that they have received little attention from psychophysiologists or other scientists studying the anxiety disorders.

The eccrine glands, on the other hand, are widespread throughout the surface of the body, are innervated exlusively by the sympathetic branch of the autonomic nervous system, play a major role in thermoregulation, and respond under a variety of emotional or stressful conditions. The eccrine sweat glands are concentrated on the palms of the hands and soles of the feet. The eccrine glands in those areas are less responsive to variations in body temperature and more responsive to emotional or ideational stimuli in comparison to eccrine glands located at other locations of the body.

While both functional and neurophysiological apsects of sweating, as they relate to the process of thermoregulation, are well understood, the biological significance of "emotional sweating" is uncertain and has been debated for some time (Edelberg, 1972). From an evolutionary perspective, it is speculated that sweating from the palms of the hands and soles of the feet may have had survival value at one time. Functionally, sweaty palms and hands may serve to facilitate the gripping of objects (e.g., a weapon), increase resistance to cutting and abrasion of the skin, and enhance tactile sensitivity, all changes that may have been helpful during a "fight-or-flight" reaction.

As previously indicated, the eccrine sweat glands are innervated solely by the sympathetic nervous system. However, this innervation is atypical in that acetylcholine rather than norepinephrine is the neurotransmitter directly involved in stimulating sweat gland activity.

Traditional measurements of EDA are obtained by placing a pair of nonpolarizing recording electrodes (e.g., silver–silver chloride) on the skin of the fingers or the palms of the hands. These serve to monitor changes in the electrical activity of the skin produced by variations in glandular activity.

Historically, two methods of recording EDA have been employed. One method involves passing a slight electrical current across a pair of electrodes which have been placed on the patient's palm or fingers. Changes in the electrical properties of the skin may then be recorded as either a change in resistance or in conductance relative to the applied voltage. If the measures obtained are recorded as units of resistance, the term *skin resistance* (SR) is employed. An inverse relationship exists between SR and sweat gland activity. That is, as the sweat glands become active, SR decreases. *Skin conductance* (SC) is the term used for EDA measures based on units of conductance. A direct relationship exists between SC and sweat gland activity such that as activity increases, SC increases and as sweat gland activity decreases, SC decreases.

In the second method of recording EDA, no external current is applied to the skin. Instead, the difference in electrical potential between an electrode placed over an active site and an electrode placed over a relatively inactive site, such as the forearm, is measured. Due to the more complex nature of the EDA waveform (i.e., biphasic) obtained by this recording technique and also the increased sensitivity of skin potential to artificial skin hydration, the measurement of either SR or SC is generally preferred (Fowles et al., 1981).

Regardless of whether measures of EDA are expressed as changes in resistance or conductance units, three types of electrodermal activity may be described. First, measures of skin conductance level (SCL) or skin resistance level (SRL) reflect the tonic level of saturation of the skin, Second, measures of skin conductance response (SCR) or skin resistance response (SRR) refer to the phasic or short-term fluctuations in the activity of the sweat glands in response to defined external stimuli. In the absence of a known environmental stimulus, electrodermal responses are called spontaneous or nonspecific responses and are designated as either SSCRs or SSRRs. Both tonic and phasic EDA measures may be recorded simultaneously from the same pair of electrodes. By applying the appropriate gain and filter settings, each component of the response may be separately and continuously recorded.

Because resistance and conductance measures are reciprocally related, transformation from one unit of measurement to the other is nonlinear. Therefore, analysis of a particular set of EDA data using both resistance and conductance units may, under certain conditions, lead to very different conclusions. On the basis of several considerations, including both biological and statistical facts, skin conductance is generally regarded as the preferable measure.

In addition to measures reflecting the magnitude and frequency of electrodermal responses, several other parameters related to the temporal characteristics of the response may be derived. For example, the measure of *response latency* is determined as the amount of time from presentation of a stimulus to the beginning of the response. The amount of time from the beginning of the response to the peak of the response is referred to as response *rise-time*. Another measure, referred to as *response recovery time,* is the time from the peak of the response to the point where the response returns to either the prestimulus level, or to the point where the response returns to 50% of the prestimulus level. Empirical studies examining the interrelationship among the various measures of electrodermal response (i.e., magnitude, frequency and temporal) have provided some support for the notion that under certain conditions, the various measures may reflect different psychological states (Lockhart, 1972; Venables & Christie, 1980).

Variables that have been demonstrated to affect EDA measures include age, sex, race, and phase of menstrual cycle. In addition, environmental factors such as ambient room temperature and humidity can also influence EDA activity. Finally, factors such as the length of the recording session, and cyclical variations in autonomic responsivity (i.e., biological rhythms) may also influence EDA measures.

The interested reader can find further discussions of the technical and methodological consideration of EDA measurement in several excellent sources (Edelberg, 1972; Venables & Christie, 1973, 1980). Recently, a committee report issued by the Society of Psychophysiological Research has published recommendations concerning acceptable methods and techniques for recording and measuring electrodermal activity (Fowles, et al., 1981).

Tonic electrodermal activity (i.e., SCL or SRL) has generally been found to be higher in anxious patients than in normal controls (Bond, James, & Lader, 1974; Connolly, 1979; Lader & Wing, 1964, 1966). It has also been found that anxious patients emit a larger number of spontaneous fluctuations in electrodermal activity compared to normal subjects (Lader, 1967; Miller & Shmavonian, 1965; Odegaard, 1932). However, several studies have failed to differentiate between anxious patients and normal subjects on the basis of either tonic or phasic EDA measures.

Lader and his colleagues (Lader, 1967; Lader & Wing, 1966) have compared the rate of habituation of the SCR in normal subjects and psychiatric patients to a series of auditory stimuli. In one study (Lader & Wing, 1966), 20 anxiety patients and 20 normal controls matched for age and sex were presented with a series of identical tones (1,000 Hz, 100 db) following a 10-minute baseline period. Measures of SCL and number of SSCRs during the baseline period were significantly higher in the anxious patients than normal subjects. In addition, during the presentation of the tone stimuli, SCL remained significantly higher in patients as compared to normals. In a second study, Lader (1967) divided the 90 patients studied into five diagnostic categories: anxiety with depression, state anxiety, agoraphobia, social phobia, and simple phobia. About two-thirds of the patients across these five groups had experienced weekly panic attacks, although the percentage within each group was not reported. These 90 patients were compared to 75 normal controls with respect to magnitude, frequency, and rate of habituation of EDA to a series of 20 consecutive tone stimuli (1,000 Hz, 100 db). The results indicated no significant differences in SCL, either among the patient subgroups or between patients and normal controls. However, patients with anxiety state, anxiety with depression, social phobia, and agoraphobia showed a slower rate of habituation to the stimuli as compared to patients with simple phobia and normal controls. No difference in the rate of habituation was observed between simple phobics and normal controls. An identical pattern of results was also obtained with respect to the number of SSCRs observed during the procedure. On the basis of correlational analysis, it was found that slow habituators demonstrated more spontaneous fluctuations, experienced higher levels of general anxiety, and experienced more frequent panic attacks than did patients who rapidly habituated to the stimuli.

We describe the Lader study in some detail because it provides a model of a carefully designed and executed psychophysiological experiment carried out in clinical psychiatry. Most important, unlike many studies in the anxiety disorder literature, an attempt was made to differentiate among several different forms of clinical anxiety. This study could serve as a basis for future work using the DSM-III categories of the anxiety.

In addition to employing measures of EDA to index states of arousal in laboratory studies of anxiety, EDA measures have also been used extensively to evaluate both the process and outcome of various therapeutic interventions for treatment of anxiety disorders. The work examining the relative efficacy of relaxation training, systematic desensitization, and various other behavioral techniques in the treatment of phobic anxiety (Katkin & Deitz, 1973) is one example. Studies demonstrating successful differentiation between phobic and nonphobic subjects based solely on EDA measures (Geer, 1964), in addition to studies showing differences in EDA in phobic subjects to feared and nonfeared objects (Frederikson, 1981; Geer, 1964), have been reported.

CONCLUDING REMARKS

Anxiety is often defined as a multidimensional phenomenon comprised of three main response components: physiological, psychological, and behavioral. Low correlations have often been observed among these three components, a situation often termed response desynchrony. It is extremely important, therefore, to carefully address the measurement technology and rationale behind each of the three components.

Cardiovascular function, electrodermal response, and respiratory function are the main parameters measured in psychophysiological assessment of anxiety. In general, patients with anxiety disorder have been found to have faster heart rate, diminished heart rate habituation to stressful stimuli, greater cardiac awareness, and greater heart rate variability than normal controls. Blood flow to the skin, splanchnic circulation, and kidneys decreases during acute anxiety, while blood flow to muscles increases.

Hyperventilation has been found to be an important component of acute panic attacks and other forms of anxiety disorder. Patients with anxiety disorder also demonstrate greater electrodermal responses to stress, more spontaneous fluctuations of skin conductance, and reduced habituation of electrodermal response to stressful stimuli than normals. These psychophysiological findings can be used to suggest hyotheses about the basic pathophysiology of anxiety.

REFERENCES

Abrahamson, D. I., & Ferris, E. B. (1940). Responses of blood vessels in the resting hand and forearm to various stimuli. *American Heart Journal, 19*, 541–553.

American Heart Association (1975). Report on the committee on Electrocardiography. Recommendations for standardization of leads and of specifications for instruments in electrocardiography and vectocardiography. *Circulation, 52*, 11–31.

Ancoli, S., Kamiya, J., & Ekman, P. (1980). Psychophysiological differentiation of positive and negative affects. *Biofeedback and Self Regulation, 5*, 356–357.

Akselrod, S. D., Gordon, D., Ubel, F. A., Shannon, D. C., Barger, D. C., & Cohen, R. J. (1981). Power spectrum analysis of heart rate fluctuations, a quantitative probe of beat to beat cardiovascular control. *Science, 2183*, 220–222.

Ax, A. F. (1953). The physiological differentiation between fear and anger. *Psychosomatic Medicine, 15*, 433–442.

Bellack, A. S., & Lombardo, T. W., (1985). Measurement of anxiety. In S. M. Turner (Ed.), *Behavior theories and treatment of anxiety*. (pp. 51–89). New York: Plenum.

Benjamin, L. S. (1967). Facts and artifacts in using analysis of covariance to undo the law of initial values. *Psychophysiology, 4*, 187–206.

Bernstein, D. A., & Nietzel, M. T. (1974). Behavioral avoidance tests: The effects of demand characteristics and repeated measures of two types of subjects. *Behavior Therapy, 5*, 183–192.

Blair, D. A., Glover, W. E., Greenfield, A. D. M., & Roddie, I. C. (1959). Excitation of cholinergic vasodilatory nerves to human skeletal muscles during emotional states. *Journal of Physiology, 148*, 633–647.

Bloom, L. J., Houston, B. K., & Burish, J. G. (1976). An evaluation of finger pulse volume as a measure of anxiety. *Psychophysiology, 13*, 40–42.

Bloom, L. J., & Trautt, G. M. (1977). Finger pulse volume as a measure of anxiety: Further evaluation. *Psychophysiology, 14*, 541–544.

Bogdonoff, M. D., Combs, J. J., Bryant, G. D., & Warren, J. (1959). Cardiovascular responses in experimentally induced alterations of affect. *Circulation, 20*, 353–359.

Bohrer, R. E., & Porges, S. W. (1982). The application of time series statistics to psychological research: An introduction. In G. Keren (Ed.), *Statistical and methodological issues in psychology and social science research*. (pp. 309–345). Hillsdale, NJ: Lawrence Erlbaum & Associates.

Bond, A. J., James, D. C., & Lader, M. H. (1974). Physiological and psychological measures in anxious patients. *Psychological Medicine, 4*, 364–373.

Borkovec, T. D., Weerts, T. C., & Bernstein, D. A. (1977). Assessment of anxiety. In A. R. Ciminero, K. S. Calhoun, & H. E. Adams (Eds.), *Handbook of behavioral assessment*. (pp. 367–428). New York: Wiley.

Brener, J. M. (1980). The measurement of heart rate. In P. H. Venerables & I. Martin (Eds.), *Techniques in Psychophysiology*. (pp. 103–131). London: Wiley.

Brown, C. C. (1967). A proposed standard nomenclature for psychophysiological measures. *Psychophysiology, 4*, 260–264.

Brown, O. R., Kloster, F. E., & Demots, H. (1975). Incidence of mitral valve prolapse in the asymptomatic normal. *Circulation*, (Supple. 2): 11–77, 51–52.

Buell, J. C. (1984). Impedance cardiography and plethismography. In. J. A. Herd, A. M. Gotto, P. G. Kaufman, & S. W. Weiss (Eds.), *Cardiovascular instrumentation: Application of new technology to biobehavioral research*. National Institute of Health Publication No. 84–1654. pp. 227–238.

Charney, D. S., Heninger, G. R., & Jatlow, P. I. (1985). Increased anxiogenic effects of caffeine in panic disorders. *Archives of General Psychiatry, 42*, 233–243.

Chesney, M. A. (1984). Non-invasive ambulatory blood pressure monitoring. In J. A. Herd, A. M. Gotto, P. G. Kaufman, & S. N. Weiss (Eds.), *Cardiovascular instrumentation: Application of new technology to biobehavioral research*. National Institutes of Health Publication No. 84–1654. pp. 79–94.

Clark, D. M., & Hemsley, D. R. (1982). Effects of hyperventilation: Individual variability and its relation to personality. *Journal of Behavior Therapy and Experimental Psychiatry, 13*, 41–47.

Clark, D. M., Salkovskis, P. M., & Chalkley, S. J. (1985). Respiratory control as a treatment for panic attacks. *Journal of Behavior Therapy and Experimental Psychiatry, 16*, 23–30.

Clark, M. E. (1978). *Therapeutic applications of physiological control: The effectiveness of respiratory pacing in reducing autonomic and subjective distress*. Unpublished doctoral dissertation, Kentucky State University, Frankfort, KY.

Cohen, H., Goodenough, D., & Witkin, H. (1975). The effects of stress on components of the respiratory cycle. *Psychophysiology, 12*, 377–380.

Cohn, M. (1982). Respiratory monitoring during sleep: inductive plethysmography. In C. Guilleminault (Ed.). Sleeping and waking disorders. Indications and techniques. (pp. 213–223). Menio Park: Addison-Wesley.

Comroe, J. H. (1974). *Physiology of respiration*, (2nd ed.). Chicago: Yearbook Medical Book Publishers Inc.

Connolly, J. F. (1979). Tonic physiological responses to repeated presentations of phobic stimuli. *Behavioral Research and Therapy, 17*, 189–196.

Cook, M. R. (1974). Psychophysiology of peripheral vascular changes. In P. A. Obrist, A. H. Black, J. Brener, & L. V. DiCara, (Eds.), *Cardiovascular psychophysiology: Current issues in response mechanism, biofeedback and methodology*. (pp. 60–64). Chicago: Aldine.

Coryell, W., Noyes, R., & Clancy, J. (1982). Excess mortality in panic disorder. *Archives of General Psychiatry, 39*, 701–703.

Cronbach, L. J., & Furby, L. (1970). How should we measure change or should we? *Psychological Bulletin, 74*, 68–80.

Dawson, M. E., Schell, A. M., & Catania, J. (1977). Autonomic activity in depressive illness. *Psychophysiology, 14*, 226.

Dudley, D. L. (1969). *Psychophysiology of respiration in health and disease*. New York: Appleton-Century-Croft.

Duffy, E. (1962). *Activation and behavior.* New York: Wiley.

Eckberg, D. L., Cavanaugh, M. S., Mark, A. L., & Aboud, F. M. (1975). A simplified neck suction device for activation of carotid baroreceptors. *Circulation, 85,* 167–173.

Edelberg, R. (1972). Electrodermal recovery rate, goal-orientation and aversion. *Psychophysiology, 5,* 512.

Ehlers, A., Margraf, J., & Roth, W. T. (1986). Experimental induction of panic attacks. In I. Hand, & H. Wittchen (Eds.), *Panic and phobias, empirical evidence of theoretical models and long term effects of behavioral treatments.* (pp. 53–66). Berlin: Springer-Verlag.

Engel, B. T. (1960). Stimulus-response and individual response specificity. *Archives of General Psychiatry, 2,* 305–313.

Engel, B. T. (1972). Operant conditioning of cardiac function: A status report. *Psychophysiology, 9,* 161–177.

Engel, B. T., & Chism, R. A. (1967). Effect of increases and decreases in breathing rate on heart rate and finger pulse volume. *Psychophysiology, 4,* 83–89.

Feleky, A. (1916). The influence of emotions on respiration. *Journal of Experimental Psychology, 1,* 218–222.

Finesinger, J. E. (1944). The effect of pleasant and unpleasant ideas on the respiratory pattern. *American Journal of Psychiatry, 100,* 649–667.

Foss, T. P. (1975). Effectiveness of breathing threapy treatment program on the reduction and management of anxiety. Unpublished doctoral dissertation, University of Maryland, College Park.

Fouad, P. G., Taruzi, R. C., Ferrerio, C. M., Fighaly, S., & Alicandri, C. (1984). Assessment of parasympathetic control of heart rate by a noninvasive method. *American Journal of Physiology, 246,* H838–H842.

Fowles, D. C., Christie, M. J., Edelberg, R., Gringe, W. W., Lykken, D. T., & Venerables, P. H. (1981). Publication recommendations for electrodermal measurements. *Psychophysiology, 18,* 3.

Fredrikson, M. (1981). Orienting and defensive responses to phobic and conditioned stimuli in phobics and normals. *Psychophysiology, 18,* 456–465.

Freedman, R. B., Iannic, P., Ettedgui, E., & Puthezath, N. (1985). Ambulatory monitoring of panic disorder. *Archives of General Psychiatry, 42,* 244–248.

Freedman, R. R., Ianni, P., Ettedgui, E., Pohl, R., & Rainey, J. M. (1984). Psychophysiological factors in panic disorder. *Psychopathology, 17,* 66–73.

Furedy, J. J., & Heslegrave, R. J. (1983). A consideration of recent criticisms of T-wave amplitude index of myocardial sympathetic function. *Psychophysiology, 20,* 204.

Garssen, B. (1980). Role of stress in the development of the hyperventilation syndrome. *Psychotherapy and psychosomatics, 33,* 214–225.

Gedder, L. A., & Baker, L. E. (1968). Principles of applied biomedical instrumentation. New York: John Wiley & Sons.

Geddes, L. A. (1970). *Direct and indirect measures of blood pressure.* Chicago: Yearbook Medical Publishers.

Geddes, L. A., Newberg, D. C. (1977). Cuff pressure oscillations in the measurement of relative blood pressure. *Psychophysiology, 14,* 198–202.

Geer, J. H. (1964). Measurement of the conditioned cardiac response. *Journal of Comparative and Physiological Psychology, 57,* 426–433.

Gelder, M. G., & Matthews, A. M. (1968). Forearm blood flow and phobic anxiety. *British Journal of Psychiatry, 114,* 1371–1376.

Ginsberg, S., & Furedy, J. J. (1974). Stimulus repetition, change, and assessment of sensitivities and relationship among an electrodermal and two plethysmographic components of the orientating response. *Psychophysiology, 11,* 35–43.

Gorman, J. M., Askanazi, J., Liebowitz, M. R., Fyer, A. J., Stein, J., Kinney, J. M., & Klein, D. F. (1984). Response to hyperventilation in a group of patients with panic disorder. *American Journal of Psychiatry, 141,* 857–861.

Gorman, J. M. Fyer, A. J., Gliklich, J., King, D., & Klein, D. F. (1981). Mitral valve prolapse and panic disorders: Effects of imipramine. In D. F. Klein & J. G. Rabkin (Eds.), *Anxiety: New research and changing concepts.* New York: Raven Press.

Gorman, J. M., Levy, G. F., Liebowitz, M. R., McGrath, P., Appleby, I. L., Dillow, D., Davies, S. O., & Klein, D. F. (1983). The effect of acute beta-adrenergic blockade on lactate-induced panic. *Archives of General Psychiatry, 40,* 425–430.

Graham, F. K. (1979). Distinguishing among orientating, defense and startle reflexes. In H. D. Kirimal, E. H. van Olst, & J. F. Orlebile (Eds.), *The orientating reflex in humans.* (pp. 137–167). Hillsdale, NJ: J. Erlbaum.

Grossman, P. (1983). Respiration, stress and cardiovascular function. *Psychophysiology, 20,* 284.

Guyton, A. C. (1985). *Textbook of medical physiology*. Philadelphia: W. B. Saunders.

Harper, M., Gurney, C., Savage, R. D., & Roth, M. (1965). Forearm blood flow in normal subjects and patients with phobic anxiety states. *British Journal of Psychiatry, 111*, 723–731.

Harris, V. A., Katkin, E. S., Lick, J. H., & Habberfield, T. (1976). Paced respiration and cardiac response to stress. *Psychophysiology, 14*, 228.

Hastrup, J. L. (1986). Duration of initial heart rate assessment in psychophysiology: Current practices and implications. *Psychophysiology, 23*, 15–17.

Heslegrave, R. J., & Furedy, J. S. (1979a). Sensitivities of HR and T-wave amplitude for detecting cognitive and anticipatory stress. *Physiology and Behavior, 22*, 17–23.

Heslegrave, R. J. & Furedy, J. S. (1979b). Carotoid and P/dt as a psychophysiology index of sympathetic myocardial effects: Some considerations. *Psychophysiology, 17*, 482–494.

Heslegrave, R. J., Ogilvie, J. C., & Furedy, J. J. (1979). Measuring baseline-treatment differences in heart rate variability: Variance versus successive difference mean square and beats per minute versus interbeat interval. *Psychophysiology, 16*, 151–157.

Hord, D. J., Johnson, L. G., & Lubin, A. (1964). Differential effects of the law of initial value (LIV) on autonomic variables. *Psychophysiology, 1*, 79–87.

Hugdahl, K. (1981). The three systems model of fear and emotion — a critical examination *Behaviour Research and Therapy, 19*, 75–85.

Jennings, R. J., Berg, K. W., Hutchenson, J. S., Obrist, P. A., Porges, S., & Turpin, G. (1981). Publication guidelines for heart rate studies in man. *Psychophysiology, 18*, 226–231.

Jennings, J. R., Stringfellow, J. C., & Graham, M. (1974). A comparison of the statistical distributions of beat-by-beat heart rate and heart period. *Psychophysiology, 11*, 207–210.

Jennings, J. R., Tahmoush, A. J., & Redmond, D. P. (1980). The non-invasive measurement of peripheral vascular activity. In P. H. Venerables & I. Martin (Eds.), *Techniques in psychophysiology*. (pp. 69–137). New York: John Wiley & Sons.

Jennings, J. R., & Wood, C. C. (1976). The readjustment procedure for repeated measures analysis of variance. *Psychophysiology, 13*, 277–278.

Katkin, E. S., & Deitz, S. R. (1973). Systematic desensitization. In W. F. Prokasy & D. Raskin (Eds.), *Electrodermal activity and psychological research*. (pp. 347–376). New York: Academic Press.

Katona, P. G., & Jih, F. (1975). Respiratory sinus arrhythmia; Non-invasive measure of parasympathetic cardiac control. *Journal of Applied Physiology, 39*, 801–805.

Kelly, D. (1966). Measurement of anxiety by forearm blood flow. *British Journal of Psychiatry, 152*, 789–798.

Kelly, D. (1968). The relationship between clinical diagnosis and anxiety assessed by forearm blood flow. *British Journal of Psychiatry, 114*, 611–626.

Kelly, D. (1980). *Anxiety and emotions*. Springfield, IL: Charles C. Thomas.

Kelly, D., Brown, C. C., & Shaffer, J. W. (1970). A comparison of physiological and psychological measurements of anxious patients and normal controls. *Psychophysiology, 6*, 429–441.

Kelly, D., & Martin, I. (1969). Antonomic reactivity, eyelid conditioning and their relationship to neuroticism and etraversion. *Behavior Research and Therapy, 7*, 233.

Kelly, D., Mitchell-Heggs, N., & Sherman, D. (1971). Anxiety and the effects of sodium lactate assessed clinically and physiologically. *British Journal of Psychiatry, 119*, 129–141.

Kelly, D., & Walter, C. (1968). The relationship between clinical diagnosis and anxiety assessed by forearm blood flow and other measurements. *British Journal of Psychiatry, 114*, 611–626.

Khachaturian, Z. A., Kerr, J., Kruger, R., & Schachter, J. (1972). A methodological note: Comparison between period and rate data in studies of cardiac function. *Psychophysiology, 5*, 539.

Knight, M. L., & Borden, R. J. (1979). Autonomic and affective reactions of high and low socially-anxious individuals awaiting public performance. *Psychophysiology, 16*, 209–213.

Konzett, H., Brener, W., & Lochs, H. (1973). Emotionally induced cardiovascular changes in man as a means for the investigation of tranquillizing drugs. *Psychopharmacologica, 30*, 75–82.

Kubicek, W. G., From, A. H., Patterson, R. P., Witsoe, D. A., Caseda, A., Lilleki, R. G., & Resek, R. (1970). Impedance cardiography as a non-invasive means to monitor cardiac function. *Journal of Association for the Advancement of Medical Instrumentation, 4*, 79–84.

Lacey, B. C. (1950). Individual differences in somatic response patterns. *Journal of Comprehensive Physiology and Psychology, 43*, 338–350.

Lacey, J. L. (1967). Somatic response patterning

and stress: Some revisions on activation theory. In M. H. Appley & R. Trumbull (Eds.), *Psychological stress: Issues in research.* (pp. 14–37). New York: Appleton-Century-Crofts.

Lacey, J. L., & Lacey, B. C. (1962). The law of initial value in the longitudinal study of autonomic constitution: Reproductibility of autonomic responses and response patterns over a four year interval. *Annals of the New York Academy of Science, 38,* 1257–1290.

Lader, M. H. (1967). Palmer skin conductance measures in anxiety and phobic states. *Journal of Psychosomatic Research, 11,* 271–281.

Lader, M. H., & Wing, L. (1964). Habituation of the psycho-galvanic reflex in patients with anxiety states and in normal subjects. *Journal of Neurology, Neurosurgery and Psychiatry, 27,* 210–218.

Lader, M. H., & Wing, L. (1966). *Physiological measures, sedative drugs and morbid anxiety.* London: Oxford University Press.

Lande, S. D. (1981). Physiological and subjective meaning of anxiety during flooding. *Behavior research and therapy, 18,* 162–163.

Lane, J. D., Greenstadt, L., Shapiro, D., & Rubinstein, E. (1983). Pulse transit time and blood pressure: An intensive analysis. *Psychophysiology, 20,* 45–49.

Lang, P. J. (1968). Fear reduction and fear behavior: Problems in treating a construct. In J. M. Schlien (Ed.), *Research in psychotherapy* (Vol. 3). Washington, DC: American Psychological Association.

Lang, P. J. (1971). The application of psychophysiological methods to the study of psychotherapy and behavior modification. In A. E. Bergin & S. L. Garfields (Eds.), *Handbook of psychotherapy and behavior change: An empirical analysis.* (pp. 75–125). New York: Wiley.

Lang, P. J. (1977). The psychophysiology of anxiety. In J. D. Cone & R. P. Hawkins (Eds.), *Psychiatric diagnosis: Exploration of biological criteria.* (pp. 178–195). New York: Spectrum.

Lang, P. J. (1980), Anxiety: Toward a psychophysiological definition. In H. S. Akiskal & W. L. Webb (Eds.), *Psychiatric diagnosis: Explorations of biological prediction.* New York: Spectrum.

Lang, P. J., Melmea, B. G., & Hart, J. H. (1975). Automating the desensitization procedure: A psychophysiological analysis of fear modification. In M. J. Kietzman (Ed.), *Experimental approaches to psychopathology.* (pp. 289–323). New York: Academic Press.

Lang, P. J., Rice, D. G., & Sternbach, R. A. (1972). The psychophysiology of emotion. In N. S. Greenfield & R. A. Sternbach (Eds.), *Handbook of psychophysiology.* (pp. 623–643). New York: Holt, Rinehart and Winston.

Lapierre, Y. D., Knott, V. J., & Gray, R. (1984). Psychophysiological correlates of sodium lactate. *Psychopharmacology Bulletin, 20,* 50–57.

Larsen, P. B., Schneideman, N., Pasin, R. D. (1986). Physiological basis of cardiovascular psychophysiology. In M. G. H. Coles, E. Donchin, & S. W. Porges (Eds.), *Psychophysiology: Systems processes and applications.* (pp. 122–165). New York: Guildford Press.

Lawler, J. E., & Obrist, P. A. (1974). Indirect indices of contractile force. In P. A. Obrist, A. H. Black, J. Brener, & L. V. Dicara (Eds.), *Cardiovascular psychophysiology: Current issues in response mechanisms, biofeedback and methodology.* (pp. 85–92). Chicago: Aldine.

Levander, S. E., Lidberg, L. & Schalling, D. (1974). Habituation of the digital vasoconstrictive orienting response. *Journal of Experimental Psychology, 102,* 700–705.

Lick, J. R., & Katkin, E. S. (1976). Assessment of anxiety and fear. In M. Hersen & A. Bellack (Eds.), *Behavioral assessment: A practical handbook.* New York: Pergamon Press.

Liebowitz, M. R., Fyer, A. J., Gorman, J. M., Dillon, D., Appleby, I. L., Levy, G., Anderson, S., Levitt, M., Palij, M., & Davies, S. O. (1984a). Lactate provocation of panic attacks: I. Clinical and behavioral findings. *Archives of General Psychiatry, 41,* 764–770.

Liebowitz, M. R., Fyer, A. J., Gorman, J. M., Dillon, D., Appleby, I. L., Levy, G., Anderson, S., Levitt, M., Palij, M., & Davies, S. O., (1984b). Lactate provocation of panic attacks. II. Biochemical and physiological findings. *Archives of General Psychiatry, 42,* 764–770.

Liebowitz, M. R., Gorman, J. M., Fyer, A. J., Levitt, M., Dillon, D., Levy, G., Appleby, I. L., Anderson, S., Palij, M., Davies, S. O., & Klein, D. F. (1985). Lactate provocation of panic attacks: II. Biochemical and physiological findings. *Archives of General Psychiatry, 42,* 709–719.

Lindsley, D. B. (1951). Emotion. In S. S. Stevens (Ed.), *Handbook of experimental psychology.* (pp. 473–516). New York: Wiley.

Lockhart, R. A. (1972). Interrlations between amplitude latency, rise time and the Edelberg recovery measure of the galvonic skin response. *Psychophysiology, 9,* 437–442.

Lovallo, W., & Zeiner, A. R. (1975). Some factors influencing the vasomotor response to cold pressor stimulation. *Psychophysiology, 13,* 499.

Lown, B., & DeSilva, R. A. (1978). Roles of

psychologic stress and autonomic nervous system changes in provocation of ventricular premature complexes. *American Journal of Cardiology, 41*, 979–985.

Lum, L. C. (1976). The syndrome of habitual chronic hyperventilation. In O. Hill (Ed.), *Modern trends in psychosomatic medicine* (Vol. 3). London: Buttersworth.

Lykken, D. T. (1972). Range correction applied to heart rate and GSR data. *Psychophysiology, 9*, 373–379.

Malmo, R. B. (1959). Activation: A neuropsychological dimension. *Psychological Reviews, 66*, 367–386.

Martin, B., & Stroufe, L. A. (1970). Anxiety. In C. G. Costello (Ed.), *Symptoms of psychopathology: A handbook*. (pp. 216–259). New York: Wiley.

Mathews, A. M., & Gelder, M. G. (1969). Psychophysiological investigations of brief relaxation training. *Journal of Psychosomatic Research, 13*, 1–12.

Mathews, A. M., & Lader, M. H. (1971). An evaluation of forearm blood flow as a physiological measure. *Psychophysiology, 8*, 509–524.

Mavissakalian, M., & Michelson, L. (1982). Patterns of psychophysiological change in the treatment of agoraphobia. *Behavior Research and Therapy, 20*, 347–356.

McCaul, K. D., Solomon, S., & Holmes, D. S. (1979). The effects of paced respiration and expectations on physiological responses to threat. *Journal of Personality and Social Psychology, 37*, 564–571.

McCollum, M., Burch, W. R., & Roesler, R. (1969). Personality and respiratory responses to sound and light. *Psychophysiology, 6*, 291–300.

McGuinness, D. (1973). Cardiovascular responses during habituation and mental activity in anxious men and women. *Biological Psychology, 1*, 115–123.

Meyers, A. W., & Craighead, W. E. (1978). Adaption periods in clinical psychophysiology research: A recommendation. *Behavior Therapy, 9*, 355–362.

Miller, J. C., & Horvath, S. M. (1978). Impedance cardiography. *Psychophysiology, 15*, 80–91.

Miller, L. H., Shmavonian, B. H. (1965). Replicability of two GSR indices as a function of stress cognitive activity. *Journal of Personality and Social Psychology, 2*, 753–756.

Mills, J. N. (1973). *Biological aspects of circadian rhythm*. London: Plenum.

Montgomery, G. K. (1977). Effects of performance evaluation and anxiety on cardiac responses in anticipation of difficult problem solving. *Psychophysiology, 14*, 251–257.

Nesse, R. M., Cameron, O. G., Curtis, G. C., McCann, D. S., & Huber-Smith, M. J. (1984). Adrenergic function in patients with panic anxiety. *Archives of General Psychiatry, 41*, 771–776.

Newlin, D. B., & Levenson, R. W. (1979). Pre-injection period: Measuring beta-adrenergic influences on the heart. *Psychophysiology, 16*, 546–553.

Obrist, P. A. (1981). *Cardiovascular psychophysiology: A perspective*. New York: Plenum Press.

Obrist, P. A., & Light, K. C. (1979). Comments on carotid dp/dt as a psychophysiological index of sympathetic myocardial effects: Some considerations. *Psychophysiology, 17*, 495–498.

Obrist, P. A., Howard, J. L., Lawler, J. E., Galosy, R., Meyers, K., & Gaebelein, C. J. (1974). Cardiac-somatic interaction. In P. A. Obrist, A. H. Black, J. Brener, & L. V. Dicara (Eds.), *Cardiovascular psychophysiology: Current issues in response mechanisms, biofeedback and methodology*. (pp. 136–162). Chicago: Aldine.

Obrist, P. A., Howard, J. L., Lawler, J. E., Sutterer, J. R., Smithson, K. W., & Martin, P. L. (1972). Alterations in cardiac contractility during classical aversive conditioning in dogs: Methodological and theoretical implications. *Psychophysiology, 9*, 246–261.

Obrist, P. A., Lawler, J. E., Howard, J. L., Smithson, K. W., Martin, P. L., & Manning, J. (1974). Sympathetic influences on the heart in humans: Effects on contractility and heart rate of acute stress. *Psychophysiology, 11*, 405–427.

Obrist, P. A., Webb, R. A., & Sutterer, J. R. (1969). Heart rate and somatic changes during aversive conditioning and simple reaction time tasks. *Psychophysiology, 5*, 696–723.

Obrist, P. A., Webb, R. A., Sutterer, J. R., & Howard, J. (1970). The cardiac-somatic relationship: Some reformulations. *Psychophysiology, 6*, 569–587.

Odegaard, O. (1932). The psychogalvonic reactivity in affective disorders. *Journal of Medical Psychology, 25*, 3–12.

Oken, D., Grinker, R. R., Heath, H. A., Korchin, S. J., Sabskin, M., & Schwartz, N. B. (1962). Relation of physiological responses to affect expression. *Archives of General Psychiatry, 6*, 336–351.

Papillo, J. F., Pijacki, R., & Tursky, B. (1984). A comprehensive software package for the management of psychophysiological experimentation. *Psychophysiological, 21*, 159.

Papillo, J. F., Tursky, B., & Friedman, R. (1981). Perceived changes in the intensity of arterial pulsations as a function of applied cuff pressure. *Psychophysiology, 18*, 283–287.

Paul, G. L., & Bernstein, D. A. (1973). *Anxiety and clinical problems: Systematic desensitization and related techniques*. New York: General Learning Press.

Pennebaker, J. W. (1982). The psychology of physical symptoms. New York: Springer-Verlag.

Porges, S. W. (1986). Respiratory sinus arrhythmia: physiological basis, quantitative methods, and clinical implications. In P. Grossman, K. H. L. Janssen, and D. Vaitt (Eds.), *Cardiorespiratory and cardiosomatic psychophysiology*. (pp. 101–115). New York: Plenum Press.

Porges, S. W., McCabe, P. M., & Yongue, B. G. (1982). Respiratory-heart-rate interactions: psychophysiological implications for pathophysiology and behavior. In J. Cacioppo and R. Petly (Eds.), *Perspectives in cardiovascular psychophysiology*. (pp. 223–264). New York: Guilford Press.

Posey, J. A., Geddy, L. A., Williams, H., & Moore, A. (1969). The meaning of the point of maximum oscillations in cuff pressure in the indirect measurement of blood pressure. *Cardiology Research Center Bulletin, 8*, 15–25.

Rachman, S. & Hodeson, R. I. (1974). Synchrony and desynchrony in fear and avoidance. *Behavior Research and Therapy, 12*, 311–318.

Roth, W. T., Tinklenberg, J. R., & Doyle, C. M. (1976). Mood states and 24-hour cardiac monitoring. *Journal of Psychosomatic Research, 20*, 179–186.

Sayers, B., McA. (1973). Analysis of heart rate variability. *Ergonometrics, 16*, 17–32.

Schandry, R. (1981). Heart beat perception and emotional experience. *Psychophysiology, 11*, 76–85.

Schneiderman, N., McCabe, P. M., & Hausman, K. A. (1984). Neurogenic influences upon the heart. In J. A. Herd, A. M. Gotto, P. G. Kaufman & S. M. Weiss (Eds)., *Cardiovascular instrumentation: Application of new technology to biobehavioral research*. (pp. 139–149). National Institutes of Health Publication No. 1 84–1654.

Schneiderman, N., & Pickering, G. W. (1986) Cardiovascular measures of physiologic reactivity. In K. A. Matthews, S. N. Weiss, T. Detre, T. M. Dembrowski, B. Falkner, S. B. Manuck, & R. B. Williams (Eds.), *Handbook of stress, reactivity and cardiovascular disease*. New York: Wiley.

Schwartz, G. E. (1977). Biofeedback and physiological patterning in human emotion and consciousness. In J. Beatty, J. Legewie, and H. Legewie (Eds.), *Biofeedback and behavior*. New York: Plenum Press.

Schwartz, G. E. (1978). Psychobiological foundations of psychotherapy and behavior change. In S. L. Garfield & A. E. Bergin (Eds.), *Handbook of psychotherapy and behavior change: An empirical analysis*. (pp. 63–99). New York: Wiley.

Schwartz, G. E., Weinberger, D. A., & Singer, J. A. (1981). Cardiovascular differentiation of happiness, saddness, anger and fear following imagery and exercise. *Psychosomatic Medicine, 43*, 343–364.

Shapiro, D., Greenstadt, L., Lane, J. D., & Rubinstein, E. (1981). Tracking cuff system for beat-to-beat recording of blood pressure. *Psychophysiology, 18*, 129–136.

Shean, G. D., & Stange, P. W. (1971). The effects of varied respiratory rate and volume upon finger pulse volume. *Psychophysiology, 8*, 401–405.

Sherwood, A., Allen, M., Obrist, P. A., & Langer, A. W. (1986). Evaluation of beta adrenergic influences on cardiovascular and metabolic adjustments to physical and psychological stress. *Psychophysiology, 23*, 89–104.

Shimizu, H. (1977). Digital cardiac meter with D. A. converter. *Psychophysiology, 14*, 417–419.

Siddle, D. A. T., Turpin, G., Spinks, J. A., & Stevenson, D. (1980), Peripheral measures. In H. M. van Praag, M. H. Lader, O. J. Rafelson & E. J. Sachar (Eds.), *Handbook of biological psychiatry: Part II — Brain mechanisms and abnormal behavior — psychophysiology*. (pp. 45–78). New York: Marcel Dekker.

Smith, T. M., Houston, B. K., & Stucky, R. J. (1984). Effects threat of shock and control over shock on finger pulse volume, pulse rate and systolic blood pressure. *Biological Psychology, 20*, 31–42.

Smith, T. W., Houston, B. K., & Zurawski, R. (1984). Finger pulse volume as a measure of anxiety in response to evaluative threat. *Psychophysiology, 21*, 260–265.

Smyth, H. S., Sleight, P., & Pickering, G. W. (1969). Reflex regulation of arterial pressure during sleep in man: A quantitative method of assessing baroreceptor sensitivity. *Circulation Research, 24*, 109–121.

Stead, E. A., Warren, J. B., Merrill, A. J., & Brannon, E. S. (1945). Cardiac output in male subjects as measured by the technique of right atrial catherization: Normal values with observations and the effects of anxiety and tilting. *Journal of Clinical Investigations, 24,* 346–331.

Steptoe, A. (1980). Blood pressure. In I. Martin & P. H. Venables (Eds.), *Techniques in Psychophysiology* (pp. 247–273). New York: Wiley.

Stevenson, I. P., Suncon, L. H., Wolf, S., Ripley, H. S., & Wolf, H. G. (1949). Life situations, emotions and extrasystolies. *Psychosomatic Medicine, 11,* 257–272.

Stevenson, I., & Ripley, H. (1952). Variations in respiration and in respiratory systems during changes in emotions. *Psychosomatic Medicine, 14,* 476–490.

Suess, W. M., Alexander, A. B., Smith, D. D., Sweeny, H. W., & Marion, R. J. (1980). The effects of psychological stress on respiration: A preliminary study of anxiety and respiration. *Psychophysiology, 17,* 535–540.

Taylor, C. B., Sheikh, J., Agras, S., Roth, W. T., Margraf, J., Ehlers, A., Maddock, R. J., & Gossard, D. (1986). Ambulatory heart rate changes in patients with panic attacks. *American Journal of Psychiatry, 143,* 478–482.

Tursky, B. (1974). The indirect recording of human blood pressure. In P. A. Obrist, A. H. Black, J. Brener, L. V. Dicara (Eds.), *Cardiovascular psychophysiology: Current issues in response mechanism, biofeedback and methodology.* (pp. 93–105). Chicago: Aldine.

Tursky, B., & O'Connell, D. N. (1966). Survey of practice in electrodermal measurement. *Psychophysiology, 2,* 237–240.

Tursky, B., Papillo, J. F., & Friedman, R. (1981). The perception and discrimination of arterial pulsations: Implications for the behavioral treatment of hypertension. *Journal of Psychosomatic Research, 26,* 485–493.

Tursky, B., Shapiro, D., & Schwartz, G. E. (1972). Automated constant cuff pressure system to measure average systolic and diastolic blood pressure in man. *IEEE Transactions on Biomedical Engineering, 19,* 271–276.

Tyrer, P. (1976). The role of bodily feelings in anxiety. *Institute of Psychiatry — Maudsley Monographs,* No. 23, Oxford University Press.

Tyrer, P., Lee, I., & Alexander, J. (1980). Awareness of cardiac function in anxious, phobic and hypochondrical patients. *Psychological Medicine, 10,* 171–174.

Van Egeren, L. F., Feather, B. W., & Hein, P. L. (1971). Desensitization of phobias: Some physiological propositions. *Psychophysiology, 8,* 213–228.

Varni, J. G., Clarke, E., & Giddon, D. B. (1971). Analysis of cyclic heart rate variability. *Psychophysiology, 8,* 406–413.

Venables, P. H., & Christie, M. J. (1973). Mechanisms, instrumentation, recording techniques and quantification of responses. In W. F. Prokasy & D. C. Raskin (Eds.), *Electrodermal activity in psychological research.* (pp. 1–124). New York: Academic Press.

Venables, P. H., & Christie, M. J. (1980). Electrodermal activity. In I. Martin and P. H. Venables (Eds.), *Techniques in Psychophysiology.* (pp. 3–67). New York: Wiley & Sons.

Weerts, T. C., & Roberts, R. (1976). The physiological effects of imagining anger-provoking and fear-provoking scenes. *Psychophysiology, 13,* 174.

Weiss, T., Dell Bo, A. D., Reichek, N., & Engelman, K. (1980). Pulse transit time in the analysis of autonomic nervous system affects on the cardiovascular system. *Psychophysiology, 17,* 202–207.

White, B. V., & Gilden, E. F. (1937). 'Cold Pressor Test' in tension and anxiety: A cardiochronographic study. *Archives of Neurological Psychiatry, 38,* 964–984.

Whitney, R. J. (1953). The measurement of volume changes in human limbs. *Journal of Physiology, 121,* 1.

Wilder, J. (1957). The law of initial values in neurology and psychiatry. Facts and problems. *Journal of Nervous and Mental Disease, 125,* 73–86.

Wilson, R. S. (1974). CARDIVAR: The statistical analysis of heart rate data. *Psychophysiology, 11,* 76–85.

Williams, R. C. Measurement of local blood flow during behavioral experiments: Principles and practice. In J. A. Hord, A. M. Gotto, P. G. Kaufmann, & S. M. Weiss (Eds.), *Cardiovascular instrumentation: Proceedings of the workshop conference on applicability of new technology to biobehavioral research.* (pp. 207–217). National Institutes of Health Publication No. 84–1654.

CHAPTER 13

Psychodynamics

Morris Eagle and David L. Wolitzky

Anxiety is a central factor in a wide range of psychopathology, and is certainly central to the psychoanalytic conception of neurosis — central in at least two ways. One, from a clinical point of view, some variant of anxiety as well as defenses against it are present in all neurotic behavior. Two, from a theoretical point of view, a discussion of the concept of anxiety in the context of psychoanalytic theory necessarily and inevitably leads one to a consideration of a network of other key psychoanalytic concepts: instinctual drive, defense, intrapsychic conflict, symptomatology, ego and superego, degree of ego strength, and so on.

A full explication of a theorist's views of anxiety almost requires a complete account of that writer's overall theory of personality, a task clearly beyond what can be presented here. We will, therefore, remain as close as possible to the main features of a given theorist's conceptualization of anxiety and provide the reader with references to the larger theory in which it is embedded.

In presenting psychodynamic theories of anxiety, the main distinction to be drawn is between the traditional Freudian theory of anxiety and other psychodynamic theories associated for example, with the work of Horney, Sullivan, Fairbairn, and more recently, Kohut. As is the case with most, if not all, post-Freudian developments, the later psychoanalytic and psychodynamic theories of anxiety take Freud's theory of anxiety as their point of departure. It is appropriate, then, to begin with Freud's conceptions of anxiety and then go on to consider briefly other psychodynamic formulations of anxiety that differ from Freud's views.

FREUDIAN THEORIES OF ANXIETY

It would be more accurate to speak of Freud's theories of anxiety rather than a single theory because, as is well known, throughout the course of his writings Freud presented a number of different conceptions of anxiety. Although Compton (1972) describes four different phases in Freud's theory of anxiety, the more customary approach is to distinguish dichotomously between Freud's earlier and later theories of anxiety.

Freud's earlier theory of anxiety

In his first or earlier theory, often referred to as his "toxic" theory, anxiety results from the transformation of nongratified and nondischarged libidinal impulses or, put in a somewhat different and more accurate way, from the transformation of the affect of a repressed impulse. Consistent with this theory, Freud believed that prolonged sexual privation and frustration or repeated practice of *coitus interruptus*, insofar as it led to the build-up of excessive excitation, could produce anxiety. Indeed, Freud initially believed that certain illnesses, such as neuresthenia and anxiety neurosis (later called "actual neurosis" — Freud, 1894/1924, did not involve psychical mechanisms, but were due to the purely physical effects of the accumulation of somatic sexual excitation. However, even when psychical factors are involved, the primary issue for Freud during this period continued to be failure to discharge affect. Thus, the central problem in hysteria was "strangulated affect," and the treatment of choice was "abreaction" of that affect. Because Freud conceptualized affect as the discharge of a quantity of excitation, the failure to discharge affect (whether because of trauma, repression, or unhealthy sexual practices) meant an increase in the sum of excitation in the nervous system. Further, any excessive increase in the sum of excitation predisposed one to anxiety and/or symptoms of one kind or another (e.g., hysterical, obsessive, or phobic), depending upon the nature of the defenses employed by the patient.

Until 1933, Freud was concerned with finding a biological explanation of anxiety. It was not until Lecture XXXII in the *New Introductory Lectures* (Freud, 1933/1964) that he gave up the idea that anxiety was transformed libido, even though he had begun to replace a reliance on economic concepts with an increasing emphasis on psychodynamic factors.

Although Freud never entirely gave up his first theory of anxiety (he only relinquished certain aspects of it), it was essentially supplanted by his second theory of "signal anxiety." Before, however, describing what has come to be known as *the* Freudian theory of anxiety, it should be noted that not all psychoanalytic theorists relinquished all the earlier theories, in particular the aspect of it having to do with the relationship between frustration of libidinal impulse (and the accumulation of excitation that such frustration creates) and the likelihood of anxiety and pathological defenses. Zetzel (1955) for example, writes that there is "evidence to suggest that unrelieved instinctual tension of any origin has results which may be clinically indistinguishable from morbid anxiety" (p. 370). Others (e.g., Rangell, 1955, 1968; Schur, 1953) have attempted to combine Freud's earlier and later theories of anxiety into a unified theory of anxiety. However, we shall put off a description of those attempts until after we have had an opportunity to present Freud's later "signal" theory of anxiety.

Freud's later theory of anxiety

One way of capturing, in abbreviated form, the major modification from Freud's earlier to his later theory of anxiety is to point out that while, in the earlier theory, anxiety is the consequence of repression (insofar as repression blocks the discharge of affect and thereby increases the sum of excitation), in the later theory, the causal direction is reversed and repression is the consequence of anxiety.

Instinctual wish, "signal anxiety," and defense

In order to explicate the above description, one must introduce the concept of "signal anxiety." By the time Freud (1926/1959) introduced his later theory of anxiety, he had already developed the so-called structural model of id, ego, and superego. According to Freud, in a situation of danger the ego is capable of generating a small quantity of anxiety which acts as a *signal* to alert the organism that danger threatens.

"Signal anxiety" is generally elicited by an instinctual wish or impulse that, in the past, has been associated with punishment and disapproval. It is the anticipated consequences following the expression (in thought or action) of the wish that constitutes the danger situation. Through the operation of the pleasure principle, defense is automatically instituted against the danger that threatens, with the result that the danger or threat is minimized.

The primary function of repression, the prototypical defense, is to banish the anxiety-producing idea or affect from consciousness. The relationship among instinctual wish, signal anxiety, and defense can be seen essentially as a negative feedback mechanism or system. Thus, an incipient thought or feeling linked to an instinctual wish elicits a small quantity of anxiety ("signal anxiety"), which then mobilizes defense, which, in turn serves to keep the incipient thought or feeling from reaching consciousness (and thereby gaining access to the motor apparatus), which then serves to reduce anxiety.

Freud posits predominant dangers appropriate to different developmental stages. Thus, birth with its sudden flood of excitation is held to be the prototype of all anxiety.[1] Then comes loss of the object, that is, of the caretaker. At a more mature developmental stage it is more loss of the object's love, rather than loss of the object, that is the primary danger and the primary source of anxiety. For the male child, castration anxiety is the major source of anxiety during the oedipal phase.[2] With formation of the superego, superego anxiety or guilt appears as a major source and form of anxiety. Anna Freud (1946) adds to this list anxiety in response to the strength or intensity of one's drives and anxiety in response to conflicts between mutually incompatible aims.[3]

The above are all referred to as danger situations. But upon what common danger do they all converge? According to Freud, the basic danger underlying all anxiety is a situation of helplessness, referred to as a "traumatic situation," in which one is at the mercy of excessive and unrelenting excitation exerted by instinctual drive. For Freud, all the sources of anxiety referred to above (loss of the object, loss of the object's love, etc.) represent the common danger of leaving the organism exposed to excessive excitation generated by nongratified instinctual drives.[4]

In an interesting paper on the Freudian theory of anxiety, Hurvich (1985) maintains that overwhelmed helplessness that can be anticipated qualifies as a basic danger situation (which he terms *annihilation anxiety*) that it is in fact the first basic danger, and as such is the prototype for the later, traditional danger situations. According to Hurvich (1985), presence of ego deficits, ego regressions, and traumatic experiences (both current and past) makes the individual more susceptible to the fear of annihilation, which is regarded as "a universal *potential* anxiety".

---

[1] The concept of signal anxiety presupposes the capacity for judgment and anticipation based on memories of prior experiences of gradations of anxiety. Psychological meanings are involved in traumatic anxiety as well, though not at birth. While Freud (1900/1953, p. 400), maintained that "the act of birth is the first experience of anxiety, and thus the source and prototype of the affect of anxiety," he also was aware (1926/1959, p. 135) that "The danger of birth has as yet no psychical content. We cannot possibly suppose that the foetus has any sort of knowledge that there is the possibility of being destroyed." It was partly on this basis that Freud rejected Rank's (1924) overly literal view of the trauma of birth and its alleged consequences (e.g., its causal role in childhood phobias).

[2] It will be noted that all the above danger — loss of the object, loss of the object's love and castration anxiety — are held initially to be real or objective dangers.

[3] Michels, Frances, and Shear (1985) refer to still another source of anxiety: a real current danger symbolically or associately linked to early actual or fantasized dangers.

[4] Note that the key idea, linking excessive excitation and anxiety, is retained from Freud's earlier theory of anxiety.

Failure of defense, pathological anxiety, and symptoms

In Freud's (1926/1959) later theory of anxiety, the adaptive function of "signal anxiety" is to mobilize defenses and thus prevent a danger situation from becoming a traumatic situation. When "signal anxiety" and defenses function adequately, the degree of anxiety experienced is limited and contained. When, however, defenses fail, anxiety of distressing and symptomatic proportions ensues. This is often experienced as an anxiety attack and/or as diffuse "free-floating" anxiety. As noted earlier, according to psychoanalytic theory, anxiety of some kind and degree is a necessary and basic element in all neurosis. Often, however, after an initial anxiety attack or period of experiencing "free-floating" anxiety, other symptoms, such as phobias, compulsions, and obsessive thoughts appear and constitute the chronic recognizable symptomatic form of the neurosis. These specific symptoms can be seen as a second line of defense, as an attempt to bind the primary diffuse anxiety to specific situations and contexts. For example, in phobias, anxiety can be contained so long as the phobic situation is avoided. Indeed, the phobic symptom can be understood as an attempt to reinstitute the function normally carried out by signal anxiety or defense, with the symptom now serving the warning and mobilizing functions normally served by signal anxiety and defense, and with an external situation and actual physical avoidance or escape substituting respectively, for an inner situation (a thought or impulse) and for a psychological defense. Thus, appearance of (or thoughts about) the phobic situation evokes moderate amounts of anxiety which then leads to physical avoidance of the danger situation, just as the small amount of "signal anxiety" leads to psychological avoidance (defense) of the instinctually related thought or feeling that is associated with the danger situation. The analogy goes further. Just as intense anxiety is experienced when signal anxiety and defense fail to banish the forbidden thought or feeling from consciousness, so it is also experienced when the phobic symptom fails to protect the individual from confronting the phobic situation. In both cases a danger situation is transformed into a traumatic situation, and the individual experiences himself or herself as helpless in the face of intense, even catastrophic, anxiety.

Roughly speaking, different kinds of anxiety can be correlated with different forms of psychopathology. The total psychic helplessness and fear of fragmentation would tend to be most characteristic of the psychoses; anxiety over loss of the object is prominent to borderline conditions, while castration anxiety and superego anxiety are seen in neurotic conditions (Bergeret, 1974; Hurvich, 1985). However, this scheme is oversimplified in that any of these anxieties can appear in connection with any of the syndromes or with any symptom. Furthermore, in view of the potential symbolic/emotional equivalence of the major types of anxiety, it needs to be established in each case to what extent the manifest anxiety expressed is the most relevant anxiety. For example, to what extent is castration anxiety being fueled by separation anxiety and vice versa?

It should be noted that this general formulation includes an implicit role for learning, at least in the maintenance of symptomatic and defense-related behavior. That is, insofar as symptoms and defense reduce or provide relief of anxiety, they are reinforced and thereby maintained (see Dollard & Miller, 1950 for a comprehensive attempt to link psychoanalytic and learning theories).

Inner conflict and anxiety

Although it has not been explicitly discussed in the preceding description, the importance of inner or intrapsychic conflict is implicit in Freud's later theory of anxiety. It will be recalled that it is an instinctual wish that mobilizes "signal anxiety" and defense. This is so because the instinctual wish has been associated with externally imposed punishment and threats of punishment (loss of the object, etc.). Were this the complete story, one could hardly speak of *inner* conflict, but only of conflict between the individual and his or her environment. According to the psychoanalytic account, however, what was originally a conflict between an instinctual wish and external prohibitions and punishments (and what was originally, therefore, objective and realistic anxiety), through the process of internalization, becomes an inner conflict. The ego comes to represent the constraints of physical and social reality (and to assess the dangers of ignoring these constraints), and the superego comes to represent moral prohibitions and constraints. Hence, one can now speak meaningfully of *intrapsychic conflict;* that is, conflict among the different psychic structures of id, ego, and superego. And one can understand how inner or intrapsychic conflict is implicated in generating anxiety. In Freudian theory, it is an instinctual wish that comes into conflict with ego and/or superego concerns and interests that is the immediate trigger for anxiety. One can also understand the intimate relationship among the triad of conflict, anxiety, and defense.[5]

Two theories of anxiety or a unified single theory?

As noted earlier, there have been a number of attempts to integrate Freud's two theories of anxiety into a single unified theory. Zetzel (1955), for example, makes the point that the internal danger situation that is signaled by "signal anxiety" is directly related to the excessive excitation that is a consequence of instinctual frustration. The most sustained and elaborate attempt to formulate a unified theory of anxiety that incorporates elements of Freud's earlier and later theories has been made by Rangell (1955, 1968). Without going into great detail, Rangell's argument is essentially that anxiety is *always* a signal of danger and *always* a reaction to a traumatic state of helplessness (in the face of instinctual discharge). The traumatic state can be mild (as in Freud's later theory of "signal anxiety") or it can be intense and severe (as in Freud's earlier theory of anxiety). In the latter case, the fear is of an ever-increasing, spiralling anxiety to the point of motor and psychic paralysis. Hence, anxiety is always set in motion by a traumatic state (mild or intense) and is always a signal of the anticipation of further danger (that the traumatic state will get worse). In both cases, anxiety has a psychological meaning. Rangell observes that one can accept Freud's clinical description of the actual or anxiety neurosis (as an experienced state of traumatic psychic helplessness and intense anxiety) without accepting Freud's explanation of this anxiety state in terms of the transformation of repressed and undischarged libido. It should be noted, however, that Rangell continues to accept the basic Freudian idea that a traumatic state is defined by an "unabsorbable excess of stimuli" generated by instinctual drive pressures (although Rangell [1955] denies "that there is a specific and exclusive relationship between anxiety and mounting *sexual* impulses. . . ." p. 395).

[5] The above formulation is based on what can be called a crime–punishment model. That is, instinctual wishes that are associated with parental (and societal) punishment become involved in conflict, anxiety, and defense. An implication of this model is that were instinctual wishes not originally associated with punishment, they would have little ability to generate conflict and anxiety. And, indeed, this is one predominant way in which Freud's theory of the relationship between instinct and anxiety has come to be interpreted by some — as reflected, for example, in the expectation that a more sexually libertarian society and childrearing system would reduce the incidence and intensity of neuroses, conflict, and anxiety. However, as has been noted (Eagle, 1984), in some of his writings, Freud (1940/1964) suggests that insofar as they represent the threat of excessive excitation, instinctual wishes and drives of *inherently* inimical to the ego and therefore, *inherently* capable of generating anxiety. Anna Freud (1946) makes this quite explicit when she refers to the "primary antagonism" between id and ego. An implication of this latter view is that to a greater or lesser extent, both a certain degree of inner conflict and anxiety are inevitable aspects of our biological and mental structure.

This chapter is not an appropriate occasion to present a critique of the psychoanalytic theory of anxiety. However, perhaps a few brief remarks are in order. First, it is clear that in discussing Freud's earlier and later theories of anxiety, Rangell is dealing with *different degrees* of anxiety — from mild to intense. "Signal" anxiety seems applicable to those instances where anxiety is mild and relatively fleeting and where defense is mobilized and instituted so that a traumatic situation is not experienced. It seems to us somewhat forced to argue that mild "signal anxiety" is generated by a mild traumatic situation. After all, it is the nature of traumatic situations that they are *not* mild, but rather inundating and unmanageable. When, by contrast, anxiety is severe (as in, for example, an anxiety attack), this suggests that the "signal" function of anxiety has failed. It is true that when people experience even intense anxiety they often fear that it will get worse and worse in an unending spiral. But this does not mean that the intense anxiety being experienced serves as a "signal" for the anticipation of even more uncontrollable and more intense anxiety — in the same sense that mild and fleeting anxiety serves as a "signal" of a traumatic situation. After all, in the former case, traumatic anxiety has already been experienced (although it can get worse and one can fear that it will get worse — anything can get worse). Another consideration that makes apparent the differences between "signal" anxiety and the anxiety characteristic of an anxiety attack is that in the former case, defenses are *effective* and *prevent* anxiety, while in the latter case, defenses have *failed* and traumatic and symptomatic anxiety is experienced.

Freud's earlier and later theories of anxiety *do* have in common the link between anxiety and the excessive excitation that is purportedly the consequence of undischarged instinctual tensions. And it is this common link that has provided the impetus for the attempts to unify the two theories. But it is the core idea that excessive excitation from frustrated instinctual drive constitutes a traumatic situation that needs to be questioned. There is little or no empirical evidence supporting this link. Furthermore, the whole idea that the danger of excessive excitation deriving from instinctual drive is what anxiety is all about is based on a model of the mind and of the nervous system that is seen by many as untenable. Of course, anxiety entails, both experimentally and neurophysiologically, *over-arousal* (which can be taken as synonymous with excessive excitation). And once one is anxious, one may fear even further arousal (captured, for example, in such experiences as fear of "splintering into pieces"). But this does not mean (a) that the neurophysiological over-arousal that is part of anxiety is caused or even related to undischarged libidinal tensions and, most important, (b) that the anxiety one experiences is occasioned by the anticipation of excessive excitation (whether or not the source of that excessive excitation is undischarged instinctual drive). It is not that anxiety is *caused* by the anticipation of excessive excitation, but rather that one aspect or feature of anxiety *is* excessive excitation (or over-arousal). What remains unclear is what causes some people to be especially prone to anxiety and the over-arousal that accompanies it. This is a variant of the question posed by Fenichel (1945) and Nunberg (1955) regarding the susceptibility of some people for a "heightened state of tension" and "readiness for anxiety." To suggest that such people are anxious because they anticipate excessive excitation seems to us to beg the question.[6]

[6] It is true that for some very anxious people, any kind or degree of excitement or arousal triggers further anxiety. They are already so over-aroused that any further arousal is experienced as unmanageable and threatening. Hence, there is something to the idea that fear or anticipation of excessive excitation can trigger anxiety. But, as we noted earlier, it does not follow that instinctual drive tensions are a primary source of such excitation. Further, one still needs to account for the initial high level of anxiety experienced by these people.

Individual differences in susceptibility to anxiety

Any comprehensive theory of anxiety would have to account for individual differences in susceptibility to experiencing anxiety. Although such individual differences have not been a primary focus to psychoanalytic theory, Freudian theorists do have some things to say about this issue. In addition, there are certain implications that can be drawn from the logic of certain aspects of psychoanalytic theory.

In its most general terms, the question is: Why do some people experience anxiety more readily and more intensely than others? Freud's early implicit answer, it will be recalled, is that those people who engage in unhealthy sexual practices in which undischarged libido is transformed into anxiety are more subject to anxiety. But this answer became unacceptable in the light of further developments in the theory of anxiety. A more complete answer would include hereditary factors, early experiences, intensity of instinctual drive, and degree of ego strength. Fenichel (1945) has noted that some people are especially prone to anxiety, in his words, to a state of "heightened inner tension." In a similar vein, Nunberg (1955) suggests that a greater "readiness for anxiety" is present in some individuals which, he argues, predisposes them to neurotic disorders. Neither Fenichel nor Nunberg say much about what they believe to be the sources of this greater readiness for anxiety. However, implicit in their descriptions and in the logic of psychoanalytic theory is the idea that constitutional factors interacting with certain early experiences would predispose one to a greater "readiness for anxiety." The particular early experiences that, from the point of view of traditional psychoanalytic theory, would seem to be especially important include parental punishment and threats of punishment associated with expressions of instinctual wishes. Such parental behavior would, it could be argued, intensify the "primary antagonism" between instinct and ego and make it more likely that the child would experience instinctual wishes as a danger (i.e., the danger of loss of the object's love and of castration, or their symbolic equivalents). Through various processes of internalization, these external "objective" dangers would eventually become internal dangers. The result is an intensification of the inner conflict between the natural expression of instinctually tinged wishes and desires and ego and superego reactions. This, in turn, would increase the likelihood of repressions of instinctual impulses which, in turn, leads to the build-up of unreleived drive excitations and thereby, to a "heightened state of inner tension" and a greater "readiness of anxiety."[7]

Following the basic logic that anything that leads to excessive excitation and/or to an increase in an individual's sense of inner danger will be likely to generate anxiety, one would expect the factors of intensification of drive and lowered ego strength to be associated with increased anxiety. The latter factor — degree of ego strength — would seem to be especially closely linked to anxiety. For any situations in which one makes the unconscious assessment that one cannot cope, and in which the consequences of that failure to cope are threatening to a core aspect of one's personality, are likely to generate anxiety. Indeed, at any given point, anxiety is likely to be functionally related, not to absolute degree of ego strength, but to a *ratio* between degree of ego strength (or degree of experienced coping ability) and the threats and demands of either an internal or external situation.

NON-FREUDIAN PSYCHODYNAMIC THEORIES OF ANXIETY

There are a number of non-Freudian, but nonetheless psychodynamic theories of anxiety that have been elaborated to a

[7] Note that aspects of Freud's earlier theory of anxiety — in which unrelieved drive tensions lead to anxiety — is retained in this formulation.

greater or lesser degree. One of the features they all seem to have in common is their rejection of the basic Freudian idea that it is an instinctual wish (and its association with punishment and excessive excitation) that triggers anxiety. This is true for the so-called neo-Freudians (e.g., Horney, Sullivan), the so-called object relations theorists (e.g., Fairbairn, Guntrip) and the more recent psychoanalytic self psychology associated with the work of Kohut. In addition, in his attachment theory, Bowlby has had a good deal to say about the causes and nature of anxiety. Obviously, we cannot cover *all* non-Freudian psychodynamic theories of anxiety in this chapter. We will, however, briefly present the ideas of Horney, Sulivan, Bowlby, Fairbairn, and Kohut. Not all of these writers have fully developed and elaborated theories of anxiety. However, all of them do offer substantive and significant revisions of Freud's theory of anxiety.

Sullivan

Perhaps no theory of personality and psychopathology since Freud's has accorded a more significant role to anxiety than that of Sullivan. As he puts it,

> I believe that it is fairly safe to say that anybody and everybody devotes much of his lifetime, a great deal of his energy — talking loosely — and a good part of his effort in dealing with others, to avoiding more anxiety than he already has, and, if possible, to getting rid of this anxiety. (Sullivan, 1953, p. 11)

As is well known, Sullivan emphasized the interpersonal field as the primary context within which to describe personality development and functioning. This focus, which has been termed a "relational/structure" model for personality, has been contrasted with Freud's so-called "drive/structure model" (Greenberg & Mitchell, 1983, p. 100). In Sullivan's system, anxiety originates not from an excess of stimulation that cannot be mastered by the ego, but from a diturbance in the emotional connection between mother and infant. Sullivan invokes the concept of empathy to explain this connection. Empathy refers to "the peculiar emotional linkage that sustains the relationship of the infant with other significant people — the mother or the nurse" (1947, p. 8). When the infant shows evidence of satisfaction of its somatic needs, for example, following feeding, there is (optimally) a biologically based tendency for this expression of pleasure to evoke delight in the mother. This is what Sullivan means by "empathic linkage" (1947, p. 8). The mother's expression of pleasure in reaction to her infant's similar expression "communicates good feeling to the infant." (At another point, Sullivan [1953, p. 37] refers to the mother's desire to satisfy its infant's needs as based on "tenderness.") The "good feeling" brings a feeling of "security," above and beyond that felt from need satisfaction. It also conveys to the infant that he or she has an *impact* on the mother (the origins of sense of power and competence).

Satisfaction needs (which refer mainly to physiological needs) and security needs (which refer primarily to psychological needs) are the two main types of organismic needs which, if not reduced by the infant's mother, give rise to strong, potentially intolerable tension states. According to Sullivan, disturbances in maternal empathy are caused by the mother's anxiety which via a process of emotional contagion becomes the direct, immediate cause of the infant's anxiety. This point bears emphasis because the caretaker may show a lapse of empathy, but not necessarily become anxious (e.g., a depressed, withdrawn mother). The infant's primitive anxiety is not sharply differentiated from fear, but in the course of development begins to be experienced as one of a limited number of "uncanny" emotions (the others being awe, dread, horror, and loathing). Sullivan (1953) is trying here to convey the "paralyzing power of anxiety" in the severely anxious infant (pp. 10, 11).

Thus, Sullivan's (1953, p. 41) central theorem regarding anxiety is that "The tension of anxiety, when present in the mothering one, induces anxiety in the infant." The process by which this occurs is "thoroughly obscure," admits Sullivan (1953, p. 41), who invokes the concept of empathy as a provisional explanation.

In any case, for Sullivan, one of the first and most vital things infant's learn is the discrimination of anxious versus non-anxious states. Infants begin to regulate their conscious experiences, their behavior with others (as well as when alone), and their conceptions and opinions of themselves along lines that attempt to minimize anxiety and thereby maximize their feeling's of security. In fact, Sullivan defines security as freedom from anxiety. In postulating the caregiver as the *cause* of the infant's anxiety, Sullivan's view is quite similar to Horney's. As we shall describe later, Horney also views the infant's anxiety as caused by the parents, but in her system the emphasis is not on parental anxiety as the cause, but on hostile, rejecting parental attitudes.

According to Sullivan, experiences of "good mother" and "bad mother" are precursors of the development of the notions of "good me," "bad me," and "not-me." "Not-me" refers to disowned, unintegrated realms of experience, behavior, and thoughts/affects associated with truly intense anxiety. Experience linked with a reduction of anxiety and a sense of "good mother" become differentiated, internalized, and represented as "good me." Experience associated with maternal disapproval and increases in anxiety become represented as "bad me." Not that initially the infant comes to feel anxious via contagion from the mother's anxiety. As the child learns to differentiate himself/herself from the mother, the stress is not so much on the mother's level of anxiety, but on her level of disapproval (overtly and covertly conveyed). Though it is not emphasized, the idea seems to be that sensing the mother's disapproval (rather than her anxiety per se) is enough to induce anxiety, because the child comes to anticipate that disapproval will lead to a reduction in tenderness. (In Freudian terms, this amounts to anxiety over the potential loss of the object's love and the loss of the object per se.) Thus, without being explicit about it, Sullivan appears to have a two-factor theory of anxiety induction: (a) anxiety in the mother, and (b) disapproval by the mother. The first seems to be predominant at earlier stages and the latter at later stages of development. These two factors may often be related to each other if it is assumed that disapproval from the mother is more likely to occur in areas in which she herself is anxious or potentially anxious.

The child as well as the adult is motivated to avoid conscious awareness of the "bad me" and the "not me," as these experiences are associated with anxiety. He or she does this by developing what Sullivan calls the "self-system." The self-system, which begins in late infancy, is "an organization of experience which will ultimately be of nothing less than stupendous importance in personality" (Sullivan, 1953, p. 165). This "organization of educative experience [is] called into being by the necessity to avoid or to minimize incidents of anxiety" (Sullivan, 1953, p. 165).

The developing child stores experiences according to a gradient of anxiety. Using his or her memory and anticipation or foresight, he or she can match memories against a developing interpersonal interaction or against whatever thoughts, feelings, fantasies, and so on are starting to emerge in consciousness. The self-system thus serves a warning function regarding the probability and intensity of anxiety (not unlike Freud's notion of signal anxiety assessed by the ego). It then instigates what Sullivan calls "security operations" (analogous to defenses in Freud's theory).

These security operations become strongly entrenched, shut out information that threatens to arouse anxiety, and lend to rigidity in patterns of interpersonal behavior. Insofar as personality change requires disruption of security operations, it always meets resistance and entails the experience of anxiety.

Horney

Horney distinguishes between anxiety and fear. Both are proportional to the degree of danger sensed by the person. The difference is that in fear, the danger is objective and known, while in anxiety, it is hidden and unknown. Thus, being extremely fearful when confronted with a picture of a snake is disproportionate to the objective threat, but not to the underlying psychological meanings. Horney claims that anxiety is a central issue for all of us, that its avoidance takes many forms, and that even if it is not an obvious part of the clinical picture (e.g., in depression), it is ultimately found beneath the surface to the same degree as in patients suffering from phobias or anxiety attacks). As she puts it, not only may we "have anxiety without knowing it, but . . . anxiety may be the determining factor in our lives without our being conscious of it" (Horney, 1937, p. 40).

Horney, (1937) emphasizes that "intense anxiety is one of the most tormenting affects we can have" (p. 40), in part, because of the associated feelings of helplessness and of being caught in the grip of irrational forces.

People "seem to go to any length to escape anxiety or to avoid feeling it" (Horney, 1937, p. 40). The principal means of dealing with anxiety are rationalization, denial, avoidance (as in phobias or inhibitions), and "narcotization" (not only literally, via drugs, but through various personal, social, and/or sexual activities designed to minimize anxiety, e.g., being a workaholic).

Having described anxiety as a strong imminent danger in the face of which one feels helpless, Horney tackles the problem of the psychological conditions that give rise to anxiety. Her general hypothesis is that "any impulse has the potential power to provoke anxiety, provided its discovery or pursuit would mean a violation of other vital interests or needs, and provided that it is sufficiently imperative or passionate" (Horney, 1937, p. 53). While in the Victorian era sexual impulses were a source of danger, Horney, writing in the 1930s, claims, in italics, that "hostile impulses of various kinds form the main source from which neurotic anxiety springs" (Horney, 1937, p. 54).

According to Horney, in most instances the link between hostility and neurotic anxiety is not apparent. It is repressed because it is "unbearable to be aware that one is hostile" (p. 57). Such repression leads to "a feeling of defenselessness" which is presumed to be present in the first place. According to Horney (1937).

> The main reasons why awareness of hostility may be unbearable are that one may love or need a person at the same time that one is hostile toward him, that one may not want to see the reasons, such as envy or possessiveness, which have promoted the hostility, or that it may be frightening to recognize within one's self hostility toward anyone. (p. 57).

The first reason Horney states sounds like Freud's danger situations of loss of the object or the object's love; the second reason sounds like superego anxiety; and the third reason is unclear, though perhaps she is implying the danger of feeling overwhelmed by one's impulses.

Horney's (1950) overall view of personality development places heavy emphasis on the extent to which the tendency toward self-realization is thwarted by adverse parental influences, in particular, their own neurotic conflicts. Under these conditions "the child does not develop a feeling of belonging, of "we", but instead a profound insecurity and vague apprehensiveness" (p. 18). This is what Horney means by "basic anxiety"; in her oft-quoted definition, it is the "feeling of being isolated and helpless in a world conceived as potentially hostile" (p. 18). Intense and pervasive feelings of basic anxiety provide the impetus for the increasingly rigid trends of moving "toward, against, or away from others" (p. 19) which become progressively elaborated into the complex neurotic structures that Horney describes in great detail in her key works (1937, 1950, etc.).

Horney (1939) attempts to explain what it is that is endangered in anxiety, what the source of the danger is, and what accounts for the sense of helplessness that characterizes anxiety states. Succinctly put, what is endangered is some aspect of one's "neurotic trends," the source of the danger being anything that "is likely to jeopardize the individual's specific protective pursuits, his specific neurotic trends" (p. 199). The source of the danger is nonspecific. The sense of helplessness is part and parcel of the individual's "basic anxiety," his or her rigid, compulsive, precariously balanced self-protective devices, and neurotic conflicts. Horney contasts this view with what she considers Freud's explanation or helpless — weakness of the "ego" (p. 203). Yet her description sounds a lot like Freud's account of the failure of ego defenses and coping resources and does not avoid the tautology of saying that a person feels helpless when this person believes he or she cannot cope. To say that the individual's "security" rather than his or her "ego" is endangered does not seem to be an advance in understanding (p. 202). We say this because Freud's formulation of the basic "danger situations" includes, at least implicitly, the idea that the person's security is threatened.

Of course, Horney's criticism is not merely terminological. It is part of her wholesale rejection of Freud's theory of instinctual drives. In emphasizing self-realization as the key motive in human functioning and in viewing instinctual drive behavior not as primary, but as an attempt to deal with basic anxiety, Horney's views bear an important similarity to Kohut's (although he fails to note the contribution of his predecessors).

Object-relations theorists (Fairbain and Guntrip)

The so-called English school of object relations theorists were all strongly influenced by and owe much to Melanie Klein. However, they have diverged sufficiently from her theories and have sufficiently established their own independent line of thought to be considered separately and independently. As with most theoretical divergences from traditional Freudian theory, object relations theorists too begin with a rejection of Freudian instinct theory. The basic differences between Freudian and object relations theories are perhaps best captured by Fairbairn's (1952) statement that "libido is primarily object-seeking, (rather than pleasure-seeking)" (p. 82). Here Fairbairn is boldly stating the claim that the basic motives, needs satisfactions, conflicts, defenses, and anxieties that characterize human behavior have to do not with the instinctual drives of sex and aggression, but with object relationships. And by object relationships, Fairbairn (as well as Guntrip) refers not only to actual interpersonal relationships with other people in the external world, but also to *internalized* object relationships (i.e., relationships with *internalized objects*). Without getting into a complex discussion of the concept of internalized objects, it suffices for the present purposes to think of them as inner mental *representations* of parental and other significant figures. Internalized object relationships are relationships — that is, attitudes, feelings, expectations, and so on — toward these representations (see Eagle, 1984).

Another of Fairbairn's basic claims is that the need for objects is primary and indeed, innate rather than, as Freud claimed, secondary to or a derivative of the object's gratification of purportedly more primary instinctual drives. (This claim, of course, is, as we shall see, very similar to Bowlby's (1969) insistence that the attachment system is inborn and not a secondary derivative of other drives).

In Fairbairn's and Guntrip's object relations theory, the most intense and the most basic anxiety has to do with ego breakdown and loss of self. And that awesome and unthinkable danger is, in turn, inextricably linked to object relationships in a number of ways. Because the young infant's mode of relating is one of primary identification, loss of the object, Fairbairn tells us, is equivalent to loss of the self. In this sense, separation anxiety is the basic anxiety. As Guntrip (1968) puts it, "separation anxiety then is a pointer to the last and worst fear, fear of the loss of the ego itself" (p. 128).

While primary identification and near complete dependence are normal in infants and young children, it is their persistence into adult life that, according to Fairbairn, constitutes the basic problem of all psychopathology. Fairbairn argues that all neurotic and psychotic symptoms are either (a) effects of or (b) defenses against conflicts attendant upon a persistent state of infantile dependence. The basic conflict that is central to a wide range of pathology is one "between an extreme reluctance to abandon infantile dependence" (p. 39) and "a longing to advance to an attitude of mature dependence upon the [differentiated] object" (p. 38). Or, as Fairbairn puts it elsewhere, the conflict is between a "a progressive urge to surrender the infantile attitude of identification with the object and a regressive urge to maintain that attitude" (1952, p. 43).

Each side of the conflict carries with it threats of anxiety. Yielding to primary identification and infantile dependence carries the threats of engulfment and loss of identity (as well as the fear that one's intense neediness and anger at not having one's needs met will destroy the object and thereby leave one without support). On the other hand, pursuing the progressive urge toward separation and renunciation of infantile dependence generates anxiety over feeling isolated, alone, and unsupported. One, then, is impelled to retreat back to the relative safety of home base (thereby expressing the regressive side of the conflict). This step, however, while it reduces the immediate intense anxiety, does not constitute a stable solution. For, after the immediate relief, the individual will often begin to feel imprisoned and engulfed and will attempt another foray to the outside world, thereby beginning the process all over again.

Another behavioral example of this kind of conflict is provided by Guntrip (1968), who describes an "in–out" relationship pattern. The individual seeks close relationships (for mature as well as immature reasons). But because of the intensity and infantile nature of his or her needs, he or she can only develop a relationship at an infantile level. Sooner or later, the individual experiences anxiety over fears of engulfment as well as fears that the intensity of his or her needs will destroy the object. This leads to emotional (and sometimes, physical) withdrawal from the relationship, and "out" phase. However, anxiety is now generated by feeling alone and unsupported. This, then, promotes the "in" phase — and so it goes.

There is one important additional source of anxiety that we have not yet mentioned: one that relates to *internalized* object relationships. Again, without getting into the complexities of Fairbairn's and Guntrip's theoretical system of split off ego structures and corresponding internalized objects, suffice it to say here that internalized representations, insofar as they represent persecutory, negative, and regressive attitudes toward oneself and one's needs, also represent important sources of anxiety. It is as if one is carrying around within oneself an "internal saboteur" that undermines one's sense of self, one's self-esteem and sense of competence, and one's moves toward satisfaction of one's needs and toward growth and mature dependence.

It should be apparent from the earlier brief presentation of object relations theory that the basic sources of anxiety posited by that theory have to do not with instinctual drive and excessive excitation, but with the threat of ego breakdown and loss of self as a consequence of either being engulfed by the object, persecuted and attacked by an internalized object, or finding oneself isolated, alone, and without support from objects.[8] It should also

[8] It is important to point out that for Freud, too, the ultimate danger is ego damage and breakdown. But for Freud the *source* of such danger is excessive excitation resulting from ungratified instinctual drives, while, as we have seen, for object relations theorists the source of such danger lies in one's object relations (see Eagle, 1984, for a fuller discussion of this issue).

be noted that, as will become apparent, there are important links between object relations theory and the later attachment theory of Bowlby (1969, 1973, 1980) and the psychoanalytic self psychology of Kohut (1971, 1977, 1984). The rejection of Freudian instinct theory; the independent and nonderived status of object relations; the primacy given to object relations in understanding one's needs, motives, satisfactions, defenses, and anxieties; the importance of the object and separation from the object as a basic source of anxiety; and the threat of ego breakdown and self-fragmentation as the ultimate anxiety-generating danger — all these elements constitute important links among object relations theory, Bowlby's attachment theory, and Kohut's psychoanalytic self psychology.

Bowlby's Theory of Anxiety

As is well known, Bowlby's work has focused on *attachment theory* in all its ramifications.[9] Along with a wide range of infra humans, we are, Bowlby maintains, genetically predisposed to develop attachment to caretakers, the biological evolutionary function of which is to guarantee the helpless infant's physical proximity to the adult caretaker and thereby minimize the danger of death from predation. One important aspect of the attachment system is the infant's reaction to separation from the attachment figure. The child's reactions to separation include a sequence of protests (which Bowlby links to separation anxiety), despair, and detachment. The initial anxiety and protest reaction is highly adaptive insofar as it increases the likelihood of calling attention to the caretakers and therefore furthers the infant's chances of survival. Bowlby's evolutionary–ethological perspective on anxiety is given added weight by compelling evidence that nonhuman primates react in a fashion similar to human infants. They too show extreme protest and anxiety reactions to separation from their caretaker (see Bowlby, 1973, pp. 57–74).

It is clear, then, that for Bowlby the essence of anxiety is not, as it was for Freud, the threat of excessive excitation generated by the accumulation of undischarged instinctual drive tensions. Rather, it is a *direct*, innately based response to separation or threat of separation from the caretaker. Furthermore, for Bowlby, anxiety disorders in adults are a direct consequence of loss, long and frequent separations, or frequent threats of such separations during childhood.

Bowlby cites Freud's (1905) statement that "anxiety in children is originally nothing other than an expression of the fact that they are feeling the loss of the person they love" (Bowlby, 1973, p. 33). And we have also noted earlier that the basic danger situations and sources of anxiety posited in psychoanalytic theory include loss of the object and loss of the object's love. However, despite Freud's recognition of the importance of object loss and missing a loved one in generating anxiety, his interpretation of the meaning of such loss was presented in the context of instinct theory and a conception of the nervous system in which discharging excitation was its primary function. That is, as noted earlier, according to Freud, loss of the object and loss of the object's love (as well as threats of castration) are not dangers in themselves, but rather, represent dangers because they leave the individual exposed to excessive tension and excitation from unfulfilled instinctual needs and drives.

---

[9] Bowlby's attachment theory is, in part, embedded in an *ethological* point of view. However, it also clearly has its roots in psychoanalytic theory and hence, is included in a chapter on psychodynamic theories of anxiety. Bowlby himself is a psychoanalyst, engaged in psychoanalytic practice. He has also stated in the preface to his first volume (1969) that "throughout this inquiry my frame of reference has been that of psychoanalysis" and that "all the central concepts of my schema — object relations, separation anxiety, mourning, defense, trauma, sensitive periods in early life — are the stock-in-trade of psychoanalytic thinking" (p. 16).

Bowlby's work on attachment has generated insights into certain developmental phenomena, such as exploratory behavior, and into a class of pathological behaviors centering on *anxious attachment.* With regard to the latter, he has argued that overdependent and clinging behavior as well as proneness to separation anxiety have to do with anxious attachment. That is, they reflect the fact that the individual has little confidence that the attachment figure will be available and responsive.[10] Hence, the individual must remain in clingingly close contact in order to insure that the attachment figure will be available. According to Bowlby, anxious attachment is a central factor in the phobias of childhood, particularly school phobias, and adult agoraphobias (which Bowlby views as "pseudophobias"). We will return to this topic in the research section of this chapter.

The quality of the child's attachment to the caretaker is also central in the degree of independent *exploratory* behavior shown by the child. As one might expect, anxious attachment is associated with little exploratory behavior, while secure attachment is correlated with a greater degree of exploratory behavior. This makes sense in the context of attachment theory. In accord with that theory, one would expect that the child (or adult) who has a confident expectation that the attachment figure will be available (based on actual experiences of the consistent availability of the attachment figure) will feel safer to explore away from home base. Conversely, one would expect that the child (or adult) who does not have such an expectation, but rather feels insecure regarding the availability of the attachment figure, will feel less safe exploring the world away from home. In the section of this chapter that deals with research findings, we will see that there is a good deal of empirical evidence in regard to secure and anxious attachment and their relationship to exploratory behavior.

In a recent paper, Taylor (1986) has extended Bowlby's conception of separation anxiety to include the idea that "the infant's responses to separation are not due simply to the breaking of an *attachment bond,* but also to *withdrawal* of the *external biological and behavioral regulation* supplied by the mother" [author's italics] (p. 9). According to Taylor, in infancy and childhood the mother serves as an external regulator of anxiety and other psychobiological experiences and responses. In the course of normal development, which includes maturation and the internalized mental representation of the infant's tie to mother, internal homeostatic mechanisms increasingly replace external regulators. Normal development also includes the role of transitional objects that reduce "separation anxiety by evoking the *ellusion* of a reunion with the absent mother" (p. 12). According to Taylor, those people especially prone to separation anxiety and panic disorder show "impaired capacity for transitional relatedness" (p. 12) as well as general deficits in self-regulation of anxiety and other psychobiological states. These people, Taylor argues, compensate for such deficits by forming an extreme dependency on external regulatory relationships. However, Taylor goes on, such individuals remain "*predisposed* to *panic disorder* or some other *disorder of regulation* because the self fragments when faced with separation from or loss of the regulatory relationship" (p. 13).

Bowlby (1980) draws upon information processing formulations to reconceptualize Freud's concepts of repression and the unconscious so that they are compatible with recent theorizing and findings in cognitive psychology. According to Bowlby, as a result of early experiences of anxiety and pain with attachment figures and frustration of attachment needs, the attachment system may become deactivated, with the result that desires, thoughts, and feelings that are part of attachment behavior or for that matter,

---

[10] Such lack of confidence and insecurity can be the result of actual experiences of loss and abandonment or of the caretaker's inconsistency and unreliability.

any information that would activate the system, are *defensively excluded* from processing and from awareness. Bowlby notes that "the defensive exclusion that I postulate is no more than repression under another name" (p. 20). Viewed this way, repression is but one aspect of normal information processing in which some information is selectively included and some selectively excluded at different stages of processing.

Kohut's theory of anxiety

In his earlier writings, Kohut (e.g., 1971) argued that Freudian theory (including the Freudian theory of anxiety) was applicable to neuroses (or so-called "structural conflict"), while his self psychology theory was applicable to self disorders, in particular, so-called narcissistic personality disorders. Accordingly, he suggested that castration anxiety (related to incestuous and aggressive wishes and impulses) was the primary kind of anxiety in neurosis, while in narcissistic personality disorders, the central anxiety relates to such issues as "the vulnerability of the mature self" (p. 20); the "temporary fragmentation of the self" (p. 20); "the psyche's inability to regulate self-esteem" (p. 20); and the "bedrock" threat of destruction of the nuclear self (p. 117). The above type of anxiety Kohut refers to as "disintegration anxiety."

In his later work, Kohut (e.g., 1977, 1984) moves toward a position in which Freudian drive or instinct theory is rejected and is to be replaced by self psychology for *all* psychopathology (although he continues to focus in his writings on narcissistic personality disorders). However, despite this tendency, Kohut (1977) continues to distinguish between two different classes of anxiety:

1. Anxiety experiences by a person whose self is more or less cohesive. This person's anxiety is related to fear of the specific danger situations noted by Freud (e.g., fear of loss of the object's love, castration);
2. "The anxieties experienced by a person who is becoming aware that his self is beginning to disintegrate" (p. 102).

According to Kohut, Freud's discussion of the danger of excessive excitation and Anna Freud's discussion of the "dread of strength of the instincts" represent "attempts to deal with disintegration anxiety within the framework of the classical mental-apparatus psychology" (Kohut, 1977, p. 104). These dreads and dangers, Kohut maintains, belong in the framework of self psychology. For what is feared, according to the latter view, is not excessive excitation or the strength of drives, but the threatened fragmentation of the self. Further, increased and threatening intensity of drive is, according to Kohut, the *result* of (self) pathology, not its cause. In a number of places in his writings, Kohut repeatedly argues that intense and unmodulated drive (sex and aggression) expressions and impulses are not the cause of pathology, but "disintegration products"; that is, the *consequences* of a noncohesive self.

For Kohut, then, it is clear that a primary source of anxiety, particularly intense and massive anxiety, is an experience of threatened fragmentation and break-up of one's self. As to what makes one's self-organization so vulnerable to such threats, Kohut presents a quasi-developmental etiological theory in which early experiences of parental empathic mirroring and opportunities for idealization are held to be critical for the development of a cohesive self. Failure to have such early experiences contribute to the development of a noncohesive self, a condition in which one is more vulnerable to the "disintegration anxiety" discussed earlier. Part of Kohut's etiological theory of self-development and of proneness to anxiety include formulations concerning the relationship between self and so-called self-objects. The empathic response of the latter facilitates the building up of psychic structures that are capable of dealing with and containing anxiety. Conversely, when self-objects do not respond empathically, such structures are not adequate and one is more likely to experience a greater spread and greater intensity of anxiety. According to Kohut (1984), intense anxiety is triggered by the "loss of the self-object without which the self cannot continue to exist" (p. 18).

It is important to note that particularly in his later writings, Kohut (1984) maintains that we continue to need self-objects throughout our lives, although in optimal development we move from archaic to more mature self-objects. Implicit in this position is the idea that although intense "disintegration anxiety" is particularly likely to afflict someone with a noncohesive self, *some* degree of anxiety will be experienced by *anyone* who has to cope with the failure or loss of self-objects. As we shall see, although Kohut's language and theoretical context are very much his own, his emphasis on the connection between anxiety and self and self-object relationships is related to and converges on Bowlby's central claim that the core of anxiety is found in the person's separation from and loss of his or her attachment figure(s).

We cannot, of course, do full justice to Kohut's theory. The above, however, should provide some idea of how anxiety is understood in Kohut's psychoanalytic self psychology. It will be noted that in Kohut's self psychology, intense anxiety is *not* occasioned by instinctual drive impulses or inner conflicts around these impulses. Indeed, inner conflict seems to play little role in Kohut's descriptions of self pathology. In this and other senses, Kohut's theory represents a radical departure from some core assumptions of Freudian theory.

REVIEW OF RESEARCH

Over the past 40 years there have probably been more than 1,000 empirical studies of anxiety, many of which were inspired by the development of one or another anxiety scale. This voluminous literature, however, is largely irrelevant to psychodynamic theories of anxiety, even though many of the studies explicitly set out to test hypotheses that were derived from psychodynamic conceptualizations. A principal reason for this state of affairs is that in attempting to study anxiety under rigorous, controlled, laboratory conditions, the methods and procedures used often violate the terms of the theory. Rapaport (1960) made this point more than 25 years ago in his overall assessment of the experimental evidence for and against various aspects of psychoanalytic theory. In the case of anxiety, the operational measures developed have by and large not remained faithful to the theoretical concept. Furthermore, the laboratory procedures typically have not distinguished anxiety from fear nor have they used stimuli high in psychodynamic relevance. For example, pairing nonsense syllables with electric shock is not a theoretically reasonable nor an ecologically valid test of Freudian notions regarding the relationship between anxiety and suppression or repression.

Of the subset of anxiety studies that are more relevant, many did not measure anxiety directly, but assumed it to be a mediating variable. For example, in the prototypical study of perceptual defense (see Eagle & Wolitsky, 1977), the operation of anxiety was inferred from alterations in response threshold. As Erdelyi (1974, p. 256) correctly notes: "What has not been demonstrated in the laboratory . . . is the cogent fact that the perception of emotional stimuli is disrupted *because* of intentional rejection by the perceiver." And, we would add, it also would be necessary to show that the emotional stimuli are intentionally rejected (or otherwise distorted) *because* they arouse signal anxiety.

With these caveats in mind, and in view of space limitations, we will present a brief, highly selective summary of research bearing on psychodynamic views of anxiety. Most of these studies were conducted in the early 1960s, at a time when there was a peaking of interest in efforts to validate experimentally core psychoanalytic hypotheses.

Mothering styles and oral traits (including anxiety)

A number of early studies found associations between specific mothering styles and oral personality traits of anxiety and separation difficulties (Finney, 1961; Goldman-Eisler, 1951; Whiting & Child, 1953). In related work, but not dealing with type of mothering, Kagan and Moss (1962) reported that the oral traits of dependency, passivity, and separation anxiety correlate with each other and tend to persist from birth to adulthood, especially in females. While these reports are somewhat relevant to and consistent with certain psychoanalytic hypotheses (e.g., that there is something like oral traits that have an internal coherence), it will be noted that they are not especially central to core traditional psychoanalytic formulations in which forbidden instinctual wishes, conflict, defense, and the signal function are all linked together in a theory of anxiety.

Castration anxiety and anxiety over loss of love in males and females

Other examples of studies that are relevant but not central to core psychoanalytic formulations on anxiety include one showing that, as Freud predicted, anxiety regarding loss of love is more common among females than males (Manosevits & Lanyon, 1965) and another study showing that in accord with the hypothesis of castration anxiety, men are more fearful of bodily injury than women (Pitcher & Prelinger, 1963). Also related to Freud's writings on castration anxiety, Sarnoff and Corwin (1959) reported that male subjects who have a relatively high degree of castration anxiety showed a greater increase in fear of death after the arousal of sexual feelings than subjects who showed a relatively low degree of castration anxiety. As a final example of a study dealing with castration anxiety, Levin (1966) tested the psychoanalytically derived hypothesis that "intensity of the female castration complex as measured by a projective test is significantly greater in women with a masculine social role than in women with a feminine social role" (p. 183). Her results supported the hypothesis: The sample of unmarried career women in masculine occupations showed significantly higher castration complex scores than the comparable sample of married homemakers.

Lazarus and his co-workers (Lazarus, 1964) conducted a series of interesting studies in which subjects viewed a film depicting sub-incision puberty rites among the Arunta of Central Australia (cf. Schwartz, 1956). These studies were undertaken as part of a programmatic effort to investigate the effects of stress, a term many authors use as synonymous with anxiety (a usage criticized by May, 1977, who seems to view stress as an external stimulus that may or may not arouse anxiety). In using the sub-incision film, Spiesman, Lazarus, Davison, and Mordkoff (1964) note that it can evoke complex, multiple meanings and should not be thought of as arousing only castration anxiety even though the main action in the film is a ceremonial surgical operation which "consists of a deep incision made with a stone blade the full length of the ventral surface of the penis and into the scrotum. No anesthetic is used and the surgical technique assaults Western standards of sanitation and precision" (Spiesman et al., 1964, p. 23). In fact, Speisman et al. (1964) found that the segments of the film, in which the incisions are made, evoke a stronger physiological reaction and higher ratings of anxiety and tension than do scenes of nudity or relatively neutral scenes, and that these effects interact significantly with subjects' scores on paper and pencil measures of body narcissism, sadomasochism, and some MMPI scales (e.g., hysteria).

In other studies using this film, it has been found that narrative soundtracks that emphasize certain ego defenses (denial of intellectualization/reaction formation) lead to a lower level of physiological and subjective arousal/anxiety than the silent version of the film or a so-called trauma soundtrack that highlighted the threatening aspects of the film (Spiesman et al., 1964). Presenting the denial/reaction formation soundtrack prior to the showing of the film further reduced the stress reaction, a phenomenon referred to by Lazarus and Alpert (1964) as "short-circuiting of threat." Furthermore, there was some evidence that stress reduction is most effective when the style of the defense-oriented soundtrack (i.e., intellectualization vs. denial/reaction formation) is compatible with the independently assessed defensive style of the subject (Lazarus, 1964). Lazarus (1964, p. 409) is appropriately cautious in noting that "the experiments are analogues of cognitive appraisal and not ego defense." It is, of course unclear as to what extent these results can be generalized to situations of self-induced defensive operations in response to signal anxiety based on unconscious mentation. However, the fact that these findings, like the findings from studies of perceptual defense (Eagle & Wolitzky, 1977), are consistent with Freud's formulations regarding the links between anxiety and defense is encouraging.

Anxiety and fear

In one of the few studies that attempted to differentiate anxiety from fear, Sarnoff and Zimbardo (1961) reasoned that arousing a fear that would be an "emotionally appropriate reaction to environmental threat" (Sarnoff, 1971, p. 162) should lead subjects to seek affiliation. Such affiliation was reasoned to be an adaptive means of coping in that it allows for the possibility of group support and cathartic release. In contrast, stimuli that arouse anxiety are more apt to lead subjects to prefer social isolation on the assumption that subjects would not want to expose or share what they likely would regard as inappropriate emotions. High and low fear conditions were created by leading subjects to expect either strong or weak electric shock. High and low anxiety conditions were set up by leading subjects to believe that they would "suck" on objects in the room, such as baby bottles, pacifiers, lollipops, oversized nipples, and breast shields (high anxiety), or that they would put items such as whistles and pipes (shown at first as slides) in their mouths briefly (the word *suck* was not mentioned in this low anxiety condition). The results indicated that under conditions of low arousal (of fear or anxiety), most subjects chose to wait with others. Under conditions of high arousal, 95% of subjects in the high fear conditions chose to wait with others, while in the high anxiety condition, only 46% sought social contact.

The authors do not explain why the high anxiety group split almost 50–50 in their preference for social affiliation versus isolation. Although the authors do not say so, presumably what was aroused were anticipations of shame and/or guilt at the prospect of the public, blatant sucking on objects from childhood. Perhaps unmeasured individual differences in the degree to which these affects were indeed aroused and in defenses against them might account for subjects' preferences for affiliation versus isolation. In any case, this study is relevant to Freud's concept of superego anxiety, although Sarnoff and Zimbardo (1961) focused their discussion on the generality of Schachter's (1959) theory of affiliation.

Conflict and experimental neuroses

The literature on experimental neuroses is historically and conceptually derived from conditioning theory. Indeed, the phenomenon was discovered in Pavlov's laboratory. We refer to experimental neuroses in the present context because that literature demonstrates that even in animals the presence of conflict can generate anxiety and maladaptive neurotic behavior. In Pavlov's (1927) report, a circle was conditioned as a positive stimulus to feeding and an ellipse was negatively conditioned to feeding. Then the ellipse was gradually changed until it was almost indistinguishable from the circle. The animal reacted with increasing anxiety and from that point on reacted with anxiety whenever it was brought to the room in which the original experiment was conducted. Conflict was employed to produce experimental neuroses by Gantt (1944), Liddell (1944), and Masserman (1943). However, Wolpe (1966) has argued that both in animals and humans, noxious and traumatic stimuli alone, that is, without conflict, can produce anxiety and neurotic behavior. In any case, Wolpe does not appear to dispute the idea that conflict *can* produce anxiety and experimental neuroses.

Perceptual defense studies

The so-called perceptual defense studies, part of the "New Look" in perception, were at least partly inspired (more likely largely inspired) by the psychodynamic idea that motivational factors such as needs, values, personality traits, and defenses could directly influence perception. The term *perceptual defense* (introduced by Bruner & Postman, 1947), in particular, refers to delayed recognition thresholds for emotionally disturbing stimuli (e.g., tabooed words). Often, despite failure to recognize the emotionally disturbing stimulus, there is other evidence (e.g., greater galvanic skin response — McGuinness, 1949; Eriksen, 1963) that some discrimination has taken place. The delayed recognition is attributed to attempts to deal with the anxiety evoked by the emotionally disturbing stimuli. As Bruner and Postman (1947) wrote, "with increase in emotionality of stimuli, recognition may lead to anxiety and is to be avoided as long as possible" (p. 47). It will be noted that this account of delayed recognition is based on the psychoanalytic anxiety-defense model applied to perceptual recognition (rather than conscious awareness of inner wishes, impulses, and ideas). In an important sense, perceptual defense was understood as the perceptual version of repression. Given this state of affairs, it would appear that evidence for perceptual defense would constitute at least indirect experimental support for the anxiety-defense model and for the operation of repression. However, as we shall see later, there was far from universal agreement regarding how to interpret the reported phenomena.

Before dealing with different interpretations of the phenomena, it should be noted that while many subjects showed *delayed* recognition thresholds for emotionally disturbing stimuli, some subjects showed *decreased* thresholds for such stimuli. This was referred to as *perceptual vigilance* and was also held to serve a defensive function. That is, the reasoning went that while some subjects dealt with the anxiety-eliciting aspects of emotionally disturbing stimuli by delaying recognition, others dealt with such threatening stimuli by vigilantly bringing them to awareness as soon as possible (such contrasting styles were presumably analogous to repression versus defenses such as intellectualization).

The early formulations of perceptual defense stimulated intense controversy, centering on the apparent paradoxical inference that the subject delays perceiving something he or she has not yet seen. Such explanations seemed to imply an unacceptable manikin theory in which a supersensitive homunculus inside the person discriminates stimuli (before the person does) and controls perceptual activity. Given this apparent paradox, a number of different explanations for the perceptual defense phenomena were offered which seemed to bypass the need to posit unconscious processes. For example, on hypothesis offered was that tabooed words have higher recognition thresholds than neutral words because *they appear less frequently* in printed English (as measured by the Thorndike-Lorge word frequency tables). However, this explanation does not account for vigilance effects (Erdelyi, 1974). Furthermore, several studies controlled for frequency and nevertheless obtained defense and vigilance effects.

The most interesting and plausible explanation of the perceptual defense results is the *partial cue* hypothesis, An example of the partial cue formulation is Eriksen's (1963) argument that so-called perceptual defense is due to triggering of conditioned avoidance responses to fractional elements of potentially anxiety-arousing stimuli. With words, the fractional elements are letters (e.g., W, H, R) that lead the subject to at least momentarily entertain a tabooed word (e.g., *whore*) and thus lead both to a larger galvanic skin response and delayed recognition threshold (see Wolitzky & Wachtel, 1973). Support for the partial cue hypothesis comes from Anisfeld's (1968) finding that some letters occur more frequently in the initial position of pleasant words and other letters in the initial position of unpleasant words. Furthermore, in a guessing task, people "are able to approximate these objective probabilities of initial letter occurrence." These findings led Anisfeld to conclude that partial cues "allow subjects to infer the probable affective nature of words exposed below threshold for complete recognition" (p. 39).

A central question for interpretation of perceptual defense results as well as for a possible reformulation of repressions in information processing terms is whether the inferential (and other) processes that lead from partial cue to affective response (e.g., anxiety) are conscious or unconscious. If the latter, then a partial cue interpretation is consistent with the Freudian concept of unconscious processes. (For a fuller discussion of the perceptual defense issue, see Eagle & Wolitzky, 1977).

Attachment and anxiety

Security of attachment and exploratory behavior

One virtue of Bowlby's theory of attachment is that it has generated a good deal of empirical research. One such fertile area, particularly relevant in the present context, is the research on the relationship between security of attachment and degree of exploratory behavior in the young child. Ainsworth and her colleagues (e.g., Ainsworth, 1967; 1984; Ainsworth & Bell, 1970; Ainsworth, Bell, & Stayton, 1971; Ainsworth, Blehar, Waters, & Wall, 1978; Ainsworth & Wittig, 1969) have led the way in investigating this relationship. They found that securely attached babies (as measured by "the strange situation" test, e.g., see Ainsworth, 1978) show exploratory behavior when alone with mother, distress when mother leaves, and increased proximity- and contact-seeking behavior during reunion. By contrast, babies that showed an anxiously attached and resistant (ambivalent) pattern showed, prior to separation, either little exploratory behavior or exploratory behavior with little affect, intense distress during separation, and proximity- and contact-seeking mixed with passive and resistant behavior during reunion. In addition, they were very difficult to soothe. A third group of babies who were described as anxiously attached and avoidant showed some exploratory behavior pre-, during, and post-separation, but were often avoidant of mother during reunion. In a particularly poignant set of findings, Sroufe and Waters (1977) reported that the exploratory behavior shown by the anxiously attached and avoidant babies "was not accompanied by the characteristic deceleration of heart rate at moments of special interest" (Ainsworth, 1984, p. 576). Furthermore, they also found that despite their different overt behavioral reactions, the anxiously attached babies showed the same kind of acceleration of heart rate as shown by securely attached babies in reaction to mother's departures and returns.

"Secure base" effects

Others (e.g., Feldman & Ingham, 1975; Maccoby & Feldman (1972) have supported Ainsworth's general finding that exploratory play in young children (12- to 36-month-olds) decreases when the attachment figure leaves the scene. "Secure base effects" are even produced by *pictures* of mother (Passman & Erck, 1977) and by a "security blanket" for those toddlers who were attached to this kind of "transitional object" (Winnicott, 1951/1975). This was not true for toddlers who were not attached to a "security blanket."

What these and other related results indicate is that the child uses the attachment figure as a *secure base* from which to explore and learn about the world. When the attachment figure is or threatens to become unavailable, separation anxiety and attachment behavior are aroused and exploratory behavior is reduced or even abandoned. According to Ainsworth, anxiously attached babies build up a representational model of mother as someone "who cannot be trusted to be accessible and responsive, and herein lies the baby's anxiety" (1984, p. 575). By contrast, the child who has a representational model of mother as accessible and responsive has developed an internal secure base from which such qualities and behaviors as exploration, self-reliance, and security are likely to develop.

It should be noted that "secure base" effects have been found with other species, including birds and monkeys (see Rajecki, Lamb, & Obmascher, 1978 for a summary of research in this area). For example, Stettner and Tilds (1966) found that when their attachment object (a green cube) was absent, ducklings would maximize the distance between themselves and a novel stimulus, whereas when the imprinted object was present, the birds would approach the doll. A similar phenomenon was reported for young monkeys by Harlow (1958). They were more likely to approach a novel and initially frightening stimulus when a surrogate cloth mother to which they had become attached was present. When the surrogate mother was absent, they were more likely to cower in a corner.

Separation effects

Rajecki et al. (1978) have also summarized recent research on effects of separation from attachment figures in different species. In birds (e.g., Rajecki et al. 1978); dogs (e.g., Pettijohn, Wong, Ebert, & Scott, 1977); monkeys (e.g., Hinde & McGinnis, 1977); and children (e.g., Heinicke & Westheimer, 1965; Robertson & Bowlby, 1952), separation from attachment figures, including, in some cases, companions, leads initially to distress and protest. These results support Bowlby's (1969; 1973; 1980) generalization regarding attachment and separation anxiety. It seems that particularly among the young in a variety of species, some variant of separation anxiety is wired in reaction to separation from attachment figures. In other words, as Bowlby claims, this reaction is *not* a result of the attachment figure's acquiring secondary reinforcement properties based on their so-called primary drive-reducing functions (primarily, feeding).

Anxious attachment, school phobias, and agoraphobia

Bowlby (1973, chapter 18) has summarized the literature on so-called school phobias and has concluded that such "phobias" are related to some variety of anxious attachment and are more properly viewed as anxiety states than as genuine phobias. Bowlby points out that in contrast to genuine circumscribed phobias, what is most feared in school phobias (as well as agoraphobia) is not the *presence* of an object or situation, but the *absense* of the attachment figure and/or the secure base toward which the individual normally retreats. This conclusion is supported by agreement among investigators that most school-refusing children tend not to complain about features of the school such as teacher or schoolmates (e.g., Hersov, 1960) and that when such complaints do occur they are most often rationalizations. Further, anxiety is most frequently at its height prior to leaving for school rather than at school, where these children often feel secure once they get there. Bowlby's summary of clinical findings in this area leads him to describe four patterns of family interaction in which: (a) chronically anxious parent(s) retains child at home as a companion; (b) child fears something dreadful may happen to parent(s) while he or she is away at school; (c) child fears something dreadful will happen to him or her away from home; (d) parent(s) fears that something dreadful will happen to child while he or she is at school. Bowlby sees all four patterns as involving anxious attachment.

According to Bowlby (1973, chapter 19), adult agoraphobia shows striking resemblances to childhood school phobias. The primary symptom in both is fear of leaving home and both can be seen, therefore, as involving chronic separation anxiety. Bowlby (1973, p. 302) claims that what little research literature is available supports the hypothesis that agoraphobic patients show family interaction patterns similar to those seen in childhood school phobias. Also pointing to the connection between the two is the finding that many adult agoraphobics report having suffered from phobias as children, including school phobias (see Bowlby, 1973, p. 294 for a summary of this research). More recently, Klein (1981) reported that 50% of adults suffering from panic attacks show evidence of separation anxiety in childhood. He also reports that "the initial panic episode has often been preceded by significant object loss" (p. 245). In short, there is a good deal of evidence that both childhood school phobias and adult agoraphobia are anxiety states in which anxious attachment, separation anxiety, and object loss play central roles.

Anxious attachment and pathological response to loss

In the last book of his trilogy, Bowlby (1980) argues for and presents evidence supporting the hypothesis that the likelihood of pathological response to loss in adults is increased in those cases in which the prior relationship was characterized by anxious and ambivalent attachments. And, according to Bowlby, the likelihood of forming adult anxious and ambivalent attachments is, in turn, increased by childhood experiences of maternal loss and periods of absence, threats of desertion, parental separation and divorce, and parental experience of the child's need for love and care as an unwelcome burden. As Bowlby points out, the child often reacts to abandonment, desertion, and inadequate fulfillment of attachment needs with, among other feelings and behaviors, anxiety, increased demands for affection, and anger and rage when he or she does not receive it. This set of reactions is, of course, precisely what is involved in ambivalent interactions.

Taylor (1986) has presented a number of case studies in which interpersonal loss was followed by panic attacks. As noted earlier, according to Taylor, such reactions occur in individuals who show deficits in self-regulation and who depend on *external* relationships to compensate for their deficits. When that external relationship is lost, its regulatory function can be lost with it and the individual is particularly susceptible to panic disorders or some other disorder of regulation. Taylor's formulation is consistent with and similar to Kohut's (1984) writings on the role of self-object relationships in maintaining self-cohesiveness and the role of disruptions in such relationships in generating feelings of self-fragmentation and "disintegration anxiety" (which, in its quality and intensity, can be understood as a panic experience). The earlier cited finding by Klein (1981) linking panic attacks to the predisposing factor of separation anxiety in childhood and the precipitating factor of preceding "significant object loss" is consistent with both Taylor's and Kohut's formulations.

TREATMENT

Other chapters in this book deal with treatment and we do not plan to present any extensive material on psychodynamic treatment of anxiety. However, we do want to make the point that corresponding to the different psychodynamic formulations discussed earlier are different accompanying conceptions, emphases, and approaches to treatment. It seems to us that many of the changes in conceptions of psychodynamic treatment can be summed up by the generalization that there has been a relative de-emphasis of the exclusive role of insight, awareness, and understanding and a concomitantly greater emphasis on the therapeutic role of the patient-therapist relationship (see Eagle & Wolitzky, 1982). Thus, it seems clear that therapists who are influenced by object relations theory, Bowlby's attachment theory, or Kohut's self psychology would *not*, perhaps each for different reasons, describe as the primary goal of their therapy Freud's goals of making the unconscious conscious and transforming id material into ego ("where id was, there should ego be"). A therapist following attachment theory would recognize the importance of the therapist as a secure attachment figure in alleviating anxiety and in providing sufficiently safe conditions so that the patient will permit the full processing of information and signals that would normally activate the attachment system. An object relations therapist, following Fairbairn and Guntrip, would recognize the importance of a "good" object relationship in producing positive therapeutic effects. And a Kohution therapist would stress the therapeutic importance of providing primarily empathic understanding for long periods of time and of constituting a self-object for the patient. It is also worth noting Taylor's (1986) remarks that psychotherapy for panic disorders "should be based not on the traditional drive–conflict–defense model of the mind, but on current knowledge about the development of the ego and the self within the context of human relationships" (p. 16). He then suggests that for many patients with panic anxiety, the therapeutic task is to foster symbolizations "that will permit the emergence of transitional phenomena and the development of stable mental representations with anxiety-regulating functions" (p. 17). One must also help these patients "develop or restore interactional and self-regulatory processes that will help stabilize the biological control mechanism for anxiety" (p. 17). All the above therapeutic goals and conceptualizations are a far cry from the primary traditional psychodynamic goals of achieving insight into unconscious wishes and conflicts.

CONCLUDING REMARKS

We have presented a brief survey of several theories of anxiety. We do not have the space to offer a critical appraisal and systematic comparison of these theories. Instead, we shall focus briefly on extracting and stating in summary form a set of general propositions that seem to reflect the commonalities and considerable overlap among them.

1. Anxiety is a noxious subjective state (that contains affective and cognitive components) which individuals attempt to avoid and minimize once it reaches a given level.

2. Anxiety leads to defense and to symptomatic behavior.

3. Individuals differ in their tolerance for anxiety.

4. While there are individual differences in the biological predispositions to anxiety, a considerable source of variance has to do with psychological factors.

5. Individuals who have a relatively secure, cohesive sense of self, including the sense of competence and confidence to master stressful, challenging situations (e.g., feared loss of the object and/or the object's love), will be less vulnerable to anxiety and will tolerate it in more adaptive fashion.

6. The development of this type of sense of self is crucially dependent on the nature of early interactions with caretakers. In particular, to the extent that the infant/child feels loved, wanted, encouraged, but not cajoled, toward autonomous functioning consistent with his or her adaptive capacities, he or she will develop a representational model of his or her caretakers as responsive, loving, and accessible and thus an internal secure base which will complement and, to a considerable extent, supercede the external security provided by the caretakers.

7. If the secure, nonanxious attachment depicted evolves in a context in which the child also develops a realistically grounded sense of competence in being able to master and control important aspects of his or her environment (cf. Lewis & Goldberg, 1969, on contingent reinforcement) this child will have a healthy sense of self-esteem and be increasingly able to regulate his or her own internal need states, and tolerate delay, frustration, and anxiety without undue defensiveness (e.g., regressions, fixations, or turning away from reality).

This capsule sketch of some of the central ingredients of optimal personality development and their implication for the experience of anxiety seems to us to be one that could be endorsed by each of the psychodynamic theorists cited in this chapter.

Probably the major point of disagreement with regard to a theory of anxiety concerns one's view of the organism's primary motivational aims. We cannot, in this chapter, do more than state the basic issue. Greenberg and Mitchell (1983) explicate it clearly by making the distinction between what they call the "drive/structure model" versus the "relational/structure model." Freud is identified with the drive model, while the other theorists mentioned in this chapter adhere more to the relational model. The distinction between these two models rests on whether one views the discharge of libidinal and aggressive drive tensions as the orgarism's primary goal or adopts a perspective in which relationships with others are primary. In Fairbairn's terms, for example, libido is object-seeking, not pleasure-seeking. In Freud's theory of instinctual drives, the object of drive gratification is its most variable aspect and becomes attached to the drive impulse according to how suited it is for the provision of satisfaction. The issue of the primacy of an interest in relating to objects versus the extent to which the object is merely a means toward the end goal of pleasure is a central one. Much of psychoanalytic theorizing since Freud is fueled by an attempt to preserve, modify, reject, or reconcile these two models.

The main implication for theories of anxiety is that in the drive model, the threat of loss of the object and/or the object's love is that the ego would not be able to master stimulation and would be helpless in the face of mounting drive tensions. In the relational model, the basic threat is the loss of the object as well as the disruption of psychological functions served by the relationship with the object. We believe that there need not be a sharp dichotomy between some version of the drive and relational models and that some integration of the two is possible. However, this obviously remains a task for the future.

REFERENCES

Ainsworth, M. D. S. (1967). *Infancy in Uganda: Infant care and the growth of love*. Baltimore: Johns Hopkins University Press.

Ainsworth, M. D. S. (1984). Attachment. In N. S. Endler & J. McV. Hunt (Eds.), *Personality and the behavioral disorders*. (Vol. I, 2nd ed., pp. 559–602). New York: John Wiley & Sons.

Ainsworth, M. D. S., & Bell, S. M. (1970). Attachment, exploration, and separation: Illustrated by the behavior of one-year-olds in a strange situation. *Child Development, 41*, 49–67.

Ainsworth, M. D. S., Bell, S. M., & Stayton, D. J. (1971). Individual differences in strange situation behavior of one-year-olds. In H. R. Schaffer (Ed.), *The origins of human social relations*. New York: Academic Press, pp. 17–57.

Ainsworth, M. D. S., Blehar, M. C., Waters, E., & Wall, S. (1978). *Patterns of attachment: A psychological study of the strange situation*. Hillsdale, NJ: Lawrence Erlbaum Associates.

Ainsworth, M. D. S., & Wittig, B. A. (1969). Attachment and exploratory behavior of one-year-olds in a strange situation. In B. M. Foss (Ed.), *Determinants of infant behavior: Vol. IV*, London: Methuen, pp. 111–136.

Anisfeld, M. (1968). Subjective approximation of relative letter incidence in pleasant and unpleasant English words. *Journal of Verbal Learning and Verbal Behavior, 7*, 33–40.

Begeret, J. (1974). *Abreqe de la psychologique pathologique*. Paris: Masson.

Bowlby, J. (1969). *Attachment and loss: Vol. I: Attachment*. London: Hogarth Press.

Bowlby, J. (1973). *Attachment of loss: Vol. II: Separation, anxiety and anger.* New York: Basic Books.

Bowlby, J. (1980) *Loss: Sadness and depression.* New York: Basic Books.

Bruner, J. S., & Postman, L. (1947). Emotional selectivity in perception and reaction. *Journal of Personality, 16,* 69–77.

Compton, A. (1972). A study of the psychoanalytic theory of anxiety. I. The development of Freud's theory of anxiety. *Journal of the American Psychoanalytic Association, 20,* 3–44.

Dollard, J., & Miller, N. E. (1950). *Personality and psychotherapy.* New York: McGraw-Hill.

Eagle, M. N. (1984). *Recent developments in psychoanalysis: A critical evaluation.* New York: McGraw-Hill.

Eagle, M. N., & Wolitzky, D. L. (1977). Perceptual defense. *International encyclopedia of psychiatry, psychology, psychoanalysis, and neurology* (Vol. III). New York: Human Science Press.

Eagle, M., & Wolitzky, D. L. (1982). Therapeutic influences in dynamic psychotherapy: A review and synthesis. In S. Slipp (Ed.), *Curative factors in dynamic psychotherapy.* New York: McGraw-Hill.

Erdelyi, M. (1974). A new look at the New Look: Perceptual defense and vigilance. *Psychological Review, 81,* 1–25.

Erdelyi, M. H. (1985). *Psychoanalysis: Freud's cognitive psychology.* New York: W. H. Freeman.

Eriksen, C. W. (1963). Perception and personality. In J. M. Wepman & R. W. Heine (Eds.), *Concepts of personality.* Chicago: Aldine, pp. 31–62.

Fairbairn, W. R. D. (1952). *Psychoanalytic studies of the personality.* London: Routledge & Kegan Paul.

Feldman, S. S., & Ingham, M. E. (1975). Attachment behavior: A validation study in two age groups. *Child Development, 46,* 319–330.

Fenichel, O. (1945). *The psychoanalytic theory of neurosis.* New York: W. W. Norton.

Finney, J. C. (1961). Some maternal influences on children's personality and character. *Genetic Psychology Monographs, 63,* 199–278.

Freud, A. (1946). *The ego and the mechanisms of defense.* New York: International Universities Press.

Freud, S. (1924), The justification for detaching from neurasthenia a particular syndrome: The anxiety neurosis. In *Collected Papers* (Vol. I, pp. 76–106). London: Hogarth Press. (Original work published 1894).

Freud, S. (1953). The interpretation of dreams. In J. Strachey (Ed. and Trans.), *The standard edition of the complete psychological works of Sigmund Freud.* London: Hogarth Press. (Original work published 1900).

Freud, S. (1905). Three essays on the theory of sexuality. In J. Strachey (Ed. and Trans.), *The standard edition of the complete psychological works of Sigmund Freud* (Vol. 7, pp. 135–243). London: Hogarth Press.

Freud, S. (1959). Inhibitions, Symptoms and Anxiety. In J. Strachey (Ed. and Trans.), *The standard edition of the complete psychological works of Sigmund Freud* (Vol. 20, pp. 77–178). London: Hogarth Press. (Original work published 1926).

Freud, S. (1964). Anxiety and instructional life. In J. Strachey (Ed. and Trans.), *The standard edition of the complete psychological works of Sigmund Freud* (Vol. 20, pp. 81–111). London: Hogarth Press. (Original work published 1933).

Freud, S. (1964). An outline of psychoanalysis. In J. Strachey (Ed. and Trans.), *The standard edition of the complete psychological works of Sigmund Freud* (Vol. 21). London: Hogarth Press. (Original work published 1940).

Gantt, W. H. (1944). Experimental basis for neurotic behavior. *Psychosomatic Medicine Monographs, 3,* Nos. 3 and 4.

Goldman-Eisler, F. (1951). The problems of "orality" and of its origins in early childhood. *Journal of Mental Science, 97,* 765–782.

Greenberg, J. R., & Mitchell, S. A. (1983). *Object relations in psychoanalytic theory.* Cambridge, MA: Harvard University Press.

Guntrip, H. (1968). *Schizoid phenomena, object relations and the self.* New York: International Universities Press.

Harlow, H. F. (1958). The nature of love. *American Psychologist, 13,* 673–685.

Heinicke, C., & Westheimer, L. (1965). *Brief separations.* New York: International Universities Press.

Hersov, L. A. (1960). Refusal to go to School. *Journal of Child Psychology and Psychiatry, 1,* 137–145.

Hinde, R. A., & McGinnis, L. (1977). Some factors influencing the effects of temporary mother-infant separation: Some experiments with rhesus monkeys. *Psychological Medicine, 7,* 197–212.

Horney, K. (1937) *The neurotic personality of our time,* New York: Norton.

Horney, K. (1939). *New ways in psychoanalysis.* New York: Norton.

Horney, K. (1950). *Neurosis and human growth.* New York: Norton.

Hurvich, M. (1985, May). Traumatic moment, basic dangers, and annihilation anxiety.

Paper presented to the New York Freudian Society, New York.

Kagan, J. & Moss, H. A. (1962). *Birth to maturity.* New York: Wiley.

Kaufman, I. C. & Rosenblum, L. A. (1967). Depression in infant monkeys separated from their mothers. *Science, 155,* 1030–1031.

Klein, D. F. (1981). Anxiety reconceptualized. In D. F. Klein & J. Rabkin (Eds.), *Anxiety: New research and changing concepts.* New York: Raven Press, pp. 235–265.

Kohut, H. (1971). *Analysis of the self.* New York: International Universities Press.

Kohut, H. (1977). *Restoration of the self.* New York: International Universities Press.

Kohut, H. (1984). *How analysis cures.* New York: International Universities Press.

Lazarus, R. S. (1964). A laboratory approach to the dynamics of psychological stress. *American Psychologist,* 19, 6, 400–411.

Lazarus, R. S. & Alpert, E. (1964). Short-circuiting of threat by experimentally altering cognitive appraisal. *Journal of Abnormal and Social Psychology, 69,* (2), 195–205.

Levin, R. B. (1966). An empirical test of the female castration complex. *Journal of Abnormal Psychology, 71,* 181–188.

Lewis, M., & Goldberg, S. (1969). Perceptual-cognitive development in infancy: a generalized expectancy model as a function of mother–infant interaction. *Merrill–Palmer Quarterly, 15,* 82–100.

Liddell, H. D. (1944). Conditioned reflex method and experimental neurosis. In J. McV. Hunt (Ed.), *Personality and the behavior disorders.* New York: Ronald Press, pp. 389–412.

Maccoby, E. E., & Feldman, S. S. (1972). Mother-attachment and stranger-reactions in the third year of life. *Monographs of the Society for Research in Child Development, 37,* (I, Serial No. 146).

Manosevits, M., & Lanyon, R. I. (1965). Fear survey schedule: A normative study. *Psychological Reports, 17,* 699–703.

Masserman, J. H. (1943). *Behavior and neurosis: An experimental psychoanalytic approach to psychobiologic principles.* Chicago: University of Chicago Press.

May, R. (1977). *The meaning of anxiety.* New York: Norton.

McGuinness, E. (1949). Emotionality and perceptual defense. *Psychological Review, 56,* 244–251.

Michels, R., Frances, A. J., & Shear, K. (1985). In A. H. Tuma & J. Mase (Eds.), *Anxiety and the anxiety disorders,* Hillsdale, NJ: Lawrence Erlbaum Associates.

Nunberg, H. (1955). *Principles of psychoanalysis.* (M. Kahr and S. Kahr, Trans.). New York: International Universities Press.

Passman, R. H., & Erck, T. W. (1977, March). *Visual presentation of mothers for facilitating play in children: The effects of silent films of mothers.* Paper presented to the Society for Research in Child Development, New Orleans.

Pavlov, I. P. (1927). *Conditioned reflexes* (G. Anrep, Trans.). New York: Oxford University Press.

Pettijohn, T. F., Wong, T. W., Ebert, P. D., & Scott, J. P. (1977). Alleviation of separation distress in three breeds of young dogs. *Developmental psychobiology, 10,* 373–381.

Pitcher, E. G., & Prelinger, E. (1963). *Children tell stories: An analysis of fantasy.* New York: International Universities Press.

Rajecki, D. W., Suomi, S. J., Scott, E. A., & Campbell, B. (1977). Effects of social isolation and social separation in domestic chicks. *Developmental Psychology, 13,* 143–155.

Rajecki, D. W., Lamb, M. E., & Obmascher, P. (1978). Toward a general theory of infantile attachment. A comparative review of aspects of the social bond. *Behavioral and Brain Sciences, 1,* 417–464.

Rangell, L. (1955). On the psychoanalytic theory of anxiety: A statement of a unitary theory of anxiety. *Journal of the American Psychoanalytic Association IV* (3), 389–414.

Rangell, L. (1968). A further attempt to resolve the "problem of anxiety." *Journal of the American Psychoanalytic Association, 16,* 371–404.

Rank, O. (1924). *The trauma of birth.* New York: Harcourt, Brace and Company.

Rapaport, D. (1960). The structure of psychoanalytic theory. *Psychological Issues,* 2 (6). (Whole).

Robertson, J., & Bowlby, J. (1952). Observations of the sequences of response of children aged 18 to 24 months during the course of separation. *Courier, 12,* 131–142.

Sarnoff, I. (1971). *Testing Freudian concepts: An experimental social approach.* New York: Springer.

Sarnoff, I., & Corwin, S. M. (1959). Castration anxiety and the fear of death. *Journal of Personality, 27,* 374–385.

Sarnoff, I., & Zimbardo, P. G. (1961). Anxiety, fear, and social affiliation. *Journal of Abnormal and Social Psychology, 62,* 356–363.

Schachter, S. (1959). *The psychology of affiliation.* Stanford, CA: Stanford University Press.

Schur, M. (1953). The ego in anxiety. In R. M.

Loewenstein (Ed.), *Drives, affects, behavior,* (pp. 227–248). New York: International Universities Press.

Schwartz, B. J. (1956). An empirical test of two Freudian hypotheses concerning castration anxiety. *Journal of Personality, 24,* 318–327.

Spiesman, J. C., Lazarus, R. S., Davison, L., & Mordkoff, A. M. (1964). Experimental analysis of a film used as a threatening stimulus. *Journal of Consulting Psychology, 28,* 25–33.

Sroufe, L. A., & Waters, E. (1977). Attachment as an organizational construct. *Child Development, 48,* 1184–1199.

Stettner, L. J., & Tilds, B. N. (1966). Effect of the presence of an imprinted object on response of ducklings in an open field when exposed to a fear stimulus. *Psychonomic Science, 4,* 107–108.

Sullivan, H. S. (1947). *Conceptions of modern psychiatry.* Washington, DC: The William Manson White Psychiatric Foundation.

Sullivan, H. S. (1953). *The interpersonal theory of psychiatry.* New York: Norton.

Taylor, G. (1986, May). *Psychodynamic aspects of panic disorder.* Paper given at symposium on "Panic disorder": Etiology and treatment" at the Annual Meeting of the American Psychiatric Association, Washington, DC.

Whiting, J. W., & Child, I. L. (1953). *Child training and personality: A cross-cultural study.* New Haven: Yale University Press.

Winnicott, D. W. (1975). Transitional objects and transitional phenomena. In *Through pediatrics to psychoanalysis* (pp. 229–242) New York: Basic Books. (Original work published 1951).

Wolitzky, D. L., & Wachtel, P. L. (1973). Personality and perception. In B. B. Wolman (Ed.), *Handbook of general psychology.* Englewood Cliffs, NJ: Prentice-Hall.

Wolpe, J. (1966). The conditioning and deconditioning of neurotic anxiety. In C. D. Spielberger (Ed.), *Anxiety and behavior.* (pp. 179–190). New York: Academic Press.

Zetzel, E. R. (1955). The concept of anxiety in relation to the development of psychoanalysis. *Journal of the American Psychoanalytic Association, III,* 369–388.

Zetzel, E. R. (1973). Repression and anxiety. In E. R. Zetzel & W. W. Meissner (Eds.), *Basic concepts of psychoanalytic psychiatry.* New York: Basic Books, pp. 80–98.

CHAPTER 14

Stress and Vulnerability

Norman S. Endler and Jean M. Edwards

The interaction model of personality (Endler, 1983) proposes that the joint influence of both person and situation factors is important in determining behavior. This model suggests, therefore, that both individual differences (i.e., differences in vulnerability) and situation variables (i.e., stressors) must be considered in understanding anxiety related disorders. The present chapter outlines the interaction model of personality and, more specifically, interaction models of stress and anxiety.

First, however, it is necessary to discuss the meanings of the three main concepts: anxiety, stress, and vulnerability. Each of these concepts has been defined in a variety of ways and has been the subject of considerable controversy. After discussing the definitions of these concepts and presenting the interaction model, we will review relevant empirical research. Although there is very little research specifically examining the interactionist model applied to anxiety disorders as identified in the *Diagnostic and Statistical Manual III* (DSM-III: APA, 1980), there are a number of studies investigating the relationship between situational stressors and the occurrence of physical and psychological disorders, including anxiety. In addition, there is a growing literature that focuses on individual differences (i.e., differences in vulnerability) that influence the relationship between stressors and disorders. Finally, we will consider the implications of the interaction model for the study of anxiety related disorders.

DEFINITIONS OF THE CONCEPTS

Anxiety

Anxiety has been a prominent construct in many theories of personality and abnormal psychology from the writings of Freud (1933) to those of cognitive social learning theorists and interactionists (Bandura, 1982; Endler, 1983). Freudian theory emphasized anxiety and conflict in the etiology of the neuroses, and his theorizing regarding the neurotic process had a substantial and long-lasting impact on the nomenclature and classification systems applied to psychological disorders involving anxiety (Millon, 1984). The impact of Freudian theory, however, has been lessened in the current DSM-III (APA, 1980) classification system.

Developers of the DSM-III (APA, 1980) sought to eliminate theoretical and etiological implications from the classification system and to restrict the categories to descriptive criteria (Millon, 1984). The class of "anxiety disorders" has been adopted as the major category of psychological disorders in which anxiety is the predominant feature of the disturbance. Anxiety disorders are subdivided into phobic disorders, anxiety states, and posttraumatic stress disorders, each of which are further subdivided. Phobic disorders include agoraphobia (with or without panic attacks), social phobia, and simple phobia. Anxiety states include panic disorders, generalized anxiety disorder, and obsessive–compulsive disorders. Posttraumatic stress disorder is differentiated into acute and chronic or delayed disorders. Approximately 2% to 4% of the general population may at some time have experienced a disturbance that would be classified as an anxiety disorder (APA, 1980).

Behavior that is clinically labeled as an anxiety disorder represents only a small component of the phenomena that generally are included under the rubric of anxiety. Although anxiety constitutes a critical component of Freud's theory of neurosis, the concept of normal anxiety gained acceptance in the mid-1950s (May, 1977). There has developed since then extensive concern over anxiety and its contribution to physical and mental disorders, as well as its effects on the productivity and well-being of members of society (Sturgis, 1984). May (1977), for example, has labeled the mid-20th century as the "Age of Anxiety".

The theory and research on anxiety is voluminous (Endler, 1980; Spielberger, 1972). One result of this extensive interest is the variety of definitions of anxiety that exists in the literature. The term *anxiety* has been used to refer to a stimulus, response, drive, motive, and trait (Endler, 1975). Spielberger (1972) suggests that in order to reduce confusion, a distinction needs to be made between state anxiety and trait anxiety. State anxiety is a reaction "consisting of unpleasant consciously-perceived feelings of tension and apprehension, with associated activation or arousal of the autonomic nervous system" (Spielberger, 1972, p. 29). Trait anxiety

> refers to relatively stable individual differences in anxiety proneness, i.e., to differences among people in the disposition or tendency to perceive a wide range of situations as threatening and to respond to these situations with differential elevations in state anxiety. (Spielberger, 1975, p. 137)

The present chapter uses the terms *state* and *trait anxiety* as defined by Spielberger (1975) and by Endler (1975, 1980).

Stress

The concept of stress was first used in physics to indicate a mechanical force acting on a body (Harris & Levey, 1975). The stress concept was introduced into the life sciences by Selye in 1936 (Appley & Trumbull, 1967; Selye, 1956) and has become a prominent focus of theory, research, and treatment (Lazarus & Folkman, 1984; Mechanic, 1962; Meichenbaum, 1983). The prominence of the stress concept has resulted in many related areas being encompassed under this topic.

> Since the term gained some attention, and apparently some status, as a research topic, it has been used as a substitute for what might otherwise have been called anxiety, conflict, emotional distress, extreme environmental conditions, ego threat, frustration, threat to security, tension arousal, or by some other previously respectable terms. (Appley & Trumbull, 1967, p. 1).

There is considerable overlap in the literature on anxiety and stress, and in fact, the terms have often been used interchangeably (Spielberger, 1976).

As with the use of the term *anxiety*, stress has been defined in a variety of ways. Selye (1956), for example, focused on the physiological response. He defined stress as a nonspecific response of the body to any demand. The early research on stressful life events, in contrast, focused on the situation, specifically on the degree of change that had occurred in one's life (Holmes & Rahe, 1967). Definitions of stress solely in terms of response or solely in terms of situations, however, have frequently been found to be inadequate in terms of research (cf. Dohrenwend & Dohrenwend, 1974; Goldberger & Breznitz, 1982; Rabkin & Struening, 1976). There does not appear to be any single response or set of responses that are always indicative of stress. Similarly, with the exception of extreme life-threatening events, there appear to be no situations that are universal stressors. Considerable controversy, therefore, has surrounded attempts to define stress, either objectively or psychologically, and has generated interest in interaction models of stress.

Spielberger (1976) differentiates between stress, defined in terms of the objective properties of a situation, and threat, defined in terms of the individual's perception of an event as being potentially dangerous. He notes that an objectively stressful situation is typically perceived as threatening, but that individual differences can alter such perceptions. The interaction model of anxiety (Endler, 1980) similarly defines stress as a situational variable, the perception of which is influenced by individual predispositions.

Coyne and Lazarus (1980) state that the important role of personality factors in producing stress reactions requires that stress should *not* be defined in terms of either the person *or* the situation, but as a transaction between them. Stress is a "particular relationship between the person and the environment that is appraised by the person as taxing his or her resources and endangering his or her well being" (Lazarus & Folkman, 1984, p. 19). This definition of stress is based on an interaction model. In the present chapter, the term *stress* is used to refer to an interaction between the person and the environment which is perceived as taxing or exceeding one's resources. The term *stressor* is used to refer to environmental variables, with the explicit recognition that not all potential stressors do, in fact, produce stress.

Vulnerability

Individual differences in perception of and response to the same objective stressors contributed to the controversies surrounding the definition of stress. In this chapter, the term *vulnerability* is used to refer to these individual differences in susceptibility to stressors (cf. Garmezy, 1981).

The interaction model postulates that individual differences interact with specific types or ranges of environments to influence behavior. The interaction model indicates that a variety of individual differences may be implicated in determining vulnerability to specific types or intensity of stressors. These differences may be cognitive, emotional, or motivational (Endler, 1983), and may result from both genetic differences (cf. Singer, 1984) and from learning in interaction with one's environment (cf. Chess, Thomas, & Birch, 1976).

INTERACTION MODELS

The Interaction Model of Personality

Personality research and theory generally, as well as research on stress and anxiety specifically, have been influenced by four models: the trait model, the psychodynamic model, the situationism model, and the interaction model (Endler & Magnusson, 1976a). The trait model emphasizes internal factors as determinants of behavior and predicts *relative* consistency in responses across a broad range of situations. Trait approaches to stress and anxiety emphasize individual differences in predispositions and focus on assessing these differences (cf. Cattell & Scheier, 1961). The psychodynamic models also emphasize internal determinants of behavior (e.g., impulses, motives, drives, and conflicts). Freud's (1933) later theory of anxiety, for example, emphasizes the role of unconscious conflicts between various impulses, and conflicts between expression of repressed impulses and internalized societal demands. In contrast, the situationism model emphasizes external factors as determinants of behavior. Classical behavior theorists emphasize the roles of learning and of eliciting stimuli in provoking stress–anxiety responses (cf. Dollard & Miller, 1950; Watson & Rayner, 1920). Criticism of these earlier models has been articulated by Endler and Magnusson (1976b). Briefly, empirical research has demonstrated that the *interaction* of persons and situations is an important source of variance in behavior (for reviews, see Endler 1975, 1982, 1983; Endler & Edwards, 1978; Endler & Magnusson, 1976b; Mischel, 1968, 1973; Pervin, 1984; Pervin & Lewis, 1978).

The interaction model of personality (Endler, 1983) provides a theoretical perspective for examining the reciprocal influences of persons, situations, and responses. Persons and situations interact in an ongoing process, and both sets of variables affect the perception or psychological meaning of the situation, as well as the response to that situation. The interaction model of personality (Endler, 1983; Endler & Magnusson, 1976b) further proposes that the person is an active, intentional agent in the process, that with respect to person factors, cognitive, motivational, and emotional variables are important, and that the appraisal of the psychological meaning that the situation has for the individual is an essential determining factor of behavior.

Two methodological models of interactionism, the mechanistic and dynamic models (Endler & Edwards, 1978; Olweus, 1977; Overton & Reese, 1973), are discussed in the anxiety and stress literature. The hypothesis that some individuals are more susceptible to stressors or to particular types of stressors is an example of the mechanistic interaction model (cf. Rabkin, 1982). In the mechanistic model, the focus is on the interaction effect of two independent variables on the dependent variable. Its measurement model is the analysis of variance. It assumes a linear and additive relationship between person (vulnerability) and situational (stressor) factors (both independent variables) in determining appraisal and response (both dependent variables). This model clearly distinguishes between independent and dependent variables. The mechanistic interaction model examines the interdependency of determinants of behavior (independent variables), but does not examine interaction between independent and dependent variables. It focuses on unidirectional causality. "The interaction is between causes and not between cause and effect" (Overton & Reese, 1973, p. 78).

Research that examines the differential effects of stressors on individuals who differ on some measure of personality, for example, trait anxiety (Endler, 1980), or locus of control (Phares, 1976), or on Type A behavior pattern (Chesney & Rosenman, 1983), is typically formulated within a mechanistic model. Research that examines stress and vulnerability within this model varies with regard to the breadth or generality of the proposed vulnerability concepts, and with regard to the comprehensiveness of the variables considered (cf. Kobasa, 1979; Lefcourt, Martin, & Saleh, 1984). At issue is the *consistency* of vulnerability or resistance across a range of stressful situations, a controversy related to the cross-situational consistency of behavior issue that has been prominent in personality theory for over a decade (Pervin, 1984).

The dynamic model of interaction focuses on the *process* of interaction. It assumes that there is reciprocal causality among both person and situation factors and responses. Persons not only react to situations, but also select, interpret, and alter those situations in which they interact, and are in turn altered by them (Endler, 1983; Lazarus & Folkman, 1984).

"Reciprocal causation means that not only do events affect behavior of organisms but the organism is also an active agent in influencing environmental events" (Endler & Magnusson, 1976b, p. 969). Dynamic interaction is multidirectional and focuses on process changes over time.

A dynamic interaction model of stress focuses on the sequence of the stress process and proposes variables for analysis appropriate to this interaction process (e.g., appraisal of the psychological situation, in addition to examining person variables, situation variables, and outcome variables). A dynamic model examines the reciprocal causation that occurs, for example, when cognitive expectancies influence behavioral and emotional responses to a potential stressor. The feedback from these responses affects the expectancies which in turn affect future responses to the same or similar stressor (cf. Bandura, 1982; Lazarus & Folkman, 1984).

A Multidimensional Interaction Model of Anxiety

Endler (1975, 1980, 1983) has proposed a multidimensional, interaction model of anxiety that has received empirical support in both laboratory and field studies. The multidimensional interaction model of anxiety proposes that person and situation factors interact to determine situation perception and anxiety responses (Endler, 1975, 1980, 1983). Two conceptual distinctions are important in the interaction model of anxiety, the distinction between state anxiety and trait anxiety, previously discussed, and the multidimensionality of trait anxiety and the interaction of congruent dimensions of trait anxiety and situational stress (Endler, 1983).

Endler's (1975, 1980) interaction model proposes that trait anxiety is multidimensional. That is, individuals differ in anxiety proneness with respect to certain dimensions of situations. The dimensions considered include interpersonal or social evaluation threat, physical danger threat, and ambiguous threat as well as daily routines. The interaction model proposes that both the type of threat in a stressful situation and the specific dimension of trait anxiety must be considered in predicting state anxiety responses. A person by situation interaction with respect to state anxiety changes is predicted only when the dimension of trait anxiety and the type of stress situation are congruent. That is, an individual high on physical danger trait anxiety will show an increase in state anxiety when confronted with a physically dangerous situation, but not when confronted with a social evaluation situation.

The interaction model suggests that the interaction of situations (stressors) and individual predispositions (multidimensional trait anxiety, as well as other individual differences related to vulnerability) must be considered in the investigation of the etiology and maintenance of anxiety disorders. The model further emphasizes the need to assess individual predispositions with regard to specific types of stressors and questions approaches that propose global rather than specific measures for individual differences in anxiety or vulnerability.

A Dynamic Interaction Model of Stress

Lazarus and Folkman (1984) define psychological stress in terms of the individual's cognitive appraisal of a specific situation as taxing or exceeding his or her coping resources. Lazarus' model outlines an interaction *process,* particularly emphasizing the role of appraisal and coping.

Cognitive appraisal is the "person's continually re-evaluated judgments about demands and constraints in ongoing transactions with the environment and his or her resources for managing them" (Coyne & Lazarus, 1980, p. 150). These appraisal processes influence the person's stress reactions and coping responses, the various emotions experienced, and adaptational outcomes.

The appraisal process consists of primary cognitive appraisal, secondary cognitive appraisal, and reappraisal. Primary cognitive appraisal is the assessment or evaluation of a situation in terms of its significance for one's well-being. Secondary appraisal refers to the individual's judgments regarding available coping resources, options, and constraints, and is important in shaping the individual's coping responses (Lazarus & Folkman, 1984). Reappraisal refers to the process of change in judgments regarding the situation or the resources available to cope with it.

Psychological vulnerability, in Lazarus' model (Lazarus & Folkman, 1984) represents potential threat. Both cognitive appraisal and coping affect vulnerability. Individual differences that influence appraisal and coping, therefore, are important in determining psychological vulnerability.

Lazarus and Folkman (1984) propose two person characteristics (i.e., commitments and beliefs) that are important determinants of appraisals. Commitments and beliefs affect appraisals by "(1) determining what is salient for well-being in a given encounter; (2) shaping the person's understanding of the event, and in consequence his or her emotions and coping efforts; and (3) providing the basis for evaluating outcomes" (Lazarus & Folkman, 1984, p. 55). Commitments have both cognitive and motivational components. Individuals are most vulnerable (i.e., susceptible to threat) in areas where they have high commitment. Knowledge of the individual's pattern of commitments, therefore, is important in defining areas of vulnerability.

Beliefs also influence appraisals. Beliefs influence perception of the environment and the interpretation of its meaning. Two sets of beliefs, personal control beliefs and existential beliefs, are considered by Lazarus and Folkman (1984). They propose that

> A promising hypothesis is that the extent to which people feel confident of their powers of mastery over the environment or alternatively, feel great vulnerability to harm in a world conceived as dangerous and hostile, affects whether an encounter will produce threat or challenge appraisals (Lazarus & Folkman, 1984, p. 65).

Coping may be of even greater importance in determining vulnerability and adaptational outcomes than appraisal. Lazarus and Folkman define coping as "constantly changing cognitive and behavioral efforts to manage specific external and/or internal demands that are appraised as taxing or exceeding the resources of the person" (1984, p. 141). Coping is influenced by cognitive appraisal and therefore those personal characteristics (e.g., commitments and beliefs) that influence appraisal also affect the coping process. In addition, Lazarus and Folkman suggest that person variables may directly affect coping, for example, personal resources including health and energy, positive beliefs, and competencies (i.e., problem-solving and social skills). They also point out that some person variables (e.g., personal constraints and agendas) may limit choice and implementation of certain coping strategies, thereby increasing vulnerability.

Lazarus (Lazarus & Folkman, 1984) takes an emphatically transactional or dynamic interaction approach to the study of stress. Individual differences, environmental factors, and *process* variables are important. Lazarus and Folkman (1984) emphasize the importance of examining the stress, appraisal, and coping process rather than relying on static trait concepts of vulnerability.

EMPIRICAL RESEARCH ON STRESS, VULNERABILITY, AND ANXIETY

Stress is the organizing concept in most of the research reviewed in this chapter. Research has examined the relationship between stress and both psychological and physical disorders. Research on vulnerability has developed within the stress research in attempts to explain individual differences in perception of and response to objectively similar situations.

Studies of extreme environments were among the earliest research on stress. For example, Grinker and Spiegel (1945) studied the effects on both physical and psychological functioning of the effects of the stress of flying combat missions in World War II. They describe in detail the anxiety-related disorders suffered by these pilots. They found, however, that even under these severe conditions, individual differences were important in determining outcome. They concluded that the men who became psychiatric casualties could be divided into two groups: those who developed severe symptoms after exposure to minimal stress, and those who developed symptoms after exposure to severe or prolonged stress. They proposed that some other factor, in addition to the stressful experiences, contributed to the development of anxiety symptoms.

> The factor of course consists in the initial psychological preparedness of the individual to react to specific stimuli. In the presence of a previous emotional disorder, small amounts of stress to which an individual is sensitized may lead to severe symptoms. Conversely, men who have considerable psychological stability can withstand large amounts of stress before giving way to crippling symptoms (Grinker & Spiegel, 1945, p. 55).

The research on natural and manmade disasters (Adams & Adams, 1984; Baum, Fleming, & Singer, 1982; Lifton & Olson, 1976) indicates that there may be transient and long-term stress responses, including both psychosomatic reactions and emotional reactions of anxiety, depression, anger, and feelings of helplessness. Adams and Adams (1984) found evidence for postdisaster stress reactions, including increases in illness, substance abuse, and violence, in a community located near Mount Saint Helens, which erupted in May 1980. Similar effects were found in the population that experienced the catastrophe near Buffalo Creek, West Virginia (Lifton & Olson, 1976).

Baum et al. (1982) assessed responses to the stressor of the accident at the nuclear power plant at Three Mile Island. They found evidence of chronic stress after the incident; however, the stress responses were not severe nor were they manifested by all the residents. The recent accident at Chernobyl was more extensive. Studies of this incident may find more severe and more widespread stress effects.

Bonkalo (1984) reviewed the literature on the variety of transient and situational disorders that may occur in normal populations in response to situational stressors such as surgery, assault, environmental castastrophe, bereavement, combat, or imprisonment. He raises the question of the residual effects of stressful encounters on the individual's vulnerability to future stressors. Experience with any stressor is part of a complex process of reciprocal interaction. The individual comes to the situation with a variety of individual differences that influence vulnerability, and the experience affects the individual's future vulnerability, for better or worse.

The area of research that has probably contributed most to the prominence of the stress concept is the stressful life events literature (Dohrenwend & Dohrenwend, 1978, 1981; Holmes & Rahe, 1967; Rabkin & Struening, 1976). Early studies assessing the relationship between life change events and illness or distress focused on the degree of change occurring in an individual's life as a measure of the degree of stress experience. For example, the Social Readjustment Rating Scale lists life change events, such as death of a spouse, marriage, and violation of the law, each weighted for the degree of change evoked by its occurrence (Holmes & Rahe, 1967). Positive correlations between related life change events scores and illness or psychological distress have been reported frequently; however, the correlations typically have been low (Dohrenwend & Dohrenwend, 1974, 1978; Rabkin & Struening, 1976).

Again, the conclusion that has emerged from the research and critical appraisals of the life change event literature is that individuals may perceive and respond to the same objective event quite differently (cf. Antonovsky, 1974). Two important trends have developed in the stressful life events literature as a result: (a) the assessment of dimensions of appraisal, and (b) the investigation of individual difference variables that influence the perception of and response to stressful events, that is, individual vulnerability.

There have been a number of ways in which individual differences in vulnerability have been conceptualized. Much of the research, however, fall into three categories: (a) approaches that emphasize cognitive factors, that is, expectancies, beliefs, and commitments (e.g., Kobasa, 1979; Lefcourt, 1980); (b) approaches that emphasize response predispositions in interaction with a specific range of situations (e.g., Chesney & Rosenman, 1984; Endler, 1975, 1980); and (c) approaches that emphasize the interaction *process* (Lazarus & Folkman, 1984). Representative research from each of these approaches is reviewed.

Cognitive Factors that Influence Vulnerability to Stressors

Kobasa (1979) has pointed out that overall, the correlations between stressful life events and the occurrence of illness, while positive, are *not large*. She proposes a personality characteristic of "hardiness" that differentiates persons experiencing high levels of stressors without falling ill, from those who become ill under similar conditions. Hardy individuals believe that they can control or influence the events they experience. They have the ability to feel deeply committed to the life activities in which they are invloved. They anticipate change as an exciting challenge leading to personal development rather than as detrimental. A series of studies of business executives functioning in highly stressful work environments support the proposed relationship between hardiness and illness (Kobasa, 1979; Kobasa, Maddi, & Kahn, 1982; Kobasa & Puccetti, 1983). Kobasa suggests that hardiness influences both appraisal of an event and coping strategies in dealing with that event. Important components of the hardy personality include

> the cognitive appraisal effect of rendering the events as not so meaningless, overwhelming and undesirable, after all, and the action effect of instigating coping activities that involve interaction with and thereby transforming the events into a less stressful form rather than avoiding them (Kobasa et al., 1982, p. 169).

Perceived control (Lefcourt, 1980; Phares, 1976; Rotter, 1966) is a cognitive expectancy that influences vulnerability to potential stressors. Glass and Singer (1972) report a series of studies that indicate the perception of control in a stressful situation can reduce its negative effects. Individual differences in control expectancies (e.g., the Internal-External Locus of Control Expectancy [Rotter, 1966]) similarly may affect one's vulnerability to stressors.

Internal locus of control refers to a person's perception that an event is contingent upon one's own behavior or relatively permanent characteristics (e.g., traits). External locus of control is the perception that an event is not entirely contingent on one's own actions, but is the result of luck, chance, fate, or powerful others (Rotter, 1966). As a personality dimension, it has been construed as a relatively broad, generalized expectancy (Rotter, 1966, 1975), as well as more specific expectancies regarding control over limited areas of one's experiences (cf. Lefcourt, 1976; Phares, 1976).

Congruent with theoretical expectancies, locus of control has been found to influence coping activities and emotional response to stressors (Phares, 1976). For example, studies have found that internals seek and use more information than externals (Davis & Phares, 1967; Seeman, 1963; Seeman & Evans, 1962). Lefcourt (1980) reports that internals differ from externals in the utilization of coping strategies (e.g., humor), and that externals compared to internals display more indicators of tension when confronted with achievement-related failure.

Johnson and Sarason (1979) suggest that locus of control may mediate the effect of life change. As predicted, they found a significant positive correlation between anxiety and depression, and negative life change events for externals but not for internals; however, the correlations were relatively modest. Lefcourt et al. (1984)

found that locus of control regarding social interaction moderates the relationship among life events, social support, and mood.

Response Predispositions that Interact with Situations to Affect Vulnerability

Endler's (1975, 1980) model of anxiety, previously discussed, proposes that trait anxiety (i.e., the predisposition to perceive as threatening and respond with state anxiety to certain situations) is multidimensional. The differential hypothesis states that increases in state anxiety are the result of interactions between a specific dimension of trait anxiety (e.g., social evaluation) and a *congruent* stressful situation (e.g., a job interview). A series of studies by Endler and his students (Endler, 1983; Endler, Edwards, & Vitelli, 1985) and by others (e.g., Kendall, 1978) empirically supports this differential hypothesis. For example, Endler and Okada (1975), in a laboratory experiment, found changes in state anxiety in female students as a result of an interaction between the physical danger dimension of trait anxiety and a physical danger stress-or (threat of electric shock). The physical danger situation did not interact with the noncongruent dimensions of trait anxiety (i.e., social evaluation). Endler, King, Edwards, Kuczynski, and Diveky, (1983), studying Canadian high school students, and Phillips and Endler (1982), studying Canadian university students, found an interaction between social evaluation (interpersonal) trait anxiety and a stressful classroom examination situation.

Endler, Edwards, and Kowalchuk (1983) examined the interaction model of anxiety in a short-term psychotherapy situation with both male and female clients. They found a significant interaction between the social evaluation psychotherapy situation and social evaluation A-trait in predicting A-state *decreases* over the course of therapy. They also found interactions for the interpersonal and innocuous facets of A-trait, and the ambiguous trait for females.

The Type A behavior pattern is similarly a response predisposition that interacts with stressful situations. Type A is not a personality type, but a set of behaviors that emerge from an *interaction* between a challenging environment and personal predisposition. The Type A behavior pattern includes

> such behavioral dispositions as ambitiousness, aggressiveness, competitiveness and impatience; specific behaviors such as alertness, muscle tenseness, rapid and emphatic speech stylistics; and emotional reactions such as enhanced irritation and expressed signs of anger. (Chesney & Rosenman, 1983, p. 548).

Chesney and Rosenman propose that the Type A behavior pattern is characterized by a chronic struggle with time to accomplish more and more in less and less time, and by competition with other people or environmental forces. Type A behavior is particularly likely to occur in predisposed individuals challenged by situations in which their control is threatened. The term *Type A individuals* is used in this chapter to refer to individuals who manifest Type A behavior in threatening, challenging situations.

The relationship between Type A behavior and coronary heart disease was first demonstrated in the Western Collaborative Study (Chesney & Rosenman, 1983). Research has generally found that Type A individuals show greater sympathetic nervous system and cardiovascular arousal when confronted with stressors than do Type B individuals (Dembroski, MacDougall, & Shields, 1977; Glass et al., 1980). The characteristics of the situation, however, are important in eliciting these differences in Type A and Type B individuals. Situations that emphasize a challenge or that include harassment enchance the differential responses of the Type A individuals compared to Type B individuals (Glass et al., 1980).

Whereas the original concept of Type A involved a composite of a number of behaviors, more recently there is evidence that some components (e.g., hostility) may be particularly important in evoking the perception of challenge. Chesney and Rosenman (1983) suggest that research is needed to examine the interactions between characteristics of the situation and of the person in provoking the perception of challenge. In addition, they suggest a need for research on the dynamic interaction process, specifically, research focusing on the coping styles employed in challenging situations by individuals who differ in the Type A and Type B behavioral pattern.

Sensation-seeking (Zuckerman, 1974) is an individual difference variable related to a tendency to prefer, seek out, and enjoy highly varied stimulating, and exciting situations. Individuals who are high on sensation-seeking may respond quite differently to life change events from those low on sensation-seeking (Johnson & Sarason, 1979). High sensation-seekers may be less aroused and better able to cope with change. Studies have found correlations between negative life changes and problems in adjustment for subjects low on sensation- or arousal-seeking but not for those high on sensation-seeking (Smith, Johnson, & Sarason, 1978).

Interaction Process Variables that Affect Vulnerability

The theory and research by Lazarus and his colleagues (Lazarus & Folkman, 1984) demonstrate the importance of examining the stress process, particularly appraisal and coping strategies. A series of laboratory studies by Lazarus and his colleagues demonstrated the importance of the mediating role of cognitive appraisal in the stress-anxiety process (Lazarus & Launier, 1978). In these studies, cognitive appraisal was operationalized primarily by experimental manipulation and by the selection of subjects who differed in appraisal of coping styles. Speisman, Lazarus, Mordkoff, and Davison (1964), for example, exposed four groups of subjects to the same objective stimulus, a film, but varied the cognitive information accompanying the stimulus. They found, as predicted, that the levels of arousal of the subjects were influenced by the cognitive appraisal they provided.

Lazarus and his colleagues have also examined the stressors encountered in daily life and the impact that the appraisal of the stressor has on the coping strategies selected (Folkman & Lazarus, 1985). Kanner, Coyne, Schaefer, and Lazarus (1981) suggested that, in contrast to the emphasis on major life events (e.g., Holmes & Rahe, 1967), research should focus on the daily "hassles" that are an important component of the person-situation stress process. Hassles are the small daily stressors (i.e., the common annoyances that affect daily life). Kanner et al. (1981) found that hassles are a better predictor of psychological and physical symptoms than life events. Folkman and Lazarus (1980) examined the relationship among context, appraisal, and coping styles across a series of stressful life experiences reported by their subjects. Both context (e.g., whether the stressors involved health, work, family, or other concerns) and appraisal (primarily regarding control) influenced the selection of coping strategies. They found that individuals showed considerable variability in the type of coping used over the situations reported.

IMPLICATIONS OF AN INTERACTION MODEL FOR THE STUDY OF ANXIETY-RELATED DISORDERS

The present chapter has outlined the interaction model of personality and has examined the research on the relationship among stress, vulnerability, and anxiety-related disorders from this interactionist perspective.

The interaction model proposes that people and situations interact in influencing behavior. Research has confirmed this proposal. The research findings have resulted in stress being defined in terms of an interaction between the person and the environment, and an increasing number of studies include both types of variables. The interaction model, however, goes further than merely recognizing the importance of interactions and emphasizing the need for theoretical and empirical explorations of *how* persons and situations interact (Endler, 1983).

Greater conceptual and empirical specificity in identifying the variables involved in the interaction process is one strategy for accomplishing this task. For example, the conceptual distinction between state and trait anxiety and the conceptualization of trait anxiety as multidimensional have led to theoretical predictions of interactions. Chesney and Rosenman (1983) have similarly discussed the multiple components of the Type A behavior pattern. There is also a growing recognition that there is a need to specify the range of situations to which a concept applies.

In this chapter, vulnerability has been used to refer to a range of individual difference variables that increase susceptibility to stressors. The interaction model emphasizes the role of cognitive factors while recognizing that motivational and emotional factors are also important. The research we have reviewed similarly tends to implicate cognitive factors (e.g., expectancies and appraisal) in the stress process. There is, however, a wide array of variables that may be related to vulnerability, ranging from relatively stable factors to situation-specific variables: for example, intelligence; specific coping skills; physical well-being; temperament (cf. Singer, 1984); cognitive styles and schemata; and beliefs, plans, and goals; as well as transient moods and states. These vulnerability factors may be more or less important depending upon the specific stressful situation and the ongoing interaction process.

Endler (1983) has identified the analysis of the meaningful psychological situation as one of the important tasks of interactional psychology. A variety of stressors have been studied, including single catastrophic events, for example, floods and nuclear accidents; ambient environmental stressors (Evans, 1982), such as noise; and cumulative life events of both major and routine proportions. It is often the psychological dimensions of these events (e.g., perceived control), however, that are important in determining responses. There is a need for a further analysis of situations to delineate the dimensions that determine their stress-provoking potential (cf. Edwards, 1984; Endler, 1981; Magnusson, 1981).

The interaction model emphasizes the need for specificity in identifying outcomes. The DSM III (APA, 1980) proposes a number of subcategories of anxiety disorders. As Sturgis (1984) suggests, the antecedents and process of development may differ across the specific disorders. Research that examines the antecedent processes that result in specific disorders is needed. See, however, Rabkin (1982) for a discussion of the methodological problems in such research.

The model emphasizes that interaction is a *process* that involves reciprocal causality between an active organism and his or her meaningful environment. Research has focused on how stressors and individual differences in vulnerability determine the development of anxiety responses. This, however, is only one segment of the interaction process. Research is needed on the various steps in this process (cf. Bandura, 1982; Folkman & Lazarus, 1985). For example, research is needed on the influence of vulnerability factors and stressors on the chronicity or exacerbation of anxiety disorders (cf. Neufeld & Mothersill, 1980). The process of confronting recurrent or continued stressors as well as multiple stressors needs to be examined. Bandura's (1982) microanalysis of the functioning of self-efficacy in altering phobic behavior is an important model for examining the stress process. He emphasizes the reciprocal interactions among expectancies, emotions, behaviors, and situational feedback.

The interaction model also has implications for treatment. Bandura (1977) has examined the treatment of phobic disorders derived from his theory of self-efficacy and reciprocal interactions. Meichenbaum (1983) also has developed his cognitive behavior therapeutic approach from an interaction perspective. In addition, there is the need for assessment techniques and strategies that include the situational factors that interact with person factors to provoke anxiety-related disorders or to facilitate improvement. Raush, Dittmann, and Taylor (1959a, b), for example, found that interactions of both person and situation factors must be included in investigations of behavior of hyperaggressive boys and in the assessment of the effectiveness of their treatment.

CONCLUDING REMARKS

This chapter examined the relationship among stress, vulnerability, and anxiety disorders from an interactionist perspective. After discussing the definitions of the major concepts, we outlined the interaction model of personality and more specifically interaction models of anxiety and stress. Research on the relationship among stress, vulnerability, and anxiety-related disorders was then reviewed. Implications of the interaction model for the study of anxiety disorders were discussed. It was suggested that both person and situation variables must be included in theories and research on anxiety disorders, and that there was a need for conceptual and empirical specificity in the identification of these variables. The importance of analyzing all the segments of the interaction process was emphasized. Finally, it was suggested that the interaction model has important implications for both the assessment and treatment of anxiety-related disorders.

Acknowledgement — The preparation of this article was supported in part by Social Science and Humanities Research Council Leave Fellowship (451-85-3463) to Norman S. Endler.

REFERENCES

Adams, P. R., & Adams, G. R. (1984). Mount Saint Helen's ashfall: Evidence for a disaster stress reaction. *American Psychologist, 39,* 252–260.

American Psychiatric Association. (1980). *Diagnostic and statistical manual of mental disorders* (3rd ed.). Washington, DC: Author.

Antonovsky, A. (1974). Conceptual and methodological problems in the study of resistance resources and stressful life events. In B. S. Dohrenwend & B. P. Dohrenwend (Eds.), *Stressful life events; Their nature and effects* (pp. 245–258. Toronto: John Wiley & Sons.

Appley, M. H., & Trumbull, R. (1967). *Psychological stress: Issues in research.* New York: Appleton-Century-Crofts.

Bandura, A. (1977). Self-efficacy: Toward a unifying theory of behavioral change. *Pyschological Review, 84,* 191–215.

Bandura, A. (1982). Self-efficacy mechanism in human agency. *American Psychologist, 37,* 122–147.

Baum, A., Fleming, R., & Singer, J. E. (1982). Stress at Three Mile Island: Applying psychological impact analysis. In L. Bickman (Ed.), *Applied social psychology annual* (Vol. 3, pp. 217–248). Beverly Hills, CA: Sage.

Bonkalo, A. (1984). Transient and situational disorders. In N. S. Endler & J. McV. Hunt (Eds.), *Personality and the behavioral disorders* (Vol. 2, 2nd ed., pp. 897–913). New York: John Wiley & Sons.

Cattell, R. B., & Scheier, I. H. (1961). *The meaning and measurement of neuroticism and anxiety.* New York: The Roland Press.

Chesney, M. A., & Rosenman, R. H. (1983). Specificity in stress models: Examples drawn from Type A Behaviour. In C. L. Cooper (Ed.), *Stress research: Issues for the eighties* (pp. 21–34). Toronto: John Wiley & Sons.

Chess, S., Thomas, A., & Birch, H. G. (1976). Behavior problems revisited: Findings of an anterospective study. In N. S. Endler, L. R. Boulter, & H. Osser (Eds.), *Contemporary issues in developmental psychology* (2nd ed., pp. 562–568). Toronto: Holt, Rinehart and Winston.

Coyne, J. C., & Lazarus, R. S. (1980). Cognitive style, stress perception, and coping. In I. L. Kutash & L. B. Schlesinger (Eds.), *Handbook on stress and anxiety: Contemporary knowledge, theory and treatment* (pp. 144–158). San Francisco: Jossey-Bass Publishers.

Davis, W. L., & Phares, E. J. (1967). Internal-external control as a determinant of information-seeking in a social influence situation. *Journal of Personality, 35,* 547–561.

Dembroski, T. M., MacDougall, J. M., & Shields, T. L. (1977). Physiologic reactions to social challenge in persons evidencing Type A coronary-prone behaviour pattern. *Journal of Human Stress, 3,* 2–10.

Dohrenwend, B. S., & Dohrenwend, B. P. (1974). Overview and prospects for research on stressful life events. In B. S. Dohrenwend & B. P. Dohrenwend (Eds.), *Stress life events: Their nature and effects* (pp. 313–331). Toronto: John Wiley & Sons.

Dohrenwend, B. S., & Dohrenwend, B. P. (1978). Some issues in research on stressful life events. *The Journal of Nervous and Mental Disease, 166,* 7–15.

Dohrenwend, B. S., & Dohrenwend, B. P. (1981). Life stress and illness: Formulations of the issues. In B. S. Dohrenwend & B. P. Dohrenwend (Eds.), *Stressful life events and their contexts* (pp. 1–27). New York: Prodist.

Dollard, J., & Miller, N. E. (1950). *Personality and psychotherapy: An analysis in terms of learning, thinking and culture.* New York: McGraw-Hill.

Edwards, J. M. (1984). Situational determinants of behavior. In N. S. Endler & J. McV. Hunt (Eds.), *Personality and the behavioral disorders* (Vol. 1, 2nd ed., pp. 147–182). Toronto: John Wiley & Sons.

Endler, N. S. (1975). A person-situation interaction model of anxiety. In C. D. Spielberger & I. G. Sarason (Eds.), *Stress and anxiety* (Vol. 1, pp. 145–164). Washington, DC: Hemisphere Publishing Corporation.

Endler, N. S. (1980). Person-situation interaction and anxiety. In I. L. Kutash & L. B. Schlesinger (Eds.), *Handbook on stress and anxiety: Contemporary knowledge, theory and treatment* (pp. 249–266). San Francisco: Jossey-Bass.

Endler, N. S. (1981). Situational aspects of interactional psychology. In D. Magnusson (Ed.), *Toward a psychology of situation: An interactional perspective* (pp. 361–373). Hillsdale, NJ: Lawrence Erlbaum Associates.

Endler, N. S. (1982). Interactionism comes of age. In M. P. Zanna, E. T. Higgins, & C. P. Herman (Eds.), *Consistency in social behavior: The Ontario Symposium* (Vol. 2, pp. 209–249). Hillsdale, NJ: Lawrence Erlbaum Associates.

Endler, N. S. (1983). Interactionism: A personality model, but not yet a theory. In M. M. Page (Ed.), *Nebraska Symposium on Motivation 1982. Personality — Current theory and research* (pp. 155–200). Lincoln, NE: University of Nebraska Press.

Endler, N. S., & Edwards, J. (1978). Person by treatment interactions in personality research. In L. A. Pervin & M. Lewis (Eds.), *Perspective in interactional psychology* (pp. 141–169). New York: Plenum Press.

Endler, N. S., Edwards, J., & Kowalchuk, B. (1983). The interaction model of anxiety assessed in a psychotherapy situation. *The Southern Psychologist, 1,* 168–172.

Endler, N. S., Edwards, J. M., & Vitelli, R. (1985). *Situation-Response General Trait Anxiety Inventory (S-R GTA) and Present Affect Reactions Questionnaire (PARQ): A manual for trait and state anxiety.* (Psych. Rep. No. 52). York University, Toronto: York University, Department of Psychology Reports.

Endler, N. S., King, P. R., Edwards, J. M., Kuczynski, M., & Diveky, S. (1983). Generality of the interaction field studies. *Canadian Journal of Behavioural Science, 15,* 60–69.

Endler, N. S., & Magnusson, D. (1976a). Personality and person by situation interactions. In N. S. Endler & D. Magnusson (Eds.), *Interactional psychology and personality* (pp. 1–25). Washington, DC: Hemisphere Publishing Corporation.

Endler, N. S., & Magnusson, D. (1976b). Toward an interactional psychology of personality. *Psychological Bulletin, 83,* 956–974.

Endler, N. S., & Okada, M. (1975). A multidimensional measure of trait anxiety: The S-R Inventory of General Trait Anxiousness. *Journal of Consulting and Clinical Psychology, 43,* 319–329.

Evans, G. W. (Ed.). (1982). *Environmental stress.* New York: Cambridge University Press.

Folkman, S., & Lazarus, R. S. (1980). An analysis of coping in a middle-aged community sample. *Journal of Health and Social behavior, 21,* 219–239.

Folkman, S., & Lazarus, R. S. (1985). If it changes it must be a process: A study of emotion and coping during three stages of a college examination. *Journal of Personality and Social Psychology, 48,* 150–170.

Freud, S. (1933). *New introductory lectures on psychoanalysis.* New York: Norton.

Garmezy, N. (1981). Childern under stress: Perspectives on antecedents and correlates of vulnerability and resistance to psychopathology. In A. I. Rabin, L. Aronoff, A. M. Barclay, & R. A. Zucker (Eds.), *Further explorations in personality* (pp. 196–269). Toronto: John Wiley & Sons.

Glass, D. C., Krakoff, L. R., Contrada, R., Hilton, W. F., Kehoe, K., Mannucci, E. G., Collins, C., Snow, B., & Eiting, E. (1980). Effect of harassment and competition upon cardiovascular and catecholaminic responses in Type A and Type B individuals. *Psychophysiology, 17,* 453–463.

Glass, D. C., & Singer, J. E. (1972). *Urban stress: Explorations on noise and social stressors.* New York: Academic Press.

Goldberger, L., & Breznitz, S. (Eds.). (1982) *Handbook of stress.* New York: Free Press.

Grinker, R. R., & Spiegel, J. P. (1945). *Men under stress.* New York: McGraw-Hill.

Harris, W. H., & Levey, J. S. (Eds.). (1975). *The new Columbia encyclopedia* (4th ed.). New York: Columbia University Press.

Holmes, T. H., & Rahe, R. H. (1967). The Social Readjustment Rating Scale. *Journal of Psychosomatic Research, 11,* 213–218.

Johnson, J. H., & Sarason, I. G. (1979). Moderator variables in life stress research. In I. G. Sarason & C. D. Spielberger (Eds.), *Stress and anxiety* (Vol. 6, pp. 151–167). Washington DC: Hemisphere.

Kanner, A. D., Coyne, J. C., Schaefer, C., & Lazarus, R. S. (1981). Comparison of two modes of stress measurement: Daily hassles and uplifts versus major life events. *Journal of Behavioral Medicine, 4,* 1–39.

Kendall, P. C. (1978). Anxiety: States, traits-situations? *Journal of Consulting and Clinical Psychology, 46,* 280–287.

Kobasa, S. C. (1979). Stressful life events, personality, and health: An inquiry into hardiness. *Journal of Personality and Social Psychology, 37,* 1–11.

Kobasa, S. C., Maddi, S. R., & Kahn, S. (1982). Hardiness and health: A prospective study. *Journal of Personality and Social Psychology, 42,* 168–177.

Kobasa, S. C., & Puccetti, M. C. (1983). Personality and social resources in stress resistance. *Journal of Personality and Social Psychology, 45,* 839–850.

Lazarus, R. S., & Folkman, S. (1984). *Stress, appraisal and coping.* New York: Springer Publishing Company.

Lazarus, R. S., & Launier, R. (1978). Stress related transactions between person and environment. In L. A. Pervin & M. Lewis (Eds.), *Perspectives in interactional psychology* (pp. 287–327). New York: Plenum Publishing Corporation.

Lefcourt, H. M. (1976). *Locus of control: Current trends in theory and research.* New York: Halstead.

Lefcourt, H. M. (1980). Locus of control and coping with life's events. In E. Staub (Ed.), *Personality: Basic aspects and current research* (pp. 200–235). Englewood Cliffs, NJ: Prentice-Hall.

Lefcourt, H. M., Martin, R. A., & Saleh, W. E. (1984). Locus of control and social support: Interactive moderators of stress. *Journal of personality and social psychology, 47,* 378–389.

Lifton, R. L., & Olson, E. (1976). The human meaning of total disaster: The Buffalo Creek experience. *Psychiatry, 39,* 1–17.

Magnusson, D. (1981). Wanted: A psychology of situations. In D. Magnusson (Ed.), *Toward a psychology of situations: An interactional perspective* (pp. 9–32). Hillsdale, NJ: Lawrence Erlbaum Associates.

May, R. (1977). *The meaning of anxiety.* New York: W. W. Norton & Company, Inc.

Mechanic, D. (1962). *Students under stress: A study in the social psychology of adaptation.* New York: The Free Press.

Meichenbaum, D. (1983). *Coping with stress.* Toronto: John Wiley & Sons.

Millon, L. (1984). The DSM III: Some historical and substantive reflections. In N. S. Endler & J. McV. Hunt (Eds.), *Personality and the behavioral disorders* (Vol. 2, 2nd ed., pp. 675–710). Toronto: Wiley.

Mischel, W. *Personality and assessment.* (1968). New York: Wiley.

Mischel, W. (1973). Toward a cognitive social learning reconceptualization of personality. *Psychological Review, 80,* 252–283.

Neufeld, R. W. J., & Mothersill, K. J. (1980). Stress as an irritant of psychopathology. In I. G. Sarason & C. D. Spielberger (Eds.), *Stress and anxiety.* (Vol. 7, pp. 31–56). New York: Hemisphere Publishing.

Olweus, D. (1977). A critical analysis of the modern interactionist position. In D. Magnusson & N. S. Endler (Eds.), *Personality at the crossroads: Current issues in interactional psychology* (pp. 221–233). Hillsdale, NJ: Lawrence Erlbaum Associates.

Overton, W. F., & Reese, H. W. (1973). Models of development: Methodological implications. In J. R. Nesselroade & H. W. Reese (Eds.), *Life span developmental psychology: Methodological issues* (pp. 65–86). New York: Academic Press.

Pervin, L. A. (1984). *Current controversies and issues in personality.* New York: Wiley.

Pervin, L., & Lewis, M. (Eds.). (1978). *Perspectives in Interactional Psychology.* New York: Plenum Press.

Phares, E. J. (1976). *Locus of control in personality.* Morristown, NJ: General Learning Press.

Phillips, J. B., & Endler, N. S. (1982). Academic examinations and anxiety: The interaction model empirically tested. *Journal of Research in Personality, 16,* 303–318.

Rabkin, J. G. (1982). Stress and psychiatric disorders. In L. Goldberger & S. Breznitz (Eds.), *Handbook of stress: Theoretical and clinical aspects* (pp. 566–584). New York: The Free Press.

Rabkin, J. G., & Struening, E. L. (1976). Life events, stress, and illness. *Science, 194,* 1013–1020.

Raush, H. L., Dittmann, A. T., & Taylor, T. J.

(1959a). Person, setting and change in social interaction. *Human Relations, 12,* 361–378.

Raush, H. L., Dittmann, A. T., & Taylor, T. J. (1959b). The interpersonal behavior of children in residential treatment. *Journal of Abnormal and Social Psychology, 58,* 9–26.

Rotter, J. B. (1966). Generalized expectancies for internal versus external control of reinforcement. *Psychological Monagraphs, 80*(1, Whole No. 609).

Rotter, J. B. (1975). Some problems and misconceptions related to the construct of internal versus external control of reinforcement. *Journal of Consulting and Clinical Psychology, 43,* 56–67.

Seeman, M. (1963). Alienation and social learning in a reformatory. *American Journal of Sociology, 69,* 270–284.

Seeman, M., & Evans, J. W. (1962). Alienation and learning in a hospital setting. *American Sociological Review, 27,* 772–783.

Selye, H. (1956). *The stress of life.* New York: McGraw-Hill.

Singer, J. L. (1984). *The human personality.* Toronto: Harcourt Brace Jovanovich.

Smith, R. E., Johnson, J. H., & Sarason, I. G. (1978). Life change, the sensation seeking motive and psychological distress. *Journal of Consulting and Clinical Psychology, 46,* 348–349.

Speisman, J. C., Lazarus, R. S., Mordkoff, A. M., & Davison, L. A. (1964). Experimental analysis of a film used as a threatening stimulus. *Journal of Consulting Psychology, 28,* 23–33.

Spielberger, C. D. (1972). Anxiety as an emotion state. In C. D. Spielberger (Ed.), *Anxiety: Current trends in theory and research* (Vol. 1, pp. 24-49). New York: Academic Press.

Spielberger, C. D. (1975). Anxiety: State-trait process. In C. D. Spielberger & I. G. Sarason (Eds.), *Stress and anxiety* (Vol. 1, pp. 115–143). Toronto: John Wiley & Sons.

Spielberger, C. D. (1976). The nature and measurement of anxiety. In C. D. Spielberger & R. Diaz-Guerrero (Eds.), *Cross-cultural anxiety* (pp. 3–12). Washington, DC: Hemisphere Publishing Corporation.

Sturgis, E. L. (1984). Anxiety disorders. In N. S. Endler & J. McV. Hunt (Eds.). *Personality and the behavioral disorders.* (Vol. 2, 2nd ed., pp. 747–770). Toronto: John Wiley & Sons.

Watson, J. B., & Rayner, R. (1920). Conditioned emotional reactions. *Journal of Experimental Psychology, 3,* 1–14.

Zuckerman, M. (1974). The sensation seeking motive. In B. Maher (Ed.). *Progress in experimental personality research* (Vol. 7, pp. 80–148). New York: Academic Press.

CHAPTER 15

Life Events

Scott M. Monroe and Shari L. Wade

Since the development of the stress concept and its implications for health and well-being, many attempts have been made to quantify individual differences with respect to the construct. Much of this work proceeded in an isolated manner, with investigators from diverse disciplines studying stress within their own particular traditions and with their own particular endpoints of interest (Averill, 1979). Early work also often was based upon laboratory methods, some of which had questionable "ecological validity" for generalizing to the organism's or individual's natural socioenvironmental circumstances. Thus, while a broad array of disorders were linked in theory to stress, the cacaphony of methods and procedures used, combined with the divergent disorders studied within the stress paradigm, rendered comparisons across studies and disciplines difficult.

It is in this context that the study of life events emerged and took a strong methodological hold on one corner of stress research. The basic premise was that diverse aspects of life experience could be conceptualized and measured as relatively discrete events. These life events, in turn, reflected the adaptational demands, or stress, in the life of the individual. Two facets of the approach proved especially attractive. First, these events represented a common core of experiences that were relevant to most people; therefore, studying life events could be viewed as a relatively "standardized" approach to the study of stress. Second, due to the focus on actual life changes, there was a reduced concern with the issue of generalization; it seemed, in fact, that this approach provided a distillate of experiences that potentially was most informative for future functioning.

Since the publication of the first life events scale by Holmes and Rahe (1967), the life events approach to the study of stress and illness has been applied to many forms of disturbance. Experience with such work over the past 20 years now affords a more informed perspective on the issues involved. The purpose of the present chapter is to provide an overview of the relationship of life events to anxiety disorders, given the benefit of this experience. Therefore, we will first present the methodological and conceptual considerations involved with the study of life events. This will provide an important backdrop for understanding the existing research. Second, we will present a review of the literature on the topic of life events and anxiety disorders. Finally, we will conclude with the implications for future work.

PRELIMINARY CONSIDERATIONS

In order to adequately evaluate the existing research on life events and anxiety disorders, several methodological and conceptual points must be kept in mind. Virtually all the issues we raise pertain to the complexities of attempting to study the reciprocal relations between an individual and his or her social context over time. That is, while the goal of this research area is to isolate the psychosocial factors that may lead to some form of vulnerability to anxiety disorders, the complementary component of the process is the individual's influence upon his or her psychosocial context. The two are necessarily interdependent and mutually influential, representing reciprocal transactions over time (Lazarus & Folkman, 1984; Monroe & Steiner, 1986).

Three broad issues are most important for the present purposes. First, and perhaps most basic, is the issue of measurement reliability: How adequate are the prevailing methods for assessing life events? Second, what are the predominant research designs employed, and the implications of these designs for understanding associations between life events and anxiety? Finally, is there reason to believe that models of stress–disorder associations may vary in terms of the particular outcome variable under study? For instance, are the same forms of psychosocial stressors predictive of all types of anxiety disorders? It is to these issues that we now turn.

Life events assessment

By far the majority of studies have employed self-report checklists of life events. These instruments are basically similar to the original scale, the Schedule of Recent Experiences, developed by Holmes and Rahe (1967) (although they may differ with respect to the wording of items or the number of events included). The respondent is requested to fill out the questionnaire for a specified period of time, typically ranging between 3 months to 2 years (Monroe, 1982b).

A very consistent finding from reports investigating the reliability of these assessment procedures is that serious problems compromise the quality of the data obtained (Jenkins, Hurst, & Rose, 1979; Monroe, 1982a; Paykel, 1982). Virtually all studies, using different designs and self–report instruments, have found that individuals tend to underreport events, with the problem increasing proportionately to the length of the retrospective interval involved. Thus, the greater the time period covered, the higher the likelihood that more underreporting occurs. Therefore, when using such methods, it is advisable to use relatively short time periods for recall (Monroe, 1982a, 1982b).

In contrast to the findings from self–report checklists, the Bedford Life Events and Difficulties Scale, developed by Brown and Harris (1978), is a semi–structured interview to assess life events and ongoing difficulties. Appropriately trained individuals using this instrument have been found to produce highly reliable data, at least for events that are rated as "severe" (i.e., those entailing a high degree of "unpleasantness" using the system's standard rating procedures; for further information, see Brown & Harris, 1978). While this approach is not as expedient as the more popular self-report procedures, the advantages of the approach in terms of quality data outweigh the limitations for most purposes.

Several reasons exist for the discrepancy in reliability estimates for self–report versus interview–based event assessment procedures. Simple "forgetting" is the most commonly ascribed reason, with the interview–based methods apparently providing a greater opportunity for probing memory and thereby stimulating recall of past experiences. Often overlooked, however, in these studies is the important issue involving the definition of the event, and the potential variability in interpretation across individuals. With self–report procedures, much of the decision process concerning what qualifies as an event is left up to the respondent; as Brown (1981) has convincingly argued, such an approach does not ensure comparability of social experiences across individuals. More specifically, the wording of many items on self–report scales is often quite general. Events such as "serious illness in close family member" may be too ambiguous, with unwanted variability across individuals resulting from idiosyncratic interpretations of what constitutes a "serious illness" (a mild case of the flu versus a life–threatening illness) or a "close family member." Inspection of most life events scales suggests that a large number of the items included may be interpreted in such idiosyncratic ways. (Our experience, too, suggests that many individuals may lower their threshold for describing certain experiences as "events"; this seems especially true when they have a relative lack of events, yet feel compelled to provide something for the investigator.) Thus, interview–based procedures may provide both more reliable and also more accurate information.

Research Design

Perhaps the most critical feature for evaluating research in this area concerns the nature of the research design employed. Especially when studying psychological problems, there may be an inherent bias in corelating recent life events with psychological symptoms assessed at the same time (the retrospective or cross–sectional design). Individuals who are distressed may attempt to "explain away" their problems in terms of increased levels of existing life stress (Brown, 1974). For example, someone who is currently experiencing acute distress may lower his or her threshold for defining certain events as being relevant (e.g., "troubles with boss," "difficulties at work," etc.), and thereby spuriously increase his/her event scores. This point takes on added saliency, given recent estimates that a substantial proportion of individuals in the general population, and therefore a substantial proportion of respondents in life events studies, may suffer from relatively chronic psychological problems (Depue & Monroe, 1986). In cross–sectional research, when such factors are not controlled for through ancillary method procedures (see earlier discussion on definitions and criteria for events), significant associations may simply represent an artifact of the method.

Prospective research designs, wherein life events are assessed at one point in time and psychological functioning is predicted at some future date, are more useful for addressing questions concerning causality. Yet care must be exercised in such studies to ensure the appropriate sample for studying specific issues. For example, to study the *onset* of disorder, the sample should be comprised of individuals at the outset who are relatively free of the disturbance (Monroe, 1982c; Monroe, Bromet, Connell, & Steiner, 1986). Alternatively, to study the *course* of disorder, one may select individuals who are informative for the disorder in question and follow them over time, predicting variation in their presentation (i.e., maintenance or remission) as a function of antecedent life events (Monroe, Bellack, Hersen, & Himmelhoch, 1983). Conceptually, these two approaches represent very different models of stress and disorder relationships. Onset conditions for disorder may be quite different from the conditions that promote maintenance or remission of a disorder. To adequately investigate these different models, further methodological requirements are entailed. For example, to study the course of disorder, care must be taken to distinguish events that may occur as a consequence of the disorder itself (although these also may have "legitimate" effects, they may simply be a reflection of the severity of disorder). This represents a point of considerable importance, for research should be explicitly designed to investigate separately these two models of stress effects (see Depue & Monroe, 1986).

Stressor–disorder Specificity

Initial work on life events suggested that a wide variety of outcome variables were related to this form of stress. Much work consequently proceeded to investigate associations between life events and general, nonspecific dimensions of distress and/or anxiety (Depue & Monroe, 1986; Monroe, 1982c), or groupings of a wide range of divergent disturbances (Rabkin & Struening, 1976). More recently, conceptualizations have been based upon models depicting potential *qualitative* differences between event–related stress and different *classes* of disturbance. For example, the nature of the relationship between life events and anxiety disorders may be very different from the relationship between life events and other forms of psychiatric disturbance (e.g., depressive disorder or schizophrenia). Futhermore, different subtypes of anxiety disorders may be related in a very different manner to life events (e.g., simple phobias vs. agoraphobia). Consequently, at the present stage of knowledge in stressor-disorder associations, it would seem most prudent to investigate associations with life event stress for different qualities associated with the stressors and for specific classes of disturbance.

Comment

The foregoing discussion highlights several prominent issues for evaluating existing research on life events and anxiety disorders. As indicated by Rabkin (1982), little of the research on life events has been dedicated to studies of diagnostically relevant anxiety disorders, and of the existing research in this area, few studies have been performed with full attention to the considerations just outlined. Nonetheless, several investigations have shed some light on potentially fruitful avenues to pursue. We will next review studies on life events with clinically relevant samples of anxiety disorders that are informative for evaluating the status of this research literature.

ANXIETY DISORDERS AND LIFE EVENTS

In a recent review on the etiology of agoraphobia, Tearnan, Telch, and Keefe (1984) concluded that the majority of agoraphobic symptoms occur following a period of background stress or a single identifiable precipitant. These authors suggest that this disorder is commonly precipitated by interpersonal problems (such as rejection, loss, and marital conflict), or physical factors (such as childbirth and surgery). In contrast, Rabkin (1982) — reviewing essentially the same literature — concluded that investigators have failed to find a strong association between socioenvironmental stressors and the onset of anxiety disorders, and that this association was actually weakest for agoraphobia. Thus, contemporary opinions on this topic are divided, and it is our goal to provide some understanding of the major issues requiring clarification.

Owing to the relatively small number of studies on the topic of life events and anxiety disorders overall, different subgroups of anxiety disorders cannot be evaluated separately. However, it should be kept in mind that while some studies examined agoraphobia, others focused upon simple phobias or panic disorder. Overall, a number of investigations provide percentages and/or anecdotal support for the precipitating role of life events in anxiety disorders. Most important, however, little regard is typically evident for the crucial methodological or definitional issues outlined previously. In the following review, we will progress from the less rigorous clinical reports to the more methodologically sound empirical work.

Literature review

In an interesting clinical paper, Hafner (1979) reported on a sample of 36 female agoraphobics treated in his practice. However, information on demographic characteristics, diagnostic criteria for defining the sample, and the clinical course (e.g., duration of disorder) of the patients was not provided. Of these 36 women, 7 were reportedly married to "abnormally jealous men" (according to material that emerged during the course of treatment). Hafner argued that this ongoing stressor served to precipitate and/or maintain the women's agoraphobic behavior. However, the report does not discuss the incidence of stressors in the other 29 women, nor does it present evidence about the frequency of "abnormal jealousy" in the normal population. Curiously, there are several other stressful life events mentioned in his case studies that were not considered in the precipitation of the disorder. This report illustrates the importance of clarity in criteria for defining events, specificity of stress effects (i.e., onset vs. maintenance models), as well as the need for appropriate comparison groups.

In another clinically oriented article, Weekes (1978) reported that only 5% of 528 agoraphobic men and women could find *no* cause for their agoraphobia. Perhaps due to the clinical and theoretical emphasis of the article, there is no discussion of the composition of the sample (e.g., age, socioeconomic status, proportion of men and women) or of the criteria used to diagnose agoraphobia. It is claimed that for the majority of subjects the precipitant was a sudden stress (e.g., serious medical problems or bereavement) or a prolonged intensifying stress. However, one cannot ascertain from the description provided how these events were assessed, the criteria that were used to define them, the time period prior to onset of the disorder that was encompassed for the life event assessment, or the total duration of time over which subjects were required to remember (i.e., this includes the average duration of disorder, which for most samples of agoraphobics is quite lengthy). Futhermore, dating of the events with regard to the timing of disorder onset was not clear (leaving open the clear possibility of psychological problems precipitating subsequent events). Although together these two clinical reports present some interesting possibilities, the vagueness of procedures renders any evaluation of the accuracy and relevance of the findings difficult.

In a more empirical vein, Doctor (1982) assessed 404 individuals with questionnaires prior to their enrollment in a treatment program for agoraphobia. The diagnosis of agoraphobia was made by an experienced clinician based on the information provided in the questionnaire; further specification of the precise criteria was not provided. The sample was 78% female and had a mean age of 39.3 years. The subjects had been ill for an average of 11 years. Life circumstances at the time of onset were assessed through an open-ended questionnaire. No further detail about the event assessment was provided. It was reported that there were as many life circumstances as subjects, and that no single type of event was prominent. However, separation and loss (31.2%), relationship conflicts (29.97%), and increased responsibilities (20.19%) appeared to be the leading classes of events labeled as precipitants. (It is unclear from his statistics what proportion, if any, failed to report an event, because the percentages within the various classes of events approach 100 when totaled.)

Roberts (1964) considered cases of married, housebound agoraphobic women identified from the case records of women admitted to a psychiatric inpatient unit between 1946 and 1962. Cases were selected in which the core symptom was an inability to leave the home due to phobic anxiety symptoms. At the time of the initial hospitalization, these women had been housebound from 3 months to 15 years; however, the majority had been housebound for less than 1 year (at the time of hospitalization). Also, at least four of these women had been diagnosed as depressed during their hospitalization, and 11 subsequently were treated with electroconvulsive therapy (ECT) for depression. Thirty-five of an originally identified 41 women were later interviewed, 1½ to 16 years after their initial hospitalization, and an additional 3 patients were followed through physician's or report's of "significant others." Of these, 23 patients (60%) spontaneously volunteered or recalled with minimal prompting specific anxiety-provoking situations prior to their first panic attack. Marital infidelity and the heart attack of a spouse were cited as specific examples. No further information about how events were assessed or recorded is provided, and comparisons with a control group are lacking.

It is interesting to point out that of the nine patients in this sample who remained totally housebound, only one had received ECT. In contrast, 10 of the 29 patients who enjoyed some remission had been treated for depression with ECT. This finding suggests that the sample was heterogeneous. Also, the relatively short duration of time since the patients were housebound for this sample suggests that it may be somewhat anomalous. More specifically, there could exist at least two distinct subgroups: a purely agoraphobic group (without depression and exhibiting a more chronic course), and a depressed group with agoraphobic features (exhibiting a more episodic course). It is unclear what proportion of each group's disorders may have been related to initiating stressful life events. (This raises an important and intriguing issue concerning the comorbidity of anxiety and depressive disorders, a topic to which we will return in the final section.)

Ninety consecutive referrrals who reported phobias of external stimuli — regardless of the actual presenting complaint — were studied by Shafar (1976). The sample was composed of 19 men and 71 women. Of these, 75% had agoraphobic symptoms, 27% has social phobias, and 3% had monosymptomatic phobias (patients with the latter primarily had been screened out for another study). The agoraphobics had a mean onset age of 32 years, and had been ill for an average of 6½ years at the time of treatment; the social phobics had a mean onset age of 20, and had been ill for an average of 10 years. However, only 45% of the sample received a *primary* diagnosis of anxiety states; the remainder suffered from depression (19%), hysteria (19%), personality disorders (12%), and paranoid psychosis (3%). Neither the criteria used to define the primary diagnoses nor phobic symptoms were provided.

In presenting event–symptom associations, Shafar distinguished among (a) individuals who report an event, (b) individuals for whom the event had a clear antecedant temporal relationship to onset or aggravation of the disorder, and (c) individuals for whom the event constituted the chief precipitant. Unfortunately, the criteria employed to make such distinctions are not specified. In this heterogeneous sample, the author noted interpersonal problems (defined as ongoing suffering by one or both parties as a consequence of their relationship) preceded the onset of symptoms in 79 of the 90 patients. The vast majority of these patients (90%) were judged as at least partly responsible for these interpersonal difficulties. Thus, for almost all of these patients it cannot be assured that the event is unconfounded with possible prodromal or subsyndromal features of the illness. For 56 of the 79 patients, the interpersonal problem was judged to be temporally proximal to the onset, and in 43 of these 56 the interpersonal event was judged to be the main precipitant.

Fifty-seven of the 90 total patients in this study experienced other life events (i.e., not interpersonal difficulties) at the time of onset or exacerbation, and 24 of these patients were judged to have events as the primary precipitant. Among these, organic illness or operation's were the most commonly reported stressors (22 of 90), yet it was only considered the precipitant in three cases. Nineteen of the 90 subjects lost a close figure through death in the 5 years prior to onset, and this was considered the most significant factor for eight of these individuals. The remaining stressors included a mixture of physiological changes, external events, and preexisting mental illness. In all, 75 of 90 (83%) reported precipitating factors; relationship problems constituted the most significant single factor (for 57%). The possible confounding of interpersonal events and disorder, the lack of appropriate controls, the mixing of onset and maintenance models of stress effects, and the heterogeneity of primary diagnoses in the sample prohibit drawing any firm conclusions about the role of precipitants in anxiety disorders. Nonetheless, the findings are suggestive of the possible role of such stressful circumstances, particularly interpersonal problems, in the genesis of anxiety disorders.

Sheehan and colleagues (Sheehan, Sheehan, & Minichiello, 1981) presented data on 100 patients, all of whom met DSM-III (APA, 1980) criteria for panic disorder, agoraphobia, and generalized anxiety disorder. These patients were an average age of 32.5 years and had been ill for approximately 12.7 years. All evidenced significant social impairment, work impairment, and avoidance behavior, as well as no history of psychosis or physical illness (that could account for the symptoms). According to the authors, 91% of the patients could identify some precipitant in the 6-month period prior to the onset of symptoms. These precipitants included nearly all types of major life events, as well as clearly physical problems (i.e., drugs, endocrine abnormalities, and surgery). Although employing better methods for diagnoses, the study lacks a control group and a description of the methodology for assessing events.

DSM-III diagnoses of agoraphobia with panic attacks provided the basis for a sample of 58 patients (53 women and 5 men) studied by Last, Barlow, and O'Brien (1984). Events were assessed in a 45-minute, semi-structured interview. Eighty-one percent of the patients reported a precipitating event. Included among the precipitants were: interpersonal conflict (34.5%, birth/miscarriage/hysterectomy (29.3%), death/illness of significant other (15.5%), and drug reaction (12.1%). The authors collapsed these discrete events into the overarching categories of conflict events (including death/illness of a significant other) and endocrine/physiological events. Together, these two categories accounted for 91% of all the events reported. It is interesting that only 18.9% of the sample experienced psychosocial events that were clearly independent of the person's behavior, and an additional 44.7% experienced medical events of one form or another. This study employed more sophisticated methods in diagnosis, as well as in the assessment and conceptualization of events. Data from comparisons with appropriate control groups, however, would have been informative. Once again, though, the theme of two classes of events — interpersonal conflict and physiological/endocrine events — emerge as possibly being of most relevance.

Agoraphobic patients (7 men and 25 women) and patients with specific phobias (12 men and 24 women) for whom records were available were investigated by Goldstein and Chambless (1978). The sample consisted of all patients judged to have either agoraphobia or a phobia of external stimuli. The agoraphobics were an average age of 34 years, the simple phobics an average age of 38 years. No further specification of diagnostic criteria or clinical course was provided. Descriptions of the circumstances surrounding onset of the disorder were gleaned from files or therapist reports. Twenty of the 32 agoraphobics, compared to only 1 of the 36 simple phobics, reported a precipitant involving interpersonal conflict. Conversely, 17 of the simple phobics, compared to only four of the agoraphobics, indicated a "conditioning event" prior to the onset of their symptoms. (Futher definition of the category of conditioning events was not provided.) These authors concluded that agoraphobia occurs in times of increased interpersonal conflict, often arising from the feeling of being trapped in a poor marital situation; simple phobias, in contrast, stem from relatively clear conditioning events. Although the findings are suggestive, the study lacks rigor in assessing events, clarity in event definition criteria, and a nonphobic control. Moreover, once again the stressor of interpersonal conflict emerges as salient, yet continues to be difficult to interpret, for it can be confounded easily with the patient's behavior and psychopathology.

Solyom, Beck, Solyom, and Hugel (1974) examined 47 phobic patients (42 women and 5 men) that had been referred from the psychiatric outpatient departments of general hospitals or from private psychiatrists. These patients were an average of 33 years old, presented with a phobia as the primary symptom, and were free from obsessive–compulsive disorder, depression, and schizophrenia. Controls were volunteers matched on age, sex, marital status, and education. Phobic symptoms in both groups were rated on a 1 to 5-point scale. Of the patients, 92% had agoraphobia and 8% had specific phobias; 42% of the controls also reported phobias (all but one were simple phobias). The main differences between patients and controls were (a) the significantly greater incidence of agoraphobia among the patients, and (b) the clinical significance of the severity of their phobias. For the majority of patients, the phobic symptoms reportedly became continuous following a severe environmental stressor, such as the death of a relative or friend, a serious illness in a close family member, or a domestic crisis. All of these stressors occured significantly more frequently in the patients compared to the control groups. (In fact, "fright" was the only stressor that occured with equal frequency in both groups.) From the percentages presented, it appears that 100% of the patient group, versus only 16% of the control group, experienced antecedent events. However, once again there is no description of diagnostic criteria, how events were assessed, or what time period of recall was employed for controls.

Buglass and her associates (Buglass, Clarke, Henderson, Kreitman, & Presley, 1977) reported findings for 30 married agoraphobics who were taken from referrals to outpatient clinics. Agoraphobia was defined by an inability to leave the house and travel freely without accompaniment as a consequence of severe anxiety. Both the clinical and research team had to agree upon the diagnosis, and patients with markedly depressed mood were excluded. (Despite this exclusion criterion, depressive symptoms were still noted in nine of the phobic patients.) Thirty normal controls were selected from the register of the department of general practice and matched with the patients on age and social class. The data were obtained from three semi-structured interviews with the patient, her husband, and the couple together. In assessing life events, these investigators inquired into both ongoing stressors and discrete traumatic events occuring either concurrent with, or in the few days preceding, the onset of the disorder. In five cases, there was doubt about the relation of the event to the onset; however, 15 of the remaining 25 patients reported ongoing stressors. For nine of these cases, the ongoing stressor consisted of a "neurotic syndrome" (in the majority of cases, an anxiety disorder) preceding the onset of the agoraphobia. Of these nine, five also had discrete events preceding their initial symptoms.

Certain problems limit the interpretability of these findings. It is interesting that the majority of the antecendent diagnoses were anxiety disorders; although this may represent one form of an ongoing stressor, it would seem perhaps more parsimonious to consider these neurotic difficulties as prodromal symptoms rather than contributing stressors. In only 7 of the 25 patients could discrete antecedant events be identified, and for eight patients no ongoing or discrete stressor was implicated. Futhermore, although this study used controls for other aspects of the investigation (e.g., spouse's personality), it failed to report on life events for the controls. Also, by considering only events that occurred concurrent with, or in the few days preceding the onset of disorder, these authors may be unduly restricting the scope of potential precipitants, as well as increasing the likelihood that the events that were reported actually followed, rather than preceded, the onset of disorder. Moreover, this sample might not be representative of agoraphobics in general, because it consisted solely of married women who had been prescreened for depression.

More recently, Faravelli (1985) examined the incidence of life events in the 12 months preceding the onset of panic disorder. He compared 23 patients who (a) met DSM-III criteria for the diagnosis of panic disorder, *and* (b) had the onset of their symptoms within the last 4 months, to a matched group of healthy nonpatients. Events were assessed through semi-structured interviews which explored the events and the circumstances in which they occurred. The interview records were subsequently reviewed by the research staff, who were "blind" to diagnostic status. It was reported that patients experienced significantly more events ($M = 2.56$ versus 1.69 for controls, $p = .05$), and had significantly higher weighted event scores ($M = 33.18$ vs. 20.18 for controls, $p = .05$). Moreover, the additional events among the panic disorder group almost all occurred during the last month prior to onset. Significantly more of the panic disordered patients experienced a severe event, such as a serious illness or death of a close relative. This study is noteworthy in that it (a) considered relatively new rather than chronic cases (thereby minimizing recall problems), (b) employed normal controls, and (c) used final "standardized" event ratings that were unbiased by knowledge of disorder. Of course, however, the design was retrospective, still leaving open the potential for the disordered patients to try harder to "explain away" their problems by citing life stressors (Brown, 1974). Nonetheless, it represents one of the stronger pieces of evidence available linking life stress to at least this form of anxiety disorder, panic disorder. Futhermore, it suggests a time frame of relevance for assessing events prior to the onset of panic disorder.

Finally, a series of reports by Brown and his colleagues represents an important addition to the understanding of associations between life stress and anxiety disorders. This work stands apart from previous investigations in several respects, including the careful assessment of life stress, the concern for distinguishing between acute onset and chronic conditions, and the conceptualization of possible associations between anxiety disorders and depression. In earlier work, Brown and Harris (1978) suggested that individuals who exhibit high levels of anxiety with their depressions are more likely to have experienced events involving a high degree of "threat" (i.e., unpleasantness), but not necessarily involving loss experiences; in contrast, more purely depressed individuals are more likely to experience severely threatening events involving some degree of loss. (Loss was defined in terms of the loss of a valued person, health, career, material possessions, or cherished ideas.)

In an investigation designed to follow up on this issue, Finlay-Jones and Brown (1981) reported results from 164 young women who were attending a general practitioner in London and who were interviewed with both the Bedford College Life Events and Difficulties Schedule (Brown & Harris, 1978) and the Present State Examination (Wing, Nixon, Mann, & Leff, 1977). Three types of *onset* cases of psychological disorder were diagnosed: depression (17 women), anxiety (13 women), and both anxiety and depression (15 women). In other words, for the group that evidenced symptomatology that qualified for *both* a case of anxiety and depression, the authors "overroad" the typical hierarchical diagnostic procedures that preclude such mixed diagnoses. The control group comprised 80 women without a psychiatric disorder, 23 women with a chronic psychiatric disorder, and 16 with an onset of borderline disorder. For the year prior to the onset cases, these investigators found that 82% of the depression cases, 85% of the anxiety cases, and 93% of the anxiety and depression mixed cases had experienced at least one severe event, compared to 34% of the control group. In subsequent analyses, these investigators distinguished between severe events involving "loss" and "danger" (the latter defined in terms of the degree of unpleasantness associated with a future "crisis" that may occur as a result of the event having happened (see Finaly-Jones & Brown, 1981, p. 806).

These distinctions produced provocative results. Summarizing their findings, we note that (a) there was a significant association between severe danger events in the 3 months prior to onset and the subsequent development of anxiety disorder, (b) there was a significant association between severe loss events and the subsequent development of depression, and (c) mixed cases of depression and anxiety tended to be associated with both a severe danger and a severe loss event. Thus, there may be "symptom specificity" of disorder in relation to the particular type of stressful experience encountered. While replication of the findings is necessary, and further delineation of the types of anxiety disorders involved requires specification, these findings are among the most compelling in the literature for empirically demonstrating an association between life events and anxiety disorder. Such work also raises the thorny issue of comorbidity between anxiety disorders and depression, along with the accompanying implications for conceptualizing socioenvironmental correlates and/or precipitants (see also Barlow, DiNardo, Vermilyea, Vermilyea, & Blanchard, 1986; Prudo, Harris, & Brown, 1984).

CONCLUDING REMARKS

At a very general level, the studies reviewed present the picture of an association between life events and anxiety disorders. The more rigorously controlled investigations support the viability of onset models related to stress, whereas the less rigorous work typically presents affirmative findings for mixed models of stress effects; that is, both onset and maintenance/exacerbation combined. In the context of this generally supportive view, however, several important qualifications are in order. Issues requiring further discussion include (a) the limitations imposed by the methods used; (b) the association between life events and subtypes of anxiety disorders (e.g., agoraphobia vs. panic disorder); (c) the implications of depressive symptoms in the relationship between life events and anxiety disorder; (d) the characteristics of life events that may be most highly related to anxiety disorders; and (e) the elucidation of the interconnections between life events, prodromal symptoms, and formal clinical disorder.

One overarching consideration to be kept in mind is the retrospective nature of all existing studies on this topic. Although the relatively low incidence of anxiety disorders (especially agoraphobia) may prohibit longitudinal studies of incidence, the long retrospective intervals typical of these life event investigations, along with the likely tendency to "explain away" psychopathology on the grounds of "stress," should provide a cautionary tone in interpreting these findings. Still, virtually all studies provided evidence compatible with the notion that life events are of importance, and this was particularly so for some of the better controlled investigations. Therefore, accepting for the moment that life events are associated in some general manner with anxiety disorders, we now turn to several issues that may be useful for clarifying our understanding of this statement.

Several of the more methodologically sound studies implicate life events in relation to the onset of panic disorder (Faravelli, 1985), agoraphobia with panic attacks (Last et al., 1984), or anxiety disorder (Finlay-Jones & Brown, 1981). Unfortunately, no studies exist in which subgroup comparisons were made directly. (When more than one subtype has been included in the research, the subgroups have been merged and/or studied with respect to combined onset and maintenance/exacerbation models of stress effects.) One interesting aspect of this observation concerns the role of panic, for in two of the three studies it is a central feature (Last et al., 1984; Faravelli, 1985), and in the third it is a potentially prominent, but not necessary, feature (Finlay-Jones & Brown, 1981). Other, less rigorous studies also support the outcome of panic in relation to life events (e.g., Roberts, 1964). Future work would profit from designs that provide for explicit subgroup comparisons, and in particular that focus on the role of panic. It may be that, at least for some individuals, life stress contributes to the initiation of panic attacks.

Another conceptual consideration for future work concerns the overlap of symptoms between anxiety disorders and depression. It is clear from the study of Finlay-Jones and Brown (1981) that depressive symptoms could play an important part in understanding the relationship between life events and anxiety disorders. The work of Roberts (1964), also, underscored the possible moderating role of depression for the outcome of agoraphobic patients whose disturbances were thought to be related to life stress. This issue perhaps raises some of the most complicated questions concerning basic nosological considerations between the two general groupings of psychiatric disorder (Barlow et al., 1986; Gersh & Fowles, 1979). Yet, to obtain a full picture of the potential consequences of stressful life events with respect to anxiety disorders, greater conceptual and empirical attention to the role of associated depressive symptoms appears warranted.

With respect to the characteristics of events that may contribute to the onset of anxiety disorders, two points from the existing research are of interest. First, the work of Finlay-Jones and Brown (1981) points toward the differential importance of "threat" versus "danger" events, with the former related primarily to depression, the latter to anxiety disorder, and "mixed" events (i.e., both threat and danger components associated with the event) to a mixed symptom picture between depression and anxiety. This suggests that the qualities of the particular event are of a specific relevance to the form of disorder expressed. Consequently, research would profit from increased attention to these distinctions involving the stressor characteristics of the experienced event.

Futhermore, a second point concerning this theme is that a number of studies suggest that agoraphobia is associated with two distinct classes of stressors: interpersonal conflict and biological-endocrine events (Tearnan et al., 1984). It may be, as Klein (1964) has suggested, that these two classes of stressors define biologically distinct subgroups. It has been documented that agoraphobic patients overall report an increased incidence of separation anxiety in childhood (Gittelman & Klein, 1985); such individuals may be sensitized to interpersonal conflict and the threat of loss, thereby possessing a lower vulnerability to anxiety symptoms under the appropriate environmental circumstances. For other agoraphobics without such a development history, symptoms may be more directly related to neuroendocrine anomalies that produce anxiety and/or panic-like symptoms.

If, indeed, there is some validity to this conjecture, considerable complexity emerges in terms of unravelling etiological contributions for the interpersonal conflict group. As we have discussed, this class of events is problematic from the perspective of causality, yet it is perhaps the most commonly cited one across all the studies reviewed. It is plausible that individuals who are already experiencing psychological distress at least in part create the circumstances that may bring about serious interpersonal stressors; while such events may still have consequences of their own, they remain confounded with the possible prodromal features of the developing disorder. In this regard, it is intriguing to point out that past studies suggest that chronic marital difficulties (Goldstein & Chambless, 1978), or a neurotic personality (most of which were classified as anxiety disorders; Buglass et al., 1977), preceded the onset of agoraphobia. One might speculate that the personality features of this subgroup of agoraphobics predispose to both a heightened probability of the event occurring *and* a heightened sensitivity to its effects (Depue, Monroe, & Shackman, 1979; Monroe & Steiner, 1986). Attention to such subgroup distinctions and potentially related predictors represent important additions for future research.

Finally, in closing we note that virtually no attention has been directed explicitly toward the consequences of stressful life events for (a) the course of disorder, (b) treatment response, or (c) the maintenance of treatment gains. The only data thus far bearing on this issue are from investigations in which onset and exacerbation groups have been inadvertently combined, thereby rendering interpretations difficult (Depue & Monroe, 1986). This lack of attention is in contrast to the focus on these issues in the research on life events and depression (Monroe et al., 1983). Increased empirical attention to these potential stress effects may help to further clarify the role life events play in the onset, course, and remission of anxiety disorders.

Acknowledgements — This work was supported in part by a National Institute of Mental Health New Investigator Research Award in Prevention, MH-39139; and BRSG Grant RR07084–20, awarded by the Biomedical Research Grant Program, Division of Research Resources, National Institutes of Health.

REFERENCES

American Psychiatric Association. (1980). *Diagnostic and statistical manual of mental disorders* (3rd ed.). Washington, DC: Author.

Averill, J. R. (1979). A selective review of cognitive and behavioral factors involved in the regulation of stress. In R. A. Depue (Ed.), *The psychobiology of the depressive disorders: Implications for the effects of stress* (pp. 365–387). New York: Academic Press.

Barlow, D. H., DiNardo, P. A., Vermilyea, B. B., Vermilyea, J., & Blanchard, E. B. (1986). Comorbidity and depression among the anxiety disorders: Issues in diagnosis and classification. *Journal of Nervous and Mental Disease, 174,* 63–72.

Brown, G. W., & Harris, T. (1978). *Social origins of depression.* New York: The Free Press.

Brown, G. W. (1979). Meaning, measurement, and stress of life events. In B. S. Dohrenwend & B. P. Dohrenwend (Eds.). *Stressful life events: Their nature and effects.* (pp. 217–243). New York: Wiley.

Brown, G. W. (1981). Life events, psychiatric disorder, and physical illness. *Journal of Psychosomatic Research, 25,* 461–473.

Buglass, D., Clarke, J., Henderson, A. S., Kreitman, N., & Presley, A. S. (1977). A study of agoraphobic housewives. *Psychological Medicine, 7,* 73–86.

Depue, R. A., & Monroe, S. M. (1986). Conceptualization and measurement of human disorders in life stress research: The problem of chronic disturbance. *Psychological Bulletin, 99,* 36–51.

Depue, R. A., Monroe, S. M., & Shackman, S. L. (1979). The psychobiology of human disease: Implications for conceptualizing the depressive disorders. In R. A. Depue (Ed.), *The psychobioloy of the depressive disorders: Implications for the effects of stress* (pp. 3–20). New York: Academic Press.

Doctor, R. M. (1982). Major results of a large-scale pretreatment survey of agoraphobics. In R. L. Dupont (Ed.). *Phobia — a comprehensive summary of modern treatments* (pp. 203–214). New York: Brunner Mazel.

Faravelli, C. (1985). Life events preceding the onset of panic disorder. *Journal of Affective Disorders, 9,* 103–105.

Finlay-Jones, R., & Brown, G. W. (1981). Types of stressful life event and the onset of anxiety and depressive disorders. *Psychological Medicine, 11,* 803–815.

Gersh, F. S., & Fowles, D. C. (1979). Neurotic depression: The concept of anxious depression. In R. A. Depue (Ed.), *The psychobiology of the depressive disorders: Implications for the effects of stress* (pp. 81–104). New York: Academic Press.

Gittelman, R., & Klein, D. F. (1985). Childhood separation anxiety and adult agoraphobia. In A. H. Tuma & J. D. Maser (Eds.), *Anxiety and the anxiety disorders* (pp. 389–402). Hillsdale, NJ: Lawrence Erlbaum Associates.

Goldstein, A. J., & Chambless, D. L. (1978). A reanalysis of agoraphobia. *Behavior Therapy, 9,* 47–59.

Hafner, R. J. (1979). Agoraphobic women married to abnormally jealous men. *British Journal of Medical Psychiatry, 52,* 99–104.

Holmes, T. H., & Rahe, R. H. (1967). The social readjustment rating scale. *Journal of Psychosomatic Research, 11,* 213–218.

Jenkins, C. D., Hurst, M. W., & Rose, R. M. (1979). Life changes: Do people really remember? *Archives of General Psychiatry, 36,* 379–384.

Klein, D. F. (1964). Delineation of two drug-responsive anxiety syndromes. *Psychopharmacologia, 5,* 397–408.

Last, C. G., Barlow, D. H., & O'Brien, G. T. (1984). Precipitants of agoraphobia: Role of stressful life events. *Psychological Reports, 54,* 567–570.

Lazarus, R. S., & Folkman, S. (1984). *Stress, appraisal, and coping.* New York: Springer.

Monroe, S. M. (1982a). Assessment of life events: Retrospective versus concurrent strategies. *Archives of General Psychiatry, 39,* 606–610.

Monroe, S. M. (1982b). Life events assessment: Current practices, emerging trends. *Clinical Psychology Review, 2,* 435–453.

Monroe, S. M. (1982c). Life events and disorder: Event-symptom associations and the course of disorder. *Journal of Abnormal Psychology, 91,* 14–24.

Monroe, S. M., Bellack, A. S., Hersen, M., & Himmelhoch, J. M. (1983). Life events, symptom course, and treatment outcome in unipolar depressed women. *Journal of Consulting and Clinical Psychology, 92,* 338–350.

Monroe, S. M., Bromet, E. J., Connell, M., & Steiner, S. C. (1986). Life events, social support, and depressive symptoms: A one-year prospective study. *Journal of Consulting and Clinical Psychology, 54,* 424–431.

Monroe, S. M., & Steiner, S. C. (1986). Social support and psychopathology: Interrelations with preexisting disorder, stress, and personality. *Journal of Abnormal Psychology, 95,* 29–39.

Paykel, E. S. (1982). Life events and early environment. In E. S. Paykel (Ed.), *Handbook of affective disorders* (pp. 146–161). New York: Guilford.

Prudo, R., Harris, T., & Brown, G. W. (1984). Psychiatric disorder in a rural and an urban population: 3. Social integration and the morphology of affective disorder. *Psychological Medicine, 14,* 327–345.

Rabkin, J. G. (1982). Stress and psychiatric disorders. In L. Goldberger & S. Breznitz (Eds.), *Handbook of stress: Theoretical and clinical aspects* (pp. 566–584). New York: The Free Press.

Rabkin, J. G., & Struening, E. L. (1976). Life events, stress, and illness. *Science, 194,* 1013–1020.

Roberts, A. H. (1964). Housebound housewives — A follow-up study of a phobic anxiety state. *British Journal of Psychiatry, 110,* 191–194.

Shafar, S. (1976). Aspects of phobic illness — a study of 90 personal cases. *British Journal of Medical Psychology, 49,* 221–236.

Sheehan, D. V., Sheehan, K. E., & Minichiello, W. E. (1981). Age of onset of phobic disorders: A reevaluation. *Comprehensive Psychiatry, 22,* 544–553.

Solyom, L., Beck, P., Solyom, C., & Hugel, R. (1974). Some etiological factors in phobic neurosis. *Canadian Psychiatric Association Journal, 19,* 68–78.

Tearnan, B. H., Telch, M. J., & Keefe, P. (1984). Etiology and onset of agoraphobia: A critical review. *Comprehensive Psychiatry, 25,* 51–62.

Weekes, C. (1978). Simple, effective treatment of agoraphobia. *American Journal of Psychotherapy, 32,* 357–369.

Wing, J. K., Nixon, J. M., Mann, S. A., & Leff, J. P. (1977). Reliability of the PSE (9th ed.) used in a population study. *Psychological Medicine, 7,* 505–516.

CHAPTER 16

Personality Disorders and Anxiety

Allen Frances, M. Katherine Shear and Minna Fyer

The relationship between the personality and the anxiety disorders deserves (and is beginning to attract) a great deal more attention than it has heretofore received. There is a fairly obvious explanation for the dearth of previous research on this association. Until quite recently, neither the personality disorders nor the anxiety disorders had been the focus of any very extensive research efforts. Most commonly, both these disorders are seen in outpatient settings (and in less severely impaired patients). For many years, most efforts at psychiatric classification and research had been focused almost exclusively on the more severely impaired inpatients presenting with schizophrenic and major affective disorders. The diagnostic reliability for the personality and anxiety disorders was low compared to that achieved for these other disorders, and no clinical assessment instruments had yet been developed to ensure systematic and reliable assessment.

This situation has changed considerably in the last few years, and the availability of DSM-III (APA, 1980) deserves much of the credit for a renewed interest in the anxiety and personality disorders. The provision of a separate Axis II for personality disorders and of specified diagnostic criteria for them has resulted in a tremendous increase both in the reliability of personality disorder diagnosis and in the research into the nature of personality disorder and its relationship to Axis I conditions. DSM-III also provided an innovative method of classifying anxiety disorders that will not be described here, because it has already been much discussed in other sections of this book. These advances in classification have provided a foundation for research into the relationship between personality and anxiety disorders. Even though there is now little accumulated evidence, it is timely to begin a consideration of this association. We will first discuss the theoretical issues that are involved, then review the available research literature, and finally we will chart some of the issues and directions for a possible future research program in this area.

THEORETICAL ISSUES

Knowing that two variables are correlated with one another does not suggest very much about their possible causal relationships, except that it may be useful to look for one. There are several possibilities: variable **A** may influence **B**: **B** may influence **A**: **A** and **B** may both be influenced by another variable **C**: or the correlation may be coincidental rather than causal. In this section, we will assume that numerous studies will soon demonstrate a relatively frequent and two-way correlation between various anxiety and various personality disorders. We will discuss in turn the possible causal (and noncausal) relationships that may account for this.

Personality Disorders Cause or Predispose to Anxiety Disorders

This is probably the most widely discussed relationship between personality and anxiety disorder. Although there is little documentation to support this type of association, it has great face validity and clinical utility. The hypothesis is that individuals whose long-term functioning is compromised by personality disorder (and/or particular psychodynamic conflicts) are especially vulnerable to develop one or another of the more acute Axis I symptom disorders, particularly in response to stressful life circumstances.

In this model, the development of the anxiety disorder may be regarded as a complication occuring during the course of the personality disorder. It is plausible, for instance, to suppose that individuals who meet criteria for avoidant personality disorder, whether this is based on temperament, early life experience, conditioning, unconscious conflicts, and/or identification would then be more likely to develop an anxiety syndrome than those who are not avoidant. Clinical experience also suggests that patients with obsessive compulsive disorder are most likely to have premorbid personality characteristics that are compulsive. Often when the anxiety disorder remits spontaneously, or with treatment, the individual returns to the level of long-term functioning characterized by his or her personality disorder.

Anxiety Disorders Cause or Predispose to Personality Disorders

The notion that various Axis I conditions can predispose to personality disorders has been more clearly formulated and more thoroughly researched for the affective and schizophrenic than for the anxiety disorders (Akiskal, 1981; Kendler, Gruenberg, & Strauss, 1981). There is a fair body of evidence that certain personality manifestations are the result, at least in part, of the chronic mild expression of depressive, hypomanic, or schizotypal tendencies that in the more severe form might be expressed in full-blown affective or schizophrenic disorder. The causal evidence is based on course data (personality manifestations that follow an acute episode); genetic data (loading in the families of personality disorder probands for the Axis I condition and conversely, for the probands with the Axis I disorder, a family loading for the personality disorder; biological test data (e.g., similarly reduced REM sleep latency in Axis I major depressions and in patients with borderline personality disorders [Akiskal et al., 1980]); and treatment outcome data (e.g., if neuroleptics reduce thought disorder in schizotypals [Hymowitz, Frances, Hoyt, Jacobsberg, & Sickles, 1984]). That a similar spectrum relationship exists between anxiety disorders and some of the personality disorders (particularly the avoidant) seems quite likely, but has not yet been documented. Certainly, it is often difficult to disentangle the manifestations of chronic anxiety from personality disorders. If any individual has an early onset of chronic agoraphobia or generalized anxiety, this becomes so deeply and pervasively ingrained in every aspect of that person's functioning that it is impossible to say where primary anxiety disorder ends and secondary personality disorder begins.

Anxiety Disorder and Certain Personality Disorders are Both Manifestations of the Same Underlying Etiology or Pathogenesis

It seems plausible that any correlation between anxiety and personality disorders might reflect underlying shared causal factors that predispose to both. These factors might be biological (e.g., genetic predispositions operating through neuroendocrine and/or physiological mechanisms); psychological (e.g., a congruence of the wishes, fears, and defenses that make up the unconscious conflicts involved in both sets of disorders); behavioral (e.g., similar patterns of conditioning and avoidance which reinforce irrational fears common to anxiety and some personality disorders); or cognitive (i.e. similar irrational cognitions that again reinforce the irrational fears common to both). There is as yet very little evidence concerning the etiology and pathogenesis of either the anxiety or the personality disorders, although theories abound concerning both sets of conditions. We will need a great deal of additional research and probably more powerful measuring tools before we will understand the mechanisms that bring about the personality and the anxiety disorders and the possible common sources of each.

The Correlation Between Personality and Anxiety Disorders is not Meaningful in Terms of Causality

It is possible that the comorbidity between personality and anxiety disorders results from a coincidental conjunction of two groups of disorders, each of which is fairly frequently encountered independently, so that their conjoint appearance implies nothing about causality and is explainable just on the basis of probability. Supporting such a notion is the fact that anxiety and personality disorders are each very frequently encountered whenever they are assessed for systematically (Boyd et al., 1984; Pfohl, Stangl, & Zimmerman, 1984).

In order to determine whether comorbidity of personality and anxiety disorders exceeds chance association, studies must attend to the underlying base rates of each of these disorders in the population being sampled in any particular setting. If this is not assessed, it is really impossible to interpret whether associations determined in one setting indicate some meaningful association between the disorders studied and whether they will generalize to other settings. This problem has not yet been studied for the association between anxiety and personality disorders, but has emerged clearly in the studies of affective and personality disorders and amongst the various personality disorders themselves (Fyer, Frances, Sullivan, Hurt, & Clarkin, 1985). If a condition has a high base rate in a sample (say, antisocial personality disorder in a prison), it is likely to be associated with each and every other psychiatric disorder presenting in that sample setting. If a condition is not present at all in the sample (say, antisocial personality in private practice), it will not contribute to comorbidity with any of the disorders present in that sample. Based upon the base rate probabilities alone, antisocial personality will thus appear spuriously to be much more associated with anxiety disorder in a prison than in a private practice sample. The two ways of dealing with this problem are to compare comorbidity rates with base rates and also to generate results from a diversity of settings with widely differing base rates of the various disorders in order to determine that the comorbidity stands up robust-

The nosologic characteristics built into DSM-III increase the likelihood that correlations between personality and anxiety disorder will not indicate deeply meaningful causal or pathogenic relationships.

DSM-III is informed by a "splitters" preference for dividing categories into their smallest coherent descriptive unit's. Thus, a major achievement of DSM-III has been to separate Axis I from Axis II and to separate within each of the Axis I and II domains a relatively large number of supposedly discrete syndromes. A necessary consequence of this approach, however, is the perhaps artificial creation of greater opportunities for comorbidity, because the more the pie is divided into small slices (i.e., narrowly defined syndrome's), the more likely it is that any given more of these will coexist in any given patient. The DSM-III definitions establishing Axis I and Axis II are not really sharply dichotomous, especially because some anxiety disorders can have an early onset and long and continuous durations. It is, therefore, entirely possible that comorbidity between some anxiety and some personality disorders (e.g., agoraphobic and avoidant personality disorders) means no more than that one integrated syndrome has been artificially and conventionally sundered for definitional purposes into two separate diagnostic axes.

It should also be recognized that even though the comorbidity of personality and anxiety disorders may be fortuitous from a causal standpoint, it can nonetheless at the same time result in important interactions. The clinical manifestations and treatment challenges of anxiety disorders may vary greatly, depending on the presence or absence of personality disorders, even if the comorbidity is based on chance association.

In summary, then, we have discussed four possible relationships between personality and anxiety disorders, that (a) personality disorders predispose to anxiety disorders; (b) anxiety disorders predispose to personality disorders; (c) personality and anxiety disorders both arise from some common, as yet unknown, etiology; or (d) that personality and anxiety disorders segregate by chance alone and/or as a consequence of DSM-III's tendency to "split" syndromes into narrow divisions. It seems entirely plausible that all of these possible relationships may apply at least in some situations and that we should not expect the causality to be linear, uniform, or simple. Moreover, in this discussion, we have thus far ignored an additional source of complexity. The personality and anxiety disorders both also overlap frequently with the affective disorders and such additional comorbidity entails all of the issues raised already in this section, and more.

REVIEW OF THE RESEARCH

As yet, there has been very little (and at that, very unsystematic) research into the relationship between personality and anxiety disorders. This is in dramatic contrast to the dozens of studies that have investigated the comorbidity of personality and affective disorders (Docherty, Shear, & Fiester, 1986). Virtually all of the few available studies relating to personality and anxiety disorders are descriptive and cross-sectional in design. We have only a handful of inconclusive studies that provide any data at all on the possible course, genetic, biological, psychological, and treatment outcome relationships between those two groups of disorders. Futhermore, this research has generally been conducted on small numbers of patients, who are often not very clearly defined diagnostically. Moreover, many different systems of classification and assessment have been used. The studies have followed one of two directions: starting either with an identified "personality disorder" patient cohort and determining the prevalence of accompanying anxiety disorders; or the reverse, starting with an "anxiety disorder" cohort and determining the prevalence of accompanying personality disorders. There are no studies that have determined the prevalence and comorbidity of both sets of disorders in relatively unselected clinical and/or community samples.

There is another literature concerning the relationship between personality and anxiety that will not be reviewed here, because it has a different history and context and does not address either of these phenomena at the severity level of psychiatric disorder. There are many studies, usually reported in the psychology literature, correlating various dimensions of personality functioning with various dimensions of anxiety. Perhaps the best known and most influential work in this area has been conducted by Eysenck (1959). The correlation, if any, between results generated by the dimensional approaches (that have been used in the psychology literature) and the categorical disorder approaches (that have been used mostly in the psychiatric literature) is not yet at all clear.

Studies that Begin With Personality Disorder

There have been six studies (see Table 16.1) assessing the prevalence of anxiety disorders in patients who have been identified and studied primarily because they meet personality disorder criteria. The major limitations of these studies are: (a) They focus on only two of the DSM-III personality disorders, i.e., the borderline and antisocial; and (b) because the major focus in each study was on characterizing the personality disorder, the assessment and diagnosis of the concomitant anxiety disorders was performed and reported less than systematically. The prevalence rate of any anxiety disorders in these six studies ranges from 3% to 17% and is more or less comparable to that found in the general population.

However, the limitations mentioned earlier make the interpretation of these findings very difficult. It must be noted that the borderline and antisocial personality disorders are certainly not among the DSM-III personality disorders that would be most likely to coexist with or predispose to an anxiety disorder. This is confirmed by the relatively low rates of borderline and antisocial personality found in anxiety disordered individuals identified in clinical or community samples (discussed later). One would need to have available studies of the prevalence of

Table 16.1. Prevalence of Anxiety Disorders in Personality Disorder Subjects

	N	PERSONALITY DISORDER	PERCENTAGE WITH ANXIETY DISORDER
Kroll et al. 1981	21	Borderline	5 (Anxiety disorder)
Pope, Jonas, Hudson, Cohen, & Gunderson, 1983	33	Borderline	3 (Agoraphobia and panic attacks)
			3 (Panic disorders)
Carroll et al. 1981	21	Borderline	5 (Generalized anxiety disorder)
Akiskal, 1981	100	Borderline	10 (Agoraphobia and phobic disorders)
			8 (Obsessive/Compulsive)
Fyer et al. 1985	180	Borderline	5 (Most panic and agoraphobic)
Boyd et al. 1984	57	Antisocial	17.5 Any phobia
			10.5 Agoraphobia
			12.3 Simple phobia
			5.3 Panic disorder

anxiety disorders in the avoidant, compulsive, and dependent personality disorders. Futhermore, only one of these studies (Boyd et al. 1984) was at all systematic in its assessment of the criteria for the anxiety disorders. Perhaps not suprisingly, this study found by far the highest prevalence of these disorders. This suggests that there will be much higher comorbidity than heretofore has been found in studies that include the personality disorders likely to be at high risk for comorbidity (i.e., particularly the avoidant, compulsive, dependent) and that provide systematic assessment of anxiety disorder symptoms.

Studies that Began with Anxiety Disorder Patients

Three studies have investigated personality features in patients with anxiety disorders, but only one of these used DSM-III criteria to diagnose anxiety and panic disorders. Tyrer, Casey, and Gall (1983) used the Personality Assessment Schedule, a standardized interview, to assign heterogeneous groups of clinically diagnosed "neurotic patients" (anxiety, phobic, obsessional, depressive, and others) to one of five International Classification of Diseases-9 personality groups: normal, sociopathic, passive-dependent, anankastic (compulsive), or schizoid. The authors interviewed an informant about each patient's premorbid state. They found a higher prevalence of these four personality disorders in the anxiety neurotics (48%) and phobic neurotics (45%) than in the depressive neurotics (30%). The most frequent personality disorder seen among the patients with anxiety neurosis was passive–dependent (26%), whereas in both the phobic and obsessional neurotics, the most frequent personality disorder seen was anankastic (18% and 13%, respectively).

Roth, Gurney, Garside, and Kerr (1972) compared 68 anxiety state patients with 62 patients with depressive illness (as diagnosed by a structured clinical interview). Eighty-six percent of the anxiety patients had panic attacks, compared with 17% of the depressed patients. Personality traits were assessed by clinical examinations, chart review, and the Maudsley Personality Inventory. The patients in the anxiety group were found to be much more likely than those in the depressed group to have hysterical traits, as well as significant shyness, hypersensitivity, dependence, and lack of self-confidence. These studies were limited by a lack of use of specific diagnostic criteria for the personality disorders and by heterogeneity among the anxiety disorders group. The diagnostic criteria used did not differentiate panic from generalized anxiety disorder.

Friedman, Shear, and Frances (1985) used the Structured Clinical Interview for DSM-III (SCID) I and II to assess systematically for DSM-III Axis I anxiety and Axis II personality disorders in 26 currently symptomatic, panic disorder outpatients. They found a 58% prevalence of personality disorder spread fairly evenly among the DSM-III Cluster II disorders (dramatic, emotional, or erratic) and Cluster III disorders (anxious or fearful). Results were also analyzed dimensionally to include correlations with threshhold and subthreshhold manifestations of each of the personality disorders. This analysis revealed a significantly greater prevalence of Cluster III (anxious or fearful) traits among the panic disorder patients. Moreover, panic disordered patients with extensive phobic avoidance were more likely than those with limited avoidance to have a personality disorder diagnosis. It was also of great interest that those with limited avoidance were more likely to have compulsive features (which may drive these patients to participate in activities despite their fear of experiencing panic), while those with extensive avoidance in response to panic attacks were more likely to have had premorbid personality features of avoidance.

There has been one study into the incidence of personality disorder in anxiety disorder individuals identified in a community sample (Boyd et al., 1984). This was limited by the fact that only one of the DSM-III personality disorders (i.e., the antisocial) was assessed. Of the 756 community subjects with any phobia, 1.2% met criteria for antisocial personality disorder (about the same as for the community in general). Rates were higher (4.6%) for the panic disorder patients.

CONCLUDING REMARKS

Attention to the relationship between personality and anxiety disorders is important from many different standpoints both to researchers and clinicians. We will outline a number of the more pertinent issues and strategies. Because about half of anxiety disordered patients meet criteria for one or more personality disorders, research concerning anxiety disorders must include assessment for the presence or absence of Axis II disorders in order to reduce heterogeneity in comparison groups and to investigate sources of variance on descriptive, familial, biological, and outcome measures. After assessment several different design strategies are possible. Personality disordered patients can be systematically excluded from studies of anxiety disorders, or stratified systematically to different groups, or included randomly and studied naturalistically to determine correlations with dependent measures. Similarly, studies of personality disorders might assess for the presence of anxiety disorders and determine their impact on dependent measures.

It is difficult to study the specific relationship between various anxiety and personality disorders, because each of these broad categories includes a large number of subcells reducing sample sizes below that necesssary for meaningful interpretation. These are several possible strategies for handling this problem. The DSM-III personality disorders can be collapsed into just a few broader categories (e.g., the three DSM-III "clusters"), or can each be correlated dimensionally with the presence/absence or degree of anxiety disorder pathology. Because the overall severity of personality disorder pathology may be as interesting as the specific type of personality disorder that may be present, general measures of global severity need to be developed.

There is frequent overlap among personality, anxiety, and affective disorders, and all three should probably be measured in all studies even when the focus of the study is on only one. The failure to measure personality, anxiety, and depressive characteristics introduces heterogeneity and a source of variance that cannot be determined.

The proposed specific spectrum relationship between the anxiety disorders and certain of the personality disorders (e.g., the avoidant, compulsive, and dependent) will be difficult to establish without a very large sample. The association should be demonstrated in several different ways. The first method is to investigate separately patients who present with anxiety and those who present with personality disorders to determine the degree of association. Also, comorbidity should be studied in unselected samples. Second, course studies are needed to determine if specific personality disorders predispose to specific anxiety disorders and vice versa. Third, family studies are required to determine the prevalence of each condition in the relatives of probands presenting with either or both, using the same biological tests in both populations (e.g., measuring lactate response in avoidant personality disorder). And fourth, we need to determine whether similar treatments are helpful for specific anxiety and personality disorders.

Clinicians ignore the comorbidity of anxiety and personality disorders (and also for that matter, that of affective disorders with both) at great peril. There are now available a number of very effective treatments, both pharmacologic and psychotherapeutic, for the anxiety disorders. Perhaps the major factor in treatment nonresponse in these conditions is noncompliance (e.g., not taking medication or not performing behavioral exposure exercises); the major reason for noncompliance may be the presence of personality disorder. It is crucial that every clinician treating anxiety disorders have the ability to make personality disorder diagnoses and assess how their presence may affect the patient's ability to form a therapeutic alliance. Changing personality disorders is difficult, but working with and around them can be quite straightforward and within the capacity of clinicians of widely varying orientations (Widiger & Frances, 1985). It can make all the difference in achieving good patient cooperation with the treatment if clinicians tailor their prescriptions and explanations to the patient's personality style. Compulsive personality disordered patients should be told everything in great detail, given as much control as possible, and treated like colleagues in planning the treatment. In contrast, dependent personality disorder patients should not be expected to make independent decisions and instead will do better if the treatment is "handed" to them in a nurturing manner that convinces them they will be given much care. Patients meeting criteria for avoidant personality disorder will generally need reassurance that they are not being judged and will not be forced to progress at a speed that greatly exceeds their own pace. Narcissists need to be admired, schizoids need to be left relatively alone, masochists need to be commiserated with, and so forth. A supportive stance that recognizes how personality disorder shapes a patient's response to anxiety disorder and its treatment will usually improve the therapeutic relationship, patient compliance, and ultimate outcome (Kahana & Bibring, 1964).

In summary, then, anxiety disorders and personality disorders are each among the most commonly encountered of the conditions that bring people for outpatient psychiatric treatments. Most importantly, the two diagnoses often are seen in the same patient. It remains unclear, when, how, and which personality disorders cause, predispose to, and affect the presentation and treatment of which anxiety disorders, and vice versa. But it would be very surprising if further research in this area does not turn up much that will be of great interest, both theoretically and practically, to our understanding and ability to treat both the anxiety and the personality disorders. The descriptive, genetic, and treatment trial research tools are now available to make this exploration eventful and fulfilling. In the interim, clinicians of all stripes should sharpen their personality disorder diagnostic and treatment skills in order to provide optimal delivery of the very powerful treatments now available for the anxiety disorders.

REFERENCES

Akiskal, M. S., Rosenthal, T. L., Haykal, R. E., Lemmi, H., Rosenthal, H., & Scott-Strauss, A. (1980). Characterological depressions. Clinical and sleep EEG findings separating "subaffective dysthymias" from "character spectrum disorders." *Archives of General Psychiatry, 37,* 777–783.

Akiskal, H. S. (1981). Subaffective disorders: Dysthymic, cyclothymic, and bipolar II disorders in the "borderline" realm. *Psychiatric Clinics of North America, 4,* 25–26.

American Psychiatric Association. (1980). *Diagnostic and statistical manual of mental disorders* (3rd ed.). Washington, DC: Author.

Boyd, J. F., Burke, J. D., Gruenberg, E., Holzer, C. E., Rae, D. S., George, L., Karna, M., Stoltzman, R., McEvoy, L., & Nestadt, F. (1984). Exclusion criteria of DSM-III: A study of co-occurence of hierarchy free syndromes. *Archives of General Psychiatry, 41,* 988–989.

Carroll, B. J., Greden, J. T., Feinberg, M. (1981). Neuroendocrine evaluation of depression in borderline patients. *Psychiatric Clinics of North America, 4,* 89–99.

Docherty, J., Shear, T., & Fiester, S. (1986). The relationship of Axis I and Axis II disorders. In *American Psychiatric Association Annual Review.* (Ed. by Frances, A. & Haykal, R.). Washington, DC: American Psychiatric Association Press.

Eysenck, H. J. (1959). *The Maudsley Personality Inventory.* London: University of London Press.

Friedman, K., Shear, M. K., & Frances, A. (1985). DSM-III personality disorders in panic patients. *Journal of Personality Disorders: 2:* 132–136, 1987

Fyer, M. R., Frances, A., Sullivan, T., Hurt, S., & Clarkin, J. (1985). Heterogeneity of borderline personality disorder. *American Psychiatric New Research Program Abstracts.*

Hymowitz, P., Frances, A., Hoyt, R., Jacobsberg,

L., & Sickles, M. (1984). Neuroleptic treatment of schizotypal personality disorder. *Comprehensive Psychiatry: 27:* 267–271, 1986.

Kahana, R., & Bibring, G. (1964). Personality types in medical management. In N. Zimberg (Ed.), *Psychiatry and medical practice in a general hospital.* New York: International University Press.

Kendler, K. S., Gruenberg, A. M., & Strauss, J. S. (1981). An independent analysis of Copenhagen sample of the Danish adoption study of schizophrenia. II: The relationship between schizotypal personality disorder and schizophrenia. *Archives of General Psychiatry, 38,* 982–984.

Kroll, J., Sines, L., Martin, K., Lari, S., Pyle, R., & Zander, J. (1981). Borderline personality disorder. Construct validity of the concept. *Archives of General Psychiatry, 38,* 1021–1026.

Pfohl, B., Stangl, D., & Zimmerman, M. (1984). The implications of DSM-III borderline personality disorder. *Journal of Affective Disorders, 7,* 309–318.

Pope, H. G., Jonas, J. M., Hudson, J. I., Cohen, B. M., & Gunderson, J. G. (1983). The validity of DSM-III borderline personality disorder. A phenomenologic family history, treatment response and long-term follow-up study. *Archives of General Psychiatry, 40,* 25–30.

Roth, M., Gurney, C., Garside, R. F., & Kerr, T. A. (1972). Studies in the classification of affective disorders. The relationship between anxiety states and depressive illness—I. *British Journal of Psychiatry, 121,* 147–161.

Tyrer, P., Casey, P., & Gall, J. (1983). Relationship between neurosis and personality disorder. *British Journal of Psychiatry, 142,* 404–408.

Widiger, T., & Frances, A. (1985). Diagnosis and treatment of the Axis II personality disorders. *Hospital and Community Psychiatry, 36,* 619–627.

PART IV

Psychological Treatments

CHAPTER 17

Psychotherapy

Thomas E. Schacht, William P. Henry and Hans H. Strupp

Writing about psychotherapy for anxiety disorders is unexpectedly difficult because the task presupposes certain assumptions that are simultaneously reasonable and questionable. First, there is the implicit assumption that an unambiguous definition of anxiety is available. Cursory inspection of the current literature makes it clear that anxiety is far from being a consensually validated construct. While many theories of personality, psychotherapy, and abnormality invoke anxiety as a central explanatory concept, the term has been used somewhat indiscriminately to refer to a state ("she is anxious now"); a disposition or trait ("she is an anxiety-prone person"); a cause or explanation ("she overeats to ward off anxiety"); a behavioral process (e.g., cognitive-affective appraisal of threat; conditioned avoidance; a learned interpersonal response); or an epiphenomenon of neurophysiology (Borkovec, Weerts, & Bernstein, 1977; Spielberger, 1975). Any of the foregoing may, in turn, emphasize affective, cognitive, interactional, and/or physiological perspectives, both objective and phenomenological. This confusing multiplicity of views has even led some theorists to the extreme position of advocating abandonment of the term *anxiety* (Ullmann & Krasner, 1973).

A second, related assumption is that there is a validated set of clinical syndromes ("anxiety disorders," operationalized in standard nosologies such as DSM-III; American Psychiatric Association, 1980) and that different therapies may be applied to these disorders with resulting opportunities for empirical comparison of therapeutic processes and outcomes. As Barlow and Beck (1984) cogently observe, the validity of the DSM-III anxiety disorder categories is far from established. Major questions remain about such issues as the relative merits of making diagnostic assessments in dimensional versus categorical terms, the importance of individual and subsystem response patterns versus global diagnostic category membership, and the extent to which anxiety can be clearly characterized and differentiated from other dysphoric states.

Parallel questions arise regarding the conceptual status of the term *psychotherapy*. Students of psychosocial treatments are familiar with the oft-repeated observation that psychotherapy is a pluralistic enterprise and that there are hundreds of allegedly different systems of psychological intervention. The attendant risks of oversimplification in any discussion that views psychotherapy as a uniform process are well recognized (cf. Kiesler, 1966). Yet in our literature we often persist in using the term *psychotherapy* as if it possesses a clear and consensual meaning that can be easily distinguished from approaches with other names, such as *behavior therapy*, *cognitive therapy*, *hypnotherapy*, and *family therapy*.

The foregoing observations underscore the difficulty of writing simply about psychotherapy and anxiety disorders without first defining one's terms. (We are not alone in this difficulty. Several authors in a recent collection of reviews on this subject expressed cognate sentiments; American Psychiatric Association, 1983). We point out these assumptions not because our intent is to explore them deeply, but rather because they represent an underaddressed area of concern and because they form an important context for what follows.

These difficult questions arise because psychotherapy and DSM-III do not carve nature into equivalent forms. There is often a substantial incongruence between diagnosis à la DSM-III and diagnosis for psychotherapeutic intervention. This incongruence stems from discrepancies between the way problems are defined for purposes of psychotherapy and the way problems are defined in a descriptive nosology like DSM-III. In the DSM-III, mental disorders are defined via standardized lists of criteria intended to be neutral with respect to underlying theoretical assumptions. Psychotherapies, in contrast, rest upon theoretical bases that go beyond simple descriptive functions to provide conceptual frames for explaining and changing the structure, development, and dynamics of experience and behavior. Consequently, psychotherapies cannot simply appropriate DSM-III categories for their own purposes. In particular, the category *anxiety disorders* may have uncertain meaning because theories of psychotherapy also frequently define the essential nature of problems in terms that exceed the scope of DSM-III.

The relationship of anxiety to psychotherapy depends fundamentally on the model of personality and human functioning underlying the therapy. In this chapter, we will not risk attempting to define psychotherapy generically, nor will we seek to defend, integrate, or supersede the multiple available perspectives on the nature of anxiety and its place in human experience and behavior. Rather, we will describe one important emerging approach to understanding and intervention. This approach is formed from an amalgam of principles and associated practices that have gained support through years of accumulated experience as well as previous and ongoing research.

In the service of lexical simplicity, in this chapter we will refer simply to *psychotherapy*. However, central features of psychotherapy appear in approaches known elsewhere by several different names, such as Time-Limited Dynamic Psychotherapy (TLDP, Strupp & Binder, 1984); Interpersonal Psychotherapy (Anchin & Kiesler, 1982); Integrative Psychodynamic Therapy (Wachtel, 1977, 1985); and Brief Strategic Psychotherapy (Watzlawick, Weakland, & Fisch, 1974). While each of the foregoing offers a somewhat different theoretical and technical stance, they share a core vision of psychological problems, including anxiety, as self-perpetuating psychological systems embedded in patterns of repetitive interpersonal transaction. Much that is arbitrary in our discussion may easily be pointed out. In the absence of general consensus, justification for our choices regarding what to emphasize in this chapter must rely on criteria of clarity, parsimony, fruitfulness for research and/or practice, and compatibility with available evidence.

Psychotherapy assigns central importance to anxiety and strives to understand it, to place it in meaningful relationship to other psychological constructs, and to provide techniques for altering associated undesirable behavior and experience. However, it is important to understand from the outset that psychotherapy is not a specific nostrum for anxiety disorders. Rather, it is a more generic approach to a range of psychological problems in which anxiety may be experienced in different forms and it may fulfill varying psychological functions.

DESCRIPTION OF THE TREATMENT

Psychotherapeutic Understanding of Anxiety

Adaptive and symptomatic anxiety

The term *anxiety disorder*, as found in DSM-III, is characterized by a view of anxiety as "either the predominant disturbance, as in Panic Disorder and Generalized Anxiety Disorder," or as a pathological experience that occurs when "the individual attempts to master the symptoms, as in confronting the dreaded object or situation in a Phobic Disorder or resisting the obsessions or compulsions in Obsessive Compulsive Disorders" (American Psychiatric Association, 1980, p. 225).

In contrast to this view of anxiety as a pathological event, a psychotherapeutic frame of reference supports an understanding of anxiety as possessing both adaptive and pathological potential. Beck (Beck & Emery, 1985) states it well:

> Anxiety . . . is not the pathological process in so-called anxiety disorders any more than pain or fever constitute the pathological process in an infection or injury. We should not allow nature's mechanism for dramatizing the feeling of anxiety to mislead us into believing that this most salient subjective experience plays the central role in the so-called anxiety disorders. (p. 14).

Beck goes on to give a theoretical account of how "evolution favors anxious genes" (p. 4) and how natural selection may have provided adaptive pressures that shaped the present form of our capacity for anxious experience. He asks why it is that human beings evolved to have the ability to experience anxiety. What possible advantage could such a capacity have served?

In his complex response to this rhetorical question, Beck advances the argument that the human capacity for experiencing anxiety originated phylogenetically in evolutionary contexts where the major dangers were natural forces, predators, and the like. These situations often placed a survival premium on the ability to evaluate danger rapidly and automatically (i.e., "unconsciously"). Competitive advantages likewise accrued to persons able to respond effectively in a similarly rapid and automatic manner (including physiological defenses to support fight or flight).

Patterns of information processing and physiological arousal (the so-called "fight/flight-freeze-faint" reaction) that are effective in dealing with the threat of a predator, however, may atavistically over-mobilize us for coping with the ordinarily less catastrophic dangers of modern civilization. For example, the reflexive, automatic, unconscious appraisal and response necessary for rapid and efficient coping with imminent life-threatening danger is accompanied by constricted mentation. This cognitive effect of anxiety improves ability to perform simple routine tasks (like running away), but degrades performance on tasks requiring complex, time-consuming analysis and synthesis. These latter capacities may be irrelevant when one is running from a bear, but they may be crucial in successful adapting to modern dangers, especially of the psychosocial variety, where effective coping may require extended reflective consideration and delayed response.

Likewise, rather than requiring physiologically exhausting arousal, which prepares one to run fast, feel little pain, minimize blood loss, and so forth in meeting a life-threatening but typically time-limited hazard, modern dangers (such as a first date or a demanding boss) may require an opposite response of relaxation and acceptance to adapt to an extended encounter with threat. Beck's account is particularly interesting because, unlike other theorists who may assume that unconscious processing is *prima facie* more "primitive" and productive of pathology, Beck shows how both conscious and unconscious modes of appraisal and response may confer specific adaptive advantages depending on the context.

Recognizing anxiety's adaptive functions means that in psychotherapy more anxiety is not always worse than less. When anxiety is viewed as having both adaptive and pathological potentials, psychological treatment becomes more complex than simply "reducing" anxious experience. Similarly, assessment for psychotherapeutic purposes requires not only knowledge of how much anxiety an individual experiences, but also what functions that anxiety serves in his or her overall psychological economy, and in which of those functions there is some difficulty. In this perspective, symptomatic or maladaptive anxiety is understood as a skewing or derangement of a basically normal and essentially psychological function.

Therapeutic progress ordinarily takes place within an optimum range of anxiousness, achieved via a careful balancing of support and confrontation (cf. Luborsky, 1984). Deliberate provocation of anxiety may be a useful therapeutic event, even forming a technical cornerstone, as in Sifneos' (1972) Short-Term Anxiety Provoking Psychotherapy. Ausubel and Kirk (1977) argue convincingly that in certain clinical situations the presence of anxiety may be a positive sign, indicating, for example, a continuation of adaptive striving rather than a resigned defeat (depression) or a withdrawal from reality (psychosis). Correspondingly, although absence of anxiety is (puzzlingly) not included as a feature of any "anxiety" disorders, such absence may be just as maladaptive as excessively intense or overly generalized anxiety. Psychopathy is an obvious example of a disorder outside the anxiety disorder category in which inability to experience normal anxiety interferes drastically with assimilation of social norms and with the development of a morally advanced conscience.

Psychologically, normal anxiety functions as but one event in a chain of separate but interconnected events that may comprise an individual's total response to danger. The role of anxiety in this constellation of events is usually construed to be that of a danger *signal*, which may occasion any of an extremely broad range of possible coping responses. As Beck (Beck & Emery, 1985) analogizes, the function of anxiety resembles that of pain. It impels a coping response which, if effective, terminates or reduces the distress. Anxiety disorders, then, are somewhat analogous to chronic pain, in which the danger signal itself becomes a problem, disproportionate to or dissociated from objective dangers.

The dangers that occasion anxiety may be external (e.g., a rapidly approaching automobile) or internal (such as a fear of losing one's mind). Likewise, coping may involve both instrumental protective action and psychological defense. (The two become linked in numerous ways, as when belief in one's ability to execute effective action becomes a psychological defense.) The term *signal* emphasizes that anxiety is ordinarily associated with the future, with dangers that are anticipated or expected but not actually present. It is this orientation toward the future that makes anxiety a quintessentially psychological response (as compared, say, to reflexively pulling one's hand away from a hot object). Even when an objective threat is present, the anxious aspect of a person's response refers to emotions and thoughts connected to how the situation may develop and what may happen next. The vigilance and mobilization that occur in an anxious state constitute a generic preparation for identifying and coping with future dangers.

Sources of threat

Anxiety reflects perceived danger or threat to something that is felt to be basic and vital to the self. Certain danger situations may be universal, ethologically innate, or inherent in the human condition and therefore not dependent on learning or trauma for their power to evoke anxiety. Awareness of other dangers is presumably acquired (learned) in the course of life experience.

Responsiveness to certain innate dangers may be present from birth, such as fear of falling or fear of intense stimulation. Universal conditions of childhood dependency and cognitive immaturity interact with progressive developmental events to expand the catalog of danger situations and the capacity to respond. Children initially experience threats in close relationship to biological necessities (e.g., hunger, cold) but soon come to learn that alleviation of distress requires intervention by the adult caretaker. Accordingly, threats to the caretaker or to the child's relationship with the caretaker eventually complement the more directly biological dangers, as seen in fears of separation (Bowlby, 1980) or the well-documented stranger anxiety that occurs normally at about 6 months of age.

As development progresses, the capacity for appreciating dangers expands synchronously. Progress in cognitive development supports abstract thought and foresight, fostering greater awareness of self and others, and of self as an objective of others' thoughts and feelings. This development, in turn, fosters recognition that the quality of caretaking depends on how others feel. Anxiety may now occur not just in response to threatened biological needs, but also to psychosocial events, including one's own wishes if one perceives them to be at odds with those of the caretaker.

Coping abilities also develop. Various strategies emerge for maintaining a sense of security. These strategies, like the threats that inspire them, may be conscious or unconscious. One example of the latter may be found in Yalom's (1980) claims that unconscious fantasies of an ultimate rescuer are frequently a component of coping with death anxiety. Another example with a stronger research base is Siverman's (1985) work on the adaptation-enhancing qualities of subliminally stimulated symbiotic fantasies. Expansion of coping abilities also generates new coping-related sources of potential threat. Just as a young child becomes anxious at the prospect of losing his or her caretaker, a person may feel distress at the prospect of losing his or her coping strategies. Ironically, then, an individual's own conflicting wishes or perceived coping weaknesses often become a major source of internal anxiety-evoking threat.

Over time, psychological and interpersonal threats replace dangers to physical integrity as predominant sources of anxiety. Instinctually primitive sources of anxiety, such as falling or dark closed spaces, are eventually supplemented by more symbolically complex abstractions, such as fear of freedom (Yalom, 1980) or fear of success (Tresemer, 1977). Intrinsic dangers (such as fear of disintegration of one's sense of self; fear of self-criticism or lowered self-esteem; fear of experiencing or acting on dangerous wishes) complement extrinsic hazards (such as fear of rejection or assault). Some theorists (cf. review by Saarni & Azara, 1980) even suggest that development, *per se*, is a fundamental danger situation, insofar as developmental changes stem from the need to accommodate when previously successful modes of functioning are outgrown and threaten to result in adaptive failure. This idea has obvious implications for any psychotherapy that conceives of change as a developmental process (as opposed, say, to a simply soothing or healing encounter), because it implies that therapeutic change possesses an inherent capacity to evoke anxiety, albeit, it is hoped, of a different, more adaptively useful sort.

Cyclical-systems nature of problems

DSM-III understands problems in terms of the simple presence or absence of particular symptoms and signs. From the perspective of psychotherapy, however, even an exhaustive list of symptoms and signs does not identify the problem, because a list of symptoms and signs alone does not make sense of the self-defeating, self-perpetuating, and inflexible quality of neurotic problems. Psychotherapy relies on the concept of cyclical systems (Anchin & Kiesler, 1982; Wachtel, 1982; Wender, 1968) as a generic model for understanding the stability and persistence of behavioral organization in both successful and neurotic adaptations. Anxiety disorders are no exception.

A cyclical system is a pattern of thinking, feeling, perceiving, and acting that is self-justifying and self-sustaining. It may involve private experience, overt behavior, and also the reactions of other persons. Cyclical systems are typically embedded in (similarly) cyclical patterns of repetitive interpersonal transaction. That is, cyclical patterns do not remain private or solipsistic: they are by nature deeply interpersonal. If the pattern happens to support the occurrence of adaptive, pleasurable, and self-enhancing events, it may be called a *virtuous circle*. On the other hand, if the self-sustaining pattern leads to repetitive maladaptive outcomes, in which the consequences of one's own troubled actions make similar unfortunate actions more likely to occur again, then the term *vicious circle* applies.

In a cyclical system understanding, cause and effect are not reduced to simple linear relationships in which past causes determine present effects. Rather, a cyclical approach seeks an understanding framed in terms of a circle of causes and effects, mutually determining each other in self-propagating sequences and all occurring in the present. While original or repetitive developmental traumas may provide initiative, once underway, cyclical systems do not depend for their continuation on the perpetual causal influence of past events. In a cyclical system, there is not a clear beginning or end. One may enter the system at any point and, having traversed the circle of causes and effects, eventually return to the starting point.

When a therapist enters the patient's life, he or she also may become part of a cyclical system. Usually this requires no special effort on the therapist's part (just as no special effort or awareness is required of other persons in the patient's life who may play a role in a cyclical pattern). In this way, a cyclical maladaptive pattern (CMP) not only describes the patient's problem; it eventually may become part of the therapeutic relationship, bringing the problem into the here-and-now transactions with the therapist. This fact underlies a central principle of psychotherapy: namely, that patient's problems may be effectively observed, understood, and changed in the here-and-now context of the therapy relationship. While additional work is usually necessary to generalize changes in contexts outside the therapeutic relationship, the in-therapy situation provides a uniquely advantageous learning environment and a haven in which nascent changes may be encouraged and protected.

To change a cyclical system, one may interrupt the circle at any point with an intervention designed to prevent completion of the cycle and (ideally) to set an alternate more benign circle in motion. In psychotherapy, such interventions most commonly take the form of statements and questions. These serve various functions. They may draw attention to aspects of one's experience or behavior, invite change in awareness or consideration of new ideas, or offer explanation and understanding. As speech acts, the therapist's verbalizations may establish a kind of interpersonal context and relationship that seeks to replace vicious with virtuous circles of interaction. As part of seeking to understand how a CMP is manifest in the therapeutic relationship, interventions may involve attempts to change how cyclical maladaptive patterns infuse what happens between patient and therapist, influencing their perceptions of and transactions with each other in ways that, if left unexamined and unaltered, will tend to perpetuate the pattern and defeat the therapy. Despite the traditional emphasis on verbal statements as the primary mode of psychotherapeutic intervention, there is not restriction in principle on intervening in some other way that is helpful. (Wachtel, 1977, 1985, for example, has ingeniously married techniques of behavioral therapies to the insight-oriented stance of traditional interpretive therapy). No part of a cyclical system is, a priori, the best place to begin making change, although intervention at more than one point may have a better change for success.

Wachtel's (1985) case of "Ms. B." illustrates a typical cyclical maladaptive pattern. As is often the case with such patterns, Wachtel's awareness of the cyclical dynamics begins with an observation about the therapeutic relationship. He recognizes himself becoming too indulgent, too helpful, and overly ready to accommodate, assist, and give advice. Further exploration indicates that these behaviors parallel reactions that Ms. B. tends to evoke from other significant figures in her life.

By evoking helpful protective reactions from others, Ms. B. also keeps herself in the role of a pleasant but needy child. In this, she effectively prevents herself from developing mature skills which, in turn, leaves her insecure and anxious about independent functioning. She responds by continuing to evoke dependent and limiting relationships with others. To enter into such relationships, Ms. B. must either find other people who want someone dependent or she must evoke those inclinations in whomever she interacts with (including, in this case, the therapist). By choosing or creating situations in which she interacts with others who value her dependency, Ms. B. reinforces a tendency, described by Wachtel as an exaggerated but basically accurate reflection of her mother's attitude, to see others as threatened and angry with her if she does behave more competently or independently. The risk of angering others in turn evokes anxiety about possible rejection in Ms. B., to which she responds by emphasizing her dependency and continuing to restrict her independent personal development. This self-restriction defends against her fear of rejection but, self-defeatingly, also makes rejection more of a threat and perhaps a greater objective possibility because it limits her ability to cope on her own. Faced with emotional impasse, feeling helpless and anxious, Ms. B. turns to others for help, thereby closing the maladaptive circle.

A generic interpersonal CMP

Cyclic maladaptive patterns help to develop and maintain a range of psychopathological symptoms and states including, but not limited to, anxiety disorders. Regardless of the paticular form of the psychopathology, however, the CMP is typically embedded in repetitive patterns of interpersonal transaction. These interpersonal patterns are themselves often cyclically organized. Schacht, Binder, and Strupp (1984) describe a generic model for an interpersonal cyclic maladaptive pattern. Called a "dynamic focus" (a term drawn from previous literature on time-limited psychotherapy), the generic interpersonal CMP serves as a heuristic that helps clinicians generate, recognize, and organize (i.e., "focus") psychotherapeutically relevant information and intervention.

The structure of this generic interpersonal CMP was empirically derived from analysis of the categories of interpersonal information to which expert therapists addressed their interventions. The interpersonal CMP specifies four categories of information that constitute minimal requirements for a well-formed narrative about an interpersonal transaction cycle. To make minimal sense of an interpersonal transaction pattern one should know something about (a) what an interpersonal actor does (thinks, feels, believes, and so on) in relation to others; (b) what an actor expects his/her actions will lead the other to do and experience; (c) how an actor perceives the other behaving in response; and (d) how the aforementioned activities influence an actor's opinion and treatment of himself.

According, the generic format of this interpersonal CMP contains four categories of action, corresponding to the following outline:

1. *Acts of self:* These may be public or private and may vary in accessibility to awareness. Examples: "I can't stop thinking about how ugly I am when I meet someone attractive"; "I avoid eye contact with my supervisor when I'm

angry with him"; "I'm always wishing my husband would treat me better."

2. *Expectations of others' reactions.* These anticipated reactions of others to oneself may be conscious or unconscious. They often take a form such as: "If I speak up, I imagine that she will disapprove of me," or "If I ask her out she will just laugh."
3. *Acts of others toward self.* To emphasize the two-way transactional quality of these events, these acts are viewed as evoked by one's actions. Examples: "When I asked for the money he ignored me," or "When I opened my mouth he thought I was ridiculous."
4. *Acts of self toward self (introject).* This category refers to how one treats oneself (self-controlling, self-punishing, self-congratulating, and so on). Examples: "When my husband praises me I feel guilty and remind myself of how fat I am," or "When I get upset I just try to slow down and think things through step by step."

Information about the foregoing categories may be organized into an outline of a cyclical interpersonal transaction pattern. The following example (from Schacht et al. 1984, pp. 83–84) illustrates:

Acts of self: Arnold seeks acceptance from others and prevents rejection by (a) behaving in a gregarious manner which conceals his anxiety; (b) attempting to structure relationships so that issues of control and power are avoided and opportunities to give and receive nurturance are maximized; (c) responding in an overly compliant manner to others' expressed wishes so as to avoid conflict; and (d) asking others to help him reach goals of which he thinks they will approve, but which often exceed his ability or desire to actually achieve.

Expectations of others: Arnold believes that others want to control and direct his aspirations, choices, feelings, and life direction. He imagines they expect him to feel and act in ways that he is unable or unwilling to; he imagines that in failing to live up to their expectations he will be summarily rejected.

Observed reactions of others: Arnold recognizes that others offer support and encouragement. However, he construes this encouragement as concealing veiled threats of rejection and humiliation if he fails to perform what he has subtly encouraged them to encourage him to do. Arnold is unaware of his role in evoking the reactions and expectations of others.

Introject: Arnold berates himself for his perceived inadequacy and lack of "achievement." He feels depressed and unlovable. He suppresses brief experiences of anger (at those whom he imagines make demands) and he forces himself to acquiesce to what he imagines are their normative expectations.

A generic CMP for anxiety disorders

Cyclical maladaptive patterns are both highly individual and also generic. In their particulars, they typically reflect unique patterns of life history and experience. However, in their general forms, CMPs may show certain recurring structures (cf. Watzlawick et al., 1974). When the experience of anxiety is a central feature of the overall psychological picture the following generic CMP may be applicable. The structure of this model draws on a broad literature, but owes special credit to the writings of Ausubel and Kirk (1977), Beck and Emery (1985), Natzlawick et al. (1974), and Weekes (1969, 1978)).

All anxious experiences begin with the conscious or unconscious perception of a threat. If effective coping ensues, then the threat is removed or diminished. Anxiety subsequently comes to an end, completing a virtuous circle of successful adaptation. However, if ineffective coping occurs, or if the threat persists despite one's best efforts, then normal anxiety may begin the process of transformation into its cyclically maintained psychopathological counterpart.

Ineffective coping may be due to a

variety of causes, operating singly or in conjunction with each other. Beck (Beck & Emery, 1985) offers the following lists of common predisposing and precipitating factors.

Possible predisposing conditions may include:

(a) physiological predisposition, either hereditary or acquired, which produces persistent physiological abnormalities (e.g., hyperthyroidism) or which evokes sensations that lend themselves to interpretation as signs of impending disaster (e.g., mitral valve prolapse);
(b) developmental traumas that foster disabilities (e.g., repeated criticisms from perfectionistic parents who are seemingly never pleased);
(c) inadequate opportunities to learn or model effective coping strategies (e.g., overprotective parents who prevent their children from facing and mastering challenges, and who, through their protectiveness, encourage development or a self-image of weakness and inability to cope);
(d) counterproductive patterns of thinking, aspiring, valuing, choosing, and relating learned from significant others.

Possible precipitating factors include:

(a) physical disease or toxicity;
(b) severe and/or chronic stress, whose intensity, duration, or lack of controllability leads the person to become emotionally overwhelmed;
(c) specific stress impinging upon a specific emotional vulnerability or exceeding limited coping resources (e.g., promotion to a job requiring autonomous responsibility for a person heretofore highly dependent upon external structure and guidance for security);
(d) participation in an interpersonal CMP which results in repeated traumatization, and/or which evokes such consistent avoidance behavior that reality-testing becomes impaired. (In such patterns, although one's coping efforts typically serve only to make the problem worse, the anxious individual rarely recognizes this fact, and the consequent self-defeating pattern involves rigidly continuing on with "more of the same.")

Initially ineffective coping results in the experience of anxiety being maintained or even enhanced while coping efforts continue at a high level. However, human beings cannot tolerate persistent high levels of anxiety for an indefinite period, and eventually certain predictable and negative psychological events become likely. Athough they represent a kind of "last ditch" coping, these events are self-defeating in the long run and ironically tend to disable further effective coping efforts.

First, prolonged or intense anxiety may lead to a state of "sensitization" (Ausubel & Kirk, 1977; Weekes, 1969, 1978). In the sensitized state, an individual's level of vigilance is dramatically increased and, correspondingly, the threshold for a fear response is markedly lowered. A sensitized person's anxiety level does not diminish after repeated exposure to frightening stimuli. This lack of habituation stands in marked contrast to the typical response of the average nonanxious person who, with greater exposure, will show more confidence and less anxiety (cf Lader, Gelder, & Marks, 1967). (Although see Gray, 1985, for a counterargument that the reason sensitized persons do not appear to habituate is that the stressor is not continued for a long enough period. He reports research on a phenomenon known as "toughening up," which indicates that whereas acute exposure to uncontrollable stress causes helplessness, chronic exposure [over 15 consecutive days] may eliminate helplessness). Sensitization actually represents a primitive form of coping response, insofar in placing oneself in a state of general arousal and mobilization may be helpful to the extent that one remains alert to even slight signs of danger. However, a sensitized person is also more likely to respond with anxiety to an overly broad range of events, and also to experience difficulty in distinguishing safe from hazardous situations.

The second kind of predictable negative consequence of persistent anxiety is a deterioration of higher level cognitive functions. A large research literature has demonstrated that while anxiety in moderation may facilitate the performance of simple or routine tasks (especially those that merely require persistence for successful performance), it greatly hinders effective responding to novel or complex situations where improvisational skill may be more important than sheer persistence (cf. Ausubel & Kirk, 1977, for further discussion).

Anxious states are typified by a narrowed focus of attention and increased rigidity of thoughts, both of which may be adaptive in helping to prevent one's attention from wandering away from a potential danger. However, if chronic, this alteration of cognitive functioning may be associated with developmental abnormalities (as suggested by studies demonstrating a negative relationship between IQ and school achievement, on one hand, and anxiety, on the other, cf. Ausubel & Kirk, 1977). It is also possible that some forms of alexithymia — the inability to represent or communicate emotional events in words — may be developmentally related to such chronic cognitive alterations (cf. Jones, 1984).

More important, narrowed attentional focus and increased cognitive rigidity may render persons more susceptible to distorted perceptions of self and the world. Because these cognitive changes interfere with accurate or complex self-evaluation and self-criticism, they make individuals more likely to employ disabling psychological defenses which, while somewhat effective in warding off anxious experiences, may do so by disturbing perception of consensual reality and by hindering participation in the very human relationships through which one might learn better coping. Table 17.1 drawn from Ausubel and Kirk (1977), illustrates a range of such defenses. Cognitive rigidity may also increase the likelihood that persons will self-defeatingly engage in "more of the same" when coping efforts fail. Such "more of the same" responses, as Watzlawick et al. (1974) note, are often a basic factor in the establishment and maintenance of vicious circles.

The foregoing negative events typically maintain or enhance anxious experience which, in turn, supports further deterioration of coping and self-confidence. Continued interference with cognitive functions (as well as repressive or transformative defensive operations) may decrease the person's ability to identify the specific nature of the threat (as seen prototypically in the person who cannot say more than "I'm just nervous, I don't know why"). This inability to identify the precise nature of the threat responsible for one's anxious experience leads to continuation of the strategy of generalized arousal as a last ditch effort. When the source of one's anxiety cannot be identified, the anxious experience becomes "free-floating" — a state of mind that severely hampers future coping efforts because there is no concrete problem with which to grapple, save one's own anxious state of mind. Rather than endure such a state of mind, persons will often unconsciously invent some concrete threats as a means of binding anxiety. The disorder of "nerves" (Ludwig, 1982) has been interpreted as a culturally generated and sanctioned example of this process, in which ineffable psychosocial threats become routinely experienced as a culturally acceptable somatic disorder, for which one goes to a physician and gets physical treatment.

If anxiety is maintained for a sufficient period, with sufficient intensity and in the absence of adequate coping, then the presence of anxiety and the failure to cope become second-order threats. Individuals who are persistently anxious begin to question, blame, and criticize themselves for their experience. Self-esteem, linked as it is with mastery, inevitably plummets. Demoralization ensues, and the person's conceptual set toward life difficulties shifts from one of confident problem-solving to one of desperate avoidance and

Table 17.1 Examples of Anxiety Defenses

General Category	Examples
Ego Enhancement	Pursuing power, money, success, status; Boastful, belligerent demonstrations of one's power simulation of nonchalance or indifference to social convention; Advancing one's own stature by attacking others' behavior or reputations; Basking in the reflected glory of powerful persons who become psychological extensions of oneself
Conciliation	Sympathetic, charitable attitudes designed to elicit comparable lenience for oneself; Repression of hostile feelings to insure one's safety from reprisal; Failure to perceive other's hostility lest one feels obliged to retaliate and hence risk one's security; Exaggerated conformity to social demands, surrender of individuality.
Indirection	Displacement of the source of threat to a more manageable danger (phobia); Monopolization of consciousness by a displaced inoccuous threat (obsession); Compulsive perfectionism to eliminate fear of uncertainty or improvisation; Displacement of threat to another person or target (e.g., anxious parent who overprotects his or her child); Reliance on stereotyped methods of problem-solving; Delusional distortions (ideas of grandeur and persecution).
Escape	Avoidance of potential anxiety-evoking situations; Denial of anxiety; Withdrawal (asceticism, intellectualization, absorption in fantasy); Self-insulation from intimate interpersonal involvements; Compulsive, counterphobic confrontation with feared situations.

Note. Adapted from *Ego Psychology and Mental Disorder: A Developmental Approach to Psychopathology* by D. P. Ausubel and D. Kirk, 1977, New York: Grune & Stratton. Copyright 1977 by Grune & Stratton.
Adapted by permission, p. 267–268.

escape. Anxiety is no longer a signal that initiates coping, because effective coping seems unavailable. In this circumstance, the experience of anxiety is itself the threat. Rather than serving as a helpful signal of danger, anxiety now *becomes* the danger, often fraught with additional catastrophic expectations about how one's mental infirmity and persistent anxiety are a sign of impending insanity, death, or — as an anxious patient might say — "worse."

At this point, regardless of the original source of anxiety, new problems of fear of fear and fear of failure compound the original threats. Because this danger ("fear of fear") is internal, there is no escape save drastic defensive distortions, massive distractions, or tranquilizers. These solutions may even further the process of self-defeat, as Frank (1983) argues:

> medications carry meanings [and] if the patient comes to rely on medication as the essential source of relief, this perception [may weaken] the patient's incentives to develop more effective ways of coping with anxiety-arousing fantasies or situations. The result is a vicious cycle. The patient's perception of dependency on the medication undermines the sense of self-efficacy. The more incompetent the patient feels, the greater the anxiety, leading to increasing dependence on the drugs. (p. 425)

These new, second-order fears contribute to the problems of sensitization and cognitive deterioration, promoting further anxiety while continuing to interfere with effective coping. At this point a self-perpetuating anxiety process is in motion. Further chronic avoidance efforts continue to sap cognitive and physiological sources designed to work best in short-term fight or flight situations. The individual's fear of being overwhelmed leads to avoidance of being exposed to or confronting the feared situations, which insures that habituation will not occur and that cognitive distortions will not be challenged. The resulting inevitable coping failures elicit changes in self-perception and self-esteem, which themselves become second-order threats, evoking additional anxiety, and perpetuating the anxiety experience.

CASE EXAMPLE

It is extremely difficult to capture the essence of psychotherapy in written case examples. Much of what is important in psychotherapy occurs moment-to-moment, and resides in the private awareness of the participants. Even a verbatim transcript or a videotape of the therapeutic interaction may not be very revealing about the participants' experience of the exchange. Interested readers should consult Spence (1982) for an excellent in-depth discussion of the formidable problems involved in using written text to represent what happens in psychotherapy. The following case example is offered with the foregoing caveat firmly in mind.

Janice R. was an attractive 33-year-old woman, college-educated, employed in a middle-management level job, and recently married for the third time. She sought treatment for her "anxieties" at the insistence of her husband, who reportedly said he could not tolerate her fearful behavior. Ms. R. felt unable to change her "anxieties" on her own, and was afraid that this marriage would shortly end, as had her previous relationships, with her husband leaving in frustration and disgust. Her therapy was brief — six sessions on an outpatient basis.

Session One

The therapist opened the session with a simple question: "How can I help you?" to which Ms. R. replied, "I don't know, I'm just a nervous person." She went on to describe a 20-year history of multiple phobias, including fears of airplanes, thunderstorms, electricity, and wild animals. As a teenager she had also developed school and sexual phobias. At that time she became very shy, developed a spastic colon, and felt embarrassed to be in a classroom with boys. As a result of these multiple phobias, Ms. R. believed herself to be a generally "nervous person," and was inclined to think poorly of herself in a wide range of situations. She previously had been in a behavioral therapy that had emphasized desensitization, without much success, and she feared that perhaps her condition was so deep-seated that psychological help was not feasible. Although she sometimes despaired about her fears, she was only occasionally demoralized and depression was not a prominent feature of Ms. R.'s clinical picture. She was of bright normal intelligence and showed no evidence of thought disorder. She functioned well at work and there was no evidence of antisocial behavior or excessive social withdrawal. Although she used minor tranquilizers occasionally (obtained from her family physician), there were no problems with substance abuse.

After hearing an outline of Ms. R.'s complaint, the therapist devoted some time to educating her to the psychotherapeutic process. This involved explaining that the therapist's role was to listen and to try and understand what was making the trouble in her life, while her role was to speak as freely as possible about whatever came to her mind. Fees, appointments, and so on, were also discussed. In this connection, Ms. R. stated that although she had excellent insurance coverage, she preferred not to use it and to pay cash, because she was anxious about the possibility that if an insurance record existed, someone might discover she had been seeking psychological help.

From the beginning, the therapist worked from the assumption, basic to psychotherapy, that the dynamics of the patient's difficulties should be evident in the patient's here-and-now transactions in the therapeutic sessions. Accordingly, rather than spending a great deal of time focused on events that occur outside the consulting room (this includes the patient's presenting symptoms), the therapist focused initially on the patient's behavior in the sessions. It was never taken for granted that Ms. R.'s phobias were "the problem." Rather, it was assumed that they were only part of the problem, and that the rest of a cyclical maladaptive pattern remained to be elucidated. In this connection, the therapist actively considered the possibility, from the very beginning, that Ms. R.'s difficulties might be only peripherally related to her presenting complaints, and that indeed her presenting complaints might represent a kind of compromise or "lesser of evils" approach to dealing with some more fundamental and frightening threats. The likelihood of this possibility was enhanced in the therapist's mind by the fact that Ms. R.'s phobias all involved relatively infrequent situations. It did not seem plausible that fears of storms, airplanes, wild animals, and so on, would, in themselves, ordinarily be so disabling as to threaten a sound marital relationship. Furthermore, when the therapist nondirectively left Ms. R. to choose the topic of conversation for the first session, she devoted most of her time to talking about her relationships with her present and former husbands, and hardly mentioned her other fears except as evidence of her general character as a nervous person and as something that her husbands had disliked in her.

Ms. R.'s interpersonal style was strikingly deferent. She sprinkled her conversation with apologies, self-deprecating remarks, and negative social expectations, such as, "Oh, if I tell you this you're going to think I'm so foolish," "I'm sorry, I guess I didn't answer that right," or "And then I did another stupid thing." When asked anything but a routine question, she would hedge and waffle, avoiding a direct or assertive answer, while smiling and giggling almost continuously. Her conversation tended to ramble, and at times she seemed almost to babble in a high-pitched, childish voice. Silences appeared to make her extremely uncomfortable. Overall, she gave the appearance of unremitting social anxiety. Because this social anxiety — and not fears of storms, planes, and so on — was immediately felt in the therapy session, the therapist hypothesized that it would be a useful starting place for the task of attempting to understand how Ms. R. generated and maintained her anxious experience.

When asked if she was aware of these behaviors, Ms. R. blushed and replied that she was, indicating that she recalled first learning to behave in this way when her uncle molested her at age 8. She recalled using giggling and babbling to distract her uncle when he would approach her with an unwelcome touch. The therapist then inquired about how Ms. R. might currently use similar displays of anxiety to achieve other, present interpersonal goals (recall the basic principle of cyclical systems, which holds that while historical events may have been important in setting processes in motion, it is current events that are crucial in maintaining them). In pursuing this line of inquiry, the therapist eventually wondered aloud about how Ms. R. might be experiencing the therapeutic relationship at the moment, and about what she might be trying to accomplish in the session with her displays of social discomfort. This kind of inquiry is consistent with the fundamental principle that cyclical maladaptive patterns are maintained in the here-and-now, and are embedded in patterns of interpersonal transaction, including the relationship with the therapist.

Ms. R.'s initial reaction to direct inquiry about the therapeutic relationship was to blush and attempt to avoid the topic, saying that she really had "no feelings," and that if she was uncomfortable it was her fault because the therapist was obviously doing everything possible to put her at ease. After some exploration of this topic, the therapist commented that people were hardly ever without feelings, but that sometimes they might be reluctant to speak about them for fear of other people's reactions. Ms. R. again tried to avoid the topic, and the therapist gently pointed out to her that she was doing so. Ms. R. then became silent for 20 or 30 seconds, and when she resumed speaking her voice was different, deeper and more resonant, and with no trace of giggling or babbling. The therapist also observed that her posture seemed more relaxed, that she breathed more slowly and deeply, that she had settled into her chair rather than sitting on its edge, and that her knuckles, which had been white from clenched fidgeting, had turned pink again.

Ms. R. stated that she imagined the therapist thought she was an idiot, and added that giggling was just something she did to express anxiety about that. The therapist asked Ms. R. if she was aware of how she had relaxed upon deciding to bring this concern out into the open. She appeared thoughtful and replied that she hadn't previously noticed, but now that her attention was drawn to her feelings, the self-disclosure had felt good.

After further exploring Ms. R.'s thoughts and feelings about this transaction, the therapist then interpreted that perhaps she might also giggle in the hope that the therapist would join her in laughter, thereby demonstrating his willingness to suspend critical judgment of her. With this interpretation the therapist began a process of educating Ms. R. to the idea that her actions might be motivated by more than just a need to "express emotions" — that, in addition, her behaviors might also serve to evoke desired responses from others, even if she was unaware at the moment of such intentions.

Ms. R. was invited to use the intervening time before the next scheduled session to observe herself and to notice any patterns of covariation between her anxious giggling and babbling and her thoughts about the interpersonal situation at the moment. She expressed interest in this task and agreed to work at it. The therapist's intent in recommending this activity to Ms. R. was twofold. First, he hoped that effort at objective self-observation would help to change Ms. R.'s relationship to her anxiety, restoring its usefulness as a signal rather than merely a symptom. Second, he expected that the information generated in the course of this self-observation would likely prove useful in the task of trying to understand what cyclical maladaptive patterns might be operating.

Session Two

At the next session, Ms. R.'s initial behavior was similar to the previous session. She was self-deprecating, giggling, babbling, fidgeting, and so on. When the therapist pointed this out and inquired about what it might mean for her feelings in the present, Ms. R. blushed and reported feeling embarrassed that she was "doing that again." She went on to state her expectation that the therapist would think her observations about herself were silly "amateur psychology." The therapist empathized with her discomfort and then wondered aloud if handling her social anxiety through self-deprecation was burdensome. When she nodded affirmatively, he offered to collaborate with her if she wished to try to act differently with him. Ms. R. responded to this, as in the first session, with marked calming and a relaxing change in physical demeanor and voice.

She went on to offer two observations. First, she had noticed that she wore a "pasted on" smile whenever she felt uncomfortable about her own feelings. The smile served as a screen to prevent others from discerning her true emotional state. Second, Ms. R. had noticed herself smiling and giggling whenever she voiced self-deprecating remarks. When asked what might be made of this, she replied: "By putting myself down first, I steal my critic's thunder." In this connection Ms. R. also recalled how her grandmother had also giggled and laughed inappropriately, and how her mother had not liked the grandmother. She wondered aloud if such laughter might be a kind of rebellion, a way of exerting social power from a position of ostensible weakness. The therapist suggested at this point that by reducing the amount of giggling, babbling, and self-deprecation in therapy sessions, Ms. R. was communicating that she viewed him as less of a critical authority than he had seemed at the beginning of therapy. She agreed. The therapist then began to wonder about possible parallels between these dynamics of anxiety in the therapeutic relationship and the way things went in Ms. R.'s marriage. However, when asked to describe how these observations might apply to her marriage, Ms. R. again became anxious and expressed a fatalistic belief in the unchangeability of her husband's negative evaluation of her as an "anxious person."

Session Three

This session was scheduled on an "emergency" basis, because Ms. R. felt panicky. She and her husband had been discussing their mutual desire to have a child, and her fertile time of month was approaching. Ms. R. was very anxious about the possibility that she would approach her husband for sexual relations, and would be rejected. Although the mechanical aspects of their sexual relationship were satisfactory, she imagined that her need for frequent sexual contact had become an onerous burden for her husband.

Impressed by the global quality of Ms. R.'s fears at this point, the therapist felt a need to build some specific understanding of the transactions that occurred between herself and her husband. He wished to do this in a collaborative manner, with Ms. R.'s active participation, because in this way she might learn to further the process of self-inquiry on her own. (This is in line with the psychotherapeutic principle that the patient may internalize the format of a therapist's systematic inquiry, to be used as a coping skill in the therapist's absence.) The therapist therefore invited her to explore this and other problematic transactions between herself and her husband in a microscopic moment-by-moment fashion. Following the outline of the generic interpersonal CMP (see previous discussion), Ms. R. was asked to describe in detail what she did, how she expected him to respond, what she observed him do, and how she felt about herself as a result. This inquiry outline was not followed in lockstep fashion, but was used as a heuristic guide.

In the course of this conversation, the therapist and Ms. R. clarified a number of issues. For example, it became clear that Ms. R. often approached her husband for sex when what she really wanted was emotional succor and reassurance. Furthermore, her anticipatory anxiety led her to behave timidly so that rather than voicing her wishes directly, she would communicate through subtle nonverbal hints (e.g., "meaningful" touches). She viewed this as tactful, insofar as it offered her husband the opportunity to ignore her if he wished without having to resort to overt rejection. The therapist suggested to Ms. R. that she might experiment with more direct means of expression, and he rehearsed with her what she might say in some specific situations. This included practice in giving her husband explicit permission to say "no" if he wasn't interested in sexual relations. (In this way, the therapist was hoping to mitigate Ms. R.'s fears of being unable to control rejection by placing her in charge of inviting it.) He also suggested that she might offer nonsexual touching (e.g., massage) when she desired closeness but her husband was uninterested in active sex. When Ms. R. expressed some reservations about her skill in this regard, the therapist suggested that she might purchase a "how-to" manual, and that she and her husband might make a joint activity out of exploring ways to help each other feel good.

This session ended with an agreement that the patient would think about inviting her husband to come for a conjoint session. Ms. R. was anxious about asking him, but agreed when the therapist suggested that because she already felt her marriage to be on the brink of divorce, she had nothing to lose. The therapist had two goals in mind here. One was that for purposes of assessment it would be useful to see the couple together and not merely through the eyes of one partner. Second, to the extent that asking her husband to join her in therapy was a departure from her previous timid stance, Ms. R. would be therapeutically interrupting a portion of what seemed likely to be a component of an interpersonal vicious circle.

Session Four

The patient reported discussing participation in the therapy with her husband. To her pleasant surprise, he expressed interest and agreed to come at a date to be specified in the future. Ms. R. described how simply knowing that he was willing to join her had substantially reduced her level of general tension. She also reported another self-observation from her continuing task of attempting to notice covariation between anxious experiences and interpersonal situations. Ms. R. had observed, to her chagrin, that her usual chronic sense of tension (which the therapist understood as mild sensitization) was markedly decreased when she was alone. In exploring this idea, the therapist suggested that perhaps Ms. R. used her fears as a way of binding significant others to her, and that she could be free from anxiety when alone because there was no one to do this with.

Subsequently the therapist invited Ms. R. to imagine what other peoples' reactions to her fears might be. She fell silent, and then stated that she imagined they might feel helpless, controlled, and even rejected. As the session ended, Ms. R. was asked to consider having a discussion with her husband in which she would ask him to describe his views of the interpersonal effects of her fearfulness, both on other people and himself.

Session Five

This next session was held 2 weeks later because the patient had to travel out of town. In making her travel plans, she considered taking an airplane, but refrained because of continued anxiety about flying. She reported, however, that she made the decision to avoid flying more easily than she had in the past, and that she had done so without involving her husband in long, unpleasant, and unresolvable ruminations.

Ms. R. reported discussing the interpersonal impact of her fears with her husband. She had imagined him to be simply disgusted with her, and was pleased to discover that he empathized with her pain and sometimes even became angry with himself for being unable to help her. Sensing from this the husband's self-esteem may have been threatened by Ms. R.'s fears, the therapist suggested that perhaps her anxious and apologetic interpersonal style put her husband off by casting him in the role of "bad guy." By acting as if her husband were always ready to blame or reject her, Ms. R. implicitly placed him in the role of angry critic. Furthermore, in so doing she deprived him of the opportunity to act and be received as the loving, caring person he wished to be. It was suggested that eventually he might become so frustrated with his inability to provide meaningful support that he would act angrily, thereby "confirming" Ms. R.'s initial expectations.

Ms. R. responded with interest to this interpretation of a cyclical maladaptive pattern. She spontaneously voiced that looking at her marriage in this way gave her hope for changing things between herself and her husband is she could act differently. The therapist responded by suggesting that perhaps fears connected with relating to her husband were more important in her life than fears of storms, planes, and so on. Ms. R. readily agreed, volunteering that she really had little trouble living with those peripheral fears so long as they did not become the basis for relationship problems with significant others.

Session Six

Two weeks elapsed between this and the previous session due to an intervening holiday. Ms. R. came to the session feeling better than she had in months. She had taken on the task of approaching her husband openly and of refraining from displays of anxiety and insecurity. He in turn had responded with more warmth and attention than she had imagined him capable of expressing. After exploring this progress with Ms. R. in detail, and assuring himself that it represented a genuine change in concrete patterns of interaction, the therapist asked Ms. R. what her next goal was. She hesitated, then wondered if the therapist thought she could maintain these gains on her own without further therapeutic support. The therapist replied affirmatively, and then inquired about her others fears, namely, storms, airplanes, and so on, and about the unrealized plans for joint sessions with her husband.

Ms. R. stated that her fears of storms, planes and so on, were still with her, but that they were not bothersome and that she was not really motivated to work on overcoming them. As for joint sessions, she felt she was accomplishing the same goals on her own. She expressed a tentative wish to terminate therapy. After some discussion of feelings about leaving the therapy and the therapist, it was mutually agreed to discontinue therapy, with the understanding that she was welcome to return in the future should she desire help in making further changes in herself.

Comment

As retrospective accounts subject to the revisionary vagaries of memory, case histories tend to understate the role of chance and improvisation, thereby making the therapeutic process seem smoother and more planful than it really was. Even histories reconstructed from extensive notes, as in the present case, are not immune to this effect. Ms. R. was in many ways a gifted and insightful person, and her case does not provide a strong example of the difficulties a therapist often encounters in patients with rigid character problems, hostile interpersonal styles, and/or lesser capacity for productive reflection and self-mobilization. However, her case does illustrate some characteristic modes of psychotherapeutic thinking and action.

In particular, it is important to recognize that the therapist was not simply applying predetermining techniques to a standardized disorder. Rather, the therapist sought to set in motion a *process* of collaboration, exploration, and personal experimentation. This process serves to refine participants' understanding of the problem (clarifying its cyclic components, identifying the role of personal responsibility and action). The therapeutic process also generates and sustains corrective experiences — emotional, cognitive, and interpersonal — which interrupt problem cycles and replace them with more adaptive ones. The relationship of therapeutic techniques to this therapeutic process is not unitary. There are multiple ways to set a therapeutic process in motion, and none is best for all patients.

What about the outcome? If judged against changes in her fear of storms, airplanes, and so on, it might well be concluded that psychotherapy had produced essentially no change. However, if outcome is assessed against changes in cyclic maladaptive patterns, then the evaluation is more positive. Realistic change is often different from what our theoretical ideals may lead us to expect. The therapist's willingness to come to an end after a brief treatment reflects avoidance of therapeutic perfectionism, as well as recognition that simply becoming able to accept symptoms may be a positive outcome. It would have been counterproductive for the therapist to have pressed Ms. R. to continue working on unfinished issues, especially if he had attempted to use the fact that there were remaining unresolved symptoms to motivate her by undermining the importance of the changes that had been made.

A BRIEF NOTE ON RESEARCH

We have presented an approach to psychotherapy based on the concept of maladaptive cyclical systems. Is this a "brand" of therapy, or simply an integrative principle that can support a rational eclecticism? Either way, the intellectual roots of this conception are extremely diverse, spreading into modern psychoanalytic thought, the psychology of interpersonal dynamics, social learning theory, and systems theory. This diversity alone severely complicates the prospects for systematic research. It is thus not accidental that virtually all research on psychosocial treatments for anxiety disorders has focused on behavior or cognitive approaches (e.g., exposure, relaxation, suppression, etc.). Psychotherapy's complexity can be quite intimidating to a researcher. Thus, although the overall psycho*social* therapy research literature is substantial enough to support large-scale meta-analyses (cf. Smith, Glass, & Miller, 1980), systematic studies of psychotherapy, *per se*, for anxiety disorders are virtually nonexistent. The following points, among additional reasons, seem to account for this state of affairs.

First, until very recently it has been impossible to specify the ingredients of psychotherapy with sufficient precision to support meaningful research. Failure to standardize the treatment variable has severely limited the researcher's ability to make objective comparisons of different treatments or to measure the degree to which each therapist provided what was intended. The development of "manual-guided" psychotherapies (e.g., Luborsky, 1984; Strupp & Binder, 1984) offers the partially fulfilled promise of enabling researchers to know, concretely, what probably occurred in a therapy of a given type. Psychotherapy, however, poses special challenges in this regard. As Luborsky (1984) notes, it is easier to create a manual for a treatment that prescribes every therapist action than for a therapy in which little of what is to be done by the therapist is known in advance. In psychotherapy, much of what the therapist has to do must be tailor-made for the patient and the occasion, after the therapist has listened to and conceptualized the patient's problems. This greatly limits the standardization achievable via a "manual."

Second, the idea that psychotherapy research can be organized according to DSM-III diagnostic categories is highly controversial. Many researchers (including the present authors) believe that psychotherapy involves change processes that cut across diagnostic categories. Accordingly, using diagnostic classifications to structure psychotherapy research questions may be a poor strategy for discovery.

Furthermore, the classification "anxiety disorders" is relatively new. Prior to the 1980 publication of DSM-III, this category of disorders did not exist as a separate group. Consequently, anxiety disorders were not conceptually available to serve as an independent variable. The result, in the words of Barlow and Beck (1984), is that while "a large number of treatment strategies have been applied to [what probably were] the anxiety disorders, in view of the fuzziness of classification before DSM-III . . . it is not always clear what was being treated" (p. 36).

Third, research attention has been focused on more basic questions, such as "does psychotherapy work at all?" While this particular question has been answered affirmatively, psychotherapy researchers have not turned *en masse* to studies of psychotherapy for specific disorders. Comparative studies have often focused on differences between therapies (such as comparing behavior therapy, psychotherapy, and pharmacotherapy) across rather than within diagnostic categories.

Fourth, substantial research progress still awaits development of adequate conceptual tools and measures. The question of how to measure outcome continues to plague the field. Should outcome in the treatment of anxiety disorders be measured by reductions in self-reported anxiety? Changes in physiological indices of reactivity to conscious or subliminal threatening stimuli? Reports by significant others about observed changes in avoidant behaviors? Evaluations of changes in the psychological functions which anxiety serves for the patient? Changes in symptoms other than anxiety that are presumed to be etiologically related to anxiety dynamics? Changes in a cyclical pattern (cf. Strupp & Hadley, 1977)?

Even if these questions of what to measure were answered satisfactorily, the technical problems of how and when to measure remain largely unsolved. In the case of Ms. R., for example, it is clear that much of the important therapeutic work was carried on by her in between actual sessions with the therapist. Can a researcher seeking to understand Ms. R.'s therapy only study what happens between patient and therapist? Or should the investigation extend into the patient's life outside the consulting room (and, if so, how?). If psychotherapy is conceptualized as a catalyst for changes that occur elsewhere, how far in space and time should the research net extend? Research on psychotherapy for anxiety disorders, or any other disorders for that matter, has a long way to go. We are grappling with some of the issues mentioned in the preceding paragraphs in the current Vanderbilt II project, a large-scale process and outcome study of time-limited dynamic psychotherapy.

Although completion of the project is several years away, preliminary studies are beginning to illustrate possible research approaches. For example, Henry, Schacht, and Strupp (1986) examined the proposition that if a patient's symptom is embedded in maladaptive interpersonal cycles, these cycles should also be present in the therapeutic dyad. Employing a fine-grained analysis of interpersonal transactions between patient and therapist using the Structural Analysis of Social Behavior (Benjamin, 1974), eight cases (four therapists, each seeing a "good" and "poor" outcome case) were selected for study. These eight cases represented a relatively homogeneous sample, as each patient was a young man suffering from depression, anxiety, and social isolation (elevated 2–7–0 MMPI profile). Using each therapist as his own control allowed the interpersonal transactions of particular dyads to be isolated for study.

These results were quite clear-cut, and indicate that the same therapist, providing the same theoretical "brand" of therapy to similar patients, may nonetheless behave quite differently in subtle interpersonal transactions across patients. Cases in which the patient received little symptomatic relief were marked by a fairly high number of cyclic hostile exchanges in which the therapist subtly blamed and belittled the patient, and the patient responded with hostile submission and appeasement. Cases in which the patient achieved greater symptomatic relief were almost totally free of such exchanges.

CONCLUDING REMARKS

At the present time, the concept of *anxiety* is not a consensually validated construct, and may refer to a state, trait, cause, or process. Further problems arise because an atheoretical, symptom-based descriptive nosology such as DSM-III does not necessarily define clinical syndromes in a manner consistent with various theoretical approaches to the etiological understanding and treatment of anxious symptomatology. Therefore, we have not attempted to provide prescriptive therapeutic approaches for specific anxiety disorders or symptoms, but rather have outlined a clinical heuristic to help structure the search for the underlying meanings and contexts of reported symptoms, as well as to guide the process of therapy.

While ideas about the nosology, etiology, and treatment of anxiety disorders may differ among psychotherapists, the manifestations of pathological anxiety are usually evident in interpersonal transactions. Our approach to psychotherapy draws upon a variety of theoretical bases, all of which emphasize the idea that neurotic problems are best seen in the context of rigid, self-perpetuating cycles of interpersonal transactions. Although cyclical maladaptive patterns may have their roots in the patient's past experiences, they are actively maintained through present behaviors and the subsequent reactions of others in the patient's environment. Thus, the identification of these cyclical patterns, especially the linking of the patient's life experiences with ongoing behaviors within the therapeutic dyad, guides the process of therapy. We believe that this approach provides not only a useful and broadly applicable clinical heuristic, but a foundation for fruitful psychotherapy research as well. When the disorder of interest, the therapy of choice, and research strategy all employ this common metric (interpersonal transactional patterns), problem-treatment-outcome congruence (Schacht & Strupp, 1984) is achieved, and meaningful, theory-driven research is made possible.

REFERENCES

American Psychiatric Association. (1980). *Diagnostic and statistical manual of mental disorders* (3rd ed). Washington, DC: Author.

American Psychiatric Association. (1983). *Psychiatry update* (Vol. III). Washington, DC: Author.

Anchin, J. C., & Kiesler, D. J. (Eds.). (1982). *Handbook of interpersonal psychotherapy*. New York: Pergamon Press.

Ausubel, D. P., & Kirk, D. (1977). *Ego psychology and mental disorder: A developmental approach to psychopathology*. New York: Grune & Stratton.

Barlow, D. H., & Beck, J. G. (1984). The psychosocial treatment of anxiety disorders: Current status, future directions. In J. B. W. Williams & R. L. Spitzer (Eds.) , *Psychotherapy research: Where are we and where should we go?* (pp. 29–69). New York: Guilford.

Beck, A. T., & Emery, G. (1985). *Anxiety disorders and phobias: A cognitive perspective*. New York: Basic Books.

Benjamin L. S. (1974). Structural analysis of social behavior. *Psychological Review, 81*, 392–425.

Borkovec, T. D., Weerts, T. C., & Bernstein, D. A. (1977). Assessment of anxiety. In A. B. Ciminero, K. S. Calhoun, & H. E. Adams (Eds.), *Handbook of behavioral assessment*. New York: Wiley.

Bowlby, J. (1980). *Attachment and loss. (Volume 3): Loss, sadness, and depression*. New York: Basic Books.

Frank, J. D. (1983). The psychotherapy of anxiety. In *Psychiatry update* (Vol. III, pp. 418–426). Washington, DC: American Psychiatric Association.

Gray, J. A. (1985). Issues in the neuropsychology of anxiety. In A. H. Tuma & J. D. Maser (Eds.), *Anxiety and the anxiety disorders*. (pp. 5–26). Hillsdale, NJ: Lawrence Erlbaum Associates.

Henry, W. P., Schacht, T. E., & Strupp, H. H. (1986). Structural analysis of social behavior: Application to a study of interpersonal process in differential psychotherapeutic outcome. *Journal of Consulting and Clinical Psychology, 54*, 27–31.

Jones, B. A. (1984). Panic attacks with panic masked by alexithymia. *Psychosomatics, 25*(11), 858–859.

Kiesler, D. J. (1966). Some myths about psychotherapy research and the search for a paradigm. *Psychological Bulletin, 65*, 110–136.

Lader, M., Gelder, M. G., & Marks, I. (1967). Palmar skin conductance measures as predictors of response desensitization. *Journal of Psychosomatic Research, 11*, 283–290.

Luborsky, L. (1984). *Principles of psychoanalytical psychotherapy: A manual for supportive-expressive treatment*. New York: Basic Books.

Ludwig, A. M. (1982). "Nerves": A sociomedical diagnosis . . . of sorts. *American Journal of Psychotherapy, 36*(3), 350–357.

Saarni, C., & Azara, V. (1980). In R. H. Woody (Ed.), *Encyclopedia of clinical assessment* (Vol. II, pp. 575–587). San Francisco: Jossey-Bass.

Schacht, T. E., Binder, J. L., & Strupp, H. H. (1984). The dynamic focus. In H. H. Strupp & J. L. Binder, (Eds.), *Psychotherapy in a new key: A guide to time-limited dynamic psychotherapy*. New York: Basic Books.

Schacht, T. E., & Strupp, H. H. (1884, July). *Psychotherapy outcome: Individualized is nice but intelligible is beautiful*. Paper presented at Annual Meeting of the Society for Psychotherapy Research, Lake Louise, British Columbia, Canada.

Sifneos, P. (1972). *Short-term psychotherapy and emotional crisis*. Cambridge, MA: Harvard University Press.

Silverman, L. (1985). Research on pyschoanalytic psychodynamic propositions. *Clinical Psychology Review, 5*, 247–257.

Smith, M., Glass, G., & Miller, T. (1980). *The benefits of psychotherapy*. Baltimore: Johns Hopkins Press.

Spence, D. P. (1982). *Historical truth and narrative truth*. New York: W. W. Norton & Co.

Spielberger, C. D. (1975). Anxiety: State-trait-process. In C. D. Spielberger (Ed.), *Anxiety and behavior*. New York: Academic Press.

Strupp, H. H., & Binder, J. L. (1984). *Psychotherapy in a new key: A guide to time-limited dynamic psychotherapy*. New York: Basic Books.

Strupp, H. H., & Hadley, S. W. (1977). A tripartite model of mental health and psychotherapeutic outcomes: With special reference to negative effects in psychotherapy. *American Psychologist, 32*, 187–196.

Tresemer, D. W. (1977). *Fear of success*. New York: Plenum.

Ullman, L. P., & Krasner, L. A. (1973). *A psychological approach to abnormal behavior* (2nd ed.). Englewood Cliffs, NJ: Prentice-Hall.

Wachtel, P. L. (1977). *Psychoanalysis and behavior therapy: Toward an integration*. New York: Basic Books.

Wachtel, P. L. (1982). Vicious circles: The self and the rhetoric of emerging and unfolding. *Contemporary Psychoanalysis, 18*(2), 259–272.

Wachtel, P. L. (1985). Integrative psychodynamic therapy. In S. J. Lynn & J. P. Garske (Eds.), *Contemporary psychotherapies: Models and methods*. Columbus, OH: Charles E. Merrill.

Watzlawick, P., Weakland, J. H., & Fisch, R. (1974). *Change: Principles of problem formation and problem resolution*. New York: W. W. Norton & Co.

Weekes, C. (1969/1978). *Hope and help or your nerves*. New York: Bantam.

Wender, P. H. (1968). Vicious and virtuous circles: The role of deviation-amplifying feedback in the origin and perpetuation of behavior. *Psychiatry, 31*(4), 309–324.

Yalom, I. (1980). *Existential psychotherapy*. New York: Basic Books.

CHAPTER 18

Behavior Therapy

William L. Marshall and Zindel Segal

In this chapter, we will attempt to describe the major behavioral approaches that have been applied successfully to the treatment of the anxiety disorders. It particularly is appropriate that a chapter in this handbook should deal with behavior therapy, because one of the main areas of application in the early development of this approach was the anxiety disorders, and these problems have continued to attract the attention of behavior therapists. Indeed, with the simple phobias behavior therapy often is thought to be the treatment of choice, even among practitioners of quite different orientations. We hope to convince the reader that while there is much research still to be done, behavior therapy offers a good deal of promise with all of these disorders.

Two decades ago, when behavior therapy was still in its infancy, it was quite easy to characterize the approach in a way that distinguished it from other treatments of the time. Behavioral techiques of that period were accurately said to be derived from either classical or operant conditioning procedures developed in laboratory studies of learning (Kazdin, 1978). Nowadays, researchers and clinicians are not so interested in distinguishing procedures as they are in designing effective treatment programs which may combine strategies adopted from various theoretical positions. Cognitive and behavioral methods commonly are combined (Meichenbaum, 1977), and drugs and behavior therapy have been usefully integrated (Marshall & Segal, 1986). In this respect, the distinctiveness of this chapter from some of the others in this handbook has been at times difficult for us to maintain. This was particularly problematic in the area of the cognitive/subjective component of anxiety, which has long been identified by behavior therapists as a target for treatment (Lang & Lazovik, 1963), and imaginal strategies, which were included among the first behavioral interventions (Wolpe, 1958). Our presentation of treatments as behavioral was in some cases guided as much by historical precedent as by clearly distinguishable features, and in other cases by the fact that the procedures were derived from basic behavioral research (e.g., covert conditioning) or from behavioral theories (e.g., imaginal desensitization). Of course behavioral theories of disorders tend today, while retaining their bases in empirical research, to include processes describing somatic and cognitive, as well as behavioral, features and behaviors are seen as attributable to influences both external and internal (Marshall, 1982). All of this makes for better theories, more precise research, and consequently, more comprehensive treatment programs, but does tend to obfuscate differences among approaches, which is probably a good thing.

Perhaps the most important, and historically consistent, feature of behavior therapy is the interchange between detailed assessment and the application of treatment. The outcome of the initial assessment determines the choice of treatment, while the initial application of treatment may reveal a need for further assessment and a modification of the treatment program. In a sense, the group evaluation of standardized procedures offends the basic tenets of individualized behavior therapy, but it is hard to see how science could progress otherwise. This persistent dilemma for behavior therapists has not yet been satisfactorily resolved, although one infrequently employed approach has been to choose differential treatments depending upon differential assessment responses. For example, predominantly somatic or predominantly cognitive responders might be allocated to either cognitive or somatically based treatments and a comparative evaluation conducted.

We have chosen to describe behavioral treatments separately for each of the anxiety disorders because each of the categories of disorder appear to call for somewhat different approaches.

SIMPLE PHOBIAS

DSM-III (American Psychiatric Association, 1980) indicates that the simple phobia category covers irrational fears of objects or situations and is to be distinguished from agoraphobia and the social phobias. The manual suggests that the common fears of objects typically involve animals, although blood and injury phobias are prevalent, while the situational fears may involve claustrophobia (fear of enclosed spaces) or acrophobia (fear of heights), but fears associated with a variety of other situations are common. The defining characteristics of this category concern the specificity of the eliciting stimulus; that is, some clearly definable object or situation provokes fear and avoidance in the "simple" phobic, as opposed to an unspecifiable anxiety (generalized anxiety disorder), distressful interoceptive changes that are not triggered by an indentifiable external stimulus (panic disorder), distress induced by scrutiny (social phobia), or anxieties concerning a fear of fear or a loss of safety (agoraphobia). In all these anxiety disorders, problems are manifest in each of three systems: behavioral, cognitive/ subjective, and physiological (Lang, 1977). Adequate evaluation of treatment, therefore, should take each of these systems into account, and treatment itself may focus on one or more of these systems depending on the nature of the disorder or on the idiosyncracies of its expression in any one individual.

It is appropriate to begin this chapter with a consideration of treatments for the simple phobias, because it was with these problems that behavior therapy first established itself as a viable alternative to more traditional treatment approaches (Sturgis & Scott, 1984). Indeed, the most seminally important text in the history of behavior therapy was Joseph Wolpe's *Psychotherapy by Reciprocal Inhibition* (Wolpe, 1958), which dealt with the application of systematic desensitization to various neurotic complaints, including the simple phobias.

Systematic desensitization has been the most thoroughly researched, and probably the most frequently used, behavioral procedure in the treatment of simple phobias. Essentially, this technique requires that the patient be trained in muscular relaxation,[1] usually be an abbreviated ver-

[1] Actually, Wolpe suggested several alternative responses that might reciprocally inhibit anxiety, but relaxation has been the most popular.

sion of Jacobson's (1938) procedure, and then exposed, while relaxed, to a graded hierarchy (from least anxiety-provoking to most anxiety-provoking) of fear-eliciting stimuli. This exposure may occur in imagination or in vivo (real life), and despite earlier conclusions that in vivo exposure was the superior form (Emmelkamp, 1982), the evidence actually fails to demonstrate an advantage for either version, with both being equally effective and superior to control procedures (James, 1985). In any case, it is clear that desensitization, in one form or another, is very effective with simple phobias (Mavissakalian & Barlow, 1981).

The demonstrated effectiveness of desensitization did not induce complacency in behavior therapists because it apparently did not help all patients. In addition, many therapists found desensitization to be tedious and to involve far too much investment of time on the part of the therapist for it to be applied on a widespread basis. These considerations led to attempts to use taped instructions (Cotler, 1970), self-help manuals (Marshall, Presse, & Andrews, 1976), and group formats (Taylor, 1971) in treatment. These variations have proven effective, but all too often research on the value of procedural variations of desensitization has involved nonclinical, analog populations of student volunteers. Among these subjects, it appears that a wide variety of procedures, including the nonspecific features of these procedures, produce changes (Borkovec & O'Brien, 1976; Segal & Marshall, 1982), so that conclusions about relative efficacy are obscured.

The most important consequence of concerns about the effectiveness and clinical utility of desensitization has been the development of alternative strategies. Covert conditioning procedures (Cautela, 1970) involve reinforcing, in imagination, the patient's competent confrontation (again done in imagination) with the feared stimulus. This procedure is not unlike imaginal desensitization, and evaluations have demonstrated it to be effective (Guidry & Randolph, 1974; Ladouceur, 1974, 1977). However, component analyses have failed to reveal a conditioning basis to the effectiveness of covert reinforcement (Ladouceur, 1978; Marshall, Boutilier, & Minnes, 1974). It seems likely that the controlling mechanisms are much the same as imaginal desensitization, which likewise does not appear to be mediated by conditioning processes or even by the processes of reciprocal inhibition, which Wolpe thought were so crucial (Leitenberg, Agras, Butz, & Wincze, 1971; Marshall, 1975).

The two major alternatives to desensitization in the treatment of simple phobias are modeling (Bandura, 1969) and flooding (Marshall, Gauthier, & Gordon, 1979), both of which may be done in imagination or in vivo. Bandura (1971) claims that phobias typically are acquired by vicarious learning rather than by direct conditioning, and he took this to mean that procedures based on observational learning principles would eliminate fears. Modeling requires the client to observe someone else approach and behave effectively in the presence of the feared stimulus. Such observations by the phobic person are said to extinguish fears through vicarious learning processes, the mechanisms of which have been described by Bandura (1977). A series of studies have demonstrated modeling to be effective in alleviating simple phobias (Rachman, 1972; Rosenthal & Bandura, 1978), although most of this research has employed analog subjects.

Covert or symbolic modeling involves the same processes, except that the client is required to imagine a model confronting the phobic stimulus. While some studies have indicated some value for this procedure, it is not as effective as in vivo modeling and sometimes no more effective than control procedures (Kazdin & Smith, 1979; Thelen, Fry, Fehrenbach, & Frantschi, 1979). Again, this covert procedure seems remarkably like imaginal desensitization.

Perhaps the most popular and apparently the most effective, in vivo version of modeling is what is called "participant modeling," which generally has been found to be more effective than nonparticipant modeling (Bandura, Adams, & Beyer, 1977). In this approach, the therapist models appropriate nonanxious behavior in the feared situation, and the client then is given the opportunity to imitate the behavior of the therapist. The reader will recognize that there are two components to this procedure: (a) modeling, which is thought to be a crucial element, and (b) exposure in vivo to the feared situation, which is understood to simply provide opportunity to immediately practice the vicariously acquired skills. Unfortunately for the advocates of participant modeling, a careful study by Bourque and Ladouceur (1980) with acrophobics demonstrated that it was the exposure component that produced the beneficial changes; the modeling component adding nothing to the effectiveness of the procedure.

To this point, we have seen that exposure is a key element in the effective behavioral treatments reviewed so far, and, as noted earlier, it is considered to be the necessary element. From this perspective, we may consider the various strategies such as desensitization, covert reinforcement, and modeling as simply different ways of ensuring exposure. Likewise, some patients may be so afraid of experiencing fear that for them the easiest approach may be to start with an imaginal (nonconfrontative) procedure in order to prepare them for real-life confrontations with the phobic stimulus.

Given that exposure is the essential element in extinguishing fears, perhaps an effective strategy might simply involve exposure to the actual feared stimulus. Procedures of this kind were initially called "flooding" or "implosion," but now often are described as "exposure-based" techniques, which, of course, implies that how this exposure is arranged is of less importance than the fact that it occurs. Stampfl and Levis (1967) were the first to propose nongraduated exposure to the most feared situation as a treatment for phobias. Because they wished to include exposure to the inferred associated meanings of the phobic stimulus (including the client's worst nightmares about the consequences of exposure, as well as the symbolic or psychodynamic meanings of the fear), their procedure only could be conducted in imagination. Comparisons of their procedure with exposure to the actual elements of the feared stimulus have shown clear advantages for the latter approach (Marshall, Gauthier, Christie, Currie, & Gordon, 1977; Mathews & Rezin, 1977; Mathews & Shaw, 1973). Similarly, for the most part flooding in vivo appears to be more effective than imaginal flooding (Emmelkamp, 1982; Marshall et al., 1979).

There are numerous variations on flooding in vivo, with some involving a gradual approach to the feared stimulus (although typically a far faster approach than desensitization), some involving elements of modeling, some done in groups rather than individually, and some involving training in coping behaviors (e.g., relaxation or encouraging self-talk). Some of the questions common to all of these variations, for which therapists need an answer, have to do with the optimal duration of exposure necessary to eliminate the fear, and the number of sessions required for effective treatment. A corollary of the first question concerns the criteria for determining when to terminate exposure. In addition, we need to know whether or not training in coping behaviors adds anything of value to simple exposure.

We found that the best time to terminate exposure was when the patient's report that fear had dissipated was congruent with the same judgment made by an experienced observer (Gauthier & Marshall, 1977). This study, while making life easy for the practitioner in that it provided simple indices of when to end exposure, evaluated only the immediate effects of treatment, and it may be that other factors are relevant to long-term maintenance of gains.

In order to answer some of the other questions just raised, we will describe a recently completed study where we treated a commonly seen clinical phobia, fear of heights. In the first experiment

(Marshall, 1985), we allocated very fearful clients to one of five treatment groups or to a control group. Two of the treatment groups were given brief exposures that terminated while the subjects were still quite fearful. Another group was exposed until their anxiety dissipated (standard procedure), while two other groups were required to remain in the phobic situation for a period additional to that of the standard group (the prolonged procedures). This additional anxiety-free period was equal to a further third of the time taken for anxiety to dissipate. Each of these five treatment groups received three exposure sessions, all conducted in vivo by having the subjects stand at the railing of a flat roof atop a building some 40 feet from the ground and look out at the area below. In one of the prolonged exposure groups, we had clients rehearse coping self-statements (e.g., "I am handling this OK," "I am on a high place but I'm not feeling anxious," "Things look great from up here," etc.) during the anxiety-free period. The control group simply went through the rigorous pretreatment, post-treatment, and follow-up (6 months later) assessments.

The two brief exposure groups (terminated before anxiety dissipated) did not improve, nor did the control group. It is worth noting that some of the brief exposure subjects got worse, confirming, at least in these few cases, both theoretical predictions and clinical expectations about the effects of brief intense exposures to fear-evoking stimuli (Eysenck, 1968; Marshall et al., 1979). More important for clinical purposes, however, the standard group and the two prolonged groups improved significantly on the assessments conducted shortly after the third treatment session. However, the standard group showed some loss of these benefits at the follow-up evaluations, while the prolonged group, receiving practice in coping self-statements, continued to improve at follow-up. In an evaluation of the benefits of adding coping self-statements to a desensitization program, Hayes, Hussain, Turner, Anderson, and Grubb (1983) found having phobic patients practice these statements decreased anxiety during treatment, as well as producing greater gains outside treatment.

The optimal procedure for flooding in vivo, then, appears to involve exposure until anxiety has dissipated, with practice in coping behaviors carried out in the phobic situation during the anxiety-free period which follows this. Consistent with this latter requirement for training coping behaviors are the results of a recent study by Williams, Dooseman, and Kleifield (1984). They compared exposure treatment alone with what they called "guided mastery," which involved approximately the same amount of in vivo exposure, but added mastery-oriented guidance by the therapist. Initially, during exposure, the therapist accompanied the patient and offered suggestions for effectively dealing with the situation. Height phobics, for example, practiced looking at the ground far from the edge of the building and, with reassurances from the therapist, they gradually moved closer to the edge. Gradually the distance between the patient and therapist was increased until the patient could manage alone. Suggestions were made throughout to reduce defensive maneuvers and to vary the manner of approach behaviors. Guided mastery proved to be more effective than exposure alone. These researchers (Williams, Turner, & Peer, 1985) subsequently have shown guided mastery to be superior to in vivo desensitization, both immediately after treatment and at follow-up.

It has been suggested that differential responsiveness to phobic stimuli may imply differential responsiveness to treatment. Ost, Johansson, and Jerremalm (1982) identified behavioral versus physiological responders among 34 claustrophobic outpatients in terms of their predominant anxiety signs during a pretreatment phobic test. Half of each group of responders were randomly assigned to either a behavioral treatment (exposure alone) or a physiological treatment (applied relaxation). When treatments were matched with the patients' predominant anxiety signs, the greatest improvements were observed. This study suggests that there may be features of phobic subjects that make them more suited to one form of treatment than another, and these issues appear to be worthy of further investigation.

As far as the required number of treatment sessions is concerned, we typically find significant reductions in anxiety after as few as three flooding in vivo treatment sessions, and it is a rare case that requires more than six sessions. As we will see later, brief-intensive treatments such as these may not be as effective in the long-term for the more complex anxiety-based disorders, but with the simple phobias they appear to be the approach of choice. Flooding, however, may not be to everyone's liking, either for the therapist or the patient, and for this reason it is just as well that the other procedures we have described are effective. But before a clinician decides that flooding is not his/her choice, we recommend they read our chapter (Marshall & Gauthier, 1983) on failures in flooding, in order to see how flooding can be implemented in a way that maximizes its effectiveness and reduces the stress on both therapist and patient.

POSTTRAUMATIC STRESS DISORDER

This disorder is, in fact, rather like a simple phobia, where the distress is occasioned by the memories, dreams, or "flashbacks" of an actual trauma, rather than by a presently occurring stimulus. Blanchard, Kolb, Pallmeyer, and Gerardi (1982) and Malloy, Fairbank, and Keane, (1983) have demonstrated that combat stimuli trigger undesirable autonomic responses in patients suffering from posttraumatic stress disorder (PTSD), suggesting that this is indeed a variant on simple phobias, and implying that effective treatment should match that employed with such problems. However, this may be too simple-minded.

Foy, Sipprelle, Rueger, and Carroll (1984), for example, found that more than 90% of Vietnam veterans suffering from PTSD had symptoms of pervasive anxiety and disgust, pointing more to a form of generalized anxiety disorder. Birkhimer, DeVane, and Muntz (1985), in a retrospective analysis of information available on 15 PTSD patients, observed a symptom complex that included depression and poor social functioning, in addition to marked anxiety. Likewise, Green, Lindy, and Grace (1985) have noted depressive features sufficient to warrant the diagnosis of a major depressive disorder in 75% of PTSD patients; another 35% met the criteria for an anxiety disorder additional to PTSD. Clearly, the issue is far more complex than the present description in DMS-III.

Nevertheless, early accounts of treatment for PTSD were based on the idea that it was a variant of simple phobias. Moor (1945) employed an unsystematic version of desensitization successfully with these patients, and Saul, Howard, and Lenser (1946) provided graduated exposure to war movies which reduced the symptoms of PTSD in soldiers. However, Kipper (1977) was the first to describe the use of a modern behavioral approach to the treatment of PTSD among a group of Israeli soldiers suffering from fears as a result of combat in the Yom Kippur War. He used desensitization to memories of traumatic combat experiences and reported success, although this was a poorly controlled study.

Keane and his colleagues (Black & Keane, 1982; Fairbank, Gross, & Keane, 1983; Keane & Kaloupek, 1982) have engaged in research with PTSD patients over a number of years, and their studies represent the only really satisfactory application of behavioral treatments to these problems. In all of their studies they have used imaginal flooding, although they prefer to call it implosive therapy despite the fact that they simply have their patients imagine the actual traumatic scenes that appear to have triggered the symptom development.

Their first report (Black & Keane, 1982) concerned the treatment by imaginal flooding of a 55-year-old veteran with numerous extensive fears of some 36 years duration. Three 1-hour flooding sessions required him to imagine scenes of the actual combat that initiated the fears. This program proved to be very effective and the benefits were maintained at 2 years follow-up. Keane and Kaloupek (1982) provided a more sophisticated multiple-baseline analysis (Hersen & Barlow, 1976) of this treatment program. Although generalization proved to be too great to clearly infer the special effects of treatment, nevertheless, outcome was very positive. Finally, Fairbank et al. (1983) demonstrated the effectiveness of their program in yet another excellent single-case study of an unfortunate Vietnam veteran who was almost killed in an ambush and then was forced to watch helplessly as a friend was tortured, killed, and mutilated. His nightmares, flashbacks, and fears were elmininated by this program, which, in this case, included not only imaginal flooding of the original scenes, but also autogenic-type relaxation exercises prior to and immediately following the 60 to 70 minutes of exposure. At 6 months follow-up, the gains were maintained.

While this program has not been evaluated in a group study, which would reveal its value across a number of subjects and increase confidence in its specific effects, the series of studies by Keane and his colleagues represent a model for the scientific development of treatment for a previously unexamined disorder. The use of single-case studies reduces the cost of exploring and developing a new approach, and reduces the distress to a large number of patients resulting from possible failures. As we have seen, this approach also permits the refinement of the procedure. Now, however, we must await a larger study before we can confidently report the effective behavioral treatment of PTSD.

SOCIAL PHOBIAS

It recently has been observed that social phobics have been neglected in the research literature (Liebowitz, Gorman, Fyer, & Klein, 1985), but this is not as true of behavior therapists as it is of other researchers. Indeed, there is an extensive history in behavior therapy of experimental investigations of treatment for social phobias, partly because such problems allowed for the evaluation of two clearly competing hypotheses. These competing hypotheses arose from the observation that social phobics not only appear anxous when engaged in social interaction but also appear inept. On the one hand, it was claimed by Wolpe (1958), in particular, that social phobics had the skills to engage in effective behavior, but that these skills were inhibited by anxiety. In this view, the treatment of choice would be some form of anxiety management training (e.g., desensitization or flooding, etc.). Alternatively, it was argued that the reason these people were anxious was because they did not have the skills to function effectively, so they were realistically afraid of making a fool of themselves. Remember that social phobics are afraid of being negatively evaluated. According to this perspective, training in social skills would be the most effective strategy.

We have for a long time sought effective treatment programs for people who have problems in speaking before an audience, and our programmatic research of these problems illustrates the issue of the relative importance of anxiety management versus skills training. In our initial study (Marshall et al., 1976), we attempted to replicate Paul's (1966) seminal work by comparing desensitization with control procedures. Desensitization was significantly more effective than control procedures, and it markedly enhanced the subject's feelings of comfort while speaking. However, unlike Paul's findings, our results indicated that desensitization had less noticeable effects on behavioral signs of anxiety. Re-examination of Paul's study revealed that his subjects were receiving a form of skills training, as an undergraduate requirement, while they were being treated in his program. Subsequently, we compared these two components of treatment with each other and with their combination, and the outcome illustrates the differential effects. Anxiety management (whether desensitization or flooding) eliminated the distressing feelings associated with speaking before an audience, but had little effect on behavioral competencies, while skills training enhanced the overt appearance of the speakers, but left them still feeling anxious; the combination improved all aspects of the subjects' performance and experiences (Hayes & Marshall, 1984; Marshall, Parker, & Hayes, 1982; Marshall, Stoian, & Andrews, 1977). The skills training component is conducted in small groups and includes instructions regarding effective and disadvantageous behaviors displayed while speaking, and this is provided along with modeling of these behaviors by the therapist. Practice then is provided, followed by discussion and feedback which emphasizes the positive features of the performance. Finally, all subjects are verbally reinforced by the therapist for their efforts. We have demonstrated (Marshall et al., 1982) that all of these elements are necessary to maximize treatment benefits.

In a similar experimental study, this time using unassertive and socially anxious penitentiary inmates, we (Marshall, Keltner, & Marshall, 1981) again found independent effects, this time for assertiveness training and applied relaxation. Other studies have secured results consistent with our findings. For example, Trower, Yardley, Bryant, and Shaw (1978) treated socially anxious patients with desensitization and obtained benefits on their measure of social fear, but no changes on objective behavioral indices of social competence. However, in their treatment of social inadequates (i.e., skill deficient patients), social skills training was superior to desensitization.

The most obvious inference from these studies is that therapists should employ skills training with those patients who are deficient in skills, and anxiety management with those who are anxious. Ost, Jerremalm, and Johansson (1981) divided their socially distressed patients into two groups: those who displayed physiological distress at testing, and those whose behavior was disrupted. Half of each group were given social skills training, while the other half received applied relaxation. Those subjects whose treatment matched their presenting problem (i.e., skills training for skills deficient patients or applied relaxation for the anxious patients) profited most.

Finally, an important observation, noted in our most recent report (Hayes & Marshall, 1984), concerns the benefits of our public speaking training program for other social difficulties. We found that effective treatment for public speaking generalized quite dramatically, and far more than we expected, to difficulties encountered in conversations with opposite-gender partners. Given that all social phobics share in common a fear of scrutiny (regardless of the specific stimulus situation that they report to be distressing), this otherwise startling degree of generalization perhaps is understandable. Apparently, if you can learn to handle scrutiny in one situation, this prepares you to deal with other situations in which you may be evaluated. Perhaps there is no other situation in which scrutiny is perceived to be so intense, and in which vulnerabilities are so readily exposed, than in public speaking, and this also may account for the strength of the generalization.

GENERALIZED ANXIETY DISORDER AND PANIC DISORDER

We have grouped these two disorders together here, not because we wish to imply that they are diagnostically undifferentiated (although, as we will see, they are not perhaps as distinct as DSM-III suggests), but rather because the symptoms of both appear to occur independently of external stimuli. The symptoms of both these disorders arise internally, and it is the perception of these internal responses that causes the patients to report themselves as distressed. The behavioral procedures we have considered so far attempt to reduce distress elicited by an external stimulus and the inclusion of these external stimuli in treatment (i.e., exposure to them) appears to be a necessary component in successful therapy.

Treatment procedures for panic disorder (PD) and generalized anxiety disorder (GAD) will have to be different from those problems considered so far, given that no external eliciting stimulus can be identified, and perhaps it is for this reason that behavioral treatments for these disorders are not at all well-developed. Gelder (1969), for instance, declared that behavior therapy cannot be used for anxiety disorders unless situational elicitors of the anxiety can be identified. Consistent with this view, Marks, Boulougouris, and Marset (1971) found that the presence of panics indicated a poor prognosis for treatment by desensitization, which, in this case, attempted to reduce anxiety to external cues. However, there is no reason in advance to suppose that internal signs cannot serve as the stimuli to which the patient must be exposed during treatment.

Very little research has focused on the evaluation of behavioral treatments for PD or GAD, and what has been done has appeared only over the past few years. In fact, the publication of DSM-III provided an impetus for research by clearly delineating diagnostic criteria for these disorders.

The differential diagnosis of PD and GAD appears to be particularly problematic. It generally has been understood that while PD primarily is experienced by the patient as somatically based, GAD is considered to be primarily cognitive (Friedman & Jaffe, 1983). Beck, Laude and Bohnert (1974) have, indeed, discovered specific cognitions to be associated with pervasive anxiety. However, while Barlow and colleagues (Barlow, Cohen et al., 1984) found that panic patients displayed a significantly stronger somatic component to their anxiety prior to treatment, there was no difference between PD and GAD patients on a cognitive scale. Also, it is important to note that the differences on the psychophysiological measures between PD and GAD patients in this study reached acceptable levels of statistical significance on only 2 of the possible 12 measures of EMG arousal, and were absent on all of the heart rate measures. Consistent with the idea that PD and GAD patients are difficult to differentiate, Barlow, Vermilyea et al. (1984) found that some GAD patients also have panics. Observations such as these have led Barlow and Maser (in press) to conclude that panic is simply the upper end of the anxiety continuum, and Hoehn-Saric (1981) found that patients with these two disorders were very much alike in their responses to a battery of psychological tests, differing only slightly in the severity of their somatic symptoms.

On a separate issue, however, these two types of patients may differ in ways that have relevance for their complete treatment. Dealy, Ishiki, Avery, Wilson, and Dunner (1981) found that depression was far more common among those anxiety patients who had panics than it was among those who did not. Similarly, Raskin, Peeke, Dickman, and Pinsker (1982) observed that PD patients reported twice as many depressive episodes as did GAD patients.

These issues of diagnosis are relevant to our conceptualization of PD and GAD, and the nature of treatment is directly implied by the way in which we conceptualize these disorders. These issues are particularly important in considering these two problems because behavioral treatment programs are not at all well developed for either GAD (Barlow, Cohen et al., 1984) or PD (Dittrich, Houts, & Lichstein, 1983).

Given the evidence reviewed so far, GAD appears to involve both a cognitive and a somatic form of anxiety. This conceptualization, of course, implies that treatment should include both a cognitive and a somatic component. In PD, on the other hand, somatic complaints seem to dominate, implying that treatment ought to target these problems. Nevertheless, the evidence to date suggests that PD and GAD will respond to similar kinds of treatment, although the emphasis on somatic or cognitive elements in treatment may differ.

The most thoroughly evaluated behavioral strategies for the treatment of GAD have been biofeedback procedures. In these procedures it is assumed that the basis for the disorder is that one or another psychophysiological system is overaroused and is out of the patient's control. The system supposedly at fault is monitored, and the patient is provided feedback of this aberrant arousal and thereby learns to control responding. Without much in the way of a satisfactory theoretical underpinning to their choice, researchers have monitored and provided subjects experiencing anxiety with feedback from cardiovascular responses (almost always meaning heart rate), electrodermal fluctuations, electroencephalographic changes, or muscular tension (electromyographic indices) from various sites (Rice & Blanchard, 1982). Unfortunately, most of these studies employed mildly anxious students, but there were seven reports where patients were the subjects, although it is not always clear how many of the patients in these latter studies could be classified as GAD.

Nevertheless, it is possible to conclude from these studies that electromyographic (EMG) feedback, usually from the frontalis muscle group, reduces anxiety. While this appears to be generally true, it has not always been found to be the case (LeBoeuf & Lodge, 1980). When biofeedback has been found to be beneficial, the procedure is no more effective than other relaxation procedures, such as progressive relaxation training and transcendental meditation (Rice & Blanchard, 1982). In fact, in one study (Glueck & Stroebel, 1975) meditation was more effective than biofeedback, while in another (Beiman, Israel, & Johnson, 1978) relaxation training was more effective. Similarly, noncontingent biofeedback appears to be just as effective as feedback that accurately reflects responding, and there does not appear to be any consistent relationship between decreases in muscular tension produced by biofeedback training and reductions in anxiety (Rice & Blanchard, 1982). Biofeedback, then, may be of some value in the treatment of GAD, but no more than simpler, less expensive relaxation training procedures.

One behavioral technique would appear to have direct relevance for the treatment of anxiety states produced by internal changes rather than external stimuli. In anxiety management training (AMT: Suinn & Richardson, 1971), the patient first is trained to identify the internal cues to anxiety, and then is required to induce them by mental imagery. Training in muscle relaxation permits the patient during treatment to acquire control over the induced anxiety by relaxing and by employing positive mental images. Jannoun, Oppenheimer, and Gelder (1982) treated 26 anxious outpatients with AMT in three different groups which differed in terms of the time they waited before treatment commenced. These patients were described as complaining of moderate to severe generalized anxiety and panic attacks. All groups showed improvements with treatment on an assessor's ratings and on the patients' self-reports. Although a daily record of anxiety levels was kept, changes on this unfortunately were not reported. While this study leaves much to be desired, particularly in terms of outcome measures, it does suggest the possible value of this program for both PD and GAD patients.

In an effort to cover all bases, a strategy was developed by Barlow, Cohen et al. (1984) which has some merits. This program combines EMG biofeedback with relaxation training and a cognitive treatment component. The cognitive component integrates stress inoculation (Meichenbaum & Turk, 1973) with both cognitive restructuring (Beck & Emery, 1979) and training in coping self-statements (Meichenbaum, 1977). In Barlow, Cohen et al.'s study (1984), both PD and GAD patients were included and treatment outcome was compared with a waiting-list control group. Treated patients improved significantly more than controls on clinical ratings, psychophysiological measures, daily self-monitored levels of anxiety and panic, and on questionnaires that evaluated anxiety. Both groups of patients responded equally well to treatment despite some pretreatment differences, and showed continued gains during follow-up (3 months to 1 year).

This study, perhaps more than any other, revealed the potential of a well-designed comprehensive behavioral treatment program for these disorders. The changes induced were extensive and were maintained at follow-up. Questions raised by Barlow et al.'s report concern the effective components of this comprehensive package and the differential relevance of the components for PD and GAD patients. Nevertheless, these researchers clearly are leading the way in this area, and we await with optimism future reports from their center.

The treatment programs discussed so far in this section have focused on GAD patients, although Barlow et al. (1984) did include PD patients. In a program quite similar to the one just described, Waddell, Barlow, and O'Brien (1984) treated three PD patients within a multiple baseline design. Treatment combined Meichenbaum's (1977) self-statement therapy and Beck et al.'s (1974) cognitive therapy (see Chapter 19 for a description of these techniques), with attentional training and relaxation training. Attentional training, which might more accurately have been called "distraction training," taught patients to focus their attention on particular tasks rather than on the somatic signs of anxiety. Each of the patients showed reductions in both the frequency and duration of panics when treatment was introduced, but not before. Futhermore, general anxiety functioned independently of changes in the panics, suggesting quite specific treatment effects. While these results are encouraging, we await a more extensive appraisal.

Finally, some authors (e.g., Hibbert, 1984; Kerr, Dalton, & Gliebe, 1937; Lum, 1981) have suggested a causal link between panics and hyperventilation. Following this suggestion, Clark, Salkovskis, and Chalkley (1985) devised a training program to teach patients with panics to control their breathing. The patient is asked to hyperventilate until mild panic symptoms occur, whereupon they are instructed to breath diaphragmatically and to reduce their rate of breathing. These authors found dramatic decreases in panic frequency and self-reported fear during a behavioral test after only 2 weeks of treatment, and these gains were enhanced at 6-months and 2-years follow-up assessments. Futhermore, these treatment benefits occured in the absence of exposure to fear-evoking situations. Rapee (1985) confirmed these observations with a similar patient. While these reports involve only four patients, they encourage the view that training to control breathing may be a valuable addition to the more comprehensive programs offered by Barlow and his colleagues.

AGORAPHOBIA

Agoraphobia has long been considered the most debilitating of the phobias and, as such, has received sustained attention on the part of behavior therapists, who have tried to bring the knowledge gained from the successful treatment of simple or circumscribed phobias to bear on this complex disorder. This complexity stems, in part, from the clinical picture which clearly presents a phobic avoidance disorder, yet also shares features in common with mood disorders, such as anxiety states and, in a significant proportion of patients, dysphoria or depression (Thorpe & Burns, 1983).

Although the term *agoraphobia* typically is used to describe fears of going out into public places, descriptive studies that have examined associated psychopathology demonstrate that these patients present with a wide range of clinical features. Fisher and Wilson (1985) report that agoraphobics were more anxious (global and phobic anxiety, as well as more somatic anxiety symptoms), more depressed, less assertive, and felt more powerless and helpless than nonagoraphobics. The two groups did not differ in their attention to internal cues, but the agoraphobics mislabeled cues to a greater extent, tending to attribute fear to internal rather than external causes.

Vermilyea, Boice, and Barlow (1984) suggested that different patterns of responding prior to treatment might indicate a greater or lesser propensity to respond to exposure-based treatment. They categorized their subjects as high versus normal heart rate responders in a pretreatment assessment, and as treatment responders or nonresponders. High heart rate responders were significantly more likely to be treatment responders. Although these results stand in contrast to other studies that found heart rate to be an unreliable index of treatment outcome with phobics (Arena, Blanchard, Andrasik, Cotch, & Myers, 1983; Mathews, Gelder, & Johnston, 1981), the notion of subgroup analysis deserves consideration as an adjunct to the now perfunctory aggregate analyses.

This focus on refining existent methodologies also can be seen when we consider the treatment realm, where a consensus has developed pointing to in vivo exposure as an essential element in the effective treatment of agoraphobia (Barlow & Wolfe, 1981; Emmelkamp, 1982; Mathews et al., 1981). Consequently, much of the current effort in the literature is aimed at evaluating package-based permutations incorporating exposure and novel elements (e.g., exposure and cognitive restructuring, couples treatment utilizing exposure). Historically, the earliest behavioral treatments for agoraphobia matched those used in the treatment of specific phobias, namely, systematic desensitization and graded practice (Thorpe & Burns, 1983). Chambless and Goldstein (1981), however, point out that benefits derived from desensitization usually accrue during homework assignments which, of course, require real-life exposure. Subsequent research has borne out this observation by demonstrating the effectiveness of in vivo exposure techniques (Emmelkamp & Wessels, 1975; Marks, Boulougouris, & Marset, 1971; Sherman, 1972).

While behavioral treatment of phobic disorders stresses the importance of confronting the phobic situation in real life, some authors have suggested that the core conditioned stimuli in agoraphobia are not represented by any particular situation, so much as they are in the fear the client has of panicking in that situation (Chambless & Goldstein, 1982; Goldstein & Chambless, 1978). Whatever the target for treatment, prolonged exposure in vivo aims at providing clients with a lengthy enough exposure to the fear eliciting stimulus to allow them to experience a reduction of anxiety in the situation. The therapist's tasks are to aid in the selection of items for the exposure trials which will be sufficiently broad for the extinction to generalize to all untreated situations, as well as to help the client maintain exposure to the phobic stimuli in each of the situations (O'Brien & Barlow, 1984). Graduated exposure in vivo is useful with clients who cannot tolerate the high levels of anxiety that are a feature of prolonged exposure treatment. In this case, instructions to clients emphasize that they are to enter the feared situation and remain in it until they find they are becoming overly anxious, at which point they are to withdraw. The difference in rationales behind these two approaches is based on the function of avoidance behavior. In prolonged exposure, avoidance or escape is discouraged so that anxiety can be fully experienced and subsequently reduced, so that the patient can learn to associate nonanxious responses with the situation. Graduated exposure, on the other hand, is structured to prevent clients from experiencing high levels of anxiety, preferring instead that relearning occur through repeated low fear encounters with the phobic stimuli (Boudewyns & Shipley, 1983; O'Brien & Barlow, 1984).

While experts at a recent conference on anxiety-based disorders concluded that approximately 60% to 75% of agoraphobics benefit from exposure treatment (Barlow & Wolfe, 1981), the issue of failures, relapses, and limited improvements still is significant, because dropout or refusal rates associated with exposure treatment are approximately 12%. Even within the 60% to 70% responder group, some clients may not improve remarkably. For example, Marks (1971) reports that only 3 of 65 clients in his study were completely symptom-free at follow-up, while McPherson, Brougham, and McLaren (1980) offer a more optimistic figure of 18% symptom-free at follow-up. What seems to happen is that exposure confers immediate benefits, but a sizeable number of patients who show these benefits (50%, according to Munby & Johnson, 1980) relapse later on. Barlow and Beck (1984), however, consider that these data indicate the disadvantages associated with the brief intense form of exposure usually employed in outcome trials. This is particularly true in the case of dropouts, which are far higher in the intensive form (Emmelkamp & Ultee, 1974; Emmelkamp & Wessels, 1975), whereas in a self-controlled home-practice version (Jannoun, Munby, Catalan, & Gelder, 1980; Mathews, Teasdale, Munby, Johnston, & Shaw, 1977), where treatment is partner-assisted and extended over a longer time frame, dropouts and relapses are rarer. Also, the dramatic improvements that occur with brief intensive exposure treatment may seriously disrupt other aspects of the patient's functioning and interpersonal relations (Hafner, 1977, 1984; Kleiner & Marshall, 1985).

Another possible explanation for the poorer maintenance of gains following brief intensive exposure is that treatment typically is therapist-assisted, thus heightening the potential for relapse once the therapist is withdrawn (Mathews et al., 1977). When intensive treatment is offered in a group context, where members remained supportive after treatment, relapses were reduced (Hand, Lamontagne, & Marks, 1974). This finding corresponds to data reported by Sinnott, Jones, Scott-Fordham, and Woodward (1981), who showed that agoraphobics from the same neighborhood treated in groups did far better than those from different districts. Presumably, those from the same area socialized and supported each other during and after treatment far more than did those in separate neighborhoods.

The logical extension of these types of results, demonstrating the value of affiliative sources of support during exposure treatment, is the inclusion of spouses in the treatment regime. An added advantage is that such a strategy provides an opportunity for addressing interpersonal and marital issues, which some authors suggest are important in understanding the etiology and maintenance of treatment gains in agoraphobia (Hafner & Ross, 1983; Kleiner & Marshall, 1985). One of the more complete investigations addressing this question was conducted by Barlow, O'Brien, and Last (1984), who compared two groups: one in which husbands attended all sessions and participated fully in treatment, and one in which husbands were thanked for their willingness to participate but were told it was not necessary. Treatment consisted of self-initiated, graduated-exposure combined with instruction on panic management procedures, and cognitive techniques designed to prevent avoidance. Their findings indicated that including husbands produced substantial clinical advantages, with 12 out of the 14 clients in that group responding to the treatment as well as showing gains in social, work, and family functioning. Clients in the nonspouse treatment group did not do as well, and took longer to achieve benefits in social and occupational functioning. These results match those of Mathews et al. (1977), with both studies eschewing therapist-assisted in vivo exposure and finding that spouse inclusion is associated with lower attrition rates in treatment.

In a study we have recently completed (Kleiner & Marshall, 1986), we found benefits for adding to group in vivo exposure a treatment component that taught interpersonal problem-solving skills, in conjunction with assertiveness training. While this additional component did not produce any greater benefits than exposure alone immediately after treatment was terminated, at 6-months follow-up patients in the combined group displayed further improvements, while those in exposure alone did not. These results, along with those of Barlow, O'Brien, and Last (1984), suggest that while exposure may be necessary in the behavioral treatment of agoraphobia, it is not sufficient to produce maximal benefits.

The main area of concern that needs to be further developed with this disorder is the explication of reasons for treatment failures or incomplete success (O'Brien &

Barlow, 1984). Investigations of a longitudinal nature are needed that can follow clients past the termination of treatment into periods where they would be at risk for relapse. Specifications of the types of psychosocial stressors that were operating at the time of relapse, or, conversely, the social supports clients were able to utilize to prevent a relapse, would be informative. Subsequent strategies derived from these data could be incorporated into a maintenance or relapse prevention program, thereby increasing the efficiency of an already powerful intervention. In the absence of such data, Jansson, Jerremalam, and Ost (1984) have creatively designed a maintenance program designed to deal with the persistent observation of relapses. After their 32 agoraphobics completed 11 sessions of in vivo exposure treatment combined with applied relaxation training, they entered into a contract with the therapist to follow a rigorous maintenance program. This program involved a commitment from the patients' spouse (or, if unmarried, some other significant person) to ensure continued in vivo practice. High risk situations which might cause set-backs were identified and strategies for dealing with these were planned. Each patient also was required to provide the therapist with a monthly report detailing progress. Results at 6-months follow-up indicated that gains from initial treatment had been maintained, suggesting that the program was effective.

OBSESSIVE–COMPULSIVE DISORDER

While many reviews of behavioral treatments for obsessive–compulsive disorder (OCD: Rachman, 1982; Turner & Michelson, 1984) commence optimistically, pointing out the advances recorded over the past 10 years in dealing with this problem, most reviewers conclude by stressing the gaps that remain in our knowledge of this debilitating disorder. Perhaps this is a format inherent in the writing of reviews, yet the fact remains that at present there exists a viable treatment program (exposure combined with response prevention) for a disorder whose relation to other clinical syndromes (such as anxiety or depression) and whose natural course and prevelance are only poorly understood (Turner & Michelson, 1984).

Early behavioral forms of treatment were influenced by the similarity between phobias and certain types of obsessive–compulsive disorders (Beech & Vaughan, 1978). Much of the work explicating these processes was carried out by Rachman and his colleagues (e.g., Hodgson & Rachman, 1972; Roper, Rachman, & Hodgson, 1973). With respect to compulsive cleaners, they found that contamination led to an increase in subjective discomfort or anxiety, whereas the completion of the ritual produced the opposite effect. In this way, ritual performance was reinforced through anxiety reduction. Compulsive checkers tended to follow this pattern as well; however, there were some instances in which the completion of the checking ritual was followed by no change in subjective discomfort or even an increase in anxiety. It was thought that these general observations regarding the anxiety features of OCD patients would make them amenable to treatment with the fear-reducing techniques that were already proving effective with phobic anxiety. Results of cases treated with systematic desensitization were unimpressive, however, rarely exceeding a response rate of 50% in uncontrolled case reports (Emmelkamp, 1982; Meyer, Levy, & Schnurer, 1974). Commenting on these early efforts, Turner and Michelson (1984) suggest that the relatively poor efficacy of desensitization may have been due to the attenuated exposure durations afforded by this method. The imaginal presentation of contamination and checking scenarios also was thought to be weaker than the confrontation of these scenes in vivo, and, finally, the value of relaxation with patients who may be significantly depressed was called into question.

The utility of prolonged exposure in vivo, coupled with the prevention of ritual performance, as a treatment for OCD first was suggested in a series of uncontrolled reports by Meyer and his colleagues (Meyer, 1966; Meyer & Levy, 1970; Meyer et al., 1974). Meyer et al. (1974) offer the following description of their method used in the treatment of a school teacher in her mid-30s who had a 3-year history of checking behavior and fear of contamination by dust and dirt.

> The treatment itself involved continual supervision during the patient's waking hours by nurses who were instructed to prevent the patient from carrying out any rituals . . . as soon as the total elimination of rituals under supervision was achieved, the therapist increased the stress where appropriate by confronting the patient with situations which normally elicited rituals. (pp. 246–247)

Furthermore,

> restriction of rituals was attempted in the usual way. She was given a single room and made responsible for keeping it clean but was only allowed to spend a few minutes a day to do so. She was then gradually exposed to dust, made to shake a duster out her window and eventually in her room. (p. 254)

A careful reading of this description will reveal the essential components of the current behavioral treatment for OCD, namely, exposure in vivo accompanied by response prevention. A number of studies have performed component analyses of these and other treatment methods, in an effort to isolate the most effective combination. Rachman and Hodgson (1980) summarize their results as follows

> flooding is more effective than relaxation control treatment or aversion relief, equally effective as participant modelling, and probably superior to thought stopping. It is possible, however, that flooding treatment evokes more anxiety than modelling . . . and that it is less effective in reducing the interfering quality of obsessional disorder. (p. 341)

Response prevention compliments flooding procedures by allowing for a two-pronged attack on the compulsive rituals and their putative anxiety-reducing function. Exposing the patient to the contaminated stimuli leads to extinction of the associated anxiety, while preventing the rituals from occurring extinguishes the supposed avoidance response (Beech & Vaughan, 1978; Emmelkamp, 1982).

A study by Foa, Steketee, Grayson, Turner, and Latimer (1984) addresses this issue by comparing the effects of exposure in vivo alone, response prevention alone, and their combination, in a sample of 32 OCD patients. They found that all three interventions produced benefits, but that the combined treatment did best overall. There also was some evidence of treatment specificity, in that exposure alone reduced anxiety to contamination, while response prevention reduced ritual performance. Another study by this group (Foa, Steketee, & Grayson, 1985) examined the relative efficacy of imaginal and in vivo exposure with a group of compulsive checkers. In this study, exposure in vivo was as effective as imaginal exposure, prompting the authors to wonder whether the field has not prematurely abandoned the use of imaginal exposure with these patients. The important point here seems to be that they did not include a group that received exposure plus response prevention. While the response to their procedures was significant and lasting, it was not as great as with procedures that combined exposure with response prevention (Foa & Goldstein, 1978; Marks, Hodgson, & Rachman, 1975). In a direct comparison, it was found that in vivo exposure alone did not yield results as great as the combined treatment (Foa et al., 1984).

To date, a number of investigators have examined the efficacy of self-controlled, as opposed to therapist-controlled, exposure. The advantage of the former is that it can be performed at home along with instructions to refrain from engaging in rituals. Results from these studies were little different from results for treatment delivered in the usual way (Emmelkamp & Kraanen, 1977; Hoogduin & Hoogduin, 1984), suggesting at least, that the self-control procedure produces considerable savings in the therapist's time.

While much of the preceding discussion has focused on patients who present with both compulsive rituals and obsessional thinking, a small proportion of cases (approximately 15%) are characterized by disturbing cognitions alone, in the absence of rituals. In some instances, therapists have assumed that obsessions function as phobic stimuli. Desensitization has been effective in treating obsessional patients (Agras et al., 1971), and so has exposure, where the patients have been required to repeatedly entertain the troublesome thoughts for prolonged periods (Broadhurst, 1976; Emmelkamp & Giesselbach, 1981). On the other hand, Emmelkamp and Kwee (1977) found less favorable results with exposure. Other approaches simply have tried to block the obsessions. Thought stopping is such a procedure and typically involves a deliberate evocation of the obsessions followed by the therapist shouting "Stop." Over repeated trials the therapist gradually reduces the loudness of his or her command, and eventually the patient commences self-instructions to stop, which are likewise gradually faded to subvocal commands. Solyom, Garza-Perez, Ledwidge, and Solyom (1972) found some benefits for this procedure with obsessional patients, but others have had difficulty in replicating these benefits (Gullick & Blanchard, 1973; Stern, 1978; Stern, Lipsedge, & Marks, 1975). A more recent report by Turner, Holzman, and Jacob (1983) obtained positive results with thought stopping. The delivery of a more specifically aversive stimulus upon the occurrence of an obsession has been effective in a number of studies (Kenny, Mowbray, & Lalani, 1978; Kenny, Solyom, & Solyom, 1973; Mahoney, 1971), but this procedure seems to have lost favor in recent years.

Vogel, Peterson, and Broverman (1982) tested a procedure they derived from Rachman's (1976) habituation technique. In three uncontrolled cases they reported positive oucome's. They enlisted a friend to spend a good deal of time with the patient, to help administer the treatment. In their version, when the patient would seem distracted, the friend would ask him/her whether he/she was thinking about the obsession. If the answer was no, the patient was reinforced for mastery, and if the answer was yes, the patient was encouraged, nonjudgmentally, to describe aloud the content of his/her thoughts. Because the thoughts are aversive, this procedure is meant to punish them.

Given the degree of attention that OCD has received from behaviorally oriented clinicians and researchers, what can we say about the benefits that accrue from conceptualizing and treating the disorder according to this model? Emmelkamp (1982) summarizes the findings of those studies in which a long-term follow-up has been included, and concludes that the response rate of patients with OCD to behavioral treatment is 70%. Furthermore, these gains are maintained up to 4.5 years later. Our ability to comment on the long-term response among those patients whose problems are limited to obsessions is hampered by the absence of adequate follow-up assessments. Emmelkamp (1982) does report, however, that of 17 obsessional patients who were treated in his studies (of which 14 could be contacted up to 4 years later), most of the improvement occurred during the pre- to posttreatment interval with little additional change occuring during the follow-up period.

Any careful analysis of outcome needs to address itself to the question of treatment failures, and a number of writers have examined this issue with respect to both OCD (Foa, Steketee, Grayson, & Doppelt, 1983) and obsessions (Rachman, 1983). With respect to treatment of OCD by in vivo exposure and response prevention, Foa, Grayson, Steketee, Doppelt, Turner, and Latimer (1983) identified a number of variables that were predictive of outcome at posttreatment and follow-up. Patients who did best posttreatment tended to have lower levels of depression and anxiety going into treatment, and less reactivity to the types of disturbing material used in treatment. These variables also were found to interact with one another, as depressed individuals tended to respond with heightened reactivity during exposure and thus show a poorer outcome, leading the authors to wonder whether high reactivity impedes effective "emotional processing." An additional predictor of importance was habituation of reported anxiety to feared stimuli both within and between sessions. Maintenance of gains achieved in treatment was significantly related to posttreatment status and age at symptom onset, with patients who were younger at onset doing better than those who were older.

CONCLUDING REMARKS

Our review of effective treatments has revealed the need for specificity in applying behavioral methods to the amelioration of the various anxiety disorders. Each disorder seems to have sufficiently unique characteristics to require its own type of behavioral treatment or its own particular combination of techniques. However, there are some common features across the anxiety disorders that require attention. In the first place, depression seems to go hand-in-hand with most of these disorders, and yet very little is known about the precise relationship between anxiety and depression. We do not know whether depression is etiologically significant or simply a secondary response to a distressful state. What we do know, however, is that depression is relevant to the processes of treatment for anxiety and may seriously interfere with effective outcome. More research is sorely needed on this issue.

It also is clear that a common need across all the anxiety disorders is a better understanding of pretreatment differences among patients, particularly in respect to whether or not their anxiety or fear primarily is somatic or cognitive in nature. Matching treatment procedures to the type of anxiety responses displayed by the patients may very well enhance the effectiveness of intervention approaches (Lang, 1977). Similarly, long-term follow-up analyses of treated patients will help reveal the reasons for relapses, which can then inform modifications or additions to treatment programs. Relapse prevention programs have been developed for other problems and these have been found to be very effective (Marlatt & Gordon, 1980).

Exposure-based treatment appears to be a necessary element in the effective modification of all the anxiety disorders. This may be done by directly confronting the most fearful situation or by gradually approaching it (desensitization or graduated practice), or in brief intense sessions or extended over longer periods, or with a modeling component or not , by a therapist or by the patient (assisted by their spouse or not), in groups or individually, or where exposure is accompanied or not by some counter-anxiety response (e.g., relaxation). Which variation of in vivo exposure is chosen seems to depend both on the specifics of the problem and on the individual patient, as well as on the therapist's personal preferences. Variations on these themes seem to improve treatment effectiveness for some patients. We believe the evidence indicates that extended, graduated exposure, done in cohesive groups with the spouse present, and accompanied by extended home practice (again with the spouse), is most likely to be effective across most patients with agoraphobia. In the case of simple phobias, a straightforward exposure procedure alone should be sufficient, although adding training in coping behavior or coping thoughts can enhance effectiveness. The same probably is true for posttraumatic stress disorders, but there is evidence to indicate that additional problems are common with these patients. For social phobics, skills training appears to be a crucial element in effective therapy, although exposure also is necessary as part of this training. Agoraphobics appear to require additional help, particularly with interpersonal problems, while for obsessive–compulsive disorders, escape responses must be prevented during direct encounters with the eliciting stimuli.

In the case of simple phobias, social

phobias, and compulsive rituals, external events appear to elicit the problem responses and these ought to be the stimuli present during exposure treatment, although in each of these problems, anticipatory thoughts or images also may be usefully included in treatment. Posttraumatic stress disorder patients are upset by thoughts or nightmares that recall the original traumatic experience, and the power of these thoughts to elicit anxiety must be extinguished. Similarly, with obsessive patients, their distressing thoughts must be evoked during treatment if they are to be rendered inert, while for compulsive patients, both external stimuli and self-generated ruminations must be included in exposure therapy. Agoraphobics are distressed both by various situations that make them fearful and by the internal cues to anxiety, so that both these sets of events must be confronted in treatment. Finally, for both generalized anxiety and panic disorders, it is the internal signs of anxiety that must be produced in treatment if intervention is to be successful, although learning to combat these by engaging in counter-anxiety responses (e.g., relaxation) seems to be crucial. This latter point is perhaps not surprising because extinction of any response by exposure-based procedures is almost certainly not a passive process of losing an anxiety response, but rather the active acquisition of an alternative incompatible response (Mackintosh, 1974).

We believe the evidence indicates that behavioral approaches have a lot to offer in the treatment of anxiety disorders, and, indeed, they seem to us to be clearly the treatments of choice, at least with the simple phobias. We also believe that the continued development of behavioral interventions for the other disorders will lead to even better results than we have seen thus far. This is not to deny the utility of other approaches which clearly have value for some patients, nor do we deny the wisdom of combining behavioral treatment with cognitive therapy or pharmacotherapy. We do, however, believe that the evidence is very encouraging concerning the value of behavior therapy, and we would regret any loss of its unique status in the treatment of anxiety disorders.

REFERENCES

Agras, W. S., Leitenberg, H., Barlow, D. H., Curtis, N., Edwards, J., & Wright, D. (1971). Relaxation in systematic desensitization. *Archives of General Psychiatry, 25*, 511–514.

American Psychiatric Association (1980). *Diagnostic and statistical manual of mental disorders* (3rd ed.). Washington, DC: Author.

Arena, J. G., Blanchard, E. B., Andrasik, F., Cotch, P. A., & Myers, P. E. (1983). Reliability of psychophysiological assessment. *Behavior Research and Therapy, 21*, 447–460.

Bandura, A. (1969). *Principles of behavior modification*. New York: Holt, Rinehart and Winston.

Bandura, A. (1971). Vicarious- and self-reinforcement processes. In R. Glaser (Ed.), *The nature of reinforcement* (pp. 228–278). New York: Academic Press.

Bandura, A. (1977). *Social learning theory*. Englewood Cliffs, NJ: Prentice-Hall.

Bandura, A., Adams, N. E., & Beyer J. (1977). Cognitive processes mediating behavioral change. *Journal of Personality and Social Psychology, 35*, 125–139.

Barlow, D. H., & Beck, J. G. (1984). Psychosocial treatment of anxiety disorders: Current status, future directions. In J. B. W. Williams & R. L. Spitzer (Eds.), *Psychotherapy research: Where are we and where should we go?* (pp. 29–61). New York: Guilford Press.

Barlow, D. H., Cohen, A. S., Waddell, M. T., Vermilyea, B. B., Klosko, J. S., Blanchard, E. B., & Di Nardo, P. A. (1984). Panic and generalized anxiety disorders: Nature and treatment. *Behavior Therapy, 15*, 431–449.

Barlow, D. H., & Maser, J. D. (in press). Psychopathology in anxiety disorders: A report on an NIMH workshop. *Journal of Behavioral Assessment*.

Barlow, D. H., O'Brien, G. T., & Last, C. G. (1984). Couples treatment of agoraphobia. *Behavior Therapy, 15*, 41–50.

Barlow, D. H., Vermilyea, J. A., Blanchard, E. B., Vermilyea, B. B., Di Nardo, P. A., & Cerny, J. A. (1984). *The phenomenology of panic*. Unpublished manuscript, State University of New York, Albany.

Barlow, D. H., & Wolfe, B. E. (1981). Behavioral approaches to anxiety disorders: A report on the NIMH-SUNY Albany Research Conference. *Journal of Consulting and Clinical Psychology, 49*, 448–454.

Beck, A. T., & Emery, G. (1979). *Cognitive therapy of anxiety and phobic disorders*. Philadelphia: Center for Cognitive Therapy.

Beck, A. T., Laude, R., & Bohnert, M. (1974). Ideational components of anxiety neurosis. *Archives of General Psychiatry, 31*, 319–325.

Beech, H. R., & Vaughan, M. (1978). *Behavioral treatment of obsessional states*. New York: John Wiley & Sons.

Beiman, I., Israel, E., & Johnson, S. A. (1978). During training and posttraining effects of live and taped extended progressive relaxation, self-relaxation and electromyogram biofeedback. *Journal of Consulting and Clinical Psychology, 46*, 314–321.

Birkhimer, L. J., DeVane, C. L., & Muntz, C. E. (1985). Post-traumatic stress disorders: Characteristics and pharmacological response in the veteran population. *Comparative Psychiatry, 26*, 304–310.

Black, J. L., & Keane, T. M. (1982). Implosive therapy in the treatment of combat related fears in World War II veterans. *Journal of Behavior Therapy and Experimental Psychiatry, 13*, 163–165.

Blanchard, E. B., Kolb, L. C., Pallmeyer, T. P., & Gerardi, R. J. (1982). A psychophysiological study of posttraumatic stress disorder in Vietnam veterans. *Psychiatric Quarterly, 54*, 220–229.

Borkovec, T. D., & O'Brien, G. T. (1976). Methodological and target behavior issues in analogue therapy outcome research. In M. Hersen, R. M. Eisler & P. M. Miller (Eds.), *Progress in behavior modification* (Vol. 3, pp. 133–172). New York: Academic Press.

Boudewyns, P. A., & Shipley, R. H. (1983). *Flooding and implosive therapy: Direct therapeutic exposure in clinical practice*. New York: Plenum Press.

Bourque, P., & Ladouceur, R. (1980). An investigation of various performance-based treatments with acrophobics. *Behavior Research and Therapy, 18*, 161–170.

Broadhurst, A. (1976). It's never too late to learn: An application of conditioned inhibition to obsessional ruminations in an elderly patient. In H. J. Eysenck (Ed.), *Case histories in behavior therapy*. London: Routledge & Kegan Paul.

Cautela, J. R. (1970). Covert reinforcement. *Behavior Therapy, 1*, 33–50.

Chambless, D. L., & Goldstein, A. J. (1981). Clinical treatment of agoraphobia. In M. Mavissakalian & D. H. Barlow (Eds.), *Phobia: Psychological and pharmacological treatment* (pp. 103–144). New York: Guilford Press.

Chambless, D. L., & Goldstein, A. J. (1982). *Agoraphobia: Multiple perspectives on theory and treatment*. New York: John Wiley & Sons.

Clark, D. M., Salkovskis, P. M., & Chalkley, A. J. (1985). Respiratory control as a treatment for panic attacks. *Journal of Behavior Therapy and Experimental Psychiatry, 16*, 23–30.

Cotler, S. B. (1970). Sex differences and generalization of anxiety reduction with automated desensitization and minimal therapist interaction. *Behavior Research and Therapy, 8*, 273–285.

Dealy, R. S., Ishiki, D. M., Avery, D. H., Wilson, L. G., & Dunner, D. C. (1981). Secondary depression in anxiety disorders. *Comprehensive Psychiatry, 22*, 612–618.

Dittrich, J., Houts, A. C., & Lichstein, K. L. (1983). Panic disorder: Assessment and treatment. *Clinical Psychology Review, 3*, 215–225.

Emmelkamp, P. M. G. (1982). *Phobic and obsessive-compulsive disorders: Theory, research, and practice*. New York: Plenum Press.

Emmelkamp, P. M. G., & Giesselback, P. (1981). Treatment of obsessions: Relevant versus irrelevant exposure. *Behavioural Psychotherapy, 9*, 322–329.

Emmelkamp, P. M. G., & Kraanen, J. (1977). Therapist-controlled exposure in vivo vs. self-controlled exposure in vivo: A comparison with obsessive-compulsive patients. *Behaviour Research and Therapy, 15*, 491–496.

Emmelkamp, P. M. G., & Kwee, K. G (1977). Obsessional ruminations: A comparison between thought-stopping and prolonged exposure in imagination. *Behaviour Research and Therapy, 15*, 441–444.

Emmelkamp, P. M. G., & Ultee, K. A. (1974). A comparison of successive approximation and self-observation in the treatment of agoraphobia. *Behavior Therapy, 5*, 605–613.

Emmelkamp, P. M. G., & Wessels, H. (1975). Flooding in imagination vs. flooding in vivo: A comparison with agoraphobics. *Behaviour Research and Therapy, 13*, 7–16.

Eysenck, H. J. (1968). A theory of the incubation of anxiety/fear responses. *Behaviour Research and Therapy, 6*, 390–422.

Fairbank, J. A., Gross, R. T., & Keane, T. M. (1983). Treatment of posttraumatic stress disorder: Evaluating outcome with a behavioral code. *Behavior Modification, 7*, 557–568.

Fisher, L. M., & Wilson, G. T. (1985). A study of the psychology of agoraphobia. *Behaviour Research and Therapy, 23*, 97–107.

Foa, E. B., & Goldstein, A. (1978). Continuous exposure and complete response prevention in the treatment of obsessive-compulsive neurosis. *Behavior Therapy, 9*, 821–829.

Foa, E. B., Grayson, J. B., Steketee, G. S., Doppelt, H. G., Turner, R. M., & Latimer, P. R. (1983). Success and failure in the behavioral treatment of obsessive-compulsives. *Journal of Consulting and Clinical Psychology, 51*, 287–297.

Foa, E. B., Steketee, G., & Grayson, J. B. (1985). Imaginal and in vivo exposure: A comparison with obsessive-compulsive checkers. *Behavior Therapy, 16*, 292–302.

Foa, E. B., Steketee, G., Grayson, J. B., & Doppelt, H. G. (1983). Treatment of obsessive-compulsives: When do we fail? In E. B. Foa & P. M. G. Emmelkamp (Eds.), *Failures in behavior therapy* (pp. 10–34). New York: John Wiley & Sons.

Foa, E. B., Steketee, G., Grayson; J. B., Turner, R. M., & Latimer, P. R. (1984). Deliberate exposure and blocking of obsessive compulsive rituals: Immediate and long-term effects. *Behavior Therapy, 15*, 450–472.

Foy, D. W., Sipprelle, R. C., Rueger, D. B., & Carroll, E. M. (1984). Etiology of posttraumatic stress disorder in Vietnam veterans: Analysis of premilitary, military, and combat exposure influences. *Journal of Consulting and Clinical Psychology, 52*, 79–87.

Friedman, D., & Jaffe, A. (1983). Problems in family practice: Anxiety disorders. *The Journal of Family Practice, 16*, 145–152.

Gauthier, J., & Marshall, W. L. (1977). The determination of optimal exposure to phobic stimuli in flooding therapy. *Behaviour Research and Therapy, 15*, 403–410.

Gelder, M. (1969). Behavior therapy for anxiety states. *British Medical Journal, 1*, 691–694.

Glueck, B. C., & Stroebel, C. E. (1975). Biofeedback and meditation in the treatment of psychiatric illnesses. *Comprehensive Psychiatry, 16*, 303–321.

Goldstein, A. J., & Chambless, D. L. (1978). A reanalysis of agoraphobia. *Behavior Therapy, 9*, 47–59.

Green, B. L., Lindy, J. D., & Grace, M. C. (1985). Posttraumatic stress disorder: Toward DSM-IV. *Journal of Nervous and Mental Disease, 173*, 406–411.

Guidry, L. S., & Randolph, D. L. (1974). Covert reinforcement in the treatment of test anxiety. *Journal of Counseling, 21*, 260–264.

Gullick, E. L., & Blanchard, E. B. (1973). The use of psychotherapy and behavior therapy in the treatment of an obsessional disorder: An experimental case study. *Journal of Nervous and Mental Disease, 156*, 427–431.

Hafner, R. J. (1977). The husbands of agoraphobic women: Assortative mating or pathogenic interaction? *British Journal of Psychiatry, 130*, 233–239.

Hafner, R. J. (1984). Predicting the effects on husbands of behavior therapy for wives' agoraphobia. *Behaviour Research and Therapy, 22*, 217–226.

Hafner, R. J., & Ross, M. W. (1983). Predicting outcome of behaviour therapy for agoraphobia. *Behaviour Research and Therapy, 21*, 375–382.

Hand, I., Lamontagne, V., & Marks, T. M. (1974). Group exposure (flooding) in vivo for agoraphobics. *British Journal of Psychiatry, 724*, 588–602.

Hayes, B., & Marshall, W. L. (1984). Generalization of treatment effects in training public speakers. *Behaviour Research and Therapy, 22*, 519–533.

Hayes, S. L., Hussain, R. A., Turner, A. E., Anderson, N. B., & Grubb, T. D. (1983). The effect of coping statements on progress through a desensitization hierarchy. *Journal of Behavior Therapy and Experimental Psychiatry, 14*, 117–129.

Hersen, M., & Barlow, D. H. (1976). *Single case experimental designs: Strategies for studying behavior change*. New York: Pergamon Press.

Hibbert, G. A. (1984). Hyperventilation as a cause of panic attacks. *British Medical Journal, 288*, 263–264.

Hodgson, R. J., & Rachman, S. (1972). The effects of contamination and washing in obsessional patients. *Behaviour Research and Therapy, 10*, 111–117.

Hoehn-Saric, R. (1981). Characteristics of chronic anxiety patients. In D. F. Klein & J. Rabkin (Eds.), *Anxiety: New research and changing concepts* (pp. 399–409). New York: Raven Press.

Hoogduin, G. A. C., & Hoogduin, W. A. (1984). The out-patient treatment of patients with obsessional-compulsive disorder. *Behaviour Research and Therapy, 22*, 455–459.

Jacobson, E. (1938). *Progressive relaxation*. Chicago: University of Chicago Press.

James, J. E. (1985). Desenitization treatment of agoraphobia. *British Journal of Clinical Psychology, 24*, 133–134.

Jannoun, L., Munby, M., Catalan, J., & Gelder, M. (1980). A home-based treatment program for agoraphobics: Replication and controlled evaluation. *Behavior Therapy, 11*, 294–305.

Jannoun, L., Oppeinheimer, C., & Gelder, M. (1982). A self-help treatment program for anxiety state patients. *Behavior Therapy, 13*, 103–111.

Jansson, L., Jerremalm, A., & Ost, L. G. (1984). Maintenance procedures in the behavioral treatment of agoraphobia: A program and some data. *Behavioural Psychotherapy, 12*, 109–116.

Kazdin, A. E. (1978). *History of behavior modification: Experimental foundations of contemporary research.* Baltimore: University Park Press.

Kazdin, A. E., & Smith, G. A. (1979). Covert conditioning: A review and evaluation. *Advances in Behaviour Research and Therapy, 2,* 57–98.

Keane, T. M., & Kaloupek, D. G. (1982). Imaginal flooding in the treatment of a posttraumatic stress disorder. *Journal of Consulting and Clinical Psychology, 50,* 138–140

Kenny, F. T., Mowbray, R. M., & Lalani, S. (1978). Faradic disruption of obsessive ideation in the treatment of obsessive neurosis: A controlled study. *Behavior Therapy, 9,* 209–221.

Kenny, F. T., Solyom, L., & Solyom, C. (1973). Faradic disruption of obsessive ideation in the treatment of obsessive neurosis. *Behavior Therapy, 4,* 448–451.

Kerr, W. J., Dalton, J. W., & Gliebe, P. A. (1937). Some physical phenomena associated with anxiety states and their relation to hyperventilation. *Annals of Internal Medicine, 11,* 961–992.

Kipper, D. A. (1977). Behavior therapy for fears brought on by war experiences. *Journal of Consulting and Clinical Psychology, 45,* 216–221.

Kleiner, L., & Marshall, W. L. (1985). Relationship difficulties and agoraphobia. *Clinical Psychology Review, 5,* 581–595.

Kleiner, L., & Marshall, W. L. (1986). *Exposure and interpersonal skills training in the treatment of agoraphobia.* Unpublished manuscript, Queen's University, Kingston, Ontario, Canada.

Ladouceur, R. (1974). An experimental test of the learning paradigm of covert positive reinforcement. *Journal of Behavior Therapy and Experimental Psychiatry, 5,* 3–6.

Ladouceur, R. (1977). Rationale of covert reinforcement: Additional evidence. *Psychological Reports, 41,* 547–550.

Ladouceur, R. (1978). Rationale of systematic desensitization and covert positive reinforcement in deconditioning anxiety. *Journal of Behavior Therapy and Experimental Psychiatry, 5,* 3–6.

Lang, P. J. (1977). Imagery in therapy: An information processing analysis of fear. *Behavior Therapy, 8,* 862–886.

Lang, P. J., & Lazovik, A. D. (1963). Experimental desensitization of a phobia. *Journal of Abnormal and Social Psychology, 66,* 519–525.

LeBouef, A., & Lodge, J. (1980). A comparison of frontalis EMG feedback training and progressive relaxation in the treatment of chronic anxiety. *British Journal of Psychiatry, 137,* 279–284.

Leitenberg, H., Agras, W. S., Butz, R., & Wincze, J. (1971). Relationship between heart rate and behavioral change during the treatment of phobias. *Journal of Abnormal Psychology, 78,* 59–68.

Liebowitz, M. R., Gorman, J. M., Feyer, A. J., & Klein, D. F. (1985). Social phobia: Review of a neglected anxiety disorder. *Archives of General Psychiatry, 42,* 729–736.

Lum, L. C. (1981). Hyperventilation and anxiety state. *Journal of Research in Social Medicine, 74,* 1–4.

Mackintosh, N. J. (1974). *The psychology of animal learning.* New York: Academic Press.

Malloy, P. F., Fairbank, J. A., & Keane, T. M. (1983). Validation of a multimethod assessment of posttraumatic stress disorder in Vietnam veterans. *Journal of Consulting and Clinical Psychology, 51,* 488–494.

Mahoney, M. J. (1971). The self-management of covert behavior: A case study. *Behavior Therapy, 2,* 575–578.

Marlatt, G. A., & Gordon, J. R. (1980). Determinants of relapse: Implications for the maintenance of behavior change. In P. Davidson & S. Davidson (Eds.), *Behavioral medicine: Changing health lifestyles* (pp. 410–452). New York: Brunner/Mazel.

Marks, I. M. (1971). Phobic disorders four years after treatment: A prospective follow-up. *British Journal of Psychiatry, 118,* 683–686.

Marks, I. M., Boulougouris, J., & Marset, P. (1971). Flooding versus desensitization in the treatment of phobic patients: A crossover study. *British Journal of Psychiatry, 119,* 353–375.

Marks, I. M., Hodgson, R., & Rachman, S. (1975). Treatment of chronic obsessive-compulsive neurosis by in vivo exposure. *British Journal of Psychiatry, 127,* 349–364.

Marshall, P., Keltner, A., & Marshall, W. L. (1981). Anxiety-reduction, assertive training, and enactment of consequences: A comparative treatment study in the modification of nonassertion and social fear. *Behavior Modification, 5,* 85–102.

Marshall, W. L. (1975). An examination of reciprocal inhibition and counter-conditioning explanations of desensitization therapy. *European Journal of Behavior Analysis and Modification, 3,* 74–86.

Marshall, W. L. (1982). A model of dysfunctional behavior. In A. S. Bellack, M. Hersen, & A. E. Kazdin (Eds.), *International handbook of behavior modification and therapy.* (pp. 57–78). New York: Plenum Press.

Marshall, W. L. (1985). The effects of variable

exposure in flooding therapy. *Behavior Therapy, 16,* 117–135.

Marshall, W. L., Boutilier, J., & Minnes, P. (1974). The modification of phobic behavior by covert reinforement. *Behavior therapy, 5,* 469–480.

Marshall, W. L., & Gauthier, J. (1983). Failures in flooding. In E. B. Foa & P. M. G. Emmelkamp (Eds.), *Failures in behavior therapy* (pp. 82–103). New York: John Wiley & Sons.

Marshall, W. L., Gauthier, J., Christie, M. M., Currie, D. W., & Gordon, A. (1977). Flooding therapy: Effectiveness, stimulus characteristics, and the value of brief *in vivo* exposure. *Behaviour Research and Therapy, 15,* 79–87.

Marshall, W. L., Gauthier, J., & Gordon, A. (1979). The current status of flooding therapy. In M. Hersen, R. M. Eisler, & P. M. Miller (Eds.), *Progress in behavior modification* (Vol. 7, pp. 205–275). New York: Academic Press.

Marshall, W. L., Parker, L., & Hayes, B. (1982). Treating public speaking problems: A study using flooding and the elements of skills training. *Behavior Modification, 6,* 47–170.

Marshall, W. L, Presse L., & Andrews, W. R. (1976). A self-administered program for public-speaking anxiety. *Behaviour Research and Therapy, 14,* 33–39.

Marshall, W. L., & Segal, Z. (1986). Phobia and anxiety. In M. Hersen (Ed.), *Pharmacological and behavioral treatment: An integrative approach* (pp. 260–288). New York: John Wiley & Sons.

Marshall, W. L., Stoian, M., & Andrews, W. R. (1977). Skills training and self-administered desensitization in the reduction of public speaking anxiety. *Behaviour Research and Therapy, 15,* 115–117.

Mathews, A. M., Gelder, M. G., & Johnston, D. W. (1981) *Agoraphobia: Nature and treatment.* New York: Guilford Press.

Mathews, A., & Rezin, V. (1977). Treatment of dental fears by imaginal flooding and rehearsal of coping behaviour. *Behaviour Research and Therapy, 15,* 321–328.

Mathews, A. M., & Shaw, P. M. (1973). Emotional arousal and persuasion effects in flooding. *Behaviour Research and Therapy, 11,* 587–598.

Mathews, A. M., Teasdale, J., Munby, M., Johnston, D., & Shaw, P. (1977). A home-based treatment program for agoraphobia. *Behavior Therapy, 8,* 915–924.

Mavissakalian, M., & Barlow, D. H. (1981). *Phobia: Psychological and pharmacological treatment.* New York: Guilford Press.

McPherson, F. M., Brougham, L., & McLaren, S. (1980). Maintenance of improvement in agoraphobic patients treated by behavioural methods — a four-year follow-up. *Behaviour Research and Therapy, 18,* 150–152.

Meichenbaum, D. H. (1977). *Cognitive-behavior modification: An integrative approach.* New York: Plenum Press.

Meichenbaum, D. H., & Turk, D. (1973). *Stress inoculation: A skills training approach to anxiety management.* Unpublished manuscript, University of Waterloo, Ontario, Canada.

Meyer, V. (1966). Modification of expectations in cases with obsessional rituals. *Behaviour Research and Therapy, 4,* 273–280.

Meyer, V., & Levy, R. (1970). Behavioural treatment of a homosexual with compulsive rituals. *British Journal of Medical Psychology, 43,* 63–67.

Meyer, V., Levy, R., & Schnurer, A. (1974). The behavioural treatment of obsessive-compulsive disorder. In H. R. Beech (Ed.), *Obsessional states* (pp. 233–258). London: Methuen.

Moor, M. (1945). Recurrent nightmares: A simple procedure for psychotherapy. *Military Surgery, 97,* 282–285.

Munby, M., & Johnston, D. W. (1980. Agoraphobia: The long-term follow-up of behavioural treatment. *British Journal of Psychiatry, 137,* 418–927.

O'Brien, G. T., & Barlow, D. H. (1984). Agoraphobia. In S. M. Turner (Ed.), *Behavioral theories and treatment of anxiety* (pp. 143–185). New York: Plenum Press.

Ost, L., Jerremalm, A., & Johansson, J. (1981). Individual response patterns and the effects of differential behavioral methods in the treatment of social phobia. *Behaviour Research and Therapy, 19,* 1–16.

Ost, L. G., Johansson, J., & Jerremalm, A. (1982). Individual response patterns and the effects of different behavioural methods in the treatment of claustrophobia. *Behaviour Research and Therapy, 20,* 445–460.

Paul, G. L. (1966). *Insight versus desensitization in psychotherapy.* Stanford, CA: Stanford University Press.

Rachman, S. (1972). Clinical applications of observational learning, imitation and modelling. *Behavior Therapy, 3,* 379–397.

Rachman, S. (1976). The modification of obsessions: A new formulation. *Behaviour Research and Therapy, 16,* 437–443.

Rachman, S. (1982). Obsessional-compulsive disorders. In A. S. Bellack, M. Hersen, & A. E. Kazdin (Eds.), *International handbook of behavior modification and therapy* (pp. 749–766). New York: Plenum Press.

Rachman, S. (1983). Obstacles to the successful

treatment of obsessions. In E. B. Foa & P. M. G. Emmelkamp (Eds.), *Failures in behavior therapy* (pp. 35–57). New York: John Wiley & Sons.

Rachman, S., & Hodgson, R. (1980). *Obsessions and compulsions.* Englewood Cliffs, NJ: Prentice-Hall.

Rapee, R. M. (1985). A case of panic disorder treated with breathing retraining. *Journal of Behavior Therapy and Experimental Psychiatry, 16,* 63–65.

Raskin, M., Peeke, H., Dickman, W., & Pinsker, H. (1982). Panic and generalized anxiety disorders — development antecedents and precipitants. *Archives of General Psychiatry, 39,* 687–689.

Rice, K. M., & Blanchard, E. B. (1982). Biofeedback in the treatment of anxiety disorders. *Clinical Psychology Review, 2,* 557–577.

Roper, G., Rachman, S., & Hodgson, R. (1973). An experiment on obsessional checking. *Behaviour Research and Therapy, 11,* 271–277.

Rosenthal, T. L., & Bandura, A. (1978). Psychological modeling: Theory and practice. In S. L. Garfield & A. E. Bergin (Eds.), *Handbook of psychotherapy and behavior change: An empirical analysis* (2nd ed.). (pp. 621–658). New York: John Wiley & Sons.

Saul, L., Howard, R., & Lenser, E. (1946). Desensitization of combat fatigue patients. *American Journal of Psychiatry, 102,* 476–478.

Segal, Z., & Marshall, W. L. (1982). Actual versus predicted expectancies and their influence in flooding therapy. *Psychological Reports, 51,* 443–452.

Sherman, A. R. (1972). Real-life exposure as a primary therapeutic factor in the desensitization treatment of fear. *Journal of Abnormal Psychology, 79,* 19–28.

Sinnott, D., Jones, R. B., Scott-Fordham, A., & Woodward, R. (1981). Augmentation of in vivo exposure treatment for agoraphobia by the formation of neighborhood self-help groups. *Behaviour Research and Therapy, 19,* 339–347.

Solyom, L., Garza-Perez, J., Ledwidge, B., & Solyom, C. (1972). Paradoxical intention in the treatment of obsessive thoughts: A pilot study. *Comprehensive Psychiatry, 13,* 291–297.

Stampfl, T. G., & Levis, D. J. (1967). Essentials of implosion therapy: A learning-theory–based psychodynamic behavioral therapy. *Journal of Abnormal Psychology, 72,* 496–503.

Stern, R. S. (1978). Obsessive thoughts: The problem of therapy. *British Journal of Psychiatry, 133,* 200–205.

Stern, R. S., Lipsedge, M. S., & Marks, I. M. (1975). Obsessive ruminations: A controlled trial of thought-stopping technique. *Behaviour Research and Therapy, II,* 659–662.

Sturgis, E. T., & Scott, R. (1984). Simple phobia. In S. M. Turner (Ed.), *Behavioral theories and treatment of anxiety* (pp. 91–141). New York: Plenum Press.

Suinn, R. M., & Richardson, F. (1971). Anxiety management training: A nonspecific behavior therapy program for anxiety control. *Behavior Therapy, 2,* 510–698.

Taylor, D. W. A. (1971). A comparison of group desensitization with two control procedures in the treatment of test anxiety. *Behaviour Research and Therapy, 9,* 281–284.

Thelen, M. H., Fry, R. A., Fehrenbach, P. A., & Frantschi, N. M. (1979). Therapeutic videotape and film modeling: A review. *Psychological Bulletin, 86,* 701–720.

Thorpe, G. L., & Burns, L. E. (1983). *The agoraphobic syndrome: Behavioural approaches to evaluation and treatment.* New York: John Wiley & Sons.

Trower, P., Yardley, K., Bryant, B. M., & Shaw, P. (1978). The treatment of social failure: A comparison of anxiety-reduction and skills-acquisition procedures on two social problems. *Behavior Modifications, 2,* 44–60.

Turner, S. M., Holzman, A., & Jacob, R. B. (1983). Treatment of compulsive looking by imaginal thought-stopping. *Behavior Modification, 7,* 576–589.

Turner, S. M., & Michelson, L. (1984). Obsessive-compulsive disorders. In S. M. Turner (Ed.), *Behavioral theories and treatment of anxiety* (pp. 239–277). New York: Plenum Press.

Vermilyea, J. A., Boice, R., & Barlow, D. H. (1984). Rachman and Hodgson (1974). A decade later: How do desynchronous response systems relate to the treatment of agoraphobia? *Behaviour Research and Therapy, 22,* 615–621.

Vogel, W., Peterson, L. E., & Broverman, I. K. (1982). A modification of Rachman's habituation technique for treatment of the obsessive-compulsive disorder. *Behaviour Research and Therapy, 20,* 101–104.

Waddell, M. T., Barlow, D. H., & O'Brien, G. T. (1984). A preliminary investigation of cognitive and relaxation treatment of panic disorder: Effects of intense anxiety versus "background" anxiety. *Behaviour Research and Therapy, 22,* 393–402.

Williams, S. L., Dooseman, G., & Kleifield, E. (1984). Comparative effectiveness of guided mastery and exposure treatments for intractable phobias. *Journal of Consulting and Clinical Psychology, 52,* 505–518.

Williams, S. L., Turner, S. M., & Peer, D. F. (1985). Guided mastery and performance desensitization treatments for severe acrophobia. *Journal of Consulting and Clinical Psychology*, *53*, 237–247.

Wolpe, J. (1958). *Psychotherapy by reciprocal inhibition*. Stanford, CA: Stanford University Press.

CHAPTER 19

Cognitive Approaches

David M. Clark and Aaron T. Beck

In the last 15 years, research in behaviour therapy has produced a marked improvement in the effectiveness of psychological treatments for agoraphobia and simple phobias. The majority of such patients are substantially helped by graded, in vivo exposure. Similarly, encouraging, though perhaps less substantial benefits, have been produced by behavioral treatments for social phobias. By contrast, relatively little progress has been made in the development of effective psychological treatments for nonphobic (generalized) anxiety states. As the anxiety involved in such states is not strongly associated with particular situations, it has often been termed "free-floating" anxiety or anxiety "the source of which is not recognized" (Lader & Marks, 1971, p. 29). However, it has been argued (Beck, Laud, & Bohnert, 1974) that this description is mistaken and that the anxiety involved in nonphobic states is a response to identifiable but largely internal stimuli (negative thoughts and images). This suggestion, along with an increasing awareness of the importance of cognitive processes in exposure therapy (Emmelkamp 1982; Wilson, 1984), has recently led to a marked growth of interest in cognitive approaches to the treatment of anxiety disorders. Ellis (1962), Meichenbaum (1977), and Beck (1976) have all written extensively on cognitive approaches to the understanding and treatment of emotional disorders, and there is much overlap in both their theories and practical procedures. However, this chapter largely concentrates on Beck's cognitive theory and therapy, as this is arguably the most extensively elaborated cognitive approach to clinical anxiety.

The chapter is divided into three major sections. The first section describes a cognitive theory of anxiety. The second section provides a detailed account of the practical procedures involved in cognitive therapy. Neither of these sections discuss research findings in detail. Instead, these are discussed in section three, which provides a review of empirical studies that have attempted to evaluate cognitive theory and therapy.

A COGNITIVE MODEL OF ANXIETY

Cognitive therapy for anxiety is based on the same model of emotions as that used in cognitive therapy for depression and other emotional disorders (Beck, 1967, 1976). The central notion within this model is the idea that it is not events per se, but rather people's interpretation of events that is responsible for the production of negative emotions, such as anxiety, anger, or sadness. The interpretations considered important in depression relate to perceived loss of a relationship, status, or efficacy. In anxiety, the important interpretations, or cognitions, relate to perceived danger of such a loss or of damage, sickness, or death. There are numerous occasions in which individuals are in objectively dangerous situations. In such situations their perceptions are often realistic appraisals of the threat inherent in the situation. However, Beck (1976) claims that in pathological anxiety, perceptions of dangers are unrealistic, in the sense that they are overestimates of the danger inherent in a given situation. These overestimates are said to arise from one or more of the four errors listed below:

1. Overestimating the probability of a feared event.
2. Overestimating the severity of the feared event.
3. Underestimating coping resources (what you can do about it).
4. Underestimating rescue factors (what other people can do to help you).

Once an individual perceives a situation as dangerous, the "anxiety program" is automatically and reflexly activated. This is a complex constellation of cognitive, affective, and behavioural changes which we have inherited from our evolutionary past and which were probably originally designed to protect us from harm in a primitive environment. These include (a) marked changes in autonomic arousal as a preparation for flight, fight, freezing, or fainting; (b) an inhibition of ongoing behaviour; (c) selective scanning of the environment for threat. Anxiety acts as an "attention getter," forcing the individual to focus on possible sources of danger. Cognitive resources are allocated away from the processing of nonthreat material in favour of the processing of data related to danger. This reallocation of resources leads not only to the selective enhancement of stimulus configurations relevant to danger, but also to the selective suppression of data that are incongruent with perceived danger.

In primitive environments, when many dangers were life-threatening and physical (e.g., being attacked by a predator), the anxiety program would have had the useful function of spurring individuals to protect themselves or get away from dangerous situations. In contemporary life, anxiety can also serve a similarly useful function in many situations in which there is a realistic threat. However, when the problem is not an actual danger but a misperception or exaggeration of danger, the experience of anxiety is inappropriate for initiating remedial action. Instead, the symptoms of anxiety are often perceived as a further source of threat leading to a series of vicious circles which tend to maintain or exacerbate anxiety reactions. For example, a racing heart may be interpreted as evidence of an impending heart attack; blushing as an indication that one has made, or is about to make, a fool of oneself; a shaking hand as evidence of impending total loss of control; and the automatic, unrealistic nature of anxious thoughts as evidence of impending insanity. Because of this reciprocal relationship between perceived threat and the symptoms of anxiety, a large amount of cognitive therapy is devoted to dealing with fears about the behavioural, cognitive, and somatic symptoms of anxiety.

The Cognitive Content of Different Anxiety Disorders

So far in discussing the cognitive model we have not distinguished between different types of anxiety disorders. To date, only two studies (Hibbert, 1984; Rappee, 1985) have systematically investigated the cognitive content of different anxiety disorders. However, clinical experience would suggest that although some thoughts are common to most anxiety disorders, there are also marked differences in ideation between the anxiety disorders. Beck and colleagues (Beck, 1986; Beck, Emery et al., 1985) suggest that the cognitions that are particularly characteristic of each of the anxiety disorders defined by DSM-III (APA, 1980) are as follows.

Panic disorder

This is characterised by a fear of an impending internal disaster (e.g., heart attack, cessation of breathing, mental derangement) and a sense of loss of control over physical and mental functions. Many panic patients' negative thoughts can be viewed as resulting from the misinterpretation of certain bodily sensations (such as palpitations or a slight feeling of breathlessness). Furthermore, it has been suggested (Beck, Emery et al., 1985; Clark, 1986a) that panic attacks result from a vicious cycle in which catastrophic misinterpretations of bodily sensations lead to an increase in anxiety and associated sensations, which are in turn interpreted as further evidence of impending, internal disaster.

Agoraphobia

The ideation of agoraphobics who experience panic attacks includes those thoughts that we have described as characteristic of panic disorder (see Chambless, Capato, Bright, & Gallagher, 1984). In addition, there is another dimension — the belief that panic attacks are either more likely to occur or will have more serious consequences if the patient enters certain situations, or is alone or distant from safe havens (hospital, home, therapist). In contrast to agoraphobia with panic, relatively little is known about the ideation of agoraphobia without panic.

Social phobia

The central concepts relate to exaggerated fears of being evaluated, of "having one's weaknesses" exposed, and of being judged adversely by other people. The social phobic continually monitors his or her performance in social situations, fears that this performance will be viewed as evidence that he or she is inept, boring, or stupid, and expects a specific rejection or failure will have dire, long-lasting, and far-reaching implications.

Simple phobias

In both agoraphobia and social phobia, fear of fear plays a significant role. The agoraphobic interprets certain aspects of autonomic arousal as evidence of an impending internal disaster and the social phobic interprets similar somatic symptoms as evidence that he or she will not perform well and hence will be ridiculed. In simple phobias, fear of fears plays a much less prominent role. Instead, the simple phobics' ideation is almost exclusively concerned with exaggerated perceptions of the danger inherent in a particular situation (heights) or specific object (snakes, small animals). In addition, as with many other phobics, the simple phobic appears to possess a dual belief system. When removed from a feared stimulus, the simple phobic usually believes that the stimulus is harmless, but when in the presence of the stimulus, he or she usually believes that it is extremely dangerous.

Generalized anxiety disorder

There appears to be considerable variation in the ideation of patients with generalized anxiety disorder. However, Beck et al., (1974) found that most anxiety-related thoughts fell into five categories: fears of physical injury, illness, or death; fears of mental illness; fears of loss of control; fears of failure and inability to cope; and fears of rejection, domination, or depreciation. Some generalized anxiety patients experience panic attacks, though, by definition, at a lower frequency than in panic disorder. Among such patients it is likely that fears of impending internal disaster (death, insanity) or loss of control will be particularly prominent (Beck et al., 1974; Hibbert, 1984). In contrast, psychosocial fears appear to be particularly prominent in nonpanic patients. Occasionally, generalized anxiety disorder develops suddenly in an individual who is not normally prone to worry. However, more typically it has a gradual onset (Rappee, 1985) in an individual who has always had doubts and concerns about self-worth and competence.

Obsessive–compulsive disorder

Beck, Emery et al. (1985) do not specifically discuss obsessive–compulsive disorder. However, Salkovskis (1985) has recently provided a cognitive-behavioural analysis of obsessive–compulsive problems. Building on Rachman and da Silva's (1978) observation that the major difference between clinical obsessionals and normal individuals lies in the distress produced by intrusive thoughts, rather than in the occurrence of the thoughts themselves, Salkovskis (1985) suggests that intrusive thoughts are best conceptualised as cognitive *stimuli*. In some individuals, these *stimuli* are followed by cognitive *responses* (negative automatic thoughts), and it is these *responses* that are said to produce the distress associated with obsessions. Typically, the content of these cognitive responses relates to excessive beliefs concerning responsibility or blame for harm to self or others, arising either directly from performing an action or indirectly from failing to perform an action.

Hypochondriasis

To date, relatively little attention has been devoted to the cognitive processes involved in hypochondriasis. However, it seems likely that hypochondriacal complaints are at least partly based on catastrophic misinterpretations of bodily sensations and signs. As misinterpretation of bodily symptoms is also said to be central to panic, it is necessary to specify differences between the cognitive processes involved in panic and those involved in hypochondriasis without panic (Clark, 1986a). It seems likely that one important difference will be in the distinction between immediate and long-term threat. Interpretations of bodily sensations which lead patients to believe that they are in immediate danger of dying, going mad, or losing control, may be particularly characteristic of panic, while interpretations that imply some more distant danger (dying in several months' or years' time) may be more characteristic of hypochondriasis.

A second difference between hypochondriasis and panic concerns the bodily stimuli that are misinterpreted. Clinically, it would appear that a wider range of bodily stimuli are misinterpreted in hypochondriasis, and many of these stimuli are not commonly occurring elements of the anxiety response (i.e., spots, aches, and pains).

Levels of Cognition

Within Beck's cognitive model of anxiety, two differnt levels of disturbed thinking can be distinguished. The term *negative automatic thoughts* refers to those thoughts and images that are present in specific situations when an individual is anxious. For example, a socially anxious individual might have the negative automatic thought "They think I'm boring" while talking to a group of colleagues in a bar. The terms *dysfunctional assumptions and rules* refer to general beliefs that individuals hold about themselves and the world, and which are said to make them prone to interpret certain situations in an excessively negative and dysfunction fashion. For example, a socially anxious individual who frequently has the thought "They think I am boring" when talking to others may be prone to make this interpretation because of an extreme equation of self-worth with social approval ("Unless I am liked by everyone, I am worthless"). Dysfunctional beliefs and assumptions are said to result from early learning experiences and often lay dormant until activated by a specific event which meshes with them. For example, a young woman whose father died suddenly and unexpectedly at the age of 40 may develop the belief that any strong and unexpected physical complaint may lead to sudden death. However, this belief may have very little influence on her emotions or behaviour until she experiences an unusual sensation, such as blurred vision from overwork, or faintness and dizziness due to hormonal changes. These sensations could then activate the belief, leading her to become preoccupied with her health, repeatedly seek medical reassurance, and systematically misinterpret innocuous bodily sensations in a catastrophic fashion.

In line with current theories in cognitive psychology (e.g., Anderson, 1985), dysfunctional beliefs and rules which have related contents are said to be associated together within memory to form higher order cognitive structures called *schemas*. Some schemas relate only to one or two specific situations (exams, restaurants, etc.), while other schemas have much more global domains of reference. Both types of schemas can vary in their level of activation. Beck, Emery et al. (1985) call a stongly activated situation specific schema a *cognitive set* and a strongly activated general schema a *mode*. Once activated, either type of schema facilitates the processing of information consistent with the content of the schema and inhibits the processing of information inconsistent with the schema. Activated schemas also lead to an increase in false alarms consistent with the contents of the schema.

DESCRIPTION OF TREATMENT

Cognitive therapy aims to reduce anxiety by teaching patients how to identify, evaluate, control, and modify their negative automatic thoughts and associated behaviours. A variety of cognitive and behavioural techniques are used to achieve this aim. Because both cognitive and behavioural techniques are included in the treatment, some researchers and clinicians have assumed that cognitive therapy consists of the simple addition of specific cognitive procedures to a set of well-established, behavioural procedures. While it would be possible to construct a therapy along these lines, this constitutes a misunderstanding of the nature of cognitive therapy. Rather than being a collection of techniques, cognitive therapy is a coherent system of therapy which often requires a conceptual shift for therapists trained in either behaviour therapy or psychodynamic psychotherapy. The general defining characteristics of the cognitive therapy approach to treatment are outlined here. Some of these characteristics are common to both behavioural and cognitive therapies, while others are unique to cognitive therapy.

1. *Cognitive therapy is based on the cognitive model of emotional disorders.* This model is presented to the patient as the explicit rationale for treatment in general and for the selection of each specific treatment procedure.
2. *Cognitive therapy is based on an educational model.* Instead of trying to solve all a patient's problems, therapists use the management of specific problems as a way of teaching general skills for dealing with emotional difficulties.
3. *Cognitive therapy in brief and time limited.* Treatment of anxiety generally lasts between 5 and 20 sessions. This brevity encourages patient self-sufficiency and the acquisition of general skills for dealing with problems.
4. *Therapy is a collaborative effort.* Therapists and patient pointly agree on the selection of target problems and work together as a team to produce solutions for those problems. Frequent feedback is used to graduate mutual understanding. The therapist does not "lecture" the patient on the validity of a positive alternative to his or her negative thoughts. Instead, the therapeutic process is closer to that of a scientific team. The patient's negative thoughts are treated as hypotheses, and patient and therapist work together to collect evidence to determine whether the hypotheses are accurate or helpful.
5. *Cognitive therapists primarily use the Socratic method.* Instead of providing answers to a patient's negative thoughts, therapists ask a series of questions that aim to help patients to evaluate and provide their own answers to their thoughts.
6. *A sound therapeutic relationship is a necessary condition for effective cogni-*

tive therapy. In order to develop collaboration, it is essential that the patient feels he or she can trust, and will be taken seriously by, the therapist. For this reason, considerable emphasis is placed on the interpersonal skills of the therapist. These should include genuiness, warmth, openess, sincerity, and accurate empathy.

7. *Cognitive therapy is structured and problem-orientated*. Each session starts with setting an agenda specifying specific problems that will be tackled during the session. Frequent feedback is used to review progress and every session ends with the setting of homework.
8. *Homework is an essential feature of cognitive therapy*. In their homework, patients collect negative automatic thoughts and other information, conduct behavioural experiments to test their beliefs, and learn to apply the procedures they have learned in therapy to stressful situations in the outside world.

Having described the general principles of cognitive therapy, we now describe the specific procedures used in therapy. The main focus of these procedures is to help patients to identify their negative thoughts and then to challenge and test out those thoughts. First, we focus on techniques for identifying negative thoughts.

Identifying Negative Thoughts

Negative automatic thoughts are: unreasonable, dysfunctional, repetitive, and idiosyncratic. They tend to arise automatically, rather than through a process of conscious reasoning; they seem plausible to the client and tend to be accepted uncritically (Beck, Rush, Shaw, & Emery, 1979).

Some patients are able to identify their negative automatic thoughts at the start of therapy. However, many require training before they can confidently identify negative automatic thoughts. Often there appear to be two parallel streams of thought. The first, which patients can readily report, consists of thoughts such as, "I am feeling anxious" and "I was worried about how I was doing." These are more like descriptions of how the person was thinking or feeling rather than their actual thoughts. The second stream contains thoughts such as, "They'll think I am stupid," "I really screwed up," and "I won't be able to cope." These thoughts are closer to the person's actual appraisal of a situation and, as such, will determine their emotional response to the situation. However, patients sometimes find that it is intially difficult to "tune in" to this second stream of thought.

There are at least three reasons why anxious patients might find it difficult to become aware of this second stream of thought:

1. *State-Dependent Memory*. Many anxious patients are not particularly anxious when seen in the clinic. Consequently, they are likely to have relatively few anxious cognitions during a consultation. In addition, state-dependent retrieval effects (Clark & Teasdale 1982, 1985; Teasdale, 1983a) are likely to make it difficult for them to access the cognitions associated with previous anxiety states.
2. *Cognitive Avoidance*. Several forms of cognitive avoidance appear to occur in anxiety states. Patients often have a brief image or thought related to a disastrous event, become distressed, and then quickly attempt to suppress the thought or image by distracting themselves. This prevents detailed processing of the thought and so makes it difficult for the patients to become aware of the exact nature of their anxiety-related cognitions. For example, Beck, Emery et al. (1985) describe a patient who attempted to cope with his anxiety by whistling to himself as soon as he experienced an anxiety-provoking thought or image. The whistling produced a reduction in anxiety, but also appeared to interfere with recall of the cognitions that had triggered the anxiety. As dwelling on

thoughts related to anticipated disaster often produces anxiety, patients may be reluctant to retrieve and discuss the exact detail of thoughts that occurred during recent anxiety episodes. Instead, they may prefer to talk in very general terms about the topics that concern them or describe "watered down" versions of anxious cognitions. In such cases, it is important for the therapist gently to persist in questioning until appropriate cognitions are elicited. A general rule for therapists to apply to elicited cognitions is "Would I be as anxious as my patient was if I had this thought and believed it?" If the answer to this question is no, the elicited thought is probably inaccurate.

3. *Fleeting Images.* As Beck (1970) points out, many anxious patients have visual images of danger before or during anxious episodes. However, with the exception of posttraumatic stress disorder, very few patients spontaneously report the presence of such images. This may be because the images that trigger anxiety reactions can be extremely brief (less than 1 second), even when patients do not appear to be engaging in cognitive avoidance. Such brief images would be difficult to become aware of or remember. An additional feature of some images associated with high anxiety is that they are extremely bizarre. This sometimes makes patients reluctant to consider and discuss them, at least until they have been warned that bizarre images are a normal accompaniment of high anxiety.

As negative automatic thoughts are difficult to identify, cognitive therapists have devised a number of special techniques for the identification of such thoughts. Several of these techniques are outlined as follows.

Discussion of Recent Emotional Experiences

Therapists and patients work together to identify a recent event or situation that seemed to trigger an emotional reponse. Recent events are chosen, as memory for such events is usually clearest. Once an event has been identified, therapists elicit the cognitions associated with the onset and maintenance of the emotional reactions by asking questions such as, "What went through your mind just then?," "Did you have an image just then?" "When you were at your most anxious, what was the worst thing that you thought might happen?" The reader will have noticed that the question, "What were you thinking?" is not included in this list. Clinical experience indicates that, unless patients have already been trained to identify automatic thoughts, this question tends to elicit descriptions of feelings or thoughts rather than thoughts themselves. Another question that can also produce misleading answers is, "What are you afraid of?" The extent to which patients believe an anxiety-related thought often varies with their level of anxiety. When calm, patients can sometimes see that their automatic thoughts are irrational and hence tend to discount and ignore them. For example, a panic patient who is preoccupied with the idea that there may be something wrong with his or her heart may reply to the question, "What are you afraid of in an attack?" by saying, "I used to think I would have a heart attack. However, my doctor has explained that my heart is O.K. and I guess I'm just worried about the anxiety." However if asked the question, "Right in the middle of an attack, what is the worst that you think could happen?," he or she may reply, "I know what my doctor said, but in the middle of an attack I really do believe I'm about to have a heart attack."

Blackboard Technique

In cases where it is suspected that cognitive avoidance may be preventing a patient from accessing cognitions sufficiently negative to account for the degree of anxiety experienced, it can be useful to write down elicited thoughts on a blackboard or piece of paper. The sight of the first few thoughts tends to elicit the recall of further anxious thoughts. Many patients find seeing their thoughts on the board makes the thoughts appear less frightening. This encourages them to overcome cognitive avoidance and to search out their most frightening thoughts. Often the last thought to be written down is the most frightening, and also the one that is sufficiently negative to account for the anxiety experienced.

Reliving an Emotional Experience through Imagery

If direct questioning fails to elicit automatic thoughts, it can be useful to get the patient to go back to the emotional event in imagination and then replay it in great detail. The following excerpt illustrates this technique:

PATIENT: I had a bad panic attack last week which really scared me.
THERAPIST: Where were you and what were you doing?
PATIENT: I was just knitting and watching the television.
THERAPIST: Do you remember any of the thoughts you had as the panic was starting?
PATIENT: No, in fact that's one of the things which made it so frightening. It just seemed to come out of the blue.
THERAPIST: Shall we try an experiment to see if we can discover what you were thinking?
PATIENT: Okay.
THERAPIST: I'd like you to relax and close your eyes. Now, imagine you are back in your living room before the attack started. When you have a clear image, describe what is happening around you and what is going through your mind.
PATIENT: I'm on the sofa, my husband is in the armchair watching T.V. I'm not paying much attention to the T.V. I think I was thinking about my mother and the mental problems she used to have.
THERAPIST: How is your mood?
PATIENT: I'm feeling a bit tense, nothing more.
THERAPIST: Okay, carry on with the image.
PATIENT: Now the attack is starting (pause). Oh, its really weird. I had a picture of my husband doing something, but he's not, if you get what I mean. He's sitting in the chair but I see him and a man in a white coat coming through the door and I know they are coming to take me away, to lock me up forever.
THERAPIST: Do you think that picture might have triggered the panic attack?
PATIENT: I am sure it did.

Role Playing

When the triggering event is an interpersonal interaction, role playing can be more effective than imagery. The therapist plays the other person while patients play "themselves." If patients can involve themselves in the role play, automatic thoughts are often elicited. If the interaction is a protracted one, the role play can be recorded on video. The therapist can then repeatedly stop the tape and ask questions to elicit the automatic thoughts that occurred at different points during the interaction.

Exposure

As well as reviewing and recreating past emotional experiences, patients engage in activities that provoke anxiety while monitoring their thoughts. Powerful but fleeting images often occur at times when there is a sudden jump in anxiety. For this reason, patients are instructed to pay particular attention to sudden changes in anxiety.

Mood Shifts During the Session

Shifts of mood during a therapy session can be particularly useful sources of automatic thoughts. The therapist points out that a shift in mood has occurred and then attempts to determine what he or she was thinking just prior to the increase in anxiety, depression, anger, or other reaction. As with exposure, this technique has the advantage of assessing cognitions as they occur.

Determining the Meaning of a Situation

Sometimes, skillful attempts by the therapist to elicit automatic thoughts are unsuccessful. The therapist should then attempt to discern, through questioning, the specific meaning for the patient of the event that preceded the emotional response. Through discussion, patients and therapists can often agree on the meaning of an event, even though specific thoughts may not have been identified. This process then helps the patient to identify specific thoughts in future, similar situations.

Modifying Negative Thoughts

In cognitive therapy, a wide range of procedures are to help patients evaluate, control, and modify negative thoughts. As already mentioned, some of these procedures are similar to procedures used in behavior therapy. However, when there is an overlap, the way a procedure is used in cognitive therapy is often slightly different from the way it is commonly used in behaviour therapy. In this chapter, it is possible to discuss only some of the more frequently used procedures. The procedures are presented in roughly the order in which they would be used in therapy. Readers who are interested in more detailed description of cognitive therapy procedures should consult Beck (1976), Beck, Emery et al. (1985, 1979), Burns (1980), Clark and Salkovskis (in press), Emery (1981, 1982), Young (1981, 1982), and Young and Beck (1982).

Demonstrating the Relationship Between Thinking and Feeling

Before patients and therapist can work together to evaluate and modify negative thoughts, the therapist must first demonstrate the relationship between thinking and feeling. There are several ways in which this can be done. Many patients can relate to a specific vignette that does not involve themselves. An example of such a vignette is given below (taken from Beck et al., 1979, pp. 147–148):

> THERAPIST: The way a person thinks about or interprets events affects how he feels and behaves. For example, say he was home alone one night and heard a crash in another room. If he thinks, "There's a burglar in the room", how do you think he would feel?
> PATIENT: Very anxious, terrified.
> THERAPIST: And how might he behave?
> PATIENT: He might try to hide or if he was smart he would phone the police.
> THERAPIST: Okay, so in response to a thought that a burglar made the noise, the person would probably feel anxious and behave in such a way as to protect himself. Now let's say he heard the same noise and thought, "The windows have been left open and the wind has caused something to fall over". How would he feel?
> PATIENT: Well, he wouldn't be afraid. He might be sad if he thought something valuable was broken or he might be annoyed that one of the kids left the window open.
> THERAPIST: And would his behaviour be different following this thought?
> PATIENT: Sure, he would probably go and see what the problem was. He certainly wouldn't phone the police.
> THERAPIST: Okay. Now, what this example shows us is that there are usually a number of ways in which you can interpret a situation. Also, the way you interpret the situation affects your feelings and behaviour.

Such vignettes often lead to good intellectual understanding of cognitive theory. However, in order to promote emotional understanding, it is important to back them up as soon as possible with examples taken from a patient's own life. It is often possible to do this during the first session, either by capitalizing or within-session shifts in mood or by discussing a recent emotional experience. If the patient has been asked to read "coping with anxiety" (Beck, Emery et al., 1985) before the session, asking him or her to briefly summarize the contents of the leaflet can often produce some anxiety and a set of automatic thoughts ("He probably thinks I'm stupid because I can hardly remember any of it") which can be identified and challenged as a mini-illustration of cognitive therapy. Similarly, while collecting information about presenting problems, questions asked to determine whether a patient's fear of a particular situation is realistic often lead to the identification and modification of negative thoughts. For example, a 55-year-old divorcé reported feeling anxious before and after dinner parties. His negative thoughts concerned the possibility that people may not enjoy themselves and then blame him. Questioning him about whether his friends generally looked as though they enjoyed themselves during his dinner parties, whether he was 100% responsible for their enjoyment, whether there were any factors other than his behaviour that might determine their enjoyment, and whether he had any definite evidence that they did not enjoy themselves, allowed him to realize that his parties were often successful and, furthermore, even if they weren't people would not necessarily blame him. He was also able to see that if he had been able to assess some of these more positive and realistic thoughts before his last dinner party, he would have felt less anxious.

Giving Information about Anxiety

In the early stages of treatment, therapists give patients a considerable amount of information about the nature of anxiety. This includes a description of the various symptoms of anxiety, their possible evolutionary origin and function, the lack of relationship between anxiety and insanity, and the role that is played in the maintenance of anxiety by both avoidance and by negative appraisals of situations and the symptoms of anxiety. Discussion of this information is tailored to the particular needs of each client. It aims to effect problem-reduction (helps the patient to see that a series of apparently unrelated difficulties — such as insomnia, difficulty in making decisions, stomach cramps, and occasional blurred vision — are all aspects of an anxiety disorder), to help the patient to understand the cognitive model of anxiety) and to correct any misconceptions concerning the nature of anxiety. Such misconceptions often contribute to anxiety about anxiety. For example, an obsessional who frequently thought she would stab her children believed such thoughts were very unusual and took this as evidence she was going mad. Belief in her impending insanity was considerably reduced by reading Rachman and da Silva's (1978) article on normal obsessions, as a result of which she discovered that thoughts similar to her own are moderately common in the normal population.

Distraction

Patients are taught that one way of controlling their anxiety is to distract themselves from thoughts of impending danger. In the early stages of therapy, this technique is used to give patients the notion that they have some control over their anxiety, and also to help reduce high anxiety to a level at which patients can concentrate well enough to discuss their irrational beliefs. Later in therapy, distraction is used as a symptom management technique during occasions in which it would be inappropriate to spend time evaluating negative thoughts; for example, while engaged in conversation. Distraction in this context would involve becoming outwardly directed and concentrating on the conversation itself rather than on thoughts concerned with the evaluation of your own performance. Distraction can also provide the basis for a potent demonstration of the cognitive model during the initial session. Patients who are anxious in the session often notice marked reductions in anxiety if asked to describe out loud the contents of the room for a few minutes instead of dwelling on their own negative thoughts.

Activity Scheduling

Patients keep an hour-by-hour record of their activities and rate each activity for salient features such as anxiety, pleasure, and mastery. Activity schedules are used in a variety of different ways. For example, perceived time pressure can lead some patients to stop engaging in leisure and social activities that they had previously enjoyed. Often these activities contributed to their sense of self-worth and perceived control over their environment. Therefore, dropping these activites often increases anxiety and perceived vulnerability. Having identified this problem, therapist and patient can use the activity schedule to improve time management and reintroduce pleasurable activities. Activity schedules can also be used to identify periods of anxious rumination, perfectionism (indicated by highly polarised mastery and pleasure ratings), anxiety triggers, and coping strategies.

Daily Record of Dysfunctional Thoughts

Table 19.1 shows the daily record of dysfunctional thoughts. This sheet is used to record and evaluate negative automatic thoughts. Several illustrations of such thoughts and patients' rational responses to them are given in the table. Within sessions, patient and therapist work collaboratively to try to identify rational responses. Between sessions, patients attempt to put into practice the questioning skills they have learned in sessions by recording and challenging negative automatic thoughts as they arise.

Some of the questions that can profitably be used to examine and reality test negative thoughts are:

1. *"What is the evidence for this thought?" "Are there any alternative ways of looking at the situation?" "How would someone else think about the situation?"* These are some of the most commonly used questions. Butler and Mathews (1983) have shown that an anxious person's exaggerated perception of danger does not extend to other people. Perhaps for this reason, asking how someone else would view the situation can help restore perspective.
2. *"Are your judgments based on feelings rather than facts?"* Many anxious patients take their feelings of anxiety as evidence that they cannot cope with a situation even though behaviour in the situation may be appropriate and competent.
3. *"Are you thinking that because something could happen, it definitely will happen?" "Are you thinking in terms of certainties rather than probabilities?"* When anxious, patients often seem to confuse possibility with probability. They can also require unattainable levels of certainty about feared events ("I have to be absolutely certain I won't develop cancer").
4. *"Are you setting yourself an unrealistic/unattainable standard?"* Some patients set themselves excessively high standards ("I have to be at my best all the time") and then feel anxious because they are frequently in danger of falling short of their arbitary, self-imposed standard.
5. *"Are you using words or phrases that are extreme or exaggerated?"* Words such as *must, should, can't,* and *never* rarely correspond to reality and their habitual use often leads patients to underestimate their coping resources or make unrealistic demands of themselves.
6. *"Are you forgetting relevant facts or overfocusing on irrelevant facts?"* For example, forgetting previous successful performances when faced with a difficult task or committing the representiveness fallacy, "because two people I know lost their sight, I will lose mine."
7. *"Are you thinking in all or nothing terms?"* Anxiety can be associated with a tendency to evaluate the self and ongoing events in extreme, black and white terms. For example, "If people don't show that they like you, then they dislike you," "If you can't do a job perfectly, its not worth doing."
8. *"So what if it happens?" "What would be so bad about that?"* Because of cognitive avoidance, anxiety patients have often not thought through what would be so bad if the event that they fear actually happens or how likely it is to happen. Partly for this reason, pushing patients to consider the worst that would happen leads them to discover that the feared event would be much less disastrous or likely than they had tacitly assumed.

In table 19.1 we have concentrated on anxiety-related negative cognitions. Clinically, patients are often depressed as well as anxious and one of the great strengths of cognitive therapy is the fact that similar questioning techniques can be used to evaluate negative cognitions related to each of the different negative emotions. In this way, therapists can effortlessly switch between anxiety, depression, and anger problems within the same session.

So far we have mainly discussed verbal

techniques for testing and modifying negative cognitions. However, when the cognitions that provoke anxiety are recurrent, vivid images, it is sometimes necessary to work in imagery as well as using verbal thought testing. For example, a 24-year-old woman was frequently disturbed by an image in which she recollected being sexually abused by a relative when 5-years-old. Verbal discussion did little to reduce the distress associated with this image. However, visualising herself back in the situation, growing to her current size, and then dealing with the relative in an assertive and adult fashion, proved highly effective. Restructuring images was similarly effective in a 31-year-old male patient. During the early stages of cognitive therapy, his panic frequency reduced considerably and his residual attacks appeared to be triggered by an image in which he recollected a biologically oriented therapist telling him that he could not benefit from cognitive therapy because he suffered from a very serious mental disturbance that could only be controlled pharmacologically, if at all. Discussion of contradictory evidence (his improvement with cognitive therapy) had little effect. However, visualising returning to the therapist's office, explaining his progress, and berating the therapist for an inaccurate diagnosis, completely abolished the image. Further examples of using imagery in cognitive therapy are given in Beck, Emery, and Greenberg (1985).

Behavioral Experiments

In addition to discussing evidence for and against negative beliefs, cognitive therapists also encourage patients to engage in behavioral experiments to test out their beliefs. These experiments are viewed as one of the most potent ways of changing beliefs, and hence have a central role in cognitive therapy. One common experiment in the treatment of anxiety involves encouraging patients to go into situations they have previously avoided in order to see whether the things they are afraid of actually occur. Obviously, this is very similar to exposure as used in behavior therapy (c.f. Mathews, Gleder, & Johnston, 1981). Like behavior therapists, cognitive therapists encourage patients to expose themselves to feared situations repeatedly and in a graded fashion. In addition, they ask them to predict in advance what they think will happen during an exposure session and then to see whether the outcome is less (or more) negative than predicted. When making predictions, patients specify not only their predicted fear level, but also (and more important) anticipated catastrophies ("I will faint," "I will have a heart attack," "I'll make a complete fool of myself") and fears of fear ("I won't be able to cope," "The anxiety will escalate uncontrollably"). Often patients accurately predict experienced fear, but their predictions of anticipated catastrophes or fears of fear are rarely correct.

Although crucially important, exposure to feared situations forms a relatively small proportion of the behavioral experiments used in cognitive therapy. The use of non-exposure related experiments is illustrated by the following two cases.

A housewife experienced frequent panic attacks which were frightening because she believed they meant that she had a serious physical illness. Negative medical tests and reassurance from her physician failed to modify her belief. Reproduction of her feared symptoms by voluntary hyperventilation (see Clark, Salkovskis, & Chalkley, 1985) allowed her to entertain the possibility that her symptoms could simply be the result of stress-induced hyperventilation. However, she pointed out that she noticed her heart more frequently than did her husband and she thought that this must indicate that there was something wrong with it. The therapist suggested the alternative interpretation: that she noticed her heart more because she attended to it more. As a test of this hypothesis, she was asked to close her eyes and concentrate on her heart. To her great surprise, she found that simply attending to her heart enabled her to detect her pulse in her forehead, neck, arms, chest, and legs without touching any of those parts of her body.

Table 19.1. Daily Record of Dysfunctional Thoughts

Situation	Emotion(s)	Automatic Thought(s)	Rational Response	Outcome	Further[a] Action
Describe: 1. Actual event leading to unpleasant emotion, or 2. Stream of thoughts, daydream, or recollection, leading to unpleasant emotion.	1. Specify sad; anxious; angry; etc. 2. Rate degree of emotion, 1–100.	1. Write automatic thought(s) that preceded emotion(s). 2. Rate belief in automatic thought(s), 0–100%.	1. Write rational response to automatic thought(s). 2. Rate belief in rational response, 0–100%.	1. Rerate belief in automatic thought(s), 0–100%. 2. Specify and rate subsequent emotions, 0–100.	
In bedroom. No pictures. Just woken up. Used glasses lying about, some crumbs on the floor.	Anxious 100.	I am in a mess. The house is a mess and I ought to get on with it *right now.*	I don't have to do it right now. If I take a few minutes to wake up and have a cup of tea, I'll be able to do it better. Even if I don't do it it isn't going to make any difference.	Anxious 20.	Try it out — take time to wake up and do something you enjoy in the morning first. (Exercise).
Becoming uncomfortable with telling my therapist — a stranger — my dsyfunctional thoughts	Anxious 95.	He must think I'm mad. Writing all these thoughts down makes me feel "sick." 75%	Who cares what he thinks if he can help lighten my mood. 100%.	1.0% 2. Anx. 0.	
While driving, hypersensitive to sounds.	Anxious 80.	This "stuff" (symptoms of anxiety) is scaring me. 100%.	It won't kill me. 100%.	1.20% 2. Anx. 0.	
Attending a social function at my husband's work. Don't know many people and most of them know each other. Not being included in the conversation.	Anxious 70.	I am boring tonight. ↓	There are lots of explanations for people having difficulty talking to a stranger other than finding them boring. Also, I'm not evaluating other people, so why should they be evaluating me.	1.10% 2. Anx. 0.	Next time: 1. Give the other people some "free information" about me to help them include me in their conversation.

That means I am a boring person. ↓	If I am boring tonight that doesn't mean I'm always boring. Anyway, nobody is boring through and through.	2. Ask them about themselves.
Everyone hates a boring person, therefore nobody will like me.	You don't have to be the life and soul of a party to be liked. Many "quiet" people are liked and loved by others.	3. Stop mind-reading.

[a] This column, which is not included in published versions of the dysfunctional thought record (Beck, Rush, Shaw & Emery, 1979. *Cognitive therapy of depression.* New York: Guilford Press, p. 288), illustrates the fact that discussion of rational responses is often followed up by behavioral assignments which provide further tests of the rational response and/or implement anxiety management strategies suggested by the rational response.

A businessman felt extremely anxious when speaking in public and avoided doing so whenever possible. His major fear was that his colleagues would see that he was anxious and, as a consequence, cease to respect him. He believed that because he *felt* anxious, others must be able to see that he was anxious. In order to test this prediction, the therapist asked him to give a short speech while being videotaped. During the taping he felt very anxious. However, to his amazement, he was unable to detect any external signs of anxiety when subsequently viewing the video.

Often a series of interconnected behavioural experiments and discussions reviewing past experience are used to help patients gather evidence against their negative beliefs. This process of gradually accumulating evidence is illustrated by the case of a housewife with hypochondriacal concerns about cancer. Despite medical reassurance to the contrary, she strongly believed that she had throat cancer. When asked for her evidence for this belief, she pointed out that she frequently had a feeling of discomfort on the surface of her throat and had difficulty swallowing. Both of these symptoms were taken to indicate the presence of cancer. As an alternative, the therapist suggested the hypothesis that the symptoms might be generated by her thoughts about cancer, and consequent focusing of attention on her throat, following the death of an acquaintance from throat cancer. Several procedures were used to distinguish between these two hypotheses. These included:

1. Discussing the extent to which her throat problem was consistent with available information on throat cancer. Following this discussion, she agreed that if she had throat cancer, she would have already deteriorated markedly, but instead, her problem had stayed at a constant level for over 2 years.
2. Collecting evidence to demonstrate that she notices her throat sensations because of an anxiety problem rather than cancer. This included discussing instances from childhood when she had difficulty swallowing because she was forbidden to do so (eating sweets in church), eating segments of oranges and nuts while concentrating on her throat during treatment sessions (this made it more difficult to swallow), and reviewing the extent to which her awareness of her throat sensations varied with the extent to which she was engrossed in activities.
3. Cutting down on behaviours that increased the throat sensations. During sessions it was noticed that she frequently stroked her throat. She explained that this was to ease the feeling of constriction. However, experimentation revealed that it had the opposite effect. After a few minutes of intentional stroking, the throat sensations markedly increased and they subsequently declined when she resisted stroking her throat for a similar period of time.

These procedures considerably reduced her belief that she had throat cancer, but she was still somewhat aware of her throat. In discussing factors that might maintain this awareness, the patient reported that following an early sexual experience she had always avoided having her throat kissed. It was suggested that this avoidance may maintain her preoccupation with her throat. To test this hypothesis, a programme of graded exposure to being kissed on the throat by her husband was introduced. As predicted, this produced a generalized reduction in awareness of her throat.

Assumption Techniques

As well as modifying the particular thoughts that occur in anxiety-provoking situations, cognitive therapy also aims to modify dysfunctional assumptions. As discussed in the introduction, these are general beliefs that predispose individuals to negative emotional reactions. In cognitive therapy for depression (Beck et al., 1979), modification of assumptions occur toward the end of therapy and is largely intended as a means of preventing relapse. In cognitive therapy for anxiety, modification of assumptions has a more prominent role in the earlier phases of treatment. This is particularly true of patients with generalized anxiety states. These individuals are anxious across a wide range of situations, but the anxiety often seems to be based on a relatively small number of general themes or global beliefs relating to long-standing concerns about self-worth and competence. In such cases, identification and modification of assumptions occurs relatively early in therapy, and may be particularly important for achieving and maintaining substantial reductions in anxiety.

Although anxiety-related assumptions probably revolve around a small number of themes (Beck, Emery et al., 1985, p. 289), the exact wording of an assumption is often highly idiosyncratic. Therapists use a variety of techniques to identify assumptions (see Emery, 1981, p. 192). Two of the most common techniques are looking for themes in weekly records of dysfunctional thoughts, and using the downward arrow technique (Burns, 1980, p. 235). In the latter technique, instead of answering an automatic thought, patients attempt to identify the belief behind the thought by repeatedly asking themselves, "If this thought was actually true, what would it mean to me?"

Figure 19.1 illustrates a dysfunctional assumption and the patient's rational responses to that assumption. The patient was suffering from a generalized anxiety state and described himself as being anxious in a wide range of situations and for approximately 80% of each day. In discussing the situations in which he became anxious, it rapidly emerged that almost all of the situations triggered performance worries. These worries appeared to arise on the assumption shown on the flashcard in Figure 19.1.

Several techniques were used to help the patient challenge and modify the assumption. After a *historical review,* he was able to see that the belief was probably the result of his early reinforcement history. This knowledge helped him to gain some distance from the belief. Discussion of the possible *advantages and disadvantages* of holding the belief helped him to see that although valuing success increases motivation to achieve, the extreme form of his belief led to constant anxiety and probably also underachievement. As in many cases of generalized anxiety, the assumption reveals that the patient has considerable doubts about his self-worth. In order to try to counteract these doubts and *build his self-esteem,* he made a list of his assets and discussed with the therapist the evidence for and against his perceived deficits. Finally, he was encouraged to *act against the assumption.* In this way, he found that he could enjoy life even when adopting a pattern of behaviour that was different from that which was implied by the assumption.

REVIEW OF RESEARCH

For convenience, our review of the literature is divided into two sections: studies concerned with the cognitive theory of anxiety and studies concerned with evaluating the effectiveness of cognitive therapy as a treatment for anxiety. Generalization from analogue to clinical populations is often problematic. For this reason, we have mainly restricted the review to studies investigating clinical populations. Analogue studies are only discussed when they address a question that has so far not been addressed in a clinical sample.

Studies investigating the cognitive theory of anxiety

The cognitive theory of anxiety proposes that cognitions concerned with the perception of danger mediate the relationship between anxiety-eliciting events (both internal and external) and the initiation and/or maintained activation of the complex constellation of physiological, cognitive, and behavioural responses, which we have called the "anxiety program." At least four testable predictions can be derived from this theory. These are:

Figure 19.1. Flashcard for Dealing with a Basic Assumption

1. *The Assumption*

I hold the belief that "I am inadequate unless I succeed. All my past successes count for nothing unless I succeed again today. Nobody will love me unless I succeed."

2. *Rational Responses and Plan for Change*

It is understandable why I hold this belief because in the past my parents have never given me unambiguous praise for my successes, but instead always suggested that there is another unseen important hurdle to attack.

However, this belief is untrue because there are things about me from my past that are good and that nobody can take away from me. Also, I am the same person when I do poorly in school. No member of my family or friends treats me differently. They still love me.

In addition, the belief is dysfunctional because it makes me constantly anxious.

As I have held this belief for a long time, I will have to work hard at changing it and it will take a while. Two things I can do to help change it are (a) to make a list of my assets, and (b) spend a little time each day doing something simply for the pleasure of doing it, not for what it will accomplish.

1. The thinking of anxious patients will be characterised by thoughts concerned with the perception of danger.
2. Within individuals, anxiety ratings will correlate with the believability and frequency of thoughts concerned with danger.
3. The temporal occurrence of thoughts concerned with danger will be such that they *could* logically contribute to the initiation or maintained activation of the anxiety program.
4. Experimental manipulations of the frequency and believability of thoughts concerned with the perception of danger will have systematic effects on patients' levels of anxiety. Increasing the frequency and believability of danger related interpretations of events should increase anxiety and decreasing the frequency and believability of danger related interpretations of events should decrease anxiety.

Six studies have investigated the first prediction in clinical populations, and each of these studies has found that the thinking of anxious patients is indeed characterised by thoughts concerned with perceived danger. Beck et al. (1974) interviewed 32 anxiety state patients. All reported experiencing thoughts concerned with psychosocial or physical threat while anxious, and many also reported experiencing images or similar content. In a second study of anxiety states, Hibbert (1984) identified similar thoughts to those observed by Beck et al. (1974) and, in addition, found that there were some differences in the types of danger-related thoughts reported by patients with and without panic attacks. These differences were subsequently replicated by Rappee (1985). Last and Blanchard (1982) studied nine anxious individuals who met DSM-III criteria for phobic disorders. When interviewed, all but one were able to specify an anticipated catastrophic outcome associated with their phobic object, and most experienced thoughts related to this outcome while imagining themselves in the phobic situation. Beidel, Turner, and Dancu (1985) asked socially anxious and non-anxious individuals to fill in a cognition checklist after participating in a series of standardized social interactions and found that socially anxious individuals were more likely to endorse thoughts concerned with negative self-evaluation and perceived inability to cope. Finally, Butler and Mathews (1983) used a questionnaire to investigate the effects of anxiety on subjective probabilities. Compared to normal controls, anxiety state patients (and also depressives scoring high on a state anxiety scale) overestimated the probability of future hypothetical negative events, but did not differ from normals in their estimates of the probability of future positive events.

Last, O'Brien, and Barlow (1985) tested Prediction 2 during the course of a study of cognitive-behavioural and behavioural treatments for agoraphobia. During weekly visits to a shopping mall, six agoraphobic patients kept a record of their thoughts by speaking them into a microphone attached to a microcassette recorder. These thoughts were subsequently categorised as negative, positive, or neutral by independent raters. Consistent with prediction, there was a significant positive correlation between percentage of negative thoughts and anxiety ratings in five cases, and a positive, but nonsignificant, correlation in the remaining case. However, caution should be exercised in interpreting the results of this study, as it is likely that subjects' anxiety ratings would have systematically declined during the course of the study, and the reported correlations appear not to have been corrected for such serial dependency.

Although these studies are consistent with the first two predictions, it could be argued that the observed correspondence between anxiety and danger-related thoughts is a demand effect. Perhaps subjects guessed the experimenters' hypothesis and then responded accordingly. In an ingenious analogue study, Sewich and Kirsch (1984) were able to discount this possibility by leading one of their groups of subjects to believe that the experimenter expected that loss-related thoughts would be associated with anxiety. Despite this manipulation, danger-related thoughts were reported significantly more often than loss-related thoughts.

As there appears to be a genuine association between danger-related thoughts and anxiety, it is appropriate to enquire into the nature of the cognitive process that may give rise to danger-related thoughts. In one of the first studies to do this, Butler and Mathews (1983) found that anxiety state (and depressed) patients were more likely than normals to interpret ambiguous events in a negative fashion. Subsequent studies have concentrated on attentional processes (Mathews & McLeod, 1985, 1986; McLeod, Mathews, & Tata, 1986; Watts, McKenna, Sharrock, & Trezise, 1986). Taken together, these studies suggest that, compared to normals, anxious patients allocate more processing resources to cues related to danger. Anxious patients appear to be more likely to notice threat-related material and also may be more likely to dwell on this material. Both of these effects would be likely to lead an individual to systematically overestimate the degree of danger inherent in a given situation.

The findings discussed so far demonstrate that there is a close relationship between activation of the anxiety program and danger-related cognitions. Clearly, this is a necessary requirement for the cognitive theory. However, the existence of this relationship does not in itself demonstrate that danger-related cognitions mediate the initiation and maintained activation of the anxiety program. On the basis of correlational data alone, it could equally easily be argued that danger-related cognitions are reflections of changes in the activation of the anxiety program, rather than variables of primary etiological importance. More substantial evidence for the cognitive theory would be provided by studies testing Predictions 3 and 4.

Prediction 3 relates to the relative temporal sequence of danger-related cognitions and other aspects of the anxiety program. If danger cognitions only ever occurred after the peak of an anxious episode, then these cognitions would clearly not play an important role in the production of anxiety. However, this does not appear to be the case. Three studies have attempted to established the temporal sequence of events in anxiety episodes, and each study has produced results consistent with the mediation hypothesis. Beck et al. (1974) reported that most anxiety state patients were able to identify danger-related thoughts just before the onset and/or exacerbation of an anxiety episode. Last and Blanchard (1982) obtained essentially similar results with phobics. All of their subjects reported having at least one catastrophic thought before their anxiety peaked. In approximately half of these subjects, danger-related thoughts appeared to have been the first event in the anxious episode. In the remaining half, subjects reported an immediate fear response during which they were not able to spot catastrophic thoughts. However, this immediate response was then followed by catastrophic thoughts, which were, in turn, followed by an anxiety peak. Finally, Hibbert (1984) also reported sequencing data consistent with the mediation hypothesis.

Prediction 4 is concerned with the effects of systematically varying the frequency and believability of negative thoughts. Several experiments have manipulated the frequency and/or believability of negative thoughts in depressed patients. In general, the results of these experiments have provided support for the cognitive theory of depression (see Fennell & Teasdale, 1984; Teasdale, 1983b) Remarkably, no comparable experiments have so far been reported with anxious patients.

To summarize, three of the four predictions derived from the cognitive mediation hypothesis have been confirmed. The fourth prediction has still to be investigated. It is hoped that both this prediction and other aspects of the cognitive model will be investigated in future studies. For example, one particularly interesting additional question concerns the use of training procedures to help some individuals identify negative automatic thoughts. Do these procedures produce verdical reports of cognitive processes, or do they represent artificial or other types of change?

Studies investigating the effectiveness of cognitive therapy

Cognitive therapy is now well established as a treatment for depression. Six studies (Beck, Hollon, Young, Bedrosian, & Budenz, 1985; Blackburn, Bishop, Glen, Whalley, & Christie, 1981; Hollon, De Rubeis, & Evans, 1983; Murphy, Simons, Wetzel, & Lustmann, 1984; Rush, Beck, Kovacs, & Hollon, 1977; Teasdale, Fennell, Hibbert, & Amies, 1984) have found that in the short term, it is as effective, or more effective, than tricyclic antidepressants, and there is some evidence that is may be associated with a lower relapse rate than drug treatment (Blackburn, Eunson, & Bishop, 1986; Simmons, Murphy, Levine, & Wetzel 1986). By contrast, relatively few studies have investigated cognitive therapy's effectiveness in anxiety disorders.

Treatment procedures similar to those described in this chapter and in cognitive therapy manuals (Beck et al., 1979; Beck, Emery et al.) have been used in three case series, each of which obtained promising results. Hollon (1980) reported that cognitive therapy was successful in treating two patients suffering from generalized anxiety with panic attacks. Waddell, Barlow, and O'Brien (1984) also found cognitive therapy helpful in three panic disorder patients. Finally, Clark (1986b) treated six patients who were mainly suffering from nonphobic anxiety disorders. All patients improved, with considerable reductions in anxiety and depression being observed after as few as eight sessions.

To date, the promising results obtained in case studies with nonphobic patients have not been further investigated in controlled trials. However, treatments closely related to cognitive therapy have proved effective. Barlow et al. (1984) found that panic disorder and generalised anxiety patients given cognitive treatments plus relaxation and EMG biofeedback improved significantly more than waiting list controls. Clark et al. (1985) investigated the effectiveness of respiratory control as a treatment for panic patients with and without associated avoidance. This treatment is based on the hypothesis (Clark, 1986a) that panic attacks result from the catastrophic misinterpretation of certain bodily sensations and is probably best categorized as a variant of cognitive therapy. Substantial reductions in panic frequency occurred during the first 2 weeks of treatment; these were further improved upon with additional treatment and maintained at the year follow-up. Similar results were obtained in a subsequent replication study (Salkovskis, Jones, & Clark, 1986). Neither study included a waiting list control. However, the authors argued that the results could not be due to spontaneous remission, as they established a stable baseline and then observed significant improvements from that baseline in a shorter period than the baseline itself. Butler, Cullington, Hibbert, Klimes, and Gelder (in press) investigated the effectiveness of anxiety management training in generalized anxiety patients. Patients given this treatment, which includes individualized identification and challenging of negative thoughts, improved significantly more than waiting list controls.

Although the utility of cognitive therapy in the treatment of nonphobic anxiety seems promising, its contribution to the treatment of phobics is not well defined in current research. No studies have used a complete cognitive therapy treatment programme. However, four studies of social anxiety have investigated treatments that include cognitive procedures. Wolfe and Fodor (1977) compared a behavioral treatment (modeling plus behavior rehearsal) with a cognitive-behavioral treatment (modeling plus behavior rehearsal plus Rational Emotive Therapy (RET)) in female outpatients reporting difficulties in assertion. Compared to waiting list and consciousness raising control groups, both treatments led to significant improvements on a behavioral measure of assertiveness but, during the very short period of treatment (2 weeks), only the cognitive-behavioral treatment led to improvements in situationnal fear. Stravynski, Marks, and Yule (1982) compared social skills training with social skills plus a cognitive modification procedure and found that social phobics improved to a significant but similar extent with both treatments. Butler, Cullington, Munby, Amies, and Gelder (1984) compared exposure, exposure plus anxiety management, and a wait group. At the end of treatment, both treatment groups showed significant and similar improvements in phobic severity, but only the exposure plus anxiety management group improved on measures related to fear of negative evaluation. At 6-months follow-up, more pronounced differences were observed, with anxiety management being significantly better than exposure alone on four out of six social variables. Emmelkamp, Mersch, Vissia, and van der Helm (1985) compared exposure in vivo with two cognitive treatments, which were given in the absence of exposure in vivo, and found significant improvements on most measures with all three treatments. However, as in the Butler et al. (1984) study, only the cognitive treatments changed negative beliefs. Finally, Jerremalm, Jansson, and Ost (1986) compared individualised self-instructional training (SIT), applied relaxation (AR), and a wait group, in social phobics who were defined as predominantly cognitive reactors or predominantly physiological reactors of the basis of their responses to a behaviour test. Within both patient groups, SIT was superior to wait list. In addition, when there were significant differences between SIT and AR, these always favoured SIT (6 out of 20 SIT vs AR comparisons were significant).

Several studies have investigated the effectiveness of cognitive procedures in the treatment of simple phobias and agoraphobia. In simple phobias, Biran and Wilson (1981) found exposure in vivo to be superior to a form of cognitive restructuring which was given in the absence of exposure. However, most cognitive therapists believe that exposure in vivo is a crucial component in the treatment of phobias. For this reason, the more interesting question is: Can exposure in vivo be potentiated by adding to it the additional procedures that are used in cognitive therapy? Three studies (Emmelkamp, Kuipers, & Eggeraat, 1978; Emmelkamp & Mersch, 1982; Williams & Rappoport, 1983) have addressed this issue in agoraphobia and each produced negative results. However, all of these studies appear to have used contrived and restricted variants of cognitive therapy procedures which bear little resemblance to the actual practice of cognitive therapy. As stated earlier in this chapter, cognitive therapy is a complex treatment which uses a very wide range of techniques to identify and modify dysfunctional thinking. Two of the most central belief modification procedures are within-session discussions of the evidence for and against patients' *idiosyncratic* dysfunctional thoughts and behavioural experiments which are designed to test the validity of these thoughts. Relatively little attention appears to have been directed to detailed discussion and evaluation of idiosyncratic thoughts (for example, in Williams and Rappoport's study, negative thoughts were discussed in 1- and 2-minute intervals between exposure assignments), and no mention is made of the use of behavioural experiments, even though these form a crucial part of cognitive therapy (see above).

CONCLUDING REMARKS

In summary, we propose that the available evidence suggests that cognitive therapy is a promising approach to the treatment of anxiety, especially in nonphobic disorders. However, final evaluation of the effectiveness of this approach must await the publication of large-scale, well-conducted, controlled trials. The results of such trials are most likely to be clearly interpretable if researchers pay particular attention to the following points: (a) tackling idiosyncratic beliefs, (b) using behavioral experiments, and (c) training therapists. As Ost and Jansson (1987) have pointed out, cognitive therapy is a complex system of therapy and particular attention needs to be paid to providing therapists with adequate training and supervision in the use of the treatment.

Acknowledgements — The authors are grateful to Gillian Butler, Melanie Fennell, Michael Gelder, and Paul Salkovskis for helpful comments on an earlier draft on this chapter.

REFERENCES

American Psychiatric Association (1980). *Diagnostic and statistical manual of mental disorders* (3rd ed.). Washington, DC: Author.

Anderson, J. R. (1985). *Cognitive psychology and its implications* (2nd ed.) New York: W. H. Freeman and Co.

Barlow, D. H., Cohen, A. S., Waddell, M. T., Vermilyea, B. B., Klosko, T. S., Blanchard, E. B., & DiNardo, P. A. (1984). Panic and generalized anxiety disorders: Nature and treatment. *Behavior Therapy, 15*, 431–449.

Beck, A. T. (1967). *Depression: Clinical, experimental and theoretical aspects*. New York: Harper and Row.

Beck, A. T. (1970). Role of fantasies in psychotherapy and psychopathology. *Journal of Nervous and Mental Disease, 150*, 3–17.

Beck, A. T. (1976). *Cognitive therapy and the emotional disorders*. New York: International Universities Press.

Beck, A. T. (in press). Cognitive approaches to anxiety disorders. In B. F. Shaw, Z. V. Segal, T. M. Vallis, & F. E. Cashman (Eds.), *Anxiety disorders: Psychological and biological perspectives*. New York: Plenum.

Beck, A. T., Emery, G., & Greenberg, R. L. (1985). *Anxiety disorders and phobias: A cognitive perspective*. New York: Basic Books.

Beck, A. T., Hollon, S. D., Young, J. E., Bedrosian, R. C., & Budenz, D. (1985). Treatment of depression with cognitive therapy and amitriptyline. *Archives of General Psychiatry, 42*, 142–148.

Beck, A. T., Laude, R., & Bohnert, M. (1974). Ideational components of anxiety neurosis. *Archives of General Psychiatry, 31*, 319–325.

Beck, A. T., Rush, A. J., Shaw, B. F., & Emery, G. (1979). *Cognitive therapy of depression*. New York: Guilford Press.

Beidel, D. C., Turner, S. M., & Dancu, C. V. (1985). Physiological, cognitive and behavioural aspects of social anxiety. *Behaviour Research and Therapy, 23*, 109–117.

Biran, M., & Wilson, G. T. (1981). Treatment of phobic disorders using cognitive and exposure methods: a self-efficacy analysis. *Journal of Consulting and Clinical Psychology, 49*, 886–899.

Blackburn, I. M., Bishop, S., Glen, A. I. M., Whalley, L. J., & Christie, J. E. (1981). The efficacy of cognitive therapy in depression: A treatment trial using cognitive therapy and pharmacotherapy, each alone and in combination. *British Journal of Psychiatry, 139*, 181–189.

Blackburn, I. M., Eunson, K. M., & Bishop, S. (1986). A two-year naturalistic follow-up of depressed patients treated with cognitive therapy, pharmacotherapy and a combination of both. *Journal of Affective Disorders, 10*, 67–75.

Burns, D. D. (1980). *Feeling good*. New York: New American Library.

Butler, G., Cullington, A., Hibbert, G., Klimes, I., & Gelder, G. (in press) Anxiety management for persistent generalized anxiety. *British Journal of Psychiatry.*

Butler, G., Cullington, A., Munby, M., Amies, P., & Gelder, M. (1984). Exposure and anxiety management in the treatment of social phobia. *Journal of Consulting and Clinical psychology, 52*, 642–650.

Butler, G., & Mathews, A. (1983). Cognitive processes in anxiety. *Advances in Behaviour Research and Therapy, 5*, 51–62.

Chambless, D. L., Caputo, G. C., Bright, P., & Gallagher, R. (1984). Assessment of fear of fear in agoraphobics: the body sensations questionnaire and the agoraphobic cognitions questionnaire. *Journal of Consulting and Clinical Psychology, 52*, 1090–1097.

Clark, D. M. (1986a). A cognitive approach to panic. *Behaviour Research and Therapy, 24*, 461–470.

Clark, D. M. (1986b). Cognitive therapy for anxiety. *Behavioural Psychotherapy, 14*, 283–294.

Clark, D. M., & Salkovskis, P. M. (in press). A cognitive-behavioural treatment for panic attacks. In W. Huber (Ed.), *Proceedings of the 2nd European Conference in Psychotherapy Research*. Belgium: University of Louvain Press.

Clark, D. M., Salkovskis, P. M., & Chalkley, A. J. (1985). Respiratory control as a treatment for panic attacks. *Journal of Behaviour Therapy and Experimental Psychiatry, 16*, 23–30.

Clark, D. M., & Teasdale, J. D. (1982). Diurnal variation in clinical depression and accessibility of memories of positive and negative experiences. *Journal of Abnormal Psychology, 91*, 87–95.

Clark, D. M., & Teasdale, J. D. (1985). Constraints on the effects of mood on memory. *Journal of Personality and Social Psychology, 48*, 1595–1608.

Ellis, A. (1962). *Reason and emotion in psychotherapy*. New York: Lyle Stuart.

Emery, G. (1981). *A new beginning: How to change your life through cognitive therapy* New York: Simon and Schuster.

Emery, G. (1982). *Own your own life*. New York: New American Library.

Emmelkamp, P. M. G. (1982). *Phobic and obsessive-compulsive disorders*. New York: Plenum Press.

Emmelkamp, P. M. G., Kuipers, A. C. M., & Eggeraat, J. B. (1978). Cognitive modification versus prolonged exposure in vivo: A comparison with agoraphobics as subjects. *Behaviour Research and Therapy, 16*, 33–41.

Emmelkamp, P. M. G., & Mersch, P. P. (1982). Cognition and exposure *in vivo* in the treatment of agoraphobia: short-term and delayed effects. *Cognitive Therapy and Research, 6*, 77–88.

Emmelkamp, P. M. G., Mersch, P. P., Vissia, E., & van der Helm, M. (1985). Social phobia: a comparative evaluation of cognitive and behavioural interventions. *Behaviour Research and Therapy*, 23, 365–369.

Fennell, M. J. V., & Teasdale, J. D. (1984). Effects of distraction on thinking and affect in depressed patients. *British Journal of Clinical Psychology*, 23, 65–66.

Hibbert, G. A. (1984). Ideational components of anxiety: Their origin and content. *British Journal of Psychiatry, 144*, 618–624.

Hollon, S. D. (1980). Cognitive-behavioural treatment of drug-induced pansituational anxiety states. In G. Emery, S. D. Hollon, & R. C. Bedrosian (Eds.), *New directions in cognitive therapy: A casebook*. pp. 120–138 New York: Raven Press.

Hollon, S. D., De Rubeis, R. J., & Evans, M. D. (1983, December). *Final report of the cognitive-pharmacotherapy trial: Outcome, prophylaxis, prognosis, process and mechanism*. Paper presented at the World Congress on Behaviour Therapy, Washington, DC.

Jerremalm, A., Jannsson, L., & Ost, L. G. (1986). Cognitive and physiological reactivity and the effects of different behavioral methods in the treatment of social phobia. *Behaviour Research and Therapy, 24*, 171–180.

Lader, M., & Marks, I. M. (1971). *Clinical anxiety*. London: Heineman.

Last, C. G., & Blanchard, E. B. (1982). Classification of phobic versus fearful non-phobics: Procedural and theoretical issues. *Behavioral Assessment, 4*, 195–210.

Last, C. G., O'Brien, G. T., & Barlow, D. H. (1985). The relationship between cognitions and anxiety: A preliminary report. *Behavior Modification, 9*, 235–241.

MacLeod, C., Mathews, A., & Tata, P. (1986). Attentional bias in emotional disorders. *Journal of Abnormal Psychology, 95*, 15–20.

Mathews, A., Gelder, M. G., & Johnston, D. W. (1981). *Agoraphobia: Nature and treatment*. New York: Guilford Press.

Mathews, A., & MacLeod, C. (1985). Selective processing of threat cues in anxiety states. *Behaviour Research and Therapy, 23*, 563–569.

Mathews, A. & MacLeod, C. (1986). Discrimination of threat cues without awareness in anxiety states. *Journal of Abnormal Psychology, 95*, 131–139.

Meichenbaum, D. (1977). *Cognitive-behavior modification*. New York: Plenum Press.

Murphy, G. E., Simons, A. D., Wetzel, R. D., & Lustmann, P. J. (1984). Cognitive therapy and pharmacotherapy singly and together in the treatment of depression. *Archives of General Psychiatry, 41*, 33–41.

Ost, L. G., & Jansson, L. (1987). Methodological issues in cognitive-behavioral treatments of anxiety disorders. In L. Michelson, & M. Asher (Eds.), *Cognitive-behavioral assessment and treatment of anxiety disorders*, pp. 105–145. New York: Guilford Press.

Rachman, S. J., & da Silva, P. (1978). Abnormal and normal obsessions. *Behaviour Research and Therapy, 16*, 233–248.

Rappee, R. M. (1985). Distinctions between panic disorder and generalized anxiety disorder: Clinical presentation. *Australian and New Zealand Journal of Psychiatry, 19*, 227–232.

Rush, A. J., Beck, A. T., Kovacs, M., & Hollon, S. D. (1977). Comparative efficacy of cognitive therapy and pharmacotherapy in the treatment of depressed out-patients. *Cognitive Therapy and Research, 1*, 17–37.

Salkovskis, P. M. (1985). Obsessional–compulsive problems: A cognitive-behavioral analysis. *Behaviour Research and Therapy, 23*, 571–584.

Salkovskis, P. M., Jones, D. R. O., & Clark, D. M. (1986). Respiratory control in the treatment of panic attacks: Replication and extension with concurrent measurement of behaviour and pCO_2. *British Journal of Psychiatry, 148*, 526–532.

Sewitch, T. S., & Kirsch, I. (1984). The cognitive content of anxiety: Naturalistic evidence for the predominance of threat-related thoughts. *Cognitive Therapy and Research, 8,* 49–58.

Simmons, A. D., Murphy, G. E., Levine, J. L., & Wetze, R. D. (1986). Cognitive therapy and pharmacotherapy for depression. Sustained improvement over one year. *Archives of General Psychiatry, 43,* 43–48.

Stravynski, A., Marks, I. M., & Yule, W. (1982). Social skills training with and without cognitive modification. *Archives of General Psychiatry, 39,* 1378–1385.

Teasdale, J. D. (1983a). Affect and accessibility. *Philosophical Transactions of the Royal Society of London* (Series B), *302,* 403–412.

Teasdale, J. D. (1983b). Negative thinking in depression: Cause, effect or reciprocal relationship? *Advances in Behaviour Research and Therapy, 5,* 3–25.

Teasdale, J. D., Fennell, M. J. V., Hibbert, G. V., & Amies, P. L. (1984). Cognitive therapy for major depressive disorder in primary care. *British Journal of Psychiatry, 144,* 400–406.

Waddell, M. T., Barlow, D. H., & O'Brien G. T. (1984). A preliminary investigation of cognitive and relaxation treatment of panic disorder: Effects on intense anxiety vs 'background' anxiety. *Behaviour Research and Therapy, 22,* 393–402.

Watts, F. N., McKenna, F. P., Sharrock, R., & Trezise, L. (1986). Colour naming of phobia-related words. *British Journal of Psychology, 77,* 97–108.

Williams, S. L., & Rappoport, A. (1983). Cognitive treatment in the natural environment for agoraphobics. *Behavior Therapy, 14,* 299–313.

Wilson, G. T. (1984). Fear reduction methods and the treatment of anxiety disorders. In *Annual Review of Behavior Therapy* (Vol. 9), pp. 95–131. New York: Guilford Press.

Wolfe, J. L., & Fodor, I. G. (1977). Modifying assertive behaviour in women: A comparison of three approaches. *Behavior Therapy, 8,* 567–574.

Young, J. E. (1981). Cognitive therapy and loneliness. In G. Emery, R. Bedrosian & S. Hollon (Eds.), *New directions in cognitive Therapy.* New York: Guilford Press.

Young, J. E. (1982). Loneliness, depression and cognitive therapy: Theory and application. In L. A. Peplau & D. Perlman (Eds.), *Loneliness: A source book of current theory, research and therapy.* New York: John Wiley & Sons.

Young J. E., & Beck, A. T. (1982) Cognitive therapy: Clinical applications. In A. J. Rush (Ed.), *Short-term psychotherapies for depression.* (pp. 182–214). New York: Guilford Press.

CHAPTER 20

Marital and Family Therapy

R. Julian Hafner

This chapter competes for the reader's attention with four others offering different psychological approaches to treatment. In reality, there is a substantial overlap between marital, psychotherapeutic, behavioral, cognitive, and hypnotic treatments for anxiety disorders. Thus, marital/family therapy will be considered here as one component of treatment, and not as an exclusive or unitary approach. Even so, the problem remains of selecting patients who are likely to benefit from marital/family therapy, and of then determining how much of it should be added to the therapeutic mix.

The severity of the disorder and precise diagnostic category are useful preliminary guides to the applicability of marital/family therapy. In general, the more severe and persisting is the disorder, the greater is the likelihood that direct attention to marital/family factors will be a prerequisite for successful treatment.

Diagnostic category helps to predict the value of marital/family therapy in two ways. First, by virtue of the relationship between diagnosis and specific intrapsychic and interpersonal processes, and second, through the compounding influence of severity. Levels of overall psychopathology vary considerably across different diagnostic categories. For the purposes of this chapter, both the DSM-III (APA, 1980) and the ICD-9 diagnostic systems will be used.

There is little evidence that marital/family factors routinely require direct attention in the treatment of simple phobias or social phobias, and the same is true of uncomplicated or "pure" cases of panic disorder and generalized anxiety disorder (GAD). However, uncomplicated cases are comparatively rare in routine clinical practice. Frequently, features common to both panic disorder and GAD coexist in the same patient, often together with symptoms listed in the DSM-III category of "somatoform disorders." Where bodily complaints and preoccupations are marked, particularly if they can be construed as abnormal illness behaviour (Pilowsky, 1978), then direct attention to marital/family factors may be critical for an optimal treatment outcome.

In agoraphobia and obsessive–compulsive disorder, attention to marital/

family factors is often central to therapy. Once again, uncomplicated cases of agoraphobia are comparatively rare, the more usual presentation being what Goldstein and Chambless (1978) termed "complex" agoraphobia, which (unlike "simple" agoraphobia) they regard as arising primarily out of marital conflict. Such cases often have features reminiscent of somatoform disorders and social phobias; depression and obsessive–compulsive symptoms are frequently prominent. Indeed, Salzman (1982) has put forward the argument that complex agoraphobia is simply one manifestation of obsessive–compulsive disorder.

In spite of these diagnostic complexities and ambiguities, routine attention to marital/family factors appears worthwhile in complex agoraphobia, in severe obsessive compulsive disorder, and in panic disorder and GAD when complicated by abnormal illness behavior. Thus, the rest of this chapter will mainly relate to these diagnostic categories, and particularly to agoraphobia, because it is so common in clinical practice. Furthermore, because this chapter is concerned primarily with the treatment of adults, couples therapy will be its main focus.

DESCRIPTION OF TREATMENT

The idea of marital therapy for anxiety disorders is, strictly speaking, illogical. The term *marital therapy* clearly suggests the marriage itself as the primary focus of therapy. However, a majority of married patients with severe or persisting anxiety disorders, together with their spouses, regard direct attention to the patient's symptoms as the only logical approach to treatment (Vandereycken, 1983). In such circumstances, an offer of marital therapy is likely to be regarded as irrelevant, misconceived, or even harmful. Unless this fundamental problem is addressed from the outset, couples therapy for anxiety disorders is unlikely to be fully successful. As Cochrane (1973) has pointed out, it is not enough merely to engage such couples in marriage therapy: They are often highly skilled at preserving indefinitely the patient's symptoms as a displaced focus of marital dissatisfaction. If confronted too forcefully about the contribution of marital dynamics to symptom maintenance, they often drop out of therapy.

Cobb, McDonald, Marks, and Stern (1980) have shown empirically that although conjoint marital therapy improved the marriages of patients with severe phobic/obsessive compulsive disorders, it did not improve the patients' symptoms. In contrast, conjoint behavior therapy that focused on the patients' symptoms improved both the symptoms and the marriage.

As Goldstein and Chambless (1981) have put it:

> The agoraphobic and her husband are legitimately focused on the very real effects of this crippling syndrome on their lives. The subtleties of interpersonal and intrapsychic conflict seem largely irrelevant in the face of such a disability . . . . For this reason we find it more useful to begin by accepting that the phobias and panic are of primary importance at the moment. (p. 125)

Many psychodynamically oriented therapists express major reservations about the idea of a couples approach that focuses directly on the patient's symptoms, and Goldstein and Chambless (1981) themselves acknowledge that this might be viewed as "joining the resistance" (p. 125). In adopting such an approach myself, which I termed *spouse-aided therapy* (Hafner, 1981b), a major problem was to avoid duplicity. Informing a couple that the focus of treatment will be on the patient's symptoms, while at the same time covertly planning to directly examine and modify the marriage relationship, seems duplicitous. This is particularly so when the spouse is suspected of contributing to symptom maintenance. Such deceit, when exposed, is likely to damage, perhaps irreparably, the therapist-couple relationship. In an attempt to avoid this and other dilemmas, spouse-aided therapy has been developed to its current state, an outline of which now follows.

Spouse-aided therapy

Assessment interviews

Most married patients with severe, persisting anxiety disorders have a history of repeated failure to respond to a range of medical and psychological treatments. Thus, they and their spouses bring a powerful ambivalence with them into their assessment interviews: Expectations of treatment failure may outweigh hopes of success, but desperation forces the couple to continue searching for "a cure." I will illustrate later how this very ambivalence can be used to protect the therapist from being deceitful toward the spouse.

Assessing the patient

Patient and spouse should be offered separate assessment interviews. Once an adequate history has been taken from the patient, and the diagnosis confirmed, it is necessary to elicit his or her views on the origins of the disorder and on the desirability of a couples approach to treatment.

Most patients equate couples therapy with marriage therapy, the idea of which usually evokes anxiety. Such anxiety generally derives from a fear that the spouse will reject or abandon them if the marriage relationship is questioned or challenged. From the patient's perspective, the spouse is dutifully remaining in a difficult marriage in order to support and care for his/her disability and distress. The greater the patient's psychological disability, the more he/she feels dependent on the spouse's good will.

The patient's dilemma about couples therapy can be resolved if the therapist proposes the idea of inviting the spouse to be involved as a *co-therapist*. However, when the spouse is hostile and/or overcontrolling, this maneuver greatly increases the patient's ambivalence about therapy, because it appears to magnify the prospect not only of success, but also of failure.

At this point, the patient is faced with the critical decision of whether or not to *trust* the therapist. The precise chemistry of this decision is probably beyond scientific analysis. However, the likelihood of the patient agreeing to spouse-aided therapy is enhanced by openness, honesty, and sincerity in the therapist, and by reassurance that the spouse will be treated with the utmost tact and respect. Once the patient has agreed to proceed with spouse-aided therapy, the therapist has accepted an unusually large burden of responsibility. He or she must guard not only against his or her own negative countertransference toward the patient, but must also be prepared to protect the patient from the negative transference (or, strictly speaking, countertransference) of the spouse.

It should now be clear that in accepting an offer of spouse-aided therapy, the patient is often taking a big risk. For this reason alone (and there are often other reasons to which the therapist may not be privy), it is inappropriate to try and persuade a clearly reluctant patient to proceed. Only if the patient gives considered and informed consent can the therapist move to the next stage, which is to invite the spouse to an assessment interview.

Interviewing husbands

Of numerous articles that describe the spouses of patients with severe phobic-anxiety or obsessive–compulsive disorders, virtually all refer primarily to husbands. While psychotherapists generally agree that husbands often play a central role in precipitating or perpetuating their wives' symptoms (Chambless & Goldstein, 1981; Fry, 1962; Goodstein & Swift, 1977; Holmes, 1982: Quadrio, 1983, 1984; Schwartz & Val, 1984; Symonds, 1971; Webster, 1953), there is very little consensus about how this actually occurs.

There is also disagreement about the willingness of husbands to join their wives in conjoint therapy. Forrest (1969) found that he was able to constructively engage only 1 of 18 such husbands in couples therapy, whereas Matthews, Gelder, and Johnston (1981) found that it was very unusual for conjoint therapy to be unworkable: "a marriage must be very severely disturbed before this happens, since relationships usually improve as the partners work together on the agoraphobic problem" (p. 112). However, in attempting, like Matthews et al., to involve spouses in patients' behavioral treatment, Benjamin and Kincey (1981) reported: "Some of our patients' relatives showed extremely negative attitudes towards the patients' treatment and refused to be involved" (p. 427). They noted also: "It seems likely that the inferred disturbances in interpersonal relationships were important in the onset, persistence and severity of the symptoms concerned" (p. 425).

Part of the difference between the findings of Matthews et al. and Benjamin and Kincey is probably attributable to the fact that the former routinely excluded cases of "complex" agoraphobia, whereas the latter deliberately included them.

In my own clinical practice, it is common for husbands to be initially hostile to me as a therapist, particularly if their wives have failed repeatedly to respond to individual therapy. Hurvitz (1967) has elaborated some mechanisms whereby such hostility is generated. Thus, a major initial task is to identify and modify this hostility so that it does not become an obstacle to therapy.

It is helpful if, as early as possible, the therapist acknowledges the strength of the husband's commitment to the marriage hitherto, congratulating him on remaining married to someone suffering from a disabling, persisting, and disrupting condition of uncertain origin. It should then be pointed out that, where mental health experts have repeatedly failed to help his wife, and perhaps have even exacerbated some of her problems, he should not blame himself for the failure thus far of his own efforts, even if these may at times have inadvertently made his wife worse. During the ensuing discussion, nearly all husbands request advice about optimal ways of helping their wives.

Inquiry should then be made about the husband's willingness to be involved as a co-therapist. At this stage I generally state clearly that I will probably fail to help the patient without the husband's active help and cooperation. This often sharply intensifies the husband's ambivalence, because it creates the opportunity for him to gratify any overt or repressed hostility and rivalry toward me by sabotaging my therapeutic efforts and turning me into a "failure." In practice, very few husbands reject the offer of a role as co-therapist, even though it has become apparent that this will probably require a direct examination of aspects of the martial relationship.

Interviewing wives

Basically similar strategies are required to enlist the wives of male patients as cotherapists. However, even greater emphasis must be placed on the strength of the marriage and the devotion, loyalty, and self-sacrifice of the spouse. Most wives of men with severe, persisting anxiety disorders have devoted several years or more to looking after their disabled husbands. Any suggestion that they may inadvertently have contributed to their husband's symptoms is likely to enrage them unless it is handled very cautiously and tactfully indeed. This crucial issue is best broached by seeking wives' views as to why their husbands have remained ill in spite of their efforts to help them. Most wives then admit to feelings of frustration and guilt which, if empathized with, generally permit an honest discussion of the wives' feelings and behavior toward the patient.

Before ending the assessment interview, it is advisable to assess the spouse's personal adjustment, and to give him or her the opportunity of discussing any personal problems. Occasionally, problems are revealed that require therapy in their own right, although more commonly they can be dealt with during spouse-aided therapy. It is also essential to elicit potential obstacles to spouse-aided therapy, such as a lack of commitment to the marriage, or clandestine extramarital liaisons.

Establishing treatment goals

Assuming that no obstacles to spouse-aided therapy have emerged during the individual assessment interviews, both partners are invited to a conjoint session aimed at establishing *treatment goals*. Unless the spouse has identified personal problems or symptoms requiring attention, treatment goals should be directly related to the patient's symptoms.

In order to counter the couple's ambivalence to the therapist, to each other, and to the process of therapy, it is essential that both partners are *actively involved* in establishing treatment goals. By thus accepting direct responsibility for a central aspect of the treatment process, the marriage partners are limited in their ability to blame each other, or the therapist, for subsequent problems in therapy. Moreover, if either partner attempts to sabotage treatment, he or she is compelled to acknowledge that the sabotage is directed at his or her own efforts, as well as those of the therapist or spouse.

Before treatment goals can be established, therapist, patient, and spouse must reach broad agreement about the nature and severity of the patient's symptoms. This task often takes up most of the first conjoint session, but it is time well spent, because it permits the spouse to understand more about the real nature of the patient's symptoms and problems.

Initial obstacles to establishing treatment goals include:

1. Failure to agree on the nature and extent of the patient's symptoms. This is most likely to occur where couples' communication is poor, and mutual hostility, mistrust, and suspicion is high. In such cases, two or three conjoint sessions may be required before agreement is reached on suitable treatment goals.
2. A rigid adherence to an illness model. Here, the couple has identified so strongly with the idea that the patient's symptoms are the product of a mysterious illness entirely beyond the personal control or responsibility of either, that neither partner feels able to take an active part in the treatment process. Two or three sessions may be required before they modify their views, in the course of which considerable anger may be released toward the therapist. Later, this anger is usually redirected toward those whom the couple blame for causing them to overvalue the illness model as an explanation for the patient's symptoms.
3. The patient's extreme passivity or dependency. If the patient has been severely distressed and disabled by an anxiety disorder for several years or more, and particularly if he or she is clinically depressed, then it may be impossible for him or her to generate any appropriate treatment goals. This is even more likely to be the case where strong conditioning to the medical model has occurred also.

   Patients who are extremely dependent on their spouses and/or others may have become so used to other people making decisions for them that they cannot initially generate treatment goals for themselves. This is a particularly difficult problem if the patient's spouse has become used to exercising rigid or near-absolute control over the patient.

If, after two or three conjoint sessions, it proves impossible for the above or other reasons to establish mutually agreed-upon treatment goals, then spouse-aided therapy cannot proceed. Alternative therapy arrangements should be discussed. At this point, a course of medication for depression and/or anxiety and obsessive–compulsive symptoms is often appropriate. Although most patients will have previously taken tricyclics, monoamine oxidase inhibitors, and/or benzodiazepines, dosages may have been inadequate. If patients respond to medication, they often become able to set appropriate treatment goals. Occasionally, response to medication is sufficient to preclude the need or desire for spouse-aided therapy.

Working at treatment goals

Problems in implementing treatment goals are inevitable. Identifying reasons for failure or difficulty requires *direct examination of marital interaction* as part of analyzing the couple's shared and individual problem-solving activities. This requires the couple to accept that attention to the marriage relationship has become a central aspect of the initial treatment contract, which was to work together at resolving the patient's symptoms and problems.

By the time attitudes, beliefs, and behavior that directly or indirectly perpetuate the patient's symptoms are revealed in both marriage partners, the therapist should have developed a good working relationship with the couple. Thus, it becomes possible to confront either or both about these problems without alienating them from therapy. Nonetheless, considerable tact, resourcefulness, and ingenuity are required in order to get couples to address the real origins of the patient's symptoms. Examples of how this may be achieved are provided in Section 4 of this chapter.

REVIEW OF RESEARCH

The widespread acceptance of DSM-III has created problems about the relevance of pre-existing research into the marital context of anxiety disorders. Thus far, nearly all such research has been aimed at either the broad diagnostic category of anxiety neurosis, or the specific category of agoraphobia.

In order to utilize these research findings, it is necessary to preserve the ICD-9 diagnostic category anxiety neurosis, a category that Tyrer (1984), among others, believes has been abandoned prematurely. For example, the DSM-III classification of anxiety disorders does not reflect the clinical reality that severely anxious patients usually present with a wide range of symptoms, including depression, which transcend the specific DSM-III categories. Moreover, Hallam (1978) has argued convincingly that there is no adequate scientific basis for a dinstinction between agoraphobia and anxiety neurosis in general.

Thus, with regard to research that is not based on DSM-III, findings about the marital context of agoraphobia will be generalized to the diagnostic category *anxiety neurosis*, a category that will be viewed in parallel with the DSM-III concept of anxiety disorders.

Marriage and agoraphobia

The psychiatric literature on agoraphobia is notable for opposing view on the role of marriage in precipitating or perpetuating the disorder. As we have seen, there are those, primarily psychotherapists, who emphasize the central role of marital factors; and there are those, primarily clinical researchers, who largely disregard the marriage relationship (Klein, Zitrin, Woerner, & Ross, 1983; Sheehan, Ballenger, & Jacobsen, 1980), or who explicitly reject its relevance (Buglass, Clarke, Henderson, Kreitman, & Presley, 1977; Cobb, Matthews, Childs-Clarke, & Blowers, 1984; Rapp & Thomas, 1982).

As the DSM-III points out, agoraphobia often co-exists with depression, anxiety, rituals, ruminations, minor checking compulsions, and social phobias. Depression has a particularly intimate relationship with agoraphobia (Bowen & Kohout, 1979), and Clancy, Noyes, Hoenk, and Slymen (1978) observed that presence of depression reduced the responsiveness of agoraphobia to treatment. However, the level at which associated symptoms may be regarded as requiring treatment in their own right is essentially arbitrary. For example, Buglass et al. (1977) excluded from their study any agoraphobic patients with marked depressive mood change or significant social phobias. On the basis of their findings they concluded that marital factors were irrelevant to the agoraphobia. In contrast, Holmes (1982) included patients with depression and other major symptoms and problems in addition to agoraphobia. He concluded that marital interaction was often central to symptom maintenance, and that worthwhile improvements occurred only if treatment focused on altering the marital system rather than on the patient alone.

These two reports reflect a general trend in the literature: Studies that exclude patients with major symptoms and problems in addition to their agoraphobia usually discount the need for direct intervention in the marriage; in contrast, studies that include such patients generally advocate couples therapy as a central aspect of treatment. This trend, hitherto poorly recognized, has been a major contributor to disagreement about the relevance of marital factors to agoraphobia, and, by implication, to severe, persisting anxiety disorders in general.

Simple versus Complex Agoraphobia

It was noted earlier that Goldstein and Chambless (1978) proposed that agoraphobia should be divided into "complex" and "simple" categories. Working independently of Goldstein and Chambless, I also defined two relatively distinct types of agoraphobia (Hafner, 1977, 1982b), and these broadly coincided with the proposed complex and simple categories. Combining the clinical findings of Goldstein and Chambless with my own empirical data, the following picture emerges.

Complex agoraphobia is generally precipitated or compounded by marital conflict. It is characterised by a wide range of major additional psychological problems, particularly hypochondriasis, generalized anxiety, obsessive–compulsive symptoms, social phobias, and depression. (Bowen and Kohout [1979] found that over 90% of 55 agoraphobic patients suffered from a primary affective disorder.) Complex agoraphobia is nearly always associated with major personality abnormalities, the most common being unusual dependency linked with a strong tendency to blame and criticize other people. This personality abnormality does not usually change after behavioral treatment, to which patients' initial response is not uncommonly positive. However, partial or complete relapse is frequent, usually in relation to marital difficulties that are precipitated or exacerbated by the patient's initial response to treatment.

Simple agoraphobia occurs against a background of accumulating life stress and intrapsychic conflict; patients commonly report specific traumatic events as precipitating factors. The disorder is rarely complicated by significant hypochondriasis, generalized anxiety, obsessive–compulsive symptoms, or social phobias, although concurrent mild to moderate depression is not uncommon. Many patients with simple agoraphobia have mild personality abnormalities, of which a tendency to excessive guilt and self-blame is a prominent feature. However, such abnormalities are largely reversed after behavior therapy, to which these patients generally respond well. If marital difficulties occur after effective behavior therapy, these are rarely associated with persisting relapse of the patients' agoraphobia.

The Over-Representation of Simple Agoraphobia in Clinical Research

The most influential experimental studies of agoraphobia in recent years have primarily concerned drugs and behavior therapy, either alone or in combination. Selection criteria for these studies have, in general, been strongly biased in favour of simple agoraphobia. For example, Zitrin, Klein, Woerner, and Ross (1983) and Marks et al. (1983) excluded patients with "more than moderate" levels of depression from their large-scale, long-term studies of agoraphobia. The precise number of patients who were deliberately excluded, or who refused to participate, is not reported in either of the above studies, a deficiency that is almost universal in this type of research.

In one of the very few studies that provide the relevant data, Jannoun, Munby, Catalan, and Gelder (1980) rejected 19 out of 53 patients from their behavioral treatment program because they failed to meet entry criteria, which included *the absence of symptoms requiring treatment in their own right*. Six more of the original 53 patients refused treatment (and one dropped out after only two sessions because of unspecified "family problems"). Thus, barely 50% of patients initially referred actually entered treatment.

Even after exclusion of agoraphobic patients with significant depression or other symptoms and problems, the number of treatment dropouts from large-scale experimental studies is generally substantial. In an extensive review, Mavissakalian and Michelson (1982) concluded that the overall percentage of dropouts is at least 25%. Thus, on average, it is likely that *less than 50%* of referred patients actually complete treatment.

Although exclusion of complex cases of agoraphobia from systematic research trials can be justified on methodological grounds, few researchers have acknowledged the implications of this: namely, that their findings are based on unrepresentative cases. Thus, the fairly good results of trials of behavioral and drug treatments for agoraphobia are in large part attributable to a preselection of "simple" cases, which in general, are likely to respond to "simple," unimodal or bimodal therapies.

It is in patients with complex agoraphobia that marital issues are most likely to be relevant to symptom formation and maintenance. Yet patients with complex agoraphobia are generally excluded from systematic research trials, or exclude themselves by declining or dropping out of treatment. It is therefore not surprising that research workers have generally ignored or rejected marital factors in their conceptualization of agoraphobia and related disorders. Nonetheless, because at least 70% of agoraphobic patients are married (Vose, 1981), this is a major clinical and theoretical issue urgently requiring resolution.

Although little is known about reasons for dropping out, Sheehan et al. (1980) found that the *clinical* characteristics of those who remained in treatment did not differ significantly from those who dropped out. Furthermore, there was no differential treatment effect on dropout rate. This suggests that *background* rather than clinical factors are major determinants of dropout. In relation to this, Lazarus (1966) and Goodstein and Swift (1977) described husbands who undermined their wives' response to behavior therapy for agoraphobia because they preferred them to be dependent. Only when the husbands themselves entered therapy did the wives improve, an observation made also by Webster (1953). If marital factors are indeed major contributors to refusal, dropping out, or failure in experimental treatment programs, then this is further evidence that marital problems are substantially underrepresented in those patients who enter and complete therapy.

Recent Experimental Findings

Presumably, husbands who are willing to be constructively and systematically involved in therapy or research are unusually sympathetic and cooperative toward their wives. That these attributes in husbands contribute to satisfactory levels of marital adjustment is suggested by the work of Cobb et al. (1984), who systematically involved spouses in a study comparing individual and conjoint therapy in the treatment of 18 married agoraphobics. On a questionnaire measure of marital dissatisfaction, patients' pretherapy scores averaged only 1.12 out of a maximum possible score of 8. This mean score is almost identical to that found by Milton and Hafner (1979) in a group of maritally *satisfied* agoraphobic patients with mainly simple agoraphobia, and it coincides with the normal population mean. Milton and Hafner used an earlier version of Cobb et al.'s marital questionnaire, dividing the total score by the number of scales to produce a *mean* score, so that for direct comparison, Cobb et al.'s marital data must be divided by a factor of 10.

Cobb et al. (1984) found that the patients with "bad" marriages responded as well to behavior therapy as did the patients with good marriages, and that conjoint therapy conferred no treatment benefits. They conclude that "agoraphobia would appear to be primarily a problem arising from the individual" (p. 287). Because there were in fact no demonstrably bad marriages among their patients, the authors' conclusions appear to be a further example of generalization from a population of agoraphobics with good marriages to the entire population of agoraphobics. This fact is underlined when their data are compared with those on the maritally dissatisfied group of (complex) agoraphobic patients from Milton and Hafner's (1979) study. Before therapy, these patients' mean marital dissatisfaction score was 3.1, nearly 3 times higher than that reported by the patients in Cobb et al.'s study. This score was comparable with that of patients seeking therapy specifically for marital problems (mean 3.2). The relapse rate in the maritally dissatisfied group was five times higher than in the maritally satisfied group, and at 6-months follow-up, the former group scored significantly higher on measures of phobic and general symptoms than did the latter. Others have reported a significant relationship between marital dissatisfaction before behavior therapy and subsequent relapse (Bland & Hallam, 1981; Hafner, 1977) or poor outcome (Hudson, 1974; Thomas-Peter, Jones, Sinnot, & Scott-Fordham, 1983).

In a follow-up study of patients treated by Marks et al. (1983), Monteiro, Marks, and Ramm (1985) came to conclusions very similar to those of Cobb et al. (1984). However, patients were excluded from the treatment phase of the study if they revealed a depressed mood that was more than moderate, and 38% dropped out of treatment. Thus, it is likely that simple agoraphobics with good marriages were substantially overrepresented in those who completed treatment, and on whom the findings are based. Indeed, the mean pretreatment marital questionnaire score of Monteiro et al.'s 27 married patients was only 1.5 (out of a maximum of 8). This is comparable to the mean score of Milton and Hafner's (1979) maritally satisfied group, and to that of Cobb et al.'s (1984) patients.

Barlow, O'Brien, and Last (1984) conducted a study with aims very similar to those of Cobb et al. (1984), but of superior design and methodology. They randomly allocated 28 married agoraphobic patients to individual or conjoint behavioral treatment. Conjoint treatment produced significantly better results than individual therapy, which was associated with a deterioration on several measures after 6 weeks of therapy. The benefits of conjoint treatment were most pronounced in patients with relatively poor marriages. In light of these findings, Barlow and Beck emphasized the importance of further research on marital interaction in agoraphobia.

Arrindell and Emmelkamp (1985) found very few differences between the husbands of agoraphobic women and normal control husbands. They therefore concluded that marital factors were unlikely to be particularly relevant in female agoraphobics. However, all their subjects were *research volunteers*. Therefore, it is likely that unusually cooperative people with fairly satisfactory marriages were strongly overrepresented in the sample, which probably contained few, if any, cases of complex agoraphobia.

In a study of unusual methodological sophistication and rigor, Arnow, Taylor, Agras, and Telch (1985) compared the effectiveness in 24 agoraphobic women of Couples Relaxation Training and Couples Communication Skills Training as a *supplement* to partner-assisted exposure therapy. Patients in the communication skills group improved significantly more than did patients in the relaxation group, a superiority that was maintained at 8-months follow-up. Arnow et al. concluded that communication training "may help couples to identify and change patterns of interaction that impede agoraphobics' progress in overcoming phobic avoidance."

Conclusions

It is clear from the preceding that systematic research into the marital context of agoraphobia is in its infancy. Research in this area will always be unusually difficult because of the problems of involving in clinical research patients with major personality abnormalities and related marital problems, and because of the methodological problems of analyzing marriage relationships and changes in them. The failure of most research workers to acknowledge that their findings are based mainly on atypical, "simple" cases means that existing research is of modest value to clinicians dealing primarily with "complex" cases. This point has been succinctly made by Barlow (1981): "At present, clinical research has little or no influence on clinical practice." (p. 147)

Ideally, this section should conclude with a review of systematic research into the marital context of obsessive compulsive disorder, panic disorder, and GAD. If such research exists, I am not aware of it. However, some clinically relevant issues in these disorders will be addressed in the next section.

CASE ILLUSTRATIONS

It was pointed out in the previous section that almost all work on the marital context of agoraphobia has been based primarily on women, who comprise at least 80% of those who seek treatment for the disorder (Thorpe & Burns, 1983). However, the work of Myers et al. (1984) has suggested a 6-month community prevalence of at least 1.5% in men aged 18 to 64, a figure somewhat higher than previously suspected.

If recent work on the relationship between alcohol dependence and anxiety disorders is taken into account (Bowen, Cipywnyk, D'Arcy, & Keegan, 1984; Stockwell, Smail, Hodgson, & Canter, 1984), the real figure is probably higher still. At least one third of men with alcohol dependency appear to have an underlying anxiety disorder, of which agoraphobia is probably the most common. Myers et al. (1984) found a 6-month community prevalence of alcoholism of nearly 10% in men aged 18 to 64. If only one fifth of such men suffer from underlying agoraphobia, then the true 6-month prevalence of this condition in men approaches 3.5%. Thus, agoraphobia and panic disorder (and perhaps GAD) are probably far greater problems for men than realized hitherto. Hence, this section will be devoted to anxiety disorders in men.

Case 1

James A, 39, was referred to me with a 7-year history of phobic/obsessive–compulsive symptoms of increasing severity. He had married Susan when he was 24 and she 23, and the couple had two sons, aged 8 and 13.

James' symptoms had started shortly after an accident in his home workshop. A chain saw which he was operating slipped and gashed him in the groin. He was very fortunate to escape major injury and, although the gash required several sutures, it healed rapidly. Within a week of the accident, James developed panic attacks at work, with which he coped by getting Susan to drive him there and back, and by making sure he could contact her at all times. Six months later he had developed troublesome agoraphobic symptoms, which prevented him from using public transport, although by this time he was able to drive himself to and from work, albeit with considerable anxiety. Concurrently, James developed extensive obsessive–compulsive symptoms, which included complex checking rituals aimed at securing the family home against nocturnal intruders.

The symptoms stabilized at this level for about 3 years, but James' job involved an increasing amount of local travel, and in the 2 to 3 years before he came to see me, this had become more and more of an ordeal. James' main problem was a fear that he might have injured someone on the road, and he felt compelled to repeatedly drive back in order to check this. He was also very fearful that he would be falsely or mistakenly accused of causing a death with his car. Even short local journeys were either impossible or took several hours, unless James was accompanied, in which case his fears lessened considerably.

The following emerged during two assessment interviews. James recalled that his father, to whom he had not been close, had died about 10 years before the chainsaw accident. He was able to check the precise date of both his injury and his father's funeral. To his astonishment, he found that they had occurred on exactly the same date, 10 years apart. James had felt little grief about his father's death, but was very worried about how he would cope with the eventual death of his mother, to whom he was extremely close. This closeness was greatly resented by Susan, who had also become very frustrated and resentful about James' symptoms. Susan's own mother had died when Susan was 12, and she did not appear to have worked through her grief about this. Partly as a result, Susan was very overprotective toward their two sons, and was unshakeably committed to remaining a full-time mother and housewife, at least until the younger son was 14 or 15 years old. After assessment, the couple agreed to spouse-aided therapy.

Confronted with the fact that the accident that had precipitated his symptoms occurred on the 10th anniversary of his father's death, James accepted, after considerable discussion, the need to do some grief work. Susan was less sure about this, although she accepted it as a valid treatment goal. However, she actively interfered with James' initial attempts to work through his grief. For example, she ridiculed James' tears (which both had traditionally regarded as a sign of weakness and "femininity" in men), and hid the photographs of James' father which were to have provided a preliminary focus for his grief work.

It thus became necessary to help Susan to acknowledge her unresolved grief about her mother, and this required three conjoint sessions. Subsequently, James and Susan worked together on their grief problems. Within 3 months, James had resolved much of his grief, although Susan was considerably slower. From this time, James' obsessive–compulsive and phobic symptoms lessened progressively, although his driving problems remained troublesome. It was not until Susan changed her rigid attitudes about full-time motherhood that further progress was made: By agreeing to consider taking a part-time job outside the home, Susan relieved James of the feeling that he *had* to continue in his current job in order to support his family. Moreover, he was able to contemplate fulfilling a strong wish to devote more time and energy to the children without feeling that Susan resented this as "poaching on her territory." He became more relaxed about his work, and, within 8 months of the start of therapy (after a total of 12 conjoint sessions), he was virtually symptom-free.

Comment

Had James been treated individually, therapy would probably have been undermined by Susan's attitude to grief work and her rigid view of sex roles. Marital conflict would have increased as a result, and this would have exacerbated James' symptoms. However, spouse-aided therapy allowed the couple to feel closer because of its emphasis on working together at specified treatment goals. Nonetheless, there was much heated, "irrational," and emotionally charged argument between the couple during therapy; this often had the flavor of both partners working through "transference" issues in relation to each other. But because this was done on a face-to-face basis, rather than indirectly through a therapist, many "transference" issues were resolved very rapidly. Working through such issues together is for some couples a major aspect of spouse-aided therapy, but it can occur only after the real origins of the patient's symptoms have been acknowledged by both partners. In relation to this, the extent to which material should be "interpreted" in a psychodynamic sense requires very careful judgment. In James' case, although "Oedipal" themes were obvious to me, interpretation of these did not appear to be an essential aspect of therapy.

Case 2

Richard B, aged 31, had experienced his first panic attack at age 21 after smoking some marijuana. He had married Carol, then 20, about 3 months previously. Over the subsequent 10 years, he had never been entirely free of panic attacks, although their frequency and severity varied greatly. During his first few panic attacks, in which palpitations were prominent, Richard had been convinced that he was about to die from a heart attack. In relation to this fear he had consulted numerous specialists, but without being adequately reassured. In the 4 to 5 years before coming to see me, his life had been dominated by a need to be within close reach of medical help: "When I have a bad panic I sometimes flee to a doctor or medical place so they can fix me up if I have a heart attack." On several occasions he had sat for 2 to 4 hours in the accident and emergency department of the local hospital, without seeking any medical attention, but simply waiting for his panic and fear to subside. Although Richard realized that this behavior was irrational (and, from a medical perspective, represented "abnormal illness behavior"), he felt powerless to prevent it, because of his overwhelming anxiety and fear of death. In the past 2 to 3 years, Richard had become increasingly agoraphobic, primarily because he had noticed an increased tendency to panic in public places, which he therefore avoided if possible. Treatment with imipramine and benzodiazepines had not prevented major panic attacks, although immediately swallowing or chewing a tranquilizing tablet helped him to cope with relatively minor ones.

Richard was academically very gifted, and had started a promising career as a junior faculty member in a reputable university. However, he resigned at age 27 when panic attacks, anxiety, and general health worries made lecturing and other academic duties too much of an ordeal.

By this time, the couple had two young daughters. Carol had a rather stereotyped view of sex roles, and regarded being a wife and mother as a full-time, exclusive commitment. She had unwittingly contributed to Richard's anxiety symptoms by placing great emphasis on his career success, from the idea of which she obtained considerable vicarious gratification. Thus, Richard felt trapped in a career path toward which he was in fact very ambivalent.

After his resignation, Richard's anxiety symptoms were compounded by a sense of failure and despair. The marriage deteriorated when it became clear that Richard was unable to resume teaching. Whereas Carol had previously responded to Richard's panic attacks with sympathy and reassurance, she now sometimes reacted with hostility: "For God's sake *have* a bloody panic attack and die, won't you!" Richard found such responses to be "totally destructive, utterly horrendous, plunging me into despair and rage, because no one seemed to understand how unbearably frightening the attacks were."

Out of financial necessity, but with extreme reluctance, Carol resumed work as a stenographer while Richard remained at home. She was full of anger about this enforced role reversal, but felt guilty about attacking Richard for disabilities that seemed attributable to an illness beyond his control. Richard was angry about Carol's unwillingness to be affectionate and reassuring, although at times she still responded to the physical manifestations of his panics with nurturing and sympathy. This inadvertently reinforced them. The couple was on the brink of separation when I first saw Richard, and both agreed readily to spouse-aided therapy.

Treatment goals focused initially on Richard's panic and agoraphobia. Conjoint training in paradoxical intention and related cognitive techniques was employed for the panic, and for the agoraphobia I supervised the couple in the use of the exposure in vivo manual written by Mathews et al. (1981). However, as Richard's symptoms improved, the couple clashed increasingly over his unwillingness to resume full-time teaching. Richard insisted that he was no longer interested in an academic career, but preferred instead to teach half-time. He wished to devote as much time and effort to raising his daughters as to earning a living. The resulting arguments increased the frequency of Richard's panic attacks, and he relapsed, once again becoming "unable," rather than unwilling, to teach.

Subsequently, several sessions were devoted to discussing role-sharing as a valid option rather than an unwanted aberation forced upon them by Richard's ill health. Carol proved flexible enough to see the advantages that might emerge from a whole-hearted commitment to role-sharing. This resulted in an improvement in the marriage and in Richard's symptoms. He was then able to obtain a half-time teaching post, and Carol reduced her stenographer's work to 3 days a week. Once the couple had adjusted to the new situation, Richard's panic attacks and agoraphobia improved further, although alone and together with Carol he had to spend many hours over several months working at his residual symptoms. Therapy occupied a total of 15 one-hour sessions over 6 months. At the 2-year follow-up, Richard was virtually free of anxiety symptoms, and the couple regarded their marriage as fairly harmonious.

CONCLUDING REMARKS

The principals of spouse-aided therapy can be utilized in a variety of family settings. For example, one or both parents and/or other relatives can be enlisted as co-therapist(s) in the treatment of severely disturbed adolescents. In such circumstances, parent-aided therapy or family-resource therapy are more suitable terms of description. Once the idea of using the patient's family and/or friends as a major therapeutic resource is accepted, a whole range of innovative therapeutic options is revealed. However, for these to be applied safely and effectively, therapists must be skilled in dealing with the issues of transference and countertransference.

I am aware that focusing on men in the clinical section of this chapter leaves me open to the charge of overlooking women's health issues. Readers with this view are invited to read some material that redresses the balance (Hafner, 1986a). For both sexes, I believe that sex-role conflict and strain are often critical in the development and maintenance not only of anxiety disorders, but also of other common psychiatric conditions (Hafner, 1986b). However, sex-role difficulties are a *general* factor, and but one of several common sources of contemporary conflict and stress. Precisely how a person reacts to such stress and conflict is a function of more specific genetic, biological, and early developmental factors. Mental health workers differ widely with regard to the emphasis that they place on biological versus psychosocial factors. The direction of my own bias is obvious.

Personal bias notwithstanding, evidence is steadily accumulating that attention to marital and family factors is often critical to a good outcome in the treatment of severe, persisting anxiety disorders. Evidence is also accumulating for important clinical differences between men and women with anxiety disorders (Chambless & Mason, 1986; Hafner, 1981a, 1982a; Liotti & Guidano, 1976; Mavissakalian, 1985; Wolfe, 1984). It is now clear that therapists who ignore sex role and gender issues in anxiety disorders, or who are inflexible in their attitudes to sex roles, are unlikely to be fully effective in their therapeutic endeavors.

REFERENCES

American Psychiatric Association. (1980). *Diagnostic and statistical manual of mental disorders* (3rd ed.). Washington, DC.

Arnow, B. A., Taylor, C. B., Agras, W. S., & Telch, M. J. (1985). Enhancing agoraphobia treatment outcome by changing couple communication. *Behavior Therapy, 16*, 452–467.

Arrindell, W. A., & Emmelkamp, P. M. G. (1985). Psychological profile of the spouse of the female agoraphobic patient: Personality and symptoms. *British Journal of Psychiatry, 146*, 405–414.

Barlow, D. H. (1981). On the relation of clinical research to clinical practice: Current issues, new directions. *Journal of Consulting and Clinical Psychology, 49*, 147–155.

Barlow, D. H., O'Brien, G. T., & Last C. G. (1984). Couples treatment of agoraphobia. *Behavior Therapy*, **15**, 41–58.

Benjamin, S., & Kincey, J. (1981). Evaluation of standardized behavioural treatment for agoraphobic in-patients administered by untrained therapists. *British Journal of Psychiatry, 138*, 423–428.

Bland, K., & Hallam, R. S. (1981). Relationship between response to graded exposure and marital satisfaction in agoraphobics. *Behaviour Research and Therapy, 19*, 335–338.

Bowen, R. C., Cipywnyk, D., D'Arcy, C., & Keegan, D. (1984). Alcoholism, anxiety disorders and agoraphobia. *Alcoholism: Clinical and Experimental Research, 8*, 48–50.

Bowen, R. C., & Kohout, J. (1979). The relationship between agoraphobia and primary affective disorders. *Canadian Journal of Psychiatry, 24*, 317–322.

Buglass, D., Clarke, J., Henderson, A. S., Kreitman, N., & Presley, A. S. (1977). A study of agoraphobic housewives. *Psychological Medicine, 7*, 73–86.

Chambless, D. L., & Goldstein, A. J. (1981). Clinical treatment of agoraphobia. In M. Mavissakalian & D. H. Barlow (Eds.), *Phobia: Psychological and pharmacological treatment*. New York: Guilford Press.

Chambless, D. L., & Mason, J. (1986). Sex, sex role stereotyping, and agoraphobia. *Behaviour Research and Therapy, 24*, 231–235.

Clancy, J., Noyes, R., Hoenk, P. R., & Slymen, D. J. (1978). Secondary depression in anxiety neurosis. *Journal of Nervous and Mental Disease, 166*, 846–850.

Cobb, J. P., Mathews, A. M., Childs-Clarke, A., & Blowers, C. M. (1984). The spouse as co-therapist in the treatment of agoraphobia. *British Journal of Psychiatry, 144*, 282–287.

Cobb, J. P., McDonald, R., Marks, I. M., & Stern, R. (1980). Marital vs. exposure therapy: Psychological treatments of co-existing marital and phobic-obsessive problems. *Behavior Analysis and Modification, 4*, 3–16.

Cochrane, N. (1973). Some reflections on the unsuccessful treatment of a group of married couples. *British Journal of Psychiatry, 123*, 395–401.

Forrest, A. D. (1969). Manifestations of 'hysteria': Phobic patients and hospital recidivists. *British Journal of Medical Psychology, 42*, 263–270.

Fry, W. F. (1962). The marital context of an anxiety syndrome. *Family Process, 1*, 245–252.

Goldstein, A. J., & Chambless, D. L. (1978). A reanalysis of agoraphobia. *Behavior Therapy, 9*, 47–59.

Goldstein, A. J., & Chambless, D. L. (1981). Denial of marital conflict in agoraphobia. In A. S. Gurman (Ed.), *Questions and answers in the practice of family therapy*. New York: Brunner/Mazel.

Goodstein, R., & Swift, K. (1977). Psychotherapy with phobic patients: the marriage relationship as the source of symptoms and the focus of treatment. *American Journal of Psychotherapy, 31*, 285–292.

Hafner, R. J. (1977). The husbands of agoraphobic women and their influence on treatment outcome. *British Journal of Psychiatry, 131*, 289–294.

Hafner, R. J. (1981a). Agoraphobia in men. *Australian and New Zealand Journal of Psychiatry, 15*, 243–249.

Hafner, R. J. (1981b). Spouse-aided therapy in psychiatry: An introduction. *Australian and New Zealand Journal of Psychiatry, 15*, 329–337.

Hafner, R. J. (1982a). Behaviour therapy for agoraphobic men. *Behaviour Research and Therapy, 21*, 51–56.

Hafner, R. J. (1982b). The marital context of the agoraphobic syndrome. In D. L. Chambless & A. J. Goldstein (Eds.), *Agoraphobia: Multiple perspectives on theory and treatment*. New York: John Wiley & Sons.

Hafner, R. J. (1986a). Marital therapy for agoraphobia. In N. S. Jacobson & A. S. Gurman (Eds.), *Clinical handbook of marital therapy*. New York: Guilford Press.

Hafner, R. J. (1986b). *Marriage and mental illness: A sex roles perspective*. New York: Guilford Press.

Hallam, R. S. (1978). Agoraphobia: A critical review of the concept. *British Journal of Psychiatry, 133*, 314–319.

Holmes, J. (1982). Phobia and counterphobia: Family aspects of agoraphobia. *Journal of Family Therapy, 4*, 133–152.

Hudson, B. (1974). The families of agoraphobics treated by behaviour therapy. *British Journal of Social Work, 4*, 51–59.

Hurvitz, N. (1967). Marital problems following psychotherapy with one spouse. *Journal of Consulting and Clinical Psychology, 31*, 38–47.

Jannoun, L., Munby, M., Catalan, J., & Gelder, M. (1980). A home-based treatment programme for agoraphobia: Replication and controlled evaluation. *Behavior Therapy, 11*, 294–305.

Klein, D. F., Zitrin, C. M., Woerner, M. G., & Ross, D. C. (1983). Treatment of phobias II. Behavior therapy and supportive psychotherapy. Are there any specific ingredients? *Archives of General Psychiatry, 40*, 139–145.

Lazarus, A. A. (1966). Broad spectrum behaviour therapy and the treatment of agoraphobia. *Behaviour Research and Therapy, 4*, 95–97.

Liotti, G., & Guidano, V. (1976). Behavioural analysis of marital interaction in male agoraphobic patients. *Behaviour Research and Therapy, 14*, 161–162.

Marks, I. M., Gray, S., Cohen, D., Hill, R., Mawson, D., Ramm, E., & Stern, R. S. (1983). Imipramine and brief therapist-aided exposure in agoraphobics having self exposure homework. *Archives of General Psychiatry, 40*, 153–162.

Matthews, A. M., Gelder, M. G., & Johnston, D. W. (1981). *Agoraphobia: Nature and treatment*. London: Tavistock.

Mavissakalian, M. (1985). Male and female agoraphobia: Are they different? *Behaviour Research and Therapy, 23*, 469–471.

Mavissakalian, M., & Michelson, L. (1982). Agoraphobia: Behavioral and pharmacological treatments, preliminary outcome, and process findings. *Psychopharmacology Bulletin, 18*, 91–103.

Milton, F., & Hafner, R. J. (1979). The outcome of behavior therapy for agoraphobia in relation to marital adjustment. *Archives of General Psychiatry, 36*, 807–811.

Monteiro, W., Marks, I. M., & Ramm, E. (1985). Marital adjustment and treatment outcome in agoraphobia. *British Journal of Psychiatry, 146*, 383–390.

Myers, J. K., Weissman, M. M., Tischler, G. L., Holzer, C. E., Leaf, P. J., Orvaschel, H., Anthony, J. C., Boyd, J. H., Burke, J. D., Kramer, M., & Stoltzman, R. (1984). Six-month prevalence of psychiatric disorders in three communities. *Archives of General Psychiatry, 41*, 959–967.

Pilowsky, I. (1978). A general classification of abnormal illness behaviours. *British Journal of Medical Psychology, 51*, 131–137.

Quadrio, C. (1983). Rapunzel and the pumpkin-eater: Marital systems of agoraphobic women. *Australian Journal of Family Therapy, 4*, 81–85.

Quadrio, C. (1984). The families of agoraphobic women. *Australian and New Zealand Journal of Psychiatry, 18*, 164–170.

Rapp, M. S., & Thomas, M. R. (1982). Agoraphobia. *Canadian Journal of Psychiatry, 27*, 419–425.

Salzman, L. (1982). Obsessions and agoraphobia. In D. L. Chambless & A. J. Goldstein (Eds.), *Agoraphobia: Multiple perspectives on theory and treatment*. New York: John Wiley & Sons.

Schwartz, L. S., & Val, E. R. (1984). Agoraphobia: Multimodal treatment approach. *American Journal of Psychotherapy, 38*, 35–46.

Sheehan, D. V., Ballenger, J., & Jacobsen, G. (1980). Treatment of endogenous anxiety with phobic, hysterical, and hypochondriacal symptoms. *Archives of General Psychiatry, 37*, 51–59.

Stockwell, T., Smail, P., Hodgson, R., & Canter, S. (1984). Alcohol dependence and phobic states: II. A retrospective study. *British Journal of Psychiatry, 144*, 58–63.

Symonds, A. (1971). Phobias after marriage. Women's declaration of dependence. *American Journal of Psychoanalysis, 31*, 144–152.

Thomas-Peter, B. A., Jones, R. B., Sinnot, A., & Scott-Fordham, A. (1983). Prediction of outcome in treatment of agoraphobia. *Behavioural Psychotherapy, 4*, 320–328.

Thorpe, G. L., & Burns, L. E. (1983). *The agoraphobic syndrome*. New York: John Wiley & Sons.

Tyrer, P. (1984). The classification of anxiety. *British Journal of Psychiatry, 144*, 78–83.

Vandereycken, W. (1983). Agoraphobia and marital relationship: Theory, treatment and research. *Clinical Psychology Review, 3*, 317–338.

Vose, R. H. (1981). *Agoraphobia*. London: Faber and Faber.

Webster, A. (1953). The development of phobias in married women. *Psychological Monographs, 67*, 1–18.

Wolfe, B. E. (1984). Gender imperatives, separation anxiety, and agoraphobia in women. *Integrative Psychiatry, 2*, 57–61.

Zitrin, C. M., Klein, D. F., Woerner, M. G., & Ross, D. C. (1983). Treatment of phobias 1. Comparison of imipramine hydrochloride and placebo. *Archives of General Psychiatry, 40*, 125–137.

CHAPTER 21

Assessment and Treatment Using Hypnosis

David Spiegel and Herbert Spiegel

The recent and growing attention paid to anxiety disorders stems from two roots. One is a recognition of their much higher prevalence than had previously been thought, largely through the work of the Epidemiological Catchment Area study, which documented a prevalence of as high as 15% (Myers et al., 1984). The second has been research demonstrating the somatic determinants and concomitants of this state of psychological discomfort (the emotional equivalent of physical pain), which Sullivan (1954) once described as "to an incredible degree a sign that something ought to be different at once." Like pain, anxiety has an important signal function, directing our attention toward the solution of pressing problems. And yet, like pain, it can become the problem in and of itself. It may (a) initiate irrational avoidance behavior, as in phobias; (b) lead to a state of sudden psychosomatic discomfort as in panic attacks; or (c) become a chronic inhibitor of psychological comfort and social function, as in generalized anxiety disorders.

WHY HYPNOSIS?

Hypnosis is especially relevant to the treatment of anxiety disorders because of its efficacy in offering access to control of the relationship between psyche and soma. The anxiety state itself can be conceptualized as a non–self-correcting feedback, or feedforward (Pribram, 1971) system, in which mental or social stress provokes an exaggerated somatic response with increased catecholamine secretion, elevations in heart rate and blood pressure, diaphoresis, flushing, muscle tension and chest pain, which in turn stimulate further psychological anxiety. The stimuli that set off this snowball effect are often not in themselves devoid of anxiety-producing characteristics; for example, anticipatory anxiety is a normal preparatory process for coping with stress. The anxious patient simply overreacts to them somatically and psychologically. From a cognitive behavioral point of view, previous experiences of such distress can create a mental set that even more easily stimulates both the somatic and the psychological discomfort. It may become chronic or situation-induced, but it involves mutual noncorrecting reinforcement between brain and body.

Hypnosis is a state of aroused dissociated focal concentration with a relative suspension of peripheral awareness. There is a substantial literature demonstrating hypnosis to be a state generally characterized by cognitive awareness and physical relaxation. While it has been shown (Banyai & Hilgard, 1976) that even an individual actively pedaling an exercycle can experience the full array of hypnotic phenomena, most hypnotic inductions and the experience of most hypnotized individuals involve somatic metaphors associated with relaxation; for example, floating, breathing deeply and easily, and feeling a physical sense of comfort. One of the hallmarks of the hypnotic experience is dissociation (Hilgard, 1977). A narrowing of the boundaries of consciousness in the hypnotized state relegates certain perceptions and experiences to the periphery of awareness. A person may act on the basis of this information; for example, a posthypnotic instruction that his/her hand will feel light and want to float up in the air, and yet will dissociate awareness of the instruction. Indeed, the hand itself may feel as if it is not as much a part of the person's body as the other hand. Two important messages are conveyed by this experience:

1. The unitary perception of experience can indeed be separated or dissociated. Thus, the overwhelming mental set of a state like anxiety can be subdivided into a series of mental and physical experiences that need not be identical or mutually reinforcing.
2. The experience teaches subjects that they have more control over their bodies than they had previously thought and they can produce rather than simply experience changes in somatic sensation. Thus, while hypnosis has been widely misunderstood as a loss of control, it is in fact an occasion to learn techniques for the enhancement of control, especially of mind over somatic process.

Research on hypnosis has demonstrated that the capacity to experience it is a stable and measurable trait. A number of well-standardized hypnotizability scales have been devised for use in both the laboratory (SHSS:C: Weitzenhoffer & Hilgard, 1962) and the clinic (HIP: Spiegel & Spiegel, 1978). Hypnotizability is greatest during the human life cycle in latency in childhood (Morgan & Hilgard, 1973) and declines gradually through adulthood, but so gradually that it is as stable a measure as IQ (Morgan, Johnson, & Hilgard, 1974). About two out of three people in a large psychiatric outpatient population were found to be significantly hypnotizable enough to use the phenomenon for clinical purposes (Stern, Spiegel, & Nee, 1978–1979), and 1 out of 10 are highly hypnotizable. There is no point in attempting to use hypnosis with someone who is not hypnotizable, but a majority of psychiatric outpatients have enough hypnotic ability that the use of the technique may be worth a try. This is important, because it is possible to exclude on the basis of 5 to 10 minutes of testing those individuals who would benefit more from some other approach.

Severe anxiety has been shown to interfere with hypnotizability (Spiegel, Detrick, & Frischholz, 1982). Patients with generalized anxiety disorder (using RDC criteria: Spitzer, Endicott, & Robins, 1975) obtained hypnotizability scores that were little more than half those of normals, and a distribution of scores that was quite similar to the observed among schizoprenics. Interestingly, those patients with generalized anxiety disorder who were receiving benzodiazepines had hypnotizability scores that, while still lower than normal, were twice the extremely low scores of those who were not receiving medication for their anxiety ($N = 18$, $p < .07$; Spiegel, 1980). Thus, the benzodiazepines appeared to partially reverse the anxious interference with hypnotic responsivity. Hypnosis is therefore likely to be of most use only among those patients with less severe anxiety or with anxiety that is partially treated using pharmacological or other techniques. There is no reason to believe that such combined modality treatment would be any less appropriate in treating anxiety than it has been shown to be with depression (Crasilneck & Hall, 1985; Dimascio, Weissman, Prusoff, Swilling, & Klerman, 1979; Weissman, 1979).

Some research has suggested that hypnotizability may be a factor in phobic anxiety disorders in particular (Frankel & Orne, 1976). The hypothesis is that hypnotizable individuals subjected to a phobic stimulus go into a kind of spontaneous trance experience, hence the analogy between phobic states and dissociative experiences. While this study has been confirmed by several others (Gerschman, Burrows, Reade, & Foenander, 1979; Kelly, 1984), it is limited by the fact that the important moderating effect of age was not adequately controlled for in the original study, and indeed the phobics were significantly younger than the control population. Thus, the difference could conceivably be accounted for on the basis of age alone, because hypnotizability decreases with age (Morgan & Hilgard, 1973). The Kelly (1984) study is limited by the fact that several of the statistical tests performed violated basic assumptions and are therefore invalid. Our attempt to replicate the finding in a much larger sample of phobics demonstrated no differences between phobics and a similar control group of smokers (Frischholz, Spiegel, Spiegel, Balma, & Markell, 1982). However, it is certainly possible that some phobic states involve spontaneous hypnotic phenomena.

The clinical association between hypnotizability and another disorder often classified as an anxiety disorder (i.e., posttraumatic stress disorder [PTSD]), is more compelling. Many of the symptoms of PTSD can be seen as dissociative symptoms: the exaggerated startle response and stimulus sensitivity, the sense of unreality and deadening of responsiveness to pleasurable stimuli, and the frankly dissociative episodes in which certain trauma victims relive the previous trauma as though it were happening in the present seem indeed to be spontaneous trance phenomena. Recent reports show reasonably high hypnotizability among PTSD patients (Spiegel, Hunt, & Dondershine, 1987; Spiegel, 1983; Stutman & Bliss, 1985). These studies demonstrate that, as a rule, patients with phobic anxiety disorders and posttraumatic stress disorders should be at least as hypnotizable as the overall population if not more so, and suggest that hypnosis may be spontaneously invoked in certain traumatic or phobic situations.

There is a substantial literature linking hypnotic responsivity to control over a variety of somatic processes. These include blood flow (Dubin & Shapiro, 1974), blood pressure (Case, Fogel, & Pollack, 1980), and skin temperature (Grabowska, 1971). There is also evidence that hypnotic experience can profoundly influence such anxiety-related phenomena as gastric acid secretion (Spiegel & Klein, 1984). Hypnotized individuals instructed to eat an imaginary meal experienced a 234% increase in gastric acid secretion; they decreased it 19% even in the face of a pentagastrin challenge when the hypnotic experience was to relax but not think of food. In a recent study (Spiegel, Cutcomb, Ren, & Pribram, 1985), we demonstrated that highly hypnotizable individuals were able to suppress their cortical evoked response to a visual stimulus while hallucinating a box obstructing their view of the stimulus generator. High hypnotizables in a trance instructed to attend to the stimulus generator had normal responses. It was only when in trance they were told to hallucinate an obstruction to the stimulus that their cortical response diminished. The studies of power spectral analysis of the EEG among high and low hypnotizables in and out of trance are similar. There are very few reliable and repeatable electroencephalographic differences that differentiate the hypnotic from the nonhypnotic state per se. The findings are more related to the content of the experience within the states than to the state itself. Thus, the hypnotic state is one of profound and responsive psychophysiological relatedness. The content of the hypnotic experience directs the somatic response.

Treatment Strategies Employing Hypnosis

There are a variety of strategies for treating anxiety with hypnosis. They tend to share structured cognition, imagery, and physical relaxation. Techniques include diverting attention away from the anxiety-provoking stimulus or restructuring the subject's approach to the problem coupled with a dissociated somatic experience (i.e., learning to associate attention to the feared stimulus with a somatic experience of comfort rather than tension). This approach has elements in common with systematic desensitization (Frankel, 1976; Lazarus, 1973), the difference being that the treatment is less systematic and therefore less cumbersome and tedious. Rather than constructing a hierarchy in which the subject learns to dissociate or extinguish the typical somatic response of tension in the face of a feared stimulus, the hypnotized person can often learn in a minute or two to maintain the somatic sense of floating relaxation, while subjectively experiencing situations that previously evoked a full-blown anxiety or panic reaction.

The hypnotic session itself is best structured as both a demonstration of the degree of symptom relief available to the patient and also an instruction in the use of self-hypnosis in the future. Patients can best be taught to prevent and control physical discomfort not by direct instructions to "relax," a cognitive term which often produces physical tension (it is often associated with tension-producing situations in which the subject's natural response was viewed as unwelcome by someone else such as a doctor about to give a shot). Rather, affiliation with a physical metaphor or image inferring relaxation is encouraged. Subjects are invited to imagine floating in a hot bath or a lake and may be told that each breath out will leave them feeling a bit more comfortable, that they will be able to breathe more deeply and easily. A baseline of physical comfort is established, and efforts are made to maintain this baseline, no matter what other cognitive tasks are undertaken in the trance. Often patients will suggest metaphors that to them personally convey greater physical comfort, and this creative use of hypnotic metaphors is encouraged as engaging patients in the task and helping them to enrich the depth of meaning.

Initially, this physical imagery can be usefully linked to a visual image of comfort. Subjects are instructed to picture an imaginery screen in their mind's eye, a movie screen or a TV screen, or a piece of clear blue sky, and to picture on that screen a pleasant scene, somewhere they enjoy being. This may be a favorite outdoor spot, or a comforting room at home. Subjects are then reminded that their store of memories and associations can provide both emotional and physical comfort. They are then instructed that no matter what subsequent images they see on the screen, they are to try to maintain the sense of floating relaxation in their bodies. If they start to lose that relaxation, they need to stop what is happening on the screen, reestablish the floating, if necessary by returning to the pleasant image, and then go on about their work. This provides an informal and rapid means of desensitization (i.e., uncoupling or dissociating the physical tension from any psychological tension inherent in the mental image).

The next task involves picturing on the screen some image that represents an aspect of their anxious preoccupations. It may be an image of a person they fear, a forthcoming operation, or anything else that tends to provoke anxiety. This in itself can be helpful in that it provides a cognitive framework and dimensions to the anxiety, converting it from the nonspecific uneasiness (which is anxiety) to a fear of something that carries with it the possibility of corrective action. Not uncommonly, at this point subjects begin to look more restless physically, and inquiries are made about whether the floating is maintained. Usually it is not. Subjects are repeatedly encouraged to reestablish the sense of floating before proceeding. The subjects can then be instructed to divide the screen into three parts, a central receiving screen on which they become receptive to their own ideas, but experience them as outside their own bodies, projected onto the screen. The sinistral side can be used as the "worry screen," on which subjects can place a problem that requires sustained attention. The right side of the screen can be used to try out dealing with the problem on the left. All of this is done with frequent verbal communication to the therapist while the patients are in trance, with the discipline of maintaining the floating physical relaxation.

One patient had severe phobic anxiety about an operation for the removal of a large spinal cord tumor which had a 10% chance of leaving him quadriplegic. He had endangered himself by putting off the operation and then appearing for it so intoxicated that the procedure had to be put off again. He was highly hypnotizable (13 of 16 points on the Hypnotic Induction Profile [HIP: Spiegel & Spiegel, 1978], and he was astounded to find himself picturing himself in the operating room while maintaining a physical sense of floating relaxation. He had never been able to think about the operation without the usual autonomic responses of anxiety, to the point that he was convinced he was having a heart attack. His ability to look at what he feared in the trance state while maintaining a physical sense of floating gave him a surprising sense of control over the response to the threat. He was instructed to induce self-hypnosis not only to prepare for the procedure, but as a way of escaping to a pleasant place during uncomfortable times in the hospital. The message he received was: "My body has to be there, but I don't."

There are as many varieties of approaches to problems as there are varieties of phobias. Many of them emphasize different kinds of cognitive restructuring of the patient's view of the problem while maintaining a physical sense of floating relaxation (Spiegel & Spiegel, 1978). Patients with aviophobia, for example, can be taught to combine the sense of floating with the motion of the plane as it takes off. They have a physical sense of floating with the plane. The second major concept is to have them think of the plane as an extension of their body rather than feeling trapped inside the plane. They are instructed to view it the way they would a bicycle, an extension of their body to help facilitate their ability to get from one place to another more quickly. Again, this enables them to link their newly discovered somatic comfort with a psychological state of reduced anxiety. Their body is linked to the plane, and the plane is in turn an extension of their body. The third concept is to have them concentrate on the difference between a possibility and a probability. Many phobics immobilize themselves by imagining scenarios of disaster which are indeed possible but are extremely unlikely. They experience a possibility as a probability. The very existence of the fantasy seems to overshadow the low probability of its occurring. This approach provides a way of enabling them to face feared circumstances while maintaining a competing concept of the low likelihood that the disaster may occur, for example, the feared air crash. Facing this, however, is important because it is part of the rubric of teaching patients not *not* to worry, but rather *how* to worry. They can learn to focus their attention on a strategy for coping with the situation rather than fighting the fear.

There are analogous restructuring paradigms for problems such as acrophobia, in which patients are encouraged to view gravity not as something likely to pull them off a cliff or a building, but rather something that roots them to the ground. Some agoraphobic patients have found it useful to imagine a clear plastic bubble which surrounds them and gives them a sense of transporting with them a personal area of safety analogous to the one they experience at home. This is used even when they travel outside, again linking it to the physical sense of floating relaxation.

The treatment of animal phobias follows

similar lines. Physical relaxation is induced among patients with either visualization of the feared stimulus animal, or with a cognitive restructuring paradigm in which the patient may think through the distinction between, for example, wild and tame animals in the case of a dog phobia (Spiegel & Spiegel, 1978). This enables them to accept, but modulate rather than struggle against their fear. Many phobic patients become strangely passive in the face of the feared animal, "waiting to see what the animal will do." This self-imposed passivity often accentuates anxiety, and is otherwise out of character — they would never be so restrained and passive in the presence of another person, let alone another type of animal. Recognizing this is often helpful in itself. One patient with an extended history of a severe and incapacitating dog phobia became so excited at conceptualizing "dog" as "friend" that she bought a dog and named it after her therapist! The transference implications were never unraveled, but she remained symptom-free for years.

Other approaches to the use of hypnosis in treating anxiety include mixtures of two classical hypnotic approaches: direct suggestion and distraction. Erickson (1967) would frequently instruct patients in a trance to imagine that they were literally somewhere else, away from the feared experience, or that they were disconnected from their own bodies, while directly suggesting experiences of increased physical and emotional comfort. Other therapists emphasize primarily direct suggestion, giving repeated instructions to patients that they will feel more comfortable and better able to master their own anxiety (Crasilneck & Hall, 1985). This approach capitalizes on the suspension of critical judgment and compulsive compliance associated with the hypnotic state. One potential drawback of some direct suggestion techniques is that they may foster dependence on the therapist for repeated hypnotic instructions and thus may not fully elicit the optimal participation of the patient in the treatment. The range of hypnotic techniques includes classical direct suggestion, distraction from the feared stimulus, and cognitive restructuring of the fear situation coupled with training in hypnotically induced physical relaxation.

Other approaches involve use of hypnosis in uncovering repressed material, usually about traumatic experiences, which seems to be associated with the complaint of anxiety (Crasilneck & Hall, 1985; Erickson, 1967). Techniques such as hypnotic age regression, in which the patient relives previous experiences as though they were occurring in the present, and the use of an imaginary screen to review life events among less highly hypnotizable individuals, are useful. The crucial point is that by itself, uncovering material is insufficient. What is most important is to help the patient to work through the material and integrate it into consciousness in an acceptable manner (Freud, 1914/1958). Traumatic anxiety is perpetuated because the experience of the self in the trauma is demoralizing. The patient comes to feel that the traumatized self is the real self, hence the loss of enjoyment in normal life, and the painful anxiety associated with intrusive thoughts in posttraumatic stress disorder (American Psychiatric Association, 1987). Hypnosis can be helpful in providing the patient with a more complex self-image in relation to the trauma. For example, a Vietnam combat veteran with severe post-traumatic stress disorder found himself unable to accept the combat death of a Vietnamese child he had "adopted" during the war. He had been amnesic to several days' events immediately after the death, and because he was extremely hypnotizable (15 of 16 points on the Hypnotic Induction Profile), hypnotic age regression was used to uncover them. He was then taught to picture on an imaginary screen two conflicting scenes: the child's grave on one side, and a previous birthday party when they had happily shared cake and presents. Using this image, he was able to more effectively grieve and accept the boy's death (Spiegel, 1981).

In general, uncovering techniques should be used as a last rather than a first resort in the treatment of anxiety. Most often, briefer and more straightforward approaches, which combine cognitive restructuring and imagery involving the anxiety-producing stimulus along with physical relaxation, suffice for symptom control. In some cases, use of imagery and cognitive restructuring must be expanded to facilitate working through earlier traumatic material that is clearly related to current symptoms of anxiety. Hypnosis is especially helpful in providing intense, focused concentration on the therapeutic strategy coupled with enhanced control over somatic response.

OUTCOME STUDIES

Outcome studies have generally shown some efficacy of hypnosis and that hypnotizability is a predictive factor of success (McGuinness, 1984). Study of a single-session treatment employing hypnosis for flying phobia with an average 7-year follow-up showed 52% of patients as either improved or cured (Spiegel, Frischholz, Maruffi, & Spiegel, 1981). Furthermore, those classified by the Hypnotic Induction Profile (HIP: Spiegel & Spiegel, 1978) as hypnotizable were significantly (χ^2 (2) = 8.8, $p < .005$) more likely to respond (66% responded) than those who were not so classified (43% responded). The fact that some nonhypnotizables did respond indicates that hypnosis is simply a vehicle for facilitating treatment. The cognitive restructuring and any nonhypnotic means of inducing physical relaxation, (e.g., simply sitting quietly and breathing deeply) are also important factors in controlling phobic anxiety.

There have been a number of outcome studies comparing various uses of hypnosis with behavioral techniques in the treatment of performance anxiety and phobias. There is substantial overlap in the use of both techniques, especially because many of the relaxation procedures used in systematic desensitization and reciprocal inhibition are richly identical to hypnotic induction procedures (Lazarus, 1973). Furthermore, the ideas behind them are quite similar: Confront an anxiety-producing stimulus while maintaining a physical state of relaxation. The major difference is that the hypnotized individual is simply instructed to maintain relaxation initially established when confronting the feared stimuli, whereas often in the behavioral approaches the effort is more gradual (with a hierarchy being constructed), so that the challenge to physical relaxation is increased gradually rather than immediately. Nonetheless, it would be hard to imagine that even a moderately hypnotizable individual being instructed in the physical relaxation techniques incorporated into many behavioral paradigms could experience them without going into a hypnotic trance.

The majority of controlled studies to be reviewed have been carried out among volunteers and college students, and therefore the inferences that can be made from them to the clinical situation are somewhat limited. However, several studies have been conducted with patients. Marks, Gelder, and Edwards (1968) found both systematic desensitization and hypnosis with suggestion to be effective in treating phobic outpatients, but systematic desensitization was more effective. On the other hand, Glick (1970) found significantly greater improvement among nine phobics treated using hypnosis than among 14 patients treated with systematic desensitization. The only other controlled study employing patients who sought treatment was conducted by Lazarus (1973). Lazarus found that people seeking help with hypnosis tended to respond better when they were treated with hypnosis rather than a very similar treatment labeled relaxation training. His point was that fulfilling the patient's expectation seemed to enhance the treatment effect. The disorders treated included headaches as well as requests for relaxation, which can presumably indicate a complaint of anxiety. His point was that fulfilling the request for a treatment involving hypnosis seemed to provide some diferential advantage.

In several other studies, volunteers were recruited because of specific problems, but they had not identified themselves as patients. Horowitz (1970) found that respondents with snake phobias were significantly improved using several treatment strategies using hypnosis, relaxation, suggestion, and fear arousal. While all resulted in improvement compared to controls, relaxation and suggestion were significantly more effective. This study is important in that it demonstrates that the type of strategy employed is a significant variable in outcome, which makes sense, because hypnosis is not in itself a form of treatment, but rather, a state of concentration, which can then be focused on a specific treatment strategy. Some are clearly better than others. O'Brien, Cooley, Ciotti, and Henninger (1981) used a similar type of sample and found treatment employing hypnosis more effective than systematic desensitization and relaxation. The treatment employing hypnosis was more intensive, however, than the systematic desenzitization treatment, and the samples were not exactly comparable. In several other studies, students with test anxiety were exposed to a variety of treatments and the results compared. Melnick and Russell (1976) found systematic desensitization superior to guided imagery employing hypnosis, while Spies (1979) found both types of treatment effective in reducing test anxiety. Paul (1969a) took groups of normal students and presented them with stressful imagery. He found that both relaxation training and hypnosis induced relaxation and reduced physiological arousal and subjective distress, although there was an edge for relaxation training on the physiological measures. In a second study (Paul, 1969b), he found similar improvement in both groups, but an advantage for relaxation training.

It is of interest that two of the three controlled studies conducted with actual patient populations show an advantage for hypnosis, especially when the patients request hypnosis, as in the Lazarus study. Studies among student volunteers who are symptomatic with snake phobias or test anxiety show mixed results, with no clear advantage for either hypnosis or systematic desensitization as a group. Studies in which stress was induced in normal volunteers show some advantage for relaxation training over hypnosis. While there are some exceptions to this generalization, it is of interest. It may have to do with expectancy, as noted by Lazarus (1973), or symptom severity. One can presume that those who present themselves as patients seeking treatment are more severely impaired by their symptoms than those who respond to a newspaper advertisement, and clearly both these groups are more impaired than those who have no symptom complaint and respond to a stress-reducing situation. Perhaps hypnotic techniques have an advantage when the condition is more severe. Some investigators have suggested that the depth of relaxation and intensity of visualization is greater in hypnosis than simple relaxation techniques (Glick, 1970). It may also be that the student samples may have been responding to a possible bias among researchers that behavioral techniques were superior to those employing hypnosis. In any event, taken as a whole, these studies indicate that hypnosis and other relaxation techniques are in many ways similar, results are by and large comparable, but that certain factors may give an advantage to one over another; for example, hypnotizability (O'Brien et al., 1981; Spiegel et al., 1981), and a request for the use of hypnosis (Lazarus, 1973).

CONCLUDING REMARKS

One unique advantage of hypnotic techniques is that rapid and reliable means of assessing hypnotic responsivity are available for clinical use. Thus, within 10 minutes a clinician can make an informed decision regarding the patient's ability to successfully utilize treatment techniques employing hypnosis. Roughly one third of patients will not be able to make reasonable use of hypnosis. In those cases, behavioral techniques and pharmacotherapy should be given preference. One factor other than low hypnotizability that should be taken into account in evaluating poor treatment response is secondary gain. Some hypnotizable individuals may be especially sensitive to subtle or overt environmental factors that reinforce symptomatology. It may be necessary to resolve these factors either through psychotherapy with the patient, or direct intervention with the family or legal issues surrounding disability, before any improvement can be expected.

A second advantage of hypnotic techniques is that patients can be taught to employ them at any time on their own; for example, in preparation for facing a feared situation or when they feel a panic or anxiety attack coming on. Having something to resort to at all times can in itself reduce the feedback and feedforward cycle of anxiety. In addition, the hypnotic induction itself can lower physiologic arousal, interrupt the snowball effect of anxiety, and enable the subject to concentrate intently on a cognitive strategy that can help them incorporate their anxious preoccupation in a broader perspective which makes it more manageable. The sense of psychological control over somatic process is often quite reassuring, even if the changes in physiological processes are minimal. Restructuring techniques with hypnosis can be employed as an adjunctive tool in the management of a variety of disorders. While some of the most extremely anxious patients may temporarily lose access to their own hypnotic capacity, a substantial number of them are hypnotizable to a sufficient degree that a treatment trial is warranted. The potential for internalizing psychological control over somatic process represented by hypnosis can be an important resource in the management of anxiety and phobic disorders.

REFERENCES

American Psychiatric Association (1987). *Diagnostic and statistical manual of mental disorders* (3rd Ed. Revised). Washington, DC: Author.

Banyai, E. I., & Hilgard, E. R. (1976). A comparison of active-alert hypnotic induction with traditional relaxation induction. *Journal of Abnormal Psychology, 85*, 218–224.

Case, D. B., Fogel, D. H., & Pollack, A. A. (1980). Intrahypnotic and long-term effects of self-hypnosis on blood pressure in mild hypertension. *International Journal of Clinical and Experimental Hypnosis, 28*, 27–38.

Crasilneck, H. D., & Hall, J. A. (1985). *Clinical hypnosis: Principles and applications* (2nd Ed.), New York: Grune & Stratton.

Dimascio, A., Weissman, M. M., Prusoff, B. A., Nu, C., Swilling, M., & Klerman, G. L. (1979). Differential symptom reduction by drugs and psychotherapy in acute depression. *Archives of General Psychiatry, 36*, 1450–1456.

Dubin, L. L., & Shapiro, S. S. (1974). Use of hypnosis to facilitate dental extraction and hemostasis in a classic hemophiliac with a high antibody titer to factor VIII. *American Journal of Clinical Hypnosis, 17*, 79–83.

Erickson, M. H. (1967). Advanced techniques of hypnosis and therapy. In J. Haley (Ed.), *Selected papers of Milton H. Erickson*. New York: Grune & Stratton.

Frankel, F. H. (1976). *Hypnosis: Trance as a coping mechanism*. New York: Plenum Press.

Frankel, F. H., & Orne, M. T. (1976). Hypnotizability and phobic behavior. *Archives of General Psychiatry, 33*, 1259–1261.

Freud, S. (1958). Remembering, repeating, and working-through. (Further recommendations on the technique of psycho-analysis II). In J. Strachey (Ed. and Trans.), *The standard edition of the complete psychological works of Sigmund Freud* (Vol. 12, pp. 145–156). London: Hogarth Press. (Original work published 1914).

Frischholz, E. J., Spiegel, D., Spiegel, H., Balma, D. L., & Markell, D. S. (1982). Differential hypnotic responsivity of smokers, phobics, and chronic pain control patients: A failure to confirm. *Journal of Abnormal Psychology, 91*, 269–272.

Gerschman, J., Burrows, G. D., Reade, P., & Foenander, G. (1979). Hypnotizability and the treatment of dental phobic illness. In G. D. Burrows, D. R. Collison, & L. Dennerstein (Eds.), *Hypnosis 1979* (pp. 33–39). Amsterdam: Elsevier/North-Holland Biomedical.

Glick, B. S. (1970). Conditioning therapy with phobic patients. Success and failure. *American Journal of Psychotherapy, 24*, 92–101.

Grabowska, M. J. (1971). The effect of hypnosis and hypnotic suggestion on the blood flow in extremities. *Polish Medical Journal, 10*, 1044–1051.

Hilgard, E. R. (1977). *Divided consciousness: Multiple controls in human thought and action*. New York: John Wiley & Sons.

Horowitz, S. L. (1970). Strategies within hypnosis for reducing phobic behavior. *Journal of Abnormal Psychology, 75,* 104–112.

Kelly, S. F. (1984). Measured hypnotic response and phobic behavior: A brief communication. *International Journal of Clinical and Experimental Hypnosis, 32,* 1–5.

Lazarus, A. A. (1973). "Hypnosis" as a facilitator in behavior therapy. *International Journal of Clinical and Experimental Hypnosis, 21,* 25–31.

Marks, I. M., Gelder, M. G., & Edwards, G. (1968). Hypnosis and desensitization for phobias: A controlled prospective trial. *British Journal of Psychiatry, 114,* 1263–1274.

McGuinness, T. P. (1984). Hypnosis in the treatment of phobias: A review of the literature. *American Journal of Clinical Hypnosis, 26,* 261–269.

Melnick, J., & Russell, R. W. (1976). Hypnosis versus systematic desensitization in the treatment of test anxiety. *Journal of Counseling Psychology, 23,* 291–295.

Morgan, A. H., & Hilgard, E. R. (1973). Age differences in susceptibility to hypnosis. *International Journal of Clinical and Experimental Hypnosis, 21,* 78–85.

Morgan, A. H., Johnson, D. L., & Hilgard, E. R. (1974). The stability of hypnotic susceptibility: A longitudinal study. *International Journal of Clinical and Experimental Hypnosis, 22,* 249–257.

Myers, J. K., Weissman, M. M., Tischler, G. L., Holzer, C. E., Leaf, P. J., Orvaschel, H., Anthony, J. C., Boyd, J. H., Burke, J. D., Kramer, M., & Stoltzman, R. (1984). Six-month prevalence of psychiatric disorders in three communities, 1980–1982. *Archives of General Psychiatry, 41,* 959–967.

O'Brien, R., Cooley, L. E., Ciotti, J., & Henninger, K. M. (1981). Augmentation of systematic desensitization of snake phobia through post-hypnotic dream suggestion. *American Journal of Clinical Hypnosis, 23,* 231–238.

Paul, G. (1969a). Inhibition of physiological response to stressful imagery by relaxation training and hypnotically suggested relaxation. *Behaviour Research and Therapy, 7,* 249–256.

Paul, G. (1969b). Physiological effects of relaxation training and hypnotic suggestion. *Journal of Abnormal Psychology, 74,* 425–437.

Pribram, K. H. (1971). *Languages of the brain: Experimental paradoxes and principles in neuropsychology.* Monterey, CA: Wadsworth.

Spiegel, D. (1980). Hypnotizability and psychoactive medication. *American Journal of Clinical Hypnosis, 22,* 217–222.

Spiegel, D. (1981). Vietnam grief work using hypnosis. *American Journal of Clinical Hypnosis, 24,* 33–40.

Spiegel, D. (1983, October). Hypnotizability and the differential diagnosis of psychopathology. In Symposium conducted at the meeting of the Society for Clinical and Experimental Hypnosis, Cambridge, MA. John Nemiah, MD, Chairperson.

Spiegel, D., Cutcomb, S., Ren, C., & Pribram, K. (1985). Hypnotic hallucination alters evoked potentials. *Journal of Abnormal Psychology, 94,* 249–255.

Spiegel, D., Detrick, D., & Frischholz, E. (1982). Hypnotizability and psychopathology. *American Journal of Psychiatry, 139,* 431–437.

Spiegel, D., Frischholz, E. J., Maruffi, B., & Spiegel, H. (1981). Hypnotic responsivity and the treatment of flying phobia. *American Journal of Clinical Hypnosis, 23,* 239–247.

Spiegel, D., & Klein, K. (1984, October). Hypnotic control of gastric acid secretion. Paper presented at the annual scientific meeting of the Society for Clinical and Experimental Hypnosis, San Antonio, TX.

Spiegel, H., & Spiegel, D. (1978). *Trance and treatment: Clinical uses of hypnosis.* New York: Basic Books.

Spies, G. (1979). Desensitization of test anxiety: Hypnosis compared with biofeedback. *American Journal of Clinical Hypnosis, 21,* 108–111.

Spitzer, R. L., Endicott, J., & Robins, E. (1975). *Research diagnostic criteria (RDC) for a selected group of functional disorders.* New York: Biometrics Research, New York State Psychiatric Institute.

Stern, D. B., Spiegel, H., & Nee, J. C. (1978–1979). The hypnotic induction profile: Normative observations, reliability, and validity. *American Journal of Clinical Hypnosis, 31,* 109–132.

Stutman, R. K., & Bliss, E. L. (1985). Posttraumatic stress disorder, hypnotizability, and imagery. *American Journal of Psychiatry, 142,* 741–743.

Sullivan, H. S. (1954). *The psychiatric interview* (pp. 100–101). New York: W. W. Norton & Co.

Weissman, M. M. (1979). The psychological treatment of depression. *Archives of General Psychiatry, 36,* 1261–1269.

Weitzenhoffer, A. M., & Hilgard, E. R. (1962). *Stanford hypnotic susceptibility scale, Form C.* Palo Alto, CA: Consulting Psychologists Press.

PART V

Pharmacological Treatments

CHAPTER 22

Benzodiazepines

A Review of Benzodiazepine Treatment of Anxiety Disorders: Pharmacology, Efficacy, and Implications for Pathophysiology

Scott W. Woods and Dennis S. Charney

The benzodiazepines are among the most commonly prescribed of drugs. Benzodiazepines are most frequently prescribed for anxiety disorders, although they are used for indications as varied as anesthesia, status epilepticus, and chloroquine toxicity (Greenblatt & Shader, 1974; Ward, 1985). This chapter critically reviews the treatment of anxiety disorders with benzodiazepines. Initially, the history of the benzodiazepine drugs and the receptors to which they bind will be discussed. Then follow reviews of benzodiazepine clinical pharmacology, anxiolytic efficacy, and adverse effects, and a section on the clinical pharmacologic management of anxiety with illustrative brief case reports. Finally, the implications of benzodiazepine efficacy for the pathophysiology of anxiety disorders and the future of anxiolytic pharmacology will be considered.

THE HISTORY OF BENZODIAZEPINE DEVELOPMENT

Chlordiazepoxide was the first benzodiazepine synthesized and the first to reach clinical use. The anxiolytic properties of chlordiazepoxide came to light through a combination of serendipity and keen observation (Cohen, 1970). Chlordiazepoxide was discovered by a pharmaceutical company medicinal chemist whose goal was to develop new psychopharmacologic drugs by essentially random screening of multiple easily synthesized compounds (Sternback, 1979). One such class of novel compounds was then known as the heptoxdiazines. Of 40 heptoxdiazine derivatives initially synthesized, all proved to have no pharmacologic activity. Chlordiazepoxide, the result of the last experiment planned for the heptoxdiazines, was assumed also to be inert and was set aside without pharmacologic testing. Two years later, in a cleanup of the laboratory, a chemist recognized that the structure of chlordiazepoxide differed from that of earlier analogues and sent it for testing, where its potent properties were discovered. The compound was almost abandoned again when the initial clinical trials using high doses in geriatric patients demonstrated no unique properties (Cohen, 1970).

The first clinical report of the effectiveness and safety of chlordiazepoxide in anxious patients appeared in March 1960 (Harris, 1960; see also Kinross-Wright, Cohen, & Knight, 1960). Chlordiazepoxide proved to have several advantages over drugs in use for anxiety at that time (Table 22.1). It was less sedating and much less lethal when taken in overdose than the barbiturates or meprobamate, and it was free of the potent neurological side effects of the neuroleptics (Cohen, 1970). Multiple other benzodiazepines have subsequently been synthesized, developed, and marketed so that there are currently 12 such drugs available for use in the United States (see Table 22.2) and several more worldwide.

Table 22.1. Historical Evolution of Drug Treatments for Anxiety

Alcohol
Opiates
Bromides
Chloral hydrate, paraldehyde
Barbiturates (e.g., phenobarbital)
Propanediol carbamates (e.g., meprobamate)
Anticholinergics and antihistamines (e.g., diphenhydramine)
Methaqualone and similar drugs
Neuroleptics (e.g, chlorpromazine)
Antidepressants (e.g., imipramine)
Beta-adrenoceptor antagonists (e.g., propranolol)
Benzodiazepines
Buspirone

Note. Modified from "Anxiolytic Profiles" by S. Gershon and A. S. Eison, 1983, *Journal of Clinical Psychiatry, 44*, p. 45. Copyright 1983 by Physicians Postgraduate Press Inc Memphis Tennessee, U.S.A. Reprinted by permission.

THE BENZODIAZEPINE RECEPTOR AND THE MECHANISM OF ANXIOLYTIC ACTION OF BENZODIAZEPINES

The 1977 discovery of a brain neuronal receptor with high affinity and specificity of the benzodiazepine drugs (Mohler & Okada; Squires & Braestrup, 1977) has led to a virtual explosion in knowledge regarding how the benzodiazepines work to reduce anxiety and may help to elucidate a neurobiological basis for some of the anxiety disorders effectively treated by benzodiazepines. There is convincing preclinical evidence that drug occupation of these high affinity neuronal receptor sites mediates most of the behavioral and pharmacologic effects of the benzodiazepines; this has been clearly demonstrated by the blockade of benzodiazepine behavioral effects by new drugs that specifically inhibit benzodiazepine binding to these receptors without producing an intrinsic effect (for review, see Haefely, 1985). In addition, the affinity of various benzodiazepines for the neuronal receptors correlates highly with the potency of the drugs in animal models predictive of anxiolytic effects (Braestrup & Squires, 1978; Mohler & Okada, 1978) and with clinical potency (Tallman, Paul, Skolnick, & Gallager, 1980). While as many as four subtypes of the neuronal benzodiazepine receptor have been proposed (for review, see Williams, 1983), some of the subtypes may actually be different affinity states of the same receptors (Gee, Yamamura, Roeske, & Yamamura, 1984). "Non-neuronal" benzodiazepine receptors also exist whose function is unknown but which do not appear to mediate benzodiazepine behavioral effects (Haefely, 1985); the affinity of various benzodiazepines for the non-neuronal sites does not

Table 22.2. Some Characteristics of Benzodiazepines Available for Use in the United States

Benzodiazepine	Year Introduced	Approved Indications	Brand Name(s)	Generic Availability	Approximate Clinical Anxiolytic Dose Equivalency (mg)	Rate of Appearance After Oral Dose	Mean Time of Peak Plasma Concentration (hours)	Overall Rate of Elimination	Mean Elimination Half-Life (hours)
Chlordiazepoxide	1960	Anxiety Alcohol withdrawal Preoperative sedation	Librium Libritabs Clipoxide SK-Lygen (Limbitrol) (Librax) (Menrium)	Yes	25	Intermediate	—	Slow	—
Diazepam	1961	Anxiety Alcohol withdrawal Muscle spasm Status epilepitcus Preoperative sedation	Valium Valrelease	Yes	10	Rapid	0.9	Slow	40–60
Oxazepam	1963	Anxiety Anxiety associated with depression Alcohol withdrawal	Serax	No	30	Intermediate to slow	2.3	Intermediate to rapid	8.5
Flurazepam	1970	Insomnia	Dalmane	No	—	Rapid to intermediate	1	Slow	82
Clorazepate	1972	Anxiety Alcohol withdrawal Seizure disorders	Tranxene	No	15	Rapid	1.2	Slow	60
Clonazepam	1974	Seizure disorders	Konopin	No	*	Intermediate	1.8	Intermediate	27
Lorazepam	1977	Anxiety Anxiety associated with depression Preoperative sedation	Ativan	Yes	2	Intermediate	1.9	Intermediate	14
Prazepam	1977	Anxiety	Centrax	No	20	Slow	7.8	Slow	60
Temazepam	1981	Insomnia	Restoril	No	—	Intermediate to slow	2.5	Intermediate	15
Alprazolam	1981	Anxiety Anxiety associated with depression	Xanax	No	1	Intermediate	1–2	Intermediate	11
Halazepam	1981	Anxiety	Paxipam	No	40	Intermediate to slow	2	Slow	80
Triazolam	1983	Insomnia	Halcion	No	—	Intermediate	1–2	Rapid	3

Note. Derived from Fann, Pitts, & Wheless, 1982; Greenblatt, Abernethy, Divoll, Harmatz, & Shader, 1983; Greenblatt, Divoll, Abernethy, Ochs, & Shader, 1983 (Figures 1 and 20); Greenblatt, Shader, & Abernethy, 1983 (Table 1); Greenblatt, Shader, & Koch-Weser, 1975; Greenblatt, Shader, MacLeod, & Sellers, 1978; Dawson, Jue, & Brogden, 1984; Kaplan, Alexander, Jack, Puglisi, deSilva, Lee, & Weinfeld, 1974; *Physician's Desk Reference*, 1986. Values for the time of peak plasma concentration and elimination half-life are the mean of values obtained in healthy young volunteers. The mean half-life is that of the longest acting active metabolite.
*Clonazepam is increasingly prescribed for anxiety, but the dose equivalency is not yet established.

correlate with behavioral potency (Syapin & Skolnick, 1979). The neuronal benzodiazepine receptors are structurally and functionally coupled to a subpopulation of receptors for gamma-aminobutyric acid ($GABA_A$ receptors) (for reviews, see Costa & Guidotti, 1985; Tallman & Gallager, 1985), to a channel for chloride anions, and to receptors for barbiturates, picrotoxin, and other drugs, all of which appear to be linked into oligomeric, supramolecular, multireceptor units (Olsen, 1981, 1982; Tallman, Thomas, & Gallager, 1978) (see Figure 22.1a).

The primary pharmacologic effects of benzodiazepines appear to be due to their potentiation of the actions of GABA at $GABA_A$ receptors. GABA is an inhibitory neurotransmitter said to be present in 30% of brain synapses (Tallman & Gallager, 1985). The general consequence of GABA occupation of $GABA_A$ receptors is to increase flux of the negative chloride ions through chloride channels into the cell, thereby hyperpolarizing the cell and inhibiting its function (for review, see Tallman & Gallager, 1985). Strong evidence indicates that benzodiazepines act to increase the inhibitory effect of GABA by increasing the affinity of $GABA_A$ receptors for GABA and thus prolonging the opening of the chloride channel (for reviews, see Costa & Guidotti, 1985; Haefely, 1985; Tallman & Gallager, 1985) (see Figure 22.1b). In the absence of GABA, benzodiazepines do not produce their biologic effects (Bormann & Clapham, 1985). While the neurochemical consequences of neuronal benzodiazepine receptor activation appear to be mediated entirely via modulation of GABA-ergic activity, the likely corollary that the behavioral effects of neuronal benzodiazepine occupation also are mediated by potentiation of GABA function has not yet been proven conclusively (for reviews, see Gray, Quintero, Mellanby, & Buckland, 1984; Sanger, 1985).

A fascinating variety of compounds, among them those not defined structurally as benzodiazepines, interact with the neuronal "benzodiazepine" receptors (Haefely, 1985; Tallman & Gallager, 1985). Some of these compounds produce pharmacologic effects that are different from, or even opposite to, those of the benzodiazepine drugs. A functional typology of compounds acting as the benzodiazepine receptor has been proposed (Braestrup & Nielsen, 1983): "agonists" refer to those compounds that, like benzodiazepine drugs, have anxiolytic, sedative, and anticonvulsant properties and potentiate the effects of GABA; "inverse agonists" refer to those compounds that, in a manner opposite to that of benzodiazepine drugs, have anxiogenic, stimulant, and proconvulsant actions and reduce the effets of GABA (see Figure 22.1c); "antagonists" bind to the benzodiazepine receptor and block the actions of agonists and inverse agonists, but themselves have little or no intrinsic effect. Finally, partial agonists have maximal effects similar to, but weaker than, those of full agonists and reduce the effects of full agonists when coadministered. Partial inverse agonists also exist.

An extensive search is underway for endogenous neuromodulators that interact with benzodiazepine receptors. Thus far, no candidate has been generally accepted, although several have been discarded (Alho, et al. 1985; Wu, Lin, Su, & Yang, 1984; for reviews see Costa & Guidotti, 1985; Haefely, 1985; Tallman & Gallager, 1985). One promising possibility is a peptide named DBI (diazepam binding inhibitor). DBI or one of its metabolites may prove to be an endogenous benzodiazepine inverse agonist (see Figure 22.1c). DBI binds to the benzodiazepine receptor, produces anxiety-like behavior in laboratory animals, and is present in the human brain (Costa & Guidotti, 1985). It is possible that benzodiazepine drugs may eventually prove to reduce anxiety in some patients by specifically counteracting an abnormality in the endogenous, benzodiazepine neuromodulator-receptor-effector system.

PHARMACOKINETICS

The benzodiazepines available for clinical use in the United States as of October

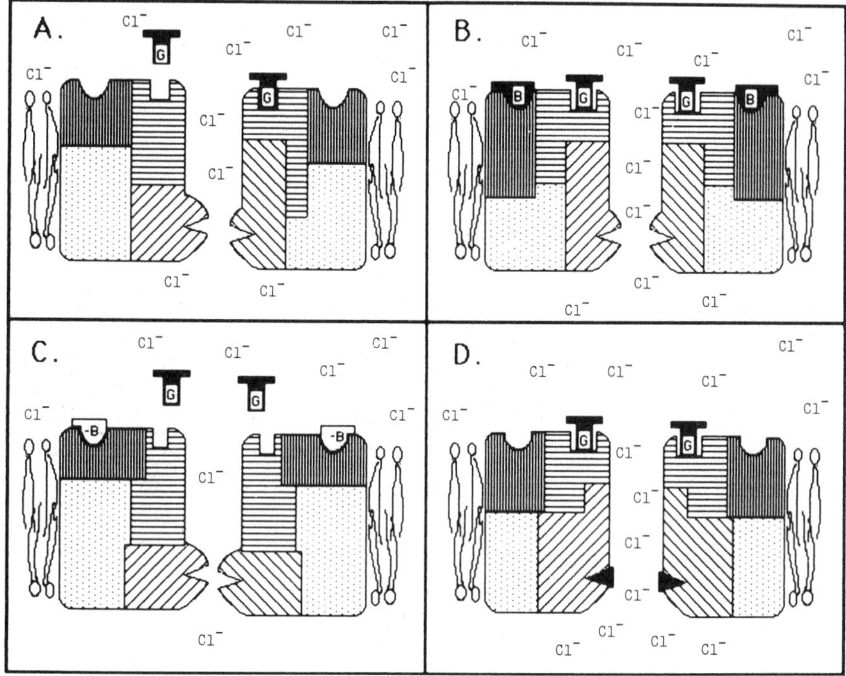

Figure 22.1. Schematic representation of drug and neurotransmitter effects at the benzodiazepine-GABA-receptor chloride ionophore complex. The main figure in each panel depicts a cross section of neuronal cell membrane, containing a lipid bilayer and the multireceptor protein moieties. The top of each panel represents extracellular fluid, and the bottom, intracellular fluid. It is postulated that increased firing of this neuron is related to anxiety. The chloride channel within the receptor complex is shown in each panel as the central space containing chloride ions. The semicircular indentations represent benzodiazepine recognition sites; the rectilinear indentations, GABA recognition sites; and the triangular indentations, barbiturate or picrotoxin sites. *Panel A.* The drug-free state. The submaximal affinity of the GABA sites for GABA (G) is shown by the incomplete saturation of the GABA receptors. The effect of GABA to prolong opening of the chloride channel is portrayed in this static drawing as a partial opening of the channel on the side where GABA is bound. *Panel B.* Benzodiazepine agonists (B) are bound to the benzodiazepine recognition site, inducing a conformational change in the complex, as shown by an altered internal, structure. The conformational change results in an increased affinity of the GABA receptor for its ligand, depicted as a widening of the GABA receptor sites and by the increased GABA binding. As a result of the increased GABA binding, the chloride channel has a higher probability of being open, and more chloride ions enter the neuron, hyperpolarizing it and inhibiting its function. *Panel C.* Benzodiazepine inverse agonists (-B) bind to the benzodiazepine site, alter the internal structure of the complex, decrease the affinity of the GABA receptors for GABA, and decrease the probability of the chloride channel being open, thereby increasing cell firing. *Panel D.* Barbiturates (dark triangles) bind to their receptors within the channel, increase the probability of channel opening by increasing the affinity of the GABA receptors, and also directly alter the conformation of the channel itself. The neuron is thus markedly hyperpolarized, possibly leading to greater sedation than observed with the benzodiazepines or obtundation at higher doses.

1986 are listed in Table 22.2 along with the indications for which they are approved by the Food and Drug Administration. The differences in approved indications do not, however, necessarily indicate differences in therapeutic effectiveness. All currently available benzodiazepines show anxiolytic, sedative, and anticonvulsant properties in animal models (Greenblatt, Shader, & Abernethy, 1983), and all interact with benzodiazepine receptors and thus presumably share the same mechanism of action (see previous section). Differences in clinical indications may relate to pharmaceutical company marketing strategies as well as to pharmacological differences. There are, however, differences in the potency (see Table 22.2) and pharmacokinetics of the benzodiazepines that may have clinical significance in selected situations.

Benzodiazepine treatment of anxiety disorders is usually accomplished by the oral route. The onset of anxiolytic effect of oral benzodiazepine is primarily determined by the rapidity with which active drug appears in the blood. Oral absorption is most rapid for diazepam and clorazepate dipotassium (Table 22.2), and anxiolytic effects with these drugs are often seen within minutes. The rapid effect is advantageous in some patients, but can be disadvantageous in patients who perceive the rapid onset of side effects such as drowsiness as a frightening loss of control. Prazepam, which is slowly metabolized to the active drug nordiazepam, has the slowest onset of action among available anxiolytics (Greenblatt, Shader, & Abernethy, 1983), and may, therefore, be desirable or undesirable, respectively, in patients who wish a gradual onset of action or in whom the drug is prescribed on an as-needed basis for occasional brief episodes of anxiety.

The duration of anxiolytic effect after single doses is largely determined by the rate at which the drug is taken up from the blood by non-neuronal tissues (Greenblatt, Divoll, Abbernethy, Ochs, & Shader, 1983). Diazepam rapidly diffuses into adipose tissue and therefore has a shorter duration of effect after a single dose than does, for example, lorazepam, which enters adipose tissue more slowly (Greenblatt, Divoll, et al., 1983).

The effect of benzodiazepines during the following chronic treatment are related to whether the drug has metabolites that are pharmacologically active and to the rate of elimination from the body of active substances. The rate of elimination of active substances has consequences for the frequency with which the drug must be taken, accumulation of drug during chronic treatment, and the occurrence of withdrawal after discontinuation of chronic treatment (van Rooyen & Offermeier, 1985). Benzodiazepines such as oxazepam, clonazepam, lorazepam, and alprazolam have no active metabolites and tend to have faster rates of eliminations and shorter durations of actions, while diazepam, chlordiazepoxide, prazepam, and halazepam do produce active metabolites which are eliminated more slowly (see Table 22.2). The elimination of active substances from the body is governed by the rapidity of metabolism by the liver (Bellantuono, Reggi, Tognoni, & Garattini, 1980; Greenblatt, Divoll, et al., 1983; Greenblatt, Shader, & Abernethy, 1983; Rooyen & Offermeier, 1985). Oxazepam and lorazepam do not require one of the steps (oxidation) of hepatic metabolism and, other considerations being equal, are theoretically to be preferred in patients with liver disease or in the elderly (especially elderly males) whose oxidative metabolism by the liver proceeds more slowly (Greenblatt, Divoll, et al., 1983; Rooyen & Offermeier, 1985). Clonazepam requires an additional hepatic metabolic step called acetylation; its effects may be prolonged in the subgroup of the population who are "slow acetylators" (van Rooyen & Offermeier, 1985). It is a common clinical observation that benzodiazepines with shorter half-lives, such as alprazolam or oxazepam, may need to be administered four or even five times daily, whereas prazepam, diazepam, or helazepam, with long half-lives, can often be administered but once daily.

In the blood, most benzodiazepines are more than 90% bound to plasma proteins including albumin; clonazepam, which is only 40% to 50% bound, is an exception

(Greenblatt, Shader, & Abernethy, 1983). Hypoalbuminemia has been associated with a higher incidence of benzodiazepine side-effects (Bellantuono et al., 1980).

BENZODIAZEPINE EFFICACY IN ANXIETY DISORDERS

In the late 1970s and early 1980s, more rigorous psychiatric diagnostic criteria, including the DSM-III criteria, were introduced and gained acceptance (American Psychiatric Association, 1980; Spitzer & Endicott, 1977). The most significant change in the nosology of the anxiety disorders was the emphasis on the recognition of panic attacks. A panic attack is characterized as a discrete episode of anxious or fearful mood accompanied by physical symptoms, whose onset is abrupt and whose duration is usually measured in minutes to hours. Recognition of the importance of panic attacks resulted in the separation of DSM-II anxiety neurosis into two DSM-III diagnoses: panic disorder and generalized anxiety disorder. The role of panic attacks in agoraphobia was also appreciated.

For a review of more than 200 pre-DSM-III benzodiazepine-controlled clinical trials, see Greenblatt and Shader, 1974. They conclude that there is substantial evidence for the efficacy in anxious patients of all the benzodiazepines then marketed as anxiolytics. Occasionally, other reviewers have reached more guarded conclusions (Shapiro, Struening, Shapiro, & Milcarek, 1983; Solomon & Hart, 1978). The present review will focus on recent benzodiazepine efficacy studies that have categorized anxious patients according to DSM-III or similar conventions. We will follow the currently proposed revisions in DSM-III and consider together patients with panic disorder and those with agoraphobia with panic attacks (Ballenger, 1984; Spitzer, 1986).

Benzodiazepine Efficacy in Panic Disorders

The panic attack is the cardinal clinical feature in patients with panic disorders. Associated symptoms such as anticipatory anxiety, generalized anxiety, phobic avoidance, and depressed mood are often present. Some antidepressant drugs, such as imipramine hydrochloride and phenelzine sulfate, are of proven effectiveness in blocking panic attacks during chronic treatment (Ballenger, 1986; Goodman & Charney, 1985). Until recently, most clinicians believed that benzodiazepines could help allay anticipatory anxiety in panic disorders but were not effective in blocking the panic attacks (Klein, Gittelman, Rifkin, & Quitkin, 1980; Matuzas & Glass, 1983; Rosenbaum, 1982; Shader, Goodman, & Gever, 1982; Sheehan, 1982b). This belief was based primarily on the observation that many patients who had been prescribed benzodiazepines without improvement then went on to enjoy a cessation of their attacks during antidepressant treatment (Klein et al., 1980; Sheehan, 1982a).

Alprazolam was the first benzodiazepine to be shown effective for the panic attacks of panic disorder (Sheehan, 1982a). Alprazolam was first tried in panic patients (Sheehan, Coleman, et al., 1984) because of the effectiveness of antidepressants in this disorder and the possibility that alprazolam might have antidepressant properties (Fabre, 1976; for reviews, see Dawson, Jue, & Brogden, 1984; Straw, 1985). The effectiveness of alprazolam for panic attacks has subsequently been confirmed in multiple centers (see Table 22.3). Alprazolam has been shown to prevent panic attacks as effectively, or nearly as effectively, as imipramine or phenelzine (Charney et al., in press; Rizley, Kahn, McNair, & Frankenthaler, 1986; Sheehan et al., 1984). Anticipatory anxiety, generalized anxiety, phobia, and depression associated with panic attacks can also respond to alprazolam treatment. The average daily dosage of alprazolam required to block panic attacks (20–60 mg diazepam-equivalent) is higher than the dosage usually used for generalized anxiety (see Table 22.3 and 22.4).

There is now emerging evidence that other benzodiazepines besides alprazolam, and perhaps all other benzodiazepine anxiolytics, are also effective in blocking panic attacks. Studies suggest that diaze-

Table 22.3. Studies of Benzodiazepine Effectiveness in Panic Disorders

Drug	Study	N	Method	Daily Mean Dose (mg)	Diazepam Equivalent Dose (mg)
Alprazolam	Chouinard et al., 1982	14	DB PG comparison with placebo	2.0	20
	Pies, 1983	1	CS	1.5	15
	Shehi & Patterson, 1984	16	CS combination with propranolol	1.5–3	15–30
	Sheehan, Coleman et al., 1984	32	SB crossover comparison with ibuprofen	5.8	58
	Sheehan, Claycomb et al., 1984	30	DB PG comparison with IMI, phenelzine, and placebo	3.9	39
	Mark, 1984	50	CS	2.2	22
	Charney & Heninger, 1985	14	DB PB	5.6	56
	Ballenger et al., 1985	250	DB PG comparison with placebo	6.0	60
	Woods et al., 1986	8	SB PB	3.1	31
	Rizley et al., 1986	22	DB PG comparison with IMI	2.8	28
	Alexander & Alexander, 1986	27	Private practice CS	3.9	39
	Liebowitz et al., 1986	34	Prospective CS	4.5	45
	Ravaris et al., 1986	8	DB PG comparison with propanolol	2–10	20–100
	Dunner et al., 1986	11	DB PG comparison with DZ and placebo	4.0	40
	Charney et al., 1986	18	SB PB NR comparison with IMI and TRZ	3.1	31
	Charney & Woods, submitted	15	DB PG comparison with LZ	2.9	29
Diazepam	Taylor et al., 1982	10	SB crossover comparison with placebo	12	12
	Noyes et al., 1984	21	DB crossover comparison with propranolol	30	30
	Dunner et al., 1986	14	DB PG comparison with ALP and placebo	44	44
Clonazepam	Fontaine & Chouinard, 1984	12	CS	6–9	*
	Fontaine, 1985	10	CS	3–6	*
	Beaudry et al., 1986	8	CS	3.9	*
	Spier et al., 1986	50	CS	1.9	*
	Tesar & Rosenbaum, 1986	10	CS	3.7	*
	Beckett et al., 1986	1	CS	3.0	*
Lorazepam	Charney & Woods, submitted	14	DB PG comparison with ALP	5.7	28
Bromazepam	Beaudry et al., 1984	1	CS	18	15
Chlordiazepoxide	McNair & Kahn, 1981	17	DB PG comparison with IMI	55	22

The **N** reported is the number of patients initially assigned to receive the drug described.
The mean daily dose refers to the mean dose of patients completing the trial.
The diazepam equivalents are clinical approximations.
*Diazepam equivalent for anxiety is not well-established.

Abbreviations:

ALP — alprazolam
BT — behavior therapy
CS — case study
DZ — double-blind
IMI — imipraimine
LZ — lorazepam
mg — milligrams
NR — non-random assignment
PA — panic attack
PB — comparison to placebo baseline
PD — panic disorder
PG — parallel
PT — groups
SB — psychotherpay
TRZ — single-blind trazodone

Results	Comment
79% improved at 4 w, 36% greatly	No specific PA measures. Most patients received concomitant BT.
"Substantial reduction in panic attacks"	Diagnosis of PD not definite. PT not mentioned.
"Almost total relief of panic" in 2w	Concomitant propranolol may permit lower doses of ALP. PT not mentioned.
ALP effective based on global outcome	PA outcome unclear. PT not mentioned.
Effective for PA's	Not yet published
88% improved	Weekly supportive therapy in all cases
Effective for PA's; 50% panic-free	Not formally reported as an outcome study. Concomitant BT.
All three drugs more effective than placebo	PT not mentioned
Effective for PA's	Not formally reported as an outcome study. Concomitant BT.
Both effective for PA's; ALP more quickly	Concomitant supportive PT
100% improved; 85% panic-free at 5 months	No PT given
76% improved; 44% panic-free at 12 w	No systematic PT given
Both drugs effective	PT not mentioned
Both active drugs more effective for PA's than placebo	No PT given
Both effective for PA's; ALP more quickly	Concomitant BT
60% of ALP and 57% of LZ patients panic-free at 6 w	Trial in progress. Concomitant BT.
Not effective	PA's not specifically measured. Low dose. Duration unclear. No PT.
Marked or complete improvement in 67%. Effective for PA's.	Only 2-week duration. No PT given.
Both active drugs more effective for PA's than placebo	No PT given
PA's markedly improved in 83%	PT not mentioned
Moderate or marked improvement in 80%	PT not mentioned
Near remission in 75%	PT not mentioned
78% responded	PT not mentioned
Patients had been treatment-refractory; all responded	PT not mentioned
Effective for PA's	PT not mentioned
57% panic-free with LZ; 60% with ALP	Trial in progress. Concomitant BT in both groups.
Remission of PA's	PT not mentioned
Similar effect of the two drug on global outcome; IMI more effective on a specific panic measure	Outcome of each drug individually not described. PT not mentioned.

Table 22.4. Studies of Benzodiazepine Efficacy in Generalized Anxiety Disorder

Study	Benzodiazepine Drug(s)	Daily Dose (mg)	Diazepam Equivalent Dose (mg)	N	Method	Comment
Feighner et al., 1982	DZ	15	15	23	DB comparison to buspirone	Both groups improved somewhat. Only 43% of DZ patients were improved.
Fontaine et al., 1983	DZ BRZ	15 18	15 15	16 16	DB comparison of DZ, BRZ, and placebo	BRZ superior to DZ on some measures
Elie & Lamontagne, 1984	DZ ALP	16 2	16 20	24 24	DB comparison	DZ superior on some measures but differences not clinically striking
Ceulemans et al., 1985	LZ	4	20	22	DB comparison with ritanserin and placebo	68% improved with LZ; 40% with placebo 76% with ritanserin 10 mg daily
Buchsbaum et al., 1985	CLZ	22.5	15	9	DB comparison with placebo	CLZ more effective
Downing & Rickels, 1985	DZ	26	26	220	SB PB	The most anxious patients had the best response
Jacobson et al., 1985	DZ	14	14	13	DB comparison to buspirone	Both drugs equally effective at 4 weeks; DZ superior at 2 weeks
Hoehn-Saric & McLeod, 1986	ALP	NR	—	30	DB comparison with IMI	Both drugs effective

Note. Dose, diazepam equivalents, *N*, and abbreviations as in Table 22.3. BRZ — bromazepam; CLZ — clorazepate; NR — not reported.

pam, clonazepam, lorazepam, and possibly bromazepam and chlordiazepoxide block panic attacks when used in dosages equipotent to the dosages of alprazolam typically prescribed for panic (see Table 22.3). A double-blind random-assignment study comparing alprazolam at a mean dosage of 4.0 mg per day and diazepam at a mean dosage of 44 mg per day to placebo has shown the two active drugs equally effective in blocking panic attacks (Dunner, Ishiki, Avery, Wilson, & Hyde, 1986), and double-blind random-assignment studies in progress comparing alprazolam to lorazepam are yielding similar results (Woods, Charney, & Heninger, unpublished data; K. Rickels, M. D., personal communication).

There are several reasons why the effectiveness of benzodiazepines in blocking panic attacks may have been previously overlooked. First, physicians typically did not prescribe benzodiazepines in sufficiently high dosages and on the schedule that is necessary to block panic attacks. Most panic patients prescribed benzodiazepines had been instructed to take as little as possible as seldom as possible. A second reason is that, although early benzodiazepine efficacy studies in anxious patients undoubtedly included patients with panic attacks whose attacks benefited from treatment (e.g., Krakowski, 1963), the systematic observation of benzodiazepine effectiveness for panic was never made because clinical attention and the rating instruments used were not focused specifically on the attacks. Third, preclinical studies reporting pharmacologic differences between alprazolam and other benzodiazepines (Eriksson, Carlsson, Nilsson, & Soderpalm, 1986; Kornecki, Ehrlich & Lenox, 1984; Sethy & Hodges, 1982) may have distracted attention from the potent agonist effect at benzodiazepine receptors which alprazolam shares with other benzodiazepine anxiolytis.

Finally, results from an early study (McNair & Kahn, 1981) suggesting that benzodiazepines might be effective for panic were not appreciated. McNair and Kahn (1981) compared patients completing an 8-week trial in which they were randomly assigned to chlordiazepoxide or imipramine (13 completers in each group). This study has been widely cited as supporting the belief that the most benzodiazepines were not effective for panic attacks, although the authors themselves do not come to this specific conclusion. The actual response of the patients to chlordiazepoxide treatment was not reported in this study; the data analysis presented relates exclusively to the comparative efficacy of the two drugs. Some of the patients' self-ratings suggested that imipramine was more effective than chlordiazepoxide; however, these findings need not indicate that chlordiazepoxide was ineffective. In fact, the similar effects of the two drugs on the patient global improvement ratings and the psychiatrist observer ratings would suggest that chlordiazepoxide is an effective medication in panic patients.

Benzodiazepine Efficacy in Generalized Anxiety Disorder (GAD)

A large number of studies have documented the efficacy of benzodiazepines in mixed anxiety states. There is no persuasive evidence that any benzodiazepine is more effective than any other in such patients (Ballenger, 1984; Greenblatt & Shader, 1974; Klein et al., 1980; Mavissakalian, 1982; Rosenbaum, 1982) Although these studies undoubtedly contained many patients suffering from GAD, they do not help to evaluate the specific efficacy of benzodiazepines in generalized anxiety patients.

Recently, several studies have specifically evaluated patients with GAD (see Table 22.4). Three of these studies compared benzodiazepine efficacy to that of placebo; in all three, the active drug was superior. In two studies, each of which compared the effects of two different benzodiazepines, the similarities between the two drugs were more striking than the differences. The average diazepam-equivalent daily dosage used in these studies appears to be roughly half that found effective in panic disorders (see Tables 22.3 and 22.4). It is not clear whether this apparent difference in dosage requirement between the two disorders reflects a difference in the underlying pathophysiology of the disorders, or methodologic differences between the studies. The benzodiazepine dosage in four of these GAD studies may not have been increased gradually over several weeks, as is normal in panic studies, and two other studies (Buchsbaum, et al., 1985; Fontaine, Annable, Chouinard, & Ogilvie, 1983) used fixed-dosage designs. In the one study that appeared to encourage the use of higher dosages (up to 40 mg diazepam per day), the average patient took 26 mg per day (Downing & Rickels, 1985).

Benzodiazepine Efficacy in Obsessive–Compulsive Disorder (OCD)

There have been no well-designed double-blind studies of benzodiazepine efficacy in OCD. A number of pre–DSM-III studies suggest that diazepam (Rao, 1964; Waxman, 1977), oxazepam (Orvin, 1967), and bromazepam (Burrell, Clupan, Newton, Ogg, & Short, 1974; Lin & Chen, 1979; Okuma, Nakao, Ogura, Kishimoto, & Majima, 1971; Tjandra & Kusumanto, 1975) may have some effect. Design problems complicate the interpretation of these studies. Recent case reports document the efficacy of alprazolam in some OCD patients (Hardy, 1986; Tesar & Jenike, 1984; Tollefson, 1985). Because several well-designed studies have documented the effectiveness of chlorimipramine and other antidepressants in OCD (for reviews, see Goodman & Charney, 1985; Insel & Murphy, 1981), the role of benzodiazepines in this disorder currently appears to be adjunctive or as second-line drugs in patients refractory to the antidepressants. Well-designed studies with benzodiazepines are in order. Several lines of evidence suggest, however, that OCD may not be best classified as an anxiety disorder (Cameron, Thyer, Nesse, & Curtis, 1986; Insel, Zahn, & Murphy, 1985).

Benzodiazepine Efficacy in Posttraumatic Stress Disorder (PTSD)

There have been no double-blind studies of the efficacy of any medication in PTSD. Some authors (van der Kolk, 1983) believe that the benzodiazepines may have some beneficial effect and recommend prescribing these drugs on an as-needed basis rather than in a fixed daily dosage to reduce problems associated with tolerance. The reported similarity of PTSD flashbacks to panic attacks (Mellman & Davis, 1985) may suggest a role for the benzodiazepines in this disorder. Preliminary results from an open trial of alprazolam in 18 PTSD patients indicate that the patients were improved by 1.5 to 4.5 mg daily (Dunner, Edwards, & Copeland, 1985). Because many other classes of psychotropic medication can at times be of some benefit to these patients, the specific role of benzodiazepines in PTSD in unclear.

Benzodiazepines for Other Anxiety States

There are no controlled studies of benzodiazepines specifically in social phobia patients (Liebowitz, Gorman, Fyer, & Klein, 1985) or in simple phobia patients, to our knowledge. One study showed that agoraphobic and social phobic patients benefited from both diazepam and chlorimipramine, but did not report treatment responses independently for each diagnosis (Allsopp, Cooper, & Poole, 1984). Benzodiazepines can be effective in the management of anxiety occuring in the context of a maximally treated medical or surgical illness (Finkel, 1978; Greenblatt & Shader, 1974; Jones & Chouinard, 1985).

UNWANTED EFFECTS

Although a large number of unwanted effects have been attributed to benzodiazepines (for reviews, see Edwards, 1981; Greenblatt & Shader, 1974), these drugs are among the safest available. This paradox is the probable result of idiosyncratic or random events occurring in the millions of patients who have been prescribed benzodiazepines. Many adverse effects are reported as single cases in the medical literature; often, when the patients cannot be rechallenged with the drug, it is difficult to be certain that the adverse effect was caused by the drug and not merely coincidental. Case reports cannot reveal the frequency of an adverse effect, which must be studied by surveying large numbers of patients.

Central Nervous System Effects

Reported adverse effects of benzodiazepines upon the central nervous system are listed in Table 22.5. Two epidemiologic studies have shown that drowsiness occurs in 4% to 9% of patients receiving chlordiazepoxide or diazepam and ataxia in as many as 2% (Miller, 1973; Svenson & Hamilton, 1966). All other side effects occurred in fewer than 1% of the patients. This pattern has been confirmed for the newer benzodiazepines as well. It should be noted that drowsiness often occurs in patients treated with placebo. Sedation from benzodiazepines is more common in the elderly (Boston Collaborative Drug Surveillance Program, 1973). In the vast majority of patients, benzodiazepine-induced sedation disappears with time or a reduction in dose.

A potentially serious adverse effect of benzodiazepines is their reported tendency to impair laboratory psychomotor performance and, therefore, possibly driving or the operating of machinery (for reviews see McNair, 1973; Wittenborn, 1979). A relationship between traffic accidents and benzodiazepines was suggested the same year that chlordiazepoxide was introduced (Murray, 1960). However, despite the gravity of this possible adverse effect, it is difficult to interpret the clinical relevance of this literature (Greenblatt, Shader, & Abernethy, 1983). Most studies

Table 22.5. Central Nervous System Adverse Effects of the Benzodiazepines

Adverse Effect	Frequency (percentage)	References
Drowsiness	4–9	Greenblatt & Shader, 1974; Edwards, 1981
Ataxia	< 2	Greenblatt & Shader, 1974
Amnesia	*	Romney & Angus, 1984; Sandyk, 1985
Psychomotor impairment	*	Edwards, 1981
Muscle weakness	< 1	Greenblatt & Shader, 1974
Dysarthria	< 1	Greenblatt & Shader, 1974
Diplopia	< 1	Greenblatt & Shader, 1974
Blurred vision	< 1	Greenblatt & Shader, 1974
Confusion	< 1	Greenblatt & Shader, 1974
Dizziness	< 1	Greenblatt & Shader, 1974
Hostility	< 1	Greenblatt & Shader, 1974; Edwards, 1981; Hall & Zisook, 1981
Depression	*	Greenblatt & Shader, 1974; Edwards, 1981
Mania	*	See text
Parkinsonism	*	Mackie, 1971; Suranyi-Cadotte et al., 1985
Hypnogogic hallucinations	*	Viscott, 1968
Increased dreaming	*	Greenblatt & Shader, 1974
Stuttering	*	Elliott & Thomas, 1985

*Not established.

have used laboratory tests of driving skills, which may or may not predict real-life driving ability. The epidemiologic studies confuse the effects of the drugs and the illnesses for which they are prescribed. The most relevant comparison between anxious patients blindly receiving benzodiazepine for several weeks and anxious patients blindly receiving placebo on real-life driving performance does not seem to have been investigated. In the absence of clear guidelines, the prudent physician should monitor his or her patients for the presence of sedation and caution them about possible impairment of driving skills.

Benzodiazepines can have measurable amnestic effects; specifically, they appear to interfere with consolidation of short-term memory. Unfortunately, the published studies of this effect in humans have all involved volunteers or short-term administration to surgical patients (Romney & Angus, 1984). The effects on memory in anxious patients taking benzodiazepines over relatively long periods are not known. Clinical experience suggests that patients, their families, and their employers rarely notice any functionally significant effect. One study in volunteers showed some tolerance to this effect after 3 weeks of chronic diazepam administration (Ghoneim, Mewaldt, Berie, & Hinrichs, 1981).

Hostility may be released or induced by benzodiazepine treatment and can range from verbal anger to physical assaultiveness out of character for the patient. It is difficult to predict which patients are at risk, but severe manifestations of this kind are fortunately rare. Most benzodiazepines have been implicated (Fouilladieu, D'Enfert, & Conseiller, 1984; Greenblatt & Shader, 1974; Hall & Zisook, 1981), including those only recently available (Gardner & Cowdry, 1985; Rapaport & Braff, 1985; Rosenbaum, Woods, Groves, & Klerman, 1984). Oxazepam, for reasons that are not clear, may not share this effect (Kochansky, Salzmann, Shader, Harmatz, & Ogletree, 1975). The release of hostility often, but not always, occurs early in treatment and may be dose-related. The effect on hostility of benzodiazepines in most patients, however, appears to be to reduce it (Rickels & Downing, 1974).

Precipitation of mania by alprazolam has been reported several times recently (Arana, Pearlman, & Shader, 1985; France & Krishnan, 1984; Goodman & Charney, in press; Klein, Uhde, & Post, 1986; Pecknold & Fleury, 1986; Remick, 1985; Rush, Schlesser, & Erman, 1984; Strahan, Rosenthal, Kaswan, & Winston, 1985). Mania has rarely been reported with other benzodiazepines (Ayd, 1962). This proliferation of case reports suggests that precipitation of mania may be more common with alprazolam than with other benzodiazepines. Goodman and Charney's case, in which alprazolam but not lorazepam induced mania, also supports this view. This property of alprazolam may be related to its ability to affect β-adrenergic receptor function (Sethy & Hodges, 1982).

Hematologic, Hepatic, Thyroid, Renal, Dermatologic, and Miscellaneous Effects

Various reversible skin rashes occasionally are attributable to benzodiazepines. Effects on other organ systems, if they occur at all, are rare (Edwards, 1981; Greenblatt & Shader, 1974). Recent case reports have suggested a relationship between benzodiazepines and hepatitis (Judd, Norman, Marriott, & Burrows, 1986; Roy-Byrne, Vittone, & Uhde, 1983), ejaculatory inhibition (Munjack & Crocker, 1986), inhibition of female orgasm (Sangal, 1985), and sexual precocity (Choonara, Rosenbloom, & Smith, 1985).

Safety of Chronic Treatment

Studies of the long-term use of benzodiazepines document that many patients appear to continue to benefit from prescription of a benzodiazepine for more than a few months and that continued benzodiazepine use for periods of up to 5 years, if needed, appears to be safe (Bowden & Fisher, 1980; Laughren, Battey,

Greenblatt, & Harrop, 1982; Rickels, Case, Downing, & Winokur, 1983). Withdrawal syndromes are more common upon abrupt benzodiazepine discontinuation if treatment had continued beyond 4 to 8 months (Covi, Lipman, Pattison, Derogatis, & Uhlenhuth, 1973; Rickels et al., 1983).

Abuse, Addiction, Tolerance, and Withdrawal

The question of whether chronically anxious patients who take benzodiazepines over long periods are "addicted" is a complex one. Benzodiazepines can produce euphoria when taken in large doses, but such abuse by anxious patients without a history of other drug abuse is rare (Marks, 1978; Owen & Tyrer, 1983; Petursson & Lader, 1981). Although tolerance to the sedative and anticonvulsant effects of the benzodiazepines occurs quickly, tolerance to the anxiolytic effects or escalation of the dose are observed infrequently (Owen & Tyrer, 1983; Petursson & Lader, 1981; Rickels et al., 1983). Withdrawal syndromes can often occur on abrupt discontinuation after chronic administration of benzodiazepines. This indicates physical dependence, but not, necessarily, in our opinion, addiction. When anxiety disorder patients are tapered gradually off benzodiazepines, the large majority have no severe withdrawal symptoms. Return of the original symptoms upon gradual tapering documents a need for continued treatment rather than addiction.

Benzodiazepine withdrawal syndrome can often be distinguished from a return of the pretreatment anxiety symptoms on the basis of specific withdrawal symptoms (see Table 22.6), such as increased sensitivity to light, noise, or other sensations; abnormal perception of motion; and muscle twitching (Busto et al., 1986; Owen & Tyrer, 1983). More serious withdrawal symptoms, such as seizures, are fortunately uncommon, occurring in less than 5% of patients undergoing abrupt withdrawal (Owen & Tyrer, 1983). Patients taking therapeutic doses of benzodiazepine for more than 4 to 8 months are at greater risk for withdrawal (Covi et al., 1973; Rickels et al., 1983). Withdrawal has been observed after as few as 6 weeks of treatment (Murphy, Owen, & Tyrer, 1984; Power, Jerrom, Simpson & Mitchell, 1985). Onset of withdrawal may range from 0.75 to 10 days and may last 5 to 20 days, depending on the half-life of the individual drug (Busto et al., 1986; Owen & Tyrer, 1983). Evidence suggests that benzodiazepines with shorter half-lives, such as oxazepam, lorazepam, and alprazolam, may tend to cause more severe withdrawal syndromes (Busto et al., 1986; Kales, Soldatos, Bixler, & Kales, 1983; Lapierre, 1981; Tyrer, Rutherford, & Huggett, 1981). Recent case reports suggest that seizures may occur more often on withdrawal from shorter-acting than from longer-acting drugs (Ananth, 1983; Barton, 1981; Breier, Charney, & Nelson, 1984; Kahan & Haskett, 1984; Khan, Joyce, & Jones, 1980; Levy, 1984; Noyes et al., 1986). "Rebound anxiety" appears to be part of the withdrawal syndrome occurring with short-half-life drugs rather than a distinct clinical entity (Kales et al., 1983). Gradual dosage reduction, over a period of several weeks or more, produces milder withdrawal syndromes than abrupt discontinuation (Busto et al., 1986; Tyrer, Owen, & Dawling,

Table 22.6. Benzodiazepine Withdrawal Symptoms

Specific Symptoms (20% of cases)	Nonspecific Symptoms (50% of cases)
Seizures	Anxiety
Delirium	Insomnia
Increased intensity of sensations	Irritability
Abnormal perception of motion	Nausea
Muscle twitching	Palpitations
Psychosis	Headache and muscle tension
Anorexia	Tremor

Modified from "Benzodiazepine Dependence: A Review of The Evidence" by R. T. Owen and P. Tyrer, 1983, *Drugs, 25,* p. 392. Copyright 1983 by *ADIS Puss, Ltd.* Reprinted by permission. Birkenhead, New Zealand.

1983; Harrison, Busto, Naranjo, Kaplan, & Sellers, 1984). Abrupt discontinuation is seldom, if ever, indicated. Evidence suggests that as many as 30% to 50% of patients taking therapeutic doses of benzodiazepines for 6 months or more will develop a mild withdrawal syndrome without seizures when the drug is withdrawn over a 3-month period (Tyrer et al., 1983).

Preliminary evidence indicates that propranolol hydrochloride, clonidine hydrochloride, and carbamazepine may be effective in permitting more rapid, less symptomatic benzodiazepine withdrawal (Abernethy, Greenblatt, & Shader, 1981; Keshavan & Crammer, 1985; Klein et al., 1986; Tyrer, Rutherford, & Haggett, 1981). Preclinical work suggests that intermittent co-administration of a benzodiazepine receptor antagonist during benzodiazepine treatment might be able to prevent subsequent withdrawal upon abrupt discontinuation of the benzodiazepine (Gonsalves & Gallager, 1985).

Overdose

When taken in an accidental or intentional overdose as a single drug, benzodiazepines are among the safest of medications: In a review of 1,239 drug-related deaths, only 2 were attributable to diazepam alone (Finkle, McCloskey, & Goodman, 1979). This record of safety contrasts with the well-known high potential for lethality in overdoses with barbiturates, meprobamate, or antidepressants. However, benzodiazepine overdose can be lethal if the benzodiazepine is taken in combination with alcohol or other drugs (Greenblatt & Shader, 1974).

Benzodiazepine Use in Pregnancy and the Perinatal Period

The use of benzodiazepines during pregnancy and the perinatal period is to be discouraged, as is the use of any medication. Benzodiazepines should be used during these times only after a careful assessment of the specific risks of continuing and of discontinuing benzodiazepine treatment in each individual. Common sense dictates that, if maternal health will nor permit the drug to be stopped altogether, the dosage should be minimized.

Specific risks of maternal benzodiazepine treatment to the fetus or infant appear to exist at several points during pregnancy and the puerperium (for reviews, see Bellantuono et al., 1980; Weber, 1985). Maternal benzodiazepine treatment during the first trimester may increase the risk of a wide variety of congenital anomalies, although not all studies agree. The best established congenital anomaly associated with maternal benzodiazepine use is cleft lip and/or cleft palate, which may be increased by a factor of two to six times (Weber, 1985). Maternal benzodiazepine use before delivery can cause hypothermia, respiratory depression, "floppy infant syndrome" (Cree, 1973; Drury, 1977), and benzodiazepine withdrawal symptoms in the newborn (Weber, 1985). Benzodiazepines are likely to be excreted into breast milk and can cause lethargy, poor feeding, and weight loss in the breast-fed infant (Bellantuono et al., 1980; Weber, 1985).

Interactions with Other Drugs and Foods

A number of commonly prescribed drugs interact with benzodiazepines (see Table 22.7). Some of these interactions have documented clinical significance. Clorazepate dipotassium requires stomach acid for conversion to the active drug nordiazepam and, therefore, should not be prescribed in conjunction with antacids. Food, aluminium antacids, or a large volume of water taken with any benzodiazepine each slow gastric emptying and, therefore, drug absorption. This effect may be utilized to therapeutic benefit in patients who experience transient sedation soon after taking each dose. When patients smoke, are unable to discontinue caffeine or theophylline, or require phenytoin or barbiturate treatment,

Table 22.7. Interactions of Benzodiazepines With Other Drugs and Foods

Drug	Interaction	Reference	Comment
Oral contraceptives	Prolong BZ half-life	Abernethy et al., 1982	Clinical significance unclear. Mechanism of interaction is impairment of hepatic oxidative metabolism. May not apply to oxazepam or lorazepam, which do not require oxidation.
Theophylline	Antagonizes BZ sedation	Henauer et al., 1983	Clinical significance possible. Receptor mechanism possible.
Caffeine	Antagonizes BZ sedation	Downing & Rickels, 1981	Clinical significance possible. Receptor mechanism or hepatic enzyme induction are possible.
Cigarettes	Antagonize BZ sedation Reduce ALP half-life	Downing & Rickels, 1981 Smith et al., 1983	Clinical significance possible. Mechanism may be hepatic enzyme induction.
Digoxin	BZs increase digoxin levels	Castillo-Ferrando et al., 1980 Tollefson et al., 1984	Patients developed digoxin toxicity
Antacids	Impair absorption of clorazepate	Shader et al., 1978	Effect specific for clorazepate, which requires acidity in stomach for conversion to desmethyldiazepam, the active substance, which is then absorbed.
	Aluminum antacids slow BZ absorption	Greenblatt et al., 1983	Aluminum slows gastric emptying.
Cimetidine	Prolongs BZ half-life	Klotz & Reimann, 1980 Desmond et al., 1980 Abernethy et al., 1983 Ruffalo et al., 1981	Can be clinically significant. Impairment of oxidative metabolism.
Beta-blockers	Prolong BZ half-life	Ballenger, 1984 Hawksworth et al., 1984	β-blockers decrease hepatic blood flow
Sedatives and ethanol	Additive sedation	Ballenger, 1984 Sellers & Busto, 1982	Can be of great clinical significance, but most patients can have a drink or two without problems.
Food	Slows BZ absorption	Greenblatt et al., 1983	Food slows gastric emptying
Volume of fluid	Slows BZ absorption	Richards et al., 1986	Slows gastric emptying
Phenytoin	Reduce BZ half-life	Scott et al., 1983 Vajda et al., 1971	Hepatic enzyme induction
Barbiturates	Reduce BZ half-life	Scott et al., 1983	Hepatic enzyme induction
Heparin	BZs can prolong partial thromboplastin time	Routledge et al., 1980	Monitor PTT carefully

induction of hepatic oxidative enzymes may result in a requirement for higher dosages of benzodiazephine. The clinician should be alert for the possibility of drug accumulation in patients requiring benzodiazepines in combination with oral contraceptives, cimetidine, or beta-blockers. Lower benzodiazepine dosages may be required. Digoxin levels and the partial thromboplastin time should be carefully monitored in patients requiring digoxin or heparin in combination with benzodiazepines.

Finally, patients should be cautioned that additive sedating effects may occur when benzodiazepines are taken together with alcohol, barbiturates, antihistamines, or other sedating drugs. The danger of the interaction with alcohol is not so serious that patients taking benzodiazepines need abstain from alcohol altogether. Social drinking in true moderation is usually tolerated quite well in patients chronically tolerated with benzodiazepines (Ballenger, 1984). When drinking alcohol for the first time after beginning a benzodiazepine, patients should plan to be in a safe place or to have a companion in case an unexpectedly strong potentiation of sedation should occur.

CLINICAL MANAGEMENT AND CASE REPORTS

Diagnosis

Before initiating treatment for an anxiety disorder, care should be taken to ensure that the patient does not have a treatable medical or surgical illness that is the cause of the anxiety symptoms. Such illnesses include hyperthyroidism, complex partial seizure disorder, caffeinism, Cushing's disease, pheochromocytoma, paroxysmal tachycardia, and ischemic cardiovascular disease. Ordinarily, normal findings on a careful history, physical and neurologic examination, and screening laboratory examination render these illnesses sufficiently unlikely that treatment for an anxiety disorder may be then initiated. Occasionally, a patient must be referred for further diagnostic procedures such as CAT scan, EEG, stress ECG, Holter monitoring, or angiography. Patients who present with diagnosable anxiety disorder in addition to a previous diagnosis of hypoglycemia (Uhde, Vittone, & Post, 1984), temperomandibular joint syndrome, irritable colon (Lydiard, Laraia, Howell, & Ballenger, 1986), hyperventilation syndrome, mitral valve prolapse (Gorman, Fyer, Gliklich, King, & Klein, 1981), premenstrual syndrome (Sandberg, Fyer, & Endicott, 1986), or hiatal hernia should receive specific treatment for their anxiety disorder. Often the symptoms of the associated diagnosis will improve when the anxiety disorder responds to treatment.

Pharmacotherapy, Psychotherapy, or Both?

Patients with severe anxiety disorders or those with moderate anxiety who are refractory to, or unsuitable for, psychotherapy should receive drug treatment. Patients with mild anxiety disorders causing little impairment, those with adjustment disorders, or those philosophically opposed to drug treatment should be offered psychological treatments. Patients with moderate to severe agoraphobia, social phobia, or obsessive-compulsive disorder should be offered behavioral or other psychological therapies in combination with drug treatment. Similarly, anxious patients with coexisting significant depression or difficulty coping with stressful life events should also be offered concomitant psychological treatment.

Which Drug to Use?

In the treatment of panic disorders, we believe that the tricyclic drugs (e.g., imipramine hydrochloride) ordinarily remain the drugs of first choice because of their slight edge in effectiveness over the benzodiazepines (see previous section) and the ease with which treatment is withdrawn. The effectiveness of the tricyclics has been documented for more than

20 years (Klein & Fink, 1962). However, the benzodiazepines become the drugs of first choice in situations where their more rapid response is necessary or where tricyclics are poorly tolerated. Among the benzodiazepines, alprazolam probably remains the best initial choice because of the currently greater wealth of research data supporting its efficacy; however, future studies may soon demonstrate advantages of the longer-acting benxodiazepines over alprazolam. The monoamine oxidase inhibitors, although extremely useful, remain drugs of third choice, in our opinion, because of the necessity for patients to adhere to a low-tyramine diet. Clonidine (Liebowitz, Fyer, McGrath, & Klein, 1981) and beta-blockers (Noyes et al., 1984; Ravaris, Friedman, & Hauri, 1986; Shehi & Patterson, 1984) may benefit some patients.

For generalized anxiety disorder, the benzodiazepines are the drugs of first choice, followed by the tricyclics. The newly available nonbenzodiazepine drug buspirone will play a prominent role in the treatment of GAD if studies documenting its efficacy (discussed later) are confirmed in clinical practice. For obsessive-compulsive disorder, antidepressants, such as imipramine or trazodone hydrochloride, are to be preferred as the initial drug treatment. There are insufficient data to suggest a drug of choice for PTSD or social phobia. Simple phobia appears to be best treated by behavioral methods.

What Dosage of Benzodiazepine to Use?

In panic patients for whom benzodiazepines are indicated, the drug is best begun in a total daily diazepam equivalent dose of 10 to 15 mg, divided appropriately based on the half-life of the drug chosen. At intervals of 3 to 7 days, the dosage may be increased by 5 to 10 mg diazepam-equivalent per day as sedation permits. Usually 1 week is sufficient time to observe the maximal therapeutic benefit of a given dosage. The typical panic patient will respond at approximately 30 to 40 mg diazepam-equivalent per day. In occasional patients, dosages as low as 5 mg or as high as 100 mg or more diazepam-equivalents per day are optimal. The goals of treatment should be "no attacks, no phobias, and no side effects." The typical patient with GAD may respond to 15 to 20 mg diazepam-equivalent per day. Benzodiazepine dosage for OCD, PTSD, and social phobia must be adjusted empirically.

Case 1. Efficacy of Benzodiazepine for Panic Attacks and Agoraphobia at a Low Dose

Mr. A, a 20-year-old professional downhill ski racer, had a 1-year history of panic attacks occurring several times each week. He had previously been confined to a couch in his living room for several weeks. At the time of evaluation, his phobia had somewhat improved, but he remained unable to work or to go more than a short distance from home without a companion. Treatment was initiated with clonazepam 1 mg PO BID. Mr. A was followed for 6 more months and never had another attack. Tolerance did not occur. He quickly overcame all his phobias without specific instruction. He had no side effects and, in fact, claimed that the clonazepam gave him "a better feel for the snow" while racing.

Case 2. High-Dose Benzodiazepine Effective and Safe

Mr. B, a 23-year-old factory worker, had been treated by the referring psychiatrist for severe panic disorder including two to three attacks per day for 6 years. He had had only a partial response to alprazolam 6 mg per day and little response to adequate trials of several tricyclics and monamine oxidase inhibitors in combination with low-dosage benzodiazepine and weekly psychotherapy. Along with behavior therapy, drug treatment was initiated with lorazepam. As the dosage was gradually increased, Mr. B enjoyed a progressively satisfactory partial response until the attacks ceased altogether at a dosage of 24 mg per day. He had no side effects.

Case 3. Combination Treatment with Antidepressants

Ms. C, a 26-year-old secretary, had a 2-year history of frequent panic attacks and agoraphobia and a 1-year history of major depression. She was terrified of her upcoming wedding ceremony. She did not improve with behavior therapy and placebo for 4 weeks. Alprazolam, in doses up to 3 mg per day for 4 weeks, helped her attacks somewhat, but seemed to exacerbate her depression. Alprazolam was reduced to 2 mg per day, and imipramine was co-prescribed and increased to 200 mg at bedtime. Over the next 3 weeks, both her panic attacks and major depression remitted. She was able to enjoy her wedding.

Management of Side Effects

Drowsiness, the most common side-effect of benzodiazepines, usually disappears within a few days. Occasionally, the dose must be reduced and can often then be increased again a few days later without difficulty. Some adverse effects require permanently reducing the dose or discontinuing the drug.

Case 4. Hypomania Responsive to Reduced Dose — Efficacy Maintained

Ms. D, a 48-year-old secretary, had a 30-year history of panic attacks and agoraphobia, but no personal or family history of major depression or mania. Alprazolam was begun at 0.5 mg TID. Two days later, Ms. D called to report feeling less anxious but euphoric and "speeded up." She had been sent home from work because of giddiness and singing on the job. The dosage was reduced to 0.5 mg BID. The hypomanic symptoms quickly resolved and the panic attacks remained in remission.

Case 5. Dysarthria and Ataxia

Mr. E, a 36-year-old truck driver, reported a 20-year history of weekly panic attacks including palpitations and tremor. Previous treatment with diazepam had left him too sleepy to work. Lorazepam was prescribed and increased to 2 mg TID without drowsiness or benefit. Four weeks after beginning lorazepam, he called to report a new kind of attack characterized by slurred speech and wobbly gait along with his typical anxiety symptoms. He was not sedated. An emergency room visit and neurologic consultation with CAT scan and EEG revealed only normal findings. There being no other obvious explanation, the new symptoms were attributed to panic attacks which had suddenly begun to manifest additional new and quite unusual symptoms. Over the next several weeks, the "new" attacks continued twice a week despite changing the lorazepam to alprazolam, 1 mg TID, and raising and lowering the alprazolam dose. Mr. E continued to have his "old" typical panic attacks as well. One day, Mr. E was examined during a "new" attack, which by then had changed to consist only of slurred speech and gait disturbance without concomitant anxiety. The alprazolam was tapered and discontinued, and the "new attacks" stopped. His original panic attacks subsequently responded to imipramine.

Duration of Treatment

Little research data are available to guide the clinician in how long to continue drug treatment for anxiety disorders. One study suggests that nearly 50% of GAD patients may no longer need benzodiazepine after only 6 weeks of treatment (Rickels et al., 1983). Relapse rates of 15% to 33% are reported after discontinuation of imipramine in panic patients (see Ballenger, 1986). Relapse rates after comparable treatment with benzodiazepines are not known. The only published study of discontinuation in panic patients used a treatment period of only 8 weeks and withdrew the patients very quickly (Pecknold & Swinson, 1986). The best available recommendation for treating panic patients with benzodiazepines is to attempt gradual withdrawal after 6 to 12 months (Ballenger, 1986; Sheehan, 1985) and, if relapse occurs, every 6 months or so thereafter. There is a critical need for research in this area.

CONCLUDING REMARKS

Implications of Benzodiazepine Anxiolytic Efficacy for the Pathophysiology of Anxiety Disorders

The evidence that benzodiazepines are effective in the treatment of anxiety disorders invites speculation about the possibility that, in some patients, benzodiazepines may represent a targeted compensation for a specific biochemical defect in an endogenous benzodiazepine neuromodulator neuroreceptor/effector system. Possible biochemical abnormalities in anxiety disorders could include hyperactivity of an endogenous inverse agonist neuromodulator (e.g., DBI, see first section) or hypoactivity of an endogenous agonist. Alternatively, alterations of benzodiazepine recognition site density or affinity or abnormal coupling of the benzodiazepine site to the chloride ionophore or the GABA or picrotoxin sites could exist.

The possibility that one or more of these abnormalities could underlie the anxiety disorders receives support from recent studies in basic and clinical neuroscience. Brain benzodiazepine receptors in living healthy human subjects have been visualized with positron emission tomography (PET scan) using a radio-labeled benzodiazepine receptor antagonist, 11-C-RO 15-1788 (Persson et al., 1985). "Stress" in laboratory rats significantly changes the density of benzodiazepine binding sites (Medini, Novas, & De Robertis, 1983; Robertson, Marton, & Candy, 1978), and the density of low-affinity GABA binding sites (Biggio et al., 1984). The benzodiazepine inverse agonist FG 7142 has been shown to be anxiogenic in man (Dorow, Horowski, Paschelke, Amin, & Braestrup, 1983).

Abnormalities of endogenous benzodiazepine function could occur in areas of the brain believed important in anxiety, such as the cerebral cortex, the septohippocampal system, or the amygdala (Gray, 1982; Mondlock & Davis, in press). Benzodiazepine receptors are located in these areas (Mohler & Okada, 1977; Squires & Braestrup, 1977). Other abnormalities of endogenous benzodiazepine function could exist at benzodiazepine receptors located on noradrenergic neurons in the locus coeruleus (Braestrup & Nielson, 1983; Tallman, et al., 1980) or on serotonergic neurons in the dorsal raphe (Gallager, 1978; Thiebot, Hamon, & Soubrie, 1982). Noradrenergic and serotonergic neurons project to the frontal and limbic areas possibly related to anxiety, and abnormal regulation of noradrenergic or serotonergic function has been implicated in the pathophysiology of anxiety disorders (Charney & Heninger, in press; Charney, Heninger, & Breier, 1984; Redmond, 1979). Efforts are underway to investigate possible abnormalities of endogenous benzodiazepine or benzodiazepine receptor function in anxious patients by pharmacologic challenges using benzodiazepine agonists, antagonists, and inverse agonists and by neuroreceptor imaging techniques such as PET scanning.

The Future of Anxiolytic Pharmacotherapy — The Search for Anxioselective Anxiolytics

Table 22.8 summarizes the behavioral pharmacologic properties of the benzodiazepines. These properties are responsible for many of the unwanted effects of currently available benzodiazepines. New drugs that possess many of these pharmacologic properties are likely to offer no significant advantage over existing drugs. A search is underway for new anxiolytics that are "anxioselective" (Gershon & Eison, 1983; Goldberg, Salama, Patel, & Malick, 1983; Williams, 1983). An ideal anxioselective anxiolytic would be clinically effective but would not cause sedation, tolerance, withdrawal, or interaction with alcohol. Possible anxioselective compounds are currently divided into three main groups: (a) those that do not interact with the benzodiazepine-GABA-picrotoxin-receptor chloride ionophore complex in any way but, rather, exert anxiolytic effects via actions on other

Table 22.8. Pharmacologic Properties of Benzodiazepines

Anxiolysis
Muscle relaxation
Sedation
Anticonvulsant properties
Interaction with alcohol
Development of tolerance
Withdrawal syndrome

neuronal systems (e.g., buspirone); (b) those that interact with the complex but do not bind to the benzodiazepine receptor site on the complex; and (c) those compounds that are partial agonists at the benzodiazepine site. Although some of the drugs in these three groups have been withdrawn from clinical trials, an understanding of their mechanisms of action is relevant because new drugs with these mechanisms are likely to be developed in the future.

A member of the first group, buspirone, is a novel drug for which there is substantial evidence of efficacy in generalized anxiety disorder (Cohn, Wilcox, & Meltzer, 1986; Feighner, Merideth, & Hendrickson, 1982; Goldberg & Finnerty, 1979, 1982; Jacobson, Dominguez, Goldstein, & Steinbook, 1985; Rickels et al., 1982). Buspirone has no anticonvulsant, sedative, muscle relaxant, or alcohol-interactive properties; studies further suggest that buspirone has no potential to produce tolerance or abuse (see Eison & Temple, 1986; Taylor, Eison, Riblet, & Vandermaelen, 1985, for reviews) and that it may improve driving performance (Smiley & Moskowitz, 1986). Buspirone was marketed under the trade name BuSpar in October 1986. Gepirone, an analogue of buspirone, has also shown anxiolytic efficacy (Cott, Kurtz, Robinson, & Temple, 1986). Neither drug interacts in an important way with the benzodiazepine-GABA-multireceptor complex (Eison & Temple, 1986; Goldberg et al., 1983; Taylor et al., 1985). Both appear to exert their anxiolytic effects by reducing serotonin function through agonism at an inhibitory presynaptic subtype of serotonin receptors, the 5-HT_{1A} receptor (Eison & Temple, 1986; Cott et al., 1986).

Ritanserin, a serotonin receptor antagonist, has shown some efficacy in GAD patients (Ceulemans, Hoppenbrouwers, Gelders, & Reyntjens, 1985). Fenobam appears to be another anxiolytic drug without effect at the benzodiazepine receptor (LaPierre & Oyewumi, 1982; Goldberg et al., 1983; Pecknold, McClure, Appelteauer, Wrzesinski, & Allen, 1982). It has been withdrawn from clinical trials because of uncertain bioavailability.

A number of classes of putative anxioselective anxiolytic compounds interact with the benzodiazepine-GABA-picrotoxin-chloride ionophore complex but do not bind to the benzodiazepine recognition site. These include the pyrazolopyridines, the GABA agonists, and the cyclopyrolones. The pyrazolopyrines tracazolate, etazolate, and cartazolate are effective in animal models of anxiety and are less sedating than the benzodiazepines. The pyrazolopyridines increase the affinity of the benzodiazepine site and increase the number of GABA sites, apparently by binding to the picrotoxin site (Gershon & Eison, 1983, Goldberg et al, 1983; Olsen, 1982; Wiliams, 1983) (see Figure 22.1d). Cartazolate showed some efficacy in anxious patients (Sakalis, Sathananthan, Collins, & Gershon, 1974), but the three pyrazolopyridines appear to have been withdrawn from clinical trials because of bioavailability or toxicity problems. The diaryltriazine LY 81067 appears to act via mechanisms similar to the pyrazolopyridines. EMD-28422, an adenosine analogue, and the dibenzocycloheptenimine MK-801 increase benzodiazepine receptor number (for reviews, see Gershon & Eison, 1983; Goldberg et al., 1983; Williams, 1983); the latter appears quite sedating. Compounds that act as direct agonists at GABA sites, such as muscimol, progabide, and THIP, have thus far been reported to have only weak anxiolytic effects in clinical trials (Hoehn-Saric, 1983; Lloyd et al., 1983; Tamminga, Crayton, & Chase, 1978). The cyclopyrrolones, zopiclone and suriclone, are less sedating than the benzodiazepines (Goldberg et al., 1983) but otherwise appear to have the pharmacologic properties of full benzodiazepine agonists (Goldberg et al., 1983; Sanger, Joly, & Zivkovic, 1985; Trifiletti & Snyder, 1984). While they inhibit benzodiazepine binding, it has been shown that they do so not by binding competitively to the benzodiazepine site, but by interacting with a novel site on the multireceptor complex (Trifiletti & Snyder, 1984). Clinical studies suggest anxiolytic and hypnotic effects in man (Gotfryd, 1984; Nicholson & Stone, 1983; Wickstrom & Giercksky, 1980).

A model has been proposed through which drugs that bind directly to the benzodiazepine site, but that function as partial agonists rather than full agonists at the receptor, could produce anxiolytic effects but not sedative effects (Ehlert, Roeske, Gee, & Yamamura, 1983). All currently available benzodiazepines are full agonists. It is possible that drugs with partial agonist properties would not cause withdrawal syndromes on discontinuation, because partial agonists by definition have some antagonist properties, and administration of a benzodiazepine antagonist has been shown to reverse biochemical evidence of benzodiazepine tolerance in experimental animals Gonsalves & Gallager, 1985). The triazolopryidazine CL218, 872 and the pyrazoquinoline CGS9896 appear to be benzodiazepine receptor partial agonists and to have activity in animal models predictive of anxiolytic efficacy (Gee et al., 1984; Gershon & Eison, 1983; Goldberg et al., 1983; Williams, 1983). Both compounds are anticonvulsants but have little muscle-relaxant or sedative properties. Unfortunately, both compounds proved to have hepatotoxic effects and have been withdrawn from clinical trials. The quinoline derivatives PK 8165 and PK 9084 are benzodiazepine receptor partial agonists in vitro, but recent work has shown them devoid of activity in vivo (Keane, Simiand, & Morre, 1984). The new compound under development by Lorex Pharmaceuticals, alpidem, may also be a benzodiazepine partial agonist. The development of a safe, anxioselective benzodiazepine receptor partial agonist drug is a research area of active interest.

The benzodiazepines are effective, and often remarkably effective, agents for the treatment of panic and generalized anxiety disorders. In general, they are quite safe. Their main drawbacks are that they may impair psychomotor performance and that they must be tapered gradually when they are discontinued after chronic treatment. It is likely that the research efforts outlined here will eventually result in new drugs that retain or improve upon the effectiveness of the benzodiazepines in anxiety disorders while possessing fewer adverse effects. When this occurs, the new drugs will largely replace the benzodiazepines in clinical psychiatric practice, just as the benzodiazepines have replaced the barbiturates, meprobamate, and bromide salts.

REFERENCES

Abernethy, D. R., Greenblatt, D. J., Divoll, M., Arendt, R., Ochs, H. R., & Shader, R. I. (1982). Impairment of diazepam metabolism by low-dose estrogen-containing oral-contraceptive steroids. *New England Journal of Medicine, 306*, 791–792.

Abernethy, D. R., Greenlatt, D. J., Divoll, M., Moschitto, L. J., Harmatz, J. S., & Shader, R. I. (1983). Interaction of cimetidine with the triazolobenzodiazepines alprazolam and triazolam. *Psychopharmacology, 80*, 275–278.

Abernethy, D. R., Greenblatt, D. J., & Shader, R. I. (1981). Treatment of diazepam withdrawal syndrome with propranolol. *Annals of Internal Medicine, 94*, 354–355.

Alexander, P. E., & Alexander, D. D. (1986). Alprazolam treatment for panic disorders. *Journal of Clinical Psychiatry, 47*, 301–304.

Alho, H., Costa, E., Ferrero, P., Fujimoto, M., Cosenza-Murphy, D., & Guidotti, A. (1985). Diazepam-binding inhibitor: A neuropeptide located in selected neuronal populations of rat brain. *Science, 229*, 179–181.

Allsopp, L. F., Cooper, G. L., & Poole, P. H. (1984). Clomipramine and diazepam in the treatment of agoraphobia and social phobia in general practice. *Current Medical Research and Opinion, 9*, 64–70.

American Psychiatric Association. (1980). *Diagnostic and statistical manual of mental disorders* (3rd ed.). Washington, DC: Author.

Ananth, J. (1983). Abstinence syndrome from therapeutic doses of oxazepam. *Canadian Journal of Psychiatry, 28*, 592.

Arana, G. W., Pearlman, C., & Shader, R. J. (1985). Alprazolam-induced mania: Two clinical cases. *American Journal of Psychiatry, 142*, 368–369.

Ayd, F. J. (1962). Clinical appraisal of chlordiazepoxide. *Journal of Neuropsychiatry, 9*, 172–180.

Balleger, J. C. (1984). Psychopharmacology of the anxiety disorders. *Psychiatric Clinics of North America, 7*, 757–771.

Ballenger, J. C. (1986). Pharmacotherapy of panic disorders. *Journal of Clinical Psychiatry, 47* (Supple.), 27–32.

Ballenger, J. C., Burrows, G. D., Noyes, R., Lydiard, R. B., Norman, T., Chandhry, D. R., & Zitrin, C. M. (1985, May). Alprazolam treatment of agoraphobia/panic disorder. In *Abstracts of the Sccientific Proceedings of the 138th Annual Meeting of the American Psychiatric Association* p. 129, Dallas, TX.

Barton, D. F. (1981). More on lorazepam withdrawal. *Drug Intelligence and Clinical Pharmacology, 15*, 134.

Beaudry, P., Fontaine, R., Chouinard, G. (1984). Bromazepam, another high-potency benzodiazepine, for panic attacks. *American Journal of Psychiatry, 141*, 464–465.

Beaudry, P., Fontaine, R., Chouinard, G., Annable, L. (1986). Clonazepam in the treatment of patients with recurrent panic attacks. *Journal of Clinical Psychiatry, 47*, 83–85.

Beckett, A., Fishman, S. M., & Rosenbaum, J. F. (1986). Clonnazepam blockade of spontaneous and CO_2 inhalation-provoked panic in a patient with panic disorder. *Journal of Clinical Psychiatry, 47*, 475–476.

Bellantuono, C., Reggi, V., Tognoni, G., & Garattini, S. (1980). Benzodiazepines: Clinical pharmacology and therapeutic use. *Drugs, 19*, 195–219.

Biggio, G., Concas, A., Serra, M., Sabis, M., Corda, M. G., Nurchi, V., Crisponi, C., & Gessa, G. L. (1984). Stress and beta-carbolines decrease the density of low-affinity GABA bindig sites: An effect reversed by diazepam. *Brain Research, 305*, 13–18.

Bormann, J., & Clapham, D. E. (1985). γ-Aminobutyric acid receptor channels in adrenal chromaffin cells: A patch-clamp study. *Proceedings of the National Academy of Science U.S.A.*, 82, 2168–2172.

Boston Collaborative Drug Surveillance Program. (1973). Clinical depression of the central nervous system due to diazepam and chlordiazepoxide in relation to cigarette smoking and age. *New England Journal of Medicine, 288*, 277–280.

Bowden, C. L., & Fisher, J. G. (1980). Safety and efficacy of long-term diazepam therapy. *Southern Medical Journal, 73*, 1581–1584.

Braestrup, C., & Nielsen, M. (1983). Benzodiaze pine receptors. In L. Iverson, S. D. Iverson, & S. M. Snyder (Eds.), *Handbook of psychopharmacology* (pp. 285–384). New York: Plenum Publishing Corp.

Braestrup, C., & Squires, R. F. (1978). Brain specific benzodiazepine receptors. *British Journal of Psychiatry, 133*, 249–260.

Breier, A., Charney, D. S., & Nelson, J. D. (1984). Seizures induced by abrupt discontinuation of alprazolam. *American Journal of Psychiatry, 141*, 1606–1607.

Burrell, R. H., Culpan, R., Newton, K., Ogg, G., & Short, J. (1974). Use of bromazepam in obsessional, phobic, and related states. *Current Medical Research & Opinion, 2*, 430–436.

Buchsbaum, M. S., Hazlett, E., Sicotte, N., Stein, M., Wu, J., & Zetin, M. (1985). Topographic EEG changes with benzodiazepine administration in generalized anxiety disorder. *Biological Psychiatry, 20*, 832–842.

Busto, U., Sellars, E. M., Naranjo, C. A., Cappell, H., Sanchez-Craig, M., & Sykora, K. (1986). Withdrawal reaction after long-term therapeutic use of benzodiazepines. *New England Journal of Medicine, 315*, 854–859.

Cameron, O. G., Thyer, B. A., Nesse, R. M., & Curtis, G. C. (1986). Symptom profiles of patients with DSM-III anxiety disorders. *American Journal of Psychiatry, 143*, 1132–1137.

Castillo-Farrando, J. R., Garcia, M., & Carmona, J. (1980). Digozin levels and diazepam. *Lancet, 2*, 368.

Ceulemans, D. L. S., Hoppenbrouwers, M.-L. J. A., Gelders, Y. G., & Reyntjens, A. J. M. (1985). The influence of ritanserin, a serotonin antagonist, in anxiety disorders: A double-blind placebo-controlled study versus lorazepam. *Pharmacopsychiatry, 18*, 303–305.

Charney, D. S., & Heninger, G. R. (1985). Noradrenergic function and the mechanism of action of antianxiety treatment. I. The effect of long-term alprazolam treatment. *Archives of General Psychiatry, 42*, 458–467.

Charney, D. S., & Heninger, G. R. (1986). Serotonin function in panic disorders: The effect of intravenous tryptophan in healthy subjects and panic disorder patients before and during alprazolam treatment. *Archives of General Psychiatry, 43*, 1059–1065.

Charney, D. S., Heninger, G. R., Breier, A. (1984). Noradrenergic function in panic anxiety: Effects of yohimbine in healthy subjects and patients with agoraphobia and panic disorder. *Archives of General Psychiatry, 41*, 751–763.

Charney, D. S., & Woods, S. W. (submitted for publication). Benzodiazepine treatment of panic disorder: A comparison of lorazepam and alprazolam.

Charney, D. S., Woods, S. W., Goodman, W. K., Rifkin, B., Kinch, M., Aiken, B., Quadrino, L. M., & Heninger, G. R. (1986). Drug treatment of panic disorder: The comparative efficacy of imipramine, alprazolam, and trazodone. *Journal of Clinical Psychiatry, 47*, 580–586.

Choonara, I. A., Rosenbloom, L., & Smith, C. S. (1985). Clonazepam and sexual precocity. *New England Journal of Medicine, 312*, 185.

Chouinard, G., Annable, L., Fontaine, R., & Solyom, L. (1982). Alprazolam in the treatment of generalized anxiety and panic disorders: A double-blind, placebo-controlled study. *Psychopharmacology, 77*, 229–233.

Cohen, I. M. (1970). The benzodiazepines. In F. J. Ayd & B. Blackwell, (Eds.), *Discoveries in biological psychiatry* (pp. 130–141). Philadelphia: J. B. Lippincott.

Cohn, J. B., Wilcox, C. S., & Meltzer, H. V. (1986). Neuroendocrine effects of buspirone in patients with generalized anxiety disorder. *American Journal of Medicine, 80* (Suppl. 3B), 36–40.

Costa, E., & Guidotti, A. (1985). Endogenous ligands for benzodiazepine recognition sites. *Biochemical Pharmacology, 34*, 3399–3403.

Cott, J. M., Kurtz, N. M., Robinson, D. S., & Temple, D. L. (1986). Clinical anxioselective activity of gepirone. In American Psychiatric Association, *New Research Abstracts*, p. 27.

Covi, L., Lipman, R. S., Pattison, J. H., Derogatis, L. R., & Uhlenhuth, E. H. (1973). Length of treatment with anxiolytic sedatives and response to their sudden withdrawal. *Acta Psychiatrica Scandinavica, 49*, 51–64.

Cree, J. E. (1973). Diazepam in labour: Its metabolism and effect on the clinical condition and thermogenesis in the newborn. *British Medical Journal, 4*, 251.

Dawson, G., Jue, S. G., & Brogden, R. N. (1984). Alprazolam: A review of its pharmacodynamic properties and efficacy in the treatment of anxiety and depression. *Drugs, 27*, 132–147.

Desmond, P. V., Patmardhan, R. V., Schenker, S., & Speeg, K. V. (1980). Cimetidine impairs elimination of chlordiazepoxide (Librium) in man. *Annals of Internal Medicine, 93*, 266–268.

Dorow, R., Horowski, R. Paschelke, G., Amin, M., & Braestrup, C. (1983). Severe anxiety induced by FG7142, a β-carboline ligand for benzodiazepine receptors. *Lancet, 2*, 98–99.

Downing, R. W., & Rickels, K. (1981). Coffee consumption, cigarette smoking, and reporting of drowsiness in anxious patients treated with benzodiazepines or placebo. *Acta Psychiatrica Scandinavica, 64*, 398–408.

Downing, R. W., & Rickels, K. (1985). Early treatment response in anxious outpatients treated with diazepam. *Acta Psychiatrica Scandinavica, 72*, 522–528.

Drury, K. A. D. (1977). Floppy-infant syndrome: Is oxazepam the answer? *Lancet*, II, 1126.

Dunner, F. J., Edwards, W. P., & Copeland, P. C. (1985). Clinical efficacy of alprazolam in PTSD patients. In American Psychiatric Association, *New Research Abstracts*, p. 50.

Dunner, D. L., Ishiki, D. Avery, D. H., Wilson, L. G., & Hyde, T. S. (1986). Effect of alprazolam and diazepam on anxiety and panic attacks in panic disorder: A controlled study. *Journal of Clinical Psychiatry, 47*, 458–460.

Edwards, J. G. (1981). Adverse effects of anti-anxiety drugs. *Drugs, 22*, 495–514.

Ehlert, F. J., Roeske, W. R., Gee, K. W., & Yamamura, H. I. (1983). An allosteric model for benzodiazepine receptor function. *Biochemical Pharmacology, 32*, 2375–2383.

Eison, A. S., & Temple, D. L., Jr. (1986). Buspirone: Review of its pharmacology and current perspectives on its mechanism of action. *American Journal of Medicine, 80* (Suppl 3B), 1–9.

Elie, R., & Lamontagne, Y. (1984). Alprazolam and diazepam in the treatment of generalized anxiety disorder. *Journal of Clinical Psychopharmacology, 4*, 125–129.

Elliott, R. L., & Thomas, B. J. (1985). A case report of alprazolam-induced stuttering. *Journal of Clinical Psychopharmacology, 5*, 159–160.

Eriksson, E., Carlsson, M., Nilsson, C., & Soderpalm, B. (1986). Does alprazolam, in contrast to diazepam, activate alpha-2-adrenoceptors involved in the regulation of rat growth hormone secretion? *Life Sciences, 38*, 1491–1498.

Fabre, L. F. (1976). Pilot open label study with alprazolam (U-31, 889) in outpatients with neurotic depression. *Current Therapeutic Research, 19*, 661–668.

Fann, W. E., Pitts, W. M., & Wheliss, J. C. (1982). Pharmacology, efficacy, and adverse effects of halazepam, a new benxodiazepine. *Pharmacotherapy, 2*, 72–79.

Feighner, J. P., Merideth, C. H., & Hendrickson, M. A. (1982). A double-blind comparison of buspirone and diazepam in outpatients with generalized anxiety disorder. *Journal of Clinical Psychiatry, 43*(12, Sec. 2), 103–107.

Finkle, B. S., McCloskey, K. L., & Goodman, L. S. (1979). Diazempam and drug-associated deaths. *Journal of the American Medical Association, 242*, 429–434.

Finkel, S. (1978). Antianxiety effects of lorazepam in patients with cardiovascular symptomatology. *Journal of Clinical Psychiatry, 39* (10, Sec. 2), 35–40.

Fontaine, R. (1985). Clonazepam for panic disorders and agitation. *Psychosomatics, 26*(12, Suppl.), 13–18.

Fontaine, R., Annable, L., Chouinard, G., & Ogilvie, R. I. (1983). Bromazepam and diazepam in generalized anxiety: A placebo-controlled study with measurement of drug plasma concentrations. *Journal of Clinical Psychopharmacology, 3*, 80–87.

Fontaine, R., & Chouinard G. (1984). Antipanic effect of clonazepam. *American Journal of Psychiatry, 141*, 149.

Fouilladieu, J.-L. D'Enfert, J., & Conseiller, C. (1984). Benzodiazepines. *New England Journal of Medicine, 310* , 464.

France, R. D., & Krishnan, K. R. (1984). Alprazolam-induced manic reaction. *American Journal of Psychiatry, 141*, 1127–1128.

Gallager, D. W. (1978). Benzodiazepines: Potentiation of a GABA inhibitory response in the dorsal raphe nucleus. *European Journal of Pharmacology, 49*, 133–143.

Gardner, D. L., & Cowdry, R. W. (1985). Alprazolam-induced dyscontrol in borderline personality disorder. *American Journal of Psychiatry, 142*, 98–100.

Gee, K. W., Yamamura, S. H., Roeske, W. R., & Yamamura, H. I. (1984). Benzodiazepine receptor heterogeneity: Possible molecular basis and functional significance. *Federation Proceedings, 43*, 2767–2772.

Gershon, S., & Eison, A. S. (1983). Anxiolytic profiles. *Journal of Clinical Psychiatry, 44*(11, Sec. 2), 45–56.

Ghoneim, M. M., Mewaldt, S. P., Berie, J. L., & Hinrichs, J. V. (1981). Memory and performance effects of single and 3-week administration of diazpem. *Psychopharmacology, 73*, 147–151.

Goldberg, H. L., & Finnerty, R. J. (1979). The comparative efficacy of buspirone and diazepam in the treatment of anxiety. *American Journal of Psychiatry, 136*, 1184–1187.

Goldberg, H. L., & Finnerty, R. (1982). Comparison of buspirone in two separate studies. *Journal of Clinical Psychiatry, 43*, 87–91.

Goldberg, M. E., Salama, A. I., Patel, J. B., & Malick, J. B. (1983). Novel non-benzodiazepine anxiolytics. *Neuropharma cology, 22*, 1499–1504.

Goodman, W. K., & Charney, D. S. (1985). Therapeutic applications and mechanisms of action of monoamine oxidase inhibitor and heterocyclic antidepressant drugs. *Journal of Clinical Psychiatry, 46*(10, Sec. 2), 6–22.

Goodman, W. K., & Charney, D. S. (1987). A case of alprazolam, but not lorazepam, inducing manic symptoms. *Journal of Clinical Psychiatry, 48*, 117–118.

Gonsalves, S. F., & Gallager, D. W. (1985). Spontaneous and RO 15-1788 induced reversal of subsensitivity to GABA following chronic benzodiazepines. *European Journal of Pharmacology, 110*, 163–170.

Gorman, J. M., Fyer, A. J., Gliklich, J., King, D., & Klein, D. F. (1981). Mitral valve prolapse and panic disorders: Effect of imipramine. In D. F. Klein & J. Rabkin, (Eds.), *Anxiety: New research and changing concepts*. New York: Raven Press, pp. 317–326.

Gotfryd, M. A. (1984). A double-blind comparative study of suriclone, lorazepam, and placebo. *Clinical Neuropharmacology, 7* (Suppl. 1), 626–627.

Gray, J. A. (1982). *The neuropsychology of anxiety*. New York: Oxford University Press.

Gray, J. A., Quintero, S., Mellanby, J., & Buckland, C. (1984). Some biochemical, behavioral, and electrophysiological tests of the GABA hypothesis of anti-anxiety drug action. In N. G. Bowery (Ed.), *Actions and interactions of GABA and benzodiazepines*. New York: Raven Press, pp. 224–281.

Greenblatt, D. J., Abernethy, D. R., Divoll, M., Harmatz, J. S., & Shader, R. I. (1983). Pharmacokinetic properties of benzodiazepine hypnotics. *Journal of Clinical Psycopharmacology, 3*, 129–132.

Greenblatt, D. J., Divoll, M., Abernethy, D. R., Ochs, H. R., & Shader, R. I. (1983). Benzodiazepine kinetics: Implications for therapeutics and pharmacogeriatrics. *Drug Metabolism Reviews, 14*, 251–292.

Greenblatt, D. J., & Shader, R. I. (1974). *Benzo-*

diazepines in clinical practice. New York: Raven Press.

Greenblatt, D. J., Shader, R. I., & Abernethy, D. R. (1983). Current status of benzodiazepines. *New England Journal of Medicine, 309*, 354–358, 410–416.

Greenblatt, D. J., Shader, R. I., & Koch-Weser, J. (1975). Flurazepam hydrochloride. *Clinical Pharmacology and Therapeutics, 17*, 1–14.

Greenblatt, D. J., Shader, R. I., Macleod, S. M., & Sellers, E. M. (1978). Clinical pharmacokinetics of chlordiazepoxide. *Clinical Pharmacokinetics, 3*, 381–394.

Hall, R. C. W., & Zisook, S. (1981). Paradoxical reactions to benzodiazepines. *British Journal of Clinical Pharmacology, 11*, 99S–104S.

Haefely, W. (1985). Tranquilizers. In D. G. Graham-Smith (Ed.), *Psychopharmacology 2, part 1: Preclinical psychopharmacology* (pp. 92–182). New York: Elsevier.

Hardy, J. L. (1986) Obsessive compulsive disorder. *Canadian Journal of Psychiatry, 31*, 290.

Harris, T. H. (1960). Methaminodiazepoxide. *Journal of the American Medical Association, 172*, 1162–1163.

Harrison, M., Busto, U., Naranjo, C. A., Kaplan, H. L., & Sellers, E. M. (1984). Diazepam tapering in detoxification for high dose benzodiazepine abuse. *Clinical Pharmacology and Therapeutics, 36*, 527–533.

Hawksworth, G., Betts, T., Crowe, A., Knight, R., Nyemitei-Addo, I., Parry, K., Petrie, J. C., Raffle, A., & Parsons, A. (1984). Diazepam/beta-adrenoceptor antagonist interactions. *British Journal of Clinical Pharmacology, 17*(Suppl. 1), 695–765.

Henauer, S. A., Hollister, L. E., Gillespie, H. K., & Moore, F. (1983). Theophylline antagonizes diazepam-induced psychomotor impairment. *European Journal of Clinical Pharmacology, 25*, 743–747.

Hoehn-Saric, R. (1983). Effects of THIP on chronic anxiety. *Psychopharmacology, 80*, 338–341.

Hoehn-Saric, R., & McLeod, D. R. (1986, April). *Alprazolam versus imipramine: Effects on anxiety.* Paper presented at the Panic Disorder Biological Research Workshop, Washington, DC.

Insel, T. R., & Murphy, D. L. (1981). The psychopharmacological treatment of obsessive-compulsive disorder: A review. *Journal of Clinical Psychopharmacology, 1*, 304–311.

Insel, T. R., Zahn, T., & Murphy, D. L. (1985). Obsessive-compulsive disorder: An anxiety disorder? In A. H. Tuma & J. D. Maser (Eds.), *Anxiety and the anxiety disorders* (pp. 577–589). Hillsdale, NJ: Lawrence Erlbaum Associates.

Jacobson, A. F., Dominguez, R. A., Goldstein, B. J., & Steinbook, R. M. (1985). Comparison of buspirone and diazepam in generalized anxiety disorder. *Psychotherapy, 5*, 290–296.

Jones, B. D., & Chouinard, G. (1985). Clonazepam in the treatment of recurrent symptoms of depression and anxiety in patients with systemic lupus erythematosis. *American Journal of Psychiatry, 142*, 354–355.

Judd, F. K., Norman, T. R., Marriott, P. F., & Burrows, G. D. (1986). A case of alprazolam-related hepatitis. *American Journal of Psychiatry, 143*, 388–389.

Kahan, B. B., & Haskett, R. F. (1984). Lorazepam withdrawal and seizures. *American Journal of Psychiatry, 141*, 1011–1012.

Kales, A., Soldatos, C. R., Bixler, E. O., & Kales, J. D. (1983). Rebound insomnia and rebound anxiety: A review. *Pharmacology, 26*, 121–137.

Kaplan, S. A., Alexander, K., Jack, M. L., Puglisi, C. V., deSilva, J. A. F., Lee, T. L., & Weinfeld, R. E. (1974). Pharmacokinetic profiles of clonazepam in dog and humans and of flunitrazepam in dog. *Journal of Pharmaceutical Sciences, 63*, 527–529.

Keane, P. E., Simiand, J., & Morre, M. (1984). The quinolines PK 8165 and PK 9084 possess benzodiazepine-like activity invitro but not in vivo. *Neuroscience Letters, 45*, 89–93.

Keshavan, M. S., & Crammer, J. L. (1985). Clonidine in benzodiazepine withdrawal. *Lancet*, I, 1325–1326.

Khan, A., Joyce, P., & Jones, A. V. (1980). Benzodiazepine withdrawal syndromes. *New Zealand Medical Journal, 92*, 94–96.

Kinross-Wright, J., Cohen, I. M., & Knight, J. A. (1960). The management of neurotic and psychotic states with RO 5-0690 (Librium). *Diseases of the Nervous System, 21*, 23–26.

Klein, D. F., & Fink, M. (1962). Psychiatric reaction patterns to imipramine. *American Journal of Psychiatry, 119*, 432–438.

Klein D. F., Gittelman, R., Rifkin, A., & Quitkin, F. (1980). *Diagnosis and drug treatment of psychiatric disorders* (p. 562). Baltimore: Williams and Wilkins.

Klein, E., Uhde, T. W., & Post, R. W. (1986). Preliminary evidence for the utility of carbamazepine in alprazolam withdrawal. *American Journal of Psychiatry, 143*, 235–236.

Klotz, U., & Reimann, I. (1980). Delayed clearance of diazepam due to cimetidine. *New England Journal of Medicine, 302*, 1012–1014.

Kochansky, G. E., Salzman, C., Shader, R. I., Harmatz, J. S., & Ogletree, A. M. (1975). The differential effects of chlordiazepoxide and oxazepam on hostility in a small group settings. *American Journal of Psychiatry, 132,* 861–863.

Kornecki, E., Ehrlich, Y. H., & Lenox, R. H. (1984). Platelet-activating factor-induced aggregation of human platelets specifically inhibited by triazolobenzodiazepines. *Science, 226,* 1454–1456.

Krakowski, A. J. (1963). Long-term study of a new psychotropic drug in private practice. *Psychosomatics, 4,* 44–51.

LaPierre, Y. D., & Oyewumi, L. K. (1982). Fenobam: Another anxiolytic. *Current Therapeutic Research, 31,* 95–101.

LaPierre, Y. D. (1981). Benzodiazepine withdrawal. *Canadian Journal of Psychiatry, 26,* 93–95.

Levy, A. B. (1984). Delirium and seizures due to abrupt alprazolam withdrawal: Case report. *Journal of Clinical Psychiatry, 45,* 38–39.

Liebowitz, M. R., Fyer, A. J., Gorman, J. M. Campeas, R., Levin, A., Davies, S. R., Goetz, D., & Klein, D. F. (1986). Alprazolam in the treatment of panic disorders. *Journal of Clinical Psychopharmacology, 6,* 13–20.

Liebowitz, M. R., Fyer, A. J., McGrath, P., & Klein, D. F. (1981). Clonidine treatment for panic disorder. *Psychopharmacology Bulletin, 17,* 122–123.

Liebowitz, M. R., Gorman, J. M., Fyer, A. J., & Klein, D. F. (1985). Social phobia: Review of a neglected anxiety disorder. *Archives of General Psychiatry, 42,* 729–736.

Lin, H.-N., & Chen, C.-C. (1979). A double-blind test on the effect of bromazepam in obsessive-compulsive neurosis. *Journal of the Formosan Medical Association, 78,* 267–275.

Lloyd, K. G., Morselli, P. L., DePoortere, H., Fournier, V., Zivkovic, B., Scatton, B., Broekkamp, C., Worms, P., & Bartholini, G. (1983). The potential use of GABA agonists in psychiatric disorders: Evidence from studies with progabide in animal models and clinical trials. *Pharmacology, Biochemistry, and Behavior, 18,* 957–966.

Laughren, T. P., Battern, Y., Greenblatt, D. J., & Harrop, D. S., III. (1982). A controlled trial of diazepam in chronically anxious patients. *Acta Psychiatrica Scandinavia, 65,* 171–179.

Lydiard, R. B., Laraia, M. T., Howell, E. F., & Ballenger, J. C. (1986). Can panic disorder present as irritable bowel syndrome? *Journal of Clinical Psychiatry, 47,* 470–473.

Mackie, L. (1971). Drug antagonism. *British Medical Journal 222,* 1401.

Mark, S. L. (1984). Agoraphobia and panic disorder: Treatment with alprazolam. *Texas Medicine, 80,* 50–52.

Marks, J. (1978). *The benzodiazepines: Use, overuse, Misuse, abuse.* Lancaster, U.K.: M.T.P. Press.

Matuzas, W., & Glass, R. M. (1983). Treatment of agoraphobia and panic attacks. *Archives of General Psychiatry, 40,* 220–222.

Mavissaklian, M. (1982). Pharmacologic treatment of anxiety disorders. *Journal of Clinical Psychiatry, 43,* 487–491.

McNair, D. M. (1973). Antianxiety drugs and human performance. *Archives of General Psychiatry, 29,* 611–617.

McNair, D. M., & Kahn, R. J. (1981). Imipramine compared with a benzodiazepine for agoraphobia. In D. F. Kleine & J. Rabkin (Eds.), *Anxiety: New research and changing concepts* (pp. 69–80). New York: Raven Press.

Medini, J. H., Novas, M. L., & DeRobertis, E. (1983). Changes in benzodiazepine receptors by acute stress: Different effect of chronic diazepam or RO 15-1788 treatment. *European Journal of Pharmacology, 96,* 181–185.

Mellman, T. A., & Davis, G. C. (1985). Combat-related flashbacks in post-traumatic stress disorder: Phenomenology and similarity to panic attacks. *Journal of Clinical Psychiatry, 46,* 379–382.

Miller, R. R. (1973). Drug surveillance utilizing epidemiologic methods: A report from the Boston Collaborative Drug Surveillance Program. *American Journal of Hospital Pharmacy, 30,* 584–592.

Mohler, H., & Okada, T. (1977). Benzodiazepine receptor: Demonstration in the central nervous system. *Science, 198,* 849–851.

Mohler, H., & Okada, T. (1978). The benzodiazepine receptor in normal and pathological human brain. *British Journal of Psychiatry, 133,* 261–268.

Mondlock, J., & Davis, M. (in press). Lesions of the amygdala, but not the cerebellum or red nucleus block fear-enhancement of acoustic startle. *Behavioral Neuroscience.*

Munjack, D. J., & Crocker, B. (1986). Alprazolam-induced ejaculatory inhibition. *Journal of Clinical Psychopharmacology, 6,* 57–58.

Murphy, S. M., Owen, R. T., & Tyrer, P. J. (1984). Withdrawal symptoms after six weeks' treatment with diazepam. *Lancet, II,* 1389.

Murray, N. (1960). Methaminodiazepoxide. *Journal of the American Medical Association, 173,* 1760–1761.

Nicholson, A. N., & Stone, B. M. (1983). Zopiclone: Sleep and performance studies in health man. *Pharmacology, 27*(Suppl. 2), 92–97.

Noyes, R., Anderson, D., & Clancy, J. (1984). Diazepam and propranolol in panic disorder and agoraphobia. *Archives of General Psychiatry, 41*, 287–292.

Noyes, R., Perry, P. J., Crowe, R. R., Coryell, W. H., Clancy, J., Yamaha, T., & Gabel, J. (1986). Seizures following the withdrawal of alprazolam. *Journal of Nervous and Mental Disease, 174*, 50–52.

Okuma, T., Nakao, T., Ogura, C., Kishimoto, A., & Majima, K. (1971). Effect of 7-bromo-5-(2-pyridyl)-3H-1, 4-benzodiazepin-2 (1H)-one, bromazepam (RO5-3350), a new minor tranquilizer, on psychoneurosis with special reference to obsessive-compulsive symptoms. *Folia Psychiatrica et Neurologica Japonica, 25*, 181–193.

Olsen, R. W. (1981). GABA-benzodiazepine-barbiturate receptor interactions. *Journal of Neurochemistry, 37*, 1–13.

Olsen, R. W. (1982). Drug interactions at the GABA receptor-ionophore complex. *Annual Review of Pharmacology and Toxicology, 22*, 245–277.

Orvin, G. (1967). Treatment of the phobic obsessive compulsive patient with oxazepam. *Psychosomatics, 8*, 278–280.

Owen, R. T., & Tyrer, P. (1983). Benzodiazepine dependence: A review of the evidence. *Drugs, 25*, 385–398.

Pecknold, J. C., & Fleury, D. (1986). Alprazolam-induced manic episode in two patients with panic disorder. *American Journal of Psychiatry, 143*, 652–653.

Pecknold, J. C., McClure, D. J., Appeltauer, L., Wrzesinski, L., & Allan, T. (1982). Treatment of anxiety using fenobam (a non-benzodiazepine) in a double-blind standard (diazepam) placebo-controlled study. *Journal of Clinical Psychopharmacology, 2*, 129–133.

Pecknold, J. C., & Swinson, R. P. (1986). Taper withdrawal studies with alprazolam in patients with panic disorder and agoraphobia. *Psychopharmacology Bulletin, 22*, 173–176.

Persson, A., Ehrin, E., Eriksson, L., Farde, L., Hedstrom, G.-G., Litton, J.-E., Mindus, P., & Sedval, G. (1985). Imaging of 11-C-labeled RO 15-1788 binding to benzodiazepine receptors in human brain by positron emission tomography. *Journal of Psychiatric Research, 19*, 609–622.

Petursson, H., & Lader, M. H. (1981). Benzodiazepine dependence. *British Journal of Addiction, 76*, 133–145.

Physicians' desk reference (40th ed.). Ovadell, NJ: Medical Economics Company Inc.

Pies, R. (1983). Alprazolam for panic disorder and depression. *American Journal of Psychiatry, 140*, 640.

Power, K. G., Jerrom, D. W. A., Simpson, R. J., & Mitchell, M. (1985). Controlled study of withdrawal symptoms and rebound anxiety after six week course of diazepam for generalized anxiety. *British Medical Journal, 290*, 1246–1248.

Rao, A. V. (1964). A controlled trial with Valium in obsessive compulsive state. *Journal of the Indian Medical Association, 42*, 564–567.

Rapoport, M., & Braff, D. L. (1985). Alprazolam and hostility. *American Journal of Psychiatry, 142*, 146.

Ravaris, C. L., Friedman, M. J., & Hauri, P. J. (1986). Xanax and Inderal in panic and phobic patients. In American Psychiatric Association, *New Research Abstracts*, p. 26.

Redmond, D. E., Jr (1979). New and old evidence for the involvement of a brain norepinephrine system in anxiety. In W. E. Fann (Ed.), *The phenomenology and treatment of anxiety* (pp. 153–203). New York: Spectrum Press.

Remick, R. A. (1985). Alprazolam-induced manic switch. *Journal of Clinical Psychiatry, 46*, 406–407.

Richards, D. G., McPherson, J. J., Evans, K. T., & Rosen, M. (1986). Effect of volume of water taken with diazepam tablets on absorption. *British Journal of Anesthesia, 58*, 41–44.

Rickels, K., Case, W. G., Downing, R. W., & Winokur, A. (1983). Long-term diazepam therapy and clinical outcome. *Journal of the American Medical Association, 250*, 767–771.

Rickels, K., & Downing, R. W. (1974). Chlordiazepoxide and hostility in anxious outpatients. *American Journal of Psychiatry, 131*, 442–444.

Rickels, K., Weisman, K., Norstad, N., Singer, M., Stoltz, D., Brown, A., & Danton, J. (1982). Buspirone and diazepam in anxiety: A controlled study. *Journal of Clinical Psychiatry, 43*(12, Sec. 2), 81–86.

Rizley, R., Kahn, R. J., McNair, D. M., & Frankenthaler, L. M. (1986). A comparison of alprazolam and imipramine in the treatment of agoraphobia and panic disorder. *Psychopharmacology Bulletin, 22*, 167–172.

Robertson, H. A., Martin, I. L., & Candy, J. M. (1978). Differences in benzodiazepine receptor binding in Maudsley reactive and Maudsley non-reactive rats. *European Journal of Pharmacology, 50*, 455–457.

Romney, D. M., & Angus, W. R. (1984). A brief

review of effects of diazepam on memory. *Psychopharmacology Bulletin, 20,* 313–316.

Rosenbaum, J. F. (1982). The drug treatment of anxiety. *New England Journal of Medicine, 306,* 401–404.

Rosenbaum, J. F., Woods, S. W., Groves, J. E., & Klerman, G. L. (1984). Emergence of hostility during alprazolam treatment. *American Journal of Psychiatry, 141,* 792–793.

Routledge, P. A., Kitchell, B. B., Bjornsson, T. D., Skinner, T., Linnoila, M., & Shand, D. G. (1980). Diazepam and N-desmethyldiazepam redistribution after heparin. *Clinical Pharmacology and Therapeutics, 27,* 628–632.

Roy-Byrne, P., Vittone, B. J., & Uhde, T. W. (1983). Alprazolam-related hepatotoxicity. *Lancet, 2,* 1037–1038.

Ruffalo, R. L., Thompson, J. F., & Segal, J. L. (1981). Diazepam-cimetidine drug interaction: A clinically significant effect. *Southern Medical Journal, 74,* 1075–1078.

Rush, A. J., Schlesser, M. A., & Erman, M. (1984). Alprazolam in bipolar I depressions. *Pharmacotherapy, 4,* 40–42.

Sakalis, G., Sathananthan, G., Collins, P., & Gershon, S. (1974). SQ 65,396: A nonsedative anxiolytic? *Current Therapeutic Research, 16,* 861–863.

Sandberg, D. P., Fyer, A. J., & Endicott, J. (1986). Premenstrual changes in anxiety patients. In American Psychiatric Association, *New Research Abstracts,* p. 35.

Sandyk, R. (1985). Transient global amnesia induced by lorazepam. *Clinical Neuropharmacology, 8,* 297–298.

Sangal, R. (1985). Inhibited female orgasm as a side effect of alprazolam. *American Journal of Psychiatry, 142,* 1223–1224.

Sanger, D. J. (1985). GABA and the behavioral effects of anxiolytic drugs. *Life Sciences, 36,* 1503–1513.

Sanger, D. J., Joly, D., & Zivkovic, B. (1985). Behavioral effects of nonbenzodiazepine anxiolytic drugs: A comparison of CGS 9896 and zopiclone with chlordiazepoxide. *Journal of Pharmacology and Experimental Therapeutics, 232,* 831–837.

Scott, A. K., Khir, A. S., Steele, W. H., Hawsksorth, G. M., & Petrie, J. C. (1983). Oxazepam pharmacokinetics in patients withepilepsy treated long-term with phenytoin alone or in combination with phenobarbitone. *Journal of Clinical Pharmacology, 16,* 441–444.

Sellers, E. M., & Busto, U. (1982). Benzodiazepines and ethanol: Assessment of the effects and consequences of psychotropic drug interactions. *Journal of Clinical Pharmacology, 22,* 249–262.

Sethy, V. H., & Hodges, D. H., Jr. (1982). Alprazolam in a biochemical model of depression. *Biochemical Pharmacology, 31,* 3155–3157.

Shader, R. I., Georgotas, A., Greenblatt, D. J., Harmatz, J. S., & Divoll Allen, M. (1978). Impaired absorption of desmethyldiazepam from clorazepate by magnesium aluminum hydroxide. *Clinical Pharmacology and Therapeutics, 24,* 308–315.

Shader, R. I., Goodman, M., & Gever, J. (1982). Panic disorders: Current perspective. *Journal of Clinical Psychopharmacology, 2,* 25–105.

Shapiro, A. K., Struening, E. L., Shapiro, E., & Milcarek, B. I. (1983). Diazepam: How much better than placebo? *Journal of Psychiatric Research, 17,* 51–73.

Sheehan, D. V. (1982a). Current views on the treatment of panic and phobic disorders. *Drug Therapy, 12,* 179–187.

Sheehan, D. V. (1982b). Panic attacks and phobias. *New England Journal of Medicine, 307,* 156–158.

Sheehan, D. V. (1985). Monoamine oxidase inhibitors and alprazolans in the treatment of panic disorder and agoraphobia. *Psychiatric Clinics of North America, 8,* 49–62.

Sheehan, D. V., Coleman, J. H., Greenblatt, D. J., Jones, K. J., Levine, P. H., Orsulak, P. J., Peterson, M., Schildkraut, J. J., Uzogara, E., & Watkins, D. (1984). Some biochemical correlates of panic attacks and their response to a new treatment. *Journal of Clinical Psychopharmacology, 4,* 66–75.

Sheehan, D. V., Claycomb, J. B., Surman, O. S., & Gelles, L. (1984, May). *Comparison of alprazolam, phenelzine, imipramine, and alprazolam in the treatment of the panic attacks and phobias.* Paper presented at the 137th Annual Meeting of the American Psychiatric Association, Los Angeles.

Shehi, M., & Patterson, W. (1984). Treatment of panic with alprazolam and propranolol. *American Journal of Psychiatry, 141,* 900–901.

Smiley, A., & Moskowitz, H. (1986). Effects of long-term administration of buspirone and diazepam on driver steering control. *American Journal of Medicine, 80*(Suppl. 3B), 22–29.

Smith, R. B., Gwilt, P. R., & Wright, C. E. (1983). Single and multiple dose pharmacokinetics of oral alprazolam in healthy smoking and nonsmoking men. *Clinical Pharmacology, 2,* 139–143.

Solomon, K., & Hart, R. (1978). Pitfalls and prospects in clinical research on antianxiety drugs: Benzodiazepines and placebo — a research review. *Journal of Clinical Psychiatry, 39,* 823–831.

Spier, S. A., Tesar, G. E., Rosenbaum, J. F., & Woods, S. W. (1986). Treatment of panic disorder and agoraphobia with clonazepam. *Journal of Clinical Psychiatry, 47,* 238–242.

Spitzer, R. L. (1986, May). Diagnosis and classification of anxiety disorders. In *Abstracts of the Scientific Proceedings of the 139th Annual Meeting of the American Psychiatric Association*, Washington, DC, p. 42–43.

Spitzer, R. L., & Endicott, J. (1977). *Research diagnostic criteria (RDC)* (3rd Ed.). New York: Biometrics Research.

Squires, R., & Braestrup, C. (1977). Benzodiazepine receptors in rat brain. *Nature, 266,* 732–734.

Sternbach, L. H. (1979). The benzodiazepine story. *Journal of Medicinal Chemistry, 22,* 1–7.

Strahan, A., Rosenthal, J., Kaswan, M., & Winston, A. (1985). Three case reports of acute paroxysomal excitement associated with alprazolam treatment. *American Journal of Psychiatry, 142,* 859–861.

Straw, R. N. (1985). Brief review of published alprazolam clinical studies. *British Journal of Pharmacology, 19,* 575–595.

Suranyi-Cadotte, B. E., Nestoros, J. N., Nair, N. P. V., Lal, S., & Gauthier, S. (1985). Parkinsonism induced by high doses of diazepam. *Biological Psychiatry, 20,* 451–460.

Svenson, S. E., & Hamilton, R. G. (1966). A critique of over emphasis on side effects with the psychotropic drugs: An analysis of 18,000 chlordiazepoxide-treated cases. *Current Therapeutic Research, 8,* 455–464.

Syapin, P. J., & Skolnick, P. J. (1979). Characterization of benzodiazepine binding sites in cultured cells of neural origin. *Journal of Neurochemistry, 32,* 1047–1051.

Tallman, J. F., & Gallager, D. W. (1985). The GABA-ergic system: A locus of benzodiazepine action. *Annual Review of Neuroscience, 8,* 21–44.

Tallman, J. F., Paul, S. M., Skolnick, P., & Gallager, D. W. (1980). Receptors for the age of anxiety: Pharmacology of the benzodiazepines. *Science, 207,* 274–281.

Tallman, J. F., Thomas, J. W., & Gallager, D. W. (1978). GABA-ergic modulation of benzodiazepine binding site sensitivity. *Nature, 274,* 383–385.

Tamminga, C. A., Crayton, J. W., & Chase, T. N. (1978). Muscimol: GABA Agonist therapy in schizophrenia. *American Journal of Psychiatry, 135,* 746–747.

Taylor, C. B., Kenigsberg, M. L., & Robinson, J. M. (1982). A controlled comparison of relaxation and diazepam in panic disorder. *Journal of Clinical Psychiatry, 43,* 423–425.

Taylor, D. P., Ecison, M. S., Riblet, L. A., & Vandermaelen. (1985). Pharmacologic and clinical effects of buspirone. *Pharmacology, Biochemistry, and Behavior, 23,* 687–694.

Tesar, G. E., & Jenike, M. A. (1984). Alprazolam as treatment for a case of obsessive-compulsive disorder. *American Journal of Psychiatry, 141,* 689–690.

Tesar, G. E., & Rosenbaum, J. F. (1986). Successful use of clonazepam in patients with treatment-restistant panic disorder. *Journal of Nervous and Mental Disorders, 174,* 477–482.

Thiebot, M. H., Hamon, M., & Soubrie, P. (1982). Attenuation of induced anxiety in rats by chlordiazepoxide: Role of raphe dorsalis benzodiazepine binding sites and serotonergic neurons. *Neuroscience, 7,* 2287–2294.

Tjandra, J., & Kusumanto, R. (1975). Treatment of ambulatory neurotic patients with RO 5-3350 in Jakarta. *Medical Journal of Malaysia, 30*(1, Suppl.), 83–86.

Tollefson, G. (1985). Alprazolam in the treatment of obsessive symptoms. *Journal of Clinical Psychopharmacology, 5,* 39–42.

Tollefson, G., Lesar, T., Grothe, D., & Garvey, M. (1984). Alprazolam-related digoxin toxicity. *American Journal of Psychiatry, 141,* 1612–1614.

Trifiletti, R. R., & Snyder, S. H. (1984). Anxiolytic cyclopyrrolenes zopiclone and suriclone bind to a novel site linked allosterically to benzodiazepine receptors. *Molecular Pharmacology, 26,* 458–469.

Tyrer, P., Owen, R., & Dawling, S. (1983). Gradual withdrawal of diazepam after long-term therapy. *Lancet, I,* 1402–1406.

Tyrer, P. Rutherford, D., & Shtuggett, (1981). Benzodiazepine withdrawal symptoms and propranolol. *Lancet, I,* 520–527.

Uhde, T. W., Vittone, B. J., & Post, R. M. (1984). Glucose tolerance testing in panic disorder. *American Journal of Psychiatry, 141,* 1461–1463.

Vajda, F. J. E., Prineas, R. J., & Lovell, R. R. H. (1971). Interaction between phenytoin and the benzodiazepines. *British Medical Journal, 1,* 346.

van der Kolk, B. A. (1983). Psychopharmacological issues in posttraumatic stress disorder. *Hospital and Community Psychiatry, 34,* 683–691.

van Rooyen, J. M., & Offermeier, J. (1985). Pharmaokinetics of the benzodiazepines. *South African Medical Journal, 26*(Suppl.), 10–13.

Viscott, D. S. (1968). Chlordiazepoxide and hallucinations. Report of cases. *Archives of General Psychiatry, 19,* 370–376.

Ward, J. (1985). Vital uses of diazepam in third world countries. In D. E. Smith & D. R. Wesson (Eds.), *The benzodiazepins: Current standards of medical practice* (pp. 167–175). Hingham, MA: MTP Press.

Waxman, D. A. (1977). A clinical trial of clomipramine and diazepam in the treatment of phobic and obsessional illness. *Journal of International Medical Research, 5,* 99–109.

Weber, L. W. D. (1985). Benzodiazepines in pregnancy-academic debate or teratogenic risk? *Biological Research in Pregnancy, 6,* 151–167.

Whitehead, W. E., Blackwell, B., & Robinson, A. (1978). Effects of diazepam on phobic avoidance behavior and phobic anxiety. *Biological Psychiatry, 13,* 59–64.

Wickstrom, E., & Giercksky, K. E. (1980). Comparative study of zopiclone, a novel hypnotic and three benzodiazepines. *European Journal of Clinical Pharmacology, 17,* 93–99.

Williams, M. (1983). Anxioselective anxiolytics. *Journal of Medicinal Chemistry, 26,* 619–628.

Wittenborn, J. R. (1979). Effects of benzodiazepines on psychomotor performance. *British Journal of Clinical Pharmacology, 7,* 61–67.

Woods, S. W., Charney, D. S., Loke, J., Goodman, W. K., Redmond, D. E., Jr., & Heninger, G. R. (1986). Carbon dioxide sensitivity in panic anxiety: Ventilatory and anxiogenic response to carbon dioxide in healthy subjects and patients with panic anxiety before and after alprazolam treatment. *Archives of General Psychiatry, 43,* 900–909.

Wu, J. Y., Lin, H. S., Su, Y. Y. T., & Yang, C. Y. (1984). Isolation and purification of benzodiazepine receptor and its endogenous ligand. *Neuropharmacology, 23,* 881–883.

CHAPTER 23

Beta-adrenergic Blockers

Russell Noyes, Jr.

In the past decade, growing concern over the dependence potential of benzodiazepines has intensified the search for alternatives. This search has, at times, focused upon the beta-adrenergic receptor blocking drugs despite uncertainty about their effectiveness (Cole, Altesman, & Weingarten, 1980; Cuche & Deniker, 1980; Kelly, 1980; Middlemiss, Buxton, & Greenwood, 1981; Noyes, 1982, 1985; Peet, 1984; Tyrer, 1980). Soon after their introduction into medical therapeutics, these drugs were found capable of controlling the autonomic hyperactivity associated with anxiety disorders. There followed a series of controlled trials examining the extent and range of their efficacy. However, because of methodologic shortcomings in this research and concurrent developments in the treatment of these conditions, there is still no consensus about the place of beta-blocking drugs in the overall treatment of anxiety disorders.

The beta-blocking drugs appear to have certain advantages over the benzodiazepines, the chief ones being that they lack addictive potential, are not sedating, and are free of cognitive impairment at anti-anxiety doses (Turner, 1977). Unfortunately, they appear to be less effective than the benzodiazepines, and this more than counterbalances their advantages in terms of safety. Also, with introduction of panic disorder into the DSM-III (APA, 1980), questions about the usefulness of beta-blocking drugs in this new category were raised that have not been completely answered. A further challenge to these drugs has come from the tricyclic antidepressants that have become more widely used in the treatment of panic disorder and generalized anxiety disorder. And, as new anti-anxiety drugs are introduced, the usefulness of beta-blocking agents may become even more limited.

Still, the last chapter has not been written. Fresh interest has arisen in the effect of beta-blockade on performance anxiety and the possible benefits for patients suffering from social phobias (Liebowitz, Gorman, Fyer, & Klein, 1985). Also, the finding of an additive interaction between beta-blockers and benzodiazepines has stirred interest in the value of combining them (Hallstrom, Treasaden, Edwards, & Lader, 1981). Beyond this, a number of new beta-blocking drugs have been introduced that may have fewer side effects and, for that reason, be relatively more effective anxiolytics (Tollefson, 1984). Drugs that are more selective and that enter the central nervous system less readily may be superior in this regard. Finally, the reader should keep in mind that shortcomings of available research have kept us guessing about the actual worth of these drugs (Hayes & Schulz, 1983). Enthusiastic reports and reviews exist that are difficult to completely discount (Pitts & Allen, 1979; Suzman, 1976).

ADRENERGIC FUNCTION AND BLOCKADE

Adrenergic function

Since the early observations of Cannon (1920), the role of sympathetic nervous system activation in stress and anxiety has been recognized. Under stress, epinephrine is released from the adrenal medulla that mediates the sympathetic response. Plasma and urinary levels of epinephrine and norepinephrine are elevated in patients with panic disorder and, after attacks, levels of urinary MHPG, the principal metabolite of epinephrine, are elevated (Uhde, Boulenger, Vittorre, & Post, 1984). The findings of increased catecholamine levels are consistent with physiologic evidence of increased sympathetic tone (Gorman, 1984). Anxious patients have increased heart rate and forearm blood flow and decreased finger pulse volume. They also have increased sweat gland and muscle activity, while salivary gland activity is reduced. Their electroencephalograms show increased beta and diminished alpha activity.

Efforts to induce or block anxiety by pharmacologic means also point to the importance of autonomic nervous system functioning in patients with anxiety disorders. Early investigators observed that injections of epinephrine provoked anxiety attacks in anxious neurotics and, more recently, infusions of the beta receptor agonist, isoproterenol hydrochloride, have induced attacks in patients with panic disorder as well (Rainey & Nesse, 1985). Successful demonstration of the anxiolytic properties of beta-receptor blocking drugs has provided further evidence along these lines. Patients with panic disorder appear to benefit from such drugs, although the panic attacks themselves may not be blocked (Gorman et al., 1983; Kathol et al., 1981). It has generally been assumed that the peripheral beta-blockade produced by these drugs is responsible for their anxiety-relieving effects (Granville-Grossman, 1974).

Evidence has also accumulated for the role of central adrenergic functioning in anxiety production (Hoehn-Saric, 1982). In cerebrospinal fluid, positive correlations between concentrations of norepinephrine and state anxiety have been found in depressed patients and between levels of anxiety and concentrations of MHPG in normal volunteers. Also, plasma levels of MHPG have been shown to correlate with state anxiety in normal and panic disorder patients, and urinary levels of the substance have been correlated with anxiety in depressed patients. Sixty percent of this MHPG is estimated to have a central origin. These findings are consistent with other human and animal research pointing to central adrenergic system activation in anxiety.

Studies of the locus coeruleus in monkeys have yielded further evidence for involvement of the noradrenergic neurotransmitter system in anxiety (Redmond, 1977). This is a major noradrenergic nucleus located in the pons, with projections to the cerebral cortex, cerebellum, limbic system, and spinal cord. It contains nearly half of the noradrenergic neurons in the brain. Electrical and pharmacologic activation of the locus coeruleus produces behaviors like those observed in monkeys exposed to threats in the wild. In contrast, electrical lesions and pharmacological inhibition of the nucleus abolish these behaviors. Centrally acting drugs that increase locus coeruleus activity and that release norepinephrine, such as yohimbine hydrochloride and piperoxane, induce anxiety in animals and man, while drugs that inhibit the locus coeruleus, such as clonidine hydrochloride and benzodiazepines, reduce anxiety (Redmond, 1979).

Adrenergic blockade

Sympathetic nervous system activity is mediated, in part, by the interaction of neurotransmitters with receptors in various tissues. The receptors in the sympathetic nervous system have been classified as alpha and beta, according to the response of various tissues to neurotransmitters or sympathomimetic amines (Greenblatt & Shader, 1972). Beta receptors have also been identified in the central nervous system. Drugs that interfere with the ability of amines to interact with these receptors are referred to as adrenergic receptor blocking agents. These drugs have major importance in the management of cardiovascular disorders, including hypertension, angina pectoris, and cardiac arrhythmias (Gilman, Goodman, Rall, & Murad, 1985). Propranolol hydrochloride was the first member of the class of drugs to be widely used, and it remains the most important. It is a highly potent, nonselective beta-adrenergic blocking agent with no intrinsic sympathomimetic activity. Propranolol decreases heart rate and cardiac output and decreases blood pressure in resting subjects.

Because it is nonselective, propranolol blocks receptors in bronchial smooth muscle and skeletal muscle. Consequently, it interferes with bronchodilatation produced by sympathomimetic amines and with glycogenolysis that occurs in response to hypoglycemia. Because of these actions, the drug is not usually administered to patients with bronchial asthma and must be used cautiously in diabetics receiving hypoglycemic agents. Such unwanted actions prompted the search for beta-blocking drugs that might be cardioselective. Several beta-blocking agents are now available, but in high doses they inhibit beta 2 receptors as well. Among the nonselective beta-blocking drugs, propranolol (Inderal®), timolol maleate (Blocadren®), nadolol (Corgard®), pindolol (Visken®) and oxprenolol (Trasicon®) are currently available in the United States; among the selective, beta 1 blocking agents, metaprolol (Lopressor®) and atenolol (Tenormin®) have been approved for use.

Propranolol is almost completely absorbed following oral administration (Gilman, Goodman, Rall, & Murad, 1985). It is metabolized in the liver, and nearly a third is removed on first passage through the portal circulation. There is a great variation in this presystemic elimination which contributes to substantial variability in plasma concentrations among individuals. A twofold accumulation occurs during the first 24 hours of continuous administration and the elimination half-life gradually lengthens from 3 to 4 hours. The ingestion of food reduces first-pass metabolism and increases the drug's availability. Atenolol and nadolol are relatively long-lasting, beta-blocking drugs with half-lives of 6 to 8 and 16 to 20 hours, respectively. Neither is extensively metabolized, but excreted unchanged in the urine.

CLINICAL INVESTIGATIONS

Controlled studies

Early observers noted that propranolol controlled the tachycardia associated with anxiety and that neurotic patients who had cardiac symptoms improved on the drug (Besterman & Friedlander, 1965). This led to systematic investigation of its efficacy in anxiety disorders. Granville-Grossman and Turner (1966) were the first to demonstrate, in a double-blind trial, that propranolol was more effective than placebo in the treatment of anxiety. They reported that, in a dose of 80 mg daily, the drug significantly reduced the autonomic but not the psychological symptoms of their patients. Based on this observation they hypothesized that propranolol's efficacy was related to its peripheral beta-adrenergic receptor blocking action and suggested that patients with autonomic symptoms might respond best to the drug (Granville-Grossman, 1974).

A series of controlled studies (Table

23.1) tend to confirm these original observations. In 6 out of 13 studies in which a beta-blocking drug was compared to placebo, the active drug proved more effective. Propranolol was the drug employed in eight studies, while oxprenolol was used in three, and practolol and sotalol in one each. Although not well described, the patients in most studies suffered from what, in the current classification, would be called generalized anxiety disorders (American Psychiatric Association, 1980). However, most of these studies involved small numbers of patients, low doses of drug, and brief periods of drug administration. Most were studies employing crossover designs in which drugs were given for 1- or 2-week intervals. On account of their design limitations and lack of clinically relevant outcome measures, it is difficult to draw firm conclusions from them (Hayes & Schulz, 1983).

In two studies, the observation by Granville-Grossman and Turner concerning the effect of beta-blocking drugs on somatic symptoms was confirmed. Tyrer and Lader (1974b) found propranolol superior to placebo in patients with mainly somatic symptoms, but not in those with predominantly psychological symptoms. Bonn, Turner, and Hicks (1972) also found greater relief of somatic symptoms in patients receiving practolol. However, in other studies patients with predominantly somatic symptoms appeared to respond no better than those with psychological symptoms (Burrows et al., 1976; Johnson, Singh, & Leeman, 1976). In one study comparing propranolol and placebo, a significant reduction in the psychological symptoms of anxiety was reported, the possible result of administering higher doses (Kathol et al., 1981). Thus, while the autonomic symptoms of anxiety appear to be a target of beta-blocking drugs, further confirmation of their specificity is needed.

Because panic attacks involve a surge of autonomically mediated symptoms, it has been suggested that beta-blocking drugs might be useful in controlling attacks. In fact, patients have been described whose attacks appeared to respond to beta-blockade (Heiser & Defrancisco, 1976). Also, in one controlled study, a series of patients with panic disorder responded better to propranolol than they did to placebo (Kathol et al., 1981). However, when panic attacks were specifically monitored, they showed little change in frequency or severity with propranolol compared to diazepam, which effectively controlled them (Noyes et al., 1984). In addition, propranolol appeared ineffective in blocking lactate-induced panic attacks, although, in this study, it was only administered in single doses prior to infusion (Gorman et al., 1983). Consequently, there is presently little evidence of any antipanic effect of beta-blocking drugs.

Comparison with benzodiazepines

Recent studies indicate that beta-blocking drugs are relatively weak anxiolytics that are less effective than the benzodiazepines (Table 23.2). In four out of six studies in which these drugs were compared, the benzodiazepine proved to be superior (Burrows et al., 1976; Hallstrom et al., 1981; Johnson et al., 1976; Noyes et al., 1984; Tyrer & Lader, 1974b; Wheatley, 1969). The majority involved propranolol and diazepam, standards for each class. Their relative efficacy can be gauged clinically from a crossover design study comparing them in patients with panic disorder and agoraphobia (Noyes et al., 1984). In this trial, patients received a median of 30 mg diazepam and 240 mg propranolol. Eighty-six percent showed at least moderate improvement on diazepam, whereas only 33% experienced this degree of improvement with propranolol. Hallstrom et al. (1981), who reported similar findings, observed an additive effect of combining the two drugs. Thus, slight but important additional benefits were experienced by patients when propranolol was added to the diazepam they were already receiving. This positive interaction is consistent with the differing modes of action — one central and the other peripheral — of the drugs. Few controlled studies comparing beta-blockers with other types of anti-anxiety drugs, namely, tricyclic antidepressants and monoamine

Table 23.1. Controlled Studies Comparing Beta-Blocking Drugs with Placebo in Patients with Anxiety Disorders

Study	*N*	Patient Sample	Beta-Blocking Drug	Daily Dose (mg)	Study Design	Duration of Trial (weeks)	Superior to Placebo	Comment
Granville-Grossman & Turner (1966)	15	Predominant anxiety symptoms	Propranolol	80	Crossover	1	Yes	Autonomic symptoms responded to propranolol.
Suzman (1971)	40	Uncomplicated anxiety syndromes	Propranolol	160[a]	Placebo substitution	Variable	Yes	Psychological symptoms were relieved.
Bonn et al. (1972)	15	Predominant anxiety symptoms	Practolol	400	Crossover	2	Yes	Practolol has little access to the central nervous system.
Ramsey et al. (1973)	14	Neurotic anxiety	Propranolol	160	Crossover	1	No	Propranolol ineffective in relieving central symptoms of anxiety.
Tyrer & Lader (1973)	14	Chronic anxiety	Sotalol	124	Crossover	2	No	Observer preference approached superiority for sotalol.
Kellner et al. (1974)	22	Anxiety disorders, nonpsychotic	Propranolol	112[a]	Crossover	1	No	No important anti-anxiety effects of propranolol drug observed.
Tanna et al. (1977)	28	Chronic anxiety neurosis	Propranolol	40 120	Crossover	1	Yes	40-mg Dose ineffective, but no important side effects at either dose.
Kathol et al. (1980)	26	Panic disorder and agoraphobia	Propranolol	160	Crossover	2	Yes	Psychological symptoms responded as well as autonomic symptoms.

[a]Flexible dose administered.

oxidase inhibitors, have been reported (Munjack et al., 1985; Silverstone, 1974).

Performance anxiety

Beta-blocking drugs are capable of blunting the anxious response to stressful circumstances. Two investigators, for example, demonstrated beneficial effects of oxprenolol on the discomfort associated with civil disturbances in Belfast, Northern Ireland (Elsdon-Dew, 1975; McMillan, 1975). Beta-blockade may not only reduce stress-related anxiety, but the physiologic response to stress as well. Reductions in stress-induced tachycardia, plasma lipid elevations, and cardiac rhythm disturbances have been reported, causing certain investigators to suggest that beta-blocking drugs be used to combat the effects of emotional and environmental stress (Davidson & Taylor, 1978; Taggart & Carruther, 1972; Taggart, Carruther, & Somerville, 1973). Whether any amelioration of stress response contributes to the reduced morbidity or mortality of patients with cardiovascular disease receiving beta-blocking drugs is difficult to say.

Because of their inhibition of the stress response, beta-blocking drugs have been used to counteract performance anxiety. In a series of controlled studies (Table 23.3), the effects of these drugs on volunteers exposed to a variety of performance situations have been examined. Most have compared the effects of single doses of drug and placebo on subjective distress and objective performance. In six studies, musicians playing stringed instruments were studied (Brantigan, Brantigan, & Joseph, 1982; James et al., 1977; James, Burgoyne, & Savage, 1983; James & Savage, 1984; Liden & Gottfries, 1974; Neftel et al., 1982). Subjects reported less anxiety after receiving a beta-blocking drug than after placebo in all but one of these studies, and their performance, as assessed by blind raters, was better with the drug in three out of five. The investigators speculated that this may have been due to a reduction in stress-related tremor (James, 1984). However, little indication of the extent of this improvement was provided and no effect could be demonstrated after the first session in two studies. It is noteworthy that a beta-stimulating drug produced an increase in "stage fright" in one group of musicians.

The effect of beta-blocking drugs has also been explored for the control of anxiety provoked by examinations and public speaking (Table 23.3). It is well known that anxiety and heightened arousal serve to enhance cognitive performance. Beyond a certain point, however, anxiety produces a deterioration in ability to perform certain tasks. In an effort to reduce the anxiety, Krishnan (1976) gave 10 mg of oxprenolol or 2 mg of diazepam twice daily to undergraduates suffering from "exam nerves." Students who received the beta-blocking drug performed better when their scores were compared with instructor expectations even though those who received the benzodiazepine believed they had done better. Drew, Barnes, and Evans (1985) also observed beneficial effects of beta-blockade on examination performances, noting that subjects with the highest anxiety benefited most. However, improved performance was not observed in all studies and, when it occurred, improvement may have been limited to those who were impaired to begin with. Another series of studies has examined the effect of administering beta-blockers in competitive situations calling for motor coordination (Donaldson, Grant-Thomson, Morwood, O'Connor, & Tippett, 1980; Foster, Evans, & Hardcastle, 1978; Gibbons & Phillips, 1976; Nakano, Gillespie, & Hollister, 1978; Siitonen & Janne, 1976; Siitonen, Sonck, & Janne, 1977). They have shown that subjective distress is sometimes reduced and performance enhanced where stress-induced tremor is controlled. However, they also indicate that beta-blockers may impair cognitive functioning and motor coordination (Broadhurst, 1980; Hartley et al., 1983).

Phobic disorders

Reports of successful control of performance anxiety stimulated interest in the treatment of social phobics with beta-

Table 23.2. Controlled Studies Comparing Beta-Blocking Drugs with Other Drugs in Patients with Anxiety Disorders

Study	*N*	Patient Sample	Beta-Blocking Drug (Daily Dose in mg)	Comparison Drugs (Daily Dose in mg)	Study Design	Duration Trial (weeks)	Superior to Placebo	Comparison Drug Superior	Comment
Wheatley (1969)	105	Anxiety neurosis acute and chronic	Propranolol (90)	Chlordiazepoxide (30)	Parallel	6	—	No	Drugs equally effective, but chlordiazepoxide better for depressed mood and insomnia.
Tyrer & Lader (1974a)	12	Chronic anxiety	Propranolol (120)	Diazepam (10)	Crossover	1	Yes	Yes	Diazepam preferred over propranolol, but propranolol equally effective for patients with prominent somatic symptoms.
Silverstone (1974)	95	Anxiety symptoms	Oxprenolol (60)	Benzoctamine (30)	Parallel	4	No	Yes	Benzoctamine was superior to oxprenolol after 2 weeks, but dose of oxprenolol inadequate.
Johnson et al. (1976)	29	Clinical anxiety	Oxprenolol (240)	Diazepam (15)	Parallel	3	No	Yes	Patients with somatic anxiety did not favor oxprenolol.
Burrows et al. (1976)	62	Anxiety symptoms	Oxprenolol (80–560)	Diazepam (5–35)	Parallel	3	No	No	Oxprenolol and diazepam equally effective in patients with somatic and psychic anxiety.
Becker (1976)	46	Anxiety with or without depression	Propranolol (240)	Oxprenolol (240)	Parallel	2	—	No	Propranolol and oxprenolol proved equally effective.
Hallstrom et al. (1981)	24	Chronic anxiety	Propranolol (180)	Diazepam (22.5)	Crossover	2	No	Yes	Combination of propranolol and diazepam superior to diazepam alone.
Noyes et al. (1984)	21	Panic disorder and agoraphobia	Propranolol (240)	Diazepam (30)	Crossover	2	—	Yes	Propanolol ineffective in controlling panic attacks.
Munjack et al. (1985)	23	Panic disorder and agoraphobia	Propranolol (160)	Imipramine (175)	Crossover	6	—	No	Half of subjects became free of panic attacks on both drugs.

Table 23.3. Controlled Studies of the Effects of Beta-Blocking Drugs on Performance Anxiety

Study	N	Activity	Beta-Blocking Drug	Single Dose (mg)	Comparison Drug	Subjective Response	Improved Performance	Comment
Liden & Gottfries (1974)	15	Musical performance	Alprenolol	50 100	Placebo	Yes	—	No difference in response to high and low dose.
Krishnan (1976)	32	Examination performance	Oxprenolol	80	Diazepam 4 mg	Yes	Yes	Diazepam increased confidence, but did not improve performance.
James et al. (1977)	24	Musical performance	Oxprenolol	40	Placebo	Yes	Yes	Improvement not sustained on second occasion, tremor decreased by propranolol.
Brantigan et al. (1982)	29	Musical performance	Propranolol	40	Placebo	Yes	Yes	Saliva production increased by drug, betastimulating drug increased performance anxiety.
Krope et al. (1982)	49	Examination performance	Mepindolol	5	Placebo	No	No	Performance not impaired by mepindolol.
	55	Examination performance	Mepindolol	10	Placebo	No	No	—
Neftel et al. (1982)	22	Musical performance	Atenolol	100	Placebo	Yes	No	Technical performance not significantly improved by atenolol.
James et al. (1983)	30	Musical performance	Pindolol	5	Placebo	Yes	No	Improved performance in subgroup of better players.
Hartley et al. (1983)	16	Public speaking	Propranolol	40	Placebo	Yes	Yes	Propranolol reduced anxiety and anxious behavior, but caused memory impairment.
James & Savage (1984)	33	Musical performance	Nadolol	40	Diazepam 2 mg	No	Yes	Nadolol improved, but diazepam impaired certain aspects of performance.
Drew et al. (1985)	35	Examination performance	Propranolol	120	Placebo	—	Yes	Subjects who experienced anxiety benefited most from propranolol.

[a]Continuous administration.

blocking drugs (Liebowitz et al., 1985). However, only one controlled study has been reported to date (Falloon, Lloyds, & Harpin, 1981). In that study, a small number of patients were given propranolol or placebo while undergoing social skills training. No differences between the effects of drug and placebo were observed. Recently, however, Gorman et al. (1985) carried out an uncontrolled trial of atenolol in social phobics, with promising results. Five of 10 patients had a marked, and 4 a moderate, response to the treatment. There were few side effects as might be expected from a drug with minimal penetration of the central nervous system. The drug appeared to reduce the autonomic response to phobic stimuli. A controlled comparison of atenolol, phenelzine sulfate, and placebo is in progress.

Beta-blocking drugs have also been administered during exposure to phobic situations in the hope of enhancing the effect of the behavioral treatment (Table 23.4). Several investigators gave single doses of a beta-blocker just before treatment sessions (Bernadt, Silverstone, & Singleton, 1980; Gaind, Suri, & Thompson, 1975; Hafner & Milton, 1977; Tyrer & Lader, 1974a). The beta-blocker abolished the tachycardia associated with exposure and, in two instances, reduced the anxiety during treatment sessions. However, this did not lead to improved treatment outcome. For example, Gaind, Suri and Thompson (1975) found that oxprenolol increased the comfort of specific phobics during sessions, but resulted in higher phobic and avoidance scores at the end of treatment. Similarly, Hafner and Milton (1977) observed that agoraphobics who received propranolol before exposure had a worse treatment outcome. Thus, in single doses, beta-blocking drugs do not appear to enhance the outcome of behavior therapy. They appear to be like the benzodiazepines in this regard.

CLINICAL APPLICATION

Patient selection

Available evidence suggests that the benzodiazepines are more effective agents for the short-term treatment of the DSM-III (American Psychiatric Association, 1980) anxiety disorders: generalized anxiety disorder, panic disorder, and agoraphobia. Consequently, beta-blocking drugs should usually be reserved for patients with generalized anxiety disorder in whom benzodiazepines are contraindicated. Patients with unstable personality disorders fall into this category as do patients with histories of alcohol or drug abuse. Also included are patients with chronic illnesses who may require pharmacotherapy on a long-term basis. Panic attacks appear to be relatively little affected by beta-blocking drugs, and imipramine is the current drug of choice for panic disorder and agoraphobia (Noyes, 1986). Tricyclics and monoamine oxidase inhibitors are capable of blocking attacks and may even have specific antipanic properties (Noyes, 1987).

Patients belonging to the above-mentioned diagnostic categories, who have prominent autonomic symptoms of anxiety or who are preoccupied with such symptoms, appear most apt to benefit from a beta-blocking drug. Such symptoms are often a focus of apprehension or, if physiologic changes are visible to others, social embarrassment. On low dosages, patients often report that the physical symptoms of anxiety are controlled even though psychological ones are little affected. Anxiety associated with functional heart disturbances or prominent cardiovascular symptoms may also respond (Imhof & Brunner, 1970). Beta-blockers are recommended for patients whose symptoms are associated with mitral valve prolapse, a defect found in a variable proportion of patients with panic disorder (Crowe, 1985; Klein & Gorman, 1984). It should be noted, however, that there is no proof that the drugs are effective in these patients (Winkle et al., 1977).

There is preliminary evidence that social phobics may benefit from beta-blocking drugs (Liebowitz et al., 1985). If the phobic reaction is circumscribed, as in a phobia of public speaking, single doses may be administered before confronting the phobic situation. However, where the

Table 23.4. Controlled Studies Examining the Effect of Adding a Beta-Blocking Drug to Behavior Therapy for Phobic Disorders

Study	*N*	Subjects	Beta-Blocking Drug (Daily Dose in mg)	Comparison Drugs (Daily Dose in mg)	Behavior Therapy	Study Design	Superior to Placebo	Comments
Tyrer & Lader (1974a)	32	Situational fears	Propranolol (120) + propranolol (120)	Diazepam (6)	Exposure to phobic stimulus	Parallel, single dose	No	Propranolol more effective than placebo in phobic situation itself.
Gaind et al. (1975)	6	Simple phobics	Oxprenolol (160)	—	Exposure in vivo	Crossover, single dose	No	Subjects receiving oxprenolol more comfortable during exposure.
Hafner & Milton (1977)	23	Agoraphobics	Propranolol (40)	—	Exposure in vivo	Parallel, single dose	No	Propranolol group showed significantly less improvement 3 months after treatment.
Bernadt et al. (1980)	22	Simple phobics	Tolamolol (200)	Diazepam (10)	Exposure in vivo	Crossover, single dose	No	Tolamolol abolished tachycardia, but had no beneficial subjective or behavioral effects.
Falloon et al. (1981)	16	Social phobics	Propranolol (160–320)	—	Social skills training	Parallel, continuous administration	No	Propranolol added nothing to an effective behavioral treatment.
Campos et al. (1984)	21	Air travel phobics	Timolol (20)	—	Exposure in vivo	Parallel, continuous administration	No	Timolol inhibited tachycardia, but did not reduce anxiety during flights.

reaction is generalized to multiple social situations, then regular daily dosing may be more appropriate. Performance anxiety that is associated with impairment and that threatens an individual's career warrants a diagnosis of social phobia and appropriate treatment. Too often, persons with this illness use alcohol or sedative drugs in an effort to control their symptoms. But in so doing, they increase their impairment and run the risk of dependence (Aimes, Gelder, & Shaw, 1983). Social phobics experience autonomic dysfunction (e.g., blushing, sweating, trembling) which they feel exposes their loss of control to others. Beta-blocking drugs may reduce such reactions, thereby increasing patients' sense of self-control and self-confidence.

Precautions

Beta-blocking drugs are well tolerated providing they are not administered to patients in whom certain important functions are maintained by sympathetic stimulation (Shand, 1978). They are contraindicated in patients with congestive heart failure, brachycardia, or conduction defects. The cardiac function of such patients may be supported by increased sympathetic tone, a reduction of which may result in decompensation. Likewise, patients with bronchial asthma should not receive the drug because interruption of the bronchodilating effect of catecholamine stimulation may precipitate an asthmatic attack. Also, caution should be observed in administering beta-blockers to patients who are prone to hypoglycemic reactions or are taking hypoglycemic agents. These drugs may block sympathetically mediated glycogenolysis that occurs in response to hypoglycemia. Patients receiving beta-adrenergic stimulating drugs (e.g. epinephrine, amphetamine) should probably not receive beta-blocking drugs.

Dosage adjustment

The anti-anxiety dosage range for propranolol is 40mg to 320 mg daily (Hawkins, 1975; Suzman, 1971). Beta-blockade lasts for 8 to 12 hours after a single dose so that the drug needs to be administered three or four times daily. Because it is relatively short acting, with a half-life of 2 to 6 hours, a steady state is established quickly (Evans & Shand, 1973). And, because the response develops rapidly, dose adjustment can be accomplished without delay. This adjustment is important in view of the variable metabolism of propranolol. The dose required to achieve a given blood level may vary 20-fold from one individual to the next (Shand, 1978). For this reason, indicators of physiologic activity can be important. A fall in resting heart rate is a reliable indicator of beta-blockade and should be monitored during the period of dosage adjustment. If the rate falls below 50 beats per minute, further dosage increases should be delayed. While no correlation between blood level and anxiety reduction has been demonstrated, a blood level of 50 to 100mg/ml is generally felt to produce satisfactory beta-blockade (Shand, 1978). Beta-blocking drugs should be discontinued gradually to minimize physiologic rebound. Abrupt withdrawal may cause a transient increase in sympathetic activity accompanied by anxiety symptoms (Garbus, Weber, Priest, Brewer, & Hubbell, 1979; Prichard, Tomlinson, Walden, & Bhattacharjeel, 1983).

Propranolol is the beta-blocking drug employed in most of the controlled studies and remains the standard for treatment of anxiety disorders. However, a number of new drugs have recently become available that are likely to have anti-anxiety effects as well (Chaturvedi, 1985; Gorman et al., 1985; Tollefson, 1984). In that case, they may have a number of advantages (Tollefson, 1984). Drugs that are hydrophilic, rather than lipophilic, reach the central nervous system in lower concentrations and, for that reason, may have fewer CNS side effects. Nadolol and atenolol are hydrophilic drugs. Drugs that are eliminated by the kidneys tend to be less variable in their availability and slower in their metabolism (van Zweiten & Timmermans, 1985). This means that dosing is more uniform and can be accomplished on a once daily basis. Nadelol and atenolol have these characteristics. It is not clear whether selectivity is associated with the anxiety-reducing properties of beta-blocking drugs. There is no reason, at least for the present, to choose a selective drug except on the basis of its side effect profile.

Side effects

The most common side effects of beta-adrenergic receptor blocking drugs involve the gastrointestinal tract and central nervous system (Greenblatt & Koch-Weser, 1973; Stephen, 1966). Nausea, abdominal distress and diarrhea, or constipation may occur. Nervous system effects include dizziness, insomnia, fatigue, and depressed mood. These side effects are rarely severe and may subside following a reduction in dosage or continued use of the drug. Delirium and depression are adverse reactions that are probably rare. Delirium has been observed in patients placed on dosages of propranolol in the neighborhood of 2,000 mg daily (Yorkston, Zaki, Malik, Morrison, & Havard, 1974). Isolated reports of its occurrence at lower dosages have appeared. Although depression was reported in a substantial proportion of patients receiving propranolol for hypertension, the criteria for depression were vague and no confirmation of the report has been forthcoming (Fitzgerald, 1967; Waal, 1967). Side effects such as depressed mood, fatigue, and insomnia may be difficult to distinguish from a depressive syndrome. The long-term safety of beta-blocking drugs is still under study (Editorial, 1978).

Single dose

If a beta-blocking drug is given for a circumscribed social phobia, then the drug may be administered in single doses before exposure to the phobic situation (James, 1984). Before using the drug in such situations, the patient may take several doses to learn about the drug's effects and become comfortable with them. A dose that attenuates the anxiety-induced tachycardia is usually sufficient. The drug chosen for use may depend upon the target symptoms and the duration of exposure to the phobic situation. A nonselective drug may be more suitable for controlling tremor, and short-acting drugs like propanolol or oxprenolol preferable for brief exposure.

CONCLUDING REMARKS

In summary, we can say that beta-adrenergic blocking drugs have anti-anxiety properties that may be useful in some patients. On clinical grounds, their appeal lies in their lack of addictive potential, while on theoretical grounds, they arouse interest because they act upon the adrenergic receptors that are believed to play an important role in the mediation of anxiety. It is unfortunate that, at this late stage, so many questions remain unanswered and that, with rapid development of other treatments, these questions may not be addressed.

REFERENCES

Aimes, P. L., Gelder, M. G., & Shaw, P. M. (1983). Social phobia: A comparative clinical study. *British Journal of Psychiatry, 142*, 174–179.

American Psychiatric Association (1980). *Diagnostic and statistical manual of mental disorder* (3rd ed.), Washington, DC: Author.

Becker, L. J. (1976). Oxprenolol and propranolol in anxiety states. A double-blind comparative study. *South African Medical Journal, 50*, 627–629.

Bernadt, M. N., Silverstone, T., & Singleton, W. (1980). Behavioral and subjective effects of beta-adrenergic blockade in phobic subjects. *British Journal of Psychiatry, 137*, 452–457.

Besterman, E. M. M., & Friedlander, D. H. (1965). Clinical experience with propranolol. *Postgraduate Medical Journal, 4*, 526–535.

Bonn, J. A., Turner, P., & Hicks, D. (1972). Beta-adrenergic receptor blockade with practolol in treatment of anxiety. *Lancet, 1*, 814–815.

Brantigan, C. O., Brantigan, T. A., & Joseph, N. (1982). Effect of beta-blockade and beta-stimulation on stage fright. *American Journal of Medicine, 72*, 88–94.

Broadhurst, A. (1980). The effect of propranolol on human psychomotor performance. *Aviation Space Environment Medicine, 51*, 176–179.

Burrows, G. D., Davies, B., Fail, L., Poynton, C., & Stevenson H. (1976). A placebo controlled trial of diazepam and oxprenolol for anxiety.

Psychopharmacology, 50, 177–179.

Campos, P. E., Solyom, L., & Koelink, A. (1984). The effects of timolol maleate on subjective and physiological components of air travel phobia. *Canadian Journal of Psychiatry, 29,* 570–574.

Cannon, W. B. (1920). *Bodily changes in pain, hunger, fear and rage.* New York: Appleton.

Chaturvedi, S. K. (1985). Metaprolol, a new selective beta-blocker in anxiety neurosis. *Psychopharmacology, 85,* 488.

Cole, J. O., Altesman, R. I., & Weingarten, D. H. (1980). Beta-blocking drugs in psychiatry. In J. O. Cole (Ed.), *Psychopharmacology update* (pp. 43–68). Lexington, MA: Collamore Press.

Crowe, R. R. (1985). Mitral valve prolapse and panic disorder. *Psychiatric Clinics of North America, 8,* 63–72.

Cuche, H., & Deniker, P. (1980). Psychiatric uses of beta-blockers. *Pharmakopsychiatrie Neuro-Psychopharmakologie, 13,* 267–272.

Davidson, C., & Taylor, S. H. (1978). Stress and beta-blockers in cardiology. In P. Kielholz (Ed.), *A therapeutic approach to the psyche via the beta-adrenergic system* (pp. 61–69). Baltimore: University Park Press.

Donaldson, E., Grant-Thomson, J., Morwood, N., O'Connor, N., & Tippett, R. (1980). Pilot study on the value of a beta-blocking drug in initial helicopter training. *Aviation, Space and Environment Medicine, 51,* 926–929.

Drew, P. J. T., Barnes, J. N., & Evans, S. J. W. (1985). The effect of acute β-adrenoceptor blockade on examination performance. *British Journal of Clinical Pharmacology, 19,* 783–786.

Editorial. (1978). Long term safety of receptor-blocking drugs. *Lancet, 1,* 1242–1243.

Elsdon-Drew, R. W. (1975). Clinical trials of oxprenolol in anxiety. *Scottish Medical Journal, 20,* 286–288.

Evans, D. H., & Shand, D. G. (1973). Disposition of propranolol. V. Drug accumulation and steady-state concentrations during chronic oral administrations in man. *Clinical Pharmacology and Therapeutics, 14,* 487–493.

Falloon, I. R. H., Lloyd, G. G., & Harpin, R. E. (1981). Real-life rehearsal with nonprofessional therapists. *Journal of Nervous and Mental Disease, 169,* 180–184.

Fitzgerald, J. D. (1967). Propranolol-induced depression. *British Medical Journal, 2,* 372–373.

Foster, G. E., Evans, D. F., & Hardcastle, J. D. (1978). Heart rates of surgeons during operating and other clinical activities and their modification by oxprenolol. *Lancet, 1,* 1323–1325.

Gaind, R., Suri, A. K., & Thompson, J. (1975). Use of beta-blockers as an adjunct in behavioral techniques. *Scottish Medical Journal, 20,* 284–286.

Garbus, S. B., Weber, M. A., Priest, R. T., Brewer, D. D., & Hubbell, F. A. (1979). The abrupt discontinuation of antihypertensive treatment. *Journal of Clinical Pharmacology, 19,* 476–486.

Gibbons, D. O., & Phillips, M. (1976). The effect of acebutolol on tachycardia and performance during competitive rifle shooting. *British Journal of Clinical Pharmacology, 3,* 516–517.

Gilman, A. G., Goodman, L. S., Rall, T. W., & Murad, F. (Eds.). (1985). *The pharmacological basis of therapeutics* (7th ed., pp. 192–203). New York: Macmillan.

Gorman, J. M. (1984). The biology of anxiety. In L. Grinspoon (Ed.), *Psychiatry update, Volume III* (pp. 467–482). Washington, DC: American Psychiatric Association Press.

Gorman, J. M., Levy, G. F., Liebowitz, M. R., McGrath, P., Appleby, I. L., Dillon, D. J., Davies, S. O., & Klein, D. F. (1983). Effect of acute beta-adrenergic blockade on lactate-induced panic. *Archives of General Psychiatry, 40,* 1079–1082.

Gorman, J. M., Liebowitz, M. R., Fyer, A. J., Campeas, R., & Klein, D. F. (1985). Treatment of social phobia with atenolol. *Journal of Clinical Psychopharmacology, 5,* 298–301.

Granville-Grossman, K. L. (1974). Propranolol, anxiety and the central nervous system. *British Journal of Clinical Pharmacology, 1,* 361–363.

Granville-Grossman, K. L., & Turner, P. (1966). The effect of propranolol on anxiety. *Lancet, 1,* 788–790.

Greenblatt, D. J., & Koch-Weser, J. (1973). Adverse reactions to propranolol in hospitalized medical patients: A report from the Boston Collaborative Drug Surveillance Program. *American Heart Journal, 86,* 478–484.

Greenblatt, D. J., & Shader, R. I. (1972). On the psychopharmacology of beta-adrenergic blockade. *Current Therapy Research, 14,* 615–625.

Hafner, J., & Milton, F. (1977). The influence of propranolol on the exposure in vivo of agoraphobics. *Psychological Medicine, 7,* 419–425.

Hallstrom, C., Treasaden, I., Edwards, J. G., & Lader, M. (1981). Diazepam, propranolol and their combination in the management of chronic anxiety. *British Journal of Psychiatry, 139,* 417–421.

Hartley, L. R., Uugapen, S., Davie, I., &

Spencer, D. J. (1983). The effect of beta-adrenergic blocking drugs on speakers' performance and memory. *British Journal of Psychiatry, 142*, 512–517.

Hayes, P. E., & Schulz, C. S. (1983). Use of beta-adrenergic blocking agents in anxiety disorders and schizophrenia. *Pharmacotherapy, 3*, 101–117.

Hawkins, J. R. (1975). Clinical experience with beta-blockers in consultant psychiatric practice. *Scottish Medical Journal, 20*, 294–298.

Heiser, J. F., & Defrancisco, D. (1976). The treatment of pathological panic states with propranolol. *American Journal of Psychiatry, 133*, 1389–1394.

Hoehn-Saric, R. (1982). Neurotransmitters in anxiety. *Archives of General Psychiatry, 39*, 735–742.

Imhof, P., & Brunner, H. (1970). The treatment of functional heart disorders with beta-adrenergic blocking agents. *Postgraduate Medical Journal, 46*, 96–99.

James, I. M. (1984). Practical aspects of the use of beta-blockers in anxiety states: Situational anxiety. *Postgraduate Medical Journal, 60* (Suppl. 2), 19–25.

James, I. M., Burgoyne, W., & Savage, I. T. (1983). Effect of pindolol on stress-related disturbances of musical performance: Preliminary communication. *Journal of the Royal Society of Medicine, 76*, 194–196.

James, I. M., Pearson, R. M., Griffith, D. N. W., & Newbury, D. (1977). Effect of oxprenolol on stage fright in musicians. *Lancet, 2*, 952–954.

James, I. M., & Savage, I. (1984). Beneficial effect of nadolol on anxiety-induced disturbances of performance in musicians: A comparison with diazepam and placebo. *American Heart Journal, 108*, 1150–1155.

Johnson, G., Singh, B., & Leeman, M. (1976). Controlled evaluation of the beta-adrenoceptor blocking drug oxprenolol in anxiety. *Medical Journal of Australia, 1*, 909–921.

Kathol, R., Noyes, R. Jr., Slymen, D. J., Crowe, R. R., Clancy, V., & Kerber, R. G. (1980). Propranolol in chronic anxiety disorders: A controlled study. *Archives of General Psychiatry, 37*, 1361–1365.

Kellner, R., Collins, C., Shulman, R. S., & Pathak, D. (1974). The short-term antianxiety effects of propranolol HCL. *Journal of Clinical Pharmacology, 14*, 301–304.

Kelly, D. (1980). Clinical review of beta-blockers in anxiety. *Pharmakopsychiatrie Neuro-Psychopharmakologie, 13*, 259–266.

Klein, D. F., & Gorman, J. M. (1984). Panic disorders and mitral prolapse [Monograph]. *Journal of Clinical Psychiatry, 2*, 14–17.

Krishnan, G. (1976). Oxprenolol in the treatment of examination stress. *Current Medical Research and Opinion, 4*, 241–243.

Krope, P., Kohrs, A., & Ott, H. (1982). Evaluating mepindolol in a test model of examination anxiety in students. *Pharmacopsychiatria, 15*, 41–47.

Liden, S., & Gottfries, C. G. (1974). Beta-blocking agents in the treatment of catecholamine-induced symptoms in musicians. *Lancet, 2*, 529.

Liebowitz, M. R., Gorman, J. M., Fyer, A. J., & Klein, D. F. (1985). Social phobia: Review of a neglected anxiety disorder. *Archives of General Psychiatry, 42*, 729–736.

McMillan, W. P. (1975). Oxprenolol in the treatment of anxiety due to environmental stress. *American Journal of Psychiatry, 132*, 965–966.

Middlemiss, D. N., Buxton, D. A., & Greenwood, D. T. (1981). Beta-adrenoceptor antagonists in psychiatry and neurology. *Pharmacology and Therapeutics, 12*, 419–437.

Munjack, D. J., Rabel, R., Shaner, R., Staples, F., Braun, R., & Leonard, M. (1985). Imipramine versus propranolol for the treatment of panic attacks: A pilot study. *Comprehensive Psychiatry, 26*, 80–89.

Nakano, S., Gillespie, H. K., & Hollister, L. E. (1978). Propranolol in experimentally induced stress. *Psychopharmacology, 59*, 279–284.

Neftel, K. A., Adler, R. H., Kapelli, L., Rossi, M., Dolder, M., Kaser, H. E., Bruggesser, H. H., & Vorkauf, H. (1982). Stage fright in musicians: A model illustrating the effect of beta-blockers. *Psychosomatic Medicine, 44*, 461–469.

Noyes, R. Jr. (1982). Beta-blocking drugs and anxiety. *Psychosomatics, 23*, 155–170.

Noyes, R. Jr. (1985). Beta-adrenergic blocking drugs in anxiety and stress. *Psychiatric Clinics of North America, 8*, 119–132.

Noyes, R. Jr. (1987). The psychopharmacology of phobic disorders. In R. D. Burrows, T. R. Norman, & B. Davies (Eds.), *Drugs in psychiatry*. New York: Elsevier.

Noyes, R. Jr., Anderson, D. J., Clancy, J., Crowe, R. R., Slymen, D. J., Ghoneim, M. M., & Hinrichs, V. V. (1984). Diazepam and propanolol in panic disorder and agoraphobia. *Archives of General Psychiatry, 41*, 287–292.

Noyes, R. Jr., Chaudhry, D., Domingo, D. (1986) Pharmacologic treatment of phobic disorders. *Clinical Psychiatry, 47*, 445–452.

Peet, M. (1984). Beta-blockade in anxiety. *Postgraduate Medical Journal, 60* (Suppl. 2), 16–18.

Pitts, F. N. Jr., & Allen, R. (1979). Beta-adrenergic blocking agents in the treatment of anxiety. In W. E. Fann, I. Karacan, & A. D. Pokorny (Eds.), *Phenomenology and treatment of anxiety* (pp. 337–349). New York: Spectrum Publishers.

Prichard, B. N. C., Tomlinson, B., Walden, Z. J., & Bhattacharjeel, P. (1983). The β-adrenergic blockade withdrawal phenomenon. *Journal of Cardiovascular Pharmacology, 5,* 556–562.

Rainey, J. M., & Nesse, R. M. (1985). Psychobiology of anxiety and anxiety disorders. *Psychiatric Clinics of North America, 8,* 133–144.

Ramsay, I., Greer, S., & Bagley, C. (1973). Propanolol in neurotic and thyrotoxic anxiety. *British Journal of Psychiatry, 122,* 555–560.

Redmond, D. E. (1977). Alterations in the function of the nucleus locus coeruleus: A possible model for studies of anxiety. In I. Hanin (Ed.), *Animal models in psychiatry and neurology.* New York: Pergamon Press.

Redmond, D. E. (1979). New and old evidence for the involvement of a brain norepinephrine system in anxiety. In W. E. Fann, I. Karacan, A. D. Pokorny, & R. L. Williams (Eds.), *Phenomenology and treatment of anxiety.* New York: Spectrum Publications.

Shand, D. G. (1978). Propranolol: Resolving problems in usage. *Drug Therapy, 8,* 53–59.

Siitonnen, L., & Janne, J. (1976). Effect of beta-blockade during bowling competitions. *Annals of Clinical Research, 8,* 393.

Siitonen, L. A., Sonck, T., & Janne, J. (1977). Effect of beta-blockade on performance: Use of beta-blockade in bowling and shooting competitions. *Journal of International Research, 5,* 359–366.

Silverstone, J. T. (1974). Some new approaches to the treatment of anxiety. *Psychopharmacological Bulletin, 10,* 10–11.

Stephen, S. A. (1966). Unwanted effects of propranolol. *American Journal of Cardiology, 18,* 463–472.

Suzman, M. M. (1971). The use of beta-adrenergic blockade with propranolol in anxiety syndromes. *Postgraduate Medical Journal, 47,* 104–108.

Suzman, M. M. (1976). Propranolol in the treatment of anxiety. *Postgraduate Medical Journal, 52,* 168–174.

Taggart, P., & Carruther, M. (1972). Suppression by oxprenolol of adrenergic response to stress. *Lancet, 2,* 256–258.

Taggart, P., Carruther, M., & Somerville, W. (1973). Electrocardiogram, plasma catacholamines and lipids, and their modification by oxprenolol when speaking before an audience. *Lancet, 2,* 341–346.

Tanna, V. T., Penningroth, P. R., & Woolson, R. F. (1977). Propranolol in the treatment of anxiety neurosis. *Comprehensive Psychiatry, 18,* 319–326.

Tollefson, G. (1984). Use of a long acting peripheral beta-blocker, nadolol, in panic disorder. *Journal of Clinical Psychopharmacology, 4,* 170–171.

Turner, P. (1977). Clinical and experimental studies on the central effects of beta-blockade in man. In P. Kielholz (Ed.), *Beta blockers and the central nervous system* (pp. 35–38). Bern: Huber.

Tyrer, P. J. (1980). Use of beta-blocking drugs in psychiatry and neurology. *Drugs, 20,* 300–308.

Tyrer, P. J., & Lader, M. H. (1974a). Physiological and psychological effects of — chronic anxiety. *Clinical Pharmacology and Therapeutics, 14,* 418–426.

Tyrer, P. J., & Lader, M. H. (1974a). Physiological and psychological effects of – propranolol, +-propranolol and diazepam in induced anxiety. *British Journal of Clinical Pharmacology, 1,* 379–385.

Tyrer, P. J., & Lader, M. H. (1974b). Response to propranolol and diazepam in somatic anxiety. *British Medical Journal, 2,* 14–24.

van Zwieten, P. A., & Timmermans, P. B. M. W. M. (1983). Differential pharmacological properties of β-adrenoceptor blocking drugs. *Journal of Cardiovascular Pharmacology, 5* (Suppl. 1), 15–75.

Uhde, T. W., Boulenger, J. P., Vittore, B. J., & Post, R. M. (1984). Historical and modern concepts of anxiety: A focus on adrenergic function. In J. C. Ballenger (Ed.), *Biology of agoraphobia* (pp. 1–26). Washington, DC: American Psychiatric Association Press.

Waal, H. J. (1967). Propranolol-induced depression. *British Medical Journal, 2,* 50.

Wheatley, D. (1969). Comparative effects of propranolol and chlordiazepoxide. *British Journal of Psychiatry, 115,* 1411–1412.

Winkle, R. A., Lopes, M. G., Goodman, D. J., Fitzgerald, J. W., Schroeder, J. S., & Harrison, D. C. (1977). Propranolol for patients with mitral valve prolapse. *American Heart Journal, 93,* 422–427.

Yorkston, J. M., Zaki, S. A., Malik, M. K. U., Morrison, R. C., & Havard, C. W. H. (1974). Propranolol in the control of schizophrenic symptoms. *British Medical Journal, 4,* 633–635.

CHAPTER 24

Tricyclic Antidepressants

Michael E. Thase and James E. Shipley

Tricyclic antidepressants (TCAs) and a variety of loosely related heterocyclic (HCAs) medications have gained an increasingly important role in the treatment of anxiety disorders. This chapter will summarize the clinical pharmacology of these drugs and review research on their efficacy in a variety of clinical anxiety states.

DESCRIPTION OF THE TREATMENT

The TCAs have been used in clinical practice for nearly three decades. The term *tricyclic* reflects the basic three-ring chemical structure of these compounds (see Baldessarini, 1983, for two-dimensional structural representations of these compounds); it also serves as a type of shorthand to separate TCAs from a distinctly different group of drugs with anti-anxiety and antidepressant properties known as monoamine oxidase inhibitors (MAOIs). The TCAs evolved from a larger family of tricyclic drugs (phenothiazines), which play a central role in treatment of psychotic states. Tricyclics differ from phenothiazines in that a sulfur atom in the center (nonaromatic) ring has been replaced by an ethylene bridge. This substitution results in a major change in how the TCA drug appears in three-dimensional space, hence altering its affinity for various neurochemical receptor sites (Barchas, Berger, Ciaranello, & Elliott, 1977). Tricyclic antidepressants, thus, do not have clinically significant antipsychotic effects.

The thymoleptic (mood altering) actions of imipramine hydrochloride (IMI), the first TCA approved for clinical use, were discovered somewhat accidently in the mid-1950s, when Kuhn (1958) observed improvements in mood, sleep, and energy (but not antipsychotic effects) in an institutionalized population. The efficacy of IMI and a number of other TCAs subsequently has been convincingly established for treatment of selected depressive syndromes (see, for example, Appleton & Davis, 1980; Klein, Gittelman, Quitkin, & Rifkin, 1980). Their potential value as treatments for anxiety neuroses initially was investigated in the early 1960s by Donald Klein and co-workers (1964, 1967). Klein found that IMI was preferentially effective in anxiety states characterized by spontaneous panic attacks, whether or not accompanied by agoraphobia. Imipramine was noted to block or diminish the frequency of such panic attacks, with secondary improvements in generalized anxiety and avoidance behavior apparently following successful treatment of the panic episodes (Klein, 1964). Conversely, IMI and related drugs were not observed to have a major impact on specific phobias not characterized by panic attacks (Klein, 1967). These observations proved instrumental in the subsequent establishment of panic disorder as a distinct condition, and led to further research on use of TCAs in anxiety disorders.

Imipramine has remained the most widely prescribed TCA in research concerning anxiety disorders (and probably in clinical practice), although there are now six other tricyclics approved by the Food and Drug Administration (FDA) for use in the United States for treatment of depression (see Table 24.1). These TCAs differ from IMI in terms of modifications of the center ring (amitriptyline hydrochloride), side chain (desipramine hydrochloride), or both (nortriptyline hydrochloride, protriptyline hydrochloride, trimipramine maleate, and doxepin hydrochloride). Such modifications do not affect the antidepressant efficacy of these TCAs, but do alter the affinity of each of these drugs for selected neurotransmitter systems (Baldessarini, 1983; Barchas, Berger, Ciarenello, & Elliott, 1977). It is not yet known if such modifications alter the potency of particular TCAs for blocking panic attacks, although such changes may have an impact on the efficacy of TCAs for treatment of obsessive-compulsive disorder (Zohar & Insel, in press). One additional TCA, clomipramine (or chlorimipramine; CMI) widely used as an antidepressant and anti-anxiety drug in both Europe and Canada, and has shown particular promise in the treatment of panic and obsessive-compulsive disorders (to be discussed in detail later). Clomipramine also is of interest because it is available for use in intravenous injections. This approach has been recommended for patients with severe, refractory conditions (Warneke, 1984). Clomipramine remains under continued study and may yet be approved for use in the United States. It is

Table 24.1. Tricyclic and Heterocyclic Antidepressants Used for Treatment of Anxiety Syndromes

General Name	Common Brand Name(s)	Daily Dosage Range (mg)[b]
Amitriptyline	Amitril, Elavil, Endep	10–300
Clomipramine	Anafranil[a]	25–300
Desipramine	Norpramin, Pertofrane	25–300
Doxepin	Adapin, Sinequan	25–300
Imipramine	Janimine, SK-Pramine, Tofranil	10–300
Nortriptyline	Aventyl, Pamelor	10–300
Protriptyline	Vivactil	5–60
Trimipramine	Surmontil	25–300
Amoxapine	Asendin	50–600
Maprotiline	Ludiomil	25–400
Trazodone	Desyrel	25–600

[a]Not yet approved by FDA for use in the United States.
[b]Higher dosages sometimes are used, under closely controlled circumstances, in patients who tolerate the medication well and who are not responding to treatment.

interesting that none of the TCAs have been approved for treatment of anxiety disorders by the FDA at this time (mid-1986).

In addition to the TCA family of drugs, three "second-generation" antidepressant drugs have been approved by the FDA for treatment of depression and currently are available in this country: maprotiline hydrochloride, amoxapine, and trazodone hydrochloride (see Table 24.1). These drugs have antidepressant efficacy roughly equivalent to IMI, although their side-effect profiles may differ somewhat from the TCAs (see Rudorfer, Golden, & Potter, 1984). In current practice, these second-generation drugs may be primarily useful in patients who are allergic, intolerant, or refractory to TCAs (Thase, in press). A limited amount of clinical data has emerged concerning use of HCAs in anxiety disorders; this literature will be reviewed later in the chapter.

Before turning to a discussion of the clinical pharmacology of the TCAs and HCAs, it might be useful to first consider some of the basic principles of drug treatment. First, and foremost, the diagnosis of the condition should be established as clearly as practically possible before pharmacologic treatment is initiated. With respect to the anxiety disorders, it is important to rule out, or clarify, the possibile role of medical factors in the etiology of the syndrome. Organic anxiety syndromes are not uncommon in medical practice, and a physical examination and basic laboratory studies are recommended prior to pharmacologic treatment in most circumstances. An electrocardiogram (ECG) also routinely should be obtained in all individuals over age 40 to evaluate pretreatment cardiac rhythm and conductance status; serial ECGs subsequently may prove useful in monitoring patients who require high dosage of TCAs (Klein et al., 1980). Further, an electroencephalogram (EEG) may be indicated to rule out temporal-lobe dysrhythmias in selected cases in which paroxysmal anxiety attacks are accompanied by symptoms suggestive of epilepsy (i.e., out of body experiences, derealization, aura sensations, visual or olfactory hallucinations, etc.). The treatment clinician also should carefully ascertain a history of drug and alcohol usage patterns, including intake of caffeine, nicotine, and other stimulants. This is important because anxiety symptoms sometimes reflect an undetected substance withdrawal syndrome and because anxiety disorders may predispose individuals for alcohol or sedative abuse (Munjack & Moss, 1981). Ongoing substance abuse also may seriously compromise therapeutic interventions. Further, individuals with anxiety disorders may be exquisitely sensitive to the anxiogenic effects of caffeine (Boulenger, Uhde, Wolf, & Post, 1984). Whenever an underlying medical condition or substance abuse disorder is identified, it should be treated and corrected, if possible, before initiating therapy with a TCA or related drug.

Second, clear target symptoms should be identified and monitored over the course of treatment. In general, these symptoms will be associated with sufficient distress and/or impairment to warrant exposure to the potential side effects and risks of pharmacotherapy. Suicidal ideation should be assessed in all patients, including those who do not appear "depressed," as persons with anxiety disorders have been shown to have increased mortality due to suicide (Coryell, Noyes, & House, 1986) *and* because all TCAs and most HCAs may be lethal agents when taken as an overdose (Preskorn & Irwin, 1982).

Third, patients' expectations and apprehensions regarding pharmacologic treatment need to be carefully explored and discussed. Answering questions regarding the lack of potential addictiveness of treatment, the anticipated time-frame of response, potential side effects, and expected therapeutic results facilitates development of a collaborative working alliance and may short-circuit subsequent developments leading to noncompliance or premature termination of treatment.

Fourth, if pharmacotherapy is initiated, it is important to allow enough time to properly evaluate the effects of each drug trial. Evidence suggests that the antipanic or antiobsessional effects of TCAs may take somewhat longer than the traditional 4- to 6-week standard trial utilized in the treatment of depression (Mavissakalian, Turner, Michelson, & Jacob, 1985; Zitrin, Klein, Woerner, & Ross, 1983), particularly if it is necessary to slowly increase the dosage over a number of weeks. Moreover, it is important to push each drug to the maximum tolerated dosage before considering the treatment trial to be a failure. It is common in tertiary referral centers to evaluate supposedly "refractory" patients who simply have not received adequate treatment. Conversely, the urge to try to augment response in patients receiving TCAs by adding a second agent (i.e., an antipsychotic or a benzodiazepine) should be resisted until the full benefits of a maximally tolerated dosage have been evaluated.

The dosages of TCAs and HCAs commonly utilized in clinical practice are summarized in Table 24.1. The "right" dosage of a medication for a given patient actually represents a cost/effect ratio, balancing the burden of side effects versus therapeutic benefit. Using IMI treatment of panic disorder as a prototype, individuals may respond to dosages as low as 5 to 20 mg/day or as high as 300 to 400 mg/day (Ballenger, 1986; Liebowitz, 1985). Unfortunately, few guidelines exist to enable the treating clinician to predict which patients will benefit from low-dose or high-dose therapy; some investigators accordingly begin all patients on low dosages (i.e., 10 mg twice each day) (Ballenger, 1986). In our experience, a majority of patients tolerate larger initial dosages (i.e., 25 mg twice each day), with reduction of the dose necessary in about 25% of patients due to intolerable side effects. Nevertheless, the dosage of medication generally is slowly increased over several weeks, or longer if necessary, by increasing the dosage by one pill (i.e., 10 mg or 25 mg of IMI) every few days. A dosage in the range of 150 to 200 mg/day of IMI can usually be reached within 3 to 4 weeks, with further increases up to 300 mg/day over the next several weeks if no therapeutic effect is observed *and* if the dosage is relatively well-tolerated.

Occasional individuals will benefit from even higher dosages, in the range of 350 to 500 mg/day. Such patients may be rapid metabolizers of the medication and hence need a higher-than-normal dosage to achieve and maintain an acceptable response. Because such dosages fall outside of the realm of standard practice, it is important to carefully document the side-effect profile, lack of response to lower dosages, and the absence of significant cardiovascular effects through obtaining periodic ECGs and monitoring of pulse and lying/standing blood pressure at each visit.

There is not, as of yet, a clear consensus as to what constitutes an adequate treatment trial for anxiety disorders. Certainly, a minimum period of 4 weeks of treatment after achieving the maximally tolerated dosage should be completed before a TCA trial is considered ineffective. It also is unclear if obtaining periodic plasma drug levels will improve the precision of pharmacologic treatment. The utility of plasma TCAs levels remains controversial in the depression literature (Task Force on the Use of Laboratory Tests in Psychiatry, 1985), and substantially less research has been conducted with respect to anxiety disorders (see, for example, Ballenger et al., 1984; Marks et al., 1983; Mavissakalian, Perel, & Michelson, 1984; Thoren, Asberg, Cronholm, Jornestadt, & Traskman, 1980). It is our opinion that monitoring blood levels may be useful in selected patients who fail to respond to conventional dosages of IMI or related TCAs, both to document compliance (or lack thereof) and to ascertain if an apparently adequate oral dosage is associated with a low level of medication in the patients' systems. This practice should take into account, however, the observation that some patients respond quite nicely to small dosages of TCA, with apparently minuscule (at least by treatment of depression standards) plasma drug levels (Sweeney, Gold, Pottash, & Martin, 1983–84).

The use of divided daily dosages of TCAs and related drugs remains the standard of practice in treatment of the anxiety disorders. Divided administration of TCAs is somewhat inconvenient for patients, but permits a close titration of the dosage and may lessen side effects by lowering peaks in blood levels. All TCAs and HCAs are rather rapidly absorbed following oral ingestion, with peak blood levels obtained within several hours after intake (Perel, 1983). With the possible exception of the second-generation drug trazodone, these drugs also have a long (i.e., >16 hours) elimination half-life (Perel, 1983). This means that it takes at least 16 hours for one half of a given dose to be eliminated from the bloodstream. One practical implication of such a long half-life is that it takes 4 to 6 days, or sometimes longer, for a stable dosage to reach a steady level in the patient's blood stream (and, presumably, the brain). Another possible implication is that it may be feasible to switch some patients to once-a-day dosing, usually at bedtime, after the effective dosage has been established. Bedtime dosing facilitates compliance and may be especially helpful in patients with insomnia, a common symptom of most anxiety disorders (Insel, Gillin, Moore, Mendelson, Loewenstein, & Murphy, 1982; Reynolds, Shaw, Newton, Coble, & Kupfer, 1983). However, it should be noted that while single daily dosing is practiced widely in the treatment of depression (Thase, in press), empirical data supporting its use are, as of yet, lacking for the anxiety disorders. Accordingly, we recommend that this option be considered only in patients who have responded well to treatment at a stabilized dosage and/or for those patients with persistent insomnia. Further, the clinician should be prepared to shift the dosage back to a divided schedule if bedtime dosing is not tolerated or if it is associated with a breakthrough of symptomatology.

All TCAs and HCAs are metabolized in the liver; most compounds have metabolites that possess some degree of clinical efficacy (Perel, 1983). This is particularly true for IMI and amitriptyline, which are metabolized to desipramine and nortriptyline, respectively. Caution, therefore, is needed in prescription of these medications to patients who have impaired hepatic metabolism, and when patients are taking other medications that alter the activity of liver degradative enzymes (i.e., anticonvulsants or cimetadine).

After achieving an acceptable drug response, a period of continuation treatment generally is recommended. In practice, this may extend from 3 to 12 months. Relapses commonly occur after tapering TCA treatment (Telch, Tearnan, & Taylor, 1983); it is useful to prepare patients for such occurrences so that they are not perceived as too demoralizing. Long-term maintenance treatment would be recommended for individuals who have had several relapses following drug discontinuation, although it should be recognized that the prophylactic efficacy of ongoing TAC treatment of anxiety disorders has not yet been empirically established. Again, it is useful to reassure patients that the TCAs are not addicting or habit forming.

Mechanism(s) of Action

Despite concerted research activity over the past several years, the exact mechanism(s) of therapeutic action of TCAs and related drugs remain unknown. (This statement also applies to the antidepressant effects of these agents, despite over 20 years of research activity.) It seems likely, however, that TCAs and related drugs may be effective in different types of anxiety states, such as panic disorder and obsessive-compulsive disorder, via different mechanisms (Ballenger, 1986; Zohar & Insel, in press).

Antidepressant drugs *are* well-known to affect a variety of neurotransmitter systems in the brain and in the peripheral nervous system. Perhaps the most widely studied neurochemical effect of these drugs is their ability to block re-uptake of norepinephrine and serotonin at the synapse, resulting in at least a temporary functional increase in these neurotransmitters (see Baldessarini, 1983). This observation initially was felt to represent the mechanism underlying antidepressant efficacy of TCAs, although much subsequent research has gravely shaken the bases for this hypothesis (see, for example, Zis & Goodwin, 1982). Of potential relevance to work on obsessive-compulsive disorder (OCD), however, is the characterization of TCAs according to their relative potencies to inhibit reuptake of norepinephrine and serotonin. For example, some TCAs (i.e., nortriptyline or desipramine) are potent norepinephrine re-uptake inhibitors with weak effects on serotonin re-uptake, whereas others (i.e., amitriptyline or chlorimipramine) have preferential impact on reuptake of serotonin (Baldessarini, 1983). Serotonergic drugs, and in particular chlorimipramine, have the strongest evidence supporting efficacy in OCD (see Ananth, 1983), while at least one group has found poor response to the noradrenergic drug desipramine in patients with this condition (Zohar & Insel, in press). There is insufficient evidence at this time to attempt to correlate the relative reuptake-inhibiting potency of TCAs and related drugs with respect to efficacy in panic disorder and/or generalized anxiety states. Of note, IMI is a compound with clearly mixed re-uptake effects, by virtue of its own serotonergic effects and the noradrenergic effects of its demethylated metabolite, desipramine (Baldessarini, 1983).

Other neurochemical effects of TCAs and related drugs include anticholinergic and antihistaminic affects, as well as down-regulation of beta-adrenergic receptors (Baldessarini, 1983; Charney, Menkes, & Heninger, 1981). The former actions have not been closely linked to either antidepressant or antipanic effects, although they are closely related to selected, clinically significant side effects (discussed later). Down-regulation of beta-adrenergic receptor sensitivity may prove substantially related to the mechanism of treatment response, particularly because this effect develops slowly over the course of several weeks of treatment, and hence may parallel the timing of treatment response (Charney et al., 1981). Tricyclic treatment also generally results in decreased turnover of whole body norepinephrine (reflecting changes in output of norepinephrine from the brain and periphery), perhaps in tandem with changes in receptor sensitivity (Jimerson, 1984). This finding is particularly relevant given evidence of increased noradrenergic function in at least some types of anxiety disorders (Charney, Heninger, & Brier, 1984; Ko et al., 1983; Nesse, Cameron, Curtis, McCann, & Huber-Smith, 1984; Redmond, 1979) and the observation that some TCAs decrease the firing rate of nonadrenergic cells in the locus coeruleus, the major norepinephrine nucleus in the brain (Nyback, Walters, Aghajanian, & Roth, 1975; Svensson & Usdin, 1978). This argument is strengthened by preliminary clinical reports linking the antipanic efficacy of IMI to reductions in plasma norepinephrine metabolites (Ballenger et al., 1984; Ko et al., 1983) or decreased norepinephrine turnover (Charney & Heninger, 1985).

With respect to treatment of panic disorder and agoraphobia, it is clear that pharmacologic blocking or attenuating the occurrence of spontaneous panic attacks is necessary for effective drug treatment (Ballenger, 1986; Liebowitz, 1985). Further, such treatment also has been shown to block the occurrence of panic attacks precipitated in laboratory settings via intravenous infusion of lactate (Liebowitz, Fyer, et al., 1984; Rifkin, Klein, & Levitt, 1981). Several groups have proposed that this effect is directly linked to the earlier-noted ability of TCAs and related drugs to decrease firing of norepinephrine neurons in the locus coeruleus (Ballenger et al., 1984; Redmond, 1979). Studies are underway examining other potential physiological processes linking panic attacks with lactate infusions, which may further elucidate the mechanism(s) of action of TCAs in blocking panic attacks in response to provocative challenges (Carr & Sheehan, 1984; Shear, 1986).

Alternative mechanisms may be necessary to account for the efficacy of TCAs and related drugs in OCD and generalized (i.e., nonpanic) anxiety states. Among several possible mechanisms, Marks

(1982) has argued that drugs such as IMI are effective through a broad "patholytic" action, which would presumably include antidepressant effects as well as nonspecific sedation. This notion is indirectly supported by studies documenting high rates of depression in anxiety disorder samples (see Breier, Charney, & Heninger, 1984), reports of biological similarity between OCD and endogenous depression (Insel, Gillin, et al., 1982; Insel, Kalin, Guttmacher, Cohen, & Murphy, 1982; Insel, 1985; Rapoport et al., 1981), and recent family studies linking panic disorder and agoraphobia with melancholia (Leckman, Weissman, Merikangas, Pauls, & Prusoff, 1983; Munjack & Moss, 1981). Evidence supporting this notion includes studies correlating anti-obsessional or anti-anxiety effects with improvements in mood and depressive symptomatology, as well as Marks' own work (Marks, Stern, Mawson, Cobb, & McDonald, 1980; Marks et al., 1983) suggesting an absence of IMI effect in nondepressed patients with obsessive-compulsive disorder or agoraphobia.

Although the notion of a general patholytic effect should not be discounted in clinical practice, several lines of evidence indicate that such an effect, in and of itself, is not the sole mechanism of action. First, results of several studies indicate that at least two clinically effective antidepressants, desipramine (Zohar & Insel, in press) and the MAOI clorgyline (Insel et al., 1983) lack anti-obsessional efficacy. A simple patholytic explanation could not account for such specificity. Second, desynchrony of outcome on antipanic and antidepressant dimensions has been reported (Nurnberg & Coccaro, 1982), suggesting that for at least some patients, response can be achieved for one condition (i.e., panic disorder), but not another (i.e., depression), with a given drug treatment. Conversely, Mavissakalian, Turner, Michelson, and Jacob (1985) found that the antidepressant effects of clomipramine and placebo did not significantly differ in a controlled study of OCD, whereas clomipramine was significantly more effective than placebo on measures of obsessive and compulsive symptomatology. Third, the nonspecific sedative effects of TCAs vary widely across drugs, and one agent known to block panic attaccks, desipramine (Rifkin et al., 1981), has virtually no sedative actions (Klein et al., 1980). Moreover, psychophysiological studies suggest that successful drug treatment of panic disorder (with or without agoraphobia) often is accompanied by *increased* autonomic reactivity (Michelson & Mavissakalian, 1985). Hence, antipanic effects in such patients could not be attributed to an overall reduction in arousal level. Finally, a number of controlled studies of panic disorder and/or agoraphobia have found treatment with TCAs to be equally effective in subgroups of patients with and without prominent depressive symptomatology (Ballenger et al., 1984; Flament et al., 1985; Sheehan, Ballenger, & Jacobsen, 1980; Thoren et al., 1980; Zitrin, Klein, & Woerner, 1980; Zitrin et al., 1983).

Side Effects

The TCAs have a plethora of side effects, whose impact may range from mildly annoying to very distressing (Klein et al., 1980). Although a majority of patients with anxiety disorder can tolerate an adequate trial of TCA, attrition rates of approximately 30% to 40% during controlled clinical trials (see Telch et al., 1983) attest to the fact that these drugs are difficult for many individuals to take.

Perhaps the most interesting type of side effect encountered in treatment of anxiety disorders is a paradoxical reaction characterized by increased arousal, restlessness, worsening insomnia, and increased anxiety; patients with such reactions appear literally "wired" on TCAs. Ballenger (1986) has described this reaction as amphetamine-like, although it generally is not associated with any subjective experience of euphoria. Several investigators have estimated that about 25% of patients with panic disorder and/or agoraphobia experience such a reaction (Ballenger, 1986; Liebowitz, 1985). We also have observed this reaction in patients with generalized anxiety and obsessive-compulsive disorder. It is interesting that the frequency of the over-arousal reaction appears to be about three to five times more common in anxiety disorder patients when compared to depressed patients (cf. Klein et al., 1980). Needless to say, it is a highly uncomfortable and aversive experience and often leads patients to abruptly discontinue the TCA.

The only practical method to manage an over-arousal reaction is through dosage reduction, that is, to a level below the threshold necessary to elicit such symptomatology. In practical terms, this might mean reducing the dosage to as low as 5 or 10 mg per day of IMI or its equivalent. The dosage can then be slowly increased, by 5 to 10 mg per week, until a therapeutic effect is achieved or until the reaction is re-experienced. In the latter case, it is our experience that alternative classes of medications (i.e., MAOIs or alprazolam) should be considered instead of pursuing another TCA. There are no data from controlled studies to suggest which TCAs are more likely to elicit this reaction, although it is our experience that desipramine and, to a lesser extent, IMI are more likely to do so than more sedating drugs, such as doxepin or the nontricyclic trazodone.

A second major class of side effects are related to anticholinergic effects. Such side effects include dry mouth, blurry vision, urinary hesitancy, and constipation. A majority of patients treated with a standard TCA such as imipramine will experience at least mild anticholinergic side effects (Klein et al., 1980). In most cases, such annoying symptoms can be readily coped with by temporary dosage adjustment or by ancillary interventions (i.e., dietetic hard candy to facilitate saliva formation or use of increased fiber, fluids, and/or stool softeners for constipation). More extreme interventions, such as use of the cholinergic agonist bethanechol chloride, are sometimes needed to counter more distressing anticholinergic side effects, including urinary retention. However, availability of alternative antipanic drugs with fewer anticholinergic side effects may make substitution of a different drug a more parsimonious option. In clinical practice, demethylated TCAs (nortriptyline or desipramine) may have more favorable anticholinergic profiles than their parent drugs (amitriptyline and IMI), although in our experience patients with exquisite anticholinergic sensitivity also often cannot tolerate these agents. In such cases, trazodone may be preferred (because of its virtual lack of anticholinergic effects) or a switch to an alternative class of medication (i.e., an MAOI or alprazolam) may be in order.

Excessive daytime sedation is most clearly linked to the TCAs' antihistaminic side effects. Patients with such a reaction may report sensations such as a hangover, fatigue, heavy feelings in the limbs, or having "cotton" in their head. Again, demethylated TCAs may be better tolerated. Trazodone also is highly sedating, although this effect may not be due to an antihistaminic mechanism (Rudorfer et al., 1984). Sedative effects often can be readily dealt with by temporary dosage reduction or by consolidating the dosage of medication at bedtime.

Cardiovascular side effects are the most worrisome unwanted actions of TCAs. Principal side effects include orthostatic hypotension (i.e., a drop in blood pressure upon postural change) and altered cardiac conduction. Postural hypotension during TCA treatment is probably related to alpha-adrenergic blockade (Preskorn & Irwin, 1982). As mentioned earlier, checking blood pressure and pulse in lying (or sitting) and standing positions prior to beginning pharmacotherapy and across the course of treatment is an important safeguard. Postural drops in blood diastolic pressure greater than 10 to 20 mm Hg often associated with lightheadedness and, in extreme cases, can produce syncope (fainting spells). Dosage reduction and careful instructions regarding avoiding sudden posture changes usually suffice in milder cases; patients with more marked orthostatic blood pressure changes may need to be withdrawn from the medication and treated with an alternative approach. Trazodone treatment also is associated with lightheadedness, although its effects on blood pressure may be less prominent (Rudorfer et al. 1984).

Most TCAs and related drugs cause a mild degree of tachycardia, which usually is benign and does not require dosage modification (Klein et al., 1980). Palpitations also may be experienced, although these drugs curiously possess at least some degree of antiarrhythmic action. However, TCAs also delay cardiac conduction and can produce prolongations of the P-R interval, causing a first-degree heart block. Preexisting cardiac conduction problems represent a relative contraindication for therapy with TCAs; ECGs should be monitored serially in all older patients. Doxepin initially was felt to be a more benign TCA with respect to cardiovascular effects, although more recent work has led to revision of this view (see Luchins, 1983). Trazodone may have fewer clinically significant effects on cardiac conduction (Rudorfer et al., 1984), although even it is not without some adverse effects (Janowsky et al., 1983).

Miscellaneous effects of TCAs include goose bumps, weight gain, erectile or orgasmic dysfunctions, excessive sweating, headaches, lowering of the seizure threshold, myoclonic jerks, and nightmares. Allergic reactions occur in about 1% to 5% of cases treated, and may take the form of a skin rash and/or liver inflammation and jaundice (Klein et al., 1980). Treatment with TCAs, as with most any drug, rarely can affect bone marrow production, leading to decreased levels of red and/or white blood cells.

Clinical studies indicate that the "second-generation" heterocyclic antidepressants may have somewhat more favorable side-effect profiles (Rudorfer et al., 1984). However, as experience with these drugs increases, reports of other troublesome reactions have proliferated. For example, maprotiline is associated with a higher-than-expected incidence of seizures (see Dessain, Schatzberg, Woods, & Cole, 1986), whereas amoxapine, by virtue of dopamine-blocking actions, can cause galactorrhea and extrapyramidal symptoms (and, at least theoretically, tardive dyskinesia) (Rudorfer et al., 1984). Trazodone, while having a more favourable overall side-effect profile, recently has been associated with priapism, a painful and potentially irreversible erection of the penis (Pass, 1985; Raskin, 1985).

REVIEW OF THE RESEARCH

Panic Disorder and Agoraphobia

Results of both open and controlled studies indicate that between 70% and 90% of patients able to take IMI experience significant improvements, as reflected by cessation or diminution of panic attacks (Ballenger, 1986; Liebowitz, 1985). Six of seven published placebo-controlled trials have documented the superiority of IMI over inactive pharmacological treatment in patients with panic attacks and/or agoraphobia (Klein, 1964, 1967; Mavissakalian & Michelson, 1986; Sheehan et al., 1980; Zitrin et al., 1980; Zitrin et al., 1983). The seventh trial (Marks et al., 1983) found no advantage for IMI (mean dosage: 158 mg/day at Week 14) over placebo in agoraphobics also receiving treatment with systematic self-directed exposure. Although the authors of this report proposed that the lack of an antiphobic effect may have been due to the fact that patients in their sample were not clinically depressed (i.e., no chance for a general patholytic effect), other investigators have suggested that inadequate dosage of IMI and/or methodological factors may have obscured detection of a significant drug effect (Matuzas & Glass, 1983). Nevertheless, the proportion of studies demonstrating a significant difference favoring IMI over placebo (6/7) compares favorably with the literature concerning IMI's antidepressant response (cf. Klein et al., 1980).

Several groups have compared IMI to alternative active treatments. Sheehan et al. (1980) found IMI to be roughly equal to the MAOI phenelzine sulfate (both drugs were superior to placebo), although phenelzine appeared to be somewhat better tolerated in this study. Munjack et al. (1985) found IMI to be equivalent to propranolol hydrochloride, a beta-blocker, in a randomized, open-label crossover design. McNair and Kahn (1981) found significant antipanic (but not antiphobic) effects favoring IMI over chlordiazepoxide hydrochloride in agoraphobics; these findings were extended in a subsequent report including a more heterogeneous sample of anxious outpatients (Kahn et al., 1986).

Results of three published clinical trials also support the efficacy of clomipramine (CMI) over placebo (Amin, Ban, Pecknold, & Klinger, 1977; Escovar & Lanelbloom, 1976; Karabanow, 1977). However, these older reports generally involve mixed diagnostic samples, including some patients with social phobias or OCD. Gloger, Grunhaus, Birmacher, and Troudart (1981), studying a more homogeneous group of patients meeting DSM-III (American Psychiatric Association, 1980) criteria for panic disorder ($n = 8$) or agoraphobia ($n = 12$), reported a 75% response rate to clomipramine in an open clinical trial. Further, Allsopp, Cooper, and Poole (1984) found clomipramine to be somewhat more effective than diazepam after 12 weeks of treatment in a small double-blind trial of patients with agoraphobia or social phobia.

There are no published placebo-controlled trials examining the efficacy of other FDA approved antidepressants in panic disorder or agoraphobia. A spate of clinical reports (see Ballenger, 1986) suggests that each of the TCAs and maprotiline and trazodone may be capable of blocking panic attacks. It is interesting that buproprion, a nonsedative HCA without marked adrenergic effects (no longer available in the United States), was not found to be effective in one small ($n = 13$) single-blind trial (Sheehan, Davidson, Manschreck, & Van Wyck Fleet, 1983).

Generalized Anxiety and Mixed Anxiety-Depression Syndromes

Few studies have specifically addressed the efficacy of TCA treatment in patients meeting DSM-III criteria for generalized anxiety disorder (GAD). One recently published report, summarizing a multicenter collaborative study, compared IMI (mean dose: 122.5 mg/day at Week 8) against chlordiazepoxide hydrochloride (Librium®) and placebo (Kahn et al., 1986). The outpatient sample ($n = 223$) was heterogeneous and "primarily anxious," as classified by DSM-III (APA, 1980) and standard clinical rating scales. Results of "primarily depressed" patients were reported separately (Lipman et al., 1986). Overall results favored IMI over chlordiazepoxide and placebo on a number of measures; such effects were independent of pretreatment ratings of anxiety and depression. Further, when 35 patients with possible panic or agoraphobic syndromes were removed from the analysis to constitute a sample more analogous with GAD, the same general pattern of results emerged (Kahn et al., 1986). However, IMI's effects on one depression measure (Raskin scale) and physician's ratings of Global Improvement were slightly less robust after exclusion of panic/agoraphobia cases.

A number of clinical trials have examined the effectiveness of TCAs, particularly doxepin, in outpatients with mixed anxiety/depression syndromes (see Appleton & Davis, 1980; Klein et al., 1980). Overall, doxepin was found to be superior to placebo in six out of six reports, and equivalent to chlordiazepoxide or diazepam in 19 out of 19 studies reviewed. Although TCAs may have somewhat greater side effects in such samples (Haskil, Gambill, Gardos, McNair, & Fisher, 1978; Kleber, 1979), these results support the use of TCAs in patients with mixed anxiety/depression syndromes. Further, the report of Kahn et al. (1986) suggests that therapeutic effects on generalized anxiety are not limited to patients with prominent depressive symptoms.

Several reports also suggest that low-dose combinations of TCAs and either benzodiazepines or antipsychotics are effective in mixed anxiety/depression syndromes (see Klein et al., 1980). Although some evidence suggests that such combinations may have more rapid or complete responses (i.e., Sussex Clinical

Trials Group, 1985), it is our opinion that the risks of combining of these drugs (i.e., tardive dyskinesia or acute pyramidal syndromes with neuroleptics and risk of dependence developing with benzodiazepines) can be avoided, in most cases, by simply using larger doses or an alternative TCA or HCA.

The interest in doxepin as a possible "drug of choice" for anxiety/depression reflects both the sedating nature of this compound and marketing strategies of its manufacturers. Less sedating TCAs also have been shown to have effects that match or surpass benzodiazepines (Kahn et al., 1986; Kleber, 1979). More recently, considerable attention has been devoted to the sedating second-generation drug trazodone in this clinical population (Davis & Vogel, 1981).

In retrospect, it is unclear what proportion of patients with mixed anxiety/depression would meet current criteria for GAD, major depression, or both diagnoses. This distinction may have more significance for research than clinical practice, although there are some conflicting reports concerning the prognostic significance of anxiety features in depression. Several studies in the affective disorders literature suggest that presence of features of generalized anxiety may predict a poorer response to TCAs when compared to uncomplicated depressions (see Thase, in press). These observations are supported by results of a recent open clinical study (Grunhaus, Rabin, & Greden, 1986), in which patients with panic disorder *and* major depression responded more poorly to TCAs than patients with only depression. It is curious that other groups have found that the presence of panic attacks (as a symptom of depression, not as a concurrent disorder) predicts favorable response to antidepressant treatment (Liebowitz, Quitkin et al., 1984). It may be that a full anxiety disorder syndrome antedating onset of depression conveys negative prognostic significance, whereas panic attacks as an isolated feature of the depressive episode is a positive predictive sign. This confusing area certainly requires further study.

Obsessive–Compulsive Disorder

Obsessive–compulsive disorder (OCD) historically has been one of the most refractory conditions in the era of psychotropic drugs (Goodwin, Guze, & Robins, 1969). In practice, it is not uncommon to interview patients with OCD who have been subjected to multiple unsuccessful treatment trials with benzodiazepines, neuroleptics, lithium, and/or numerous antidepressants. Among the TCAs, the most encouraging results have been reported for clomipramine (CMI), which unfortunately has not yet been approved for use in this country by the FDA.

Early open clinical studies suggested that CMI, in dosages similar to those used in treat depression, may exert specific effects on both obsessions and compulsions in patients previously refractory to other treatments (see Ananth, 1983). More recently, a series of double-blind clinical trials have confirmed these observations (Ananth, Pecknold, Van Den Steen, & Engelsmann, 1981; Flament et al., 1985; Insel et al., 1983; Marks et al., 1980; Montgomery, 1980; Thoren et al., 1980; Volavka, Neziroglu, & Yaryura-Tobias, 1985; Zohar & Insel, in press). All studies published to date utilizing a placebo comparison group have documented significant effects favoring CMI after 4 to 6 weeks of treatment (Flament et al., 1985; Insel et al., 1983; Marks et al., 1980; Montgomery, 1980; Thoren et al., 1980). Such results are striking in that more robust drug effects often are apparent over several months of continued treatment (Mavissakalian et al., 1985; Stroebel, Szarek, & Glueck, 1984). Pooling results across these studies, significant improvement is achieved by at least two thirds of patients receiving CMI. Further, available results suggest efficacy in most clinical forms of OCD, including patients with obsessions only, as well as those with rituals but not obsessions (Thoren et al., 1980).

Several groups have contrasted CMI against other TCAs, such as amitriptyline (Ananth et al., 1981), imipramine (Mavissakalian et al., 1985; Volavka et al., 1985), nortriptyline (Thoren et al., 1980), and desipramine (Insel, Mueller, Alterman, Linnoila, & Murphy, 1985; Zohar & Insel, in press). Insel et al. (1983) also contrasted CMI against clorgyline, an experimental MAOI. Although these studies generally suggest that some patients benefit from treatment with IMI, amitriptyline, desipramine, or nortriptyline, response rates to these drugs appear to be inferior to CMI. Further, clorgyline was found to be relatively ineffective.

In keeping with the hypothesis of a serotonergic basis underlying CMI's efficacy in OCD, a number of reports have emerged suggesting anti-obsessional effects of treatments that enhance serotonergic tone, including lithium (Stern & Jenike, 1983), L-tryptophan (Yaryura-Tobias & Bhagavan, 1977), and trazodone (Prasad, 1984b, 1985). Such studies require replication using placebo-controlled designs. Zimelidine, which also is a potent serotonin re-uptake blocker, has been reported to be effective in an open clinical trial (Kahn, Westenberg, & Jolles, 1984) and under double-blind conditions (Prasad, 1984a). However, Insel and associates (1985) failed to demonstrate a clinically significant effect for zimelidine in a placebo-controlled, crossover study of 16 patients with OCD, despite documenting a significant drug effect on cerebrospinal fluid levels of 5-hydroxyindoleacetic acid, the principal metabolite of serotonin. Further, zimelidine nonresponders subsequently improved with treatment with CMI.

As discussed earlier, Marks (1982) has argued that the anti-obsessional effects of CMI and other TCAs may be related to antidepressant effects. Marks et al. (1980) found that CMI was effective only in OCD patients with prominent depressive symptoms. Mavissakalian et al. (1985) similarly observed a substantial covariation between improvements in depressive and obsessive–compulsive symptoms. However, a number of investigators, including Mavissakalian et al. (1985) have subsequently demonstrated that non-depressed patients with OCD can respond to CMI (Flament et al., 1985; Insel et al., 1983; Thoren et al., 1980; Volavka et al., 1985).

Social and Simple Phobias

Few empirical studies have been published to suggest that TCAs have a prominent role in treatment of specific phobias. For example, Liebowitz, Gorman, Fyer, and Klein (1985) concluded in a recent review that "there is a paucity of studies of tricyclics in social phobics, (p. 734)" after excluding those trials that involved patients with panic or agoraphobia. As reviewed earlier, Allsopp et al. (1984) found CMI to be superior to diazepam in their sample with social phobia or agoraphobia, although the relative efficacy of treatment in social phobics was not separately reported. Imipramine also may be helpful in treatment of school phobia, although this condition has been suggested to be an age-appropriate expression of agoraphobia (see Klein et al., 1980). In an influential series of studies, Zitrin and associates (Zitrin, Klein, & Woerner, 1978; Zitrin et al. 1980, 1983) reported a distinct lack of efficacy for IMI in the treatment of patients with simple or specific phobias; the simultaneous presence of spontaneous panic attacks (i.e., a mixed phobia presentation) was necessary for the drug to convey therapeutic value in such patients. Thus, the so-called "antiphobic" effects of TCAs may relate more specifically to two components, improvements that follow successful blockade of panic and relief of generalized anxiety, rather than actual direct effects on phobias.

Posttraumatic Stress Disorder

No controlled clinical trials have, as of yet, been published concerning the efficacy of TCAs in posttraumatic stress disorder (PTSD). A number of clinical reports suggest that TCAs may be symptomatically helpful, particularly in patients with depressive features, panic attacks, or night terrors (see Burstein, 1984; Ettedgui & Bridges, 1985). Results of one recent retrospective study (n = 17) suggest that a TCA treatment of PTSD may effect rates of improvement comparable to that seen in treatment of panic disorder (Falcon, Ryan, Chamberlain, & Curtis, 1985).

CASE ILLUSTRATIONS

Case #1

Mr. K, a 41-year-old unemployed former schoolteacher, was referred for evaluation by a psychiatrist in private practice. He had been in treatment for much of the past 12 years for generalized anxiety, depression, somatization, and a "cardiac" phobia. The referring doctor felt that his condition was intractable and questioned whether Mr. K's progressively worsening condition might be associated with some sort of secondary gain. Over the years, Mr. K had been treated with a variety of benzodiazepine tranquilizers and antipsychotic drugs. Past attempts to treat his condition with amitriptyline and doxepin had not been successful, principally due to anticholinergic side effects. At the time of referral, he was taking haloperidol (5 mg b.i.d.) and trazodone (150 mg/day) without clear benefit.

Mr. K reported his condition dated to an initial "anxiety attack," experienced in the classroom in front of his students. He vividly recalled his heart pounding in his chest, intense psychic anxiety, a choking sensation, tingling in his limbs, and the clear sense that he was dying of a heart attack. The onset of this episode shortly followed his mother's death from a myocardial infarction. The episodes began to occur with increasing regularity; each was severe and each new episode added to his growing conviction that he had heart disease. Detailed and frequent medical assessments proved negative, but he could not be reassured. After several years, he left his teaching position, partly in response to growing embarrassment over having to leave the classroom repeatedly in a state of panic. He developed more free-floating anxiety symptoms, as a consequence of anticipation of the unpredictable, intense attacks. Psychotherapy helped him see connections between his own fears and his mother's death, but did not reduce the frequency of these attacks. He was not able to succeed at a series of sales jobs, as he frequently missed appointments due to the attacks. The family's financial status suffered and he felt increasingly frustrated, pessimistic, and demoralized. His wife assumed many of his out-of-the-house duties and she had to return to work to support the family. Mr. K frequently contemplated suicide as a means of ending his suffering.

At the time of referral, he was virtually housebound and met DSM-III (APA, 1980) criteria for both major depression and agoraphobia with panic attacks. He reported having at least one attack each day, with perpetual worry over when the next attack would occur. He also had drug-induced Parkinsonism, with tremors and bradykinesia. His energy level and Parkinsonian side effects improved simply by discontinuing the haloperidol and trazodone. Therapy with desipramine, 25 mg/day, was selected given his prior sensitivity to anticholinergic effects. Desipramine was increased slowly, by 25 mg per week, until near complete blockade of panic attacks was achieved on 100 mg/day. Suicidal ideation abated and his sleep, mood, and appetite normalized. He was able to obtain a new sales job 2 months into treatment.

Mr. K remained preoccupied with his heart, however, and these fears heightened when he would experience an occasional, milder panic attack. Cognitive-behavioral therapy proved useful in helping him begin to test and challenge these fears. Mr. K continued to improve slowly, rebuilding his professional and interpersonal life. After 9 months of pharmacotherapy, he asked to come off the medication to "test" if he was fully recovered. The chances of a relapse were discussed, and he opted to discontinue the desipramine. During the next year, he experienced one clear-cut panic attack, with an associated increase in his concern about his heart. A booster therapy session helped him to place this episode into perspective and he remained off medication.

Case #2

Mrs. H, a 35-year-old homemaker, presented for treatment reporting persistent, intrusive thoughts and images about her deceased brother. Mrs. H described, with some embarrassment, that she experienced nearly continuous thoughts and images about having had intercourse and oral sex with her brother. She related that he had died in a car accident 4 years earlier and that they had never, *ever* actually had sexual relations. Despite realizing that these thoughts were untrue, she could not make them go away. In fact, trying to forbid them seemed to increase their frequency. The thoughts had been increasing in frequency and intensity for the past 2 years. She also had begun to worry that she would develop similar thoughts about her children. Twice-weekly psychotherapy and diazepam was not helpful; Mrs. H actively resisted the interpretation that her obsessions reflected forbidden, unconscious desires.

Mrs. H met DSM-III criteria for obsessive–compulsive disorder. An initial trial of IMI, in doses up to 250 mg/day, proved somewhat helpful in lessening her overall distress and improving sleep, but did not affect the frequency or intensity of the obsessions. Arrangements were made for Mrs. H to see a consultant in Canada, where treatment with clomipramine is approved. A complete response was achieved after 10 weeks of treatment with CMI (200 mg/day). Mrs. H has remained on CMI at this dosage for the past year. She has not been interested in tapering the CMI due to fear of having a relapse.

Case #3

Ms. S, a 22-year-old college student, sought treatment because of progressively worsening "nervousness." She described herself as having always been shy and high-strung. Moreover, during the past year, as college graduation approached, she reported increasing tension, apprehension, autonomic arousal (diarrhea and sweaty palms), and insomnia. She reported having problems concentrating at school and an unexplainable fear that she would die in her sleep. She found that two or three beers temporarily helped, although she recognized that this was not a useful solution, as her father was an alcoholic.

Ms. S. met DSM-III criteria for generalized anxiety disorder. She also appeared mildly depressed, but her mood state clearly was more anxious. Her history revealed two episodes of panic attacks, which was insufficient to diagnosis as a full-blown panic disorder. Medical work-up, including thyroid function studies, was normal. Treatment options were discussed and she favored a pharmacologic approach. She agreed to abstain from alcohol. Imipramine was selected instead of a benzodiazepine because of Ms. S's fears of becoming addicted. She was not able to tolerate an initial starting dose of 50 mg at bedtime due to increased insomnia, tachycardia, and light-headedness. A reduced dosage of 10 mg b.i.d. was well-tolerated. Progressive increases of 10 to 20 mg/week similarly were well tolerated, so that by Week 6 of treatment Ms. S was taking 100 mg each day. At this point, she reported feeling much better. Generalized anxiety had lessened and her sleep and concentration had returned to normal. Pharmacotherapy was continued for 4 additional months, then tapered and discontinued without recurrence of symptoms. Ms. S remained fairly well for nearly 2 years, at which point she re-experienced anxiety and depressive symptoms during a time of stress at work. A second course of IMI treatment again was effective.

CONCLUDING REMARKS

Trycyclic antidepressants have emerged as effective pharmacologic treatments of a range of anxiety disorders. These medications (particularly IMI and CMI) are useful as a primary treatment, or in combination with psychosocial interventions, for a majority of individuals with panic disorder, agoraphobia, generalized anxiety, and obsessive–compulsive disorder. Further study is needed to confirm their utility in posttraumatic stress disorder and social phobia. The only anxiety disorders for which TCAs do not appear useful are the specific (simple) phobias.

It would be premature to assert that the

TCAs are the treatment of choice for these conditions. They have documented efficacy and little abuse potential, but do have multiple annoying side effects and can be lethal when taken in overdose. A substantial amount of research is yet needed to establish the relative merits and risks of TCAs versus other effective pharmacologic treatments. Additional studies also are needed to further compare treatment with TCAs and promising psychological approaches, both alone and in combination with pharmacotherapy.

REFERENCES

Allsopp, L. F., Cooper, G. L., & Poole, P. H. (1984). Clomipramine and diazepam in the treatment of agoraphobia and social phobia in general practice. *Current Medical Research and Opinion, 9,* 64–70.

American Psychiatric Association. (1980). *Diagnostic and Statistical manual of mental disorders* (3rd ed.). Washington, DC: Author.

Amin, M. M., Ban, T. A., Pecknold, J. C., & Klinger, A. (1977). Clomipramine (Anafranil) and behavior therapy in obsessive–compulsive and phobic disorders. *Journal of International Medical Research, 5* (5, Suppl.), 33–37.

Ananth, J. (1983). Clomipramine in obsessive–compulsive disorder: A Review. *Psychosomatics, 24,* 723–727.

Ananth, J., Pecknold, J. C., Van Den Steen, N., & Engelsmann, F. (1981). Double-blind comparative study of clomipramine and amitriptyline in obsessive neurosis. *Progress in Neuropsychopharmacology, 5,* 257–262.

Appleton, W. S., & Davis, J. M. (1980). *Practical clinical psychopharmacology* (2nd ed.). Baltimore, MD: Williams & Wilkins.

Baldessarini, R. J. (1983). *Biomedical aspects of depression.* Washington, DC: American Psychiatric Press.

Ballenger, J. C. (1986). Pharmacotherapy of the panic disorders. *Journal of Clinical Psychiatry, 47* (6, Suppl.), 27–32.

Ballenger, J. C., Peterson, G. A., Laraia, M., Hucek, A., Lake, C. R., Jimerson, D., Cox, D. J., Trockman, C., Shipe, J. R., Jr., & Wilkinson, C. (1984). A study of plasma catecholamines in agoraphobia and relationship of serum tricyclic levels to therapeutic response. In J. C. Ballenger (Ed.), *Biology of agoraphobia* (pp. 27–63). Washington, DC: American Psychiatric Press.

Barchas, J. D., Berger, P. A., Ciaranello, R. D., & Elliott, G. R. (1977). *Psychopharmacology.* New York: Oxford University Press.

Boulenger, J. P., Uhde, T. W., Wolf, E. A., III., & Post, R. M. (1984). Increased sensitivity to caffeine in patients with panic disorders. *Archives of General Psychiatry, 41,* 1067–1072.

Breier, A., Charney, D. S., & Heninger, G. R. (1984). Major depression in patients with agoraphobia and panic disorder. *Archives of General Psychiatry, 41,* 1129–1135.

Burstein, A. (1984). Treatment of post-traumatic stress disorder with imipramine. *Psychosomatics, 25,* 681–687.

Carr, D. B., & Sheehan, D. V. (1984). Evidence that panic disorder has a metabolic cause. In J. C. Ballenger (Ed.), *Biology of agoraphobia* (pp. 99–111). Washington, DC: American Psychiatric Press.

Charney, D. S., & Heninger, G. R. (1985). Noradrenergic function and the mechanism of action of antianxiety treatment: II. The effect of long-term imipramine treatment. *Archives of General Psychiatry, 42,* 473–481.

Charney, D. S., Heninger, G. R., & Breier, A. (1984). Noradrenergic function in panic anxiety. *Archives of General Psychiatry, 41,* 751–763.

Charney, D. S., Menkes, D. B., & Heninger, G. R. (1981). Receptor sensitivity and the mechanism of action of antidepressant treatment. *Archives of General Psychiatry, 38,* 1160–1180.

Coryell, W., Noyes, R., Jr., & House, J. D. (1986). Mortality among outpatients with anxiety disorders. *American Journal of Psychiatry, 143,* 508–510.

Davis, J. M., & Vogel, C. (1981). Efficacy of trazodone: Data from European and United States studies. *Journal of Clinical Psychiatry, 1,* (6, Suppl.), 27–34.

Dessain, E. C., Schatzberg, A. F., Woods, B. T., & Cole, J. O. (1986). Maprotiline treatment in depression. *Archives of General Psychiatry, 20,* 680–685.

Escovar, J., & Lanelbloom, P. (1976). Treatment of phobic neurosis with chlomipramine: A controlled clinical trial. *Current Therapy and Research, 20,* 680–685.

Ettedgui, E., & Bridges, M. (1985). Posttraumatic stress disorder. *Psychiatric Clinics of North America, 8,* 89–103.

Falcon, S., Ryan, C., Chamberlain, K., & Curtis, G. (1985). Tricyclics: Possible treatment for posttraumatic stress disorder. *Journal of Clinical Psychiatry, 463,* 385–389.

Flament, M. F., Rapoport, J. L., Berg, C. J., Sceery, W., Kilts, C., Mellstrom, B., & Linnoila, M. (1985). Clomipramine treatment of childhood obsessive–compulsive disorder. *Archives of General Psychiatry, 42*, 977–983.

Gloger, S., Grunhaus, L., Birmacher, B., & Troudart, T. (1981). Treatment of spontaneous panic attacks with chlomipramine. *American Journal of Psychiatry, 1383*, 1215–1217.

Goodwin, D. W., Guze, S. B.., & Robins, E. (1969). Follow-up studies in obsessional neurosis. *Archives of General Psychiatry, 20*, 182–187.

Grunhaus, L., Rabin, D., & Greden, J. F. (1986). Simultaneous panic and depressive disorder: Response to antidepressant treatments. *Journal of Clinical Psychiatry, 47*, 4–7.

Haskell, D. S., Gambill, J. D.; Gardos, G., McNair, D. M., & Fisher, S. (1978). Doxepin or diazepam for anxious and anxious-depressed outpatients? *Journal of Clinical Psychiatry, 39*, 135–139.

Insel, T. R. (1985). Obsessive–compulsive disorder. *Psychiatric Clinics of North America, 8*, 105–117.

Insel, T. R., Gillin, J. C., Moore, A., Mendelson, W. B., Loewenstein, R. J. & Murphy, D. L. (1982). The sleep of patients with obsessive–compulsive disorder. *Archives of General Psychiatry, 39*, 1372–1377.

Insel, T. R., Kalin, N. H., Guttmacher, L. B., Cohen, R. M., & Murphy, D. L. (1982). The dexamethasone suppression test in patients with primary obsessive–compulsive disorder. *Psychiatry Research, 6*, 270–275.

Insel, T. R., Mueller, E. A., Alterman, I., Linnoila, M., & Murphy, D. L. (1985). Obsessive–compulsive disorder and serotonin: Is there a connection? *Biological Psychiatry, 203*, 1174–1188.

Insel, T. R., Murphy, D. L., Cohen, R. M., Alterman, I., Kilts, C., & Linnoila, M. (1983). Obsessive–compulsive disorder: A double-blind trial of clomipramine and clorgyline. *Archives of General Psychiatry, 40*, 605–612.

Janowsky, D., Curtis, G., Ziscook, S., Kuhn, K., Resovsky, K., & LeWinter, M. (1983). Trazodone-aggrevated ventricular arrhythmias. *Journal of Clinical Pshychopharmacology, 3*, 372–376.

Jimerson, D. C. (1984). Neurotransmitter hypotheses of depression: Research update. *Psychiatric Clinics of North America, 7*, 563–573.

Kahn, R. J., McNair, D. M., Lipman, R. S., Covi, L., Rickels, K., Downing, R., Fisher, S., & Frankenthaler, L. M. (1986). Imipramine and chlodiazepoxide in depressive and anxiety disorders: II. Efficacy in anxious outpatients. *Archives of General Psychiatry, 43*, 79–85.

Kahn, R. S., Westenberg, H. G. M., & Jolles, J. (1984). Zimeldine treatment of obsessive–compulsive disorder. *Acta Psychiatrica Scandinavica, 69*, 259–261.

Karabanow, O. (1977). Double-blind controlled study in phobias and obsessions. *Journal of International Medical Research, 5*, (5, Suppl.), 42–48.

Kleber, R. J. (1979). A double-blind comparative study of desipramine hydrochloride and diazepam in the control of mixed anxiety/depression symptomatology. *Journal of Clinical Psychiatry*, 40, 165–170.

Klein, D. F. (1964). Delineation of two drug-responsive anxiety syndromes. *Psychopharmacologia, 5*, 397–408.

Klein, D. F. (1967). Importance of psychiatric diagnosis in prediction of clinical drug effects. *Archives of General Psychiatry, 16*, 118–126.

Klein, D. F., Gittelman, R., Quitkin, F., & Rifkin, A. (1980). *Diagnosis and treatment of psychiatric disorders (2nd ed.).* Baltimore, MD: Williams & Wilkins.

Ko, G. N., Elsworth, J. D., Roth, R. H., Rifkin, B. G., Leigh, H., & Redmond, E., Jr. (1983) Panic-induced elevation of plasma MHPG in phobic-anxious patients: Effects of clonidine or imipramine. *Archives of General Psychiatry, 40*, 425-430.

Kuhn, R. (1958). The treatment of depressive states with G-22355 (imipramine hydrochloride). *American Journal of Psychiatry, 115*, 459–464.

Leckman, J. F., Weissman, M. M., Merikangas, K. R., Pauls, D. L., & Prusoff, B. A. (1983). Panic disorder increases risk of major depression, alcoholism, panic, and phobic disorders in affectively ill families. *Archives of General Psychiatry, 40*, 1055–1060.

Liebowitz, M. R. (1985). Imipramine in the treatment of panic disorder and its complications. *Psychiatric Clinics of North America, 8*, 37–47.

Liebowitz, M. R., Fyer, A. J., Gorman, J. M., Dillon, D., Appleby, I. L., Levy, G., Anderson, S., Levitt, M., Palij, M., Davies, S. O., & Klein, D. F. (1984). Lactate provocation of panic attacks. *Archives of General Psychiatry, 41*, 764–770.

Liebowitz, M. R., Gorman, J. M., Fyer, A. J., & Klein, D. F. (1985). Social phobia. *Archives of General Psychiatry, 42*, 729–736.

Liebowitz, M. R., Quitkin, F. M., Stewart, J. W., McGrath, P. J., Harrison, W., Rabkin, J., Tricamo, E., Markowitz, J. S., & Klein, D. F.

(1984). Phenelzine *v* imipramine in atypical depression. *Archives of General Psychiatry, 41,* 669–677.

Lipman, R. S., Covi, L., Rickels, K., McNair, D. M., Downing, R., Kahn, R. J., Lasseter, V. K., & Faden, V. (1986). Imipramine and chlordiazepoxide in depressive and anxiety disorders: I. Efficacy in depressed outpatients. *Archives of General Psychiatry, 43,* 68–78.

Luchins, D. J. (1983). Review of clinical and animal studies comparing the cardiovascular effects of doxepin and other tricyclic antidepressants. *American Journal of Psychiatry, 140,* 1006–1009.

Marks, I. (1982). Are there anticompulsive or antiphobic drugs? Review of the evidence. *Psychopharmacology Bulletin, 18,* 78–84.

Marks, I. M., Gray, S., Cohen, D., Hill, R., Mawson, D., Ramm, E., & Stern R. S. (1983). Imipramine and brief therapist-aided exposure in agoraphobics having self-exposure homework. *Archives of General Psychiatry, 40,* 153–162.

Marks, I. M., Stern, R. S., Mawson, D., Cobb, J., & McDonald, R., (1980). Clomipramine and exposure for obsessive–compulsive rituals. *British Journal of Psychiatry, 136,* 1–25.

Matuzas, W., & Glass, R. M. (1983). Treatment of agoraphobia and panic attacks. *Archives of General Psychiatry, 40,* 220–222.

Mavissakalian, M., & Michelson, L. (1986). Agoraphobia: Relative and combined effectiveness of therapist-assisted *in vivo* exposure and imipramine. *Journal of Clinical Psychiatry, 47,* 117–122.

Mavissakalian, M., Perel, J. M., & Michelson, L. (1984). The relationship of plasma imipramine and *N*-desmethylimipramine to improvement in agoraphobia. *Journal of Clinical Psychiatry, 4,* 36–40.

Mavissakalian, M., Turner, S. M., Michelson, L., & Jacob, R. (1985). Tricyclic antidepressants in obsessive–compulsive disorder: Antiobsessional or antidepressant agents? II. *American Journal of Psychiatry, 142,* 572–576.

McNair, D. M., & Kahn, R. J. (1981). Imipramine compared with a benzodiazepine for agoraphobia. In D. F. Klein & J. G. Rabkin (Eds.), *Anxiety: New research and changing concepts* (pp. 69–80). New York: Raven Press.

Michelson, L., & Mavissakalian, M. (1985). Psychophysiological outcome of behavioral and pharmacologic treatments of agoraphobia. *Journal of Consulting and Clinical Psychology, 53,* 229–236.

Montgomery, S. A. (1980). Clomipramine in obsessional neurosis: A placebo controlled trial. *Pharmaceutical Medicine, 1,* 189–192.

Munjack, D. J., & Moss, H. B. (1981). Affective disorder and alcoholism in families of agoraphobics. *Archives of General Psychiatry, 38,* 869–871.

Munjack, D. J., Rebal, R., Shaner, R., Staples, F., Braun, R., & Leonard, M. (1985). Imipramine versus propranolol for treatment of panic attacks: A pilot study. *Comprehensive Psychiatry, 26,* 80–89.

Nesse, R. M., Cameron, O. G., Curtis, G. C., McCann, D. S., & Huber-Smith, M. J. (1984). Adrenergic function in patients with panic anxiety. *Archives of General Psychiatry, 41,* 771–776.

Nurnberg, H. G., & Coccaro, E. F. (1982). Response of panic disorder and resistance of depression to imipramine. *American Journal of Psychiatry, 139,* 1060–1062.

Nyback, H. V., Walters, J. R., Aghajanian, G. K., & Roth, R. H. (1975). Tricyclic antidepressants: Effects of the firing rate of brain noradrenergic neurons. *European Journal of Pharmacology, 32,* 302–312.

Patt, N. (1985). More on trazodone and priapism. *American Journal of Psychiatry, 142,* 783–784.

Perel, J. M. (1983). Tricyclic antidepressant plasma levels, pharmacokinetics, and clinical outcome. In L. Grinspoon (ed.), *Psychiatry Update, Vol. II* (pp. 491–511). Washington, DC: American Psychiatric Press.

Prasad, A. (1984a). A double blind study of imipramine versus zimelidine in treatment of obsessive compulsive neurosis. *Pharmacopsychiatry, 17,* 61–62.

Prasad, A. (1985). Efficacy of trazodone as an antiobsessional agent. *Pharmacology Biochemistry & Behavior, 22,* 347–348.

Prasad, A. J. (1984b). Obsessive–compulsive disorder and trazodone. *American Journal of Psychiatry, 141,* 612–613.

Preskorn, S. H., & Irwin, H. A. (1982). Toxicity of tricyclic antidepressants: Kinetics, mechanism, intervention: A review. *Journal of Clinical Psychiatry, 43,* 151–156.

Rapoport, J., Elkins, R., Langer, D. H., Sceery, W., Buchsbaum, M. S., Gillin, J. C., Murphy, D. L., Zahn, T. P., Lake, C. R., Ludlow, C., & Mendelson, W. (1981). Childhood obsessive–compulsive disorder. *American Journal of Psychiatry, 138,* 1545–1554.

Raskin, D. E. (1985). Trazodone and priapism. *American Journal of Psychiatry, 142,* 142–143.

Redmond, D. E., Jr. (1979). New and old evidence for the involvement of a brain norepinephrine system in anxiety. In W. E. Fann (Ed.), *Phenomenology and treatment of anxiety* (pp. 153–203). New York: Spectrum Press.

Reynolds, C. F., III, Shaw, D. F., Newton, T. F., Coble, P. A., & Kupfer, D. J. (1983). EEG sleep in outpatients with generalized anxiety: A preliminary comparison with depressed outpatients. *Psychiatry Research, 8,* 81–89.

Rifkin, A., Klein, D. F., & Levitt, M. (1981). Blockade by imipramine or desipramine of panic induced by sodium lactate. *American Journal of Psychiatry, 138,* 676–677.

Rudorfer, M. V., Golden, R. N., & Potter, W. Z. (1984). Second generation anti-depressants *Psychiatric Clinics of North American, 7,* 519–547.

Shear, M. K. (1986). Pathophysiology of panic: A review of pharmacologic provocative tests and naturalistic monitoring data. *Journal of Clinical Psychiatry, 47,* (6, Suppl.), 18–26.

Sheehan, D. V., Ballenger, J., & Jacobsen, G. (1980). Treatment of endogenous anxiety with phobic, hysterical and hypochondriacal symptoms. *Archives of General Psychiatry, 37,* 51–59.

Sheehan, D. V., Davidson, J., Manschreck, T., & Van Wyck Fleet, J., (1983). Lack of efficacy of a new antidepressant (bupropion) in the treatment of panic disorder with phobias. *Journal of Clinical Pharmacology, 3,* 28–31.

Stern, T. A., & Jenike, M. A. (1983). Treatment of obsessive–compulsive disorder with lithium carbonate. *Psychosomatics, 24,* 671–673.

Stroebel, C. F., Szarek, B. L., & Glueck, B. C. (1984). Use of clomipramine in treatment of obsessive–compulsive symptomatology. *Journal of Clinical Psychopharmacology, 4,* 98–100.

Sussex Clinical Trials Group. (1985). Separate and combined anxiolytic and antidepressant treatment of mixed anxiety/depression. *Acta Psychiatrica Scandinavica, 72,* 81–88.

Svensson, T. H., & Usdin, T. (1978). Feedback inhibition of brain noradrenaline neurons by tricyclic antidepressants. *Science 202,* 1089–1091.

Sweeney, D. R., Gold, M. S., Pottash, A. L. C., & Martin, D. (1983–84). Plasma levels of tricylic antidepressants in panic disorder. *International Journal of Psychiatry in Medicine, 13,* 93–96.

Task Force on the Use of Laboratory Tests in Psychiatry (1985). Tricyclic antidepressants — blood level measurements and clinical outcome. *American Journal of Psychiatry, 142,* 155–162.

Telch, M. J., Tearnan, B. H., & Taylor, C. B. (1983). Antidepressant medication in the treatment of agoraphobia: A critical review. *Behavior Research and Therapy, 21,* 505–517.

Thase, M. E. (in press). The biomedical approach to affective disorders. In R. L. Morrison & A. S. Bellack (Eds.), *Medical factors and psychological disorders: A handbook for psychologists.* New York: Plenum Press.

Thoren, P., Asberg, M., Cronholm, B., Jornestedt, L., & Traskman, L. (1980). Clomipramine treatment of obsessive–compulsive disorder. I. A controlled clinical trial. *Archives of General Psychiatry, 37,* 1281–1285.

Volavka, J., Neziroglu, F., & Yaryura-Tobias, J. A. (1985). Clomipramine and imipramine in obsessive–compulsive disorder. *Psychiatry Research, 14,* 83–91.

Warneke, L. B. (1984). The use of intravenous chlorimipramine in the treatment of obsessive–compulsive disorder. *Canadian Journal of Psychiatry, 29,* 135–141.

Yaryura-Tobias, J. A., & Bhagavan, H. N. (1977). L-tryptophas in obsessive–compulsive disorders. *American Journal of Psychiatry, 134,* 1298–1299.

Zis, A. P., & Goodwin, F. K. (1982). The amine hypothesis. In E. S. Paykel (Ed.), *Handbook of effective disorders* (pp. 175–190). New York: Guilford.

Zitrin, C. M., Klein, D. F., & Woerner, M. G. (1978). Behavior therapy, supportive psychotherapy, imipramine, and phobia. *Archives of General Psychiatry, 35,* 307–316.

Zitrin, C. M., Klein, D. F., & Woerner, M. G. (1980). Treatment of agoraphobia with group exposure *in vivo* and imipramine. *Archives of General Psychiatry, 37,* 63–72.

Zitrin, C. M., Klein, D. F., Woerner, M. G., & Ross, D. C. (1983). Treatment of phobias: I. Comparison of imipramine hydrochloride and placebo. *Archives of General psychiatry 340,* 125–138.

Zohar, J., & Insel, T. R. (in press). Obsessive–compulsive disorder: Psychobiological approaches to diagnosis, treatment, and pathophysiology. *Biological Psychiatry.*

CHAPTER 25

Monoamine Oxidase Inhibitors

David V. Sheehan and Ashok B. Raj

Monoamine oxidase inhibitor (MAOI) drugs are enjoying a renaissance. This is because recent reports have shown them to be very effective in therapy for panic disorder (Sheehan, Ballenger, & Jacobson, 1980), atypical depression (West & Dally, 1959), and tricyclic/electroconvulsive therapy refractory endogenous depression. There are suggested uses for these drugs in migrane headaches (Anthony & Lance, 1969), resistant narcoleptic states (Wyatt, Fram, Buchbinder, & Snyder, 1971), and as an adjunct in the treatment of hypertension (Gibbs, 1966). There is growing acceptance and awareness that with proper dietary precautions they are well tolerated (Raskin, Schulterbrandt, Reating, Crook, & Oolle, 1974). Blackwell (Blackwell, Marley, Price, & Taylor, 1967) has found that patients ingesting high-risk food products rarely experience adverse hypertensive effects. Studies show that most patients do not find it difficult to follow the necessary diet and do not feel deprived by it (Orlosky, 1982).

HISTORICAL SUMMARY

There is now strong suggestive evidence from several double-blind placebo-controlled studies in the past 15 years that MAO inhibitors are effective in the treatment of panic disorder. This observation has gained wide clinical acceptance since the late 1970s. Concurrently and largely as a result of these observations, the MAOIs are now more widely prescribed for this condition than they were 10 years ago. Although at first many clinicians inexperienced in the use of MAOIs were uncomfortable prescribing them, the body of knowledge that has accumulated through their more widespread use has generated useful and practical guidelines so that they can now be used with greater effect and safety than in previous decades.

GENERAL DESCRIPTION

The MAO inhibitors are related chemically to isoniazid and iproniazid, which were studied in the 1950s for their antitubercular activity. Iproniazid, the parent compound of current MAO inhibitors, was noted to have significant mood-elevating properties and antidepressant effects (Crane, 1957). The currently available MAOIs result from attempts to synthesize MAO inhibitors that would have the benefits of iproniazid without its adverse effects. In the United States, only three MAO inhibitors are available for prescription: (a) phenelzine sulfate, (b) isocarboxazid, and (c) tranylcypromine sulfate. Phenelzine and tranylcpromine account for over 90% of all the MAOIs prescribed (Blackwell et al., 1967).

As a family of drugs, the MAOIs can be divided into two classes: the hydrazines and the nonhydrazines. Phenelzine and isocarboxazid are hydrazine MAO inhibitors, while tranylcypromine is a nonhydrazine. Each class is associated with different side effects and different therapeutic effects that may dictate the choice of the drug for an individual patient. The hydrazines are structurally related to iproniazid, while the nonhydrazine tranylcypromine is not. The hydrazine and nonhydrazine MAOIs differ in several ways:

1. The nonhydrazine (tranylcypromine) is five times more likely to predispose to hypertensive reactions than the hydrazines (Blackwell et al., 1967). One study found 17.2 deaths per year per million prescriptions for phenelzine and 13.7 deaths per year per million prescriptions for tranylcypromine (Girdwood, 1974). This is four times greater than the death rate attributed to imipramine hydrochloride (Girdwood, 1974), but approximately half the estimated mortality rate associated with electroconvulsive therapy (ECT) (Freedman, Kaplan, & Sadock, 1975). Forty-three percent of the deaths with phenelzine and 90% of the deaths with tranylcypromine are due to hypertensive crises (Freedman et al., 1975). The difference is thought to be due to tranylcypromine's greater ability to inhibit MAO enzyme A in the intestine and liver. This enzyme acts as a defense by inactivating ingested pressor amines such as tyramine in cheese.
2. The hepatotoxicity associated with MAO inhibitors is believed to be due to the free hydrazine group. Ten percent of tranylcypromine (a nonhydrazine) deaths and 43% of phenelzine (a hydrazine) deaths were due to hepatocellular damage (Blackwell et al., 1967).
3. The hydrazines, at therapeutic doses, are more effective overall as mood elevators, antipanic drugs, and antiagoraphobic drugs than tranylcypromine (the nonhydrazine). This is based on our clinical experience and merits more definitive empirical evaluation.
4. Tranylcypromine, in our experience, is associated with lower degrees of subjectively disruptive side effects than the hydrazine MAO inhibitors.
5. The hydrazine MAOIs cause "irreversible" MAO inhibition, in contrast to the reversible MAO inhibition caused by the nonhydrazines (Natoff, 1965). In practice, this means that if a hydrazine MAO inhibitor is discontinued, it will take several days, perhaps even as long as 2 to 3 weeks for the body to adequately reconstitute or replace its lost stores of MAO enzymes. Until adequate MAO stores are reconstituted, the patient remains at risk to develop a hypertensive reaction if tyramine or contraindicated drugs are used prior to this time. It is prudent, therefore, for patients to remain on their restricted diet for at least 2 weeks after stopping an MAO inhibitor. With a nonhydrazine tranylcypromine, intestinal MAO inhibition is maximal in 1 to 2 hours after ingestion, but 80% recovery has occurred by 4 hours, at which time the liver MAO is only 32% of normal (Natoff, 1965). When the tranylcypromine blood level drops to zero, the MAO inhibition is largely reversed (Natoff, 1965). However, it is prudent to maintain these patients on the MAOI restrictions for at least a week after tranylcypromine has been stopped.
6. Tranylcypromine acts more rapidly than the hydrazine MAO inhibitors

(Hutchinson & Smedberg, 1963; Linge, 1964). As a working rule, it is best to expect that at least 3 to 6 weeks will be needed to obtain a significant and stable clinical effect with either the hydrazines or the nonhydrazines.

MECHANISM OF ACTION

Monoamine oxidase inhibitors inhibit monoamine oxidase, an enzyme found principally in the liver, intestine, blood, and nervous system that alters (inactivates) monoamines, for example, norepinephrine, serotonin, dopamine, and tyramine. However, it is not clear that this effect is central to their therapeutic action. This catalytic effect on the oxidative deamination of monoamines results in higher levels of these amines at nerve endings in the central nervous system. However, they have many other effects in widespread areas of the central nervous system, any one of which might be more central to their observed clinical effects (Blackwell, 1966; Perry & Hanson, 1973). The current state of our knowledge of their exact mechanism of action is very limited at this time.

SYNDROMES THEY TREAT

Major indications for MAOIs are in the treatment of severe anxiety disorders and depression. Although their main use was initially in the treatment of depression, controlled studies by the Clinical Research Committee found them less effective than ECT or imipramine in the treatment of endogenous depression. Subsequently, they were relegated to the role of drugs of second choice in the treatment of depression, and then only when all other measures had failed. Because the doses used in the above studies on depression were not optimal by today's standards, it is possible that MAOIs were shortchanged. However, it is not clear that even under optimal circumstances they offer any significant advantages over tricyclics for patients with atypical vegetative signs of endogenous depression.

There is now general agreement that they are often very effective for endogenous depression. However, they also appear to be effective for all subtypes of depression, not just those considered "atypical" on the basis of hypersomnia, hyperphagia, anxiety, or somatisation. There is at least some evidence suggesting that the drugs may be particularly effective in depressions without the "classical endogenicity" (Pare, 1985).

In 1960, a Boston psychiatrist, Dr. R. Arnot, first described the use of an antidepressant drug for the treatment of anxiety symptoms in anxious patients (Arnot, 1960). This short anecdotal paper described the anxiolytic effect of hydrazine MAO inhibitors he had observed in his clinical practice. Over the next several years there was a series of uncontrolled studies that proposed that certain MAO inhibitors were effective in treating anxiety attacks, cases of severe phobic anxiety, and what was called "atypical depression" (Kelly, Guirguis, Frommer, Higgs, & Sargant, 1970; King, 1962; Kline, 1967; Roth & Myers, 1969; Sargant, 1962, 1966; West & Dally, 1959). These reports did not clearly delineate the syndromes being treated. It was never clear whether these MAOI sensitive disorders were several distinct clinical entities or were merely all sectors of one larger polysymptomatic disorder associated with attacks of anxiety; multiple phobias; or hysterical, hypochondriacal, depressive, and obsessive/compulsive symptoms.

These anecdotal observations were confirmed more scientifically in 1973 in three controlled studies on agoraphobic and socially phobic patients. The methodologic limitations of these studies left certain questions unanswered (Lipsedge, Hajioff, & Huggins, 1973; Solyom et al., 1973; Tyrer, Candy, & Kelly, 1973). They did not make any distinction between spontaneous (unexpected) panic attacks, situational panic attacks, limited symptom attacks, anticipatory anxiety, and avoidance behavior. The outcome measures used then would not be considered adequate today to help sort out the impact of the MAO inhibitors of several different sectors of the disorder. These distinctions have direct implications in practice. For example, it was unclear if the MAOIs affected the unexpected panic attacks and avoidance behavior in a different way. In addition, these studies had small sample sizes, used doses that would now be considered only marginally therapeutic, and were conducted for relatively short periods of time. These studies used either phenelzine or iproniazid. There are still no double-blind placebo-controlled studies documenting the efficacy of isocarb oxazid, tranylcypromine, or nialamide for the treatment of anxiety disorders.

In a double-blind placebo-controlled study we compared phenelzine with imipramine and placebo in the treatment of panic attacks and multiple phobias (Sheehan et al., 1980). Both phenelzine and imipramine were significantly superior to placebo on all the dimensions of the disorder measured, even at the relatively modest fixed doses used in the study. An unexpected finding was that phenelzine showed a consistent trend to be superior to imipramine, and this achieved statistical significance on two of the phobia disability outcome scales. (Sheehan et al., 1980).

Although the MAOIs have been branded as drugs of questionable efficacy, or at least only second best in power (Clinical Psychiatry Committee, 1965), it now appears that in the case of panic related disorders (including agoraphobia) phenelzine was not only remarkably effective, but in panic it might have a margin of superiority in efficacy over the tricyclic antidepressants at optimal dosages of both. Although the dosages in the study were only marginally therapeutic by today's standards (the study was done between 1973 and 1975), we have recently replicated these findings in another double-blind study using dosages of both drugs that are considerably higher (Sheehan, Claycomb, & Surman, 1984). Agoraphobics who have been on both drugs at different times during the course of their treatment usually report that they found phenelzine more effective overall than imipramine even when the doses of both drugs were increased to achieve optimal therapeutic effect. In cases of mild to moderate severity, both drugs are usually adequately effective, but in the really severe, intractible cases, the extra power of the phenelzine over the imipramine is usually more apparent.

Although it has been reported anecdotally (Sheehan & Claycomb, 1983; Sheehan, Claycomb, & Kouretas, 1960) that both tranylcypromine and isocarboxazid are effective in panic attacks and agoraphobia, there are no double-blind studies yet documenting their efficacy. Clinically, it appears as if the hydrazine MAOIs (phenelzine and isocarboxazid) are more potent at optimal doses in anxiety disorders than the nonhydrazine MAOI tranylcypromine. However, this observation remains to be tested under controlled conditions.

MAOIs are effective in the treatment of panic anxiety even when there is no evidence of significant clinical depression and even in the absence of vegetative signs of depression (Sheehan et al., 1980). From these studies we have concluded that phenelzine is effective in this polysymptomatic anxiety syndrome which appears to be distinct from endogenous depression.

There has been some debate in the literature over how exactly to characterize the anxiety syndrome that responds to MAO inhibitors. The recent literature suggests that they are effective for panic disorder and agoraphobia, as if these two conditions were distinct. The MAO inhibitors also appear to be effective for degrees of pathological anxiety that are milder than and do not quite meet full criteria for panic disorder. Indeed, some of these patients deny experiencing panic attacks, but only complain of recurrent limited symptom attacks either with or without anxiety.

The cardinal feature for the MAOI responsive anxiety syndrome is the presence of sudden unexpected anxiety attacks that occur with little or no provocation. They are interspersed with spontaneous attacks of somatic symptoms from the cluster we associate with anxiety neurosis (such as lightheadedness, skipping or racing of the heart, shortness of breath, hypochondriasis, or parasthesias). Such a symptom may occur in isolation as well as in an attack with several other symptoms. As a result of these attacks, avoidance develops to situations associated in the past with such attacks. Over time these patients progressively acquire more phobias until they are sufficiently polyphobic and symptomatic to be considered agoraphobic. The agoraphobia is merely a late complication of the disorder (Sheehan & Sheehan, 1983) and is associated with fears of crowded places, traveling far from secure places, or being left alone. The MAO inhibitors are most effective against the core spontaneous or unexpected anxiety attacks. They have some, but a less dramatic effect, on the anticipatory anxiety to the phobias. Anticipatory anxiety is largely conditioned and usually requires repeated in vivo exposure in addition to drug therapy before being extinguished. The MAO inhibitors, particularly phenelzine, have a confidence-enhancing, energizing, assertive effect that motivates the phobic patient to face the feared situation. This helps the patient carry through on plans for in vivo exposure, reducing the phobic anxiety, decreasing the disability, and encouraging a return to the mainstream of life.

Although the hydrazine MAO inhibitors are marginally better then imipramine in their ability to block unexpected anxiety attacks, it is these other features that give the hydrazines the advantage as more effective rehabilitators. Because the terms *panic disorder* and *agoraphobia* are only the severe end of the spectrum of the anxiety syndrome that is sensitive to MAO inhibitors, I have used, in the past, the term *endogenous anxiety* to delineate the larger anxiety disease category that is MAOI-sensitive. The endogenous anxiety group would include those patients with panic disorder, and/or agoraphobia, and approximately three quarters of all patients who meet criteria for generalized anxiety disorder but who have unexpected, unprovoked, sudden surges of these attacks described earlier without having them to a sufficient intensity, frequency, or severity to meet criteria for panic disorder and agoraphobia. If the use of these drugs is limited rigidly only to the more severe cases, many of the mildly to moderately disabled patients will not get adequate treatment, although they may need an MAO inhibitor to recover. The delineation of this MAOI-sensitive anxiety syndrome has been described in more detail elsewhere (Sheehan, 1983, 1986; Sheehan & Sheehan, 1982a, b).

WHEN NOT TO USE MAO INHIBITORS

It is generally inadvisable to use MAO inhibitors in younger patients because of their potential noncompliance. They are contraindicated in patients with a pheochromocytoma or impaired cardiac function. They are not absolutely contraindicated in patients with hypertension. Because MAO inhibitors have a direct hypotensive effect, they assist in lowering the patient's blood pressure further. Indeed, it is usually necessary to lower the patient's existing antihypertensive medication as the MAOI dose reaches optimal levels.

As with other psychotropic drugs, special caution is needed when using MAOIs in the elderly, although they are not contraindicated. The major problem encountered in the elderly is hypotension; for this reason, tranylcypromine is a preferable choice and is usually better tolerated by the elderly than the hydrazine MAO inhibitors.

Although MAO inhibitors are not contraindicated in epilepsy, hyperthyroidism, diabetes, or impaired renal function, the dosage requires more cautious adjustments, may need to be lower than usual, and any concomitant medication used may require alteration.

Because MAO inhibitors are rarely associated with hepatotoxity, special caution is needed in patients who have hepatic disease. Tranylcypromine is preferable in liver disease to other MAO inhibitors because it is less frequently associated with hepatotoxicity. It is also prudent to monitor liver function tests at regular intervals and to avoid any contact with victims of infectious mononucleosis and viral hepatitis.

Monoamine oxidase inhibitors can be used for patients with asthma, especially in those who do not have status asthmaticus or who do not require epinephrine in emergencies. In mild to moderate asthma, an acute asthmatic attack can be managed by steroids, for example, beclomethasone dipropionate (Vanceril® Inhaler) or intravenous hydrocortisone.

Although the safety of MAO inhibitors in pregnancy has not been established empirically, neither is there substantial evidence that they are predictably associated with ill effects to the pregnancy. Several cases of women taking MAO inhibitors through their pregnancy are known to the author without any apparent short- or long-term ill effects to mother or child. However, drug-free pregnancy is always ideal, and the risk/benefit ratio to the mother and infant must be evaluated in each case and caution exercised. It remains to be demonstrated that frequent panic attacks, unexpected anxiety symptoms, and depression are not harmful to a pregnancy.

In all of the high risk cases just discussed, informed discussion with the patient and the family are warranted. Good patient compliance, careful monitoring, and close frequent supervision by the physician can make the difference between a good stable outcome and troublesome complications.

PREPARING THE PATIENT

Monoamine oxidase inhibitors should be prescribed with the same careful preparation and monitoring as used in prescribing insulin for a diabetic. Preparation and education of the patient and his or her family are critical for optimal results. Casual prescription is an invitation to therapeutic failure at best, or serious medical complications at worst. We consider involvement of key family members or a friend most valuable, because this enhances patient compliance to the treatment regimen and reinforces the patience and persistence necessary to tolerate the frequent disruption and lack of progress in the early weeks of treatment. With rising public medical sophistication, the average patient both expects and deserves informed explanation. With proper preparation, patients learn what to expect and how to cope with any difficulties that arise. This increases confidence in the physician, puts patients at ease, and insures greater compliance and a better chance of success. Because these drugs are subjectively unpleasant to take in the early weeks of treatment, many patients will want to stop taking the medications at the first sign of side effects or subjective disruption. Warning the patient about what he or she will expect and preparing her/him thoroughly for the experience and how to handle it is the best insurance for a successful outcome.

There are four essential points to be considered in preparing the patient:

1. Food, drug, and drink restrictions on MAOIs.
2. Practical instructions for patients taking MAO inhibitors.
3. Dosage schedule.
4. Side effects.

Because much of the information that the doctor gives to the patient is often quickly forgotten by the patient, we recommend giving the patient printed information on these four points to bring home for future reference. To assist the implementation of this recommendation, Appendices 25.1, 25.2 and 25.3 can be given to the patient. Let us examine the four essential points of preparation in sequence.

Food, Drug, and Drink Restrictions

A comprehensive list of these restrictions is provided in Appendix 25.1. These restrictions should be observed for 2 days before and for 2 weeks after stopping the last dose. Many such lists are overinclusive and too complicated to be useful. Patients should be given reliable printed lists for reference that they can easily carry with them. Appendix 25.1 is not intended to be scientifically precise, but it is practical, safe, and reliable. For example, we recommend that *all* cheeses be avoided without exception because it is not possible to predict from variety, appearance, or flavor how much tyramine they contain. The tyramine increases with aging. Similarly, with beer, wine, and sherry, although the tyramine content varies, all should be avoided. It is easier for patients to remember and it is safer. The "yeast extracts," marmite and bovril, consumed primarily in England, are likely to cause hypertensive reactions (Blackwell & Marley, 1966a, b; Blackwell et al., 1967; Sjogvist, 1965). Breads and cakes in which Baker's yeast has been used are safe. Broad beans are rarely consumed in the United States, but are frequently eaten in England. They are large, pale green, kidney shaped, and laterally flattened beans and contain the amino acid "dopa."

Many clinicians are under the mistaken belief that the MAO inhibitors themselves can cause unexpected hypertensive reactions. This is not correct. The apparent mechanism is that the MAO inhibitor inactivates monoamine oxidase A, a defense mechanism in the intestine and liver that protects patients against monoamines (e.g., tyramine) that exist in certain aged and fermented foods. If this defense mechanism is inactivated, any ingested tyramine will pass through the intestine and liver into the bloodstream without being inactivated and when it accumulates in the general circulation, it can lead to a surge of blood pressure (Blackwell & Marley, 1966a, b). The MAO inhibitors themselves only set the patient up to be vulnerable to tyramine by inactivating the defense mechanism against it. However, if the tyramine or its equivalent is not ingested, no hypertensive reaction can occur. The direct effect of the drugs themselves is to lower blood pressure.

A small rise in blood pressure is not usually felt by the patient unless the systolic pressure rises to over 170 to 200 mm Hg. Consequently, just because a patient reports that she or he is feeling nothing unusual after taking small quantities of cheese does not mean his or her blood pressure did not rise or that this is safe. Such deliberate infractions of the restrictions on two or more occasions warrants discontinuation of the drug and switching to alternative therapy.

Cheese

We advise patients to avoid *all* cheese, unless they know the tyramine content is low *each time* they eat it. It is not possible to tell the tyramine content of any cheese by appearance, brand, or type. It may vary from batch to batch and the tyramine is not necessarily evenly distributed throughout the cheese. While it is theoretically true that a few cheeses may, at times, have low tyramine, this is too often untrustworthy and inconsistent. If any exceptions are made in permitting a few cheeses, patients are liable to "try others out in small amounts to see if anything happens." This is extremely dangerous and the clinician who in any way encourages this is medicolegally indefensible.

A little background on cheese will help understand why this is so. If fresh milk is allowed to stand long enough, it turns sour and the increased acidity curdles the milk, separating it into flocculated proteins, fat, and fluid whey. When the fluid is removed, a fresh acid curd cheese remains.

To make good cheese, a curdling agent (such as rennet) is added to milk that has been previously soured and is at the correct temperature. The rennet, with the milk's calcium, helps convert the protein casein into an insoluble curd — which is the main element of cheese. The cheesemaker separates the whey from the curd particles. The curd is then ripened. Casein, which is the most important protein in cheese, contains 21 amino acids. As it decomposes (ripens), these amino acids are liberated throughout the cheese to influence its taste and aroma. One of these amino acids is tyrosine.

The offering agent with MAO inhibitors is most frequently tyramine. Tyramine is formed through the action of mold or yeast on tyrosine. Tyrosine is a dietary amino acid and is a precursor of norepinephrine and dopamine. Normally, when we eat tyramine in our diet (e.g., as cheese) it is altered or detoxified in the intestine and liver by MAO enzymes to *p*-hydroxyphenylacetic acid, in which form it passes harmlessly into the general circulation. On taking an MAO inhibitor, this defense mechanism (or tyramine alteration) by the MAO enzyme is inactivated, and the tyramine is free to get into the general circulation. From here it reaches sympathetic postganglionic nerve endings, where it displaces stored norepinephrine stoichiometrically. The resulting massive release of norepinephrine to receptor sites leads to the hypertensive and related autonomic changes.

No two cheeses are made in exactly the same way. There are endless variations from the type of milk; the souring; the temperature; and the curdling, draining, and ripening process. Ultimately, it is a local, sometimes quite an individual, process.

Processed cheese can also be highly variable. Pasteurized processed cheese is a dairy product resulting from the mixing and heating of several lots of natural cheeses with suitable emulsifying agents into a homogeneous mass followed by cooling. It may contain fruits, vegetables, and meats. Only some cheeses are protected by laws that restrict the use of the name and guarantee origin and production method. You may think that all those of the same name have the same tyramine content, but they may have been made elsewhere with a different production method. Some cheese shops ripen young cheeses in their own cellars just prior to marketing. After it is sent to market, the cheese may continue to ripen on the shelf while awaiting purchase.

The bottom line is that there are far too many variables outside the consumer's control and beyond standardization that can influence the tyramine content and have potentially fatal consequences to a patient on an MAOI. To play it safe, avoid all cheese.

Drinks

Wine: There is so much variability in the preparation of wines that one cannot always be assured that the tyramine content will not vary. It is safer to avoid all of them, although some may contain much more tyramine than others.

Sherry: All true sherries are fortified wines that come from a small region (50,000 acres) around Jerez de la Frontora in Spain. The name *sherry* is a corruption of *Jerez*. Sherries are prepared through a complex process (called *solera*) that involves the blending of fresh wine with older wines, in which the older sherries are said to "educate" the younger ones. Because there are too many individual variables that can influence the final product, it is safer to avoid all sherries, because their tyramine content is unpredictable and variable.

Brandy: The name *brandy* identifies any spirits distilled from fruit, for example, grapes, cherries, plums, or peaches. The term is more commonly used to mean a distilled wine, for example, *cognac* or *armagnac*. Cognac is the best known. It originates from an unremarkable wine. It is the process of distillation and aging that concentrates and refines it to give it its unique taste. The final cognac is a blend. Because French law requires that any cognac must be aged for at least 4 years, this results in the youngest spirit in the blend having to be 4 years old, with the other parts being older. The greater the percentage of older spirits in the blend, the more expensive the cognac. All brandies should be avoided, although some have more tyramine than others.

Champagne: Champagne is a blend of wines. By French law and European common market agreement, only a wine that (a) is made by blending three varieties of grapes (chardonnay, pinot noir, pinot meunier) from different years and from different fields or areas within a limited zone in the champagne region of France, and (b) follows a carefully regulated process called *la methode champenoise* can call itself champagne. Red wine grapes are a major component of champagne. Champagne has many imitators which are merely sparkling wines. It is safer to avoid all champagnes because one cannot rely on them having a low tyramine content.

Vermouth is an aperitif wine and should be avoided by patients taking MAOIs. Other aperitif wines to be avoided include Byrrh, Dubonnet, and Quinquina.

Liqueur: Liqueurs are usually made by adding an infusion of fruits or herbs to grain alcohol, brandy, or whiskey. It is safer for MAOI-medicated patients to avoid all liqueurs because the tyramine content varies among them. This includes Benedictine, Calisay, chartreuse, cointreau, crème de cacao, crème de cassis, crème de menthe, crème de rose, crème de vanille, crème de Yvette, curaçao, Grand Marnier, Jummel, maraschino, noyau, prunelle, Southern Comfort, Swedish Punch, and triple sec.

Avoid any mixed drinks including cocktails, because many contain wines and brandies. Martinis and Manhattans, for example, are made with vermouth. Grenadine, an artifically flavored syrup for sweetening drinks, can also cause a hypertensive reaction with MAO Inhibitors.

Drinks that have not been associated with hypertensive reactions include gin, vodka, and whiskey. It should be reemphasized that the alcohol content of the drink is no predictor of its susceptibility to cause hypertensive reactions.

Not only should these drinks be avoided as drinks, but foods prepared with any of them also need to be avoided. The cooking may reduce the alcohol content, but does not remove the tyramine!

Practical Instructions for Patients taking MAO Inhibitors

These are detailed in Appendix 25.2 and can be given on a printed form to the patient and reviewed with him or her. These instructions include questions frequently asked by patients on MAO inhibitors with instructions on how to resolve these questions. They outline some of the more common expected side effects and problems that may emerge in the initial weeks of treatment. They may serve as a focus for any additional verbal instructions the clinician wishes to give the patient.

Item 3 in these instructions describes the symptoms of the hypertensive reaction to the patient and what course of action he or she should take if it occurs. Typically, there is a headache that first occurs in the occiput and the temples and is described as truly explosive and distinct in quality and location from a common tension headache. However, the patient can be reassured that such reactions are very rare indeed and the majority, in our experience, have occurred in those who are deliberately noncompliant. In the event this rare reaction does occur, the patient should be instructed to go to the nearest emergency room and have his or her blood pressure checked and, if necessary, treated. Patients should be warned against the natural inclination to lie down and wait, because this position only increases the intracranial blood pressure and compounds the danger to the patient.

Dosage Schedule and Adjustment Instructions

In prescribing an MAO inhibitor, it is first prudent to identify a patient's past history of drug tolerance, fear of medication, weight, and age. When this is clarified, an appropriate schedule for starting and building up the dosage can be discussed with him or her. These instructions should then always be written out in detail. A sample chart that we use in prescribing MAO inhibitors is outlined in Appendix 25.3 as a suggested reference point. A suitable regimen is to start with 15 mg of phenelzine after the evening meal for the first 3 days. On Day 4, one tablet is taken after breakfast and one after the evening meal. This dosage is maintained for another 3 days until Day 8, when 15 mg (one tablet) is prescribed after each meal. If the side effects, particularly postural hypotension, are significant, the patient continues on this dosage until tolerance to the side effects permits a further increase of the dose by another tablet. If the patient experiences no side effects, the dose is increased in further increments of 15 mg (one tablet) every week.

The best single guide to the correct therapeutic dosage is the dosage at which the patient begins to experience some postural hypotension. This is best identified by checking the patient's blood pressure sitting and standing at each visit from the very first visit. When the patient reaches the correct therapeutic dosage, the clinician will usually notice a small drop in the patient's blood pressure when the patient stands and a delayed recovery of this drop to normal. For example, if a patient's blood pressure is normally 120/80, when the patient reaches the correct therapeutic dose, his or her blood pressure may drop to 100/70, and whe he or she suddenly stands up, it may drop further to 100/65. Frequently, this is not associated with any subjective feeling of change. In more marked cases, the patient may experience a darkening of vision when changing posture. This is usually transient and mild. A subjective report of lightheadedness on the patient's report is notoriously unreliable as a guide to postural hypotension, because many anxious patients already experience lightheadedness as a prominent symptom in their anxiety syndrome. The lightheadedness of the anxiety syndrome is distinct from the darkening of vision experienced by patients when they get postural hypotension.

Fine Tuning of Dosage

In the course of adjusting the dosage upward, patients will usually experience some side effects at first to which they will later develop a tolerance. If they lose the benefit they have gained as well as the side effects, further increases in the dosage may be necessary. One peculiar pharmacokinetic property of hydrazine MAO inhibitors is an apparent sigmoid shaped (s-shaped) dose response curve. This means that at doses close to the effective therapeutic dosage, even very small changes in the dosage can bring about a significant increase both in benefit and in side effects. For this reason, half-tablet doses are sometimes necessary to achieve the optimal therapeutic benefit. For example, a patient may experience little or no side effects and benefit at 45 mg per day of phenelzine. When he or she increases the dosage to 60 mg per day, the patient experiences too much postural hypotension, and yet complete blockade of symptoms. At 3½ tablets per day, this patient may derive optimal benefit.

Some patients will gain weight after several months on MAO inhibitors and as a result, the previous dosage they were on is no longer sufficient to control their symptoms. In such cases, further increase in the dosage by ½ to 1 tablet are usually all that are necessary to regain the full therapeutic benefit. Some of these tablets are difficult to split in half, but patients should be encouraged to cut the tablets in these cases when necessary. Frequently, at a therapeutic dosage the full side effects of the drug do not occur immediately on reaching the dosage, but only after 2 or 3 days at that dosage. This is one reason it is prudent to leave 5 to 7 days between dosage increases in the higher dosage ranges. When the dosage is increased after the 4th week, usually the benefit comes within about 5 days of the onset of side effects, and usually when the dosage is reduced, it may take approximately 3 days before the previously experienced side effects of the higher dosage subside. Consequently, the clinician regulating the dosage in these cases must hold a steady course and not overreact to transient effects of the dosage in either direction. Over the course of long-term management, patients may require such adjustment up and down in their dosage in order to maintain the benefit or diminish the side effects.

How High Can the Dosage Go?

Approximately 40% of patients get satisfactory benefit at three tablets (45 mg) of phenelzine per day. Approximately 40% of patients derive benefit at four tablets (60 mg) of phenelzine per day. About 15% of patients need five or six tablets per day. Less than 5% of patients need doses higher than 90 mg per day. As a general working rule, if a patient is at 90 mg of phenelzine (Nardil®) per day or 90 mg of isocarboxazid or tranylcypromine and is not experiencing any demonstrable side effects or benefit, it is likely that the patient is metabolizing the drug rapidly and could derive benefit at a higher dosage. In such cases, it appears justified to make further cautious but steady increases in the dosage to even higher levels. In such cases, the clinician will usually observe the clinical benefit occurring within 5 to 7 days of the patient's experiencing the typical side effects. In a large population of our patients on MAO inhibitors, no patient ever required a dosage of any of the MAO inhibitors higher than 12 tablets per day. However, there are rare severe cases of this disorder where patients who have failed on every other drug have responded well in our experience to 10, 11, or 12 tablets of these drugs per day without experiencing significant side effects and whose lives were significantly changed by their having this medication. Failure to increase the dosage in these cases would only unnecessarily condemn these patients to a life of disability.

In cases where patients require higher-than-recommended dosages, it is prudent to advise them that you are moving the dosage into a range above the recommended level (informed consent). It is also prudent to monitor their ECG and vital signs at the higher dosages. Elderly patients and younger patients generally tolerate MAOIs less well than adults. As a result, lower dosages should be used at first and the dosage adjustments should be slower and more cautiously implemented in these cases.

Distribution of Doses

Some have recommended giving the total daily dose once daily (usually at bedtime), while others recommend using divided doses during the day. Giving one dose at night may enhance compliance and decrease daytime side effects; however, MAOIs can produce significant postural hypotension and insomnia. A large dose at once increases the likelihood of a sudden fall, especially at night if the patient has to get out of bed to urinate. We prefer to prescribe the drug in two or three divided doses after meals, and not to take any doses later than 6:00 p.m. because of the activating properties of the drug (see Appendix 25.3). With tranylcypromine, distributing most of the daily doses to the earlier part of the day is often particularly important to avoid insomnia.

We usually recommend to patients that they take the tablets at the end of a meal because there is a small amount of tyramine in the average meal that will prevent their blood pressure from dropping too low. If the patient goes on a strict diet, he or she may become more hypotensive and experience more marked side effects.

Length of Adequate Trial

It is important to stress to the patient repeatedly that he or she should not expect any significant stable benefit from these drugs for at least 3 to 4 weeks after starting them. Promises to the contrary can lead to unnecessary disappointment and even premature noncompliance or termination of the drug. Failure to improve even slightly or even a brief regression in the early weeks of treatment are not cause for concern but are a call for perseverance. Sometimes patients will develop an amphetamine-like hypomania in the first week of treatment on a MAO inhibitor, and feel a significant improvement only to lose it in the second and third weeks and finally to regain it again after the fourth week of treatment. The clinician should anticipate this and not overreact or prematurely terminate the trial until the patient has had an adequate dosage for an adequate period of time. It is usually unwise to terminate a trial of an MAO inhibitor until the patient has been on an adequate dosage for at least 8 weeks. There are some patients in our experience who do not derive any significant benefit from these drugs until they have been on the drug 6 to 8 weeks in spite of adequate compliance to the dosage schedule regimen. In general, if patients have not responded between the 8th and the 10th weeks, it is rather unlikely that they will get a therapeutic effect after this time.

Monitoring Blood Levels to Guide Dosage Adjustment

The question of monitoring platelet MAO levels is sometimes raised as a suggestion in guiding the dosage adjustment. Although it has some research interest, it is probably not yet of practical utility to use platelet MAO levels to monitor the dosage of MAO inhibitors. It has been recommended that patients should achieve at least 80% MAO inhibition if they are to derive a therapeutic effect. However, if a patient has 85% MAO inhibition and has no significant side effects or benefit at that dosage, the sensible clinician would not hestiate to increase the dosage further to attempt to derive further benefit for the patient. In order to use platelet MAO levels as a guide to dosage, it is necessary to take platelet MAO levels before the drug is prescribed. The platelets must be prepared in a speical way within 4 hours of the blood drawing, otherwise the results will not be reliable. The facilities to do this are not easily available to the average clinician. At this time, the ability to directly measure blood levels of the MAO inhibitors is not available to the clinician. Their predictive value has not been established.

Long-Term Monitoring

It is always necessary to take a careful medical history and to measure vital signs, particularly blood pressure sitting and standing and pulse sitting and standing, before prescribing the drug. The blood pressure and pulse (sitting and standing) should be routinely checked and recorded at each subsequent visit. Doing a routine series of lab tests, such as a complete blood count, liver and renal functions tests, and an ECG, are a wise precaution and provide a baseline against which to measure any future deviations. It is a sensible precaution to monitor the liver function tests and ECG approximately once every 6 to 12 months as long as the patient continues to take the drug. Although small elevations in liver enzymes are not unusual while taking these medications, these are not usually of serious consequence unless the liver enzyme elevation is quite marked. Another useful monitoring device over the months and years of a patient's treatment is to have the patient complete a few simple scales that they can self-rate in the 10 minutes prior to each visit. These will serve as useful reference points to compare fluctuations in the patient's illness and response to treatment over long periods of time.

Length of Medication Treatment

When the patient has had a significant remission in his/her symptoms, some clinicians recommend lowering the dose to a maintenance level for long-term management. We have found that this frequently leads to a recurrence of some of the patient's symptoms. However, the clinician needs to be flexible and should not hesitate to maintain the patient on the optimal therapeutic dosage for several months or up to a year, should that become necessary. It is generally not recommended that the medication be discontinued any sooner than 6 months. We prefer that the patient be asymptomatic for at least 6 months before the medication is discontinued. In withdrawing the patient from medication, it is again wise to do it slowly. Withdrawal symptoms for MAOIs have been described in the literature Naylor, 1987. If a patient has been doing well for several months and is ready to start tapering the drug, we recommend that the patient decrease the dosage by one tablet every 2 or 3 weeks. This will help sort out any withdrawal effect from a true recurrence of the condition. If the patient gets progressively worse as the dosage decreases, then it is likely he or she is having a true recurrence of the original disorder.

During long-term management, the patient should have vital signs monitored carefully and be seen at least once every 4 months after he or she is stablized. When the medication is discontinued completely, further follow-up visits once or twice a year are recommended to insure that the patient does not become disabled again should he or she experience a recurrence.

Relapses After Medication is Stopped

Relapses are more common after these medicines are stopped than we have been willing to admit in the past. In the case of panic disorder patients treated for up to a year on phenelzine, we found 71% had some relapse of symptoms within 3 months of discontinuing the drug. Many more patients are being kept on these medications for long periods of time than the literature reflects at this time. As long as the clinician justifies this in his or her records and monitors the patient sensibly, this should be acceptable. Future generations will be much less hesitant about treating these patients chronically with medicine than we are.

The importance of the careful adjustment and titration of the dose of MAO inhibitors cannot be overemphasized. It is the single most important variable that can make the difference between success and failure.

Side Effects

Nonserious Side Effects

MAOIs can cause a variety of side effects, ranging from mild to serious. The subjectively unpleasant but not serious side effects usually occur early and subside as treatment continues. They can often be minimized by adjusting the dosage and rarely necessitate discontinuation of the medication. These irritating, but not serious, side effects include:

1. Dry mouth is easily tolerated, but if it is severe and associated with a bad taste it may respond to sugarless gum or citrus fruit lozenges. If accompanied by cheilosis (a raw soreness in the angles of the mouth), lyseine administered two tablets daily is usually helpful within 5 to 7 days.
2. Dizziness, lightheadedness, fatigue, tiredness, coldness, and restlessness are usually tolerated by the patient and subside with time.
3. Constipation is common and occasionally alternates with diarrhea early in treatment, particularly with tranylcypromine. Patients should be warned to expect this and advised to manage themselves with increased fluid and bulk (high fiber) intake like regular bran or Metamucil® and stool softeners if necessary. Irritating laxatives should be avoided.
4. Cardiac side effects include bradycardia and postural hypotension. Arrhythmias are rare with MAOIs. MAOIs have cardiac effects significantly different from those associated with tricyclics. For example, phenelzine significantly shortens the QTc interval, but has no effect on PR or QRS intervals. Postural hypotension is very common.

   Indeed, the presence of postural hypotension is the best single guide clinically to the optimal therapeutic dosage. Many patients with endogenous anxiety complain of lightheadedness and unsteadiness at rest as part of their syndrome. However, this is unlike the postural hypotension they experience with MAOIs. Patients soon learn to distinguish between these two types of "lightheadedness." The critical distinction revolves around a *darkening of vision* with postural change on the drug, as opposed to a lightheaded unsteady disoriented sensation associated with the anxiety disorder. To minimize the postural hypotension, patients are encouraged to take their medication after meals. They are warned against getting up too rapidly from a prone or seated position. Drinking small amounts of tea or coffee during the day usually results in a minor rise in blood pressure of 5 to 20 mm Hg, which is often sufficient to counteract the hypotension.
5. Patients may report a blowing, popping, or blocking sensation in their

ears. Some of these symptoms are associated with hypotension and are apparently benign.

6. Excessive sweating, flushing, chills, and sensitivity to cold are frequently reported.
7. The patient may report isolated forgetfulness of things, particularly forgetting the names of common objects, and losing his or her train of thought; this normalizes when the dosage is reduced or the medication is discontinued.
8. Genitourinary symptoms, such as the inability to experience or a delay in reaching orgasm or ejaculation, are more common than reported and should be anticipated because the patient may not spontaneously mention them. Patients should be told that these symptoms are not permanent, and a reduction in the dosage is not always indicated. Patients often develop a gradual tolerance to this side effect. Delayed micturition with associated nocturia responds to a reduction in dosage and only very rarely produces urinary retention.
9. Muscle twitching, body jerking upon falling asleep, and leg cramps are usually minor problems requiring no intervention.
10. Neurological side effects include hyperreflexia and shock-like "electric sensations." The shock-like sensations are usually experienced in the extremities, especially on moving the head or eyes laterally, and most frequently occur after the 4th to 6th month of treatment when the dosage is high. Rarely, patients on long-term MAOI therapy develop a neuropathy including a carpal tunnel syndrome secondary to vitamin B-$_6$ deficiency. Both the shock-like sensations and the neuropathy may respond to the administration of pyridoxine (vitamin B-$_6$), 300 to 400 mg per day (Sheehan & Claycomb, 1983; Sheehan et al., 1960).
11. Some patients may experience a periodic generalized edema on hydrazine MAOIs. This usually subsides within a week without special intervention, but occasionally can be troublesome and persist for months. This edema sometimes responds to high doses of vitamin B-$_6$. Lowering the dosage or switching to a nonhydrazine MAOI may be indicated in severe cases. It may also be a complication of a significant weight gain and often subsides when the patient drops their weight below a certain threshold by strict dieting.
12. Many patients gain weight after a few months on an MAO inhibitor. Some patients on hydrazine MAO inhibitors gain as much as 30 to 40 lbs. First, there seems to be a generalized appetite stimulation after the second month. These patients will begin eating more of everything, especially sweet and fattening foods. In addition, the drug appears to stimulate a specific compulsive craving for certain foods such as donuts, cookies, cakes, or ice cream. These are true cravings and patients report eating large amounts of these foods with little satiation of their appetite. Finally, it seems that MAOIs produce an increase in weight without any apparent increase in caloric intake. This responds to a reduction or discontinuation of the drug.
13. Some patients may experience a transient hypomania in the initial 3 months of treatment. They may become euphoric, exuberant, energized, extroverted, assertive, and even agressive. They talk more, accomplish more in their everyday activities, and in general feel good about themselves. This only very rarely leads to a more severe manic episode. In general, however, clarification of the problem with the patient and the patient's family is usually sufficient to prevent matters from getting out of hand. Only rarely is it necessary to lower the dosage, which will moderate the hypomania. Usually the hypomania is self-limiting and subsides after the 4th month of treatment. Rarely, a disinhibition syndrome associated with antisocial behavior including petty

crimes and promiscuity and often associated with diminished guilt is seen in individuals who were previously socially compliant.

14. MAO inhibitors, in general, shorten sleep time and disrupt the normal circadian rhythym. The patient may sleep less at night but feel intermittently drowsy during the day, alternating with periods of energy. He or she may have alternating episodes of drowsiness and marked energy. MAOIs at higher levels suppress REM sleep, which produces a shortening of time spent sleeping at night. Usually this insomnia is not especially upsetting to the patient and is often associated with adequate energy and functioning during the day.

The overriding principle when prescribing these drugs is to reach an optimal balance between producing side effects and gaining therapeutic benefit. Patients should be advised not to stop the medication abruptly, but to decrease it gradually over a period of days to weeks. A recommended schedule would be to decrease the dose by one tablet every 3–7 days. Even then, withdrawal symptoms of nausea, generalized itching, malaise, lack of energy, headaches, and vivid nightmares may occur. These symptoms, particularly the itching, may last as long as 2 or 3 weeks.

Abrupt discontinuation of MAO inhibitors (phenelzine and tranylcypromine) have been associated with delirium (confusional psychosis) (Frankel & Raskin, 1985; Liskin, Roose, Walsh, & Jackson, 1985; Roth, 1985).

Serious Side Effects

Three rare but serious side effects can occur with MAO Inhibitor use: (a) hypertensive reactions; (b) hepatotoxicity; and (c) potentiation of effects of other drugs.

Hypertensive Crisis. The MAO inhibitors are *hypo*tensive agents and do *not* themselves alone cause hypertension. They merely inhibit intestinal and hepatic MAO (MAO-A) which acts as a defense — in the gastrointestinal tract and liver — against ingestion of pressor amines like tyramine. When MAO is inactivated by these drugs, the patient is vulnerable to foods, drugs, or drinks with pressor amines of the phenylethylamine group in an unmodified form. These enter the bloodstream, act on peripheral adrenergic receptors, and release nonadrenaline from stores in the sympathetic nerve terminals causing sudden rises in blood pressure within 10 to 35 minutes after the food is ingested (Blackwell et al., 1967; Blackwell & Marley, 1966a, b; Sjogvist, 1965). These amines are found especially in fermented, decaying, or overripe foods, after bacteria facilitate breakdown of amino acids and increase the tyramine content. The extent of the reaction depends on several factors (Blackwell et al., 1967):

1. The amount of tyramine eaten. Six milligrams of tyramine causes a moderate BP increase, 10 mg a marked pressor effect, and 25 mg a severe hypertensive crisis.
2. Size of the meal and food content.
3. How rapidly the stomach empties.
4. Type of MAO inhibitor — more common with tranylcypromine.
5. Duration of treatment — greater effect over first few weeks.
6. Size of last dose of MAO inhibitor.
7. Interval between dose and ingestion of food (Blackwell et al., 1967). By inactivating a defense mechanism in the liver and intestine, MAOIs predispose patients to developing hypertensive reactions if the patient ingests tyramine. The hypertensive reaction, when it occurs, is described as unmistakable even by patients who have many anxiety symptoms. It begins suddenly, within 5 minutes to 1½ hours after ingesting the tyramine. There is a heavy, thumping increase in heart rate. The blood vessels in the neck, face, and head throb. A sudden severe, pulsating headache follows, which is confined initially to the occiput or temporal regions, but later spreads all over the head. Patients may feel that their head is about to explode and that it is very

"full." Flushing and profuse sweating, nausea, vomiting, and high temperature frequently accompany the attack. Neck stiffness, photophobia, and pulse irregularities occur less frequently. The attack may last minutes to several hours. Patients vary greatly in the threshold at which they experience these symptoms, although most are symptomatic at systolic blood pressures of 200 mm Hg. Even after the acute episode has subsided and the blood pressure has been lowered, the headache may persist for 2 or 3 days.

Treatment of Hypertensive Crisis from MAOIs. When treating a hypertensive crisis that resulted from MAOIs, the following information is important: If the blood pressure is dangerously high, treatments to lower it should be instituted immediately. The most effective recommended treatment is to give phentolamine mesylate, 5 mg intravenously. This should be administered *very* slowly to avoid producing an excessive hypotensive effect. Concomitant administration of a diuretic is often necessary, because the vasodilators are associated with fluid retention. Furosemide, 40 mg, has a dual advantage. It both counteracts the fluid retention and reduces the blood pressure. Patients should always be admitted overnight and watched carefully for several hours, even after their blood pressure drops, lest it rise again because the phentolamine is short-acting and the tyramine is still usually being absorbed from their gastrointestional tract. We do not recommend giving patients prescriptions for chlorpromazine to treat a hypertensive reaction, because they could take it by mistake while they are having a hypotensive episode.

Below we discuss the choice of drugs available to use in the management of hypertensive crisis, beginning with the old standards and then progressing to the newer ones:

1. *Phentolamine* (Regitine®) — 5 mgs IV *slowly*. Its duration of action is shorter and it has both the advantage and disadvantage that the drop in blood pressure is not sustained. It is an alpha-adrenergic blocker and works both pre- and postsynaptically.
2. *Phenoxybenzamine* hydrochloride — 100 mg in 250 ml of 5% dextrose solution infused over 90–120 minutes. It is an alpha-adrenergic blocker and acts at both pre- and postsynaptic levels.
3. *Diazoxide* (Hyperstat®) — It is a direct vasodilator that has minimal effects on venous circulation. It probably acts by blockade of calcium receptors or inhibition of calcium release in the vascular smooth muscle, thus inhibiting calcium dependent action of the contractile process. The resulting arteriolar dilatation causes a decrease in peripheral resistance and blood pressure; reflex tachycardia; and increased cardiac output and stroke volume. The usual dose is 5 mg/kg (300 mg) administered as a rapid, undiluted intravenous push over 10 to 30 seconds. Onset of action is in 1 to 5 minutes, while the duration of effect is 4 to 12 hours. If a satisfactory response is not obtained in 30 minutes after injections, an additional dose of 300 mg may be given. Some patients respond with a marked decrease in blood pressure, leading to hypotension. One way of minimizing this problem is to administer the diazoxide in 3 divided doses of 2 mg/kg (100 mg) IV push every 5 minutes, for a total of 300 mg. The clinical response compares well with a single 300-mg dose and hypotensive episodes are less (Ram & Kaplan, 1979). The maximum dose of diazoxide is 1200 mg in 24 hours. Side effects are sodium and water retention (a diuretic can be administered concurrently), hypotension, and hyperglycemia (due to inhibition of insulin).
4. *Sodium nitroprusside* (Nipride®) — It relaxes all vascular smooth muscles resulting in arteriolar dilation, decreased peripheral resistance, and venous dilatation (venous pooling and decreased venous return).

The usual starting dose of nitroprusside is 0.5 to 1.5 μ/kg per minute as a continuous intravenous infusion. Maintenance dose is from 0.5 to 10 μg/kg per minute. Onset of action is immediate. If a patient becomes hypotensive, the infusion should be discontinued and the blood pressure will rise in a few minutes.

Side effects are nausea, vomiting, hypotension, abdominal pain, and palpitations. Normally, nitroprusside is metabolized to cyanide and this to thiocyanate. If hepatic function is poor, then this conversion may be incomplete and signs of cyanide poisoning may appear — hypotension and metabolic acidosis. Patients with renal impairment may have reduced clearance of thiocyanate — leading to thiocyanate toxicity, nausea, vomiting, diarrhea, arthralgia, muscle cramps, twitching, psychosis, irritability, tinnitus, and depressed thyroid function. This toxicity may also occur if they have been receiving nitroprusside for over 72 hours. If levels exceed 10 mg/100 ml, nitroprusside administration should be discontinued.

This drug should be used only in a setting where blood pressure can be closely or continuously monitored and the infusions given by infusion pump or electronic microdrip regulation to avoid catastrophic changes in blood pressure.

5. *Calcium Channel Blockers* — Recently, nifedepine has been suggested as an important alternative in the treatment of certain hypertensive emergencies (Bertel et al., 1983; Cockhill & Remick, (in press); Weidmann, Gerber, & Laederach, 1985). A single dose of 5 to 20 mg sublingually or orally, acutely and effectively reduced blood pressure without causing a rapid drop and thus reduces the risk of major side effects such as stroke, angina, myocardial infarction, and death. In fact, it reduces peripheral blood pressure with no effect or increased cerebral flow.

   Following sublingual administration of nifedipine, the reduction in blood pressure is maximal at 15 to 30 minutes; improvement may last up to 4 hours. The response takes only slightly longer after oral administration. Individual decreases in blood pressure correlate strongly with pretreatment blood pressure. An exaggerated fall to hypotensive levels was not encountered with nifedipine monotherapy, but may sometimes occur with the use of higher doses (15–20 mg) in patients already on diuretics or other potent antihypertensives.

   Other calcium antagonists, such as verapamil or diltiazam given intravenously, were found to be effective in some patients with hypertensive crisis. Short-term calcium antagonist therapy is relatively free of serious side effects.

Hepatotoxicity. Hepatotoxicity is extremely rare in patients on MAO inhibitors. It may present with a flu-like syndrome, while severe cases present with jaundice. The mechanism appears to be hepatocellular damage rather than the cholestatic jaundice seen with chlorpromazine. For medicolegal reasons, it is wise to check the liver function tests every 6 months or at the onset of a skin rash, unusual nausea, fever, eosinophilia, or unexplained illness. A small elevation of liver enzymes, however, is not necessarily sufficient cause for stopping the medication and is usually reversible with reduction in dosage or changing to a nonhydrazine MAOI. Fatal progressive necrotizing hepatocellular damage has been reported in a few patients. It has been suggested that MAOIs may increase the susceptibility to hepatitis and mononucleosis virus.

Interaction with Other Drugs. MAOIs can alter enzyme systems in the liver and elsewhere in the body other than monoamine oxidase. Drugs that are metabolized by these enzymes are potentiated or interfered with. Consequently, these drugs must be used with greater caution, and in lower doses or, if possible, not at all (Sjogvist, 1965). Particular attention needs to be paid to the following drugs:

1. **Sympathomimetic amines and local anesthetics**. Indirect-acting sympatho-

mimetic amines displace norepinephrine from storage sites in nervous tissue and can lead to severe hypertensive reactions. These include amphetamine, methylphenidate, ephedrine, phenylpropanolamine, and tyramine. Especially dangerous are the over-the-counter preparations containing these amines and used by patients as cold and cough remedies and nasal decongestants. Although, theoretically, direct acting sympathomimetic amines such as epinephrine and norepinephrine should be safe, it is best to avoid them because they may also act by an indirect action (Boakes, Tech, Barar, Benedikter, & Prichard, 1973; Elis, Laurence, Mattie, & Prichard, 1967). Although found on many lists of drugs to avoid, local anesthetics like novacaine and xylocaine are safe in small amounts as long as they do not contain sympathomimetic vasoconstrictors. When dental work has to be done, we advise our patients to use the pure local anesthetics without epinephrine and have not encountered any problems with this regimen.

Epinephrine and norepinephrine are reported to be "safe" when taken concurrently with MAOIs (Boakes et al., 1973; Elis et al., 1967). We would recommend a more conservative approach until there is more evidence to support these observations. For example, epinephrine may theoretically cause some hypertensive effect by an indirect as well as by its own direct effect on the adrenergic receptor terminals (Boakes, Laurence, Lovel, O'Neil, & Verrill, 1972; Svedmyr, 1968). However, this question warrants further study.

2. **Opiates**. Narcotics should not be used with MAO inhibitors because fatal interaction with MAOIs has been reported, especially with meperidine hydrochloride. We recommend using codeine for patients in severe pain and have never encountered any severe ill effect from the interaction of these moderate doses of codeine and MAO inhibitors. It is not clear that patients always get a hypertensive reaction from the interaction of opiates and MAO inhibitors. Some of the complications may have resulted from severe hypotension and/or hyperpyrexia. We have seen a moderately severe hypertensive reaction in a patient who unwittingly took a small dose of dextromethorphan polistirex in combination for a severe cough. In a small number of patients, the interaction with MAOIs is unpredictable and life threatening complications can occur with extreme rapidity.
3. **Antihypertensive Agents**. Because MAOIs are hypotensive agents, adding them to an existing antihypertensive drug will only amplify the hypotension. Usually a small adjustment of the antihypertensive drug is all that is required. With higher doses and more powerful antihypertensives, greater care should be exercised. Guanethidine and other alpha blockers should be avoided and alphamethyl-dopa has been reported to cause interractions with MAOIs.
4. **Anesthetic Drugs**. We have encountered no problems with patients on MAO inhibitors who have had routine inhalation anesthesia. It is best to discontinue the drugs 2 weeks before elective surgery. However, this is not always possible. Barbituate (La Roche & Brodie, 1960), atropine, scopolamine, and other anticholinergic agents are significantly potentiated, but not contraindicated. This is particularly true if they are given intravenously or subcutaneously. The importance of telling the anesthesiologist they are taking a MAOI should be stressed to all patients.

The most common problem that arises during emergency surgery with an MAOI is a *hypo*tensive reaction. in such cases, anesthesiologists should avoid the powerful pressor agents, because this could lead to hypertensive interaction with the MAOI. Using hydrocortisone intravenously, as in the days before the new pressor agents were available, is a safer way of raising the blood pressure if it falls. Barbituates are potentiated when used concomitantly with MAOIs, but they are not contraindicated. Usually all that is necessary is a small modification in the dosage.

Stopping MAOIs before surgery is, therefore, not always necessary. One study of 27 MAOI-treated patients undergoing anesthesia for a variety of reasons found no serious complications. One case of hypotension was quickly and safely treated with I.V. phenylephrine. With a few precautions (avoiding indirect acting pressor agents such as tyramine and ephedrine and narcotics such as meperidine), MAOI-treated patients can undergo surgery safely (El Ganzouri, Ivankovich, Braverman, & McCarthy, 1985).

5. **Psychiatric Drugs**. No problems of interaction have arisen in our experience with concomitant use of benzodiazepines, antipsychotic drugs, or lithium. There have been several reviews of the interaction of tricyclic antidepressants and MAO inhibitors (Kline, 1969; Simmons, Carr, & Ross, 1970). The conclusion of these reports is that in appropriately selected patients, the concomitant use of tricyclics and MAO inhibitors has low potential for serious toxicity. In general, however, it appears safer to start both drugs together and avoid tranylcypromine because of its higher incidence of hypertensive reactions.

Pare (1965) states that the combination of MAOIs with chlorimipramine can be dangerous, while combinations with other cyclic antidepressants are as safe as MAOIs alone when it comes to hypertensive reactions. It has been suggested that both drugs be started together and that in using the combination, amitriptyline is recommended over imipramine (Ashcroft, 1975). Isocarboxazid is said to be safer in combination with tricyclics because it is a "pure MAO Inhibitor", unlike phenelzine and tranylcypromine, which have "amine releasing properties", making them more likely to predispose the patient to hypertensive attacks (Pare, 1965). It is not clear how much weight should be given to the above observations, because other authors have not followed these guidelines and report no ill effects. Some of the serious reactions noted with this TCA-MAOI combination have apparently involved malignant hyperthermia rather than a hypertensive crisis. Tricyclics may not protect against hypertensive reactions in patients taking MAOIs as some have suggested (Abrams, Schulman, & White, 1985; Pare, Al Mousawi, & Sandler, & Glover, 1985). There is some suggestion that the combination of a tricyclic (amitriptylene) with an MAO inhibitor (isocarboxazid) may be more likely to induce mania (20% incidence) than either the tricyclics or the MAO Inhibitors alone (10% incidence each) (de la Fuente, Berlanga, & Leon-Andrade, 1986).

Kline (1969) reports no difficulties arising from the combination of MAOIs with each other. It should probably only be done as a last resort. Until we have further evidence that such combinations are safe, in switching from a hydrazine to a nonhydrazine, it is advisable to wait at least 1 week. One report suggests that waiting 2 weeks between stopping one MAO Inhibitor and starting another may not always be necessary. It does not always lead to a hypertensive reaction or malignant hyperthermia (True, Alexander, & Carter, 1985).

6. **Alcohol**. Some alcohol drinks (e.g., gin, vodka, whiskey) other than wine, sherry, cognac, beer, and ale, if used in moderation, can be consumed by patients on MAO inhibitors. However, this should not be encouraged, because alcohol is potentiated when taken with MAOIs.

7. **Antiparkinsonism Drugs**. There are conflicting reports in the literature on the safety of the combination of MAOIs (phenelzine) and amantadine

hydrochloride, with one paper reporting a hypertensive reaction (Jack & Daniel, 1984), while another reports the safe use of the combination in Parkinson's disease (Greenberg & Meyers, 1985). L-dopa is contraindicated with MAOIs. With other antiparkinsonism drugs, there may be little more than potentiation of the anticholinergic side effects.

8. **Central Stimulants**. Combining central stimulants (methylphenidate or dextroamphetamine) with an MAO inhibitor can be safe and effective in otherwise treatment-resistant patients, particularly those who become hypotensive while taking MAOIs alone (Feighner, Herbstein, & Damlouji, 1985). With such a combination, the MAOI should be started first and the central stimulant later. Initially, only low doses should be used and careful monitoring is essential (Feighner et al., 1985).
9. **Insulin**. MAOIs may lower blood sugar and potentiate hypoglycemic agents and, in diabetics on insulin, may interfere with medical management. However, most cases can be managed successfully by close monitoring of serum glucose and a possible reduction in the dosage of insulin. In socially isolated outpatients, such concurrent therapy has been reported to induce a prolonged serious hypoglycemic state (American Pharmaceutical Association, 1976).
10. **Dilantin**. We have seen two cases of apparent enhanced dilantin toxicity in epileptics previously stabilized on dilantin. Great caution must be used should an MAOI be necessary for a patient with epilepsy.
11. **The "Serotonin Syndrome" with L-Tryptophan**. There have been several reports of a potentially hazardous "serotonin syndrome" when daily doses of as little as 2 mg of L-tryptophan were used with MAOIs. This syndrome varied in different patients, but was a neurotoxic syndrome appearing within 2 to 3 hours of the addition of L-tryptophan. It was characterized by myoclonus, fasiculations, hyperreflexia, shivering, confusion, disorientation, agitation, hypomania, unsteadiness, a drunken feeling, diaphoresis, teeth chattering, and tremor. The symptoms usually resolve spontaneously within 8 to 12 hours of stopping the drugs (Goff, 1985; Jack, 1986; Levy, Bucher, & Votolato, 1985).
12. **Caffeine**. Drinks and foods containing caffeine should be avoided by patients with anxiety disorders. However, when they are used in moderation (not more than two cups of coffee per day) we have not encountered any difficulties from interactions with hydrazine MAOIs. They are best avoided with tranylcypromine because of its greater propensity to hypertensive reactions.
13. **Parenteral Drugs**. Parenteral administration of all drugs to patients on MAOIs should be avoided when possible, and where a choice exists, the oral drug should be given.

MANAGEMENT OF MAO INHIBITOR POISONING

MAO Inhibitor Overdose

These drugs can be highly toxic. In over 50% of published reports of MAO inhibitor overdoses, death has resulted (Simmons et al., 1970). They have a low therapeutic index, i.e., the ratio of the toxic dose to the therapeutically effective dose is small. Death has been reported with eight times the usual dose of phenelzine (375 mg) and six times the usual dose of tranylcypromine (170 mg) (Tucker & Sirisinha, 1965). However, people have survived overdoses of 350mg of tranylcypromine or phenelzine in the range of 375 mg to 1,500 mg. Survivors of iproniazid (1,750 mg) isocarboxazid (300–500 mg) and nialamide (400–1,500 mg) intoxications have been reported. Death from nialamide poisoning (5,000 mg) has been reported. Autopsy and animal studies show congestion of various organs, enlargement of liver and spleen, and inflammatory changes in the brain — these changes are nonspecific. Histochemical (David, Bartlett, & Termini, 1968) studies in one case showed no demonstrable MAO activity in sections of the patient's liver, brain, and kidneys 3 days after the overdose. This suggests that liver biopsy may be a direct technique to monitor severity or recovery in an overdose.

The clinical picture in intoxication may be influenced by the additional ingestion of tyramine-containing products, sympathomimetic agents, or other psychotropics. For example, instead of the expected hypotension directly resulting from the MAOI overdose, the patient may be hypertensive from the ingested sympathomimetic agent. Characteristically, there is a lag period following the overdose of 8 to 12 hours. During this period, the vital signs may be normal and the only abnormal signs are those of the primary psychiatric disorder. This lag period may be due to the enzyme-inhibiting effects of the MAOIs causing an accumulation of amines in the brain tissue. Later signs of central nervous system overstimulation begin — thrashing movements of the extremities, profuse sweating, restlessness, irrational behavior, convulsions, and coma. Hyperpyrexia is a common feature and cause of death (108–110° F). Increased respiratory rate, tachycardia, dilated pupils, hyperactive deep tendon reflexes, or involuntary movements of face and jaw may be noted. There may be associated hypotension or hypertension.

Management of MAO Inhibitor Overdose

A specific antidote for MAOI overdose is not available. Recommended measures include:

1. Anyone suspected of an MAO inhibitor overdose should be observed in the hospital for at least 24 hours. This is to avoid a misdiagnosis due to the characteristic lag period.
2. MAO inhibitor delays gut motility, and gastric lavage should be performed up to several hours postingestion.
3. The excretion of tranylcypromine is influenced by urinary pH. Urine pH can be altered by administration of ammonium chloride toward the acid side. At pH 5, the excretion is seven times as high as in alkaline urine (after sodium bicarbonate) (Turner, Young, & Paterson, 1967).
4. Avoid use of narcotics, barbituates, or tranquilizers — their effects are prolonged due to MAO inhibition and may complicate the clinical picture.
5. Monitor ECG, blood pressure, and temperature.
6. Send urine for hemoglobin and myoglobin analysis. Monitor output of urine.
7. Get readings on blood gases and pH, serum glucose, electrolytes, calcium, magnesium, CPK, LDH, pyruvate, lactate, creatinine, PT, PTT, and platelet count.
8. Give I.V. fluids — 5% dextrose.

Hemodialysis

The extent of protein binding of MAO inhibitors is unknown. The small molecular size and structural similarity of tranylcypromine sulphate to amphetamine and epinephrine suggests that it is dialyzable. Several cases of improvement after dialysis over a 6-hour period have been reported (Matter, Donat, Brill, & Ginn, 1965; Versaci, Nakamoto, & Kolff, 1964). Dialysis also eliminates the risk of drug potentialization by the supportive use of narcotics, barbituates, or tranquilizers.

Malignant hyperthermia

In malignant hyperthermia, the temperature rises rapidly, reaching as high as 110° F within 24 hours of toxic overdose, and is often the cause of death. Other causes of death are hypertension or hypotension. The hyperpyrexia is most probably due to malfunction of the thermoregulatory hypothalamic center and massive heat production from the overactive musculature. Similar rapid and fatal rises in body temperature have been observed in idiopathic malignant hyperthermia, neuroleptic malignant syndrome, heat stroke, and any extreme fever.

Primary malignant hyperthermia is an inherited condition. It is triggered by stress or exposure to depolarizing skeletal muscle relaxants (succinylcholine chloride) and volatile hydrocarbon anaesthetics (halothane, trichloroethylene, cyclopropane, ethylene, and ether) (Willner, 1984). Part of the hyperthermia is due to muscle rigidity caused by abnormality in the excitation-contraction coupling mechanism in skeletal muscle. Re-uptake of calcium ions by the sarcoplasmic reticulum is impaired. Some of the temperature rise may be due to an increase in circulating catecholamines. Release of catecholamines from the adrenal medulla is calcium-ion dependent. Acidosis also stimulates release of catecholamines (Nahar, Ligore, & Mehlman, 1960). Neuroleptic malignant syndrome (NMS) is an uncommon, but life-threatening complication of treatment with neuroleptic drugs (Guze & Baxter, 1985). Its core features are hyperthermia, hypertoxicity of skeletal muscles, and fluctuating consciousness, along with autonomic instability. Thus, there are similarities in features between idiopathic malignant hyperpyrexia, neuroleptic malignant syndrome, and hyperpyrexia due to MAO inhibitor overdose. What the common thread is, if any, is unclear. However, dantrolene sodium has been found useful in malignant hyperthermia (Kolb, Horner, & Nartz, 1982) and in heat stroke. There are reports of it being helpful in decreasing the hyperpyrexia and muscle rigidity seen in neuroleptic malignant syndrome (Guze & Baxter, 1985). Malignant hyperthermia is considered to be of postsynaptic (peripheral) origin (Bergman, 1975) while NMS is considered to be a presynaptic (central) condition (Granato et al., 1983). However, despite probable dysfunction of hypothalamic thermoregulatory centers in NMS and MAO inhibitor toxicity, it is probable that a large part of the heat production is due to tonic skeletal muscle contractions. Dantrolene is a potent muscle relaxant helpful in NMS. We suggest it should be helpful in treating hyperthermia from MAO inhibitor toxicity.

Managment of Malignant Hyperthermia. Dantrolene apparently prevents the release of calcium ions from the sarcoplasmic reticulum in the presence of normal depolarization of the sarcolemma, that is, uncoupling of the excitation-contraction mechanism, leading to muscle relaxation and decrease in body temperature.

As described earlier, immediate measures following overdose or adverse reaction with MAO inhibitors are gastric lavage, acidification of urine, IV fluids, correction of acid/base balance, and, perhaps, hemodialysis. If the temperature begins to rise, the following additional steps are taken (Marmor, 1983):

A. Commence active cooling with:
   1. Hypothermia blanket, ice bags in axilla and groin, icewater sponging, and fans.
   2. Iced normal saline solution intravenously, 100 ml every 10 minutes for 30 minutes. Ringers lactate should be avoided, as it contains calcium.
   3. Iced saline lavage of stomach and rectum.

B. Begin drug therapy with:
   1. Dantrolene sodium 1 mg/kg by rapid IV. If symptoms persist or reappear, the dose may be repeated to a cumulative dose of 10 mg/kg. Reversal is usually achieved with a cumulative dose of 2.5 mg/kg.
   2. Steroids may be useful. Bicarbonate may be needed to combat acidosis.
   3. Heparinization may be helpful in treating disseminated intravascular coagulation if it occurs.
   4. The patient should be monitored for 72 hours, as retriggering may occur.
   5. Post-crisis treatment is 4 to 8 mg/kg/day orally of dantrolene for 1 to 3 days to prevent recurrence.

Serious adverse reactions associated with chronic oral dantrolene therapy (hepatitis, seizures, pleural effusions) have *not* been reported with short-term IV therapy for hyperpyrexia.

CONCLUDING REMARKS

In spite of their well known disadvantages and restrictions, the MAO inhibitors remain remarkably effective drugs for a variety of psychiatric syndromes in the anxiety–depressive neurotic spectrum. They can succeed where other available psychotropics fail. Prescribing them requires skill and patience from the clinician and special compliance from the patient. When the guidelines offered by this chapter are followed, the clinician will find that the challenge of using them skillfully will be rewarded by some of his or her most gratifying clinical successes.

REFERENCES

Abrams, J. H., Schulman, P., & White, W. B. (1985). Successful treatment of a monoamine oxidase inhibitor-tyramine hypertensive emergency with intravenous labetatol. *New England Journal of Medicine, 313*(1), 52.

American Pharmaceutical Association Monographs. (1976). The National Society of Pharmacists. *Evaluation of drug interactions: Insulin–phenelzine* (2nd ed.), 110–112.

Anthony, M., & Lance, J. W. (1969). Monoamine oxidase inhibition in the treatment of migraine. *Archives of Neurology, 21*, 263–268.

Arnot, R. (1960). Calming effects of the monoamine oxidase inhibitors. *Diseases of the Nervous System, 11*, 448.

Ashcroft, G. W. (1975). Psychological medicine: Management of depression. *British Medical Journal, 2*, 372–376.

Bergman, J. A. (1975, March). Idiopathic malignant hyperthermia: Review and report of a case. *Archives of Opthalmology, 93*, 232–235.

Bertel, O., Coven, D., Radeu, E. W., Muller, J., Lang, C., & Duback, U. C. (1983). Nifedipine in hypertensive emergencies. *British Medical Journal, 286*, 19.

Blackwell, B. (1966). Clinical and pharmacological interactions of MAO inhibitors, amines and foodstuffs. Unpublished *M.D. thesis, Cambridge University*, Cambridge, England.

Blackwell, B., & Marley, E. (1966a). Interactions of yeast extracts and their constitutents with MAO inhibitors. *British Journal of Pharmacology, 26*, 142–161.

Blackwell, B., & Marley, E. (1966b). Interactions of yeast extracts and their constituents with MAO inhibitors. *British Journal of Pharmacology, 26*, 120–141.

Blackwell, B., Marley, E., Price, J., & Taylor, D. (1967). Hypertensive interaction between monoamine oxidase inhibitors and food stuffs. *British Journal Psychiatry, 113*, 349–365.

Boakes, A. J., Laurence, D. R., Lovel, K. W., O'Neil, R., & Verrill, P. J. (1972). Adverse reactions to local anesthetic/vasoconstrictor preparation. *British Dental Journal, 133*, 137–140.

Boakes, A. J., Tech, D. C., Barar, F. S. K., Benedikter, L. T., & Prichard, B. N. C. (1973). Interaction between sympathomimetic amines and antidepressent agents in men. *British Medical Journal, 1*, 311–315.

Clinical Psychiatry Committee of the Medical Research Council. (1965). Clinical trial of the treatment of depressive illness. *British Medical Journal, 1*, 881.

Cockhill, L., & Remick, R. A. (In Press). *Blood pressure effects of monoamine oxidase inhibitors — the highs and lows.* Paper presented to Canadian Psychiatric Associations. 34th Meeting, Banff, September 1984. (In Press Canadian Journal of Clinical Psychiatry).

Crane, G. E. (1957). Iproniazid phosphate (Marslaid): A therapeutic agent for mental disorders and debilitating diseases. *Psychiatric Research Report, 8*, 142–152.

David, J., Bartlett, E., & Termini, B. A. (1968). Overdosage of psychotropic drugs: A review. *Disorders of the Nervous System, 29*, 246–256.

DeCastro, R. M. (1985). MAOIs, the "cheese" reaction, and sleep apnea. *Journal of Clinical Psychopharmacology, 5*, 59.

de la Fuente, J. R., Berlanga, C., & Leon-Andrade, C. (1986). Mania induced by tricyclic-MAOI combination therapy in bipolar treatment resistant depression: Case reports. *Journal of Clinical Psychiatry, 47*, 40–41.

El Ganzouri, A. R., Ivankovich, A. D., Braverman, B., & McCarthy, R. (1985). Monoamine oxidase inhibitors: Should they be discontinued preoperatively? *Anesthesia and Analgesia, 64*, 592–598.

Elis, J., Laurence, D. R., Mattie, H., & Prichard, B. N. C. (1967). Modification by MAO inhibitors of the effect of some sympathomimetics on blood pressure. *British Medical Journal, 2*, 75–78.

Feighner, J. P., Herbstein, J., & Damlouji, N. (1985). Combined MAOI, TCA and direct stimulant therapy of treatment resistant depression. *Journal of Clinical Psychiatry, 46*, 206–209.

Frankel, D. A., & Raskin, D. E. (1985). Psychosis following phenelzine withdrawal. *Journal of Clinical Psychopharmacology, 5,* 360.

Gibbs, R. H. S. (1966). Essential hypertension in general practice. An evaluation of paragyline hydrochloride. *Practitioner, 196,* 426–430.

Girdwood, R. H. (1974). Death after taking medicaments. *British Medical Journal, 1,* 501–504.

Goff, D. C. (1985). Two cases of hypomania following the addition of L tryptophan to an MAO inhibitor. *American Journal Psychiatry, 142,* 1487–1488.

Granato, J. E., Stern, B. J., Ringel, A., Karim, A. H., Krumholz, A., Coyle, J., & Adler, S. (1983). Neuroleptic malignant syndrome: Successful treatment with dautrolene and bromocreptine. *Annals of Neurology, 14,* 89–90.

Greenberg, R., & Meyers, B. S. (1975). Treatment of major depression and Parkinsons disease with combined phenelzine and amantadine. *American Journal Psychiatry, 142,* 273–274.

Guze, B. H., & Baxter, L. R., Jr. (1985). Current concepts, neuroleptic malignant syndrome. *Medical Intelligence, 313,* 163–166.

Hutchinson, J. T., & Smedberg, D. (1963). Treatment of depression: Comparative study of ECT and six drugs. *British Journal of Psychiatry, 109,* 536–538.

Jack, R. A. (1986). Myoclonus, hyperreflexia, and diaphoresis. *Canadian Journal of Psychiatry, 31,* 178.

Jack, R. A., & Daniel, D. G. (1984). Possible interaction between phenelzine and amantadline. *Archives of General Psychiatry, 41,* 726.

Kalinowsky, L. B. The convulsive therapies. In *Comprehensive textbook of psychiatry* Freedman, D. M., Kaplan, H. I., & Sadock, B. J. (eds.). (2nd ed., p. 1973). Baltimore: Williams & Wilkins.

Kelly, D., Guirguis, W., Frommer, E., Higgs, N. M., & Sargant, W. (1970). Treatment of phobic states with antidepressants. *British Journal of Psychiatry, 116,* 387–398.

Kennedy, S. H., Piran, N., & Garfinkel, P. E. (1985). Monoamine oxidase inhibitor therapy for anorexia nervosa and bulimia: A preliminary trial of isocarboxazid. *Journal Clinical Psychopharmacology, 5,* 279–285.

King, A. (1962). Phenelzine treatment of Roths calamity syndrome. *Medical Journal Australia, 1,* 879–883.

Kline, N. S. (1969). *Depression: Its diagnosis and treatment* (p. 38). New York: Brunner/Mazel.

Kline, N. S. (1967). Drug treatment of phobic disorders. *American Journal of Psychiatry, 123,* 1447–1450.

Kolb, M. E., Horne, M. L., & Nartz, R. (1982). Deutrolene in malignant hyperthermia. *Anesthesiology, 56,* 254–262.

Kronig, M. H. (1986). Case report of successful treatment of bulimia with isocarboxazid. *American Journal of Psychiatry, 143,* 551–552.

La Roche, M. M., & Brodie, B. B. (1960). The lack of relationship between inhibition of monoamine oxidase and the potentiation of Hexobarbital hypnosis. *Journal Pharmacologic Experimental Therapy, 130,* 134–137.

Levy, A. B., Bucher, P., & Votolato, N. (1985). Myoclonus, hyperreflexia, and diaphoresis in patients on phenelzine — Tryptophan combination treatment. *Canadian Journal of Psychiatry, 30,* 434–436.

Linge, E. A. (1964). Combined drug therapy compared with electric shock in psychotic depression. *American Journal of Psychiatry, 120,* 808–810.

Lipsedge, J. S., Hajioff, J., Huggins, P., Napier, L., Pearce, J., Pike, D. J. & Rich, M. (1973). The management of severe agoraphobia: A comparison of iproniazid and systematic desensitization. *Psychopharmacologia, 32,* 67–80.

Liskin, B., Roose, S. P., Walsh, B. T., & Jackson, W. K. (1985). Acute psychosis following phenelzine discontinuation. *Journal of Clinical psychopharmacology, 5,* 46–47.

Marmor, M. (1983). Malignant hyperthermia. *Survey of Opthamology, 28,* 117–127.

Matter, J. B., Donat, P. E., Brill, M. L., & Ginn, H. E. (1965). *Archives of International Medicine, 116,* 18–20.

Nahar, G. G., Ligore, J. C., & Mehlman, B. (1960). Effects of pH changes on O_2 uptake and plasma catecholamine levels in the dog. *American Journal of Physiology, 198,* 60–66.

Natoff, I. L. (1965). Toxic reactions to foodstuffs during therapy with monoamine oxidase inhibitors. *Medical Proceedings, 11,* 101–104.

Naylor, M. W., Grunhaus, L., & Cameron, O. (1987). Myoclonic seizures after abrupt withdrawal from phenelzine and alprazolam. *Journal of Nervous and Mental Disease, 175,* 111–114.

Orlosky, M. (1982). MAO inhibitors in sickness and health. *Biological Therapies in Psychiatry, 5,* 25–27.

Pare, C. M. B. (1965). Treatment of depression. *Lancet, 1,* 923–925.

Pare, C. M. B. (1985). The present status of MAO inhibitors. *British Journal of Psychiatry, 146,* 576–584.

Pare, C. M. B., Al Mousawi, M., Sandler, M., & Glover, V. (1985). Attempts to attenuate the "cheese effect": Combined drug therapy in depressive illness. *Journal of Affective Disorders, 9*, 137–141.

Perry, T. L., & Hanson, S. (1973). Sustained drug induced elevation of brain GABA in the rat. *Journal of Neurochemistry, 21*, 1167–1175.

Ram, C. V. S., & Kaplan, N. M. (1979). Individual titration of diazoxide dosage in the treatment of severe hypertension. *American Journal of Cardiology, 43*, 627.

Raskin, A., Schulterbrandt, J. G., Reating, N., Crook, T. H., & Odle, D. (1974). Depression subtypes in response to phenelzine, diazepam, and a placebo: Results of a nine hospital collaborative study. *Archives of General Psychiatry, 30*, 66–75.

Roth, S. (1985). More on psychosis following phenelzine discontinuation. *Journal of Clinical Psychopharmacology, 5*, 360–361.

Roth, M., & Myers, D. H. (1969). Anxiety neurosis and phobic states: Diagnosis and management. *British Medical Journal, 1*, 559–562.

Sargant, W. (1966). Psychiatry in general teaching hospitals. *British Medical Journal, 2*, 257–262.

Sargant, W. (1962). The treatment of anxiety states in atypical depression by monoamine oxidase inhibitor drugs. *Journal of Neuropsychiatry, 3* (Suppl. 1), 96–103.

Sheehan, D. V. (1983). *The anxiety disease*. New York: C. Scribners & Sons.

Sheehan, D. V. (1986). *The anxiety disease* (rev. ed.). New York: Bantam Paperback Books.

Sheehan, D. V., Ballenger, J., & Jacobson, G. (1980). The treatment of endogenous anxiety with phobic, hysterical and hypochondriacal symptoms. *Archives of General Psychiatry, 37*, 51–59.

Sheehan, D. V., & Claycomb, J. B. (1983). The use of MAO inhibitors in clinical practice. In T. C. Manschreck (Ed.), *Psychiatric medicine update. Massachusetts General Hospital Review for Physicians.* New York: Elsevier.

Sheehan, D. V., Claycomb, J. B., & Kouretas, N. (1960). MAO inhibitors: Prescription and patient management. *International Journal of Psychiatry in Medicine, 10*, 99–121.

Sheehan, D. V., Claycomb, J. B., & Surman, O. S. *The relative efficacy of phenelzine, imipramine, alprazolam, and placebo in the treatment of panic attacks and agoraphobia.* Paper presented at meeting on Biology of Panic Disorders, Boston, November 5, 1983 and the annual meeting of the American Psychiatric Association, Los Angeles. May 1984.

Sheehan, D. V., & Sheehan, K. H. (1982a). The classification of anxiety and hysterical states. Part 1. Historical review and empirical delineation. *Journal of Clinical Psychopharmacology, 2*, 235–243.

Sheehan, D. V., & Sheehan, D. H. (1982b). The classification of anxiety and hysterical states. Part 2. Towards a more heuristic classification. *Journal of Clinical Psychopharmacology, 2*, 386–393.

Sheehan, D. V., & Sheehan, K. H. (1983). The classification of phobic disorders. *International Journal of Psychiatry in Medicine, 12*, 243–264.

Simmons, A. V., Carr, D., & Ross, E. J. (1970). Case of self-poisoning with multiple antidepressant drugs. *Lancet, 1*, 214.

Sjogvist, F. (1965). Interaction between MAO inhibitors and other substances. *Proceeds of the Royal Society of Medicine, 58*, 967–978.

Solyom, L., Heseltine, G. F. D., McClure, D. J., Solyom, C., Ledwidge, B., & Steinberg, G. (1973). Behavior therapy vs. drug therapy in the treatment of phobic neuroses. *Canadian Psychiatric Association Journal, 18*, 25–31.

Stewart, J. W., Walsh, B. T., Wright, L., Roose, S. P., & Glassman, A. H. (1983). An open trial of MAO inhibitors in bulimia. *Journal of Clinical Psychiatry, 45*, 217–219.

Svedmyr, N. (1968). The influence of a tricyclic antidepressive agent (protriptyline) on some of the circulatory effects of nonadrenaline and adrenaline in man. *Life Sciences, 7*, 77–84.

True, B. L., Alexander, B., & Carter, B. (1985). *Drug intelligence and clinical pharmacy, 19*, 825–826.

Tucker, E., & Sirisinha, I. (1965). Toxicity of monoamine oxidase inhibitors. Report of a fatal case with histochemical findings and a review of the literature. *Alabama Journal Medicine, 2*, 301–304.

Turner, P., Young, J. H., & Paterson, J. (1967). Influence of urinary pH on the excretion of tranylcypromine sulphate. *Nature, 215*, 881–882.

Tyrer, P., Candy, J., & Kelly, D. A. (1973). A study of the clinical effects of phenelzine and placebo in the treatment of phobic anxiety. *Psychopharmacologia, 32*, 237–254.

Versaci, A. A., Nakamoto, S., & Kolff, W. J. (1964). Phenelzine intoxication. Report of a case treated by hemodialysis. *Ohio Medical Journal, 60*, 770–771.

Walsh, B. T., Stewart, J. W., Roose, S. P., Gladis, M., & Glassman, A. H. (1984). Treatment of bulimia with phenelzine. A double blind, placebo controlled study. *Archives of General Psychiatry, 41*, 1105–1109.

Weidmann, P., Gerber, A., & Laederach, K. (1985). Calcium antagonists in the treatment of hypertension: A critical overview. *Advanced Nephrology, 14,* 197–232.

West, E. D., & Daily, P. S. (1959). Effects of iproniazid in depressive syndrome. *British Medical Journal, 1,* 1491–1494.

Willner, J. (1984). Pediatric annals. *Malignant hyperthermia, 13,* 128–134.

Wyatt, R. J., Fram, D. H., Buchbinder, R., & Snyder, F. (1971). Treatment of intractable narcolepsy with monoamine oxidase inhibitors. *New England Journal of Medicine, 285,* 987–991.

Appendix 25.1. Monoamine Oxidase Inhibitors and Alprazolam

DIETARY RESTRICTIONS FOR PATIENTS TAKING MAOIs[a]	DANGER OF BLOOD PRESSURE RISE[b]
A. Foods	
1. All cheese	3
All foods containing cheese (pizza, fondue, many Italian dishes, and salad dressings)	3
Fresh cottage cheese; cream cheese are safe in moderate amounts	Safe
Sour Cream	2
2. All fermented or aged foods, especially aged meats or aged fish (aged corned beef, salami, fermented sausage, pepperoni, summer sausage, pickled herring)	2
3. Liver (chicken, beef, or pork liver)	2
Liverwurst	2
4. Broad bean pods (English bean pods, Chinese pea pods)	3
5. Meat extracts or yeast extracts	2
Baked products raised with yeast (bread) are safe	Safe
Yeast is safe	Safe
6. Spoiled fruit (spoiled bananas, pineapple, avocados)	2
Fresh fruits are safe	Safe
B. Drinks	
1. Red wine, sherry, vermouth, cognac	2
2. Beer and ale	2
3. Other alcoholic drinks are permitted in true moderation (gin, vodka, whiskey)	Safe
C. Drugs	
1. Cold medications (Dristan, Contac)	3
2. Nasal decongestants and sinus medicine	3
3. Asthma inhalants	3
Pure steroid asthma inhalants, for example, Vanceril, are safe	Safe
4. Allergy and hay fever medication	2
5. Narcotics, for example, Demerol	3
Codeine is safe	Safe
6. Amphetamines	3
Antiappetite (diet) medicine	2
7. a. Sympathomimetic amines — Direct acting (epinephrine, isoproterenol, methoxamine, levarterenol, norepinephrine)	2
b. Indirect acting (amphetamines, methylphenidate, phenylpropanolamine, ephedrine, cyclopatamine, pseudoephedrine, tyramine)	3
c. Direct and indirect acting Vetaraminol, phenylephrine	3
8. a. Local anesthetics with epinephrine	3
b. Local anesthetics without epinephrine (Carbocaine)	Safe
9. Levodopa for Parkinsonism	2
Dopamine	2
10. Diabetics on insulin may have increased hypoglycemia requiring a decreased dose of insulin (otherwise safe)	Blood sugar ↓
11. Patients on hypotensive agents for high blood pressure may have more hypotension requiring a decrease in their use of hypotensive agent (otherwise safe)	Blood Pressure ↓
12. Antihistamines	2

Note: The following foods have been rarely reported to cause hypertensive reactions with MAOIs. The evidence supporting these claims is weak and often based on a single isolated case. Warnings based on such evidence have been uncritically perpetuated especially in view of the large numbers of patients on MAOIs who eat these foods with no problem.

In practice, a blanket prohibition of these foods in small quantities seems unjustified unless they are clearly spoiled or decayed and except for specific patients in whom they have already caused symptoms.

Chocolate	1	Sauerkraut	1	Worcestershire sauce	1
Anchovies	1	Mushrooms	1	Soy sauce	1
Caviar	1	Beet root (beers)	1	Licorice	1
Coffee	1	Rhubarb	1	Snails	1
Colas	1	Curry powder	1	Yogurt	1
Figs. raisins, dates	1	Junket	1		

Note. From "The Use of MAO Inhibitors in Clinical Practice," in *Psychiatric Medicine Update, Massachusetts General Hospital Review for Physicians* edited by T. C. Manschreck, 1983, New York; Elsevier. Copyright 1983 by Elsevier. Reprinted by permission. pp. 148–149.

[a]Avoid for 2 days before and for 2 weeks after stopping drugs.

[b]Minimal danger, 1; Moderate danger, 2; Very dangerous; 3.

Appendix 25.2.

CONTINGENCY INSTRUCTIONS FOR PATIENTS TAKING MAOIs

While taking this medication:

1. Avoid all the restricted food and drugs mentioned in Appendix 25.1. Be particularly careful to avoid those foods and drugs marked 2 and 3.
2. In general, all the foods you should avoid are decayed, fermented, or aged in some way. Avoid any spoiled food even if it is not on the list.
3. Eating one of the restricted foods above may cause a sudden elevation of your blood pressure. When this occurs, you get an explosive headache, particularly in the back of your head and temples, that is different from a common headache.
   Your head and face will feel flushed and full, your heart may pound, and you may perspire heavily and feel nauseated. This may be a high blood pressure reaction and requires immediate attention.
4. If this rare reaction occurs, do not lie down as this further elevates the blood pressure in your head. Go to the nearest emergency room for evaluation and treatment. (The drug phentolamine, administered intravenously, slowly, in doses of 5 mg lowers the blood pressure to normal within minutes.)
5. If you need medical or dental care while on this medication, show these restrictions and instructions to your doctor.
6. If you get a cold or flu, you may use aspirin or Tylenol. For a cough, glycerin cough drops or *plain* Robitussin may be used.
7. All laxatives or stool softeners for constipation may be used.
8. For infections, all antibiotics may be safely prescribed (penicillin, tetracycline, erythromycin).
9. Avoid all other medications without first checking with physician. This especially includes any over the counter medicines bought without prescription, for example, cold tablets, nose drops, cough medicine, diet pills.
10. Side effects such as postural lightheadedness, constipation, delay in ejaculation and orgasm, muscle twitching, drowsiness, dry mouth, fluid retention, insomnia, and delay in starting urination are quite common.
11. Lightheadedness may occur following sudden changes in position. This can be avoided by getting up slowly. If the tablets are taken with meals, this and the other side effects are lessened.
12. The medication is rarely effective in less than 3 weeks.
13. Care should be taken while operating any machinery or while driving, as some patients have episodes of drowsiness in the early phase of treatment.
14. Take the medication precisely as directly. Do not regulate the number of pills or abruptly stop the medication without first consulting physician.
15. Despite the side effects and special dietary restrictions, your medication (an MAOI) is safe and effective when taken as directed.
16. If any special problems arise, call physician.

Note. "The Use of MAO Inhibitors in Clinical Practice" by D. V. Sheehan and J. B. Claycomb, In *Psychiatric Medicine Update. Massachusetts General Hospital Review for Physicians*, edited by T. C. Manschreck, 1983, New York: Elsevier. Copyright 1983 by Elsevier. Reprinted by permission. p. 151.

Appendix 25.3. Directions for taking MAO inhibitors[a]

BREAKFAST	LUNCH	EVENING MEAL	BEDTIME	DAY
NUMBER OF TABLETS				
0	0	1	0	1–3
1	0	1	0	4–7
1	1	1	0	8–12
1	1	2	0	13–19
2	1	2	0	20–26
2	2	2	0	27–33
2[b]	2	3	0	34–40
3[b]	2	3	0	41–47

[a]10 mg tablets of Parnate or Marplan or 15 mg tablets of Nardil.
[b]For Parnate and Marplan only — not Nardil.

- If no side effects (drowsiness) or benefit occurs with medications, increase dose to next level.
- When coming off MAO inhibitors do not reduce dose suddenly at a rate faster than one tablet every 3 days, ideally one tablet every 2 weeks.
- There are food or drug restrictions with MAO inhibitors.
- Caution when driving and operating high speed equipment is necessary.
- Avoid alcohol consumption.

CHAPTER 26

Combined Pharmacological and Psychological Treatment

Michael J. Telch

The past two decades have witnessed significant advances in our understanding of the nature and treatment of agoraphobia. Psychological treatments derived from classical conditioning theory and its variants have had a profound impact on the anxiety disorders, especially the phobias. More recent advances in psychological theory (i.e., Bandura, 1977; Foa & Kozak, 1986; Lang, 1977; Rachman, 1983) have further enhanced our understanding of the processes governing fear reduction.

While an impressive body of research has demonstrated the efficacy of psychological procedures that facilitate the patient's exposure to fear-evoking situations (cf. Emmelkamp, 1982; Marks, 1978; Tearnan & Telch, 1983), many patients undergoing exposure-based treatments exhibit some residual impairment in functioning (Barlow, O'Brien, & Last, 1984; McPherson, Brougham, & McLaren, 1980). Expanding exposure-based treatments to include components such as marital communication training (Arnow, Taylor, Agras, & Telch, 1985) or cognitive therapy (Williams & Rappoport, 1982) have shown relatively small gains in treatment efficacy.

The conceptualization of agoraphobia as a classically conditioned fear response to public places has been rejected and replaced with more comprehensive psychological models that take into account cognitive processes, early childhood experiences, stress, interpersonal conflict, trait anxiety, and biologic vulnerabilities. A review of psychological theories for agoraphobia is beyond the scope of this chapter. The interested reader is referred to excellent discussions by Chambless and Goldstein (1982), Halam (1985), and Mathews, Gelder, and Johnston, (1981).

Biological theories of panic disorder and agoraphobia have shown a major increase in popularity. A recent overview of progress in psychiatry published in the *Journal of the American Medical Association* was devoted almost exclusively to the topic of panic (Freedman and Glass, 1984). Several lines of empirical findings have been cited to support the thesis that panic disorder, the presumed core feature of agoraphobia, stems from an underlying biochemical abnormality. These include (a) research establishing the effectiveness of several classes of medications in eliminating panic attacks, (b) panic provocation studies suggesting that sodium lactate precipitates attacks in panic disorder patients but rarely in controls (Liebowitz, Fyer, Gorman, Dillon, et al. 1984), (c) the unusual age-of-onset distribution (Sheehan, 1982), and (d) the higher concordance rate in monozygotic than in dizygotic twins (Crowe, Pauls, Slymen, & Noyes, 1980).

Proponents of the biological position have stressed the inability of learning theory to adequately explain several key features of agoraphobia, including (a) the usual absence of a traumatic incident preceding onset, (b) the nature and spread of avoidant behavior, (c) the limited range of phobic objects, and (d) the differential effects of antidepressant medication on panic versus anticipatory anxiety (Klein, 1980).

The biologic perspective ascribes a central role to panic attacks in the onset and course of agoraphobia. Klein and others have noted that agoraphobia is almost always *preceded* by one or more episodes of spontaneous panic. While some individuals may experience recurrent panic attacks with no significant consequences, the majority of those afflicted develop strong apprehension and avoidance of situations that they believe might bring on an attack. Within this theoretical framework, anticipatory anxiety and phobic avoidance are seen as sequels of the core panic disorder.

Klein observed that imipramine appeared to block spontaneous panic but had little effect on anticipatory anxiety (Klein, 1964). This led Klein and others to propose a qualitative distinction between panic attacks and anticipatory or more generalized forms of anxiety. More recently, Sheehan (1982) has echoed Klein's position by referring to panic disorder as "endogenous" anxiety and distinguishing it from anticipatory anxiety or "exogenous" anxiety.

Within the biological framework, treatment is focused on the elimination of panic attacks through pharmacotherapy. As Klein (1984) notes, "By means of the various medications available to us, we have obtained complete removal of panic attacks in well over 95% of the patients we treated in a recent series" (p. 32). Proponents of the medical model have indicated that nonpharmacologic treatments (i.e., psychotherapy and behavior therapy) are of little value *alone* in the treatment of agoraphobia, because they fail to address the core underlying biologic disorder (Sheehan, 1982). Exposure-based therapies are viewed as potentially helpful adjuncts to medication for those refractory cases who continue to exhibit some avoidance behavior despite having their panic attacks blocked.

COMBINING PSYCHOLOGICAL AND PHARMACOLOGICAL APPROACHES

Given the complexity and multifaceted nature of the agoraphobia syndrome, combining treatment modalities that address separate symptom clusters (i.e., phobic avoidance/anxiety, spontaneous panic attacks, dysphoric mood) seems warranted. Exposure-based procedures exert their most pronounced effect on behavioral avoidance and anticipatory anxiety, but have not demonstrated strong antipanic or antidepressant effects. Patients undergoing exposure therapy to reduce phobic avoidance and anxiety may show limited progress or an increased risk for relapse if they continue to experience recurrent spontaneous panic or markedly depressed mood. Effective psychological treatments specifically targeted at the panic and depressive symptoms in agoraphobia are needed.

Several classes of antidepressant medication (i.e., tricyclics and monoamine oxidase [MAO] inhibitors) and alprazolam, a new triazolo benzodiazepine, have shown clinical usefulness in the treatment of agoraphobia and panic (Klein, 1984;

Sheehan, 1985). Advocates of the pharmacological approach claim that these medications possess strong antipanic properties that are independant of their antidepressant effects (Klein, 1984; Liebowitz, 1985; Sheehan, 1985; Zitrin, 1981). It should be noted that there currently exists much debate over the mechanism of action of these medications in treating agoraphobia (cf. Marks, 1983; Telch, Agras, Taylor, Roth, & Gallen, 1985; Telch, Tearnan, & Taylor, 1983). This issue will be discussed in more detail later in this chapter.

While antidepressants such as imipramine and phenelzine sulfate appear beneficial in suppressing panic and elevating mood, their effects on phobic avoidance and anticipatory anxiety in the absence of exposure are limited. Alprazolam, on the other hand, may have potent antipanic effects and some beneficial effect on anticipatory anxiety, but provides limited benefit on phobic avoidance or depressed mood. In our anxiety disorders clinic, many patients report past or current usage of either imipramine or alprazolam and yet continue to manifest marked disability in terms of travel restrictions and anticipatory anxiety.

Because pharmacological and psychological approaches may operate on different symptom clusters within the agoraphobia syndrome, their thoughtful combination may provide a more potent treatment for some patients. However, combined pharmacologic and psychologic treatments also may result in less than desirable outcomes. For instance, in an interesting study aimed at testing the hypothesis that experiencing anxiety during exposure is a beneficial therapeutic factor, Chambless, Foa, Groves, and Goldstein (1979) found exposure in fantasy plus intravenous methohexital sodium (Brevital®) to be significantly less effective than exposure in fantasy plus placebo.

Listed below are the four possible outcomes when combining pharmacological and psychological treatments:

1. *No change*: The benefits derived from the combined treatment would not differ from the benefits of either of the two treatments administered individually;
2. *Additive*: The benefits derived from the combined treatment would equal the sum of the benefits from the individual treatments;
3. *Potentiating (synergistic)*: The benefits derived from the combined treatment would be greater than the sum of the benefits from the individual treatments;
4. *Negative (counteractive)*: The benefits derived from combining the two treatments would be less than the benefits of either of the two treatments administered individually.

RESEARCH REVIEW

A number of controlled studies have reported on the efficacy of combining antidepressant medication with a psychological treatment in treating agoraphobia. The pharmacologic treatments most commonly studied have been the tricyclic, imipramine (Klein, 1967; Marks et al., 1983; Mavissakalian & Michelson, 1986; Sheehan, Ballenger, & Jacobsen, 1980; Telch et al., 1985; Zitrin, Klein, & Woerner, 1978, 1980; Zitrin, Klein, Woerner, & Ross, 1983) or the MAO inhibitor, phenelzine (Lipsedge et al., 1973; Mountjoy, Roth, Garside, & Leitch, 1977; Sheehan, Claycomb, & Kouretas, 1980; Solyom, Heseltine, McClure, Solyom, Ledwidge, & Steinberg, 1973; Tyrer, Candy, & Kelly, 1973). Studies examining the effectiveness of the new triazolo benzodiazepine, alprazolam, in treating agoraphobia/panic have begun to appear (Mark, 1984; Sheehan, 1985). However, these studies will not be reviewed here because none to date have looked at the combined use of alprazolam with psychological treatments.

The psychological treatments used in conjunction with pharmacologic treatment have included therapist-assisted in vivo exposure (Marks et al., 1983; Mavissakalian & Michelson, 1986; Telch et al., 1985; Zitrin et al., 1980); imaginal exposure (Zitrin et al., 1978, 1983); self-directed exposure homework (also referred to as "programmed practice": (Marks et al.,

1983; Mavissakalian & Michelson, 1986); supportive psychotherapy (Klein, 1967; Sheehan et al., 1980; Zitrin et al., 1978); and relaxation training (Marks et al., 1983). Although the nature of psychological interventions have varied among the different studies, they all include the common element of encouragement to confront fear-provoking cues outside of the therapy session. This has been proposed as a crucial therapeutic factor in the treatment of agoraphobia (Mathews et al., 1981).

The following brief review provides a sampling of research studies that have examined the combined use of pharmacological and psychological treatments for agoraphobia and panic. For a more comprehensive review of the pharmacologic treatment literature pertaining to agoraphobia, see Marks (1983) or Telch et al. (1983).

Klein and Fink (1962) initially reported on the successful use of imipramine in suppressing the panic attacks of agoraphobics. In the first controlled double-blind investigation of the use of imipramine in the treatment of agoraphobia, Klein (1964) randomly assigned 13 agoraphobics to receive imipramine or placebo. Subjects in both groups also received psychotherapy throughout a 5-week treatment. Daily dosage for imipramine began at 75 mg for the first week and was increased 75 mg each week up to a maximum dosage of 300 mg. Results demonstrated a significant superiority of imipramine over placebo on psychiatrist's ratings of overall improvement.

In a more elaborate double-blind trial, Klein and his associates (Klein, Zitrin, & Woerner, 1977; Zitrin et al., 1978, 1983) tested the relative efficacy of imipramine and behavior therapy (imaginal desensitization), imipramine plus supportive therapy, and placebo plus behavior therapy in a 26-week study. The patient population consisted of agoraphobics with panic attacks, circumscribed phobics without panic attacks, and mixed phobics with circumscribed phobias and panic attacks. Psychological treatment (imaginal desensitization or supportive therapy) was given to all subjects and consisted of 26 weekly sessions each lasting 45 minutes. Medication (imipramine or placebo) was administered throughout the course of treatment. The mean dosage for patients receiving imipramine was 180 mg/day with a range of 10 to 300 mg. The authors hypothesized that imipramine would exert a beneficial effect only for the patient groups having spontaneous panic attacks. As predicted, imipramine was found superior to placebo for the agoraphobic and mixed phobics with panic attacks, but not for the circumscribed phobics without panic attacks. The authors concluded that the imipramine effect was due to the clinical feature (i.e., spontaneous panic) common to both the agoraphobics and mixed phobics, but absent in the simple phobic group. One problem with this line of reasoning is that on their panic measures, the simple phobic group scored almost as high as the other two groups, and also showed significant improvement following treatment. Either the panic scale did not measure the phenomenon of panic or the authors erred in assuming that simple phobics do not experience spontaneous panic. Moreover, the failure to include an imipramine-only group further weakens the authors' conclusion regarding imipramine's mechanism of action. However, the results do support the conclusion that exposure is more effective when combined with imipramine than when combined with placebo.

Combining different types of phobics (i.e., agoraphobic, social phobics, and specific phobics), Solyom et al. (1973) conducted a double-blind trial comparing phenelzine and placebo in conjunction with brief psychotherapy. Both groups also were compared to a third that only received flooding in imagination. Subjects in the phenelzine and placebo groups received 45 mg/day over a 3-month period and participated in six supportive biweekly psychotherapy sessions. Subjects in the flooding condition received 12 hours of imaginal exposure to feared situations over the same 3-month period. Short-term findings indicated that all three treatment groups showed significant reductions in phobic ratings. However, the decrease in phobic ratings for the phenelzine plus psychotherapy group was significantly greater than for placebo plus psychotherapy. Contrary to Zitrin et al. (1978), subjects classified as agoraphobic improved about as much as those with specific phobias. Results of a 2-year follow-up revealed that all subjects in the phenelzine condition relapsed once the drug was discontinued, whereas only 10% of the subjects receiving flooding relapsed. The authors suggest that despite the high rate of relapse, the initial symptom suppression achieved through phenelzine may enhance the patient's motivation to remain in treatment, and thus justify its combined use with behavior therapy.

In a double-blind study designed to evaluate the combined use of imipramine and group in vivo exposure to feared situations, Zitrin et al., (1980) randomly assigned 76 agoraphobic women to receive group exposure plus imipramine or placebo. Medication (imipramine or placebo) was started 4 weeks prior to group exposure in an attempt to suppress subjects' panic attacks prior to their undergoing behavior therapy. Dosage levels began at 25 mg/day and were increased by 25 mg every other day up to 150 mg/day. Further increases up to a maximum dose of 300 mg/day were used for those patients who continued to report panic attacks. Group exposure consisted of 10 weekly sessions of 3- to 4-hour duration. Medication was given throughout treatment and continued for 12 weeks after the termination of group exposure. Results showed that both groups improved considerably by the end of treatment. However, group exposure plus imipramine was significantly superior to group exposure plus placebo on patient, therapist, and assessor ratings of overall improvement, severity of illness, spontaneous panic, and primary phobia. Significantly greater improvement for both groups was observed after 26 weeks than at 14 weeks. Unfortunately, the design of the study does not permit a determination of whether the greater improvement after 26 weeks was due to a delayed effect of the medication, longer period of self-directed exposure, or a combination of the two. The results do suggest that imipramine may be useful for enhancing the potency of group exposure therapy with agoraphobics.

In a double-blind study comparing an MAO inhibitor with a tricyclic, Sheehan, Ballenger, and Jacobsen (1980) treated 87 severe agoraphobic outpatients suffering from panic attacks with imipramine (150 mg/day), phenelzine (45 mg/day), or placebo. Patients in all groups received six hourly sessions of biweekly supportive group therapy throughout a 3-month treatment period. During group therapy, patients were encouraged to gradually approach phobic situations and were provided social reinforcement for successful performance. Results indicated that patients in the phenelzine and imipramine conditions achieved a significantly lower degree of illness, social and work disability, and avoidance behavior than patients receiving the placebo. Phenelzine was found to be statistically superior to imipramine on only 2 of the 13 scales (i.e., Symptom Severity and Avoidance scale and the Work and Social Desirability scale). Unfortunately, no data were reported on the effects of treatment on panic attacks. It is interesting that a subsample of nine patients who had specific phobias without panic attacks responded poorly to the drug treatment. This finding is consistent with Zitrin et al.'s (1978, 1983) findings that antidepressant medication confers no additional benefit to psychological treatment with simple phobics.

In a well executed 2 × 2 factorial study, Mavissakalian and Michelson (1986) compared the relative and combined effectiveness of pharmacotherapy (imipramine vs. placebo) and behavior therapy (prolonged in vivo exposure vs. discussion) in treating 62 patients meeting DSM-III (American Psychiatric Association, 1980) criteria for agoraphobia with panic attacks. Subjects in all four experimental conditions also received programmed practice (i.e., systematic behavioral instructions for self-directed exposure) similar to that employed by Marks et al. (1983). Results showed significant pre- to post-treatment improvement for all four treatment groups. Therapist-assisted exposure resulted in little added benefit on the programmed practice that all subjects were instructed to engage in between sessions. These results are consistent with Marks et al. (1983), who showed therapist-aided exposure added little to systematic self-directed exposure homework. Further support for the role of self-directed exposure comes from the authors' finding that the amount of practice predicted improvement on specific phobia measures. With respect to imipramine, their results indicated an imipramine effect on several outcome measures. However, as the authors themselves point out, the imipramine effect is really better thought of as a combined imipramine plus exposure effect given that all imipramine subjects also received programmed practice for self-directed exposure. Of particular theoretical interest was the absence of an imipramine effect on panic. While an imipramine dose-response relationship was found on phobia measures, the dose of imipramine was not related to panic blockade, nor were plasma imipramine levels. Results of the study lend further support to the hypothesis that imipramine facilitates the effects of exposure, but calls into question imipramine's mechanism of action.

Several studies have reported negative findings with respect to the facilitative effects of combining psychological and pharmacological treatments. In a well controlled 2 × 2 study of 45 agoraphobia outpatients, Marks et al. (1983) compared (a) imipramine plus therapist-aided exposure; (b) imipramine plus therapist-aided relaxation; (c) placebo plus therapist-assisted exposure; and (d) placebo plus therapist-assisted relaxation. In addition, all subjects were given a manual with structured self-exposure homework assignments. Recent evidence suggests that structured self-directed exposure homework is a potent therapeutic ingredient (Greist, Marks, Berlin, Gournay, & Norshirvani, 1980; Jannoun, Munby, Catalan, & Gelder, 1980).

Results showed that subjects improved on nearly all outcome measures and maintained their gains at the 1-year follow-up. However, there were no significant differences between imipramine and placebo groups despite imipramine plasma levels usually considered therapeutic. Therapist-assisted exposure proved to be superior to therapist-assisted relaxation. In discussing the results from this study, Marks (1983) hypothesized that the effects of imipramine on agoraphobia are primarily antidepressant in nature and that the absence of a drug effect in the present study was due to subjects' low initial depression scores. This study has been faulted for low imipramine doses and the inclusion of patients who previously had not responded to antidepressants (Liebowitz, 1985). A reanalysis of Marks' data by Raskin, Marks, and Sheehan (1983) revealed that imipramine was superior to placebo on a number of outcome measures. However, a 2-year follow-up study of these patients showed that about two thirds of the patients remained improved or much improved on phobias and spontaneous panic, with no differences between the four treatments (Cohen, Monteiro, & Marks, 1984).

In a study comparing the relative and combined effects of therapist-aided exposure and phenelzine, Solyom, Solyom, Lapierre, Peckhold, and Morton (1981) assigned 40 agoraphobics and social phobics to one of four conditions: (a) phenelzine-exposure; (b) phenelzine–no exposure; (c) placebo–exposure; (d) placebo–no exposure. Patients in all four groups received exposure homework. Results indicated that while all groups significantly decreased their phobia ratings following treatment, subjects receiving exposure improved significantly more than subjects who did not receive exposure. There were no significant differences between phenelzine and placebo, nor did phenelzine enhance the effectiveness of exposure.

These results parallel those by Marks et al. (1983). There were several interesting similarities between these two investigations that might account for their negative findings. First, both studies' mean medication dose levels have been criticized for being low. A second note of interest was the markedly lower depression scores in these two trials as compared to previous trials. If the primary mediating effect of imipramine and phenelzine is anti-depressant in nature as opposed to anti-panic, as Marks (1983) argues, then subjects' starting level of depression may predict the presence of a drug effect. It is hoped that future research will shed light on this interesting question.

COMBINED EFFECTS OF IMIPRAMINE AND EXPOSURE—SYNERGISTIC OR ADDITIVE?

In each of the previously cited imipramine trials, the medication was given in conjunction with a psychological treatment, which included as a component encouragement to enter phobic situations. Although these studies demonstrate that imipramine may facilitate the effects of exposure, the absence of an imipramine-only condition raises the question as to whether the facilitative effects of combining imipramine and exposure reflects a synergism of the two treatments or simply an additive effect. Answering this question requires a study that assesses the effects of exposure and imipramine independent of one another and compares each of these to a treatment combining exposure and pharmcotherapy. Several investigators have pointed to the confounding of imipramine and exposure and the need to examine the effects of imipramine independent of exposure (Matuzas & Glass, 1983; Telch et al., 1983; Zitrin et al., 1983).

Telch et al. (1985) recently addressed this issue. Thirty-seven severe agoraphobics with panic attacks were randomized to the following conditions: (a) imipramine alone; (b) imipramine plus intensive in vivo exposure; and (c) placebo plus intensive in vivo exposure. In order to control for the effects of exposure, subjects in the imipramine only group were given anti-exposure instructions which emphasized the importance of refraining from entering phobic situations for the first 8 weeks so that the medication would have time to build up in their systems. Diary data were collected from all participants to insure that they were complying with the no-practice instructions.

The intensive in vivo exposure treatment consisted of a total of 9 hours of therapist-assisted group exposure spread over 3 consecutive days followed by a partner-assisted home-based exposure program modeled after that of Mathews et al. (1977). Subjects and their partners were provided with slightly modified versions of the Mathews, Teasdale, Munby, Johnston, and Shaw treatment manuals and required to meet in small groups with their partners for four 90-minute weekly sessions to discuss their progress with home practice. Particular emphasis was given to helping couples overcome obstacles for home practice.

Assessments were conducted at Weeks 0, 8, and 26. Outcome measures included self-report, behavioral, and psychophysiological indices. At the 8-week assessment, subjects receiving imipramine with the no-practice instructions showed little improvement on phobic anxiety, phobic avoidance, heart rate, or panic attacks. It is interesting that subjects receiving imipramine without exposure showed a significant reduction in all three measures of depressed mood, thus attesting to the antidepressant properties of imipramine. In contrast, subjects assigned to the two exposure conditions (imipramine plus exposure or placebo plus exposure) displayed marked improvements on measures of phobic anxiety, phobic avoidance, self-efficacy, and depression. Comparisons between the combined imipramine-exposure and placebo-exposure conditions revealed a slight advantage for the combined imipramine-exposure group at 8 weeks. However, at the 26-week assessment, a clear superiority of the combined treatment emerged. Of interest was the finding that patients receiving imipramine with no-practice instructions showed significant improvement from Weeks 9 to 26 on measures of phobia once the no-practice instructions were removed. This finding further supports the potentiating effects of imipramine and self-directed exposure.

Figure 26.1 illustrates the potentiating effects of imipramine and exposure on patients' heart rate responses during the behavioral test course. Neither imipramine nor exposure produced a significant improvement in psychophysiologic responding during the test course, but the combined treatment group displayed a significant reduction in their arousal during the test course.

A similar potentiating pattern was observed for panic. As Figure 26.2 illus-

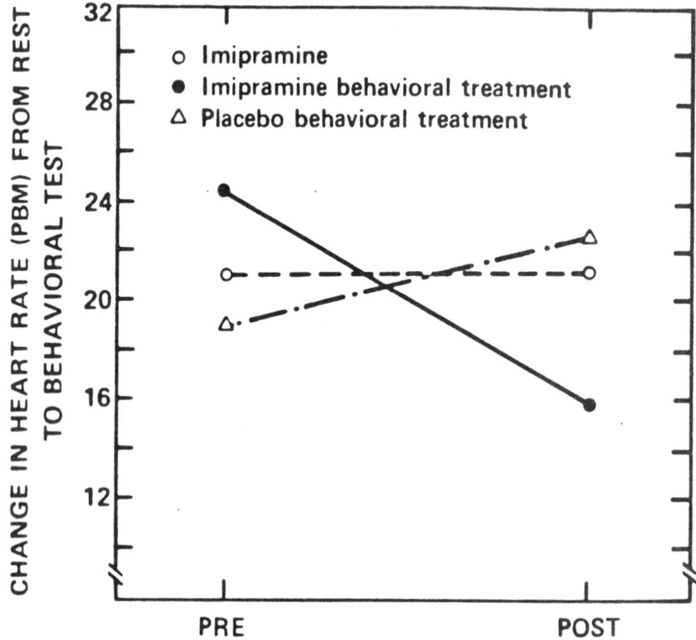

Figure 26.1. Subjects' mean changes in heart rate from rest to behavioral test walk at pre- and posttreatment. Adapted from Telch et al. (1985). Reprinted by permission.

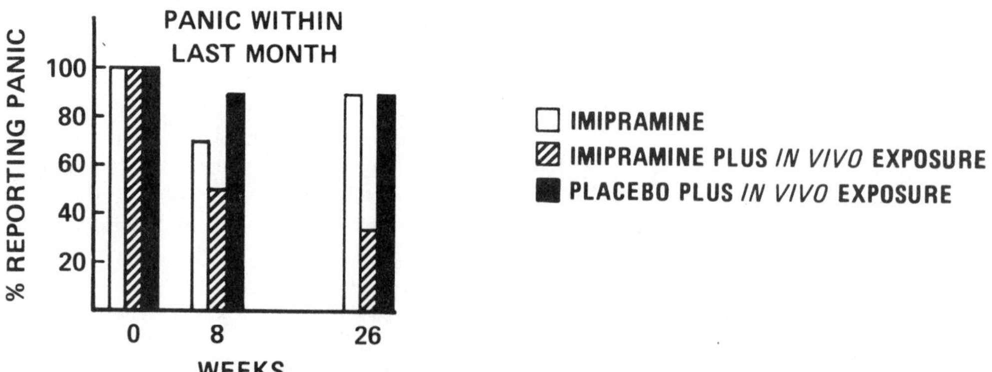

Figure 26.2. Subjects' reported panic attacks at pretreatment, posttreatment and follow-up. Adpated from Telch et al. (1985). Reprinted by permission. p. 331.

trates, antipanic effects were evident only for the combined exposure plus imipramine treatment.

The results for depression follow a somewhat different pattern, with all three groups showing similar improvement at 8 weeks. Patients receiving either imipramine alone or exposure alone showed no further improvement on depression at the 26-week assessment, whereas the combined treatment exhibited marked improvement beyond the 8-week point (see Figure 26.3).

PROPOSED MODE OF ACTION OF COMBINED PSYCHOLOGICAL AND DRUG TREATMENTS

Although the overwhelming evidence points to the efficacy of combined pharmacological and psychological approaches in the treatment of agoraphobia, much debate still exists with respect to the mechanisms governing their combined effectiveness.

Panic Suppression Hypothesis

As noted earlier, the centrality of recurrent spontaneous panic attacks in the development and maintenance of agoraphobia has become increasingly popular. One possible mechanism to account for the apparent superiority of combined pharmacological and psychological treatments is the role of panic suppression in facilitating reductions in phobic anxiety and phobic avoidance. Agoraphobics who have their spontaneous panic attacks suppressed by pharmacotherapy *and* concurrently are provided the necessary skills, support, and encouragement to venture out into situations that they previously avoided may be more willing to "test the water."

Evidence supporting the panic suppression hypothesis of antidepressants like imipramine and phenelzine come from investigations reporting that phenelzine and imipramine block lactate-induced panic attacks (Appleby, Klein, Sachar, & Levitt, 1981; Kelly, Mitchell-Heggs, & Sherman, 1971). However, this research has been plagued by some serious methodological and conceptual shortcomings which are beyond the scope of this chapter (cf. Margraf, Ehlers, & Roth, 1986, for an excellent review of the panic provocation literature).

Data pertaining to the panic suppression hypothesis from clinic-based studies are mixed. Klein and his associates have found imipramine to be superior to placebo on clinical ratings of panic in two studies (i.e., Zitrin et al., 1978, 1980), whereas, Marks et al. (1983) and Mavissa-

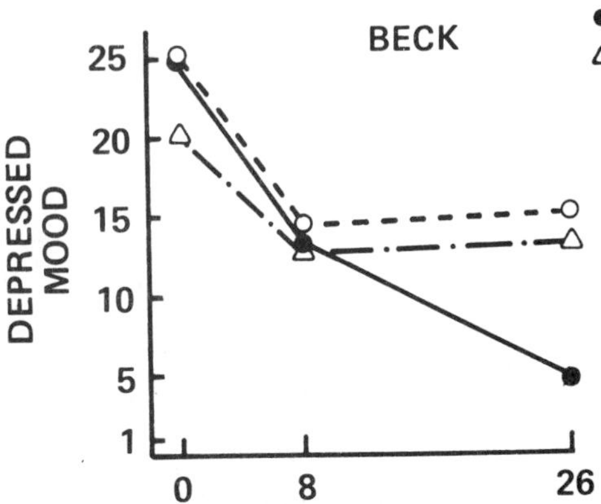

Figure 26.3. Subjects' mean scores on the Beck Depression Inventory at pretreatment, posttreatment, and follow-up. Adapted from Telch et al. (1985). Reprinted by permission. p. 331.

kalian and Michelson (1986) found no significant antipanic effect for imipramine. However, as mentioned earlier, the pharmacological effects of the medication were confounded with the effects of exposure in all of these studies.

Studies examining the panic blocking effects of imipramine or MAO inhibitors independent of exposure have been few. Tyrer et al. (1973) conducted the first double-blind trial of an MAO inhibitor (phenelzine) in the treatment of agoraphobia. Forty outpatients with a diagnosis of agoraphobia or social phobia were matched according to type of phobia, duration, sex, and level of depression and then randomly assigned to a 2-month trial of phenelzine or placebo. In the phenelzine condition, subjects started with an initial dosage of 15 mg/day and increased up to 45 mg/day after 1 week. The dosage was further increased to a maximum of 90 mg/day for those subjects who failed to improve after the first month. With the 32 subjects who completed the study, phenelzine was shown to be significantly superior to placebo on subjects' ratings of overall improvement and their ratings of secondary phobia, but not for their reported main phobia. Furthermore, improvement correlated negatively with duration of phobia and initial level of depression. At a 1-year follow-up, no differences were found between the two groups on any of the original outcome measures (Tyrer & Steinberg, 1975). The authors concluded that phenelzine given alone is no more effective in treating agoraphobia than other symptomatic treatments.

In a small pilot trial, Garakani, Zitrin, and Klein (1984) examined the effects of imipramine without psychotherapy on 10 patients with panic disorder but no phobic avoidance. The authors reported that all patients remaining in treatment ($N = 4$) exhibited a cessation of panic attacks. Mavissakalian, Michelson, and Dealy (1983) compared the effects of imipramine alone or imipramine plus self-directed exposure homework with 18 agoraphobics. Results indicated that imipramine plus exposure was significantly superior to imipramine alone on measures of panic, as well as phobia and depression. Patients receiving imipramine without exposure did show a reduction in panic, however the absence of a placebo control makes interpretation of the within-group panic changes problematic. Of particular theoretical interest was the study's analysis of the relationship between panic attacks and imipramine dose or plasma imipramine levels. Contrary to prediction, imipramine dose and imipramine plasma levels did not correlate with panic, but did correlate with phobic symptoms.

Further disconfirmatory evidence for the panic suppression hypothesis comes from the Telch et al. (1985) study in which we examined the panic suppression effects of imipramine independent of exposure to the feared situation through the utilization of an "anti-exposure" instructional set. Data collected from patients' activity diaries confirmed that they were adhering to the no-practice instructional set. Despite relatively high mean doses (above 190 mg), patients receiving imipramine plus anti-exposure instructions showed no significant reduction in panic attacks as measured by detailed panic diaries or clinical ratings of panic. It should be noted that this test of the panic suppression hypothesis was weakened by several limitations of the study — namely, the small sample size and the absence of a placebo plus anti-exposure condition. We currently are conducting a more elaborate replication of this study with a larger sample size and the inclusion of a placebo plus anti-exposure cell.

Antidepressant Hypthesis

Marks (1983) has proposed an alternative mechanism to account for the effectiveness of antidepressant medication in treating agoraphobia. He postulates that the beneficial effects of tricyclics and MAO inhibitors with agoraphobics are mediated by the drugs' antidepressant effects. In reviewing 19 studies employing antidepressant medications with phobic or obsessive-compulsive disorder, Marks concluded that in general the tricyclics and MAO inhibitors show a treatment effect for patients with high starting levels of dysphoric mood, but fail to show an effect for patient samples with low dysphoria levels. Marks argues that because antidepressants have been shown to exert a broad-spectrum effect on phobias, anxiety, panic, depression, and anger, it is premature to place panic suppression in a central explanatory role.

Two major analytic strategies have been employed to test the antidepressant hypothesis. Correlational analyses have been used to examine the relationship between depression and other indices of treatment outcome, with the prediction being that improvement should correlate positively with initial starting levels of depression. With the exception of McNair and Kahn (1981), studies have not found a positive relationship between starting levels of depression and treatment outcome. A second approach has been to group patients with respect to their starting levels of depression and compare treatment response between the depressed and nondepressed subsamples. This approach has been used by Marks (1983) and has yielded some support for the hypothesis that depressed subjects show a more favorable response to antidepressants than nondepressed subjects. However, lack of common measures across studies hinders interpretation. In addition, four of the studies included in Marks' analyses focused on obsessive-compulsive populations. It is quite possible that the role of depression in governing treatment outcome may differ between agoraphobics and obsessive-compulsives.

Data from Telch et al. (1985) fail to support Marks' antidepressant hypothesis in full. Despite high mean starting levels of depression (i.e., Beck score of 25, Zung score of 67), patients receiving imipramine in the absence of exposure showed marked improvements on depression at the 8-week posttest (i.e., Beck score of 15, Zung score of 54), with no significant improvement on measures of phobia or panic. These data suggest that elevation of agoraphobics' mood through pharmacologic channels is not sufficient to bring about changes in agoraphobic symptomology.

Dysphoria-Efficacy Hypothesis

The final mechanism to be considered involves the possible facilitative effect of mood elevation on patients' self-directed exposure. Telch et al. (1985) have proposed that elevation of mood brought about by antidepressants such as imipramine may enhance the effects of exposure through several possible channels. First, alleviation of dysphoric mood may increase the likelihood that agoraphobics will engage in self-directed exposure, either in between therapy sessions or following the termination of therapy. Anecdotally, patients frequently report bouts of depression as being a serious obstacle in their efforts to practice. Stabilization of mood through antidepressant pharmacotherapy may help eliminate this obstacle, thus increasing the total *amount* of patient-initiated exposure.

A second way in which depressed mood may interefere with self-directed exposure is through the patient's cognitive appraisal of performance accomplishments during actual practice sessions. Mood states have been shown to influence people's judgments of self-efficacy (Kavanaugh & Bower, 1985). Elevated mood raises perceived self-efficacy, whereas depressed mood lowers it. Agoraphobics who practice under conditions of despondent mood may find that negative self-evaluative thoughts which typically accompany depression may serve to undermine the adequate processing of efficacy information. In summary, the proposed dysphoria-efficacy mechanism asserts that depressed mood, if present, may attenuate the beneficial effects of exposure on patients' sense of mastery either by reducing the amount of self-initiated exposure or by attenuating the effects of exposure through negative self-evaluative processes.

The addition of antidepressant medication may reduce these dysphoria-induced efficacy inhibitory channels from operating during exposure. While this hypothesis has not been tested directly, support for this hypothesis comes from the Telch et al. (1985) study. Imipramine given in the absence of exposure produced no significant improvement in patients' self-efficacy, whereas imipramine given in conjunction with exposure produced a greater enhancement of self-efficacy than did placebo plus exposure. The postulated dysphoria-efficacy hypothesis might be tested by administering a nonpharmacologic method for alleviating depressed mood (e.g., Beck's cognitive therapy for depression), both alone and in combination with an exposure treatment. These two conditions could be compared to a third condition in which only the exposure treatment is given. To the extent that the depression treatment was effective in elevating mood, the hypothesis would predict that the combined treatment approach would show the greatest increase in self-efficacy and the most improvement on agoraphobic indices.

LIMITATIONS IN THE USE OF PHARMACOTHERAPY

Fear of Taking Medications

It has been commonly observed that a substantial number of agoraphobics are highly fearful when it comes to ingesting medications. In our imipramine study, almost 20% of the agoraphobics who contacted the clinic expressed a strong unwillingness to take a drug, even though it was presented as one that would help block their panic attacks. Among those patients who are willing to undergo pharmacologic treatment, the majority expess some fear or concern about taking medication. For some, medication concerns have very little disruptive effect and the skilled physician is able to gradually and reassuringly increase medication dose to desired levels. For others, however, anxiety with respect to medication taking can be quite disruptive even to the point of triggering panic attacks in some instances. In these cases, even the skilled physician may find it difficult or impossible to increase the patient's dose up to desired levels.

Physical Side Effects and Their Consequences

Physical side effects of pharmacotherapy deserve careful consideration. In the case of the tricyclics such as imipramine, anticholinergic side effects such as dry mouth, constipation, and agitation are common and can be quite disruptive for some patients. In addition, almost 20% of the agoraphobics placed on imipramine exhibit an extreme sensitivity to the drug, manifested by an amphetamine-like effect often resulting in insomnia, jitteriness, and irritability (Zitrin, 1981). In the case of the MAO inhibitors, postural lightheadedness, constipation, delay in urination, delay in ejaculation and orgasm, muscle twitching, sedation, fluid retention, insomnia, and excess sweating are quite common (Sheehan, Claycomb, & Kouretas, 1980). The patient on MAO inhibitors must also adhere to strict dietary prescriptions which require avoiding all foods containing cheese, all fermented food (e.g., aged meats), liver, wine, and certain medications. In the case of alprazolam, side effects include drowsiness, unsteadiness, slurring of speech, and depression (Sheehan, 1982). While the side effects of alprazolam tend to be less disruptive than with the tricyclics and the MAO inhibitors, this is counterbalanced by the difficulties associated with alprazolam withdrawal (Levy, 1984).

Physical side effects also may interact with agoraphobics' tendency to be overly fearful with respect to medication taking. The occurrence of one "true" physical side effect may produce heightened anxiety in predisposed medication phobic patients, thus leading to a host of other disruptive symptoms (e.g., palpitations) which the patient attributes to the physical effects of the drug.

One consequence of pharmacotherapy and its side effects is patient attrition. Dropout rates for the antidepressant trials with agoraphobics have typically averaged between 25% and 40%, which are well above the 10% to 20% mean dropout rate found for drug-free behavioral treatments. Medication side effects also may contribute to inadequate dose levels. As mentioned earlier, patients experiencing subjective discomfort associated with their medication taking (whether due to physical or psychological factors) often are quite reluctant to agree to increase their dose level despite reassurance from their physician.

Relapse and External Attribution of Success

Relapse upon termination of drug therapy has been a major difficulty that has yet to be adequately addressed. In the pharmacologic treatment studies to date, relapse rates have ranged from 27% to 50% (cf. Telch et al., 1983). One potential drawback in using pharmacotherapy in conjunction with psychological treatments is the tendency for patients to attribute their treatment gains to the drug and not to their own personal efforts. In our clinic we have seen patients who have been maintained on what would be considered homeopathic doses of imipramine (i.e., 8 mg) while receiving exposure therapy. Despite making impressive gains during behavioral treatment, the mere suggestion of medication withdrawal produces a marked rise in anxiety and in some cases a resumption of panic attacks. From a social learning perspective, one would predict that such external cognitive appraisal of treatment gains would interfere with the patient's development of a strong sense of efficacy to handle feared situations once they are no longer on the medication. Effective medication fading procedures need to be incorporated into combined drug and psychological treatments to help minimize faulty attributional judgments and maximize patients' sense of personal mastery. Future research is needed to identify optimal drug withdrawal strategies.

FUTURE DIRECTIONS FOR RESEARCH

Design Issues

Without exception, the studies examining the relative and combined effects of pharmacologic and psychological treatments for agoraphobia compared placebo plus a psychological treatment to either an active drug alone or an active drug plus the psychological treatment. In each study, a placebo plus psychological treatment was used to represent the psychological treatment alone. The major problem with this approach is that while comparisons between drug plus psychological treatment versus placebo plus psychological treatment allow the researcher to distinguish between pharmacologically mediated effects and psychologically mediated effects, this comparison does not permit the assessment of differential treatment outcome (Hollon & DeRubeis, 1981).

The placebo plus psychological treatment combination (whether psychotherapy or behavior therapy) is very different than psychotherapy or behavior therapy alone. Unlike psychotherapy alone, patients receiving placebo plus psychotherapy believe that they are getting medication in addition to psycotherapy. The effects of perceived medication taking on treatment outcome should not be overlooked. In an excellent discussion of this issue, Hollon and DeRubeis (1981) present data suggesting that placebo plus psychotherapy combinations may actually underestimate the effects of psychological procedures. One possible explanation for the observed negative interaction between placebo and psychological treatments was discussed earlier in the context of attributional processes and relapse. Falsely attributing treatment potency to a drug may serve to undermine the effects of the psychological treatment.

Investigators interested in evaluating the relative and combined effects of pharmacological and psychological approaches need to consider the inclusion of a psychotherapy (or behavior therapy) — no placebo condition as part of the study design. The placebo plus psychotherapy condition should be viewed as a necessary element *only* for those interested in teasing out the pharmacological versus psychological effects of a medication when administered in conjunction with a psychological treatment.

Measurement Issues

Advances in the measurement of the panic/agoraphobia syndrome will undoubtedly help to shed light on (a) a more precise deliniation of the nature of agoraphobia and panic disorder, (b) the etiologic processes governing the onset of panic attacks and agoraphobia, (c) treatment outcomes derived from existing and newly developed psychological and pharmacological treatments, (d) the mechanisms governing the independent and combined effects of both psychological and pharmacological treatments, and (e) the processes of recovery.

The use of a minimum standard set of reliable and valid self-report measures across studies would greatly facilitate intertrial comparisons and enhance interpretation of findings.

The development of more reliable and comprehensive methods for assessing panic attacks are needed. As noted earlier, despite the theoretical importance given to panic blockade among advocates of pharmacological treatments, the majority of the pharmacological trials failed to measure panic attacks (cf. Telch et al., 1983). Moreover, the assessment of panic attacks in most studies have included retrospective ratings of panic frequency and/or intensity. Patient self-monitoring of ongoing panic episodes has been employed in several studies using "panic diaries" (Taylor, Telch, & Havvic, 1982; Taylor et al., 1986; Telch et al., 1985). This type of panic assessment offers several potential advantages over retrospective ratings. First, ongoing panic monitoring helps to alleviate the potential pitfalls of retrospective ratings (e.g., reporting bias, memory decay). Second, patient monitoring of actual panic episodes provides an opportunity to collect more precise information on symptom profiles and contextual factors associated with each attack. This information can then be used to classify panic episodes into theoretically interesting categories such as spontaneous panic episodes, situational panic episodes, and anticipatory panic episodes.

In addition to panic occurrence, the assessment of patients' cognitive appraisal of panic may serve as an important index of treatment outcome as well as a useful means to test hypotheses concerning onset and recovery processes. Several distinct panic appraisal dimensions need to be considered. These include (a) perceived distress associated with specific panic sensations, (b) maladaptive beliefs concerning the anticipated adverse consequences of having a panic attack, (c) beliefs concerning the likelihood of panic occurrence in specific situations, and (d) self-efficacy in effectively coping with panic if/when it occurs. Several instruments now are available to assess these panic appraisal dimensions. Chambless and her colleagues (Chambless, Caputo, Bright, & Gallagher, 1984) have reported on the Agoraphobic Cognitions Questionnaire (ACQ) and the Body Sensations Questionnaire (BSQ) which address dimensions (a) and (b) listed above. Telch (1985) has developed the Panic Assessment Battery (PAB) which addresses dimensions (b), (c) and (d) listed above.

The use of psychophysiologic measures for process and outcome purposes deserves more attention. Recent advances in heart-rate monitoring equipment now make it possible to obtain precise measurements of heart rate on a 24-hour basis. Taylor et al. (1982) used a sophisticated ambulatory heart-rate device (Vitalog) to monitor subjects' panic episodes in their home environments. Michelson and Mavissakalian (1985) used ambulatory heart-rate monitoring to examine patterns of synchrony and desynchrony among agoraphobics undergoing behavioral and pharmacologic treatments. Because of the multidimensional nature of panic and agoraphobia complaints, further use of psychophysiologic assessment appears warranted.

Of paramount importance in the area of assessment is the need for long-term follow-up of patients who have undergone combined pharmacotherapy and psychological treatment. Relapse often has been reported as a problem with the use of pharmacotherapy with agoraphobics (Sheehan, 1982). On the other hand, several reports have esablished the durability of treatment gains for agoraphobics undergoing behavioral treatments (Marks, 1971; McPherson et al., 1980; Munby & Johnston, 1980). Unfortunately, few systematic data currently exist concerning patients' long-term status after receiving combined pharmacotherapy and psychological treatment. The most extensive longitudinal tracking of agoraphobics treated with pharmacotherapy and psychological intervention was reported by Cohen et al. (1984). They followed the patients originally treated in the Marks et al. (1983) study and found no differences between patients treated with imipramine and placebo at a 2-year follow-up. However, two thirds of the patients remained improved or much improved, which the authors attributed to the potency of the self-exposure homework that all patients received. Future studies are needed to establish the long-term benefits or risks associated with adding pharmacotherapy to exposure-based psychological treatments.

Treatment Issues

We have barely scratched the surface in understanding how best to combine drug and psychological approaches for treating agoraphobia. Critical questions with respect to the optimal sequencing of drug and psychological treatments, medication prescription parameters, psychological treatment parameters, and the tailoring of treatments to relevant patient characteristics need to be addressed.

The question of how best to sequence combined drug and psychological treatments for agoraphobia has not been studied systematically. While several studies (e.g., Mavissakalian & Michelson, 1983; Sheehan, Ballenger, & Jacobsen, 1980) initiated drug and psychological treatment simultaneously, the majority of studies began drug therapy for a period ranging from 2 to 4 weeks before initiating psychological treatment. None of the studies reviewed initiated a period of psychological treatment prior to the start of medication. Several rationales have been offered for including a pharmacotherapy period *before* initiating psychological intervention. First, providing a medication adjustment period prior to starting exposure may help to reduce the potential disruptive influence of medication side effects on the psychological treatment. This may be especially important for medications such as the tricyclics, where the side effects can be quite marked or when the psychological treatment involves active confrontation to fear-provoking situations. Future studies might consider the use of psychological interventions initiated prior to the start of drug therapy which focus on patient education and fear reduction surrounding medication use.

A second commonly cited rationale for initiating drug therapy prior to psychological intervention has been to provide ample time to activate the presumed therapeutic effects of the drug (e.g., panic blockade). The facilitation of pharmacotherapy on exposure may be attenuated if exposure is begun before the pharmacologic effects of the drug are present. This may account for the failure to find a drug-exposure facilitation in some studies (i.e., Marks et al., 1983; Solyom et al., 1981). Research examining the effects of different sequencing strategies are needed to help clarify how best to combine drugs and psychological treatments.

Other medication-related parameters may affect the efficacy of combined drug-psychological approaches in treating agoraphobia and panic. Much uncertainty still exists with respect to the relationship between medication dosage and treatment response. Several investigators have reported favorable treatment response among certain agoraphobics who were taking extremely low dosages of imipramine in conjunction with a psychological treatment (Zitrin et al., 1978). In a retrospective analysis, Mavissakalian and Perel (1985) found strong empirical support for a dose-response relationship among agoraphobics treated with imipramine and exposure. Optimal treatment response was found among those subjects on dosages of 150 mg/day or more. One should use caution in drawing conclusions from retrospective analyses of dose-response, because doses are confounded with a host of patient factors (e.g., hypochondriasis) that may affect treatment outcome. Prospective studies are needed in which agoraphobics undergoing the same psychological treatment are randomized to different fixed doses and treatment response assessed separately for each of the major symptom complaints (i.e., panic, phobia, and depression).

In addition to questions about medication dosage, further research is needed to address questions such as (a) what is the optimal duration of pharmcotherapy when used in conjunction with a psychological treatment?; (b) does the therapeutic rationale that patients receive for the drug (i.e., the drug will block your panic attacks versus the drug will help you overcome your phobias) make a difference?; and (c) are there medication fading procedures that reduce the likelihood of relapse?

Future Directions in Psychological Treatment

The efficacy of psychological approaches that encourage active confrontation and mastery over external fear-provoking cues has been clearly demonstrated in the tretment of agoraphobia. Approximately two thirds of those who undergo treatments of this type show moderate to marked improvement based on observed changes on standard self-report rating scales of anxiety and avoidance (Jansson & Ost, 1982). However, the clinical meaningfulness of these improvements has been questioned (cf. Hallam, 1985). Morever, a sizeable proportion of patients undergoing exposure-based therapies continue to exhibit some degree of psychological dysfunction and behavioral impairment (Barlow et al. 1984).

There has been a growing recognition of the conceptual inadequacies in viewing agoraphobia as a unitary fear of public places. Recent theoretical formulations have called attention to the importance of interoceptive fear cues ("fear of fear") and the cognitive appraisal of panic and its consequences in the development and maintenance of agoraphobia (Foa, Steketee, & Young, 1984; Goldstein & Chambless, 1978; Weekes, 1976). These advances in theory provide the groundwork for the development of more effective psychological treatments for agoraphobia and panic.

One exciting area for future research on psychological treatments is the development and refinement of panic innoculation and panic management strategies Relevant treatment targets include (a) reducing patients' subjective distress associated with specific panic-related physical symptoms (e.g., tachacardia, depersonalization etc); (b) correcting patients' erroneous beliefs concerning the catastrophic consequences of panic (e.g., "People will think I'm crazy," "I will have a heart attack"); and (c) increasing patients' sense of mastery in preventing, stopping, or attenuating panic. In our laboratory, we have been piloting techniques in which we individually tailor enactive experiences to patients' specific panic concerns. For instance, a patient who is most distressed over sensations of dizziness or unsteadiness during a panic attack is instructed to twirl in circles to bring on the disturbing sensation of dizziness. A patient who dreadfully fears that during a panic attack she will be forced to ask a stranger for help first observes the therapist enacting a panic attack in a public setting and asking someone for help. With firm encouragement and reassurance from the therapist, the patient then enacts a panic attack in public and practices asking someone for assistance. With respect to panic control, we are experimenting with several behavioral (i.e., training in controlled breathing) and cognitive strategies (i.e., paradoxical self-statement training—"Come on panic, hit me with your best shot"). Research along these lines really are just getting underway in a number of centers, and thus the verdict with regard to efficacy is still out.

The use of adjunct psychological therapies in conjunction with exposure needs further study. Arnow et al. (1985) found the effects of exposure could be enhanced by providing agoraphobics and their partners with marital communication skills. Strategies aimed at helping the patient manage dysfunctional mood and interpersonal conflict are just a few areas that may prove useful.

The duration of psychological treatment that typically is employed in clinical trials with agoraphobics deserves comment. Unlike in clinical practice, where psychological treatments including exposure therapies are delivered for 6 months or more, the studies examining the efficacy of combined drug and psychological treatments employed relatively brief periods of psychological treatment, ranging from 1 to 12 weeks. While moderate to marked improvement usually occurs in the majority of patients, it hardly seems surprising that with such brief treatments a sizeable proportion of patients will still exhibit some level of disability upon termination of psychological treatment. The question can then be raised: "How effective are the exposure-based therapies when delivered more intensively and over a significantly longer time frame?" Studies examining the efficacy of stronger "doses" of psychological treatments are needed.

CONCLUDING REMARKS

In reviewing the current status of research on the combined use of pharmacological and psychological approaches in treating agoraphobia and panic, several concluding comments appear warranted. With respect to clinical efficacy, there is sufficient evidence demonstrating that certain classes of medications, namely the tricyclics and MAO inhibitors, can exert a significant therapeutic effect on agoraphobic symptoms when administered in conjunction with psychological approaches that encourage the patient to confront fear provoking cues. However, the efficacy of these medications in the absence of exposure to fear-provoking situations has not been adequately demonstrated. There still is insufficient evidence to conclude whether the superiority of the combined treatment is the result of a true "potentiating effect" or the result of an "additive effect." This primarily is the result of studies not including experimental conditions that allow the efficacy of the medication to be assessed independent of the effects of exposure. It is important to note that the conclusion with respect to the superiority of the combined approach over exposure alone is limited to the period in which patients are still on medication. Continued superiority of the combined approach over exposure alone has not been demonstrated after patients have been withdrawn from medication.

With respect to mechanisms of action, the data are far from conclusive. The view proposed by biologically oriented theorists, that these drugs' primary mode of action in the treatment of agoraphobia is the pharmacological blocking of panic attacks, is becoming increasingly less tenable. While medications like imipramine can undoubtedly have antipanic effects, they have not demonstrated antipanic effects consistently. Moreover, the majority of studies have shown imipramine or phenelzine to have antiphobic and antidepressant effects as well, and, in some cases, in the absence of antipanic effects.

The hypothesis that antidepressants exert their beneficial effect on agoraphobia primarily through an antidepressant mode of action has not fared well empirically. Most studies have shown no relationship between patients' starting levels of depression and treatment response. Moreover, it has been shown that under conditions in which patients' exposure to fear-provoking situations is kept at a minimum, imipramine produces improvement in depressed mood with little or no changes in phobia or panic.

In light of the empirical evidence to

date, it appears that the tricyclics and MAO inhibitors may serve to potentiate the effects of exposure to fear-provoking cues. The mechanisms governing this potentiation are still unclear. Earlier, I proposed that the alteration in dysphoric mood brought about by the drug may potentiate the effects of exposure by increasing the likelihood that patients will engage in self-directed practice, and by correcting the devaluation of self-observed gains during exposure. Direct tests of this hypothesis currently are underway. However, it should be pointed out that the search for a unitary mode of action of these drugs on the agoraphobia/panic syndrome may be misguided. Multiple pharmacologic effects on panic/anxiety, depression, and avoidance are all possible and may vary from individual to individual. These effects must then be considered interacting with a host of psychological, social, and environmental factors.

What then are the recommendations for clinical practice with respect to the combined use of pharmacologic and psychological approaches in treating agoraphobia and panic? Mavissakalian and Michelson* (1986) have strongly recommended the combined use of imipramine and programmed practice as an efficacious and cost-effective treatment for agoraphobia. They suggest that therapist-assisted sessions then could be selectively added for the more refractory cases. While this recommendation clearly is in line with the current outcome status of combined approaches, it fails to adequately consider the drawbacks and long-term consequences in the use of pharmacotherapy agoraphobics, namely (a) the sizeable proportion of patients unwilling to go on medication, (b) problems associated with side effects, and (c) the problem of relapse and the potential for misattribution of success to an external source. These medication drawbacks, coupled with few data to support any long-term benefits after patients have been withdrawn from medication, suggest that a more appropriate recommendation may be to begin with a structured program of self-directed exposure adding therapist guided exposure if necessary. Concurrent psychological treatment focusing on other sequelae of the disorder, namely, interpersonal conflict, mood disturbance, and low self-esteem, can be addressed if needed. Pharmacologic treatment then can be selectively used for those patients whose dysphoric mood or panic fail to respond to psychological intervention.

Earlier in this chapter, I suggested that one rationale for the use of pharmacotherapy in treating agoraphobia and panic is that it addresses facets of the disorder (i.e., panic and depressed mood) that have not been adequately addressed by exposure-based therapies. In the last decade, we have witnessed significant advances in our understanding of the nature and maintenance of agoraphobia. It is hoped that these theoretical advances will lead to the development of more potent psychological treatment approaches.

REFERENCES

American Psychiatric Association. (1980). *Diagnostic and statistical manual of mental disorders* (3rd ed.). Washington, DC: Author.

Appleby, H., Klein, D. F., Sachar, P. J., & Levitt, M. (1981). The biochemical indices of lactate induced anxiety. In D. F. Klein & J. G. Rabkin (Eds.), *Anxiety: New research and changing concepts* (pp. 411–423). New York: Raven.

Arnow, B. A., Taylor, C. B., Agras, W. S., & Telch, M. J. (1985). Enhancing agoraphobia treatment outcome by changing couple communication patterns. *Behavior Therapy, 16*, 452–467.

Bandura, A. (1977). Self-efficacy: Toward a unifying theory of behavioral change. *Psychological Review, 84*, 191–215.

Barlow, D. H., O'Brien, G. T., & Last, C. G. (1984). Couples treatment of agoraphobia. *Behavior Therapy, 15*, 41–58.

*In a recent communication, Dr. Michelson has indicated that he no longer advocates this position.

Beck, A. T., Ward, C. H., Mendelsohn, M., Mock, J., & Erbaugh, J. (1961). An inventory for measuring depression. *Archives of General Psychiatry, 4,* 561–571.

Chambless, D. L., & Goldstein, A. J. (Eds.). (1982). *Agoraphobia: Multiple perspectives on theory and treatment.* New York: Wiley.

Chambless, D. L., Caputo, G. C., Bright, P., & Gallagher, R. (1984). Assessment of fear in agoraphobics: The Body Sensations Questionnaire and the Agoraphobic Cognitions Questionnaire. *Journal of Consulting and Clinical Psychology, 52,* 1090–1097.

Chambless, D. L., Foa, E. B., Groves, G. A., & Goldstein, A. J. (1979). Flooding with Brevital in the treatment of agoraphobia: Countereffective? *Behaviour Research and Therapy, 17,* 243–251.

Cohen, S. D., Monteiro, W., & Marks, I. M. (1984). Two-year follow-up of agoraphobics after exposure and imipramine. *British Journal of Psychiatry, 144,* 276–281.

Crowe, R. R., Pauls, D. L., Slymen, D. J. & Noyes, R. (1980). A genetic study of anxiety neurosis. *Archives of General Psychiatry, 37,* 77–79.

Emmelkamp, P. M. G. (1982). In vivo treatment of agoraphobia. In D. L. Chambless & A. J. Goldstein (Eds.), *Agoraphobia: Multiple perspectives on theory and treatment* (pp. 43–75). New York: Wiley.

Foa, E. B., & Kozak, M. J. (1986). Emotional processing of fear: Exposure to corrective information. *Psychological Bulletin, 99,* 20–35.

Foa, E. B., Steketee, G., & Young, M. C. (1984). Agoraphobia: Phenomenological aspects, associated characteristics, and theoretical considerations. *Clinical Psychology Review, 4,* 431–457.

Freedman, D. X., & Glass, R. M. (1984). Psychiatry. *Journal of the American Medical Association, 252,* 2223–2228.

Garakani, H., Zitrin, C. M., & Klein, D. F. (1984). Treatment of panic disorder with imipramine alone. *American Journal of Psychiatry, 141,* 446–448.

Goldstein, A. J., & Chambless, D. L. (1978). A reanalysis of agoraphobia. *Behavior Therapy, 9,* 47–59.

Greist, J. H., Marks, I. M., Berlin, F., Gournay, K., & Noshirvani, H. (1980). Avoidance versus confrontation of fear. *Behavior Therapy, 11,* 1–14.

Hallam, R. S. (1985). *Anxiety: Psychological perspectives on panic and agoraphobia.* London: Academic Press.

Hollon, S. D., & DeRubeis, R. J. (1981). Placebo-psychotherapy combinations: Inappropriate representation of psychotherapy in drug-psychotherapy comparative trials. *Journal of Consulting and Clinical Psychology, 90,* 467–477.

Jannoun, L., Munby, M., Catalan, J., & Gelder, M. (1980). A home-based treatment program for agoraphobia. *Behavior Therapy, 11,* 294–305.

Jansson, L., & Ost, L. (1982). Behavioral treatment for agoraphobia: An evaluative review. *Clinical Psychology Review, 2,* 311–336.

Kavanaugh, D. J., & Bower, G. H. (1985). Mood and self-efficacy: Impact of joy and sadness on perceived capabilities. *Cognitive Therapy and Research, 9*(5), 507–525.

Kelly, D., Mitchell-Heggs, N., & Sherman, D. (1971). Anxiety in the effects of sodium lactate assessed clinically and physiologically. *British Journal of Psychiatry, 119,* 468–470.

Klein, D. F. (1964). Delineation of two drug-responsive anxiety syndromes. *Psychopharmacologia, 5,* 397–408.

Klein, D. F. (1967). Importance of psychiatric diagnosis in prediction of clinical drug effects. *Archives of General Psychiatry, 16,* 118–126.

Klein, D. F. (1980). Anxiety reconceptualized. *Comprehensive Psychiatry, 21,* 411–427.

Klein, D. F. (1984). Psychopharmacologic treatment of panic disorder. *Psychosomatics, 25,* 32–36.

Klein, D. F., & Fink, M. (1962). Psychiatric reaction patterns to imipramine. *American Journal of Psychiatry, 119,* 432–438.

Klein, D. F., Zitrin, C. M., & Woerner, M. G. (1977). Imipramine and phobia. *Psychopharmacological Bulletin, 13,* 24–27.

Klein, D. F., Zitrin, C. M., Woerner, M. G., & Ross, D. C. (1983). Treatment of phobias: Behavior therapy and supportive psychotherapy: Are there any specific ingredients? *Archives of General Psychiatry, 40,* 139–145.

Lang, P. J. (1977). Imagery in therapy: An information processing analysis of fear. *Behavior Therapy, 8,* 862–886.

Levy, H. B. (1984). Delirium and seizures due to abrupt alprazolam withdrawal. *Journal of Clinical Psychiatry, 45,* 38–39.

Liebowitz, M. R. (1985). Imipramine in the treatment of panic disorder and its complications. *Psychiatric Clinics of North America, 8,* 37–47.

Liebowitz, M. R., Fyer, A. J., Gorman, J. M., Dillon, D., Appleby, I. L., Levy, G., Anderson, S., Levitt, M., Palij, M., Davies, S. O., & Klein, D. F. (1984). Lactate provocation of panic attacks. *Archives of General Psychiatry, 41,* 764–770.

Lipsedge, M. S., Hajioff, J., Huggins, P., Napier, L., Pearce, J., Pike, D. J., & Rich, M. (1973). The management of severe agoraphobia: A comparison of iproniazid and systematic desensitization. *Psychopharmacologia, 32,* 667–680.

Margraf, J., Ehlers, A., & Roth, W. T. (1986). Sodium lactate infusions and panic attacks: A review and critique. *Psychosomatic Medicine, 48*(1–2), 23–51.

Mark, S. L. (1984). Agoraphobia and panic disorder: Treatment with alprazolam. *Texas Medicine, 80,* 50–52.

Marks, I. M. (1971). Phobic disorders four years after treatment. *British Journal of Psychiatry, 118,* 683–688.

Marks, I. M. (1978). Behavioral psychotherapy of adult neurosis. In S. L. Garfield & A. E. Bergin (Eds.), *Handbook of psychotherapy and behavior change* (pp. 493–547). New York: Wiley.

Marks, I. M. (1983). Are there anticompulsive or antiphobic drugs? Review of the evidence. *British Journal of Psychiatry, 143,* 338–347.

Marks, I. M., & Mathews, A. M. (1979). Brief standard self-rating for phobic patients. *Behaviour Research and Therapy, 17,* 263–267.

Marks, I. M., Gray, S., Cohen, D., Hill, R., Mawson, D., Ramm, E., & Stern, R. S. (1983). Imipramine and brief therapist-aided exposure in agoraphobics having self-exposure homework. *Archives of General Psychiatry, 40,* 153–162.

Mathews, A. M., Gelder, M. G., & Johnston, D. W. (1981). *Agoraphobia: Nature and treatment.* New York: Guilford.

Mathews, A. M., Teasdale, J., Munby, M., Johnston, D., & Shaw, P. (1977). A home-based treatment program for agoraphobia. *Behavior Therapy, 8,* 915–924.

Matuzas, W., & Glass, R. M. (1983). Treatment of agoraphobia and panic attacks. *Archives of General Psychiatry, 40,* 220–222.

Mavissakalian, M., & Michelson, L. (1983). Self-directed in vivo exposure practice in behavioral and pharmacological treatments of agoraphobia. *Behavior Therapy, 14,* 506–519.

Mavissakalian, M., & Michelson, L. (1986). Agoraphobia: Relative and combined effectiveness of therapist-assisted in vivo exposure and imipramine. *Journal of Clinical Psychiatry, 47,* 117–122.

Mavissakalian, M., & Perel, J. (1985). Imipramine in the treatment of agoraphobia: Dose-response relationships. *American Journal of Psychiatry, 142,* 1032–1036.

Mavissakalian, M., Michelson, L., & Dealy, R. S. (1983). Pharmacological treatment of agoraphobia: Imipramine versus imipramine with programmed practice. *British Journal of Psychiatry, 143,* 348–355.

McNair, D. M., & Kahn, R. J. (1981). Imipramine compared with a benzodiazepine for agoraphobia. In D. F. Klein & J. G. Rabkin (Eds.), *Anxiety: New research and changing concepts* (pp. 69–80). New York: Raven Press.

McPherson, F. M., Brougham, L., & McLaren, S. (1980). Maintenance of improvement in agoraphobic patients treated by behavioural methods: A four-year follow-up. *Behaviour Research and Therapy, 18,* 150–152.

Michelson, L., & Mavissakalian, M. (1985). Psychophysiological outcome of behavioral and pharmacological treatments of agoraphobia. *Journal of Consulting and Clinical Psychology, 53,* 229–236.

Mountjoy, C. Q., Roth, M., Garside, R. F., & Leitch, I. M. (1977). A clinical trial of phenelzine in anxiety depressive and phobic neuroses. *British Journal of Psychiatry, 131,* 486–492.

Munby, M., & Johnston, D. W. (1980). Agoraphobia: The long-term follow-up of behavioural treatment. *British Journal of Psychiatry, 137,* 418–427.

Rachman, S. (1983). Fresh possibilities in the treatment of agoraphobia. *Behaviour Research and Therapy, 11,* 567–574.

Raskin, A., Marks, I. M., & Sheehan, D. V. (1983). The influence of depressed mood on the antipanic effects of antidepressant drugs. Unpublished manuscript.

Sheehan, D. V. (1982). Panic attacks and phobias. *New England Journal of Medicine, 307,* 156–158.

Sheehan, D. V. (1985). Monoamine oxidase inhibitors and alprazolam in the treatment of panic disorder and agoraphobia. *Psychiatric Clinics of North America, 8,* 49–62.

Sheehan, D. V., Ballenger, J., & Jacobsen, G. (1980). Treatment of endogenous anxiety with phobic, hysterical, and hypochondrical symptoms. *Archives of General Psychiatry, 37,* 51–59.

Sheehan, D. V., Claycomb, J. B., & Kouretas, N. (1980). MAO inhibitors: Prescription and patient management. *International Journal of Psychiatry and Medicine, 10,* 99–121.

Solyom, L., Heseltine, G. F. D., McClure, D. J., Solyom, C., Ledwidge, B., & Steinberg, G. (1973). Behaviour therapy versus drug therapy in the treatment of phobic neurosis. *Canadian Psychiatric Association, 18,* 25–31.

Solyom, C., Solyom, L., LaPierre, Y., Pecknold,

J., & Morton, L. (1981). Phenelzine and exposure in the treatment of phobias. *Biological Psychiatry, 16,* 239–247.

Spielberger, C., Gorsuch, A., & Lushene, R. (1970). *The Stait-Trait Anxiety Inventory.* Palo Alto, CA: Consulting Psychologists Press.

Taylor, C. B., Sheik, J., Agras, W. S., Roth, W. T., Margraf, J., Maddock, R. J., & Gossard, D. (1986). Ambulatory heart rate changes in patients with panic attacks. *American Journal of Psychiatry, 143,* 478–482.

Taylor, C. B., Telch, M. J., & Havvik, D. (1982). Ambulatory heart rate changes during panic attacks. *Journal of Psychiatric Research, 17,* 261–266.

Tearnan, B. H., & Telch, M. J. (1983). Phobic disorders. In H. E. Adams & J. Sutker (Eds.), *Comprehensive handbook of psychopathology.* New York: Plenum.

Telch, M. J. (1985). The panic assessment battery. Unpublished manuscript, Stanford University, Stanford, CA.

Telch, M. J., Agras, W. S., Taylor, C. B., Roth, W. T., & Gallen, C. (1985). Combined pharmacological and behavioral treatment for agoraphobia. *Behaviour Research and Therapy, 23,* 325–335.

Telch, M. J., Tearnan, B. H., & Taylor, C. B. (1983). Antidepressant medication in the treatment of agoraphobia: A critical review. *Behaviour Research and Therapy, 21,* 505–517.

Tyrer, P., Candy, J., & Kelly, D. (1973). Phenelzine in phobic anxiety: A controlled trial. *Psychological Medicine, 3,* 120–124.

Tyrer, P., & Steinberg, D. (1975). Symptomatic treatment of agoraphobia and social phobias: A follow-up study. *British Journal of Psychiatry, 127,* 163–168.

Weekes, C. (1976). *Simple effective treatment for agoraphobia.* New York: Hawthorn.

Williams, S. L., & Rappoport, A. (1982). Cognitive treatment in the natural environment for agoraphobics. *Behavior Therapy, 14,* 299–313.

Zitrin, C. M. (1981). Combined pharmacological and psychological treatment of phobias. In M. M. Mavissakalian & D. H. Barlow (Eds.), *Phobia: Nature and measurement* (pp. 35–62). New York: Guilford Press.

Zitrin, C. M., Klein, D. F., & Woerner, M. G. (1978). Behavior therapy, supportive psychotherapy, imipramine, and phobias. *Archives of General Psychiatry. 35,* 307–316.

Zitrin, C. M., Klein, D. F., & Woerner, M. G. (1980). Treatment of agoraphobia with group exposure in vivo and imipramine. *Archives of General Psychiatry, 37,* 63–72.

Zitrin, C. M., Klein, D. F., Woerner, M. G., & Ross, D. C. (1983). Treatment of phobias: Comparison of imipramine hydrochloride and placebo. *Archives of General Psychiatry, 40,* 125–138.

PART VI

Special Topics

CHAPTER 27

Anxiety Disorders in Childhood and Adolescence

Cynthia G. Last

Epidemiological studies conducted during the past two decades indicate that anxiety symptoms are quite common in children of all ages and both sexes (see Orvaschel & Weissman, 1985). Moreover, although specific incidence and prevalence rates currently are unavailable for anxiety *disorders*, the clinical literature and several empirical investigations suggest that they occur with reasonable frequency among psychiatrically ill children and adolescents.

Despite the apparent prevalence of childhood anxiety disorders, in conjunction with the marked impairment that can result from these disorders (e.g., school attendance, academic performance, peer relationships, etc.), very few empirical studies have been conducted that have focused on their nature or phenomenology. In this chapter, we first will review the DSM-III (American Psychiatric Association, 1980) classification system for childhood anxiety disorders. We then will discuss two of the disorders in detail, as to their characteristics, reliability, and validity.

DSM-III CLASSIFICATION

DSM-III distinguishes three anxiety disorders of childhood or adolescence: separation anxiety disorder, avoidant disorder of childhood or adolescence, and overanxious disorder. While anxiety is considered to be the central feature for this entire group of disorders, it is focused on specific situations in separation anxiety and avoidant disorders, and generalized to a variety of situations in the case of overanxious disorder.

According to DSM-III, the hallmark of *separation anxiety disorder* is excessive anxiety concerning separation from major attachment figures (e.g., parents) and/or from home or other familiar surroundings. In *avoidant disorder of childhood or adolescence*, anxiety is focused on contact with strangers, resulting in persistent avoidance or shrinking from both adults and peers. In contrast to both of these diagnostic categories, the essential feature of *overanxious disorder* is excessive worry and fearful behavior that is not limited to a specific situation or object.

Three other anxiety diagnoses also are included in DSM-III which may be applied to children and adolescents as well as adults. In *phobic disorder,* fear and avoidance are associated with a specific situation or object, with the exclusion of separation ("separation anxiety disorder") or contact with strangers ("avoidant disorder"). The essential feature of *panic disorder* involves panic attacks that do not occur only upon exposure of a particular phobic stimulus, life-threatening situation, or during physical exertion. Finally, *obsessive-compulsive disorder* is characterized by recurrent obsessions or compulsions.

It is interesting that separation anxiety and avoidant disorders were not included in previous versions of the DSM. By contrast, overanxious disorder ("overanxious reaction") was specified as a diagnostic category for children and adolescents in DSM-II (American Psychiatric Association, 1968). Phobic disorder ("phobic neurosis") and obsessive–compulsive disorder ("obsessive–compulsive neurosis") also were included in DSM-II, although these categories were applied to adults as well as children and adolescents. Similarly, the DSM-II diagnosis of "anxiety neurosis" was used to classify individuals of all ages whose disorders were characterized by nonphobic anxiety reactions or panic attacks. As indicated in DSM-III, this diagnostic category has since been divided into two distinct diagnoses: panic disorder and generalized anx-iety disorder (which only may be applied to persons 18 years or older).

Based on our clinical and research experience, we have found that the vast majority (76%) of youngsters referred to our childhood anxiety clinic present with either separation anxiety disorder or overanxious disorder (Last, Hersen, Kazdin, Finkelstein, & Strauss, in press). In the following section, both of these disorders are discussed in detail, with respect to their reliability and discriminative validity.

RELIABILITY

Anxiety Disorders of Childhood or Adolescence is a relatively new category, first appearing in the third version of the DSM in 1980. As such, data only recently have been collected that address the reliability of the overall diagnostic category, as well as the specific diagnoses included in the category (i.e., separation anxiety disorder, avoidant disorder, and overanxious disorder). Such information particularly is important to consider because unreliable diagnosis imposes serious constraints, or a "ceiling," on diagnostic validity.

A number of investigations have produced data on the reliability of the DSM-III subclass of Anxiety Disorders of Childhood or Adolescence. A summary of results from these studies is provided in Table 27.1 and will be described in detail here.

In an examination of the reliability of the 1978 draft of DSM-III, Williams and Spitzer (1980) evaluated clinician agreement for DSM-III diagnoses in two different field trials. During Phase I,, 71 children and adolescents were interviewed, with 60% of these cases evaluated separately (i.e., two separate interviews conducted by two different clinicians). Similarly, 55 children and adolescents were assessed during Phase II, with 67% consisting of separate evaluations.

Results from Phase I revealed poor agreement for Anxiety Disorders of Childhood or Adolescence ($\kappa = .25$, $n = 6$). When the number of such cases increased slightly during Phase II, reliability also increased ($\kappa = .44$, $n = 9$). Unfortunately, the reliability of each of the three diagnoses included in the diagnostic category was not evaluated, most probably due to the relatively small number of cases assessed during the field trials.

Werry, Methven, Fitzpatrick, and Dixon (1984) investigated the reliability of DSM-III diagnoses in 195 children and adolescents on an inpatient psychiatric unit in

Table 27.1. Reliability Studies of the DSM-III Diagnostic Category Anxiety Disorders of Childhood or Adolescence

STUDY	METHOD		κ OR %	N
Cantwell et al. (1979)[a]	Case history (written)		15%	1
Last et al. (1986)	Structured interview (test-retest)		.85	44
Mezzich & Mezzich (1985)	Case history (written)	.20	—	
Strober et al. (1981)	Structured interview (interrater)		.47	6
Werry et al. (1984)	Case history ("in vivo")		.69	24
Williams & Spitzer (1980)	Unstructured interview	I	.25	6
	(interrater and test-retest)	II	.44	9

[a]This case was diagnosed as separation anxiety disorder.

New Zealand. In this study, an "in vivo case history approach" was utilized, where both clinicians' diagnoses were based on a verbal presentation of each case. Therefore, unlike the DSM-III field trials, clinicians based their diagnoses on case histories (rather than live interviews), and were exposed to exactly the same diagnostic information. Results for anxiety disorders revealed good agreement for the overall category of Anxiety Disorders of Childhood or Adolescents (κ = .69, n = 24), as well as its subcategories (κ = .66).

Mezzich and Mezzich (1985) also used a case history approach to evaluate diagnostic agreement, although here the investigators used written presentations. The reliability coefficient for Anxiety Disorders of Childhood or Adolescence was quite low (κ = .20), although statistically significant.

In an investigation with hospitalized adolescents, Strober, Green, and Carlson (1981) examined diagnostic agreement for joint interviews conducted with a structured interview schedule. Despite statistical significance, the authors note that reliability for Anxiety Disorders of Childhood or Adolescence was lower than for any of the other categories evaluated (κ = .47, n = 6).

Using written case histories of 24 child and adolescent patients, Mattison, Cantwell, Russell, and Will (1979) investigated clinician agreement using 20 child psychiatrist raters. Data are presented for each case as percentage agreement among the raters for (a) the most common diagnosis, and (b) the second most common diagnosis. One case received a second most common DSM-III diagnosis of overanxious disorder. However, only 30% of clinicians showed agreement on this diagnosis.

In a second report by this group (Cantwell, Russell, Mattison, & Will, 1979), rather agreement with "expected diagnosis" (i.e., the diagnosis that the authors considered most appropriate) is presented for each case. One case was judged by the investigators to have a primary diagnosis of separation anxiety disorder. However, only 15% agreement was obtained for this case.

Differences in findings obtained from these studies may be due, at least in part, to variation in the experimental designs used to determine reliability. As Grove, Andreasen, McDonald-Scott, Keller, and Shapiro (1981) recently noted, a number of research designs are appropriate for use in reliability studies, each having its own particular advantages and disadvantages. For example, the written case history or case vignette approach is by far the least expensive method for evaluating reliability. However, it also is the *least stringent* because it reduces sources of variation that usually occur when rating and diagnosing patients. Indeed, the only sources of variability that influence agreement in the case history designs are differences between diagnosticians in interpreting case vignettes and applying DSM-III criteria. Thus, discrepancies due to variations in patients' accounts, clinicians' interviewing styles, and interpretation of patients' nonverbal behavior do not occur.

Given that the case history approach is less stringent, higher estimates of reliability are expected to occur. As Grove et al. (1981) indicate "if the obtained reliability in such a study is low, there is little point in doing more expensive and stringent studies" (p. 409). In other words, it is unlikely that adequate reliability will be achieved using more stringent designs, when the least stringent design already has revealed problems with diagnostic reliability.

In light of these considerations, it is somewhat surprising and discouraging that Cantwell et al. (1979), Mattison et al. (1979), and Mezzich and Mezzich (1985) obtained relatively poor diagnostic agreement using this method. By contrast, Werry et al. (1984) showed substantially better reliability using a modified version of this method, where case histories were presented verbally. But the verbal presentation may have introduced unwanted biases. Also, larger sample sizes may have contributed to the positive findings obtained by this group.

Another approach that often is used in reliability studies is the interrater agreement design. Here, one rater interviews a subject while another simultaneously observes the same interview and rates it independently (Grove et al., 1981). The main disadvantage of this design is that deceptively high agreement may result from the observer seeing the rater's movements or receiving cues. Despite this drawback, the interviewer-observer design is considered to be a more stringent test of diagnostic reliability than the case history approach. As such, findings reported by Strober et al. (1981) probably can be regarded as roughly comparable to Werry et al.'s (1984) results obtained using the in vivo case history method. However, it should be noted that for interrater agreement, kappa coefficients of .70 or greater usually are considered to represent satisfactory levels of agreement (e.g., Spitzer, Forman, & Nee, 1979). Thus, Strober et al.'s (1981) agreement for Anxiety Disorders of Childhood or Adolescence (.47) falls well below the acceptable level.

The most stringent test of diagnostic reliability is the test-retest design, where subjects initially are interviewed by one clinician and then reinterviewed, after a certain time interval, by a second clinician. The time interval between assessments can vary from short intervals (e.g., morning–afternoon) to long intervals (e.g., several months); the longer the interval, the more likely that variability due to genuine change in the patient's condition will occur. Two other sources of confound in this design include variations in the patient's report in the two interviews and differences in the interviewing style of the two diagnosticians (Grove et al., 1981). As Grove et al. (1981) point out, the test-retest design most closely approximates actual interviewer behavior in the research or clinical setting. In fact, during the DSM-III field trials (Williams & Spitzer, 1980), more than half of all interviews were conducted in this manner (i.e., separate interviews administered by two different clinicians), with the remaining cases consisting of joint interviews (i.e., interrater agreement design). Given the more stringent nature of this study's design, it is not all that surprising that kappa coefficients for Anxiety Disorders of Childhood or Adolescence were relatively low.

Recent data from Last et al. (in press) indicate that it is possible to achieve good agreement between clinicians conducting separate interviews with this population. Findings from this study revealed excellent reliability for the overall category of Anxiety Disorders of Childhood or Adolescence ($\kappa = .85$, $n = 44$). Moreover, agreement was very high for two of the three anxiety diagnoses included in this category: separation anxiety disorder ($\kappa = .81$, $n = 28$) and overanxious disorder (κ = .82, n = 32). Finally, reliability also was calculated for cases that had only one versus both anxiety disorders: separation anxiety disorder only (κ = .77, n = 12), overanxious disorder only (κ = .96), both separation anxiety and overanxious disorders (κ = .72, n, = 16).

The high level of agreement reached by these investigators most probably can be attributed to two factors: (a) use of a semi-structured interview schedule (the *Interview Schedule for Children*: Kovacs, 1978, 1983), and (b) use of a short test-retest interval (morning–afternoon). Previous research had indicated that structured and semi-structured interviews (as opposed to unstructured interviews) increase diagnostic reliability by reducing information variance (i.e., differences in the amount and kinds of information about patients available to clinicians: Endicott & Spitzer, 1978). Thus, it is possible that agreement during the DSM-III field trials might have been enhanced (and closer to findings obtained by our group) if a structured or semi-structured interview had been employed. Moreover, as mentioned earlier, use of a short test-retest interval in the Last et al. (in press) study minimized the likelihood of actual change in a patient's status, also reducing information variance.

VALIDITY

Clinical studies and case reports have provided some evidence for the "face" validity of DSM-III diagnoses of separation anxiety disorder and overanxious disorder. Although separation anxiety was not included in the DSM classification until 1980 (DSM-III), a number of publications prior to that time have referred to separation anxiety as a clinically significant phenomenon in both children and adolescents (e.g., Berg, Nichols, & Pritchard, 1969; Broadwin, 1932; Chazan, 1962; Eisenberg, 1958; Freud, 1950; Gittelman-Klein & Klein, 1971, 1973; Hersov, 1960, Johnson, Falstein, Szurek, & Svendson, 1941; Kahn & Nursten, 1962; Klein, 1964; Partridge, 1939; Smith, 1970; Warren, 1948). While most of the literature preceding DSM-III classified these children as having "school phobia," rather than separation anxiety per se, it has been noted that a large number of school phobics have clinically significant levels of separation anxiety (Berg, 1980; Bowlby, 1975; Eysenck & Rachman, 1965; Gittelman-Klein & Klein, 1980; Ollendick & Mayer, 1985; Smith, 1970), with rates estimated to range from 30% to 90% of school phobics. Similarly, the clinical literature on overanxious disorder has supported its existence as a diagnostic entity (e.g., Hewitt & Jenkins, 1946; Jenkins, 1964, 1969; Jenkins, Nureddin, & Shapiro, 1966; Lewis, 1954; Shamsie, 1968; Suh & Carlson, 1977).

According to Feighner, Robins, Guze, Woodruff, Winokur, and Munoz (1972), empirical studies aimed at establishing the validity of a diagnostic category can be divided into five types: (a) clinical description, (b) laboratory studies, (c) delimitation from other disorders, (d) follow-up study, and (e) family study. In *clinical description* studies, the clinical picture of the disorder is characterized by defining the clinical (symptomatology) and associated features (e.g., sociodemographic variables, patterns of comorbidity, etc.). Included among *laboratory studies* are anatomical, chemical, radiological, and physiological findings. *Delimitation from other disorders* emphasizes the homogeneity of a diagnostic group through exclusion of borderline and doubtful cases.

A *follow-up study* may contribute to the study of diagnostic validity in two ways. First, follow-up allows one to determine if a significant number of the original patients present with the clinical features of another psychiatric disorder at a later point in time. This may be referred to as the clinical course of the disorder or the stability of the diagnostic category. If a significant number of the index cases are found to meet criteria for any other psychiatric disorder at follow-up, this finding suggests that the original patients did not comprise a homogeneous group and that the diagnostic criteria for the disorders under investigation must be modified (Feighner et al., 1972; Guze, 1967). Second, follow-up enables one to assess whether marked differences in outcome or prognosis occur (e.g., complete recovery versus chronic illness, etc.), which again would suggest that the group is not homogeneous and that the diagnostic criteria must be modified. As Feighner et al. (1972) point out, however, marked differences in outcome

> is not as compelling in suggesting diagnostic heterogeneity as the finding of a change in diagnosis. The same illness may have a variable prognosis, but until we know more about the fundamental nature of . . . psychiatric illnesses, marked differences in outcome should be regarded as a challenge to the validity of the original diagnosis. (p. 57)

Finally, a *family study* allows one to assess whether increased prevalence of the same disorder exists among the close relatives of index cases. Such findings strongly suggest that one is dealing with a valid entity, independent of the question of etiology (i.e., heredity and/or environmental causes). It should be noted, however, that while most psychiatric illnesses have been shown to run in families, absence of an increased family prevalence does not necessarily negate the validity of a diagnostic category because not all illnesses show familial aggregation (Guze, 1967).

Clinical description

Since publication of DSM-III, only three studies have reported any information on the clinical or associated features of separation anxiety disorder (SAD) and overanxious disorder (OAD) (Bernstein & Garfinkel, 1986; Hershberg, Carlson, Cantwell, & Strober, 1982; Last et al., in press). Two of these studies (Bernstein & Garfinkel, 1986; Hershberg et al., 1982) addressed the specific question of overlap between anxiety and depressive disorders in children. Hershberg et al. (1982) found that none of 10 children diagnosed as having SAD or OAD met DSM-III criteria for major depression. By contrast, Bernstein and Garfinkel (1986) reported that the majority of their sample of 16 adolescents with SAD or OAD showed major depression.

Last et al. (in press) examined and compared the demographic characteristics and patterns of comorbidity associated with SAD and OAD in a clinical sample of 69 children and adolescents. It is interesting that the two anxiety disorders differed significantly on several dimensions: age, social class, and presence of a coexisting anxiety disorder. Children with SAD were younger and from families of lower socioeconomic status than children with OAD. Children with OAD were much more likely than children with SAD to present with an additional concurrent anxiety disorder, usually simple phobia or panic disorders.

It is important to note that Last et al. (in press) found that approximately one third of the SAD and OAD children met DSM-III criteria for major depression. While these findings correspond to those previously obtained for anxious adults (e.g. Barlow, 1985), they differ somewhat from those obtained by Bernstein and Garfinkel (1986) and Hershberg et al. (1982).

Differences in findings among our study and the two studies just cited may be due, at least in part, to differences in the age of the samples. Overall, we found that anxious children who presented with a concurrent major depression tended to be older than those who did not exhibit major depression. In the Hershberg et al. study, they reported that their anxiety group tended to be young (although specific ages were not reported), which may have accounted for the absence of depression. Alternatively, Bernstein and Garfinkel's sample consisted exclusively of adolescents, which may have increased the rates of depression observed. However, the very small number of anxious patients included in both of these studies ($n \leq 16$) restricts the interpretation, and generalizability, of their findings.

Laboratory studies

Unfortunately, as of this time, no laboratory studies have been published on SAD or OAD children.

Delimitation from other disorders

One recent study has addressed the delimitation of separation anxiety disorder from "school phobic disorder" (Last, Francis, Hersen, Kazdin, & Strauss, 1987). Unfortunately, historically, and even into the present, the label "school phobia" has been applied to two types of children: those who evidence separation anxiety and those who show a phobic reaction toward school. However, not all children with school phobia show separation anxiety problems, nor do all children with separation anxiety disorder exhibit school refusal.

The purpose of the Last et al. (1987) study was to examine and compare the clinical and associated features of separation anxiety disorder and school phobic (SP) disorder by evaluating a clinical sample of children who met DSM-III criteria for one of the two disorders (i.e, separation anxiety disorder or phobic disorder, school type). The children were assessed on a variety of dimensions, including demographic characteristics, symp tomatology, associated psychiatric disorders, and maternal psychiatric illness. Results revealed several significant differences between the two groups. Children with SAD predominantly were female, prepubertal, and from families of lower socioeconomic status, while children with SP predominantly were male, postpubertal, and from higher socioeconomic backgrounds. Children with SAD were less likely to exhibit school refusal than SP children. However, SAD children were more likely than SP children to meet criteria for an additional DSM-III diagnosis. Finally, mothers of SAD children had a rate of affective disorders four times greater than mothers of SP children.

Follow-up studies

Although several follow-up studies have been published prior to DSM-III on "school phobia," none has appeared to date on SAD or OAD.

Family studies

Only two controlled investigations have examined psychiatric illness in the relatives of SAD or OAD children (Last, Hersen, Kazdin, Francis, & Grubb, 1986; Livingston, Nugent, Rader, & Smith, 1985). Two other studies have reported on relatives of "school phobic" children (Berg, Butler, & Pritchard, 1974; Gittelman-Klein, 1975).

Berg et al. (1974) evaluated maternal psychiatric illness by examining the hospital records of 100 school phobic adolescents and a control group of 100 psychiatrically disturbed, non–school phobic adolescents. One fifth of the mothers in both groups had a history of some type of psychiatric disturbance. Of these, approximately one half were diagnosed as having an "affective disorder," which was defined as anxiety, depression, or phobias. Gittelman-Klein (1975) interviewed the parents and siblings of 42 school phobic and 42 hyperactive children to determine their psychiatric histories. Results were analyzed for three specific diagnostic categories: (a) major depression, (b) specific phobias, and (c) separation anxiety disorder. No differences appeared between the two groups of parents or siblings for major depression or specific phobias. However, the parents and siblings of school phobic youngsters were found to have a significantly higher rate of separation anxiety disorder than those in the control group.

More recently, Livingston et al. (1985) evaluated lifetime psychiatric illness in the relatives of 12 anxious (DSM-III diagnoses of SAD or OAD) and 11 depressed children using the family history method and Research Diagnostic Criteria (Endicott, Andreasen, & Spitzer, 1975). Major depression and alcoholism were the two most common diagnoses in both groups. Contrary to expectation, very few of the relatives in the anxiety group were diagnosed as having an anxiety disorder.

Each of these studies must be considered in light of its methodological limitations. In the Berg et al. (1974) investigation, diagnoses were based on written records, criteria for the diagnoses were unspecified, and anxiety and affective disorders were combined into one diagnostic category. Further, the diagnostic composition of the control group was not delineated. Although in the Gittelman-Klein (1975) study clinical interviews were conducted, these interviews were unstructured. Moreover, diagnostic criteria were not specified and diagnostic reliability was not reported. Furthermore, in both of these studies it is unclear whether interviewers were blind to children's diagnoses. Finally interpretation of findings from the Livingston et al. (1985) investigation is restricted by the very small size of the anxious group and use of the family history method, which has been shown to underdetect psychiatric illness, particularly for the anxiety disorders (Thompson, Orvaschel, & Kidd, 1982).

To build upon these studies, we (Last et al., 1986) conducted an evaluation of lifetime psychiatric illness in the mothers of anxious children using a larger sample size ($N = 58$) and an approach specifically designed to overcome the methodological limitations of prior work. Mothers were interviewed directly with a structured diagnostic interview and diagnosed by application of DSM-III criteria. Interviewers were unaware of children's diagnoses, and diagnostic agreement was evaluated by having a second clinician, also blind to children's diagnoses, independently score audiotapes of the interviews. Finally, rates of psychiatric illness in the mothers of anxious children were compared to those obtained from a psychopathological control group, which consisted of mothers of children who were psychiatrically disturbed, but did not show an anxiety or affective disorder.

Results indicated that the vast majority (83%) of mothers of children with separation anxiety disorder and/or overanxious disorder had a lifetime history of an anxiety disorder. Moreover, over one half (57%) of the mothers presented with an anxiety disorder at the same time at which their children were seen for similar problems. Both of these rates significantly differed from those obtained for controls.

Overall, these findings reveal a strong association between anxiety disorders in mothers and their children. Whether this relationship is specific to the mother-child dyad, or indicative of a more general pattern of familial aggregation, remains to be determined.

CONCLUDING REMARKS

Reliability studies conducted to date have obtained markedly different levels of agreement for the DSM-III diagnostic category Anxiety Disorders of Childhood or Adolescence. The majority of the studies reviewed showed relatively poor reliability for this category. However, reliability in each of these investigations was calculated based on a small number of cases ($n < 10$), which can seriously inflate or deflate coefficients of agreement. By contrast, two other investigations, which included much larger samples of anxious children, revealed good to excellent reliability for the diagnostic category (Last et al., 1986; Werry et al., 1984). Moreover, one of these studies (Last et al., 1986) employed a test-retest design, which generally is considered to be the most stringent test of the reliability of a diagnostic category.

Considerably more data are needed on the validity of the childhood anxiety disorders, particularly separation anxiety and overanxious disorders. Data from Last and colleagues on clinical characteristics and maternal psychiatric history warrant replication. Moreover, large-scale family and follow-up studies of this population are needed. Finally, future epidemiological studies of anxiety disorders in community samples will have a significant impact on our understanding of clinically referred anxious children.

REFERENCES

American Psychiatric Association. (1968). *Diagnostic and statistical manual of mental disorder*, (2nd ed.). Washington, DC: Author.

American Psychiatric Association. (1980). *Diagnostic and statistical manual of mental dis-*

orders, (3rd ed.). Washington, DC: Author.

Barlow, D. H. (1985). The dimensions of anxiety disorders. In A. H. Tuma & J. D. Maser (Eds.), *Anxiety and the anxiety disorders* (pp. 479–500). Hillsdale, NJ: Lawrence Erlbaum Associates, Inc.

Berg, I. (1980). School refusal in early adolescence. In L. Hersov & I. Berg (Eds.), *Out of school* (pp. 231–250). New York: John Wiley & Sons.

Berg, I., Butler, A., & Pritchard, J. (1974). Psychiatric illness in the mothers of school-phobic adolescents. *British Journal of Psychiatry, 125,* 466–467.

Berg, I., Nichols, K., & Pritchard, C. (1969). School phobia — its classification and relationship to dependency. *Journal of Child Psychology and Psychiatry, 10,* 123–141.

Bernstein, G. A., & Garfinkel, B. D. (1986). School phobia: The overlap of affective and anxiety disorders. *Journal of the American Academy of Child Psychiatry, 2,* 235–241.

Bowlby, J. (1975). *Attachment and loss. Vol. 1 Attachment.* London: Hogarth.

Broadwin, I. T. (1932). A contribution to the study of truancy. *American Journal of Orthopsychiatry, 2,* 253–259.

Cantwell, D. P., Russell, A. T., Mattison, R., & Will, L. (1979). A comparison of DSM-II and DSM-III in the diagnosis of childhood psychiatric disorders. *Archives of General Psychiatry, 36,* 1208–1213.

Chazan, M. (1962). School phobia. *British Journal of Educational Psychology, 32,* 200–217.

Eisenberg, L. (1958). School phobia: A study in the communication of anxiety. *American Journal of Psychiatry, 114,* 712–718.

Endicott, J., Andreasen, N., & Spitzer, R. (1975). *Family history research diagnostic criteria.* New York: New York State Psychiatric Institute, Biometrics Research.

Endicott, J., & Spitzer, R. L. (1978). A diagnostic interview: The Schedule for Affective Disorders and Schizophrenia. *Archives of General Psychiatry, 35,* 837–844.

Eysenck, H. J., & Rachman, S. J. (1965). The application of learning theory to child psychiatry. In J. Howells (Ed.), *Modern perspectives in child psychiatry* (pp. 104–169). Edinburgh: Oliver & Boyd.

Feighner, J. P., Robins, E., Guze, S. B., Woodruff, R. A., Winokur, G., & Munoz, R. (1972). Diagnostic criteria for use in psychiatric research. *Archives of General Psychiatry, 26,* 57–63.

Freud, S. (1950). The analysis of phobia in a five-year-old boy. Editor — Ernest Jones. Translators — Alix and James Strachey. In *Collected papers: Volume 3* (pp. 149–288). London: Hogarth Press. (Original work published 1909).

Gittelman-Klein, R. (1975). Psychiatric characteristics of the relatives of school phobic children. In D. V. S. Sankar (Ed.), *Mental health in children* (pp. 325–334). New York: PJD Publications.

Gittelman-Klein, R., & Klein, D. F. (1971). Controlled imipramine treatment of school phobia. *Archives of General Psychiatry, 25,* 204–207.

Gittelman-Klein, R., & Klein, D. F. (1973). School phobia: Diagnostic considerations in the light of imipramine effects. *Journal of Nervous and Mental Disorders, 156,* 199–215.

Gittelman-Klein, R., & Klein, D. F. (1980). Separation anxiety in school refusal and its treatment with drugs. In L. Hersov & I. Berg (Eds.), *Out of school* (pp. 321–342). New York: John Wiley & Sons.

Grove, W. M., Andreasen, N. C., McDonald-Scott, P., Keller, M. B., & Shapiro, R. W. (1981). Reliability studies of psychiatric diagnosis. *Archives of General Psychiatry, 38,* 408–413.

Guze, S. B. (1967). The diagnosis of hysteria: What are we trying to do? *American Journal of Psychiatry, 124,* 491–498.

Hershberg, S. G., Carlson, G. A., Cantwell, D. P., & Strober, M. (1982). Anxiety and depressive disorders in psychiatrically disturbed children. *Journal of Clinical Psychiatry, 43,* 358–361.

Hersov, L. A. (1960). Refusal to go to school. *Journal of Child Psychology and Psychiatry, 1,* 137–145.

Hewitt, C. E., & Jenkins, R. L. (1946). *Fundamental patterns of maladjustment: The dynamics of their origin.* Springfield: State of Illinois.

Jenkins, R. L. (1964). Diagnosis, dynamics, and treatments in child psychiatry. *Psychiatric Research Reports, American Psychiatric Association, 18,* 91–120.

Jenkins, R. L. (1969). Classification of behavior problems of children. *American Journal of Psychiatry, 125,* 1032–1039.

Jenkins, R. L., Nureddin, E., & Shapiro, I. (1966). Children's behavior syndromes and parental responses. *Genetic Psychological Monographs, 74,* 261–329.

Johnson, A. M., Falstein, E. I., Szurek, S. A., & Svendson, M. (1941). School phobia. *American Journal of Orthopsychiatry, 11,* 702–711.

Kahn, J. H., & Nursten, S. P. (1962). School refusal: A comprehensive view of school phobia and other failures of school attendance. *American Journal of Orthopsychiatry, 32,* 707–718.

Klein, D. F. (1964). Delineation of two-drug-responsive anxiety syndrome. *Psychopharmacologia, 5,* 397–408.

Kovacs, M. (1978). *The interview schedule for children (ISC): Form C, and the follow-up form.* Unpublished manuscript, University of Pittsburgh, Pittsburgh, PA.

Kovacs, M. (1983). *The interview schedule for children (ISC): Form C, and the follow-up form.* Unpublished manuscript, University of Pittsburgh, Pittsburgh, PA.

Last, C. G., Francis, G., Hersen, M., Kazdin, A. E., & Strauss, C. C. (1987). Separation anxiety and school phobia: A comparison using DSM-III criteria. *American Journal of Psychiatry, 144,* 653–657.

Last, C. G., Hersen, M., Kazdin, A. E., Finkelstein, R., & Strauss, C. C. (in press). Comparison of DSM-III separation anxiety and overanxious disorders: Demographic characteristics and patterns of comorbidity. *Journal of the American Academy of Child Psychiatry.*

Last, C. G., Hersen, M., Kazdin, A. E., Francis, G., & Grubb, H. J. (1986). Psychiatric illness in the mothers of anxious children. Manuscript submitted for publication.

Lewis, H. (1954). *Deprived children.* London: Oxford University Press.

Livingston, R., Nugent, H., Rader, L., & Smith, G. R. (1985). Family histories of depressed and severely anxious children. *American Journal Psychiatry, 142,* 1497–1499.

Mattison, R., Cantwell, D. P., Russell, A. T., & Will, L. (1979). A comparison of DSM-II and DSM-III in the diagnosis of childhood psychiatric disorders. *Archives of General Psychiatry, 36,* 1217–1222.

Mezzich, A. C., & Mezzich, J. E. (1985). Reliability of DSM-III vs. DSM-II in child psychopathology. *Journal of the American Academy of Child Psychiatry, 24,* 273–280.

Ollendick, T. H., & Mayer, J. A. (1985). School phobia. In S. M. Turner (Ed.), *Behavioral treatment of anxiety disorders* (pp. 367–411). New York: Plenum Publishing Corporation.

Orvaschel, H., & Weissman, M. M. (1985). Epidemiology of anxiety disorders in children: A review. In R. Gittelman (Ed.), *Anxiety disorders in children* (pp. 58–72). New York: Guilford Press.

Partridge, J. M. (1939). Truancy. *Journal of Mental Science, 85,* 45–81.

Shamsie, S. J. (Ed.). (1968). *Adolescent psychiatry.* Pointe Claire, Quebec: Shering Corp.

Smith, S. L. (1970). School refusal with anxiety: A review of sixty-three cases. *Canadian Psychiatric Association Journal, 126,* 815–817.

Spitzer, R. L., Forman, J. B. W., & Nee, J. (1979). DSM-III field trials: I. Initial interrater diagnostic reliability. *American Journal of Psychiatry, 126,* 815–817,.

Strober, M., Green, J., & Carlson, G. (1981). Reliability of psychiatric diagnosis in hospitalized adolescents. *Archives of General Psychiatry, 38,* 141–145.

Suh, M., & Carlson, R. (1977). Childhood behavior disorder — A family typology. *The Psychiatric Journal of the University of Ottawa, 2,* 84–88.

Thompson, W. D., Orvaschel, H., & Kidd, J. R. (1982). An evaluation of the family history method for ascertaining psychiatric disorders. *Archives of General Psychiatry, 39,* 53–58.

Warren, W. (1948). Acute neurotic breakdown in children with refusal to go to school. *Archives of Disease in Childhood, 23,* 266–272.

Werry, J. S., Methven, R. J., Fitzpatrick, J., & Dixon, H. (1984). The interdiagnoser reliability and validity of the DSM-III diagnostic system in children. Unpublished manuscript.

Williams, J. B. W., & Spitzer, R. L. (1980). Appendix F. In American Psychiatric Association, *Diagnostic and statistical manual of mental disorders,* (3rd ed.) (pp. 467–472). Washington, DC: Author.

CHAPTER 28

Anxiety in the Elderly

Roger L. Patterson

Among the problems facing the elderly, anxiety occupies a strange position. Many books and other publications on geriatrics and gerontology devote much space to the problems of dementia and depression, while hardly mentioning anxiety. Yet there are clinical opinions and data to indicate that anxiety is a more prevalent and significant problem for the elderly than is acknowledged by such publications. For example, Kalish (1977) asserted: "If there is a mental 'state' peculiar to aging, it may well be anxiety" (p. 329). Similarly, Kuhlen (1959) contends that successful aging may depend upon the management of anxiety. Eisdorfer (1977), in summarizing expressed opinions of a gathering of nationally recognized clinicians and scientists concerned specifically with anxiety and the elderly, concluded that "The consensus was that anxiety among the aged is undoubtedly a much more pervasive problem than hitherto reported" and that "a much more substantial body of basic and clinical research is needed, that the aged may manifest their problems in ways different from the young" (p. 7).

Epidemiological data from Mellinger and Balter (cited in Crook, 1985b) support Eisdorfer's (1977) view of the preeminence of anxiety in the aged. These authors conducted a national survey of American adults and found that, among those aged 65 to 79, great distress was caused by anxiety for 5.7%, mixed anxiety and depression for 9.5%, and depression for 3.8%. These figures show that, whether considered in its relatively pure form, or as a mixed condition, anxiety is a problem for a significant number of elderly Americans.

Thus, it would seem that anxiety in the elderly deserves a great deal more attention in the clinical literature. Therefore, this chapter will report on clinical features of anxiety in the elderly, followed by a discussion of some relevant research regarding both assessment and treatment.

CLINICAL ISSUES

Many clinicians and researchers in the fields of gerontology and geriatrics have written that there are important differences in both the typical etiology and the presentation of anxiety in the elderly as compared with younger people. These differences are often related to both the psychosocial situations and the physical changes typical of the older population.

Etiology

According to Verwoerdt (1981) and others, losses and threats of losses are much more likely to be anxiety- (and/or depression-) producers in the elderly. Frequent and significant losses include physical abilities, health, property, social position, opportunities for valued activities, and significant others. At the very least, some of these losses represent serious threats to self-esteem. According to the research of Spielberger and his associates (1972), threats to self-esteem alone are very effective producers of anxiety states, particularly for those who are high in "trait" anxiety. The more substantive losses or threats of losses are probably sufficient to produce anxiety in many, even in those not particularly high in trait anxiety. Busse and Pfeiffer (1973) endorse the idea that the fear of becoming disabled is a source of anxiety for some elderly persons who may be seen clinically.

In addition to serving as psychological stressors, a number of physical illnesses, most frequently found in the elderly, have been implicated in the etiology of increased anxiety. Jenicke (1983) has given his medical opinion that no fewer than 29 organic conditions may produce anxiety directly. These include cardiovascular, dietary, drug-related, endocrinologic, hematologic, immunologic, neurologic, and pulmonary problems.

Still another way in which physical problems may produce anxiety is by misattribution. Kalish (1977) suggests that some signs of aging are identical to the signs of anxiety. These include tremor, fatigue, clumsiness, unsteadiness, facial tics, quivering voice, and palpitating heart. According to Emery (1981), the elderly person may notice these physical changes occurring and mislabel them as anxiety. Such an individual may therefore come to believe that he/she has anxiety problems, which may be a self-fulfilling prophesy. Geyman (1977) thought that it is usually not possible to separate anxiety as a target symptom from physical illness and psychosocial problems in this population.

Fear of imminent death, which is more likely to be present late in life, has also received attention as a precursor of anxiety. Kalish (1985) has reviewed a large number of studies that show that fear of death in the elderly is present in a significant minority, though not as prevalent as supposed by some. For example, 10% of a multi-ethnic group in Los Angeles said that they were "afraid" or "terribly afraid" of death (Kalish & Reynolds, 1981). Evidently, there are enough such people that the clinician may encounter some of them and should be aware of the existence of the problem.

Manifestations

Many authors have offered opinions, usually based upon clinical experience, as to how anxiety may appear differently in the elderly. Most of them do agree that there are differences (e.g., Eisdorfer, 1977; Gershon, 1973; Kochansky, 1979). A summary of some of the suggested differences follows.

Pfeiffer (1977) stated that "Among older persons . . . the expression of anxiety is more commonly direct, appearing as overt fear, panic, worry, or bewilderment, and without the intricate conversion mechanisms customarily seen in younger persons' (p. 28). Other experts report that anxiety in the elderly may often be expressed as bodily concern. Gershon (1973) said that anxiety in the elderly often takes the form of a "rather primitive body-focused type" associated with "pain, disability, dyspnea, fragility, and failing body functions" (p. 184). Similarly, Busse (1975) noted that anxiety in the elderly may be displaced into high bodily concern and expressed as hypochondriacal symptoms.

Salzman and Shader (1978) have considered denial as being common in elderly people. This denial may make it more difficult for them to express their affective states.

Although, as discussed in a previous chapter, the distinction between anxiety and depression has presented problems for all ages, it may be even more of a problem in the elderly. Salzman (1977) argues that "The distinction between anxiety and depression may become blurred in the elderly" (p. 14). If, indeed, the elderly focus on bodily functions, such as problems in sleeping, eating, excretion, sexual matters, and so on, then there would be a considerable overlap of symptoms of anxiety and depression in the elderly, because these same symptoms may also be key symptoms of depression (Salzman & Shader, 1978). The resistance to the accurate report of affective states would make distinctions between anxiety and depression even more difficult.

This author would add intergenerational differences to the above factors contributing to differences in the presentation and self-description of anxiety. The use of the term *anxiety* and the current concept of it is a relatively modern innovation. Although professional concern with anxiety goes back at least to Freud and the early psychoanalysts, it was not until the 1960s and 1970s that anxiety became a popularly discussed phenomenon. People born in the earlier part of the 20th century are quite often not found to be familiar with the modern concept of the term *anxiety*. The closest approximation for many of them is "nervousness," or a "nervous condition." Such problems are likely to be attributed to some mysterious, unspecified physical problem; as when it is said that he/she has "bad nerves," or "my nerves are shot." In part, the use of such ideas and terms is related to education; but education may be confounded with age, because the post–World War II generations are generally better educated than were most of their forebears.

Jarvik and Russell (1979) have hypothesized one of the more novel ways in which anxiety may appear differently in the elderly. They sought to account for what they saw as a discrepancy between the high frequency of stress situations affecting the elderly and the relatively low frequency of reported acute and severe anxiety cases. They argue for the existence of a different response to stress endemic to older people.

Since the observations of Cannon (1929), most clinicians and researchers have accepted the proposition that people (and other animals) react to stress by attempts at "fight or flight." Jarvik and Russell (1979) note that neither of these responses may be available to an elderly person. Instead, the most appropriate response may be a third alternative termed "freeze." This freeze response is said to refer to "an interegnum, a period of relative inactivity representing the optimal response to a given threat" (p. 198). Significantly, this response is distinguished from helplessness and hopelessness, in that the occurrence of the freeze response is the result of a "conscious or unconscious appraisal which suggested it as the response most likely to enhance chances of survival" (p. 198). In addition to rather passive inactivity or "playing possum," a major way in which this response is said to differ from the usual responses to stress is that it is not necessarily associated with typical sympathetic arousal. This latter response difference is offered as an explanation for the relatively few typical severe acute anxiety reactions seen among the aged.

Perhaps the most complex view of anxiety-related problems in the elderly comes from Simon (1980). He states that anxious, depressive, hysterical, and obsessive manifestations are not usually seen in isolation in neurotic elderly, but rather are present in varying combinations and degrees at different times.

Obviously, there is considerable need for clarification of the issues of the etiology and manifestation of anxiety in the elderly. Attempts to shed light on anxiety in this population through research on assessment and treatment will be considered next.

RESEARCH

Major research questions exist in the areas of assessment and treatment of anxiety in the elderly. In light of the previous discussion, it is unfortunate that very little research has been carried out in either area. This section will inform the reader of some published information regarding these issues. In the area of treatment, the best information seems to come from case studies, a few experiments, and expert opinion.

Assessment

Three classifications of measures will be considered here: self-report, ratings by others, and physiological measures. Because of the brevity of this chapter, reviews by others will be relied upon where these are available and sufficient.

Self-report

Zung (1983) recently reviewed self-rating scales for psychopathology, and noted that the Zung Self-Rating Anxiety Scale (Zung, 1971) has been used sufficiently with the elderly so that considerable data, including cross-cultural samples as well as information on reliability, validity, and age-adjusted norms, are available.

MacDonald and Spielberger (1978) developed a special form of the State-Trait Anxiety Inventory (STAI: Spielberger, Gorsuch, & Lushene, 1970) for use with elderly Germans. Essentially, the STAI was translated into German language suitable for the elderly, and was printed in large type with additional lines on the paper to separate response choices. Normative data were obtained for the German population.

Patterson, O'Sullivan, and Spielberger (1980) validated a version of the State-Trait Anxiety Scale for Children (STAIC: Spielberger, Edwards, Lushene, Montouri, & Platzek, 1973) for use with the elderly. The rationale for this research was that a measure of state and trait anxiety in the elderly was needed for research as well as clinical reasons. But pilot work has shown that the format and the wording of the original STAIC presented difficulties for this group. The STAIC, however, measures the same constructs, and is much simpler in both format and wording. Two inappropriate questions were eliminated from the Trait scale of the STAIC, and it was retyped using larger letters. This scale was then administered to two samples of the elderly: one group lived in the community and attended a mental health day treatment program, and the other resided in a residential treatment program (Patterson et al., 1982). Self-report scores were compared with scores from the STAIC and the Anxious-Depression subscale from the Missouri Inpatient Behavior Scale (MIBS: Missouri Psychiatric Institute, undated; Sletten & Ullett, 1972). The MIBS has seven scales relating to a broad spectrum of psychopathology in state hospital inpatients, and four competency scales. MIBS normative scores are available for men and women aged 21 to 64 years, and aged 65 and older. Four types of validity were found: (a) the children's form was highly correlated with the adult form, (b) both scales were correlated with the staff ratings, (c) discriminant validity was established by the fact that the STAIC measures were not related with behavioral ratings other than "anxious-depression," and (d) residential clients' scores were significantly higher than those of community residents. The STAIC was reported to be much easier to administer, and to require less reading of items and response choices by the staff.

A somewhat different approach to the study of anxiety in the elderly is reported by Salzman (1977). He indicates that he and his associates have found 100-millimeter lines with anchoring adjectives (Harmatz, 1976) to be useful devices for measuring anxiety, particularly *state* anxiety, in the elderly. Salzman presented an example of an anxiety scale consisting of 13 such lines, each with an adjective (calm, jittery, nervous, etc.) printed above its center with words at each end (e.g., absent-severe) representing opposite extremes of the feelings indicated by the adjectives. The only response required was a mark on the line. The position of the mark represented the degree to which the subject experienced the feeling. This method was advocated because of its obvious simplicity.

In contrast to self-report scales which were developed to measure anxiety in younger populations but were later adapted for use with the elderly, Wisocki and her colleagues (Wisocki, Handen, & Morse, 1986) have taken the "Worry Scale," which was developed for use with the elderly, and shown that it is a useful general measure of anxiety, as well as of specific areas of concern. This scale asks subjects how often ("rarely" to "much of the time") they worry about 35 items in the categories of finances, health, and social conditions. Wisocki et al. document that scores on the Worry Scale correlate significantly with other anxiety scales.

In addition to self-ratings specific to anxiety, several ratings of multiple moods and affective states have been used with the elderly and have included anxiety measures. McNair (1979) and Salzman (1977) have reviewed many of these. Salzman discussed specifically the Scheier-Cattell Anxiety Battery (Scheier, Cattell, & Sullivan, 1961), the Hopkins Symptom Checklist (Derogatis, Lipman, & Covi, 1973), the Profile of Mood States (McNair, Lorr, & Droppleman, 1971), and the Multiple Affective Check List (Zuckerman, 1960). He concluded that none of these could be endorsed for several reasons: they were difficult for the elderly to use, too few data pertaining to the elderly were available for them, they were insensitive to changes in conditions, or other problems. In addition to these scales, McNair (1979) reviewed the Minnesota Multiphasic Personality Inventory (MMPI: Hathaway & McKinley, 1967), the Sixteen Personality Factor Questionnaire (16 PF: Cattell, Eber, & Tatsuoka, 1970), the Emotions Profile Index (Plutchik, 1962), as well as several others. He concluded, "There are insufficient accomplishments to provide the fundamentals of systematic psychometric knowledge about the role and value of self-measurement by elderly people" (p. 164). More recently, Woods and Britton (1985) reviewed the use of both objective and projective personality tests with the elderly and concluded that this practice was basically unsatisfactory. The possible exceptions were, "If the elderly person is cognitively, physically, and sensorily unimpaired and has above average verbal skills then one of the tests might be appropriate depending on the particular areas of interest" (p. 163). There seems to be substantial agreement among major reviewers of this area. The self-report scales that measure only anxiety seem to fare better than the multiple-score scales.

Behavior rating scales

These scales have probably achieved wider use and better reputation than have self-report measures. Obviously, they may avoid the difficulties of semantics, vocabulary, and response formats, which are not appropriate for elderly clients. They have an inherent limitation in that most definitions of anxiety include a subjective component that only the distressed person can provide.

Kochansky (1979) reviewed two such anxiety rating scales that have received some fairly widespread use. Neither of these was developed for use with the elderly, however. These are the Hamilton Anxiety Scale (HAMA: Hamilton, 1959) and the Zung Anxiety Status Inventory (ASI: Zung, 1971). The HAMA includes both observational and interview items. Factor analyses of the HAMA have identified the factors of Somatic Anxiety and Psychic Anxiety in addition to a general anxiety factor (Hamilton, 1959). A limitation of the HAMA is that its use is limited to those patients already diagnosed as having neurotic anxiety states. In a more recent review of assessments useful with the elderly, Reisberg (1983) referred to the Hamilton Scales for depression and anxiety as "Excellent, brief, standardized clinical rating instruments" (p. 19).

The Zung ASI is similar to the HAMA, in that it was designed to measure anxiety disorders rather than traits or states. It also includes mostly somatic symptoms, with additional feeling-state items. Petrie (1983), in his recent review, considers the ASI acceptable, but prefers the HAMA.

Honigfeld (1983) reviewed multiple problem rating scales potentially useful with the elderly. He reported the existence of 17 scales developed specifically for geriatric patients and 22 others that were said to be suitable for this purpose. Of these, he recommends three that contain specific anxiety or anxious/depression scales: the Psychotic Inpatient Profile (PIP: Lorr & Vestre, 1969), the Physical and Mental Impairment of Function Evaluation (PAMIE: Gurel, Linn, & Linn, 1972), and the Ward Behavior Inventory (WBI: Burdock & Hardesty, 1968). Of these, only the PIP was recommended specifically for the affectively disturbed. The WBI was said to be more useful with psychotics, and the PAMIE better for the demented. A major reason for eliminating many of the other scales is that they have a considerable degree of overlap across their items.

Although Honigfeld (1983) did not recommend it in his review, the Sandoz Clinical Assessment Geriatric Scale (SCAG: Shader, Harmatz, & Salzman, 1974) should be mentioned here, because it is probably the only psychiatric rating scale developed specifically for use with the elderly. Also, it has demonstrated reliability and validity, and has been used in several studies. The SCAG has 18 items, each measuring different symptoms, one of which is anxiety. One item probably does not allow for much sensitivity, and, as with other rating scales, self-report is omitted.

It has already been mentioned that Patterson et al. (1980) used the MIBS behavior rating scale because it had appropriate age norms based upon large numbers of mentally ill persons. However, the MIBS is limited in that it has only three items on the Anxious/Depression scale, and the norms were derived from a state-hospital population.

Psychophysiological measures

A measure of anxiety that has received recent attention is the evaluation of electroencephalographic change in response to specific stimuli (called event-related potentials or ERP). Tinklenberg, Roth, Pfefferbaum, and Kopell (1983) have reviewed studies that showed that ERP measures were useful in evaluating the relative effectiveness of anxiolytic drugs. Tinklenberg et al. claim that it would have been difficult or impossible to obtain measures with this degree of sensitivity in any other fashion. A review of EEG research and other psychophysiological work carried out with the elderly may be found in a chapter by Marsh and Thompson (1977).

Treatment

Pharmacotherapy is probably the most widespread approach to the treatment of anxiety in the elderly, and is frequently recommended if used judiciously (e.g., Ayd, 1984; Crook, 1985a). Yet, there is informed opinion that such treatment is not well-founded in research. With regard to mixed anxiety and depression, Crook (1985b) notes that the field of geriatric psychopharmacology is in its infancy. Other readings (e.g., Crook, 1985a) lead the present author to the conclusion that Crook's statement may be applicable to the whole field of geriatric psychopharmacology. To the extent that pharmacotherapy is useful, Crook (1985a) recommends the use of benzodiazepines, especially "low dose, short-acting compounds without active metabolites, such as oxazepam or lorazepam for the treatment of generalized anxiety conditions in the elderly" (p. 18). For mixed anxiety and depression, Crook (1985a, 1985b) recommends use of tricyclic antidepressants.

In spite of the ubiquitous application of drugs, Crook and others do not recommend the use of drugs without first considering altering real-life stressors affecting the person. This is accomplished through changes in life situations such as obtaining needed financial or medical assistance and/or the use of behavior therapy in particular or psycotherapy in general. The latter are recommended either as exclusive or as co-treatments with drugs. Nonpharmacological treatments have special advantages with the elderly, because this group is especially prone to paradoxical reactions and side-effects, in addition to representing complex compliance difficulties.

The status of the psychological treatment of anxiety in the elderly is that it is primarily at the case-study stage of development. Some of these case studies have included data, and these will be underscored here. Few of these, however, have included recognized single-case experimental designs to ensure that the results obtained were most likely to have been due to the planned therapeutic intervention, rather than uncontrolled concomitant factors.

A study that did use a multiple-baseline design to evaluate the results of a behavior therapy procedure was reported by Woods and Britton (1985). The subject was a 64-year-old widow who was afraid to leave her first-floor apartment. She also had a fear of heights, which precluded her using elevators in other buildings. Initial and subsequent ratings of fears of these two situations were made simultaneously, but treatment for going out preceded treatment for the fear of heights. The treatment, which was conducted in the home, was a variant of desensitization. First the client was asked to commit herself to working to overcome her problems. Subsequent sessions then involved relaxation instructions, followed by encouragement to walk increasing distances from her home.

Fear ratings decreased dramatically over a 5- to 6-month period, and self-reports of her activities confirmed by her family indicated that she was indeed leaving her apartment rather frequently. Fear of heights did not decrease during this time, so similar procedures were then introduced to treat this problem. Treatment was effective, and she then was able to ride an elevator to visit her daughter. Total treatment consisted of 22 sessions over an 8-month period of time.

Thyer (1981) similarly used desensitization with a 70-year-old woman to eliminate her fear of being attacked by dogs if she went outside. Seven in vivo sessions of exposure to dogs were effective.

Haley (1983) described the treatment of an 87-year-old moderately demented woman who became extremely anxious when she was left in a room alone. She called out loudly for her family, even if they were in another part of the house. First she was given simplified relaxation training, and the family was told to remind her to relax when they left the room. She was also provided with a message board with notes indicating to her where a family member was located when not immediately present. In addition, she was provided with a timer to indicate when someone would return, and she was informed that she would receive a reward if she refrained from crying out until the family member returned. The timer was initially set at 20 minutes; and by successive approximations toward longer intervals, it was eventually possible to leave her for 50 minutes.

Haley (1983) also describes a case of a woman who telephoned her niece up to 10 times per day. The niece was taught to extinguish the behavior by refusing to answer more than three calls per day. Role-plays of this procedure were conducted with the aunt and niece. The procedure was successful in eliminating excessive calls.

In yet a third case, Haley was successful in enabling an elderly woman to leave her room to socialize and eat with her family. In this case, the reinforcer consisted of the client helping to plan the meal if she agreed to leave her room to eat and/or socialize.

Hussian (1981) reported success in using stress inoculation training (Meichenbaum, 1977) to treat the extreme anxiety experienced by four elderly residents in riding an elevator at a long-term care facility. First, they were given informal relaxation training using primarily covert imagery. The residents were then instructed about the relationship between covert self-verbalization, anxiety, and avoidance. Next, in a group, they were asked to describe to the therapist fearful thoughts they had about riding an elevator. This was followed by education about how an elevator worked, and sessions in which they practiced verbalizing appropriate coping statements in addition to practicing covertly. Practice using the coping statements while imagining entering of words followed by attempts at recalling actual brief rides using relaxation and coping statements. Data were presented showing that the relaxation and the educational phases alone had no effect on approach behavior and self-rated anxiety. However, actual practice using coping statements and relaxation was successful in enabling all four to ride the elevator comfortably. A 2-month follow-up showed that treatment gains had been maintained.

Garrison (1978) was able to use stress-management training (Suinn & Richardson, 1971) to help an elderly resident of a long-term care facility to overcome anxiety about being near other "crazy" residents. This was accomplished in only seven sessions. Essential steps of this procedure included relaxation training, alternation of tension and anxiety, imagining the anxiety-provoking scene while relaxed, and follow-up.

Sherman (1981) presents numerous case studies in which he was able to combine environmental interventions with cognitive techniques (Beck, 1976) and other methods to treat more extensive and complex problem situations of the elderly than those just described. Such combined treatment was termed "integrative counseling." Similarly, Emery (1981) also has discussed the use of cognitive techniques with the elderly.

Hussian and Davis (1985) summarized some clinically useful techniques for reducing anxiety. Included are the reinforcement of successive approximations to the approach of a feared object or person, behavior rehearsal, and the discussion of coping ideas with a therapist.

In addition to attempts to alleviate clinically relevant anxiety per se, research has also shown that the reduction of anxiety can affect the *cognitive* performance of elderly people (see Yesavage, 1985). In one study, Yesavage, Rose, and Spiegel (1982) found that relatively brief relaxation training (progressive muscle relaxation excluding neck and back movements) had a facilitative effect on normal elderly persons who were initially high in anxiety. The task used was that of memorizing lists and riding the elevator was followed by them. Subjects low in initial anxiety showed no improvement, or actually performed more poorly after relaxation training.

This work was later replicated and expanded (Yesavage, 1984). In this research, face-name recall was used as the task, because this is a more realistic problem for many elderly persons. An experimental and a comparison group were both taught to use mnemonics. The experimental group in addition, was taught relaxation while the other group received "attitude improvement." Results showed that the experimental group showed greater improvement on the task, and the degree of improvement was correlated with anxiety reduction.

CONCLUDING REMARKS

With regard to clinical manifestations of anxiety, there seems to be some consistency in the view that a mixed condition of anxiety with depression and/or somatic concern often exists in the elderly. This somatic concern may or may not be to some degree realistic. Relatively pure anxiety states and specific fears do exist, but these are less frequently seen. The etiology of anxiety-related conditions in the elderly seems to be much more complex than in younger persons.

Research in assessment of anxiety in the elderly is minimal. Additional use of the trait-state distinction might help to clarify issues. Methods to identify specific concerns and fears would also seem to be useful.

The effectiveness of psychological treatment has been most clearly demonstrated empirically when specific fears are addressed. Considering the success of cognitive-behavioral approaches with depression, it is likely that further work in this area may be effective not only with specific fears, but also with more generalized states and more complex conditions. It is hoped that success in pharmacological treatment will be enhanced by the development of new drugs that are specifically effective with an older population (Crook, 1985a, 1985b).

REFERENCES

Ayd, F. J., Jr. (1984). Is it anxiety or depression? *Southern Medical Journal, 77*, 1269–1272.

Beck, A. T. (1976). *Cognitive therapy and the emotional disorders*. New York: International Universities Press.

Burdock, E. I., & Hardesty, A. S. (1968). *Ward behavior inventory manual*. New York: Springer.

Busse, E. W. (1975). Aging and psychiatric diseases of late life. In M. F. Reiser (Ed.), *American handbook of psychiatry* (2nd ed., Vol. 4, pp. 67–89). New York: Basic Books.

Busse, E. W., & Pfeiffer, E. (1973). *Mental illness in later life*. Washington, DC: American Psychiatric Association.

Cannon, W. B. (1929). *Bodily changes in pain, hunger, fear, and rage* (2nd ed.). New York: Appleton & Co.

Cattel, R., Eber, H., & Tatsuoka, M. (1970). *Handbook for the sixteen personality factors questionnaire*. Champaign, IL: Institute for Personality and Ability Testing.

Crook, T. (1985a). Diagnosis and treatment of mixed anxiety–depression in the elderly. *Internal Medicine for the Specialist, 6*, 154–176.

Crook, T. (1985b). Geriatric psychopathology: An overview of the ailments and current therapies. *Drug Development Research, 5*, 5–23.

Derogatis, L. R., Lipman, R. S., & Covi, L. (1973). SCL-90: An outpatient psychiatric rating scale — preliminary report. *Psychopharmacology Bulletin, 9*, 13–26.

Eisdorfer, C. (1977, November). Anxiety in the aged: Introduction and overview. In *Diagnosis and treatment of anxiety in the aged, part I: Clinical management of anxiety* (pp. 5–7; available from Hoffman-LaRoche, Inc.).

Emery, G. (1981). Cognitive therapy with the elderly. In G. Emery, S. Hollon, & R. Bedrosian (Eds.), *New directions in cognitive therapy* (pp. 84–98). New York: Guilford.

Garrison, J. E. (1978). Stress management training for the elderly: A psychoeducational approach. *Journal of the American Geriatrics Society, 26*, 397–403.

Gershon, S. (1973). Antianxiety agents. In C. Eisdorfer & W. E. Fann (Eds.), *Psychopharmacology and aging* (pp. 183–188). New York: Plenum Press.

Geyman, J. P. (1977, November). Office management of anxiety in older patients. In *Clinical management of anxiety, part IV* (pp. 5–22; available from Hoffman-LaRoche, Inc.).

Gurel, L., Linn, M. W., & Linn, B. S. (1972). Physical and mental impairment of function evaluation in the aged: The PAMIE Scale. *Journal of Gerontology, 27*, 83–90.

Haley, W. E. (1983). A family-behavioral approach of the cognitively impaired elderly. *The Gerontologist, 23*, 18–20.

Hamilton, M. (1959). The assessment of anxiety states by rating. *British Journal of Medical Psychology, 32*, 50–55.

Harmatz, J. (1976). *Tentative approaches to testing elderly volunteers in a drug trial*. Paper presented at the meeting of the American Psychological Association, Washington, DC.

Hathaway, S. R., & McKinley, J. C. (1969). *Minnesota multiphasic personality inventory manual*. Princeton, NJ: The Psychological Corporation.

Honigfeld, G. (1983). Psychopathology rating scales for use by nursing personnel. In T. Crook, S. Ferris, & R. Bartus (Eds.), *Assessment in geriatric pharmacology* (pp. 81–96). New Canaan, CT: Mark Powley Associates.

Hussian, R. A. (1981). *Geriatric psychology: A behavioral perspective*. New York: Van Nostrand Reinhold.

Hussian, R. A., & Davis, R. L. (1985). *Responsive care: Behavioral interventions with elderly persons*. Champaign, IL: Research Press.

Jarvik, L. F., & Russell, D. (1979). Anxiety, aging, and the third emergency reaction. *Journal of Gerontology, 34*, 197–200.

Jenicke, M. A. (1983). Treating anxiety in elderly patients. *Geriatrics, 10*, 115–120.

Kalish, R. A. (1977). *The later years*. Belmont, CA: Wadsworth.

Kalish, R. A. (1985). *Death, grief, and caring relationships* (2nd ed.). Monterey, CA: Brooks-Cole.

Kalish, R. A., & Reynolds, D. K. (1981). *Death and ethnicity: A psychocultural study* (2nd printing). Farmingdale, NY: Baywood.

Kochansky, G. E. (1979). Psychiatric rating scales for assessing psychopathology in the elderly: A critical review. In A. Raskin & L. Jarvik (Eds.), *Psychiatric symptoms and cognitive loss in the elderly* (pp. 125–154). Washington, DC: Hemisphere.

Kuhlen, R. G. (1959). Aging and life adjustment. In J. E. Birren (Ed.), *Handbook of aging and the individual* (pp. 314–332). Chicago: University of Chicago Press.

Lorr, M., & Vestre, N. D. (1969). The psychotic inpatient profile: A nurses' observation scale. *Journal of Clinical Psychology, 25*, 137–140.

Marsh, G. R., & Thompson, L. W. (1977). Psychophysiology of aging. In J. E. Birren &

K. W. Schaie (Eds.), *Handbook of the psychology of aging* (pp. 219–248). New York: Van Nostrand Reinhold.

McDonald, R. J., & Spielberger, C. D. (1978). *Measuring anxiety in hospitalized geriatric patients.* Berlin: Schering AG.

McNair, D. M. (1979). Self-rating scales for assessing psychopathology in the elderly. In A. Raskin & L. Jarvik (Eds.), *Psychiatric symptoms and cognitive loss in the elderly* (pp. 157–167). Washington, DC: Hemisphere.

McNair, D. M., Lorr, M., & Droppleman, L. F. (1971). *Profile of mood states: Manual.* San Diego: Education and Individual Testing Service.

Meichenbaum, D. (1977). *Cognitive-behavioral modification.* New York: Plenum Press.

Missouri Psychiatric Institute. (undated). *Missouri inpatient behavior scale (MIBS).* St. Louis: Author.

Patterson, R. L., Dupree, L., Eberly, D. A., Dee-Kelley, C., O'Sullivan, M. J., & Penner, L. A. (1982). *Overcoming deficits of aging: A behavioral treatment approach.* New York: Plenum Press.

Patterson, R. L., O'Sullivan, M. J., & Spielberger, C. D. (1980). Measurement of state and trait anxiety in elderly mental health clients. *Journal of Behavioral Assessment, 2,* 89–97.

Petrie, W. M. (1983). Psychiatric rating scales for inpatient research. In T. Crook, S. Ferris, & R. Bartus (Eds.), *Assessment in geriatric pharmacology* (pp. 59–68). New Canaan, CT: Mark Powley Associates.

Pfeiffer, E. (1977, November). Interviewing the anxious older patient. In *Diagnosis and treatment of anxiety in the aged, part II: Measurement of anxiety* (pp. 23–33; available from Hoffman-LaRoche, Inc.).

Plutchik, R. (1962). *The emotions: Fact, theories, and a new model.* New York: Random House.

Reisberg, B. (1983). The brief cognitive rating scale and global rating scale. In T. Crook, S. Ferris, & R. Bartus (Eds.), *Assessment in geriatric pharmacology* (pp. 19–35). New Canaan, CT: Mark Powley Associates.

Salzman, C. (1977, November). Psychometric rating of anxiety in the elderly. In *Diagnosis and treatment of anxiety in the aged, part II: Measurement of anxiety* (pp. 5–21; available from Hoffman-LaRoche, Inc.).

Salzman, C., & Shader, R. I. (1978). Depression in the elderly. I: Relationship between depression, psychologic mechanisms, and physical illness. *Journal of the American Geriatrics Society, 26,* 253–260.

Scheir, I. H., Cattell, R. S., & Sullivan, W. P. (1961). Predicting anxiety from symptoms of anxiety. *Psychoanalytic Quarterly, 35*(Suppl.), 114–126.

Shader, R. I., Harmatz, J. S., & Salzman, C. (1974). A new scale for clinical assessment of geriatric populations: Sandoz clinical assesment — geriatric (SCAG). *Journal of the American Geriatrics Society, 22,* 107–113.

Sherman, E. (1981). *Counseling the aging: An integrative approach.* New York: The Free Press.

Simon, A. (1980). The neuroses, personality disorders, alcoholism, drug use and misuse, and crime in the aged. In J. E. Birren & R. R. Sloane (Eds.), *Handbook of mental health and aging* (pp. 653–670). Englewood Cliffs, NJ: Prentice-Hall.

Sletten, I. W., & Ullett, G. A. (1972). The present status of automation in a state psychiatric system. *Psychiatric Annals, 2,* 77–80.

Spielberger, C. D. (1972). Conceptual and methodological issues in research on anxiety. In C. D. Spielberger (Ed.), *Anxiety: Current trends in theory and research* (Vol. 1, pp. 481–493). New York: Academic Press.

Spielberger, C. D., Edwards, C. D., Lushene, R. E., Montouri, J., & Platzek, D. (1973). *STAIC: Preliminary manual for the state-trait anxiety inventory for children.* Palo Alto, CA: Consulting Psychologists Press.

Spielberger, C. D., Gorsuch, R. L., & Lushene, R. E. (1970). *Manual for the state-trait anxiety inventory (self-evaluation questionnaire).* Palo Alto, CA: Consulting Psychologists Press.

Suinn, R., & Richardson, F. (1971). Anxiety management training: A nonspecific behavior therapy program for anxiety control. *Behavior Therapy, 2,* 498–510.

Thyer, B. A. (1981). Prolonged in-vivo exposure with a 70-year-old woman. *Journal of Behavior Therapy and Experimental Psychiatry, 12,* 69–71.

Tinklenberg, J. R., Roth, W. T., Pfefferbaum, A., & Kopell, B. S. (1983). Electrophysiological assessment techniques. In T. Crook, S. Ferris, & R. Bartus (Eds.), *Assessment in geriatric pharmacology* (pp. 221–234). New Canaan, CT: Mark Powley Associates.

Verwoerdt, A. (1981). *Clinical geropsychiatry* (2nd ed.). Baltimore: Williams & Wilkens.

Wisocki, P. A., Handen, B., & Morse, C. (1986). The worry scale as a measure of anxiety among homebound and community active elderly. *The Behavior Therapist, 5,* 91–95.

Woods, R. T., & Britton, P. G. (1985). *Clinical psychology with the elderly.* Rockville, MD: Aspen Systems Corp.

Yesavage, J. A. (1984). Relaxation and memory

training in 39 elderly patients. *American Journal of Psychiatry, 141,* 778–781.

Yesavage, J. A. (1985). Nonpharmacologic treatments for memory loss with normal aging. *American Journal of Psychiatry, 142,* 600–605.

Yesavage, J. A., Rose, T. A., & Spiegel, D. (1982). Relaxation training and memory improvement in elderly normals. *Experimental Aging Research, 8,* 195–198.

Zuckerman, M. (1960). The development of an affect adjective check list measure for anxiety. *Journal of Consulting Psychology, 24,* 457–462.

Zung, W. W. K. (1971). A rating instrument for anxiety disorders. *Psychosomatics, 12,* 371–379.

Zung, W. W. K. (1983). Self-rating scales for psychopathology. In T. Crook, S. Ferris, & R. Bartus (Eds.), *Assessment in geriatric pharmacology* (pp. 145–152). New Canaan, CT: Mark Powley Associates.

CHAPTER 29

Suicide and Anxiety

Alex D. Pokorny and James W. Lomax

Relatively little has been written on the topic of suicide and anxiety, despite the fact that anxiety probably is the most common psychiatric symptom, and suicidal behavior is an important concern. The literature is particularly sparse if consideration is limited to completed suicide.

In this chapter, we will focus on (a) the place of anxiety in the psychopathological states preceding suicide; (b) follow-up studies of anxiety neurotics, in terms of subsequent completed suicide; (c) the evidence that predisposition to suicide in anxiety is due to its correlation with depression; and (d) the recent emphasis on persons with panic disorders as especially likely to commit suicide. Finally, we will conclude with a case illustration.

A common oversimplification about suicide is that it always springs from depressive mental illness. Even those suicides due to mental illness include suicides based on paranoid delusions, panic, and so on. Kubie (1967) states that "suicide can occur at the end of many different roads." He lists and describes many mechanisms leading to suicide, two of which include an anxiety component: (a) sudden terror of recurrence of psychosis, and (b) "initial panics," occurring without warning in a seemingly calm and undisturbed life.

We reviewed several leading psychiatry textbooks for discussions of anxiety in relation to suicide. In Kolb and Brodie (1982), the section on anxiety disorders contains no mention of suicide. Similarly, the section on suicide has no mention of anxiety, though there is a reference to Barraclough's (Barraclough, Bunch, Nelson, & Sainsbury, 1974) study of 100 completed suicides, 3 of whom had experienced a phobic anxiety state.

The Comprehensive Textbook of Psychiatry (Kaplan & Sadock, 1985), in the chapter on anxiety states, makes no specific mention of suicide, although it mentions anxiety reaching "a degree of panic and terror that is far more unbearable . . . than the worst physical pains. . . ." The chapter on suicide states that suicide occurs primarily in affective disorders, and next most often in alcoholism. Phobic-anxiety state is mentioned with the miscellaneous group.

The 1985 textbook, *Psychiatry*, (Michels et al., 1985), lists in chapter 71, on suicide and attempted suicide, the leading categories of psychiatric disorders important in assessing suicidal risk: affective disorders, alcoholism, schizophrenia, and previous suicide attempt. It is mentioned that the diagnosis of suicide state or neurosis has shown up in some series of suicides and not in others. Chapter 32, on panic and anxiety disorders, mentions the Coryell, Noyes, and Clarcy (1982) study, which revealed an increased incidence of suicide among patients with panic disorder. They add that this increased suicide rate may be due to development of major depressive disorder at some point. In chapter 33 on agoraphobia, social phobia, and simple phobia, it is pointed out that such patients frequently become demoralized but are rarely truly depressed; there is no mention of suicide as a likely outcome.

The third edition of the *Diagnostic and Statistical Manual* of the American Psychiatric Association (1980) lists the characteristics and diagnostic criteria of anxiety disorders on pages 225 through 239. Suicide is not mentioned in the discussions of generalized anxiety disorder, panic disorder, or the several phobic disorders.

Thus, standard textbooks have little to say about anxiety and suicide in relation to each other. We conclude that this relationship has not been emphasized, often not even mentioned.

Because anxiety is a central concept in psychodynamics, psychopathology, and psychological defense mechanisms, it is surprising that there is little mention of anxiety in articles on dynamics of suicide. Hendin's *Suicide and Scandinavia* (1964) contains a chapter on the psychodynamics of suicide, with many formulations, such as death as self-punishment, death as rebirth, death as retroflexed murder, and so on, but does not mention anxiety.

Breed (1968) presents data from interviews with families and associates of 264 persons who completed suicide. He discusses "failure suicides," and stresses the influence of shame, guilt, and self-derogation, without mention of anxiety. Lester (1972), in an active chapter on personality correlates of suicidal inclination, mentions anxiety only as part of a dysphoric state, along with depression and hostility. Farber (1968) develops the theme that suicide is more closely related to the concept of hope than to any other concept.

Lester (1974) reviews many predictive scales, including these:

1. Devries' Inventory of 13 MMPI items. The only item in this group that taps anxiety is "Sometimes I am really very much afraid."

2. The Tuckman-Youngman and similar scales, none of which has any items suggesting anxiety.

3. The Los Angeles Suicide Prevention Center Scale, which includes as 1 of 11 symptoms, "agitation, tension, anxiety."

Lester (1972) reviews attempts to predict suicidal risk using psychological tests, in which anxiety indicators are not mentioned. Poeldinger, Gehring, and Blaser (1973) report on a study of suicide risk as related to MMPI scores, particularly on anxiety and depression measures, based on a study of 37 depressed patients, 9 of whom had attempted suicide. They found that anxiety and depression were correlated with increased risk (evidently a concurrent judgment of risk).

A recent textbook on defense mechanisms (White & Gilliland, 1975) presents current thinking regarding psychodynamics and defense mechanisms. The state of anxiety is not linked to completed suicide in any section or statement.

A rather different emphasis has appeared in recent years. The focus has shifted from anxiety in a generalized form to panic and phobic anxiety, and it seems plausible that the relationship to suicide of these subcategories is much stronger.

Sheehan (1982) has reviewed and integrated findings regarding panic attacks and phobias, suggesting that this should be viewed from a medical illness model rather than as purely a reaction to life stress or unconscious conflict. He stresses the need to view the symptom complex as a whole.

REVIEW OF THE RESEARCH: FOLLOW-UP STUDIES

If anxiety is viewed not as a symptom but as a psychiatric syndrome or disease state (anxiety state, anxiety neurosis), what is the suicide rate of such patients on follow-up?

One problem rapidly emerges: Most of the references are to the broader category "psychoneurosis," not limited to anxiety neurosis. It may well be that in the older nomenclature, anxiety neurosis was the most common type of neurosis. This might allow us to apply cautiously to anxiety neurosis the reported findings for psychoneurosis.

Levy and Southcombe (1953) report 58 suicides during a 60-year span in one state hospital. None of the subjects had a diagnosis of anxiety reaction. Sletten and Altman (1971) reported on suicides within the Missouri State Hospital System during a 10-year period. The highest rate was for "neurotic depression," with 31 per 10,000 patients per year (this equals 310/100,000/year; after this and many of the subsequent citations, we will give a suicide rate expressed as cases per 100,000 (patients or subjects) per year; these are by our own calculations). There is no mention of anxiety disorders.

Temoche, Pugh, and MacMahon (1964) identified some 1,500 suicides in Massachusetts residents during a 3-year period, and matched these against lists of patients in state, private, and Veterans Administration mental institutions in Massachusetts. They found that psychoneuroses had a standard mortality ratio of 1,840 (normal is 100), which was the second highest category after depressive psychosis, which had a ratio of 3,610. The psychoneurosis category is not broken down further.

Kerr, Schapira, and Roth (1969) report on a follow-up study of affective disorders in relation to premature death. They were able to trace 128 of 135 cases. Their subjects included 40 with phobic anxiety depersonalization state, 32 simple anxiety state, 25 endogenous depression, and 31 reactive depression. After 4 years, there were two suicides, both in male patients with anxiety states (1,786/100,000/year).

Greer and Cawley (1966) followed up 175 neurotic subjects (56 men, 119 women) for 14 years. Forty-eight were diagnosed as having anxiety reaction and 6 as having phobic reaction. After follow-up for 4 to 6 years, there were four completed suicides (457/100,000/year); they do not report the neurotic category of these four suicides. They also cite two foreign-language references. The first, Ljungberg (1957), investigated all 380 patients (135 men and 245 women) admitted to the University Psychiatric Clinic at Stockholm between 1931 and 1945 with a diagnosis of hysteria. Five years after discharge, five of these patients had committed suicide (262/100,000/year). Greer and Cawley also cite a study by Ernst (1959), who followed up 120 psychoneurotic patients who had attended a clinic in Zurich 20 years previously. Four had committed suicide (166/100,000/year).

Pitts and Winokur (1964) studied 748 consecutive admissions to the Renard Hospital in St. Louis, diagnosed according to the APA standard nomenclature. They then identified the cases with a family history of completed suicide. Of 37 patients with such a history, 25 had been diagnosed as having affective disorder and only 1 as having an anxiety reaction.

Sims (1973) did a 12-year follow-up of 157 patients with neurosis, focusing on mortality. Three had died from suicide, and in five others the death might have had a suicidal component. The suicide deaths represented 15% of the total deaths (159/100,000/year). He states that "suicide occurs with increased frequency in all neuroses — not only in neurotic depression."

Sims and Prior (1978) followed up 1,482 neurosis patients from three hospital psychiatric units for a mean of 10.9 years. Fourteen suicides occurred in this group, and 27 others were possible suicides, yielding a relative risk of 6.1 in comparison with the general population. They did not report on anxiety disorders separately. In a more recent report, Sims (1984) discusses further the same study. At the end of the follow-up period, the suicide rate was increased in both "neurotic depression" and "other neurotic disorders," although there was a greater increase in the depressed group.

Robins and associates (Robins, Murphy, Wilkinson, Gassner, & Kayes, 1959) investigated all of the suicides occurring in St. Louis during a 1-year period, interviewing close friends or relatives shortly after the suicide. They also interviewed other associates and obtained hospital records, police records, and other sources of data. They then arrived at a retrospective diagnostic classification. None of these subjects was given a diagnosis of anxiety reaction or neurosis, although a total of 25 subjects were listed as "undiagnosed but psychiatrically ill."

Barraclough and associates (Barraclough et al., 1974) reviewed 100 suicides, as defined by a coroner at inquests, by means of an extensive household interview and search of documents in each case. Diagnoses then were arrived at by a panel of three psychiatrists. Ninety-three of the 100 persons who committed suicide were diagnosed as mentally ill, 70% were diagnosed as having depressive illness, and 15% as being alcoholics. Three subjects were given a diagnosis of phobic anxiety state. These authors also listed the frequency with which 58 symptoms had been mentioned by informants as having been present in the subject. The most common ones were insomnia, 76%; weight change, 66%; looked miserable, 69%. Those symptoms suggesting anxiety scored as follows: looked anxious, 60%; difficulty in concentration, 35%; restless, 34%; complained of anxiety, 31%; trembling and shaking, 24%. The three cases of phobic anxiety states all were found in relatively young married people with anxiety symptoms of such a degree that their domestic and social lives had been severely affected. All required daytime sedation, and all had seen psychiatrists. Furthermore, the two female subjects also were dependent on barbiturates, and the male subject drank heavily. Two of the suicides occurred after loss of keenly anticipated jobs, and one after the loss of a boyfriend.

Rennie (1953) reported on 240 hospital-treated psychoneurotic patients followed up for a period of 20 years. The sample included 50 cases each of anxiety neurosis, hysteria, hypochondriasis, obsessive-compulsive state, and various fatigue states and motor neuroses. Ten of the 240 psychoneurosis patients committed suicide, reported as more than 40 times the rate for the general population during the same decade. The suicide group included three hypochondriacal patients, two neurasthenics, two obsessives, two hysterics, and one anxiety case (total psychoneurotic group = 208/100,000/year; anxiety neurosis group = 100/100,000/year).

One of us (AP) did several follow-up studies of psychiatric patients which included information on diagnosis. In one study of 44 former patients who had committed suicide (Pokorny, 1960), 9 of the 44 subjects had a primary diagnosis of neurosis, although some also had associated alcoholism.

We also studied (Pokorny, 1964) 117 completed suicides in relation to the psychiatric inpatient group from which these cases had arisen (over 11,000 first admissions). By calculating total time at risk for each diagnostic group, we derived suicide rates. The rate for the total group was 165/100,000/year, for the neurotic group, 119, and for depressive disorders, 566.

In another study, we (Pokorny, 1966) followed 618 veteran patients who had initially been seen because of suicide attempts or suicidal ideation. After a follow-up period of 1 month to 14½ years, averaging 4.6 years, 21 subjects (3.4%), all men, had committed suicide. By computation of man-years of risk for each diagnostic category, we found a suicide rate for neurosis of 241/100,000/year, and for the total group, 740.

We also did a major prospective study of 4,800 consecutive psychiatric admissions to the Houston VA Hospital (Pokorny, 1983), for a follow-up period averaging

5 years. Sixty-seven completed suicides occurred in this group, yielding an overall suicide rate of 279/100,000/year. Four hundred subjects had a diagnosis of psychoneurosis, and three suicides occurred in this group (rate of 150). When these were subdivided by type of neurosis, one completed suicide had a diagnosis of anxiety reaction, and two had depressive neurosis. Because the total sample included 216 subjects with anxiety neurosis and 116 with depressive neurosis, this yielded suicide rates of 93/100,000/year for those with anxiety neurosis and 345 for those with depressive neurosis, but these are computed on the basis of only one and two cases, respectively.

Brill and Beebe (1955) reported a follow-up of 1,475 war veterans who had been diagnosed as having psychoneurosis in the year 1944. The psychoneurosis group included all of the usual diagnoses, but exact numbers are not given for subtypes, such as anxiety neurosis, nor does the report identify in which subtype the suicides occured. By 9 years after intake, there had been six suicides, three times the expected rate (45/100,000/year).

A later report (Keehn, Goldberg, & Beebe, 1974) on a larger group of veteran subjects gives mortality rates after 24 years. This report includes 9,813 psychoneurotics and 9,942 control subjects discharged from military service at the same time. A breakdown lists 3,407 (35%) subjects with anxiety type, another 399 (4%) with neurasthenia or neurocirculatory asthenia, and 3,570 (36%) with "mixed type psychoneurosis." After 24 years, there had been 74 suicides in the psychoneurosis group and 24 in the control group, a ratio of 3.15 to 1 (31.4/100,000/yr). Unfortunately, the subtype of neurosis is not given. Noyes, Clancy, Hoenk, and Slymen (1980) interviewed 112 anxiety neurotics originally seen 6 years previously, and compared their outcomes with those of 110 surgical control subjects. The anxiety patients were socially impaired to a greater extent than the control subjects; however, the majority of anxiety neurosis patients had a favorable outcome. Brief episodes of depression developed in nearly half of the anxiety patients. There was one suicide in the anxiety group.

Miles (1977) reviewed the literature up to 1977 to arrive at an estimate of the percentage of individuals in the major psychiatric disease entities who die by suicide. He concluded that estimates for neurosis and personality disorder were difficult, due to many changes in diagnosis and the development of superimposed disorders, often more serious. The data suggest, however, that patients with anxiety states have a considerable risk of suicide. For neurotic or personality disorders combined, his estimate is 5%.

Summarizing these studies, the suicide rate in neurosis appears to be elevated, as compared to the general population, ranging from 100 to 300 per 100,000 per year. The overall population rate is about 12, and for adults, about 15 to 20. There only is fragmentary information on patients diagnosed as having anxiety neurosis. Furthermore, in some of these reports patients with complicating disorders, such as alcoholism or drug dependence, are known to have high suicide rates. Nevertheless, these fragmentary reports are consistent with the view that suicide rates in anxiety disorders are about the same as in the total group of neuroses.

As noted, a problem with the older epidemiological studies is that anxiety disorders are simply lumped in with "psychoneurosis." We can anticipate an even greater problem in looking for suicide outcome in the newer and more specific category "panic disorders." There already is at least one report that does provide such information.

Coryell et al. (1982) screened the charts of all patients with a diagnosis of anxiety neurosis discharged from their hospital between 1925 and 1955. They identified 117 patients who met criteria for panic disorder and eight with agoraphobia with panic attacks. Ninety percent of these subjects were traced successfully. Death certificates were obtained for those who had died. They found that male patients with panic disorder had a highly significant excess mortality in the last decade of follow-up; a similar trend was noted in female patients. Six of 30 subjects (20%), had died by suicide (2 women, 4 men), one within 1 year, another within 4 years, and the others from 14 to 24 years after index admission. The authors suggest that complicating syndromes, such as depression and alcoholism, may divert attention away from a pre-existing panic disorder. They state that studies with more intensive surveillance during follow-up are needed to determine whether depression and substance abuse are necessary antecedents to suicide in these patients.

THE RELATIONSHIP AMONG ANXIETY, DEPRESSION, AND SUICIDE

The correlation of anxiety with depression could account for the increased incidence of suicide in anxiety disorder. Depressive neurosis lumped among psychoneuroses could account for the increased incidence of suicide in individuals with a more broadly conceptualized psychoneurosis, rather than anxiety disorder as defined in DSM-III.

Anxiety symptoms also appear in depression. In a follow-up study of 111 nonhospitalized depressed patients for 14 years, Ziegler and Heersema (1942) report on seven patients who died by suicide, providing some interval history. One patient committed suicide after he had "become panicky and intensely anxious." From a syndrome standpoint, this person had shifted from depression to a state of anxiety.

The follow-up of 240 hospital-treated psychoneurotics by Rennie (1953) mentions that a number of the 50 anxiety neurosis cases required subsequent hospitalization for conditions other than anxiety; for example, 5 developed subsequent depression. "One patient admitted at the age of 30 with anxiety had a previous history of 4 months depression at 23, and ultimately committed suicide at 50." Another patient, "recovered from her anxiety state, remained well for 19 years, and then developed cancer phobia and an agitated depression." Two other patients were subsequently hospitalized for clear-cut depressions. In addition, 3 of the 50 anxiety patients were later hospitalized for schizophrenic conditions. Thus, diagnostic groupings are not necessarily valid for the indefinite future. Sheehan, Ballenger, and Jacobsen (1980) have discussed the relationship between treatment response to antidepressants in anxiety syndromes and possible underlying depression.

Thus, the exact relationships among anxiety, depression, and suicide are not yet clear. There may be a common biological vulnerability to depression and anxiety disorders, especially panic. Klein (D. F. Klein, personal communication, 1985) emphasizes the profound demoralization of individuals with panic attacks who are inappropriately or ineffectively treated. It also is possible to conceptualize the relationship in a psychodynamic framework.

Breier, Charney, and Heninger (1984, 1985), in reviewing this general area, state that agoraphobia/panic disorder and major depression may have a common genetic link. First-degree relatives of patients with agoraphobia/panic disorder have high rates of major depression, and certain antidepressant drugs also are effective for the treatment of agoraphobia/panic disorder. Accordingly, panic disorder emerges as a distinct psychiatric diagnosis based on descriptive, genetic, treatment, and emerging neurobiological data. On the other hand, the diagnostic validity of generalized anxiety disorder remains in question. Even though persons carrying this label may have a predictable treatment response to anxiety agents, other features examined, such as lifetime occurrence, and genetic and neurological studies, fail to support this as a distinct or separate category. Rather, it appears that generalized anxiety symptoms may occur together with panic disorder and major depression, and, in fact, may be a ubiquitous component of most psychiatric disorders. They suggest, therefore, that "generalized anxiety disorder" may actually be a prodromal, incomplete, or residual manifestation of some other psychiatric disorder. The authors do not refer to suicide in this discussion.

Because suicide does seem to occur in panic disorder, what might be the psychological aspects of such an event? Suicide is by definition a conscious act, a self-willed death, a step the individual takes deliberately knowing that it may result in death. The situation seems fairly straightforward in the case of severe depression. Although it is not possible to interview those who have completed suicides afterward, it is possible to approximate the thinking and logic of depressed persons by interviewing "near-misses" and individuals who are stopped in the act. Severely depressed persons have mood-congruent delusions, feelings of worthlessness, loss of hope, and so on, so that a decision to commit suicide is not "illogical." In the case of panic disorder, is it a blind attempt to escape from intolerable feelings (which would suggest an impulsive, unpreplanned action), or is it more a state of demoralization, shame, fear of even worse symptoms, or something like that, which might lead to a more deliberate, planned suicidal act? It will take a different kind of research than the traditional epidemiological studies to answer this. We will need to study each individual case in greater depth.

CLINICAL CONSIDERATIONS

Gittleman and Klein (Klein, personal communication, 1985) have observed that one half of adult agoraphobics have historical evidence of separation disorder of childhood. Klein has incorporated these observations into a conceptual model emphasizing ethological, behavioral, and pharmacological parameters. One of us (JL) has treated a case that illustrates the clinical correlation of panic, separation phenomena, and suicide, which is summarized here:

Case Study

Dr. A sought consultation 4 weeks after he was awakened with an episode of intense anxiety. He called a colleague at the multispecialty clinic in which he worked, who saw Dr. A at their office. Dr. A's physical findings were normal, but as he described his sudden attack of breathlessness and palpitations, he began talking about considerable stresses related to professional disappointments. He had joined the multispecialty clinic when a salaried position with a senior surgical specialist in another city had gone sour. The senior physician had promised a great deal, given "satisfactory performance" by Dr. A, including a lucrative partnership arrangement. However, the more senior physician had found much to criticize about Dr. A's conservative approaches to problems, as opposed to more aggressive surgical interventions. Dr. A had initially admired the more senior physician, particularly his self-assured, positive manner. Later, Dr. A judged that the more senior physician was doing unnecessary surgery, and with greater time exposure, his self-assured manner seemed more cavalier and excessively ambitious. Eventually, the more senior physician announced that Dr. A's "productivity" was insufficient, that he would not be renewing his salaried position, nor would he consider him for partnership in the practice. Under these conditions, Dr. A left and went to work in another community in a move that for him seemed like a disgrace. He felt demoralized, despondent, and had occasional ideas of suicide. In spite of this perspective, the new clinic was extremely pleased to have someone with Dr. A's training; he was greeted warmly, with relative fanfare.

The panic attack itself occurred during a visit from Dr. A's father who lives in another city. Dr. A's father is a retired blue collar worker whom Dr. A describes as having been rather distant and critical during Dr. A's childhood, but who now was quite proud of his son's accomplishments. Shortly after the panic episodes, Dr. A went to a medical meeting, in part for a reunion with a former mentor to discuss his professional dilemmas. Upon arriving at the meeting, however, he discovered that the mentor had died unexpectedly and suddenly, just prior to the meeting. He experienced a profound sense of loss. Upon returning home, he had a second panic attack while lying awake and reminiscing about his recent disappointments.

Dr. A was treated with expressive psychotherapy on a twice weekly basis. He has had no further panic attacks. During treatment, considerable neurotic conflict was uncovered. During the period of therapy, he became more successful and assertive in both professional and interpersonal spheres. There had been considerable revision of his unrealistic perceptions of adulthood, as a sort of trouble-free state in which he would feel calm and capable under all circumstances. For instance, he began to realize that it was normal to be anxious prior to major surgical procedures, and that his inner experience of anxiety did not mean he was "incompetent and a fake," as he had previously interpreted his doubts. His strong yearnings for closeness with an admired man or male team and his wish to be admired himself were developed in considerable detail.

As might be anticipated, Dr. A developed an idealizing transference. There were two major consequences from this transference. On the one hand, Dr. A did not have further panic attacks and had a steady increase in his productivity in every sphere of his life. However, it also became very obvious that the therapist's absences were correlated with periods of increasing nonspecific anxiety; on two such occasions, Dr. A became quite distraught.

Dr. A took the position that he needed his treatment and benefited from it greatly. He struggled with positive feelings toward the therapist about which he initially had grave misgivings because of "homosexual" implications. Eventually, he was able to accept both his dependency and positive feelings about the therapist, concluding that he could have a variety of feelings and not necessarily act on them.

About 9 months prior to the termination of his therapy (which extended over approximately 26 months), Dr. A began to consider the possibility of termination. Almost immediately, he developed a new symptom which was "the thought of suicide," as a suddenly appearing, extremely intense idea which he feared he might not be able to resist. These thoughts occurred most often on the rather long drive from the therapist's office to Dr. A's home. It was very difficult for him to put this thought into clearer words, but it had something to do with the "realization that I could commit suicide." It became obvious that the prospect of terminating and separating had evoked intense anxiety, similar to the feelings at times of missed appointments or vacations. This "thought of suicide" was also related to the original circumstances that had led him to treatment. For Dr. A, a successful and capable career meant a sort of isolation and renunciation of the dependent relationship with an admired older man, which had been an unspoken but pervasive objective of all his educational and professional efforts. His visit from the father which preceded the first panic attack was one in which his father had spoken admiringly of him and his new situation. The second attack followed the actual loss through death of a mentor whom he had seen as a person with whom he would always have a potential place should things not work out in private practice. As these issues were developed in the therapy, there was a mutual recognition that his anxiety over the homosexual implication of his relationship to his therapist and the "thought of suicide" were similar in that they were both unacceptable, crazy thoughts which entered into his consciousness when he felt a sense of separation and longing for a dependent male relationship. He made the observation that a strong loving attachment to his therapist did not oblige him to a homosexual relationship and that having a thought about suicide did not mean that he would actually have to kill himself. This seemed to fit in with the realization that his anxiety about major surgical cases did not mean he was incompetent to function as a surgeon. The suicidal thoughts and attendant anxiety slowly diminished, but there were sessions in which Dr. A felt afraid to leave his session because he might act on this impulse.

As the termination of the therapy grew closer, Dr. A began more directly and more sadly to anticipate the end of his therapy. He realized that in a profound way he could really "not go home again," at least to the sort of dependent relationship he had both dreaded and enjoyed with his father. At a surprise birthday party, Dr. A felt a deep sense of enjoyment of his new associates and friends. He was surprised at the positive way in which he was seen by his colleagues and accepted by them. During the party, however, he had recurring moments of sadness which seemed out of context, until he realized that he was wondering whether or not his wife had invited the therapist to the party. He recognized that this would be a highly unlikely thing for his wife to do, and that the thought reflected his own wish to extend the relationship with his therapist to other situations. He went on from there to a mixture of sadness and a sense of resignation that he was taking a great deal from his therapy, but the relationship with his therapist was ending. The availability of the psychotherapeutic alliance allowed Dr. A to verbalize, understand, and resolve thoughts and feelings that unaddressed would have continued to escalate the intensity, hopelessness, and despair that precedes completed suicide.

Discussion

The clinical material just related highlights the relationship of panic disorder of adult life to separation phenomena. Klein (1981) incorporates such observations in a particular theoretical and clinical framework. However, the clinical material also can be formulated in a psychodynamic manner. For Dr. A, independent and mature functioning had the overwhelming connotation of loss of a dependent relationship. At times of vacation or missed appointments, he became anxious. The frustration of intense passive wishes for an admired older man also led to an intense anger, rapidly turned against himself as the "idea of suicide." The "homosexual" implications of such yearnings made them even more difficult to acknowledge. However, as this rather classic turning of anger against the self was interpreted in a consistent and neutral fashion, Dr. A gradually acknowledged the wishes, and there followed a slow but steady decrement in the intensity of the feelings involved. In patients with less intact ego functioning, more severe regressions and even suicidal crises are not uncommon. Dr. A's ego strength and psychological mindedness made it possible for him to not only form a useful therapeutic alliance, but to think psychologically and reflectively on his inner experiences. Less fortunate individuals with panic attacks do not have this ability to experience regressive pulls in a useful manner, and for them eruption into consciousness of intensely disavowed thoughts may lead to various forms of fragmentation, including suicidal behavior as well as suicidal thoughts.

It is our contention that every patient with significant panic disorder has an increased risk of suicidal crises, particularly around separations caused by therapist vacations or instances in which there must be a change in therapists. At such times, the psychiatrist must be as sensitive to preparing the patient for interruptions and separations as he or she would be with a patient with known major depressive illness. In an expressive or insight-oriented psychotherapy, plans for termination are not met with unmixed enthusiasm. A recurrence of presenting symptoms must be expected and dealt with. For Dr. A, this meant active interpretation of both defenses and underlying impulses. For other persons with panic disorder, pharmacological interventions or even brief hospitalization may be required.

Hendin (1982) describes psychotherapeutic strategies with a variety of patients with suicidal impulses. Of particular interest is the description of a young woman, far more primitively organized than Dr. A, who made a very serious suicide attempt at the time of her therapist's vacation. Hendin's contention is that in most cases, the problem most likely to result in suicidal action is the failure to understand what was going on in the therapeutic interaction. He stresses that the therapist may assume that by providing care and concern previously missing, this will give the patient a desire to live; the patient's hidden agenda may be to prove that nothing the therapist can do will suffice. Hendin concludes that "seriously suicidal" patients are too depressed, withdrawn, or fragile to tolerate anxiety generated in psychoanalytic process; however, he also says that most suicidal patients can work psychodynamically in psychotherapy and should be tried. Apparently, by this Hendin advocates therapeutic interventions that allow the patient to acknowledge "hidden agendas," identify the disguises in which these hidden agendas are cloaked, and see themselves as active participants in their relationships and life course, instead of passive victims. Identifying unacknowledged impulses, elaborating the defenses against awareness of such impulses, and the switch from passive to active participation often are considered to be the core elements of psychoanalysis.

It is not clear in what way "seriously suicidal patients" are inappropriate for the "psychoanalytic process," as opposed to the standard psychoanalytic technique, but such patients should be seen in face-to-face individual therapy less frequently than analytic patients, and the therapist needs to be more active in confrontations that acknowledge the patient's aggressive impulses and intent. A more difficult problem is the management of intensely erotic transferences in very suicidal patients; these may be more difficult for both therapist and patient to openly acknowledge. While Hendin's advice on psychotherapeutic management is sound, the treatment process is extremely tricky and anxiety producing for both parties. Even patients with superficially intact reality testing and good work capacity may have relatively primitive impulses and motivations that can produce enormous difficulties in the management of suicidal crises.

CONCLUDING REMARKS

Considering the importance, when viewed separately, of anxiety and suicide in psychiatry, not much has been written about their relationship. Anxiety receives minimal emphasis in writings about the dynamics and mechanisms of suicide. It appears that in anxiety neurosis, the suicide rates are substantially elevated above those in the general population, but are not as high as rates in affective disorder, alcoholism, and schizophrenia. The whole issue is clouded by the unreliability and lack of systematization of psychiatric diagnosis, particularly in the past, when case series that are the basis of later epidemiological studies were being accumulated. A strong trend is emerging to separate panic disorder from anxiety reactions in general. Although these respond to antidepressants, there is increasing evidence that panic disorders are an independant biological entity, not just "masked" depression; patients with panic disorder do appear to have a high suicide rate, comparable to that in patients with affective disorders. Expressive psychotherapy is appropriate for selected patients with anxiety disorders and panic, but one must carefully evaluate the character structure in which such symptoms exist. In all such patients, regardless of the treatment modality employed, one needs to anticipate the potential emergence of suicidal impulses at fairly predictable points associated with separation and loss.

REFERENCES

American Psychiatric Association. (1980). *Diagnostic and statistical manual of mental diseases* (3rd ed.). Washington, DC: Author.

Barraclough, B., Bunch, J., Nelson, B., & Sainsbury, P. (1974). A hundred cases of suicide: Clinical aspects. *British Journal of Psychiatry, 125*, 355–373.

Breed, W. (1968). The suicide process. In N. Farberow (Ed.), *Proceedings, Fourth International Conference for Suicide Prevention,* (pp. 286–291). Los Angeles: Delmar.

Breier, A., Charney, D., & Heninger, G. (1984). Major depression in patients with agoraphobia and panic disorder. *Archives of General Psychiatry, 41,* 1129–1135.

Breier, A., Charney, D., & Heninger, G. (1985). The diagnostic validity of anxiety disorders and their relationship to depressive illness. *American Journal of Psychiatry, 142,* 787–797.

Brill, N., & Beebe, G. (1955). *A follow-up study of war neuroses.* Veterans Administration Medical Monograph, Washington, DC.

Coryell, W., Noyes, R., & Clancy, J. (1982). Excess mortality in panic disorder: A comparison with primary unipolar depression. *Archives of General Psychiatry, 39,* 701–703.

Devries, A. (1966). A Potential Suicide Personality Inventory. *Psychological Reports, 18,* 731–738.

Farber, M. (1968). Suicide and hope: A theoretical analysis. In N. Farberow (Ed.), *Proceedings, Fourth International Conference for Suicide Prevention,* (pp. 297–306). Los Angeles: Delmar.

Greer, H., & Cawley, R. (1966). *Some observations on the natural history of neurotic illness.* (Australian Medical Association Medical Monograph No. 3). Sydney: Australian Medical Publishing.

Hendin, H. (1964). *Suicide and Scandinavia.* New York: Grune & Stratton.

Hendin, H. (1982). Psychotherapy and suicide. In *Suicide in America* (pp. 160–174). New York: Norton.

Kaplan, H., & Sadock, B. (Eds.). (1985). *Comprehensive textbook of psychiatry IV* (4th ed.). Baltimore: Williams & Wilkins.

Keehn, R., Goldberg, I., & Beebe, G. (1974). Twenty-four-year mortality follow-up of army veterans with disability separations for psychoneurosis in 1944. *Psychosomatic Medicine, 36,* 27–46.

Kerr, T., Schapira, K., & Roth, M. (1969). The relationship between premature death and affective disorders. *British Journal of Psychiatry, 115,* 1277–1282.

Klein, D. (1981). Anxiety reconceptualized. In D. Klein & J. Rabkin (Eds.), *Anxiety: New research and changing concepts* (pp. 239–252). New York: Raven Press.

Kolb, L., & Brodie, H. (1982). *Modern clinical psychiatry* (10th ed.). Philadelphia: W. B. Saunders.

Kubie, L. S. (1967). Multiple determinants of suicide. In E. Schneidman (Ed.), *Essays in self-destruction* (pp. 455–462). New York: Science House.

Lester, D. (1972). *Why people kill themselves* (pp. 259–300). Springfield, IL: Charles C. Thomas.

Lester, D. (1974). Demographic versus clinical prediction of suicidal behaviors. In A. Beck, H. Resnik, & D. Lettieri (Eds.), *The prediction of suicide.* Bowie, MD: Charles Press.

Levy, S., & Southcombe, R. (1953). Suicide in a state hospital for the mentally ill. *Journal of Nervous and Mental Diseases, 117,* 504–514.

Litman, R., Farberow, N., Wold, C., & Brown, T. (1974). Prediction Models of Suicidal Behaviors. In A. Beck, H. Resnick, & D. Lettieri (Eds.), *The prediction of suicide.* Bowie, MD: Charles Press.

Michels, R., Cavenar, J., Brodie, K. H., Cooper, A. M., Guze, S. B., Judd, L. L., Klerman, G. L., & Solnit, A. J. (Eds.). (1985). *Psychiatry.* New York: Lippincott.

Miles, C. P. (1977). Conditions predisposing to suicide: A review. *Journal of Nervous and Mental Diseases, 164,* 231–246.

Noyes, R., Clancy, J., Hoenk, P., & Slymen, D. (1980, February). The prognosis of anxiety neurosis. *Archives of General Psychiatry, 37,* 173–178.

Pitts, F., & Winokur, G. (1964). Affective disorder III. Diagnostic correlates and incidence of suicide. *Journal of Nervous and Mental Diseases, 139,* 176–181.

Poeldinger, W., Gehring, A., & Blaser, P. (1973). Suicide risk and MMPI scores, especially as related to anxiety and depression. *Life Threatening Behavior, 3,* 147–153.

Pokorny, A. (1960). Characteristics of forty-four patients who subsequently commited suicide. *Archives of General Psychiatry, 2,* 314–323.

Pokorny, A. (1964). Suicide rates in various psychiatric disorders. *Journal of Nervous and Mental Disease, 139,* 499–506.

Pokorny, A. (1966). A follow-up study of 618 suicidal patients. *American Journal of Psychiatry, 122,* 1109–1116.

Pokorny, A. (1983). Prediction of suicide in psychiatric patients. *Archives of General Psychiatry, 40,* 249–257.

Rennie, T. (1953). Prognosis in the psychoneurosis: Benign and malignant developments. In P. Hoch & J. Zubin (Eds.), *Current problems in psychiatric diagnosis* (pp. 66–79). New York: Grune & Stratton.

Robins, E., Murphy, G., Wilkinson, R., Gassner, S., & Kayes, J. (Eds.). (1959). Some clinical considerations in the prevention of suicide based on a study of 134 successful suicides. *American Journal of Public Health, 49,* 888–899.

Sheehan, D. (1982, July 15). Current concepts in psychiatry: Panic attacks and phobias. *New England Journal of Medicine, 307,* 156–158.

Sheehan, D., Ballenger, J., & Jacobsen, G. (1980). Treatment of endogenous anxiety with phobic, hysterical, and hypochondriacal sympoms. *Archives of General Psychiatry, 37,* 51–59.

Sims, A. (1973). Mortality in neurosis. *Lancet,* (II), 1072–1075.

Sims, A. (1984). Neurosis and mortality: Investigating an association. *Journal of Psychosomatic Research, 28,* 353–362.

Sims, A., & Prior, P. (1978). The pattern of mortality in severe neurosis. *British Journal of Psychiatry, 133,* 299–305.

Sletten, I., & Altman, H. (1971). Suicide in mental hospital patients [Abstract]. *Scientific Proceedings, 124th Annual Meeting of the American Psychiatric Association.* Publisher is American Psychiatric Association (Wash. DC). No Editor is listed. Washington, DC. Abstract No. 250, 291–292.

Temoche, A., Pugh, T., & MacMahon, B. (1964). Suicide rates among current and former mental institution patients. *Journal of Nervous and Mental Disease, 138,* 124–130.

Tuckman, J., & Youngman, W. (1968). A Scale for Assessing Suicide Risk of Attempted Suicides, *Journal of Clinical Psychology, 24,* 17–19.

White, R., & Gilliland, R. (1975). *Elements of psychopathology: The mechanisms of defense.* New York: Grune & Stratton.

Ziegler, L., & Heersema, P. (1942). A follow-up study of one hundred and eleven non-hosptialized depressed patients after fourteen years. *American Journal of Psychiatry, 99,* 813–817.

CHAPTER 30

Medical Illness and Anxiety

Abraham J. Twerski

The mind-body dichotomy has been with us since time immemorial. Aristotle concluded that only the body can be subject to disease, and as a result of his authoritative pronouncement, afflictions of the spirit were variously relegated to supernatural origins. The impact of this type of reasoning has persisted well into the scientific era. Emotional disorders still are less respectable than "legitimate" somatic diseases, and psychological experiences such as anxiety often are considered to be the expression of a disordered, disembodied "psyche," which can be managed only by those with expertise in ministering to the latter. Treatment of anxiety thus is very often relegated to the psychiatrist, psychologist, or spiritual counselor. If the nonpsychiatric physician does treat anxiety, it generally is with the drugs of the psychiatric armamentarium.

It therefore is important to realize that anxiety frequently may be a symptom of somatic pathology. Indeed, anxiety sometimes may be the *only* symptom, or it may be so prominent that it obscures any other somatic symptom. If the psychiatrist and psychologist are not alert to the possibility of a somatic etiology for the anxiety, or if they assume that the referring physician has already ruled out somatic pathology, treatment with anxiolytic agents or psychotherapy generally is initiated. Patients may report that they have recently undergone a "complete physical evaluation" and were given a clean bill of health. As we shall see, a routine physical examination and even routine blood tests do not rule out somatic causes for emotional symptoms. In those instances where the anxiety is due to a somatic disorder, treatment with anxiolytic agents may be analagous to treatment of undiagnosed abdominal pain with analgesics, where the pain may subside but the inflamed appendix may go on to rupture.

Any discussion of anxiety therefore must include those somatic conditions that may produce these symptoms. Some of these are quite common, some very rare, but rare or common, the statistical incidence is of little interest to the afflicted patient.

CLINICAL CONSIDERATIONS AND RESEARCH REVIEW

Drugs

In our chemophilic society, it is well to remember that many people are self-medicated, and may seek medical help only when self-medication no longer is effective. It is not unlikely that the patient will withhold the truth of self-medication from the physician. Ironically, virtually all chemicals intended to *reduce* anxiety also are capable of *producing* anxiety, whether by direct effect or, more commonly, as a withdrawal phemomenon.

The chemical most widely used to achieve relaxation is ethyl alcohol. Long before gross symptoms of alcohol abuse are manifest, regular use of "moderate" amounts of alcohol can result in anxiety when there is reduction of consumption. Daily drinkers who permit themselves to overindulge on weekends, but who must restrict their intake on returning to the workplace may experience classic anxiety symptoms during the first half of the week. These people are not likely to reveal the extent of their alcohol consumption to the physician. Excessive use of alcohol is much more common than we may think. Indeed, alcohol has displaced syphilis as the "great masquerader," because it can produce varied physical and/or psychological symptoms.

For teaching purposes, I give medical students three rules to diagnose alcohol as etiologic in a patient's symptoms: (a) always suspect, (b) always ask, and (c) never believe. This overstatement obviously is a heuristic technique, but it does emphasize the importance of considering an alcohol etiology. This is one instance where the history given by the patient is not helpful, because denial of the extent of alcohol consumption is the rule. The physician suspecting alcohol excess should obtain additional data from family members where possible.

Assuaging alcohol-induced anxiety with anxiolytic drugs is hazardous for two reasons. The patient may combine the drug with alcohol and have serious additive or synergistic effects, and/or may become addicted to the anxiolytic medication itself.

We live in a culture where normal stress and tension often are considered taboo. The radio or TV repeatedly instructs us, "Do you come home from work tense or ill-at-ease? Then take ________ ." People will obtain anxiolytic drugs from well-intending physicians or pharmacists. Whereas benzodiazepines can be helpful in the short-term treatment of pathological anxiety, use of potent medications to escape from the normal stresses of life is hazardous. Continued use of benzodiazepines, even when the doses are not accelerated, may give rise to anxiety symptoms when the medication is discontinued (Lader, 1983). Furthermore, withdrawal symptoms may occur or persist for weeks and months after cessation of the medication, and both patient and physician may not associate the two (Ashton, 1984; Pertusson & Lader, 1981). I personally have seen numerous cases of severe anxiety in patients who have been using either excessive amounts of benzodiazepines, or had been on maintenance doses for extended periods. Patients with tranquilizer dependency may have prescriptions from several physicians and none may be aware of the excessive dosages.

Amphetamines and its congeners are widely used, whether as anorexics, stimulants, or as respiratory tract decongestants. Neither the patient nor the physician may implicate something as innocent as nasal spray as the offender in causing anxiety, nor is the patient apt to reveal excessive use of these agents even when such excess is gross. The wife of a physician did not reveal to her psychiatrist that she was using a pint of phenylephrine hydrochloride (Neo-Synephrine®) per month. Oral decongestants and bronchodilators may produce tachycardia, palpitation, tremulousness and hyper-irritability, as well as anxiety.

Whereas moderate use of caffeine generally is well tolerated, some people are sensitive to even relatively small doses, such as may be contained in two cups of coffee or several cans of cola. Furthermore, many people consume appreciable doses of caffeine. A person drinking eight to ten cups of coffee or tea daily plus two cans of cola, and who perhaps may use some tablets of a caffeinated headache nostrum, is consuming a quantity of caffeine that can produce or aggravate anxiety. A second-year medical student who felt that he had to keep alert to study sufficiently to rank in the upper 5% of his class admitted to a daily consumption of 40 cups of coffee. One nurse, the wife of an army officer who was scheduled for transfer to Vietnam, developed anxiety with palpitations, which were assumed to be due to the impending transfer. Prior to the onset of the anxiety, she had received a coffee brewer as a gift and her consumption of caffeine had increased. Elimination of the caffeine was followed by complete disappearance of the symptoms. It also is possible to have anxiety as a withdrawal phenomenon from caffeine.

Regular use of hypnotics, especially short-acting barbituates, may produce anxiety as a withdrawal phenomenon in the afternoons or evenings, often resulting in the patient using the hypnotic drug during the day to relieve the symptoms. This leads to the vicious cycle of medication→withdrawal anxiety→medication, so characteristic of addiction. Discontinuing or decreasing the dose of any hypnotic drug, after even 2 weeks of regular use, may result in withdrawal anxiety.

Phenothiazine derivatives in any dose may produce extrapyramidal symptoms, among which is akathesia, a restlessness characterized by consistent shuffling of the legs or an inability to sit in one place. If this is misinterpreted as anxiety, dosage of the medication may be increased in an attempt to reduce the anxiety, and the symptoms actually may be aggravated.

Patients who are on diuretics may develop hyponatremia or hypokalemia, both of which can result in anxiety as well as confusion and weakness.

Use of "recreational" drugs is widespread and all are capable of producing anxiety. Furthermore, the user of street drugs may think he or she is using one drug, while he or she has, in fact, been given another. No social class or ethnic group is immune to drug abuse, and the physician should not hesitate to pursue this line of questioning with both patient and family.

Medications that generally are not associated with causing anxiety nevertheless may produce an idiosyncratic reaction. It is therefore wise to consider *all* medications as potentially anxiety-provoking agents and, wherever possible, recommend a drug-free interval of several weeks before concluding that the anxiety is psychogenic.

Metabolic Disorders

Hyperthyroidism is a classic example of a physical disorder producing anxiety symptoms, and usually is considered in the differential diagnosis. What is less well-known is that *hypothyroidism*, instead of presenting with the typical symptoms of lassitudem, weakness, and depression, may present paradoxically with symptoms of anxiety and irritability (Watanakurakorn, Hodges, & Evans, 1965).

Any of the varieties of thyroiditis may cause sudden fluctuations in the level of circulating thyroid hormone, with consequent classic symptoms of anxiety. The telltale enlargement or tenderness of the thyroid gland may be absent, thus obscuring the correct diagnosis.

Hypoparathyroidism may manifest as severe anxiety (Boren & Brandt, 1985; Hossaine, 1970), and in the full-blown condition there also is neuromuscular irritability, carpal-pedal spasm, and urinary frequency. These may be misinterpreted as psychogenic panic attacks.

Excess or deficiency of adrenal cortical hormones (Cushing's disease or Addison's disease) may manifest prominent anxiety, and unless the associated characteristic signs and symptoms of these conditions are present, they may lead to misdiagnosis. Anxiety also occurs in the virilization syndrome in women, and although the other prominent signs in these conditions usually lead to the correct diagnosis, the anxiety may precede other manifestations (Hall, 1980).

The role of hypoglycemia in producing anxiety is controversial. Well-controlled laboratory studies tend to minimize hypoglycemia as causative (Anderson & Lev-Ran, 1985; Johnson, Door, Swenson, & Service, 1980), while anecdotal data do implicate it (Fredericks & Goodman, 1969).

These are two possible reasons for this discrepancy. First, a 5-hour glucose tolerance curve that shows the lowest blood sugar level to be within the normal range does not rule out hypoglycemia. If a particular patient has a fasting blood glucose level of 108 mg/dl and a 3-hour level of 68 mg/dl, he or she may indeed have all levels within the "normal range," but it must be remembered that this individual has had a drop of 40 mg/dl below his or her normal fasting level, and this may indicate an unstable glucose metabolism. This instability may conceivably result in even lower levels at other times. Second, even absence of symptoms coinciding with the low levels during the laboratory test does not rule out the possibility that in the stresses of real life situations a low blood sugar may contribute to the severity of the symptoms. A simple trial of a hypoglycemic diet, consisting of six feedings a day, and elimination of simple sugars, caffeine, and alcohol can be diagnositc.

The classic metabolic anxiety syndrome is, of course, pheochromocytoma. Carcinoid tumors also can produce typical anxiety symptoms. Recently, there has been increasing intertest in the premenstrual syndrome (PMS), where anxiety frequently is a major problem (Norris & Sullivan, 1983). In the latter condition, the diagnosis can be made by careful documentation, and it therefore is important that women of menstruating age keep a careful record of when their anxiety occurs. Recording of symptoms on a calendar should be done for three cycles. If the anxiety episodes are more severe during the latter half of the menstrual cycle, PMS may be a factor. Treatment with restriction of sodium and simple sugars, vitamin supplements, and, in some cases, natural progesterone may provide dramatic relief.

Neurologic Problems

Cerebral ischemia may result in anxiety, and while this anxiety indeed may be a psychologic reaction to a somatic disorder, rather than a direct sympton of the somatic pathology, the correct diagnosis obviously is essential for appropriate treatment.

Cerebral vascular insufficiency may be due to narrowing of the extracranial arteries, as with an arteriosclerotic plaque in the internal carotid artery or partial occlusion of the subclavian or innominate arteries. Anemia, cardiac arrythmias, or any condition producing hypotension may result in inadequate cerebral perfusion.

Because the ischemia often is a transient phenomenon, there may be no signs or symptoms at the time of examination. The patient who has had a transient dysarthria (episode of confusion or disorientation, dizziness, or hemiparesis), understandably may be very anxious, and because the anxiety may be the only abnormality evident to the physician on examination, the diagnosis of psychogenic anxiety may be made.

Persons who have had head injuries are apt to have *post-concussive syndrome,* with anxiety episodes occurring for months after the injury (Merskey & Woodfarde, 1972). Following viral upper respiratory infections associated with severe headaches, anxiety may occur as the sole symptom of *subclinical encephalitis* (Himmelhoch, Pincus, Tucker, & Detre, 1970). Persons with any of the convulsive disorders or other cerebral dysrythmias unassociated with seizures may manifest anxiety. In the absence of seizures of EEG abnormality, a therapeutic trial of phenytoin may be diagnositc.

Brain tumor, hepatolenticular degeneration (Wilson's disease), multiple sclerosis, combined system disease (posterolateral sclerosis), or Huntington's chorea initially may present as anxiety without accompanying neurologic findings. Anxiety also is seen in peripheral neuropathy, cerebral lues, and early myasthenia gravis (Santy, 1983).

Cardiovascular Diseases

Coronary artery disease classically is accompanied by anxiety. In the younger patient, who is considered to be an unlikely candidate for coronary artery disease, the symptoms of chest tightness and dyspnea, even when accompanied by tachycardia and diaphoresis, easily may be mistaken for psychogenic anxiety. These findings also may occur in pulmonary embolism.

One might think that congestive heart failure would not be misdiagnosed as psychogenic anxiety. I recall a 63-year-old woman brought to the psychiatric hospital because of severe anxiety. One week earlier she had been discharged from the hospital following treatment of congestive heart failure. The attending physician assumed that treatment had been adequate and that the anxiety was psychogenic. Examination following admission to the psychiatric unit revealed signs of congestive heart failure. The anxiety disappeared following adequate treatment of the circulatory problem.

Anxiety attacks are said to be more frequent in patients with mitral valve prolapse, although the etiologic relationship is unclear. Muskin (1985) notes that in 1871, DaCosta described a syndrome of anxiety symptoms associated with a systolic murmur, and that in the following 100 years we have learned that the symptoms are not merely a neurosis, but represent a discrete illness that can be effectively diagnosed and treated. On the other hand, Hicken, Andrews, and Wilcken (1983) believe mitral valve prolapse and anxiety to be independent and unrelated phenomena. Paroxysmal tachycardias also closely mimic anxiety.

Miscellaneous

There are a variety of somatic problems that may manifest anxiety, such as the collagen diseases (Ford & Siekert, 1965), chronic infections (Hall & Popkin, 1977), and exposure to toxins. Anxiety may appear as the harbinger of a malignancy (Avery, 1971; Blustein & Seeman, 1972; Fras, Litin, & Pearson, 1967), and in those conditions where early identification of the tumor is difficult, such as carcinoma of the pancreas, the correct etiology for the anxiety may be made only in retrospect. Chronic pulmonary insufficiency may produce anxiety.

Anxiety may be the most prominent complaint in early Meniere's disease, where the patient reverses the sequence, and complains of attacks of anxiety followed by dizziness, whereas the true state of affairs is that the anxiety is a reaction to the vertigo.

A syndrome that recently has come to recognition is sleep apnea. In addition to anxiety, there may be symptoms suggestive of organic brain dysfunction, such as memory impairment, confusion, deterioration of judgment, and mood changes. If it occurs in the elderly, it easily can be misdiagnosed as Alzheimer's disease or major affective disorder. Because central nervous system depressants can aggravate the condition, it is crucial that the correct diagnosis be made before trials of psychotropic medication are instituted. Most patients with sleep apnea are totally unaware that they have a sleep disturbance, and many physicians do not consider this in their differential. An excellent review of the syndrome is presented by Kwentus, Schulz, Fairman, and Isrow (1985).

Diagnosis

No diagnosis ever is made unless the physician considers it in his or her differential. The numerous somatic etiologies for anxiety thus make it mandatory that the therapists have a mental checklist and make certain that the necessary steps are taken to rule out somatic causes before embarking on a course of treatment for psychogenic anxiety.

The association of anxiety with psychogenic factors is so close in the minds of the physician and patient that erroneously attributing the symptom to a psychological etiology is quite likely to happen. The patient may associate the anxiety with any of the many stresses that are so common in everyday life, convincing both him or herself and the physician of a causal relationship. The risk of misdiagnosis is particularly great in persons who have a history of previous emotional illness.

In my book *Who Says You're Neurotic* (Twerski, 1984), I elaborated on this topic and presented actual case histories where misdiagnoses of neurosis and psychosis were made.

It also is possible for both psychogenic and somatogenic anxiety to coexist, and there may be mutual reinforcement with a resultant vicious cycle. Thus, even the discovery of a bona fide psychological cause for the anxiety by no means eliminates the need for considering a somatic origin.

Obviously, there is nothing to prevent a patient who has anxiety of psychogenic origin from subsequently developing a somatic condition that produces similar symptoms. The patient known to have anxiety or panic attacks for years may indeed suffer a myocardial infarction, develop hyperthyroidism, or have a brain tumor. Thus, it is not sufficient to rule out somatic origins for anxiety or initiation of treatment. The physician must be on the alert and institute periodic examinations, especially when there is a significant change in symptomatology.

There is no sharp demarcation line between somatogenic and psychogenic anxiety. The distress of an anxiety or panic attack is so severe that the patient may develop anxiety in anticipation of the anxiety, resulting in a constant anxiety state.

Where anxiety is constant, those somatic conditions that are likely to cause episodic anxiety may be overlooked, because the physician's focus is apt to be on the constant anxiety. Careful questioning may elicit the description of a rather steady state of anticipatory anxiety among which episodes of symptoms that are both quantitatively and qualitatively different are interspersed. For example, the patient may describe a pervasive feeling of apprehension, irritability, tension, with occasional attacks of palpitations, chest tightness, dizziness, sweaty palms, and feelings of doom.

Hyperventilation is an example of the overlapping of psychogenic and somatogenic anxiety. The hyperventilation per se frequently is secondary to psychogenic anxiety, but produces metabolic changes, such as alkalosis and/or hypocalcemia, which in turn produce severe anxiety as well as a variety of other symptoms.

Consideration of coexistence of both types of anxiety especially is important in the elderly. On the one hand, the loneliness, depression, and feelings of futility that are so prevalent among the older people who may be widowed, unemployed, economically deprived, and "shut-in," may generate functional anxiety. On the other hand, the various somatic causes for anxiety, especially circulatory problems and drugs, are more common among the elderly, whose oxygen delivery to the brain may be compromised and who are likely to be using a number of drugs that, either alone or in combination, may produce anxiety.

We cannot leave the subject of medical illness and anxiety without at least mentioning the flip side of the coin, when anxiety presents as a medical illness. Ruling out the presence of a medical illness does not mean that the patient is not in need of treatment.

A 64-year-old widow was brought to the emergency room at 2:30 a.m. with complaints of dyspnea and chest pain. She was admitted to the coronary care unit, and when several days of monitoring, which included normal ECGs, normal blood work, and normal lung scan, were completed, she was discharged with the reassurance that "There is nothing wrong with you."

On the day prior to the onset of the symptoms, this patient's daughter, a divorcée and mother of three children, all of whom lived with the patient, informed her of the glad tidings that she was soon to marry. The patient, whose life revolved around the care of her grandchildren, was suddenly faced with her life becoming meaningless. She could not permit herself to resent her daughter's marriage because this would mean that she begrudged her good fortune. She was thus torn by internal conflict.

The patient might not even have been aware of the internal turmoil, but even if she were, 2:00 a.m. is hardly an appropriate time to seek out a sympathetic listener. Her psychologic-physiologic system was clever enough to give her entree to help, and did so by producing the kind of symptoms that justify attention at this hour.

The conclusion "We can find nothing wrong with your heart and lungs" was justified. The statement "There is nothing wrong with you" was not, unless a person is consciously malingering, symptoms do not arise when there is "nothing wrong."

REFERENCES

Anderson, R., & Lev-Ran, A. (1985). Hypoglycemia: The standard and fiction. *Psychosomatic Medicine, 26,* 38–47.

Ashton, H. (1984). Benzodiazepine withdrawal: An unfinished story. *British Medical Journal, 288,* 1135–1140.

Avery, T. L. (1971). Seven cases of frontal tumor with psychiatric presentation. *British Journal of Psychiatry, 119,* 19–23.

Blustein, J. E., & Seeman, M. V. (1972). Brain tumors presenting as functional psychiatric disturbances. *Canadian Psychiatric Association Journal, 17,* 55–63.

Boren, M.., & Brandt, V. (1985). Hyperparathyroidism: Neuropsychiatric manifestations. *Psychosomatic Medicine, 26,* 597–601.

Da Costa, J. (1871). On irritable heart: A clinical study of a form of functional cardiac disorder and its consequences. *American Journal of Medical Science, 61,* 17–52.

Ford, R. G., & Siekert, R. G. (1965). Central nervous system manifestations of periarteritis nodosa. *Neurology, 15,* 114–122.

Fras, I., Litin, E. M., & Pearson, J. S. (1967). Comparison of psychiatric symptoms of carcinoma of the pancreas with those in some other intra-abdominal neoplasms. *American Journal of Psychiatry, 123,* 1553–1562.

Fredericks, E., & Goodman, H. (1969). *Low blood sugar and you.* New York: Charter Books.

Hall, R. C. W. (1980). *Psychiatric manifestations of medical illness.* New York: Spectrum Publications.

Hall, R. C. W., & Popkin, M. K. (1977). Psychological symptoms of physical origin. *Female Patient, 21,* 43–47.

Hickey, A., Andrews, G., & Wilcken, D. (1983). Independence of mitral prolapse and neurosis. *British Heart Journal, 50,* 333–336.

Himmelhoch, T., Pincus, J., Tucker, G., & Detre, T. (1983). Subacute encephalitis: Behavioral and neurological aspects. *British Journal of Psychiatry, 116,* 531–538.

Hossain, M. (1970). Neurological and psychiatric manifestations of idiopathic hypoparathyroidism. *Journal of Neurology, Neurosurgery, and Psychiatry, 33,* 153–156.

Johnson, D. D., Door, K. E., Swenson, W. M., & Service, T. (1980). Reactive hypoglycemia. *Journal of the American Medical Association, 243,* 1154.

Kwentus, T., Schulz, S., Fairman, P., & Isrow, L. (1985). Sleep apnea. *Psychosomatic Medicine, 26,* 713–724.

Lader, M. (1983). Dependence on benzodiazepins. *Journal of Clinical Psychiatry, 44,* 121–127.

Merskey, H., & Woodfarde, J. M. (1972). Psychiatric sequelae of minor head injury. *Brain, 95,* 521–528.

Muskin, P. (1985). Parrico, prolapse, and PVC's. *General Hospital Psychiatry, 7,* 219–223.

Norris, R., & Sullivan, C. (1983). *PMS/premenstrual syndrome.* New York: Rawson Associates, 187–256.

Pertusson, H., & Lader, M. H. (1981). Withdrawal from long-term benzodiazepine treatment. *British Medical Journal, 238,* 643–645.

Santy, P. (1983). Undiagnosed myasthenia gravis in emergency psychiatric referrals. *American Emergency Medicine, 6,* 397–398.

Twerski, A. J. (1984). *Who says you're neurotic?* Englewood Cliffs, NJ: Prentice Hall.

Watanakurakorn, C., Hodges, R. E., & Evans, T. C. (1865). Myxedema. *Archives of International Medicine, 116,* 183–190.

CHAPTER 31

Primary Prevention of Anxiety Disorders

Linda Dusenbury and George W. Albee

The purpose of this chapter is to examine the primary prevention of anxiety disorders. The task is somewhat unusual because, with rare exceptions involving those mental disorders with specific known organic etiologies, preventive interventions have not been aimed at specific mental disorders. Rather, attempts are made to reduce levels of psychological distress and to promote positive adjustment and/or coping skills that reduce the incidence of a whole range of disorders.

Perhaps this nonspecific approach to prevention has been the rule because specific mental disorders are rarely connected to specific causes. The stress-disorder relationship is very complex. Various emotional disorders may result from the same objective stressful event. For example, Brenner (1973) has shown that when unemployment rates go up, so do admissions to mental health facilities, as do suicide rates, spouse and child abuse, physical illnesses, and death rates. Similarly, various separate stressful events or experiences often result in the same emotional disorder. Divorce, death of a parent, traumatic early childhood, involuntary unemployment, and other such experiences may each result in depression.

Another reason for the nonspecific approach to prevention is that it may be self-defeating for prevention researchers to try to design interventions to prevent a specific mental disorder because specific disorders are relatively rare in the general population (e.g., schizophrenia has a 1% lifetime prevalence), and may take many years to manifest themselves, making it difficult to demonstrate the short-term effectiveness of a preventive intervention. Because of the nonspecific stress-disorder relationship and the low prevalence rates of specific disorders, prevention researchers have tended to design interventions to reduce psychological distress or to promote psychological well-being in general.

While it is unusual to discuss the primary prevention of a specific disorder, anxiety disorders are of particular interest to preventionists for two reasons: (a) anxiety disorders are more often associated with specific causes (i.e., highly traumatic events such as separations from parents), and (b) anxiety disorders have a particularly high rate of occurrence in the general population. Preventionists may be able to reduce the incidence of anxiety disorders specifically by identifying preventable traumatic events that many people might be expected to experience and by taking steps to reduce these, thereby interrupting the chain of fear reactions that may ultimately result in anxiety disorders.

STATEMENT OF PROBLEM

Mental health problems generally and anxiety disorder specifically are a national epidemic. Several independent surveys (Kiesler, 1980) disclose that 10% to 20% (25–50 million) of the people in the United States have serious mental health problems, and as many as 5% of the population will suffer an anxiety disorder at some point in their lifetime (Marks, 1981). The most cautious survey, conducted by Regier, Goldberg, and Taube (cited in Kiesler, 1980), estimates that 15% of the population (33 million individuals) have serious mental health problems. The most recent National Institute of Mental Health epidemiological study (see Regier et al., 1984) found 19% or 43 million American adults to have a diagnosable DSM-III (American Psychiatric Association, 1980) disorder (and this survey did not include children, adolescents, homeless people, or those in institutions; nor were persons asked about their sexual problems). Kramer (cited in Albee, 1984) has observed that the prevalence rates of mental disorders are rising steadily — particularly those disorders affecting middle-aged and older adults, age groups whose numbers are increasing throughout the world. In as many as one quarter of these disorders, anxiety is a primary symptom (Marks, 1981). In addition to those with serious mental disorders there is at least an equally large number with critical emotional crises that may contribute specifically to the experience of anxiety (e.g., involuntary unemployment, marital disruption and divorce, death of a loved one, serious illness). Kiesler posits that altogether there are about 45,000 (full-time equivalent) practicing clinical psychologists and psychiatrists in the United States. If each of these professionals were to see clients 30 hours a week for 52 weeks each year, they would provide at most 70 million hours of psychotherapeutic services. If professionals were to see each client for a total of 10 hours during the year (an absolute minimum estimate of the time needed to deal with a serious emotional problem), only seven million individuals would be helped. In fact, according to the President's Commission on Mental Health (1978), only seven million persons are seen each year in the U.S. in all mental health facilities by mental health professionals. Obviously, it is impossible to treat on a one-to-one basis the vast numbers of suffering individuals.

The key to understanding the logic of prevention is the well-established fact that widespread disorders affecting millions of persons are never brought under control or eliminated by attempts at treating affected individuals. This bedrock fact, widely understood in the field of public health but little attended to by those concerned with treating individuals, leads to the appreciation that even successful individual treatment has no effect on incidence. Successful treatment of any disease or disorder is highly desired by the affected individual and his or her family and friends. But successful treatment does nothing to reduce the incidence of the disorder. Successful coronary artery surgery may reduce discomfort, and possibly even prolong the life of the individual involved, but it has no effect on the incidence of heart disease in the next generation. Similarly, in those diseases where quick and successful treatment is available (like the use of an antibiotic with gonorrhea, syphilis, or strep infections of the throat), there has been no significant reduction in the subsequent incidence of these disorders since the treatment became available. A one-time antibiotic injection, successful in curing gonorrhea, has not reduced the incidence of gonorrhea in the population.

All of this should make it clear that widespread and popular forms of individual therapy for anxiety disorders (like the widely prescribed mild tranquilizing drugs, as well as self-medication with alcohol for the same purpose), has no effect on the incidence of anxiety disorders in the next generation. If successful prevention efforts are the only way to reduce anxiety disorders, how can we account for the widespread focus on methods of treatment, including drug therapy and psychotherapy? One answer to this paradoxical situation is that most professional in the mental health disciplines have been self-selected to be attracted by and motivated to do individual treatment. They have not been exposed to prevention principles, and have had little contact with the field of public health, where these principles have been demonstrably effective. But there is a further, more ominous kind of problem. As Kelly (1984) has shown, there is a clear relationship between political ideology and attitudes toward causation of emotional disorders and toward prevention efforts. In general, political conservatives favor individual treatment, and explanations of psychopathology rooted in biological causation. Those at the other side of the political spectrum see social factors to be more involved in causation and they are more inclined to favor prevention efforts. Because the field of psychopathology is so dominated by conservative, biologically oriented professionals, the logic of prevention efforts is not sufficiently strong to overcome attitudinal biases.

Wilson (cited in Furnham, Johnson, & Rawles, 1985) reviewed more than 20 studies on the personality of conservatives. He concluded that the conservative syndrome "represents a generalized susceptibility to experiencing threat or anxiety in the face of uncertainty" (see Furnham, Johnson, & Rawles, 1985, p. 676). It is paradoxical to discover that the anxiety of political conservatives may well be a factor in causing opposition to efforts at social change that would reduce the general level of anxiety in the population!

GENERAL DEFINITIONS OF PREVENTION

In the field of public health, *prevention* is a broad concept used to describe three levels of intervention. Primary prevention refers to proactive interventions, usually with groups, that take place before (and to prevent) the onset of the disease or condition. Targets of primary prevention are free of the condition at the time of intervention, though they may be at high risk for contracting it later. Secondary prevention refers to early interventions that take place after signs or symptoms of the disease are exhibited. Secondary prevention is actually early treatment; it attempts to return victims of disease to their original level of pre-illness functioning as quickly as possible. Tertiary prevention refers to interventions that take place after the disease is well established. Tertiary prevention is rehabilitation; it works to minimize the level of disability victims suffer. The difference between primary prevention, and secondary and tertiary prevention is that secondary and tertiary prevention work to reduce the prevalence (existing cases) of disease, while primary prevention works to reduce the incidence (new cases) of disease (Goldston, 1984). In this chapter, the term *prevention* is used to refer only to primary prevention.

Public health's concept of prevention can be used to describe the activities of professionals in the field of mental health. In public health terminology, primary prevention reduces incidence of disease by (a) neutralizing the noxious agent in the environment, (b) strengthening the host, or (c) preventing the transmission of the noxious agent to the host. There are many examples of the success of primary prevention in the field of public health. When chlorine was added to water supplies, the incidence of cholera declined; the noxious agent had been neutralized.

Vaccinations have reduced the incidence of polio, smallpox, and tetanus by strengthening the resistance of the host. Controlling the mosquito population has prevented the transmission of malaria and yellow fever.

While primary prevention cannot alleviate the current problem of the numerical discrepancy between practicing clinicians and *current* populations with mental disorder, it can help to reduce this discrepancy in the *future*. Therefore, primary prevention has become the only realistic hope of those concerned about the gap between the number of individual therapists available and the large number of individuals in need of treatment. Prevention in this context means the primary prevention of emotional or mental dysfunction. Prevention is always proactive. The target of prevention may be groups at high risk for emotional or mental dysfunction, but primary prevention is not directed at individuals already affected.

REDUCING THE INCIDENCE OF PSYCHOPATHOLOGY

Factors relating to changing the incidence of psychopathology can be understood using the following model (Albee, 1982):

$$\text{Reducing Incidence} = \frac{\text{Organic Factors} + \text{Stress} + \text{Exploitation}}{\text{Competence} + \text{Coping Skills} + \text{Self-Esteem} + \text{Support Groups}}$$

"Incidence" refers to the number of new cases of mental disorders occurring in a given time period. "Organic factors" refers to physical or biochemical conditions, such as fetal alcohol syndrome, brain damage, or malnutrition, that contribute to mental dysfunction. "Stress" refers to reactions due to difficult life situations that contribute to mental dysfunction. "Exploitation" of powerless individuals (e.g., migrant farm workers) by those in power contributes to mental dysfunction by increasing the individual's sense of helplessness. The term *competence* relates to the individual's ability to deal effectively with her/his social environment. "Coping skills" refer to the specific strategies in the individual's repertoire that are effective in manipulating the social environment. "Self-esteem" involves the individual's feelings of self-worth and quality of self-image. "Support groups" refers to persons and groups available to the individual for validation and sustenance. The incidence of various forms of psychopathology can be decreased by reducing factors in the numerator, or by increasing factors in the denominator.

ANXIETY AND THE ANXIETY DISORDERS

Our objective is to explore how the incidence of anxiety disorders might be reduced. Anxiety refers to feeling tense, nervous, or apprehensive, and is, therefore, thought of as an emotion. Anxiety is not simply emotional, however; anxiety occurs when the organism perceives threat or danger (Beck, 1985). The object of anxiety, then, is an event that might occur in the future (Spielberger, Pollans, & Worden, 1984), requiring future-oriented thought (Finley-Jones & Brown, 1981). Thus, the central feature of anxiety is cognitive (Sarason, 1985).

Anxiety can be adaptive. It motivates the organism to take evasive action or to otherwise deal with the situation in order to avoid becoming a victim. This response has been called the fight-or-flight response. It is physiological (Sarason, 1985). It involves activation of the sympathetic nervous system, which prepares the organism for physical action. Adrenalin is released, heart rate and blood pressure increase, breathing quickens, and muscles tense (Speilberger et al., 1984). Darwin suggested that anxiety or fear promoted survival because animals who became fearful in threatening situations were more likely to escape and to survive (Good & Kleinman, 1985; Speilberger et al., 1984; Tuma & Maser, 1985). Darwin believed fear and anxiety reactions evolved through natural selection (i.e., nature-favored anxious genes). As Beck points out,

> It is better to have "false positives" (false alarms) than "false negatives" (which miss the danger) in an ambiguous situation. One false negative and you are eliminated from the gene pool. Thus, the cost of survival of the lineage may be a lifetime of discomfort. (Beck, 1985; p. 4)

The problem for we civilized creatures is that the fight-or-flight response which prepares us for physical exertion often cannot be enacted. The aversive physiological symptoms that accompany activation of the sympathetic nervous system are therefore not relieved (Sarason, 1985; Spielberger et al., 1984). The response that was adaptive in the jungle or the steppes is still operational, but is often forbidden in civilization and frequently maladaptive today. In most social situations, fight or flight is not an appropriate response. Such a response must be suppressed, which may have all sorts of negative consequences of health.

Anxiety disorders result when anxiety persists and interferes with effective functioning. Anxiety disorders often involve distorted thinking or irrational assumptions. People with anxiety disorders exaggerate the danger of certain situations (Sarason, 1985). Virtually all cultures have generalized anxiety disorders, but anxiety is expressed through culturally relevant symbols (Good & Kleinman, 1985). For example, Collis (cited in Good & Kleinman, 1985) found that inability to concentrate, which is troublesome in our culture, was not a source of concern among the Yoruba of Nigeria. What was of concern for the Yoruba was not producing a large family. With the Ashanti in Ghana, a major source of worry was dreams, because dreams in this culture was taken to be evidence that one was possessed.

Anxiety disorders are one of the major classification categories in the third edition of the *Diagnostic and Statistical Manual of the American Psychiatric Association* (DSM-III: APA, 1980). Anxiety disorders typically develop during young adulthood, between the ages of 15 and 40 (Marks, 1981). Anxiety disorders include the phobic disorders, posttraumatic stress disorders, and anxiety states. The phobic disorders include agoraphobia, simple phobia, and social phobia. Posttraumatic stress disorders can be acute or chronic. Anxiety states, the most common of the anxiety disorders, include panic disorders, obsessive–compulsive disorders, and generalized anxiety disorders. Panic disorders and simple phobias are the most common, while obsessive–compulsive disorders and social phobias are rare. Finally, for anxiety that does not fit into any of these classifications, there is a miscellaneous category called atypical anxiety disorders (Spielberger et al., 1984).

In a major epidemiological study of the distribution of emotional disturbances in the adult population of the United States (see Albee, 1985, for further discussion), investigators in several American cities found anxiety disorders and phobias significantly more common in women than in men. An explanation for this significant difference was not offered by the investigators, although it is quite clear that it is much more dangerous to be a woman than a man in the United States (and in most other parts of the world). This anxiety might be related to what Freud (1936/1959) called "reality anxiety." Obviously, a way of preventing this would be to find ways to keep men from being aggressive in their physical and sexual relationships with women. Once again, it is clear that meaningful efforts at prevention must involve social and political change.

Anxiety disorders often involve conditioning (Spielberger et al., 1984). The following scenario illustrates how conditioning contributes to anxiety: A bright sixth grader is invited by her teacher to participate in a public speaking contest. The student agrees without realizing the preparation needed to speak effectively. Due to her lack of preparation, her performance is very poor. She is intensely embarrassed not only in front of her peers and favorite teachers, but in front of her parents as well. Following the experience, she comes to dread public speaking more and more. Required class reports produce such anxiety that she becomes nauseous and has to stay home on the days reports are scheduled. Later, her voice begins to quaver and embarrasses her if she so much as tries to ask a question in class. The anxiety becomes so severe by the time she enters college that she elects to drop any class that requires class discussions or class presentations. In behavioral terms, the reason that anxiety states and phobias persist is because intense emotional arousal becomes associated with a harmless stimulus (in this case public speaking) which was related to some noxious event (e.g., public embarrassment) in the past (classical conditioning). As a consequence, individuals exert tremendous energy avoiding the harmless stimulus. Every time they avoid the stimulus, they reduce the anxiety elicited by the thought of encountering the stimulus. Anxiety reduction is itself a powerful reinforcer, so the avoidance behavior is strengthened (operant conditioning). Because the stimulus is successfully avoided, the individual never discovers that the stimulus is in fact harmless. In behavioral terms, the fear never has the opportunity to be extinguished (Spielberger et al., 1984).

The precipitating noxious event believed to be common in many anxiety disorders involves traumatic personal experiences, including the disruption of early relationships (Raskin, Peeke, Dickman, & Pinsker, 1982; Spielberger et al., 1984; Tuma & Maser, 1985). For example, a precipitating event in the lives of many agoraphobics appears to be intense separation anxiety following an unexpected separation from significant adult figures during infancy and childhood. Similarly, the anxiety states also are associated with the disruption of primary relationships during childhood, as well as with poverty. Maternal anxiety also appears to increase risk, as do high parental expectations operating in combination with high parental criticism (Spielberger et al., 1984).

The causal factor in posttraumatic stress disorder is a catastrophic developmental event occurring at any time. The event itself is usually extremely dangerous and elicits tremendous anxiety. Thereafter, the internal and external cues associated with the event are conditioned to elicit the same powerful emotional reaction. People who are more anxious to begin with, or who have lower self-esteem, are at high risk to experience postraumatic stress disorders following catastrophic events (Spielberger et al., 1984).

Why should anxiety disorders relate to an initial traumatic experience? Because an initial traumatic experience elicits a state of fear in the individual which is thereafter more easily reactivated. The first time an individual experiences serious danger (e.g., rape, death of a loved one, separation, combat, a serious accident) the threat may be so powerful as to activate a new state of mind: fear. The event itself is recorded in memory and repeated in thought processes so that it stays in active memory storage. Over time, the event is reorganized and the original memory decays. The event becomes transformed in long-term memory. As time passes, the outside world is safe again, but the state of mind associated with the past event may linger. The emotional arousal associated with the state of mind is now maladaptive because the outside world is relatively safe. Any time cues originally associated with the event reactivate memories of the event, anxiety results (Horowitz, 1985).

In addition to the role conditioning plays in the experience of anxiety, another stress of approach-avoidance conflicts over sexuality is also important. Albee (1977) has argued that sexual repression has long been a major component of the Protestant ethic. In developing industrial societies, in order to move upward into the middle class, it was essential that sex and marriage be rigidly postponed to permit the acquisition of either (a) an education, or (b) capital formation, the only two routes for a poor individual to enter the middle class. Persons who could read and write, and who learned bookkeeping and clerical skills, were in great demand in the industrializing societies. Persons who could save enough money to buy scarce capital materials permitting entrepreneurship could earn their way into the middle class. The Protestant ethic was indeed the true spirit of capitalism (Weber, 1904/1958), and the repression of sexuality was critical to the ethic. Sex had to be controlled, and the Protestant ethic insisted on its sinfulness and threatened sinners with hell-fire and damnation. The anxiety that was conditioned around sexuality in the industrializing society has persisted, and so children grow up conditioned to associate anxiety with sex because their parents feel so anxious around this topic. Most preventionists argue that sex education is critically important in reducing stress and anxiety. As one excellent example of this position, Pogrebin (1983) argues for four preventive efforts that parents can make to reduce sexual anxiety in their children. These include (a) permission to feel sexual pleasure, (b) a positive attitude toward their bodies, (c) the right to sexual knowledge without sex-role distinction based on sexist attitudes, and (d) protection from sexual abuse. The more these are achieved by children as a consequence of parental modeling, the more sexual anxiety and disturbance due to sexist attitudes will be reduced in the society.

STRESS AND ANXIETY

Specific traumatic life events are clearly associated with anxiety, but nonspecific stress also and contributes to the experience of anxiety (Andrews, Tennant, Hewson, & Valliant, 1978; Spielberger et al., 1984), and research has demonstrated that various factors including coping style, self-esteem, and support networks appear to mediate the effects of stress (Andrews et al., 1978; Bandura, 1982; Geller, Swindle, & Dusenbury, 1986; Richardson & Kleinknecht, 1984; Spielberger et al., 1984; Tuma & Maser, 1985).

APPRAISAL

An important determinant of stress is an individual's appraisal of a situation. The environment places demands on the individual, but whether or not the demands will produce fear or anxiety depends on the individual's appraisal of the situation. For example, suppose assembly line workers learn the factory where they work may shut down. According to Lazarus (1980), if an individual perceives that he or she has the potential skills for dealing effectively with the stress, stress may be experienced as challenging in a positive way. For example, if a worker has been learning to use a personal computer in his spare time, he may see the factory shutdown as an excuse to look for a more rewarding job in computers. On the other hand, according to Lazarus, distress or anxiety occurs when the individual appraises a situation as dangerous or threatening because the individual perceives a lack of the skills or resources necessary to handle the situation effectively. A worker who had expected to spend his whole life working at the factory and has no other work skills may not be able to cope. The resulting anxiety is unpleasant in this case, and the individual experiencing anxiety will be motivated to take actions to reduce the anxiety. When people cannot reduce anxiety by coping with the stress or escaping it, they may be able to cope with their own reactions; for instance, they might be able to reappraise the stressor as "not so bad" or "irrelevant" or in some way manageable.

The implications of a factory shutdown may be so serious that reappraisal of the threat as irrelevant or not so bad is not possible, however. When it is not possible to reappraise a stressor as manageable or irrelevant, the individual can take intrapsychic action to reduce discomfort and disruption associated with anxiety. Intrapsychic strategies include repression or denial, which forces the anxiety provoking situation out of conscious awareness (e.g., believing the government would never let the factory go under), or rationalization or intellectualization (e.g., believing that after working hard it is acceptable to collect unemployment payments and take it easy for a while) (Lazarus, 1980). Anxiety becomes problematic when the intrapsychic strategies are detrimental to well-being, or interfere with normal functioning, or are otherwise not effective. If denial inteferes with planning for a shutdown, it is detrimental.

Some groups are more likely than others to perceive situations as threatening. Highly anxious individuals tend to engage in more catastrophisizing when thinking about future events, for example (Richardson & Kleinknecht, 1984). People with generally high levels of trait anxiety and lower self-esteem and self-confidence are more threatened by any evaluation situation. Differences in levels of trait anxiety may be the result of childhood experiences or relationships. Withdrawal of love by parents and negative evaluations by peers or teachers in the past may all contribute to general trait anxiety (Spielberger et al., 1984).

Past experiences with similar situations, as well as activated memories and awareness of relevant coping skills will all contribute to the way a situation is appraised. The experience of threat is subjective and involves apprehension or anticipation about something in the future. When appraisal of threat is realistic, given a truly dangerous situation, it appropriately activates arousal and mobilizes the individual to take evasive action. The appraisal function becomes maladaptive when there is no real danger, at least none that is proportional to the level of arousal. In this case, the evoked emotional reaction is an unnecessary anxiety state (Spielberger et al., 1984).

All people evaluate their abilities to deal with a situation, but anxious individuals are more preoccupied about this and may have many self-defeating thoughts, such as "I can't handle this" when, in fact, they do possess the necessary skills. In other words, anxious preoccupation can interfere with accurate appraisal, and lead to errors in evaluating potential danger. An adaptive response to stress is thinking about issues related to the problem at hand. It involves putting aside intrusive preoccupations about the consequences of failing to cope with the problem. Appraisal, then, has a critical function in facilitating adaptive coping (Sarason, 1985).

PREVENTING ANXIETY: SPECIFIC STRATEGIES

A conceptual model that relates incidence of anxiety disorders to traumatic experiences, stress, coping and appraisal, self-esteem, and support suggests two general intervention strategies: (a) reducing traumatic experiences or levels of stress in the environment and (b) increasing resistance to stress by promoting an individual's adaptive appraisal and coping, bolstering self-esteem, and mobilizing support.

Interventions at the Environmental Level

Interventions at an environmental level could work to eliminate traumatic events that relate to anxiety, such as sexual abuse or rape. These events are proximal causes of anxiety, however. The underlying cause of this sort of anxiety is the society that teaches macho values and sexism, in this way perpetuating and perhaps even endorsing violent or aggressive acts. Interventions at the environmental level must work to change cultural attitudes and stereotypes that account for unnecessary anxiety. For example, repression of sexuality and aggression has, according to Freud (1936/1959), resulted in anxiety over forbidden impulses. Negative cultural stereotypes about the elderly, women, and minorities may result in lowered self-esteem in these groups with resulting vulnerability to anxiety. Interventions at an environmental level are needed to reduce or eliminate social problems, such as poverty, crowding, criminality, and so on. Rutter (1979) has found these problems to have a profound cumulative effect on the mental health of people experiencing them.

Possible interventions at the environmental level include sex education and values clarification in the schools, as well as greater policing of the mass media to reduce the presentation of negative stereotypes of the elderly, minorities, and so on. Legislation and grassroots movements designed to reduce social problems are other examples of intervention at the environmental level.

Interventions at the Level of the Individual

Promoting Coping

Clearly, it takes time to change social and cultural influences, and it is not always possible to prevent traumatic events from occurring. Another approach to prevent anxiety disorders is to facilitate the individual's effective coping with anxiety. Relaxation exercises are effective techniques for coping with anxiety. The most common relaxation technique is progressive deep muscle relaxation, and the effectiveness of this technique for reducing physiological arousal is well documented. While many studies have demonstrated the effectiveness of relaxation training in the treatment of anxiety, it is surprising that relaxation has not been applied to the prevention of anxiety. An exception is the Life Skills Training (LST) program developed by Botvin (1983) to prevent cigarette smoking and substance use during adolescence. The LST program is a multicomponent curriculum that not only provides junior high school students with information about smoking, drinking, and using marijuana, but also gives students an opportunity to develop social skills, communication skills, assertiveness skills, and effective ways of coping with anxiety. The "Coping with Anxiety" component of this curriculum, which explains what anxiety is and provides training in a number of relaxation techniques, could well serve as a model for programs designed to prevent anxiety and anxiety disorders.

There are other research examples that serve as models for promoting coping and reducing anxiety. Sarason (1973) has explored various ways of reducing worry, for example. He found that providing subjects with an effective role model who described problem-solving thought processes and demonstrated problem-solving behaviors reduced anxiety for highly test-anxious subjects. A second study by Sarason and Sarason (1981) also demonstrated that subjects experienced less anxiety during problem-solving tasks after they had the opportunity to view a competent model (Sarason, 1985).

Another study by Sarason (cited in Sarason, 1985) compared the effectiveness of instructing undergraduates to focus on a task (e.g., "Concentrate on the problem") while reassuring them not be overly concerned (e.g., "Don't worry"). High worriers in both experimental groups performed better than high worriers in the control group. On the other hand, nonworriers did worse in the reassurance manipulation than in the control group. Reassurance seems to lower motivation for nonworriers. Because instruction to attend the task was helpful for all subjects, this would appear to be the more promising prevention technique in terms of facilitating coping.

Stress Inoculation

A more broad-based approach to prevent anxiety disorders is stress inoculation training. Stress inoculation involves learning about the nature of stressful experiences and how to cope with them, as well as learning new coping techniques and how to apply them to stressful situations (Bistline, Jaremko, & Sobleman, 1980; Jaremko, 1979, 1980, 1984; Jaremko, Hadfield, & Walker, 1980). It is called stress inoculation because it increases an individual's resistance to stress, analogous to the way tetanus inoculations increase resistance to tetanus. Stress inoculation helps prepare individuals for stressful experiences by informing them about what to expect. Stress inoculation usually occurs between the time individuals decide to do something that will be stressful (e.g., having surgery) and the time they actually do it.

The value of stress inoculation was first suggested in a study by Janis (1958, cited by Janis, 1983), which showed that patients who had elected to have surgery, and who were informed about unpleasant consequences they could expect, suffered fewer post-operative setbacks than patients who did not receive this preparatory information. Since this initial study, a number of experiemnts have demonstrated the positive effects of stress inoculation for people anticipating a range of stressful experiences (e.g., surgery, a new job, childbirth, relocation). Research has also demonstrated the effectiveness of this technique for reducing anxiety associated with public speaking (Jaremko, 1980). Stress inoculation increases resistance to stress in general, though there is some evidence that highly anxious individuals may find preparatory information distressing. While this technique is promising, more research is needed to determine the impact stress inoculation has on those who are already anxious (Janis, 1983).

Enhancing Support

Another strategy to prevent anxiety disorders would be to exploit the protective value of social ties. Social support appears to protect individuals experiencing stress to some extent (Miller & Ingham, 1976 [cited in Marks, 1981]). One of the best research examples of this comes from Nuckolls, Cassell, and Kaplan (1976), who report that pregnant women experiencing negative life events had 57% more birth complications when they lacked social support than women in similar situations who had good support systems.

Anxious people tend not to have the quantity or quality of supportive relationships that less anxious people enjoy, and perceive their relationships as less satisfying and more negative (Henderson & Byrne; Duncan-Jones, Adcock, Scott, & Steele [cited in Marks, 1981]). Preventive interventions that provide social support seem promising, therefore, but careful research is needed to determine whether social ties are actually lacking in the lives of anxious individuals, or whether the ties simply are perceived as less satisfying. In addition, researchers are recently becoming aware that social support can have negative consequences under some circumstances (Heller et al., 1986), and social situations may be especially threatening to the individual who is anxiety prone. How best to exploit social support remains an interesting problem for research.

Influencing Appraisal

A promising intervention strategy for the prevention of anxiety disorders involves influencing the appraisal process the individual uses to determine the extent to which an event should be perceived as threatening. In this regard, behavior therapists have begun to consider how their techniques might be applied to the area of prevention (Jaremko, 1978; Jaremko & Wenrick, 1973). An understanding of the phenomenon known as latent inhibition may contribute to the development of interventions to prevent anxiety. Latent inhibition refers to inhibition of learning. Learning is inhibited and reduced when, prior to pairing a conditioned stimulus with an unconditioned noxious stimulus, the conditioned stimulus is presented alone. This is the case because it is not as easy for an individual to associate a harmless stimulus with a noxious stimulus once the individual has habituated to the harmless stimulus in the absence of the noxious stimulus. For example, dogs exposed to a bell for a number of trials before the bell is paired with electric shock take longer to associate the bell with the shock than dogs who never heard the bell except when it was paired with shock. Research has demonstrated the effectiveness of latent inhibition for reducing later arousal and fear (Jaremko, 1978). In clinical work, latent inhibition is sometimes referred to as prophylactic systematic desensitization; it involves presenting the harmless stimulus in a relaxed setting, in the absence of the noxious (unconditioned) stimulus with which it will later be paired. Prophylactic systematic desensitization has been shown to effectively reduce arousal in public speaking and in approaching a snake (Jaremko & Wenrich, 1973).

In a more applied example, this technique has been used by hospitals to prepare children for scheduled hospitalization. Separations from parents during hospitalization increase the risk that a child will experience anxiety disorders. By introducing children to hispital staff, and familiarizing them with the hospital routine prior to a scheduled hospitalization, later anxiety associated with the hospital itself and separation can be reduced. Children are exposed to neutral elements of the hospital situation in the safety of their parents' company. The anxiety the child later experiences when separated from parents during the actual hospitalization is, in this way, less likely to become strongly associated with the hospital itself and is less likely to be constantly activated while in the hospital or when thinking about the hospital. Introducing children to the school setting and their teacher, in the company of their parents, prior to the first day of school could have the same effect.

CONCLUDING REMARKS

The review of the various strategies for the prevention of anxiety disorders raises a number of questions for research. For example, if effective coping repertoires reduce vulnerability to anxiety, can the development of these coping repertoires be promoted? What role does social support play in the development of anxiety disorders?

Longitudinal studies are needed to address these questions. However, we would argue that research into the prevention of anxiety disorders can begin immediately by providing interventions that work to reduce anxiety. In fact, at the same time that the effectiveness of interventions that provide coping skills training or social support are being evaluated, the relative contribution of coping skills and support to the experience of anxiety could be examined. The intervention would serve as the experimental manipulation.

Finally, we must return to the paradoxical situation in the broad area of intervention that emphasizes treatment and neglects efforts at prevention. The public health dictum that states "No mass disorder afflicting humankind is ever eliminated by attempts at treating the affected individual" is still valid. Logic dictates that funds for research be diverted to prevention efforts and that training in prevention be included in the professional curricula of the mental health professions. Eventually the wisdom of this redirection will be apparent. Treatment has no effect on incidence; it only affects prevalence. Unless we are prepared to walk an endless treadmill, we must re-order our priorities.

REFERENCES

Albee, G. W. (1977). The protestant ethic, sex and psychotherapy. *American Psychologist, 37,* 1043–1050.

Albee, G. W. (1982). Preventing psychopathology and promoting human potential. *American Psychologist, 37,* 1043–1050.

Albee, G. W. (1984). Prologue: A model for classifying prevention programs. In J. M. Joffe, G. W. Albee, & L. D. Kelly (Eds.), *Reading in primary prevention of psychopathology: Basic concepts* (pp. vii–xviii). Hanover, NH: University Press of New England.

Albee, G. W. (1985). The answer is prevention. *Psychology Today,* 19, 2, 60–64.

American Psychiatric Association. (1980). *Diagnostic and statistical manual of mental disorders* (3rd ed.). Washington, DC: Author.

Andrews, G., Tennant, C., Hewson, D. M., & Vaillant, G. E. (1978). Life event stress, social support, coping style, and risk of psychological impairment. *Journal of Nervous and Mental Disease, 166,* 307–316.

Bandura, A. (1982). Self-efficacy mechanism in human agency. *American Psychologist, 37,* 122–147.

Beck, A. T. (1985). Turning anxiety on its head: An overview. In A. T. Beck & G. Emery with R. L. Greenberg (Eds.), *Anxiety disorders and phobias: A cognitive perspective* (pp. 3–18). New York: Basic Books.

Bistline, J. L., Jaremko, M. E., & Sobleman, S. (1980). The relative contribution of covert rain and cognitive restricting to test anxiety reduction. *Journal of Clinical Psychology, 36,* 723–728.

Botvin, G. J. (1983). Prevention of adolescent substance abuse through the development of personal and social competence. In T. J. Glynn, C. G. Luekefeld, & J. P. Ludford (Eds.), *Preventing adolescent drug abuse: Intervention strategies* (National Institute on Drug Abuse Research Monograph 47, DHHS Publication No. ADM 83-1280). Washington, DC: U. S. Government Printing Office.

Brenner, H. (1973). *Mental illness and economy.* Cambridge, MA: Harvard University Press.

Furnham, A., Johnson, C., & Rawles, R. (1985). The determinants of beliefs in human nature. *Personality and Individual Differences, 6,* 675–684.

Finlay-Jones, R., & Brown, G. (1981). Types of stressful life events and the onset of anxiety and depressive disorders. *Psychological Medicine, 11,* 803–815.

Freud, S. (1959). *Inhibitions, symptoms and anxiety* (J. Strachey, Trans.). New York: W. W. Norton and Company. (Original work published 1936).

Goldston, S. E. (1984). Defining primary prevention. In J. M. Joffe, G. W. Albee, & L. D. Kelly (Eds.), *Readings in primary prevention of psychopathology*. Basic Concepts (pp. 31–35). Hanover, NH: University Press of New England.

Good, B. J., & Kleinman, A. M. (1985). Culture and anxiety: Cross-cultural evidence for the patterning of anxiety disorders. In A. H. Tuma & J. D. Maser (Eds.), Anxiety and the anxiety disorders (pp. 297–323). Hillsdale, NJ: Lawrence Erlbaum Associates.

Heller, K., Swindle, R., & Dusenbury, L. (1986). Component social support processes: Comments and integration. *Journal of Consulting and Clinical Psychology, 54*, 466–470.

Horowitz, M. J. (1985). Anxious states of mind induced by stress. In A. H. Tuma & J. D. Maser (Eds.), *Anxiety and the anxiety disorders* (pp. 619–631). Hillsdale, NJ: Lawrence Erlbaum Associates.

Janis, I. L. (1983). Preventing pathogenic denial by means of stress inoculation. In S. Breznitz (Ed.), *The denial of stress* (pp. 35–76). New York: International Universities Press.

Jaremko, M. E. (1978). Prophylactic systematic desensitization: An analogue test. *Journal of Behavior Therapy and Experimental Psychiatry, 9*, 5–9.

Jaremko, M. E. (1979). A component analysis of stress inoculation: Review and prospectus. *Cognitive Therapy and Research, 3*, 35–48.

Jaremko, M. E. (1980). The use of stress inoculation training in the reduction of public speaking anxiety. *Journal of Clinical Psychology, 36*, 735–738.

Jaremko, M. E. (1984). Stress inoculation training: A generic approach for the prevention of stress-related disorders. *Personnel and Guidance Journal, 62*, 544–550.

Jaremko, M. E., Hadfield, R., & Walker, W. F. (1980). Contribution of an educational phase to stress inoculation of speech anxiety. *Perceptual and Motor Skills, 50*, 495–501.

Jaremko, M. E., & Wenrich, W. W. (1973). A prophylactic usage of systematic desensitization. *Journal of Behavior Therapy and Experimental Psychiatry, 4*, 103–105.

Kelly, L. (1984). *Primary prevention ideology: An examination of the attitudes and activities of mental health professionals.* Unpublished doctoral dissertation, University of Vermont, Burlington, VT.

Kiesler, C. A. (1980). Mental health policy as a field of inquiry for psychology. *American Psychologist, 35*, 1066–1080.

Lazarus, R. S. (1980). The stress and coping paradigm. In L. A. Bond & J. C. Rosen (Eds.), *Competence and coping during adulthood* (pp. 28–74). Hanover, NH: University Press of New England.

Marks, I. (1981, December). Stress and other risk factors in anxiety disorders. In H. H. Goldman & S. F. Goldston (Eds.), Preventing Stress-related psychiatric disorders: Proceedings of a National Institute of Mental Health Research Planning Workshop held at Langley Porter Psychiatric Institute, University of California, San Francisco (pp. 77–106).

Nuckolls, K. B., Cassell, J. C., & Kaplan, B. H. (1976). Psychosocial assets, life crisis and the prognosis of pregnancy. *American Journal of Psychiatry, 134*, 90–101.

Pogrebin, L. G. (1983). Nonsexist sexuality. In G. W. Albee, S. Gordon, & H. Leitenberg (Eds.), *Promoting sexual responsibility and preventing sexual problems* (pp. 66–94). Hanover, NH: University Press of New England.

President's Commission on Mental Health (1978). *Report to the President*. Washington, DC: U. S. Government Printing Office.

Raskin, M., Peeke, V. S., Dickman, W., & Pinsker, H. (1982). Panic and generalized anxiety disorders. *Archives of General Psychiatry*, 687–689.

Regier, D. A., Myers, J. K., Kramer, M., Robins, L. N., Blazer, D. G., Hough, R. L., Eaton, W. W., & Locke, B. Z. (1984). The NIMH epidemiologic catchment area program. *Archives of General Psychiatry, 41*, 934–941.

Richardson, S., & Kleinknecht, R. A. (1984). Expectancy effects on anxiety and self-generated cognitive strategies in high and low dental-anxiety females. *Journal of Behavior Therapy and Experimental Psychiatry, 15*, 241–247.

Rutter, M. (1979). Protective factors in children's responses to stress and disadvantage. In M. W. Kent & J. E. Rolf (Eds.), *Primary prevention of psychopathology: Volume III: Social competence in children* (pp. 49–94). Hanover, NH: University Press of New England.

Sarason, I. G. (1973). Test anxiety and cognitive modeling. *Journal of Personality and Social Psychology, 28*, 58–61.

Sarason, I. G. (1985). Cognitive processes, anxiety and treatment of anxiety disorders. In A. Tuma & J. Maser (Eds.), *Anxiety and the anxiety disorders* (pp. 87–107). Hillsdale, NJ: Lawrence Erlbaum Associates.

Sarason, I. G., & Sarason, B. R. (1981). Teaching cognitive and social skills to high school students. *Journal of Consulting and Clinical Psychology, 49,* 908–918.

Spielberger, C. D., Pollans, C. H., & Worden, T. J. (1984). Anxiety disorders. In S. M. Turner, & M. Hersen (Eds.), *Adult psychopathology: A behavioral perspective* (pp. 613–630). New York: John Wiley & Sons.

Tuma, A. H., & Maser, J. D. (1985). Introduction and overview of selected issues. In A. H. Tuma & J. D. Maser (Eds.), *Anxiety and the anxiety disorders* (pp. xix–xxxv). Hillsdale, NJ: Lawrence Erlbaum Associates.

Weber, M. (1958). *The Protestant ethic and the spirit of capitalism* (T. Parsons, Trans.). New York: Scribners. (Original work published 1904–1905).

PART VII

Future Directions

CHAPTER 32

Future Directions

David H. Barlow

The future of the anxiety disorders for the near term will involve ascertaining the nature of panic and unraveling the complex relationship between panic and anxiety. Increased understanding of these complex issues may result in a greatly altered nomenclature for the anxiety disorders as well as a new generation of psychological and pharmacological treatment. In this chapter, I will review briefly evidence for the uniqueness of panic. Based on this evidence, as well as increasing information on the ubiquity of panic, and the relationship of panic to anxious apprehension, I will speculate on anxiety disorder categories that might be found in the fourth edition of the Diagnostic and Statistical Manual of the American Psychiatric Association (DSM-IV) due sometime in the 1990s.

DESCRIPTIONS OF PANIC

Subjectively, the feeling of panic is described as a rush of "apprehension, fear, or terror . . . or feeling of impending doom" (American Psychiatric Association, 1980) that is distinguished from a high level of general anxiety by its sudden onset and tendency to surge to a peak, usually within 10 minutes. The extreme fright that often accompanies the first experience of panic is evident from the recollections of patients assessed at our Phobia and Anxiety Disorders Clinic; 81% of a group of 99 patients recalled that they discontinued their activities, and approximately 25% attended an emergency medical facility or contacted a doctor or nurse in response to their first panic attack. The extent to which avoidance patterns develop alongside panic attacks varies considerably both across individuals, and within individuals across time. Agoraphobia with panic (panic disorder with agoraphobia, DSM-III-R) is assigned as a diagnosis when anticipatory anxiety concerning the attacks results in reluctance to leave the house or to enter places in which panic has been experienced. Anticipatory anxiety commonly is present in panic disorder without agoraphobia, but is not associated with marked avoidance of specific situations.

The phenomenon of panic has accumulated many descriptors and qualifiers. Among terms often utilized are spontaneous, situationsl, predicted, major, minor, and so on. In our view, the current evidence suggests that panic can be categorized best by use of the terms expected and cued and their antonyms as presented in Table 32.1. For example, claustrophobics report panicking in small enclosed places. This, then, is their reported "cue" for panic. However, as Rachman and Levitt (1985) have clearly demonstrated, claustrophobics either may expect or not expect to have a panic attack at a given time when entering a small enclosed place. Similarly, agoraphobics may identify a variety of cues for their panics, including shopping malls and crowded spaces, but also may have panics in the absence of any of these cues, as when they are in a safe place or with a safe person, for example, at home. Because identifiable cues preceding panic are in many cases cognitive (Barlow et al., 1985), the term *cue* seems preferable to the term *situational.*

Clinicians also are well aware that many patients with panic disorder with or without agoraphobia report expectations of panic in the absence of any identifiable cues. Most often this occurs when agoraphobics awaken and report that they are going to have a "bad day," which means they expect to experience a number of panics. Thus, cued panics either can be expected or unexpected and uncued panics also can be expected or unexpected.

Table 32.1. Panic Qualifiers

	Panic	
	Expected	Unexpected
Cued		
Uncued		

Naturally, the term *cued* is phenomenological in that it refers only to the patient's perception of the presence of a discriminated cue and not to the actual presence of a cue. All clinical investigators at this point in time would believe that there are clear antecedents, either biological or psychological, for all panic attacks. Nevertheless, whether the patient perceives a cue or not (regardless of the actual existence of the cue) has important implications for symptom development, particularly in terms of the development of avoidance behavior. That is, patients will tend to avoid a cue perceived to be associated with panic. While these descriptors may be useful, they do not necessarily imply that there is anything essentially unique about panic. Evidence for this uniqueness comes from several different alternative sources.

PANIC UNIQUENESS

The uniqueness of panic is an area of intense study and speculation. Justification for differentiating panic from intense generalized anxiety has been achieved by four methods of analysis, all of which fall short in some respects.

Pharmacological Dissection

The first of these methods involves the observation of differential responses to drug treatment in an observational method that came to be known as "pharmacological dissection." This was noted first by Donald Klein and his colleagues (Klein, 1964; Klein & Fink, 1962). In his early work designed to test the effectiveness of imipramine pamoate, Klein observed that this drug seemed to reduce or eliminate panic attacks but had little effect on chronic levels of anticipatory anxiety. On that basis, he assumed that panic attacks were not simply severe states of general anxiety. Klein thus "dissected" panic attacks from generalized, chronic, or anticipatory anxiety as a qualitatively different state (Klein, 1964; Klein & Fink, 1962). Unfortunately, his reasoning was based on the logical fallacy of inferring pretreatment differences from treatment effects. Also, it now seems that any number of pharmacological agents may be effective for panic (Liebowitz, 1985). However, Klein's work suggested directions for future research.

Psychological Dissection

The second method may be termed "psychological dissection." Waddell, Barlow, and O'Brien (1984) studied the differential treatment effects of a combined treatment program on chronic background anxiety and panic attacks. In their multiple-baseline across-subjects design, three subjects were treated sequentially with relaxation training and cognitive restructuring. The patients self-monitored both number and duration of episodes of intense anxiety and panic, rated as 4 or higher on a scale of 0 to 8. In addition, they recorded level of general anxiety four times each day. All three patients demonstrated marked decreases in the number of episodes of intense anxiety and panic, an improvement that was maintained at a 3-month follow-up. However, two patients exhibited a clear increase in background anxiety at the same time that episodes of intense anxiety and panic were reduced. The third patient demonstrated synchronous reductions in background anxiety and episodes of panic.

It is tempting to conclude from these results that there are two different types of anxiety that respond differentially to the same treatment procedures. However, in so doing, the same logical error for which Klein was criticized is committed. In addition, the data are limited to three patients in whom a consistent pattern of differentiation between panic and chronic anxiety was not present. These data do not exclude the possibility that panic and chronic anxiety differ quantitatively but not qualitatively, and that the impact of psychological and pharmacological treatment is noticeable in the case of only intense levels of anxiety. Moreover, a set of data collected recently from a group of 16 patients with panic disorder who underwent a comprehensive treatment at our Phobia and Anxiety Disorders Clinic indicated that both number of panics and general anxiety ratings decreased from pre- to postassessment: Mean number of panics per week decreased from 1.31 to 0.10, and mean anxiety ratings decreased from 2.31 to 1.37. However, group averages mask individual patterns of response, and it is likely that some patients within that group did not experience parallel changes in panic and generalized anxiety.

Neurobiology and Genetics

The third method reaches broadly and deeply into the areas of behavioral genetics and neurobiology to search for differential biological and genetic underpinnings to panic and generalized anxiety. Aspects of this search are reviewed elsewhere in this volume (e.g., Chapter 11). Suffice it to say here that exciting neurobiological research concentrating on neurotransmitters and various receptor systems is continuing as investigators attempt to isolate the biological basis of panic. Nevertheless, there has, as of yet, been no discovery of a biological marker for panic, as every speculative hypothesis on differential neurobiological processes has not stood up to empirical tests (Barlow, in press; Charney, Woods, Goodman, & Heninger, 1985; Margraf, Ehlers, & Roth, in press).

A seemingly more promising line of investigation has examined the genetic basis of panic. After early retrospective studies suggesting different family backgrounds in panic disorder versus generalized anxiety disorder (e.g., Raskin, Peeks, Dickman, & Pinkster, 1982), a number of studies attempted to investigate more systematically differential family aggregation of panic (e.g., Crowe, Noyes, Pauls, & Slyman, 1983; Harris, Noyes, Crowe, & Chaundry, 1983; Moran & Andrews, 1985). Other studies have examined more directly the genetic basis of panic using twin-study methodology (Torgersen, 1983). All of these studies found that panic aggregated in families or in monozygotic twins, while generalized anxiety did not. In fact, we have known for a long time that clinical anxiety seems to run in families and is probably at least partially inherited (Brown, 1942; Carey, & Gottesman, 1981; Cohen, Badel, Kilpatrick, Reed, & White, 1951; Slater & Shields, 1969). We also are quite sure that the personality trait that has been termed "neuroticism" or "emotionality" runs in families and probably has a genetic component (Broadhurst, 1975; Gray, 1982). What is new about the more recent studies, then, is the suggestion that panic is inheritable, while generalized anxiety is not. This information is directly at odds with all early studies, unless the early studies were only assessing people with panic who were classified under broader headings in use at the time, such as "anxiety neurosis," something that is impossible to ascertain at this time. But even this would not account for a person inheriting an "anxious" personality.

Because findings for a specific genetic component to panic, as opposed to generalized anxiety, are very much at odds with a broader view of the ability to inherit of anxiety, often referred to as nervousness or emotionality, it is possible that these results are artifactual. In addition to major methodological problems with existing work (Carey, 1985; Carey & Gottesman, 1981), a close examination of this literature reveals one very clear artifact that might make these findings spurious. First, studies supporting the hypothetical differential genetic contribution of panic and generalized anxiety utilized DSM-III (American Psychiatric Association, 1980) diagnostic criteria. But there is a diagnostic convention in DSM-III (not present in DSM-III-R) that generalized anxiety disorder is a residual category, to be diagnosed only in the absence of any other anxiety-based symptoms such as panic, phobic avoidance, or obsessive thoughts. In fact, data indicate that almost all patients with panic disorder also present with marked "generalized anxiety" (Barlow, Blanchard, Vermilyea, Vermilyea, & DiNardo, 1986). Therefore, the only patients included in the category "generalized anxiety disorder" in the Crowe et al. (1983) study, for example, were those not panicking at all. It is very likely that these were less severe cases. In fact, Torgersen's (1983) twin study, commonly regarded as the strongest supporting evidence for differential ability to inherit panic disorder, found a genetic contribution to neurotic disorders only among those probands who were inpatients and not those who were outpatients. Once again this may be reflecting the influence of severity on heredity, rather than differential anxiety symptoms. Cloninger, Martin, Clayton, and Guze (1981), in sketching out the natural history of panic disorder, note that one of the first symptoms recalled by patients in late childhood is "nervousness," with panic not appearing until early adulthood. Because it is difficult to find panickers without generalized anxiety, establishing different heredity rates for panic and generalized anxiety would require at least matching the two groups on severity.

Behavioral geneticists have a lot of work in front of them before we can draw any conclusions one way or the other in this very difficult but potentiallly rewarding area. It does seem safe to conclude, however, that some aspect of anxiety runs in families and probably is inheritable, but it is not entirely clear just what is inherited. Because studies suggesting differential heredity of panic and generalized anxiety have not controlled for severity, which influences the inheritance of any human trait in a very powerful way, it does not seem possible to say that specific anxiety "symptoms" are inherited differentially. Rather, the best evidence indicates that what is inherited is a "vulnerability" to develop an anxiety disorder, because even in studies suggesting a strong genetic contribution, no simple or clear mode of genetic transmission is apparent, and more of the variance seems to be accounted for by environmental influences than genetic influences (Crowe et al., 1983; Torgersen, 1983). But what exactly is this vulnerability? The strongest evidence suggests that it is a labile or overly responsive autonomic nervous system. Eysenck (1967) makes a strong case for this as the underlying biological vulnerability predisposing the development of a clinical anxiety syndrome under the right combination of environmental and psychological conditions. Even stronger evidence is provided by twin studies on the inheritance of specific autonomic nervous system traits. For example, Hume (1973) and Lader and Wing (1966) both showed that habituation of the galvanic skin response (GSR), pulse rate, and number of spontaneous fluctuations in GSR seem to be genetically determined. As McGuffin and Reich (1984) suggest, these psychophysiological characteristics may reflect the substrate on which both the personality trait of "emotionality," as well as the clinical anxiety disorders, are based.

Finally, it does not make sense at this point in time to conclude that a specific clinical anxiety symptom, whether it be an obsessional thought, a panic attack, or a phobia of enclosed spaces, would be directly inherited as one intact behavioral and emotional response, set in the same sort of simple Mendelian mode as hair and eye color. The demonstrated psychosocial influence on the formation of these behavioral and emotional patterns almost surely points to a complex biopsychosocial model of the development of panic and anxiety disorders. In fact, there is no psychiatric or emotional disorder for which a classical Mendelian mode of single-gene heredity seem applicable. Even for the major psychotic disorders, where suggestions of genetic links have long been established, almost all investigators, including geneticists, conclude that an underlying vulnerability exists that interacts with a variety of psychological and social factors to produce the disorder (McGuffin & Reich, 1984; Tsaung & Vandermay, 1980). At most, geneticists suggest that a polygenic multifactorial model might be appropriate, where the underlying genetically determined vulnerability is normally distributed across the population through the additive effect of many genes (polygenes), but where environmental factors also account for a necessary contribution (multifactorial).

In summary, neither the limited evidence from differential treatment response studies (either pharmacological or psychological), or the more robust and logically more important evidence from neurobiological or genetic studies suggest anything unique about panic at this point in time. Of course, new data always are appearing and if anything "unique" is found about panic from these areas of inquiry, it would most likely emerge from detailed studies of neurotransmitter and receptor systems.

Panic Phenomenology

Despite the relatively weak evidence provided by these approaches, a more straightforward method, often overlooked, provides more convincing evidence on panic uniqueness that may highlight what is essentially important about panic. In this approach, panic is examined directly and compared to general anxiety phenomenologically. For example, Taylor et al. (1986) were able to obtain physiological data on episodes of panic and generalized anxiety by ambulatory monitoring during day-to-day activities. Heart rate remained relatively stable during periods of intense anticipatory anxiety, at a much lower level than during panic episodes, despite the fact that episodes of anticipatory and panic anxiety were rated subjectively at similar levels of intensity. Heart rate averaged 89.2 beats per minute (bpm) during anticipatory anxiety, as compared to 108.2 bpm during panic. A similar pattern of results was observed by Freedman, Ianni, Ettedgui, and Puthezhath (1985), who compared heart rate recorded during panic attacks and during states of anxiety that were matched in terms of intensity but were not labeled as panic. The latter, which presumably represented periods of anticipatory or generalized anxiety, were not characterized by heart rate elevation.

However, even physiological comparisons involving panic episodes do not adequately rule out the possibility that panic is simply a severe level of generalized anxiety, given that the response systems of anxiety can be discordant at any given point in time, so that intensity can vary somewhat independently on subjective and physiological measures. It is for this reason that panic can be reported, on occasion, in the absence of intense physiological arousal.

Additional phenomenological evidence for differences between generalized anxiety and panic derives from studies that compare tonic arousal levels in patients with each diagnosis. Rapee (1986) recorded differences in baseline measures from 20 subjects with panic disorder and 13 subjects with generalized anxiety disorder. At rest, panic disorder subjects showed a greater tendency to overbreathe than those with generalized anxiety disorder. Rapee suggested that "such individuals may be predisposed to experiencing acute exacerbations of symptoms inasmuch as their bodies may no longer have the ability to buffer minor changes in pCO_2" (1986, p. 27). His data are consistent with evidence reported by Lum (1976) and Liebowitz et al. (1985), who reported the chronic presence of lower bicarbonate and pCO_2 levels in patients with panic disorder than in normal persons. Rapee also found that panic patients displayed higher resting heart rates than generalized anxiety patients: 92.4 compared to 76.4 bpm, respectively, replicating a similar finding from our center (Barlow et al., 1984). Liebowitz et al. (1985) noted similar heart rate differences during baseline measurement; however, patient-control differences were less marked the day before panic induction, causing them to attribute the chronic arousal in panic patients to "nonspecific apprehension."

Recently, we have demonstrated that patients with panic disorder evidence a stronger somatic component to their anxiety than do patients with generalized anxiety disorder on questionnaire measures of anxiety (Barlow et al., 1984). Subjects with panic disorder scored significantly higher on the Somatic scale of the Cognitive Somatic Anxiety Questionnaire (Schwartz, Davidson, & Goleman, 1978); the means were 23.9 and 15.5, respectively. The groups did not differ significantly with respect to cognitive scores, although GAD patients tended to score higher. Hoehn-Saric (1981) compared the scores of 15 patients with GAD to the scores of 36 mixed anxiety disorder patients suffering from panic attacks. The groups differed on a Somatic Symptom Scale, where the panic patients' high scores reflected more intense and more somatic signs of anxiety, such as muscle tension and respiratory symptoms. The prevalence of a significantly stronger somatic component for panic patients has been reported by other researchers, including Anderson, Noyes, and Crowe (1984).

Of interest is the fact that these groups do not differ on measures of general anxiety, for example, the State-Trait Anxiety Inventory (Spielberger, Gorsuch, & Lushene, 1970). Also, scores from 82 panickers and 11 GAD patients, assessed at our clinic, did not differ substantially on measures of general anxiety and depression, based on the Hamilton Anxiety and Depression Scales; anxiety ratings were 18.4 and 19.8, respectively; and depression ratings were 12.9 and 14.4, respectively. Given the large somatic component found in panic disorder patients, one might expect them to report more physical complications of their disorder than GAD patients. However, our preliminary findings suggest that panic disorder and GAD patients are equally likely to report the presence of at least one physical complication, such as migraine headaches or irritable bowel syndrome (42% and 46% of the samples, respectively). Indeed, GAD patients tended to report, on average, more somatic complications (mean = 0.82) than panic patients (mean = 0.46). However, this evidence is subject to further investigation.

In general, then, panic disorder seems to present somewhat differently and can be identified separately from intense generalized anxiety disorder on measures of phasic response, tonic response, and questionnaire measures. But there is one other phenomenological feature of panic that may, in fact, be crucial. This feature of panic is best represented by data presented in Figure 32.1, illustrating the sudden overwhelming surge of anxiety experienced both physiologically and sub-

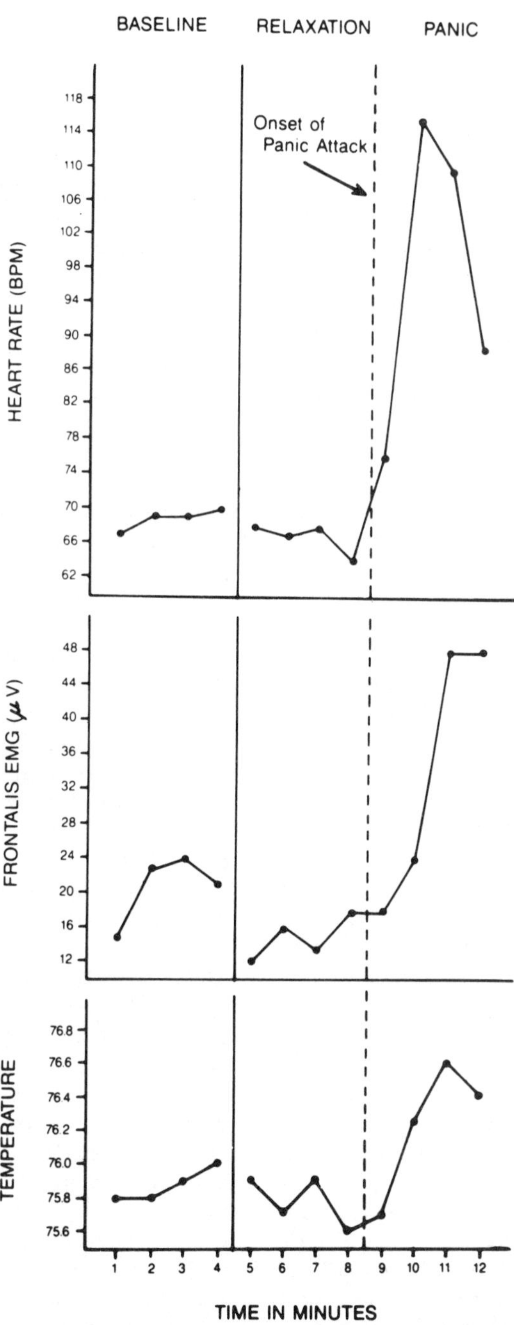

Figure 32.1. Heart rate, average integrated electromyograph (EMG), and hand-surface temperature. From "Psychophysiology of Relaxation-Associated Panic Attacks" by A. Cohen, D. Barlow, and E. B. Blanchard, 1985, *Journal of Abnormal Psychology, 94*, 96–101. Copyright 1985 by American Psychological Association. Reprinted by permission.

jectively that reaches a peak in several minutes. While the definition in DSM-III-R specifies 10 minutes, one can see that the surge presented in Figure 32.1 reached a peak in closer to 2 minutes' time (Cohen, Barlow, & Blanchard, 1985).

Now we have fascinating evidence supporting what we have known clinically for some time. Many patients become "apprehensive" about the possibility of having an unexpected or uncued panic attack. This suggests a functional relationship between these two phenomenological events that may differ depending on a variety of parameters. For example, Rachman and Levitt (1985) examined the differential consequences of expected and unexpected panics in a setting where cues for panic were readily available, specifically, a small enclosed space used to assess claustrophobia. Volunteers with moderate to severe claustrophobia were subjected to 238 trials of enclosure in a small dark room. Sixty-seven episodes of panic were experienced by 13 claustrophobics. Of those, 50 were expected and correctly predicted, while 17 were unexpected. Expected panics were not followed by any changes in feelings of safety or anticipatory anxiety preceding subsequent trials. But the experience of unexpected panic attacks greatly increased anticipatory anxiety concerning the occurrence of panic on subsequent trials (although it did not influence the probability of panic or the actual fear that was experienced during subsequent trials).

Therefore, what might be important about panic is the overwhelming suddenness or intensity of the event and whether it is expected or not. With this phenomenological difference, and the evidence for a functional relationship between anxious apprehension and panic, it may not be necessary to establish underlying biological markers or specific genetic contributions before saying panic is unique. It will be enough to say that panic is unique because it is experienced uniquely by the patient, due to the sudden surge of anxiety and the potentially unexpected nature of the event. In this respect, whether this is simply anxiety at a higher intensity or whether it is essentially a different biological event, its "uniqueness" is established and we need to attend to the functional implications of this uniqueness.

DSM-IV

The evidence now is clear that panic is a pervasive and a ubiquitous event (Barlow, in press; Barlow & Craske, in press). Not only is panic experienced occasionally by a larger percentage of the population, estimated to range from 25% to 35% in a given year, but evidence indicates that almost all patients with diagnosable anxiety disorders experience panic (Barlow et al., 1985). Differences established in this study in terms of the phenomenon of panic among the anxiety disorders had only to do with identified cues for panic on the part of the patients. Specifically, patients with panic disorder with or without agoraphobia had many subjectively determined uncued panics. Increasing evidence from a variety of sources (Barlow, in press, in press b; Beck, in press; Clarke, in press) strongly suggests that the antecedants of these "uncued" unexpected panics are specific sets of somatic events that are misinterpreted and strongly associated with anxiety. Emerging psychologically based treatments for panic with strong evidence for success target cognitive and behavioral aspects of fears of somatic or interoceptive sensations (Barlow, 1986; Barlow & Cerny, in press).

But what are the origins of panic? While etiologic issues concerning panic and anxiety are covered elsewhere in this volume (see part III), suffice it to say that panics either begin very unexpectedly against a background of acute or chronic life stress or they occur in the context of some traumatic situation, which could range widely from events such as natural disasters to being bitten by a dog. This initial panic attack, which seems to be an expression of our hardwired alarm system preparing us to fight or flee from the impending threat, either may be a true alarm, as would be the case with natural disasters or frightening encounters with aggressive dogs, or a "false" alarm, as would be the case when it occurs unexpectedly against the background of accumulating life stress (false in the sense that fight or flight is an unadaptive response to the types of threats presented by life stressors such as divorce, financial difficulties, changing jobs, etc.). What is common to both true and false alarms is that each can turn into an inappropriately "learned" alarm that becomes associated with specific antecedants, whether these antecedants are perceived by the patient or not. Once again, if they are perceived by the patient they are reported as "cues" for panic. Individuals then develop more or less severe apprehension to the possibility of panicking, depending on the presence or absence of perceived cues, the expected or unexpected quality of the panics, and the pervasiveness of the antecedants.

Based on results from future research, it is possible that all currently identified anxiety disorders, as well as some DSM-III disorders not characterized as anxiety disorders, are basically panic disorders that differ only in terms of the pervasiveness of the antecedants, the perception of the cues, and whether the panic is expected or not. Posttraumatic stress disorder and some simple phobias with traumatic etiologies would represent true alarms transformed into learned alarms. Antecedants in these conditions could be quite pervasive and include thoughts or dreams of the natural disaster, war, or traumatic encounter with an animal, and so on. Panic disorder with and without agoraphobia, as well as other phobias without a traumatic etiology such as most social and some simple phobias, simply may be false alarms that are transformed into learned alarms that are more or less highly discriminated (cued). An individual experiencing a false alarm while flying on a plane after years of successful and enjoyable flying might be said to have a phobia of flying, when in fact it is a highly discriminated panic disorder emerging out of an experience with a false alarm. Similar analyses might apply to certain social phobics, as well as almost all patients presenting with panic disorder. While the learned alarm may be more or less discriminated depending on a variety of circumstances surrounding the initial event, what is actually feared is the unexpected alarm itself, representing as it does a breakdown of control over future events. Similarly, in obsessive-compulsive disorder, alarms become learned to and associated with certain patterns of thoughts, making the antecedants in this disorder the most pervasive and unavoidable of any of the anxiety disorders. Certain historical conditions facilitate this type of learned alarm, such as the notion that horrible thoughts are the moral equivalent of horrible actions. The pervasiveness of the antecedants here would insure heroic attempts at magical avoidance in the form of rituals, as well as the severe demoralization, dysphoria, and depression that often accompanies this very severe anxiety disorder.

The one anxiety disorder that cannot be characterized as an inappropriate learned alarm would be generalized anxiety disorder, characterized by pervasive anxious apprehension concerning a number of potential future threats. While anxious apprehension is, of necessity, a part of the panic disorders in the form of anticipatory anxiety (with the exception of some highly discriminated simple phobias where complete avoidance is possible), when existing on its own it is in many ways the most difficult of all disorders to treat. Nevertheless, this type of anxious apprehension seems to be a loose cognitive-affective structure consisting of a negative feedback cycle characterized to varying degrees by components of high negative affect, arousal, self-preoccupation and self-focused attention, and perceptions of both internal and external events proceeding in an unpredictable, uncontrollable fashion. This cognitive-affective structure and its underlying biological marker of chronic overarousal seem to have deep psychological and biological roots that account for the enormous difficulty confronting clinicians in dealing successfully with this pervasive problem (Barlow, in press). These categories are represented diagramatically in Figure 32.2.

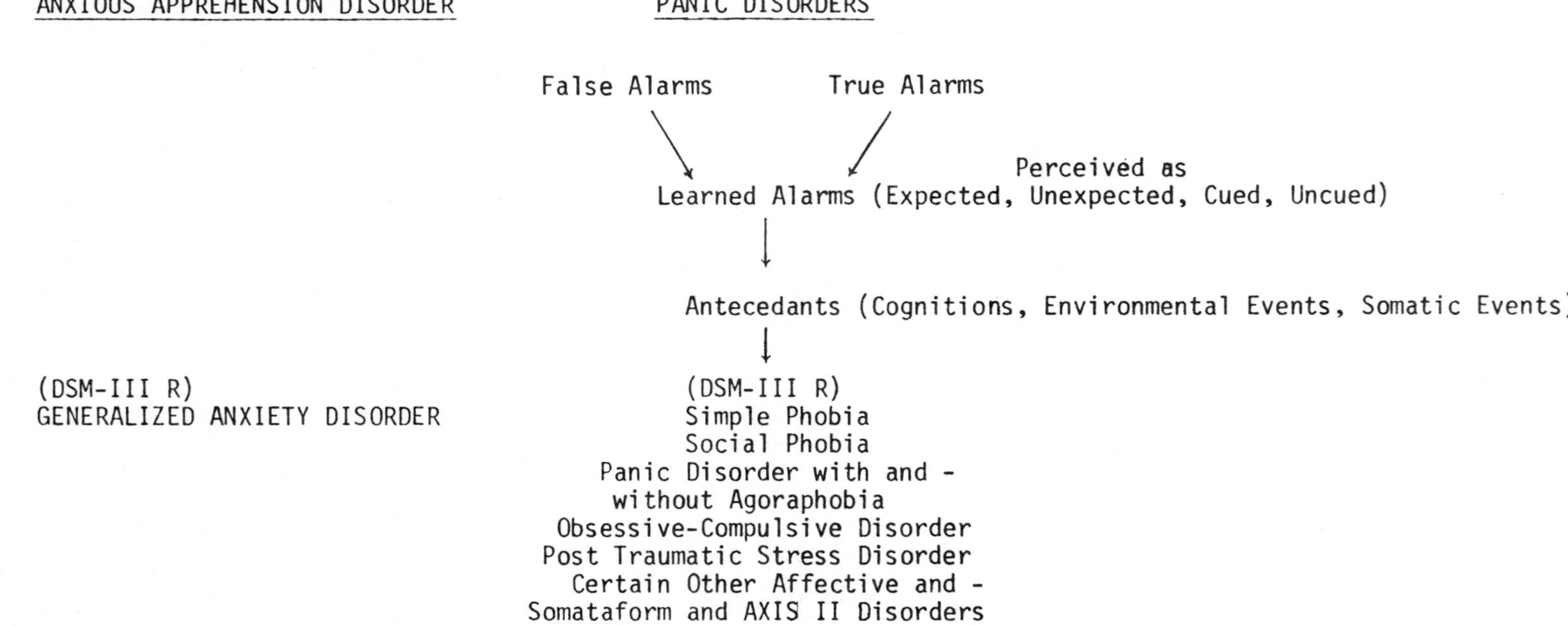

Figure 32.2. Anxious apprehension disorder (panic disorders).

Developments in thinking underlying this speculative system of classification are outlined elsewhere (Barlow, in press), but it will be clear to the reader that it is years away from confirmation. Nevertheless, progress in the past 5 years in understanding the nature of panic and its relationship to anxiety insures that we may move rather rapidly toward a goal of understanding these ancient and complex phenomena.

REFERENCES

American Psychiatric Association. (1980). *Diagnostic and statistical manual of mental disorders* (3rd ed.). Washington, DC: Author.

Anderson, D. J., Noyes, R., & Crowe, R. R. (1984). A comparison of panic disorder and generalized anxiety disorder. *American Journal of Psychiatry, 141,* 572–575.

Barlow, D. H. (1986). Behavioral conception and treatment of panic. *Psychopharmacology Bulletin, 22,* 802–806.

Barlow, D. H. (in press). *Panic, anxiety, and the anxiety disorders.* New York: Guilford Press.

Barlow, D. H., Blanchard, E. B., Vermilyea, J. A., Vermilyea, B. B., & DiNardo, P. A. (1986). Generalized anxiety and generalized anxiety disorder: Description and reconceptualization. *American Journal of Psychiatry, 143,* 40–44.

Barlow, D. H., & Cerny, J. A. (in press). *Psychological treatment of panic.* New York: Guilford Press.

Barlow, D. H., Cohen, A. S., Waddell, M., Vermilyea, B. B., Klosko, J. S., Blanchard, E. B., & DiNardo, P. A. (1984). Panic and generalized anxiety disorders: Nature and treatment. *Behavior Therapy, 15,* 431–449.

Barlow, D. H., & Craske, M. G. (in press). The phenomenology of panic. In S. Rachman & J. D. Maser (Eds.), *Panic: Psychological Perspectives.* Hillsdale, NJ: Lawrence Erlbaum Associates.

Barlow, D. H., Vermilyea, J., Blanchard, E. B., Vermilyea, B. B., DiNardo, P. A., & Cerny, J. A. (1985). The phenomenon of panic. *Journal of Abnormal Psychology, 94,* 320–328.

Beck, A. T. (in press). Cognitive approaches to panic disorder: Theory and therapy. In S. Rachman & J. D. Maser (Eds.), *Panic: Cognitive perspectives.* Hillsdale, NJ: Lawrence Erlbaum Associates.

Broadhurst, P. L. (1975). The Maudsley reactive and nonreactive strains of rats: A survey. *Behavioral Genetics, 5,* 299–320.

Brown, F. W. (1942). Heredity in the psychoneuroses (summary). *Proceedings from the Royal Society of Medicine, 35,* 785–790.

Carey, G. (1985). Epidemiology and cross-cultural aspects of anxiety disorders: A commentary. In A. H. Tuma & J. D. Maser (Eds.), *Anxiety and the anxiety disorders.* Hillsdale, NJ: Lawrence Erlbaum Associates.

Carey, G., & Gottesman, I. I. (1981). Twin and family studies of anxiety phobic, and obsessive disorders. In D. F. Klein, & J. G. Rabkin (Eds.), *Anxiety: New research and changing concepts* (pp. 117–134). New York: Raven Press.

Charney, D. S., Woods, S. W., Goodman, W. K., & Heninger, G. R. (1985). *Involvement of noradrenergic and serotonergic systems: Neurobiological mechanisms of human anxiety.* Paper presented at Annual Meeting of the American College of Neuropsychopharmacology, Maui, Hawaii.

Clarke, D. M. (in press). A cognitive model of panic. In S. Rachman & J. D. Maser (Eds.), *Panic: Cognitive perspectives.* Hillsdale, NJ: Lawrence Erlbaum Associates.

Cloninger, C. R., Martin, R. L., Clayton, P., & Guze, S. B. (1981). A blind follow-up and family study of anxiety neurosis: Preliminary analysis of the St. Louis 500. In D. F. Klein, & J. Rabkin (Eds.), *Anxiety: New research and changing concepts* (pp. 137–148). New York: Raven Press.

Cohen, M. E., Badel, D. W., Kilpatrick, A., Reed, E. W., & White, P. D. (1951). The high familial prevalence of neurocirculatory asthenia (anxiety neurosis, effort syndrome). *American Journal of Human Genetics, 3.* 126–158.

Cohen, A. S., Barlow, D. H., & Blanchard, E. B. (1985). The psychophysiology of relaxation-association panic attacks. *Journal of Abnormal Psychology, 94,* 96–101.

Crowe, R. R., Noyes, R., Pauls, D. L., & Slyman, D. (1983). A family study of panic disorder. *Archives of General Psychiatry, 40,* 1065–1069.

Eysenck, H. J. (1967). (Ed.), *The biological basis of personality.* Springfield, IL: Charles C. Thomas.

Freedman, R. R., Ianni, P., Ettedgui, E., & Puthezhath, N. (1985). Ambulatory monitoring of panic disorder. *Archives of General Psychiatry, 42,* 244–250.

Gray, J. A. (1982). *The neuropsychology of anxiety.* New York: Oxford University Press.

Harris, E. L., Noyes, R., Crowe, R. R., & Chaundhry, D. R. (1983). Family study of agoraphobia. *Archives of General Psychiatry, 40,* 1061–1064.

Hoehn-Saric, R. (1981). Characteristics of chronic anxiety patients. In D. F. Klein & J. G. Rabkin (Eds.), *Anxiety: New research and changing concepts*. New York: Raven Press.

Hume, W. I. (1973). Physiological measures in twins. In G. Claridge, S. Canter, & W. I. Hume (Eds.), *Personality differences and biological variations: A study of twins*. Oxford, England: Pergamon Press.

Klein, D. F. (1964). Delineation of two drug responsive anxiety syndrome. *Psychopharmacologia, 5,* 397–408.

Klein, D. F., & Fink, M. (1962). Psychiatric reaction patterns to imipramine. *American Journal of Psychiatry, 119,* 438.

Lader, M. H., & Wing, L. (1966). *Physiological measures, sedative drugs, and morbid anxiety*. London: Oxford University Press.

Liebowitz, M. R. (1985, December). *Pharmacological treatment of panic attacks.* Paper presented at Annual Meeting of the American College of Neuropsychopharmacology, Maui, Hawaii.

Liebowitz, M. R., Gorman, J. M., Fyer, A. J., Levitt, M., Dillon, D., Levy, G., Appleby, I. L., Anderson, S., Daly, M., Davies, S. O., & Klein, D. F. (1985). Lactate provocation of panic attacks: II. Biochemical and physiological findings. *Archives of General Psychiatry, 42,* 709–719.

Lum, L. C. (1976). The syndrome of habitual chronic hyperventilation. In O. W. Hill (Ed.), *Modern trends in psychosomatic medicine* (Vol. 3). London: Butterworths.

Margraf, J., Ehlers, A., & Roth, W. T. (in press). Current biological models of panic disorder and agoraphobia: A look at the evidence. *Behaviour Research and Therapy.*

McGuffin, P., & Reich, T. (1984). Psychopathology and genetics. In H. E. Adams & P. B. Sutker (Eds.), *Comprehensive handbook of psychopathology*. New York: Plenum Press.

Moran, C., & Andrews, G. (1985). The familial occurrence of agoraphobia. *British Journal of Psychiatry, 146,* 262–267.

Rachman, S., & Levitt, K. (1985). Panics and their consequences. *Behaviour Research and Therapy, 23,* 585–600.

Rapee, R. (1986). Differential response to hyperventilation in panic disorder and generalized anxiety disorders. *Journal of Abnormal Psychology, 95,* 24–28.

Raskin, M., Peeke, H. V. S., Dickman, W., & Pinkster, M. (1982). Panic and generalized anxiety disorders: Developmental antecedents and precipitants. *Archives of General Psychiatry, 39,* 687–689.

Schwartz, G. E., Davidson, R. J., & Goleman, D. J. (1978). Patterning of cognitive and somatic processes in self-regulation of anxiety: Effects of meditation versus exercise. *Psychosomatic Medicine, 40,* 321–328.

Slater, E., & Shields, J. (1969). Genetical aspects of anxiety. *British Journal of Psychiatry, Special Publication, 3,* 62–71.

Spielberger, C. D., Gorsuch, R. L., & Lushene, R. E. (1970). *Manual for the State-Trait Anxiety Inventory*. Palo Alto, CA: Consulting Psychologist Press.

Taylor, C. B., Sheikh, J., Agras, W. S., Roth, W. T., Margraf, J., Ehlers, A., Maddock, R. J., & Gossard, D. (1986). Self-report of panic attacks: Agreement with heart rate changes. *American Journal of Psychiatry, 143,* 478–482.

Torgersen, S. (1983). Genetic factors in anxiety disorders. *Archives of General Psychiatry, 40,* 1085–1089.

Tsaung, M. T., & Vandermay, R. (1980). *Genes and the mind. Inheritance of mental illness.* New York: Oxford University Press.

Waddell, M., Barlow, D. H., & O'Brien, G. T. (1984). A preliminary investigation of cognitive and relaxation treatment of panic disorder: Effects on intense anxiety vs. 'background' anxiety. *Behaviour Research and Therapy, 22,* 393–402.

Author Index

Subject Index

About the Editors and Contributors

Editors

Cynthia G. Last, Ph.D. is Assistant Professor of Child Psychiatry and Director of the Child and Adolescent Anxiety Disorder Clinic in the Department of Psychiatry, University of Pittsburgh School of Medicine. With Dr. Hersen, she is editor and founder of the *Journal of Anxiety Disorders*. Her books include: *Behavior Therapy Casebook* and *Issues in Diagnostic Research*. Dr. Last is the recipient of a Clinical Investigator Award from the National Institute of Mental Health. More recently, she received a research grant from NIMH to study anxiety disorders in children and adolescents. She has published numerous journal articles and book chapters on the assessment, diagnosis, and treatment of anxiety disorders in both child and adult populations.

Michel Hersen, Ph.D. is Professor of Psychiatry and Psychology at the University of Pittsburgh School of Medicine. He is Past President of the Association for Advancement of Behavior Therapy. He has co-authored and co-edited 54 books including: *The Clinical Psychology Handbook, Behavior Therapy for Children and Adolescents: A Clinical Approach, Behavior Therapy for the Developmentally and Physically Disabled, Handbook of Developmental and Physical Disabilities, Handbook of Family Violence, Psychological Evaluation of the Developmentally and Physically Disabled,* and *Research Methods in Clinical Psychology*. He has also published more than 160 scientific journal articles and is coeditor of several psychological journals: *Clinical Psychology Review, Journal of Anxiety Disorders, Journal of the Multihandicapped Person, Journal of Family Violence*, and *Behavior Modification*. His research interests include assessment and treatment of a variety of child populations, including multihandicapped children and their families, and family violence. Dr. Hersen is the recipient of several research grants from the National Institute of Mental Health, the Department of Education, the National Institute of Disabilities and Rehabilitation Research, and the March of Dimes Birth Defects Foundation.

Contributors

George W. Albee, Ph.D. is Professor of Psychology at the University of Vermont.

In 1977–78 he chaired the Task Panel on Prevention for the President's (Carter) Commission on Mental Health. One result of the Commission's report was the passage of the Mental Health System Act that established the NIMH Office of Prevention and Prevention Branch. In 1959 he wrote *Mental Health Manpower* for the President's (Eisenhower) Joint Commission on Mental Illness and Health. On the basis of that commission's report, Congress established Community Mental Health Centers throughout the country. Dr. Albee was national President of the American Psychological Association (1969–1970), and served on the APA Board of Directors until January, 1980. In 1975 Dr. Albee received the APA Distinguished Professional Contribution Award, and in 1981 he received a similar award from the APA Division of Community Psychology. He has written and spoken extensively about the prevention of psychopathology. With Dr. Justin M. Joffe he established the Vermont Conference on the Primary Prevention of Psychopathology (VCPP) in 1977, which holds an annual conference on some specific aspect of prevention and has published a series of a dozen books on prevention.

David H. Barlow is Professor of Psychology and Co-Director of the Center for Stress and Anxiety Disorders at the Department of Psychology, State University of New York at Albany. Previously he was Professor of Psychiatry and Psychology at Brown University and is Past President of the Association for Advancement of Behavior Therapy. Recent books include: Barlow, D. H., Hayes, S. C., & Nelson, R. O., *The Scientist-Practitioner: Research and Accountability in Clinical and Educational Settings*; Barlow, D. H. & Hersen, *Single Case Experimental Designs: Strategies for Studying Behavior Change, Second Edition*, both published by Pergamon Press; Barlow, D. H. & Cerny, J. A., *The Psychological Treatment of Panic*, The Guilford Press; Barlow, D. H., *Panic, Anxiety, and the Anxiety Disorders*, The Guilford Press.

Aaron T. Beck, M.D. is a University Professor of Psychiatry, Department of Psychiatry, School of Medicine, University of Pennsylvania. He has over 200 publications mainly in the areas of panic, depression, suicide, hopelessness, and anxiety. His current research is particularly focused on cognitive approaches to the understanding and treatment of panic.

Dennis S. Charney, M.D. is an Associate Professor of Psychiatry at Yale University School of Medicine and Director of the Clinical Neuroscience Research Unit at the Connecticut Research Award of the American Academy of Clinical Psychiatrists. He is the author of 200 articles, abstracts, and book chapters regarding the neurobiology of psychiatric disorders and the mechanism of action of psychotropic drugs.

David M. Clark, D.Phil. is University Lecturer in Psychology, Department of Psychiatry, University of Oxford and a Fellow of Wolfson College, Oxford. He has published numerous articles, mainly on the role of cognitive processes in personality and in the development, maintenance and treatment of emotional disorders. His current research is particularly concerned with cognitive approaches to the understanding and treatment of panic.

Linda Dusenbury, Ph.D. is Assistant Professor of Psychology in Public Health at Cornell University Medical College. With Dr. Justin Joffe, and Dr. Albee, she is editor of *Readings in Primary Prevention: Basic Concepts*. In 1984–85, while she was a National Institute of Mental Health Clinical Research Trainee at Indiana University, Dr. Dusenbury studied psychological invulnerability and stress-resistance among populations at high risk for emotional disorders. Dr. Dusenbury currently manages a large scale substance use prevention trial funded by the National Cancer Institute to test the effectiveness of a program which emphasizes the development of important personal and social skills with urban minority students. She has published journal articles and book chapters on the prevention of psychopathology and the promotion of social competence.

Morris N. Eagle (Ph.D., Clinical Psychology, New York University, 1958) has been Professor of Psychology at York University in Toronto since 1972. Between 1982 and 1985, he was Chairman of the Psychology Department and before that, Director of the Clinical Program for two years.

Currently, in addition to his faculty position at York University, he consults to the Department of Psychiatry, Toronto General Hospital and has a part-time private practice in psychotherapy.

He has authored about 75 journal articles, chapters and reviews and has authored *Recent Developments in Psychoanalysis: A Critical Evaluation*, published by McGraw-Hill in 1984.

Jean M. Edwards, Ph.D. is an Assistant Professor in the Department of Psychology, Wright State University. Her research interests include stress and anxiety and the interaction model of personality.

Paul M. G. Emmelkamp, Ph.D. is Professor of Clinical Psychology and Psychotherapy at the University of Groningen, The Netherlands. He is the author of *Phobic and Obsessive-Compulsive Disorders* and (with Dr. E. B. Foa) editor of *Failures in Behavior Therapy*. He has published numerous journal articles and book chapters on anxiety disorders, depression and marital distress. He is president of the European Association of Behavior Therapy (1987–1988).

Norman S. Endler is a Professor of Psychology at York University, North York, Ontario. He received his Ph.D. in Clinical Psychology in 1958 from the University of Illinois. His areas of interest include anxiety and stress, social interaction processes, and the interaction model of personality, and he has published numerous articles in these areas. His books include *Personality and the Behavioral Disorders* (edited with J. McV. Hunt), and *Personality at the Crossroads* and *Interactional Psychology and Personality* (edited with D. Magnusson). He has published numerous journal articles and book chapters on anxiety, conformity, interactionism and the sociology of psychological knowledge. Professor Endler is a Fellow of the Royal Society of Canada, and a Killam Research Fellow, Canada Council.

Edna B. Foa, Ph.D. is a Professor of Psychiatry and Director of the Center for the Treatment and Study of Anxiety in the Department of Psychiatry, Medical College of Pennsylvania at Eastern Pennsylvania Psychiatric Institute. Dr. Foa is an author of three books and over 80 chapters and articles. She heads research projects on the treatment of obsessive-compulsive disorders, the response of rape victims and their treatment, and to investigate the effects of anxiety on information processing and memory.

Allen Frances, M.D. is Professor of Psychiatry at Cornell University Medical College and Director of the Outpatient Department of the Payne Whitney Clinic. He is the author or editor of 8 books and of over 150 publications. Dr. Frances is the Editor of the *Journal of Personality Disorders*.

Minna Fyer, M.D. is Assistant Professor of Psychiatry at Cornell University Medical College and Associate Director of the Central Evaluation Service of the Payne Whitney Clinic.

Jack M. Gorman, M.D. is Associate Professor of Clinical Psychiatry, College of Physicians and Surgeons, Columbia University and serves as Scientific Director of the Mental Health Clinical Research Center and as Director of the Biological Studies Unit of the New York State Psychiatric Institute. He is a recipient of a Research Scientist Development Award and of a grant to study respiratory physiology in panic disorder fron the National Institute of Mental Health. He has published numerous articles and chapters on psychobiology and psychopharmacology.

Jeffrey A. Gray, M.A., Ph.D. is Professor of Psychology and Head of the Department of Psychology in the Institute of Psychiatry, University of London, England. He was previously in the Department of Experimental Psychology, Oxford University and Fellow of University College, Oxford. His books include *Pavlov's Typology, The Psychology of Fear and Stress, Elements of a Two-Process Theory of Learning* and *The Neuropsychology of Anxiety*. He has published nearly 200 articles dealing with problems in brain and behavior, psychopharmacology, learning theory and the biological basis of personality.

Ann Pollinger Haas, Ph.D. is Associate Professor of Health Sciences at Lehman College of the City University of New York, Research Associate Professor of Psychiatry at New York Medical College, and Associate Director of the Center for Psychosocial Studies. With Dr. Hendin, she has done extensive research on responses to life-threatening experiences. She is currently completing a statistical analysis of data collected from 100 Vietnam combat veterans with posttraumatic stress disorder, for which she has received a grant from NIMH. Other areas in which she has published widely include marijuana abuse and research methodologies for studying psychosocial problems. She is coauthor with Dr. Hendin of *Wounds of War* and *Living High: Daily Marijuana Use Among Adults.*

R. J. Hafner, M.D., M.Phil., F.R.A.-N.Z.C.P., M.R.C. Psych. is Clinical Associate Professor of Psychiatry at the Flinders University of South Australia, and Director of the W. A. Dibden Research Unit, Glenside Hospital, Adelaide. His interest in the marital context of psychiatric disorders and in other areas of psychiatry has yielded numerous publications in professional journals and a recent book *Marriage and Mental Illness: A Sex Roles Perspective*. He continues to be active in psychiatric research, with the marital and family context of psychological symptoms as a major focus.

Emeritus Professor Max Hamilton, M.D. was formerly Nuffield Professor of Psychiatry at the University of Leeds, England and Hon. Consultant Psychiatrist to the General Infirmary at Leeds and other hospitals in the area. He is an Honorary Member of various national associations of psychiatry and psychopharmacology and was a pioneer in research methodology and statistics in psychiatry. He is the author of two well-known rating scales for anxiety and depression and has published numerous journal articles, books and book chapters on psychiatry, psychometrics, and psychopharmacology.

Herbert Hendin, M.D. is Professor of Psychiatry at New York Medical College and President of the American Suicide Association. He also directs the Center for Psychosocial Studies, a research organization that studies psychiatric problems with social implications, including suicide, drug abuse and posttraumatic stress. He has been the principal investigator on a number of research projects concerned with posttraumatic stress disorder, and is currently doing a study of victims of violence for the Harry Frank Guggenheim Foundation. He is the author of many articles on posttraumatic stress in civilians and veterans, and co-author with Ann Pollinger Haas of *Wounds of War: The Psychological Aftermath of Combat in Vietnam.*

William P. Henry, Ph.D. is Research Assistant Professor in the Department of Psychology, Vanderbilt University, where he coordinates data analysis for a five-year NIMH-funded project on time-limited dynamic psychotherapy, and where he conducts research on interpersonal processes in psychotherapy.

Rudolf Hoehn-Saric, M.D. is Associate Professor of Psychiatry and Director of the Psychiatric Outpatient Services and the

Anxiety Disorders Clinic in the Department of Psychiatry and Behavioral Sciences, Johns Hopkins University School of Medicine. His research, conducted conjointly with Daniel R. McLeod, Ph.D., focuses on psychological, physiological and pharmacological aspects of anxiety disorders. Currently, Dr. Hoehn-Saric has a research grant from the NIMH to study somatic manifestations of anxiety, using an ambulatory monitoring device. He has authored numerous publications and is on the editorial board of the *Journal of Anxiety Disorders.*

Thomas R. Insel, M.D. is a psychiatrist and neuroscientist in the Laboratory of Clinical Science of the National Institute of Mental Health in Bethesda, Maryland. Dr. Insel has edited a book and written numerous papers in the areas of obsessive-compulsive disorder, anxiety, and neuropharmacology. He received the A. E. Bennett Award from the Society of Biological Psychiatry for his work on obsessive–compulsive disorder. His current research focus is in developmental psychobiology, studying the ontogeny of neurotransmitter and neuropeptide systems relevant to fear.

Michael J. Kozak, Ph.D., a clinical psychologist, is Assistant Professor of Psychiatry and Psychophysiology Laboratory Director at the Center for the Treatment and Study of Anxiety, Medical College of Pennsylvania at Eastern Pennsylvania Psychiatric Institute. His primary research interest is the psychophysiology of emotion, especially as related to the process and outcome of therapy for anxiety disorders.

Alan Lipschitz, M.D. is Assistant Professor of Psychiatry at New York Medical College, and Director of the Anxiety Disorders Clinic at Metropolitan Hospital, where he is Assistant Director of the Psychiatry Outpatient Department.

James Lomax, M.D. is an Associate Professor of Clinical Psychiatry at Baylor College of Medicine in Houston, Texas. He is Director of the Baylor Psychiatry Residency Program, and was formerly Director of the Baylor Psychiatry Clinic. Dr. Lomax is Board Certified in Psychiatry, a Fellow of the American Psychiatric Association, and a graduate of the Houston-Galveston Psychoanalytic Institute. Dr. Lomax is interested principally in graduate medical training, educational innovations, program evaluation, and trainee evaluation. He has done research on violent behavior, the post-traumatic stress syndrome in Vietnam veterans, correlates of suicide, and the influence of suicide of patients on treatment staff. He has also compiled a core reading list on suicide and has developed a curriculum on suicide care for psychiatry residents.

W. L. Marshall, Ph.D. is Professor of Psychology and Associate Professor of Psychiatry at Queen's University in Kingston, Ontario. He is the author of more than 70 journal articles and 20 book chapters, many of which deal with anxiety disorders. Dr. Marshall has also been a member of the editorial board of eight international journals.

Paul R. McCarthy, Ph.D. is an Instructor of Psychiatry and member of the Center for the Treatment and Study of Anxiety in the Department of Psychiatry, Medical College of Pennsylvania at Eastern Pennsylvania Psychiatric Institute. Dr. McCarthy is the recipient of an NIMH grant for the study of cognitive fear structures in anxiety disorders. Also, he is engaged in the psychophysiologic study of ANS and CNS function in obsessive-compulsive disorder.

William T. McKinney, M.D. is Professor of Psychiatry in the Department of Psychiatry at the University of Wisconsin School of Medicine. He is also a research psychiatrist at the Harlow Primate Laboratory and an Affiliate Scientist at the Wisconsin Regional Primate Research Center. He is the author of numerous journal articles and book chapters on the development and utilization of animal models in Psychiatry as well as on integrative theories of human depressive disorder. Along with Drs. Whybner and Akiskal he is the author of the book *Mood Disorders: Toward a New Psychotherapy.*

Daniel R. McLeod, Ph.D. is Assistant Professor of Psychiatry in the Department of Psychiatry and Behavioral Sciences, Johns Hopkins University School of Medicine. His research, conducted conjointly with Rudolf Hoehn-Saric, M.D., focuses on psychological, physiological and pharmacological aspects of anxiety disorders. He has published several papers in the fields of anxiety disorders and psychopharmacology. Dr. McLeod currently has a research grant from the NIAAA to study relationships between alcohol and anxiety.

Scott M. Monroe, Ph.D. is Associate Professor of Psychology and Psychiatry at the University of Pittsburgh. Dr. Monroe's research is on the affective disorders, with a special emphasis on socioenvironmental considerations. He is a recipient of a New Investigator Research Award from the National Institute of Mental Health, and serves on the editorial board of the *Journal of Abnormal Psychology, Journal of Consulting and Clinical Psychology*, and *Journal of Personality and Social Psychology: Personality*. He is currently conducting separate studies on life stress in relation to recurrent depression and adult anxiety disorders.

Patrick Murphy, (Ph.D., City University of New York). He is currently a Research Scientist at the Anxiety Clinic, New York Hospital, Payne Whitney Clinic.

Russell Noyes, Jr., M.D. is Professor of Psychiatry and Director of the Anxiety Clinic in the Department of Psychiatry, University of Iowa College of Medicine. His research in the area of anxiety disorder has involved treatment and family studies.

James F. Papillo (Ph.D., State University of New York at Stony Brook) is currently a postdoctoral fellow (MacArthur Foundation, NH124-784-700-59174) in the Department of Psychiatry and Biobehavioral Sciences, University of California, Los Angeles, California. His major areas of interest and research are visceral perception, cardiovascular psychophysiology, and the psychophysiology of emotion.

Roger L. Patterson, Ph.D. is Coordinator Day Treatment, Veteran's Administration Outpatient Clinic, Daytona Beach, Florida. He received his Ph.D. in Clinical Psychology from Florida State University in 1971. Previously he was Chairperson, Department of Aging Programs, Florida Mental Health Institute, University of South Florida. He is Fellow and Diplomat, American Board of Examiners Psychotherapy; Clinical Fellow, Behavior Therapy and Research Society; Chairperson, Special Interest Group on Aging, Association for Advancement of Behavior Therapy; Member: American Psychological Association, and others. He is a member of the editorial board of *Behavior Modifications*, and guest reviewer for several other journals. Publications include: senior author of *Overcoming Deficits of Aging: A Behavioral Approach*, editor of another book and author or co-author of a number of book chapters and journal articles.

Alex D. Pokorny, M.D. is Professor of Psychiatry and Executive Vice Chairman of the Department of Psychiatry at Baylor College of Medicine, Houston, Texas. Dr. Pokorny has published widely in the areas of suicide and self-destructive behavior, alcoholism and drug abuse, course and outcome of mental illness, psychopharmacology, and in medical education. Dr. Pokorny has been principal investigator and co-investigator on a number of research grants from the Veterans Administration and the National Institute of Mental Health. He has been on the editorial boards of *Hospital and Community Psychiatry, Suicide and Life-Threatening Behavior*, and *Alcoholism: Clinical and Experimental Research.*

Ashok B. Raj, M.D. is Assistant Professor of Psychiatry in the Department of

Psychiatry and Behavioral Medicine, University of South Florida School of Medicine. He is the Director of the Adult Anxiety Disorders Clinic at the University of South Florida Psychiatry Center and is particularly interested in the medical aspects of anxiety.

Z. V. Segal, Ph.D. is Assistant Professor of Psychiatry at the University of Toronto, and a Psychologist on the Cognitive Behavior Therapies Section of the Clarke Institute of Psychiatry. Dr. Segal is a co-editor of *Anxiety disorders: psychological and biological perspectives* to be published shortly, and he has authored numerous journal articles and book chapters.

Thomas E. Schacht, Psy.D. is Assistant Professor of Psychiatry and Family Medicine at the Quillen-Dishner College of Medicine at East Tennessee State University. He was formerly on the faculty of Vanderbilt University, where he also received a 2-year National Research Service Award at the Center for Psychotherapy Research, and where he continues research as part of a five-year NIMH-funded project on time-limited dynamic psychotherapy. He has published numerous book chapters and articles on psychotherapy and related topics.

M. Katherine Shear, M.D. is Assistant Professor of Psychiatry, Cornell University Medical College, Associate Director of the Payne Whitney Clinic Outpatient Department and Director of the Anxiety Disorders Clinic. Dr. Shear is recipient of a William Paley Fellowship in Academic Medicine.

David V. Sheehan, M.D. is Professor of Psychiatry and Director of Clinical Psychiatric Research at the University of South Florida College of Medicine. He is Professor of Psychology at the University of South Florida College of Social and Behavioral Sciences. At Harvard Medical School, where he was Assistant Professor of Psychiatry, he was on the full time faculty for 13 years. He was the Director of Anxiety Research and Director of the Psychosomatic Medicine Clinic at Massachusetts General Hospital. Dr. Sheehan was born and educated in Europe. He did his postgraduate training in psychiatry at Massachusetts General Hospital and Harvard Medical School. He has written over 100 publications, including a bestselling book on anxiety called *The Anxiety Disease*. He has lectured widely in this country and throughout the world on anxiety and phobic disorders. He lives in Tampa, Florida with his wife Dr. Kathy Harnett Sheehan and their two children.

James E. Shipley, M.D. is Assistant Professor of Psychiatry and Director of the Sleep Laboratory in the Department of Psychiatry, University of Michigan School of Medicine. Dr. Shipley's clinical practice, research, and publications center around the pathophysiology and treatment of anxiety and affective disorders.

David Spiegel, M.D. is Associate Professor of Psychiatry and Behavioral Sciences and Director of the Adult Psychiatric Outpatient Clinic at Stanford University School of Medicine. He is an authority on medical uses of hypnosis, and his numerous research publications include studies of the efficacy of hypnosis in reducing cancer pain, neurophysiological mechanisms of hypnotic perceptual alteration, and the relationship between social support and adjustment to illness. He is co-author with Herbert Spiegel, M.D., of *Trance and Treatment, Clinical Uses of Hypnosis* (1978) and has authored numerous textbook chapters on the subject. He is a member of the Editorial Boards of the American Psychiatric Press, the American Journal of Clinical Hypnosis, and the Journal of Psychosocial Oncology.

Herbert Spiegel, M.D. is an internationally prominent authority on medical hypnosis and psychotherapy. During his more than forty years in the field, he has collaborated in three books and has written some 58 journal articles and chapters.

He has contributed pioneering approaches to smoking control and the treatment of the highly hypnotizable patient. He is former Clinical Professor of Psychiatry and currently Special Lecturer at the College of Physicians & Surgeons, Columbia University.

Hans H. Strupp, Ph.D. is Distinguished Professor in the Department of Psychology, Vanderbilt University. He is a Diplomate in Clinical Psychology, American Board of Professional Psychology. He has been engaged in psychotherapy research for more than 30 years, and currently directs a 5-year NIMH-funded project on time-limited dynamic psychotherapy. His most recent book (with J. L. Binder) is *Psychotherapy in a new key: A Guide to time-limited dynamic psychotherapy*. He is a past president of the Division of Clinical Psychology of the American Psychological Association. He has also served as president of the Society for Psychotherapy research, which awarded him a Distinguished Career Contribution Award.

Michael J. Telch, Ph.D. is Assistant Professor of Psychology at the University of Texas at Austin. He is also founder and co-director of the Laboratory for the Study and Treatment of Anxiety Disorders at the University of Texas at Austin. Dr. Telch has published numerous journal articles and book chapters on the etiology and treatment of agoraphobia and panic-related disorders.

Michael E. Thase, M.D. is Associate Professor of Psychiatry in the Department of Psychiatry, University of Pittsburgh School of Medicine and Coordinator of Outpatient Studies for the Department's Mental Health Clinical Research Center. Dr. Thase's clinical practice, research, and publications focus on the psychobiology of mood disorders, including the interaction of psychosocial and biomedical factors in affective and anxiety disorders.

Svenn Torgersen, Ph.D., is Professor of Clinical Psychology, Director of Center for Research in Clinical and Applied Psychology and Chairman at Department of Psychology. He is also Research Adviser at Department of Psychiatry, Vinderen, both University of Oslo. He has published numerous articles and book chapters dealing with heredity and environment in the development of affective, anxiety and somatoform disorders, personality and borderline conditions.

Abraham J. Twerski, M.D. is Assistant Clinical Professor of Psychiatry, University of Pittsburgh School of Medicine, and Founder and Medical Director of the Gateway Rehabilitation Center in Aliquippa, PA. Dr. Twerski is the author of a book *Who Says You're Neurotic?*, which describes a number of conditions with prominent psychiatric symptoms whose major etiology is of somatic origin. Dr. Twerski has written numerous articles and several books on problems of alcohol and chemical dependency, among which are *It Happens to Doctors Too*, and *Caution: "Kindness" Can Be Dangerous to the Alcoholic.*

Shari L. Wade, M.S. is an advanced graduate student in Clinical Psychology at the University of Pittsburgh. Her interests are in life stress and coping, and her current focus of research is on life events and anxiety disorders.

Marianne Z. Wamboldt, M.D. is a psychiatrist who was a clinical fellow in the Laboratory of Clinical Science, National Institute of Mental Health, Bethesda, Maryland, at the time this paper was written. Her research interests have centered around the neuropharmacologic changes connected with parenting behavior. She has written several articles on the effects of oxytocin in mammalian parenting system. She is currently in clinical practice in the Adolescent Unit at the Psychiatric Institute in Montgomery County and continuing her research on the efficacy of tricyclics medication and adolescent depression and anxiety disorders.

Scott W. Woods, M.D. is an Assistant Professor of Psychiatry at Yale University School of Medicine and Chief of the Anxiety Disorder Clinic at the Connecticut Mental Health Center in New Haven. His major career interest is investigating the possibility of a neurobiological etiology in the anxiety disorders.

Pergamon General Psychology Series

Editors: Arnold P. Goldstein, Syracuse University

Leonard Krasner, Stanford University & SUNY at Stony Brook

Vol. 28. FELDMAN — College and Student: Selected Readings in the Social Psychology of Higher Education
Vol. 29. ASHEM & POSER — Adaptive Learning: Behavior Modification with Children
Vol. 30. BURCK et al. — Counseling and Accountability: Methods and Critique*
Vol. 31. FREDERIKSEN et al. — Prediction of Organizational Behavior
Vol. 32. CATTELL — A New Morality from Science: Beyondism
Vol. 33. WEINER — Personality: The Human Potential
Vol. 34. LIEBERT & SPRAFKIN — The Early Window: Effects of Television on Children and Youth, Third Edition
Vol. 35. COHEN et al. — Psych City: A Simulated Community
Vol. 36. GRAZIANO — Child Without Tomorrow
Vol. 37. MORRIS — Perspectives in Abnormal Behavior
Vol. 38. BALLER — Bed Wetting: Origins and Treatment*
Vol. 40. KAHN, CAMERON & GIFFEN — Methods and Evaluation in Clinical and Counseling Psychology
Vol. 41. SEGALL — Human Behavior and Public Policy: A Political Psychology
Vol. 42. FAIRWEATHER et al. — Creating Change in Mental Health Organizations
Vol. 43. KATZ & ZLUTNICK — Behavior Therapy and Health Care: Principles and Applications
Vol. 44. EVANS & CLAIBORN — Mental Health Issues and the Urban Poor
Vol. 46. BARBER, SPANOS & CHAVES — Hypnosis, Imagination and Human Potentialities
Vol. 47. POPE — The Mental Health Interview: Research and Application
Vol. 48. PELTON — The Psychology of Nonviolence*
Vol. 49. COLBY — Artificial Paranoia — A Computer Simulation of Paranoid Processes
Vol. 50. GELFAND & HARTMANN — Child Behavior Analysis and Therapy, Second Edition
Vol. 51. WOLPE — Theme and Variations: A Behavior Therapy Casebook
Vol. 52. KANFER & GOLDSTEIN — Helping People Change: A Textbook of Methods, Third Edition
Vol. 53. DANZIGER — Interpersonal Communication
Vol. 55. GOLDSTEIN & STEIN — Prescriptive Psychotherapies
Vol. 56. BARLOW & HERSEN — Single-Case Experimental Designs: Strategies for Studying Behavior Changes, Second Edition
Vol. 57. MONAHAN — Community Mental Health and the Criminal Justice System
Vol. 58. WAHLER, HOUSE & STAMBAUGH — Ecological Assessment of Child Problem Behavior: A Clinical Package for Home, School and Institutional Settings
Vol. 59. MAGARO — The Construction of Madness: Emerging Conceptions and Interventions into the Psychotic Process
Vol. 60. MILLER — Behavioral Treatment of Alcholism*
Vol. 61. FOREYT — Behavioral Treatments of Obesity
Vol. 62. WANDERSMAN, POPPEN & RICKS — Humanism and Behaviorism: Dialogue and Growth
Vol. 63. NIETZEL, WINETT, MACDONALD & DAVIDSON — Behavioral Approaches to Community Psychology
Vol. 64. FISHER & GOCHROS — Handbook of Behavior Therapy with Sexual Problems. Vol. I: General Procedures. Vol. II: Approaches to Specific Problems
Vol. 65. BELLACK & HERSEN — Behavioral Assessment: A Practical Handbook, Third Edition
Vol. 66. LEFKOWITZ, ERON, WALDER & HUESMANN — Growing Up to Be Violent: A Longitudinal Study of the Development of Aggression

Vol. 67. BARBER — Pitfalls in Human Research: Ten Pivotal Points
Vol. 68. SILVERMAN — The Human Subject in the Psychological Laboratory
Vol. 69. FAIRWEATHER & TORNATZKY — Experimental Methods for Social Policy Research*
Vol. 70. GURMAN & RAZIN — Effective Psychotherapy: A Handbook of Research*
Vol. 71. MOSES & BYHAM — Applying the Assessment Center Method
Vol. 72. GOLDSTEIN — Prescriptions for Child Mental Health and Education
Vol. 73. KEAT — Multimodal Therapy with Children
Vol. 74. SHERMAN — Personality: Inquiry & Application
Vol. 75. GATCHEL & PRICE — Clinical Applications of Biofeedback: Appraisal and Status
Vol. 76. CATALANO — Health, Behavior and the Community: An Ecological Perspective
Vol. 77. NIETZEL — Crime and Its Modification: A Social Learning Perspective
Vol. 78. GOLDSTEIN, HOYER & MONTI — Police and the Elderly
Vol. 79. MIRON & GOLDSTEIN — Hostage
Vol. 80. GOLDSTEIN et al. — Police Crisis Intervention
Vol. 81. UPPER & CAUTELA — Covert Conditioning
Vol. 82. MORELL — Program Evaluation in Social Research
Vol. 83. TEGER — Too Much Invested to Quit
Vol. 84. MONJAN & GASSNER — Critical Issues in Competency-Based Education
Vol. 85. KRASNER — Environmental Design and Human Behavior: A Psychology of the Individual in Society
Vol. 86. TAMIR — Communication and the Aging Process: Interaction Throughout the Life Cycle
Vol. 87. WEBSTER, KONSTANTAREAS, OXMAN & MACK — Autism: New Directions in Research and Education
Vol. 89. CARTLEDGE & MILBURN — Teaching Social Skills to Children: Innovative Approaches, Second Edition
Vol. 90. SARBIN & MANCUSO — Schizophrenia — Medical Diagnosis or Moral Verdict?*
Vol. 91. RATHJEN & FOREYT — Social Competence: Interventions for Children and Adults
Vol. 92. VAN DE RIET, KORB & GORRELL — Gestalt Therapy: An Introduction
Vol. 93. MARSELLA & PEDERSEN — Cross-Cultural Counseling and Psychotherapy
Vol. 94. BRISLIN — Cross-Cultural Encounters: Face-to-Face Interaction
Vol. 95. SCHWARTZ & JOHNSON — Psychopathology of Childhood: A Clinical-Experimental Approach, Second Edition
Vol. 96. HEILBRUN — Human Sex-Role Behavior
Vol. 97. DAVIDSON, KOCH, LEWIS, WRESINSKI — Evaluation Strategies in Criminal Justice
Vol. 98. GOLDSTEIN, CARR, DAVIDSON, WEHR — In Response to Aggression: Methods of Control and Prosocial Alternatives
Vol. 99. GOLDSTEIN — Psychological Skill Training: The Structured Learning Technique
Vol. 100. WALKER — Clinical Practice of Psychology: A Guide for Mental Health Professionals
Vol. 101. ANCHIN & KIESLER — Handbook of Interpersonal Psychotherapy
Vol. 102. GELLER, WINNETT EVERETT — Preserving the Environment: New Strategies for Behavior Change
Vol. 103. JENKINS — The Psychology of the Afro-American: A Humanistic Approach
Vol. 104. APTER — Troubled Children/Troubled Systems
Vol. 105. BRENNER — The Effective Psychotherapist: Conclusions from Practice and Research

Vol. 106. KAROLY & KANFER — Self-Management and Behavior Change: From Theory to Practice
Vol. 107. O'BRIEN, DICKINSON, ROSOW — Industrial Behavior Modification: A Management Handbook
Vol. 108. AMABILE & STUBBS — Psychological Research in the Classroom: Issues for Educators and Researchers*
Vol. 110. DiMATTEO & DiNICOLA — Achieving Patient Compliance: The Psychology of the Medical Practitioner's Role
Vol. 111. CONOLEY & CONOLEY — School Consultation: A Guide to Practice and Training
Vol. 112. PAPAJOHN — Intensive Behavior Therapy: The Behavioral Treatment of Complex Emotional Disorders
Vol. 113. KAROLY, STEFFEN, O'GRADY — Child Health Psychology: Concepts and Issues
Vol. 114. MORRIS & KARATOCHWILL — Treating Children's Fears and Phobias: A Behavioral Approach
Vol. 115. GOLDSTEIN & SEGALL — Aggression in Global Perspective
Vol. 116. LANDIS & BRISLIN — Handbook of Intercultural Training
Vol. 117. FARBER — Stress and Burnout in the Human Service Professions
Vol. 118. BEUTLER — Eclectic Psychotherapy: A Systematic Approach
Vol. 119. HARRIS — Families of the Developmentally Disabled: A Guide to Behavioral Intervention
Vol. 120. HERSEN, KAZDIN, BELLACK — The Clinical Psychology Handbook
Vol. 121. MATSON & MULICK — Handbook of Mental Retardation
Vol. 122. FELNER, JASON, MORITSUGU, FARBER — Preventive Psychology: Theory Research and Practice
Vol. 123. CENTER FOR RESEARCH ON AGGRESSION — Prevention and Control of Aggression
Vol. 124. MORRIS & KRATOCHWILL — The Practice of Child Therapy
Vol. 125. VARNI — Clinical Behavioral Pediatrics: An Interdisciplinary Biobehavioral Approach
Vol. 126. RAMIREZ — Psychology of the Americas: Mestizo Perspectives on Personality and Mental Health
Vol. 127. LEWINSOHN & TERI — Clinical Geropsychology: New Directions in Assessment and Treatment
Vol. 128. BARLOW, HAYES, NELSON — The Scientist Practitioner: Research and Accountability in Clinical and Educational Settings
Vol. 129. OLLENDICK & HERSEN — Child Behavioral Assessment: Principles and Procedures
Vol. 130. BELLACK & HERSEN — Research Methods in Clinical Psychology
Vol. 131. GOLDSTEIN & HERSEN — Handbook of Psychological Assessment
Vol. 132. BELLACK & HERSEN — Dictionary of Behavior Therapy Techniques
Vol. 133. COOK — Psychological Androgyny
Vol. 134. DREW & HARDMAN — Designing and Conducting Behavioral Research
Vol. 135. APTER & GOLDSTEIN — Youth Violence: Programs and Prospects
Vol. 136. HOLZMAN & TURK — Pain Management: A Handbook of Psychological Treatment Approaches
Vol. 137. MORRIS & BLATT — Special Education: Research and Trends
Vol. 138. JOHNSON, RASBURY, SIEGEL — Approaches to Child Treatment: Introduction to Theory, Research and Practice
Vol. 139. RYBASH, HOYER & ROODIN — Adult Cognition and Aging: Developmental Changes in Processing, Knowing and Thinking

Vol. 140. WIELKIEWICZ — Behavior Management in the Schools: Principles and Procedures
Vol. 141. PLAS — Systems Psychology in the Schools
Vol. 142. VAN HASSELT & HERSEN — Handbook of Adolescent Psychology
Vol. 143. BRASSARD, GERMAIN & HART — Psychological Maltreatment of Children and Youth
Vol. 144. HERSHENSON & POWER — Mental Health Counseling: Theory and Practice
Vol. 145. GOLDSTEIN & KRASNER — Modern Applied Psychology
Vol. 146. CARSTENSEN & EDELSTEIN — Handbook of Clinical Gerontology
Vol. 147. HERSEN & BELLACK — Dictionary of Behavioral Assessment Techniques
Vol. 148. VAN HASSELT, STRAIN & HERSEN — Handbook of Developmental and Physical Disabilities
Vol. 149. BLECHMAN & BROWNELL — Handbook of Behavioral Medicine for Women
Vol. 150. MAHER & ZINS — Psychoeducational Interventions in Schools: Methods and Procedures for Enhancing Student Competence
Vol. 151. LAST & HERSEN — Handbook of Anxiety Disorders
Vol. 152. KAZDIN — Child Psychotherapy: Developing and Identifying Effective Treatments
Vol. 153. RUSSELL — Stress Management for Chronic Disease
Vol. 154. HIGGINBOTHAM, WEST & FORSYTH — Psychotherapy and Behavior Change: Social, Cultural and Methodological Perspectives
Vol. 155. HUGHES — Cognitive Behavior Therapy with Children in Schools

---

*Out of print in original format. Available in custom reprint edition.